Instructor's Solutions Manual

Cindy Trimble & Associates

Beginning & Intermediate Algebra

FOURTH EDITION

Elayn Martin-Gay

PEARSON

Prentice
Hall

Upper Saddle River, NJ 07458

Editorial Director, Mathematics: Christine Hoag
Editor-in-Chief: Paul Murphy
Sponsoring Editor: Mary Beckwith
Assistant Editor: Georgina Brown
Senior Managing Editor: Linda Mihatov Behrens
Project Manager: Kristy S. Mosch
Art Director: Heather Scott
Supplement Cover Manager: Paul Gourhan
Supplement Cover Designer: Victoria Colotta
Operations Specialist: Ilene Kahn
Senior Operations Supervisor: Diane Peirano

© 2009 Pearson Education, Inc.

Pearson Prentice Hall

Pearson Education, Inc.

Upper Saddle River, NJ 07458

Pearson Prentice Hall™ is a trademark of Pearson Education, Inc.

The author and publisher of this book have used their best efforts in preparing this book. These efforts include the development, research, and testing of the theories and programs to determine their effectiveness. The author and publisher make no warranty of any kind, expressed or implied, with regard to these programs or the documentation contained in this book. The author and publisher shall not be liable in any event for incidental or consequential damages in connection with, or arising out of, the furnishing, performance, or use of these programs.

Printed in the United States of America

10 9 8 7 6 5 4 3 2 1

ISBN-13: 978-0-13-603083-6

ISBN-10: 0-13-603083-1

Pearson Education Ltd., London
Pearson Education Singapore, Pte. Ltd.
Pearson Education, Canada, Inc.
Pearson Education—Japan
Pearson Education Australia Pty, Ltd.
Pearson Education North Asia, Ltd., Hong Kong
Pearson Educación de Mexico, S.A. de C.V.
Pearson Education Malaysia, Pte. Ltd.
Pearson Education Upper Saddle River, New Jersey

Contents

Chapter 1

Answers will vary on Exercises 2–22.

Section 1.2

Practice Exercises

1. **a.** $5 < 8$ since 5 is to the left of 8 on the number line.

   b. $6 > 4$ since 6 is to the right of 4 on the number line.

   c. $16 < 82$ since 16 is to the left of 82 on the number line.

2. **a.** $9 \geq 3$ is true, since $9 > 3$ is true.

   b. $3 \geq 8$ is false, since neither $3 > 8$ nor $3 = 8$ is true.

   c. $25 \leq 25$ is true, since $25 = 25$ is true.

   d. $4 \leq 14$ is true, since $4 < 14$ is true.

3. **a.** $3 < 8$

   b. $15 \geq 9$

   c. $6 \neq 7$

4. The integer -52 represents owing the bank 52 dollars.

5. **a.** The natural number is 25.

   b. The whole number is 25.

   c. The integers are $25, -15, -99$.

   d. The rational numbers are $25, \frac{7}{3}, -15, \frac{-3}{4}, -3.7, 8.8, -99$.

   e. The irrational number is $\sqrt{5}$.

   f. The real numbers are $25, \frac{7}{3}, -15, \frac{-3}{4}, \sqrt{5}, -3.7, 8.8, -99$.

6. **a.** $0 < 3$ since 0 is to the left of 3 on the number line.

   b. $15 > -5$ since 15 is to the right of -5 on the number line.

   c. $3 = \frac{12}{4}$ since $\frac{12}{4}$ simplifies to 3.

7. **a.** $|-8| = 8$ since -8 is 8 units from 0 on a number line.

   b. $|9| = 9$ since 9 is 9 units from 0 on a number line.

   c. $|-2.5| = 2.5$ since -2.5 is 2.5 units from 0 on a number line.

   d. $\left|\frac{5}{11}\right| = \frac{5}{11}$ since $\frac{5}{11}$ is $\frac{5}{11}$ unit from 0 on a number line.

   e. $\left|\sqrt{3}\right| = \sqrt{3}$ since $\sqrt{3}$ is $\sqrt{3}$ units from 0 on a number line.

8. **a.** $|8| = |-8|$ since $8 = 8$.

   b. $|-3| > 0$ since $3 > 0$.

   c. $|-7| < |-11|$ since $7 < 11$.

   d. $|3| > |2|$ since $3 > 2$.

   e. $|0| < |-4|$ since $0 < 4$.

Vocabulary and Readiness Check

1. The <u>whole</u> numbers are $\{0, 1, 2, 3, 4, ...\}$.

2. The <u>natural</u> numbers are $\{1, 2, 3, 4, 5, ...\}$.

3. The symbols $\neq$, $\leq$, and $>$ are called <u>inequality</u> symbols.

4. The <u>integers</u> are $\{..., -3, -2, -1, 0, 1, 2, 3, ...\}$.

5. The <u>real</u> numbers are $\{$all numbers that correspond to points on the number line$\}$.

6. The <u>rational</u> numbers are $\left\{\frac{a}{b} \middle| a \text{ and } b \text{ are integers}, b \neq 0\right\}$.

7. The <u>irrational</u> numbers are {nonrational numbers that correspond to points on the number line}.

8. The distance between a number b and 0 on a number line is $|b|$.

Exercise Set 1.2

2. $9 < 15$ since 9 is to the left of 15 on the number line.

4. $2.13 > 1.13$ since 2.13 is to the right of 1.13 on the number line.

6. $20 > 0$ since 20 is to the right of 0 on the number line.

8. $-4 > -6$ since -4 is to the right of -6 on the number line.

10. $0 < 100$ since 0 is to the left of 100 on the number line.

12. $67{,}841 < 75{,}657$ since 67,841 is to the left of 75,657 on the number line.

14. $4 \geq 7$ is false, since 4 is to the left of 7 on the number line.

16. $17 > 16$ is true, since 17 is to the right of 16 on the number line.

18. $8 \cdot 8 \leq 8 \cdot 7$ is false, since 56 is to the left of 64 on the number line.

20. $4 < 7$ is true, since 4 is to the left of 7 on the number line.

22. $360 \geq 180$

24. Fifteen is greater than five is written as $15 > 5$.

26. Negative ten is less than or equal to thirty-seven is written as $-10 \leq 37$.

28. Negative seven is not equal to seven is written as $-7 \neq 7$.

30. 23 represents yards gained. -12 represents yards lost.

32. 33,000 represents an increase in population of 33,000 people.

34. 30 represents an ascent of feet. -50 represents a descent of 50 feet.

36. The tallest bar represents 287 million visitors.

38. Look for the bar with a height less than 270; 2003

40. Answers may vary

42. The number $\dfrac{1}{4}$ belongs to the sets of: rational numbers and real numbers.

44. The number $-\dfrac{1}{2}$ belongs to the sets of: rational numbers and real numbers.

46. The number 5 belongs to the sets of: natural numbers, whole numbers, integers, rational numbers, and real numbers.

48. The number $\sqrt{3}$ belongs to the sets of: irrational numbers and real numbers.

50. The number $-1\dfrac{5}{9}$ belongs to the sets of: rational numbers and real numbers.

52. False; negative numbers may be irrational.

54. True

56. False; irrational numbers are real.

58. False; $\dfrac{1}{2}$ is not an integer.

60. False; 0 is a whole number that is not positive.

62. $-200 < -20$ since -200 is to the left of -20 on the number line.

64. $7.1 > -7$ since 7.1 is to the right of -7 on the number line.

66. $\dfrac{8}{2} = \dfrac{12}{3}$ since $4 = 4$.

68. $|-20| > -200$ since $20 > 200$.

70. $0 = |0|$ since $0 = 0$.

72. $\left|\dfrac{2}{5}\right| = \left|-\dfrac{2}{5}\right|$ since $\dfrac{2}{5} = \dfrac{2}{5}$.

74. $-500 < |-50|$ since $-500 < 50$.

76. $\left|-12\right| = \dfrac{24}{2}$ since $12 = \dfrac{24}{2}$.

78. $0.96 < 0.98$ since 0.96 is to the left of 0.98 on the number line.

80. Spica is dimmer since $0.98 > 0.72$.

82. Regulus is dimmest since 1.35 is to the right of all other numbers listed.

84. $13 \geq -13$ has the same meaning as $-13 \leq 13$.

86. $3 < 5$ has the same meaning as $5 > 3$.

88. $-2 > -4$ has the same meaning as $-4 < -2$.

90. Answers may vary

Section 1.3

Practice Problems

1. a. $36 = 4 \cdot 9 = 2 \cdot 2 \cdot 3 \cdot 3$

   b. $75 = 3 \cdot 25 = 3 \cdot 5 \cdot 5$

2. a. $\dfrac{63}{72} = \dfrac{3 \cdot 3 \cdot 7}{2 \cdot 2 \cdot 2 \cdot 3 \cdot 3} = \dfrac{7}{2 \cdot 2 \cdot 2} = \dfrac{7}{8}$

   b. $\dfrac{64}{12} = \dfrac{2 \cdot 2 \cdot 2 \cdot 2 \cdot 2 \cdot 2}{2 \cdot 2 \cdot 3} = \dfrac{2 \cdot 2 \cdot 2 \cdot 2}{3} = \dfrac{16}{3}$

   c. $\dfrac{7}{25} = \dfrac{7}{5 \cdot 5}$

      There are no common factors other than 1, so $\dfrac{7}{25}$ is already in lowest terms.

3. $\dfrac{3}{8} \cdot \dfrac{7}{9} = \dfrac{3 \cdot 7}{8 \cdot 9} = \dfrac{3 \cdot 7}{2 \cdot 2 \cdot 2 \cdot 3 \cdot 3} = \dfrac{7}{2 \cdot 2 \cdot 2 \cdot 3} = \dfrac{7}{24}$

4. a. $\dfrac{3}{4} \div \dfrac{4}{9} = \dfrac{3}{4} \cdot \dfrac{9}{4} = \dfrac{3 \cdot 9}{4 \cdot 4} = \dfrac{27}{16}$

   b. $\dfrac{5}{12} \div 15 = \dfrac{5}{12} \cdot \dfrac{1}{15} = \dfrac{5 \cdot 1}{12 \cdot 15} = \dfrac{5}{12 \cdot 3 \cdot 5} = \dfrac{1}{36}$

   c. $\dfrac{7}{6} \div \dfrac{7}{15} = \dfrac{7}{6} \cdot \dfrac{15}{7} = \dfrac{7 \cdot 15}{6 \cdot 7} = \dfrac{15}{6} = \dfrac{3 \cdot 5}{2 \cdot 3} = \dfrac{5}{2}$

5. a. $\dfrac{8}{5} - \dfrac{3}{5} = \dfrac{8-3}{5} = \dfrac{5}{5} = 1$

   b. $\dfrac{8}{5} - \dfrac{2}{5} = \dfrac{8-2}{5} = \dfrac{6}{5}$

   c. $\dfrac{3}{5} + \dfrac{1}{5} = \dfrac{3+1}{5} = \dfrac{4}{5}$

   d. $\dfrac{5}{12} + \dfrac{1}{12} = \dfrac{5+1}{12} = \dfrac{6}{12} = \dfrac{1}{2}$

6. $\dfrac{2}{3} = \dfrac{2}{3} \cdot \dfrac{7}{7} = \dfrac{2 \cdot 7}{3 \cdot 7} = \dfrac{14}{21}$

7. a. $\dfrac{5}{11} + \dfrac{1}{7} = \dfrac{5 \cdot 7}{11 \cdot 7} + \dfrac{1 \cdot 11}{7 \cdot 11}$

$= \dfrac{35}{77} + \dfrac{11}{77}$

$= \dfrac{35+11}{77}$

$= \dfrac{46}{77}$

   b.

$\begin{aligned}
9\tfrac{1}{13} &= 9\tfrac{2}{26} = 8\tfrac{28}{26} \\
-5\tfrac{1}{2} &= -5\tfrac{13}{26} = -5\tfrac{13}{26} \\
&\hphantom{= -5\tfrac{13}{26}} = 3\tfrac{15}{26}
\end{aligned}$

   c. $\dfrac{1}{3} + \dfrac{29}{30} - \dfrac{4}{5} = \dfrac{10}{30} + \dfrac{29}{30} - \dfrac{4 \cdot 6}{5 \cdot 6}$

$= \dfrac{10+29}{30} - \dfrac{24}{30}$

$= \dfrac{39-24}{30}$

$= \dfrac{15}{30}$

$= \dfrac{1}{2}$

Vocabulary and Readiness Check

1. A quotient of two numbers, such as $\dfrac{5}{8}$, is called a <u>fraction</u>.

2. In the fraction $\dfrac{3}{11}$, the number 3 is called the <u>numerator</u> and the number 11 is called the <u>denominator</u>.

3. To factor a number means to write it as a <u>product</u>.

4. A fraction is said to be <u>simplified</u> when the numerator and the denominator have no common factors other than 1.

5. In $7 \cdot 3 = 21$, the numbers 7 and 3 are called <u>factors</u> and the number 21 is called the <u>product</u>.

6. The fractions $\dfrac{2}{9}$ and $\dfrac{9}{2}$ are called <u>reciprocals</u>.

7. Fractions that represent the same quantity are called <u>equivalent</u> fractions.

8. 3 of the 8 equal parts are shaded; $\dfrac{3}{8}$

9. 1 of the 4 equal parts are shaded; $\dfrac{1}{4}$

10. 5 of the 7 equal parts are shaded; $\dfrac{5}{7}$

11. 2 of the 5 equal parts are shaded; $\dfrac{2}{5}$

Exercise Set 1.3

2. $60 = 4 \cdot 15 = 2 \cdot 2 \cdot 3 \cdot 5$

4. $27 = 3 \cdot 9 = 3 \cdot 3 \cdot 3$

6. $56 = 4 \cdot 14 = 2 \cdot 2 \cdot 2 \cdot 7$

8. $32 = 4 \cdot 8 = 2 \cdot 2 \cdot 2 \cdot 2 \cdot 2$

10. $24 = 4 \cdot 6 = 2 \cdot 2 \cdot 2 \cdot 3$

12. $\dfrac{3}{6} = \dfrac{1 \cdot 3}{2 \cdot 3} = \dfrac{1}{2}$

14. $\dfrac{15}{20} = \dfrac{3 \cdot 5}{4 \cdot 5} = \dfrac{3}{4}$

16. $\dfrac{5}{9} = \dfrac{5}{9}$

18. $\dfrac{42}{45} = \dfrac{2 \cdot 3 \cdot 7}{3 \cdot 3 \cdot 5} = \dfrac{14}{15}$

20. $\dfrac{1}{8} \cdot \dfrac{3}{5} = \dfrac{1 \cdot 3}{2 \cdot 2 \cdot 2 \cdot 5} = \dfrac{3}{40}$

22. $\dfrac{7}{8} \cdot \dfrac{3}{21} = \dfrac{7 \cdot 3}{8 \cdot 21} = \dfrac{7 \cdot 3}{8 \cdot 3 \cdot 7} = \dfrac{1}{8}$

24. $\dfrac{7}{12} \div \dfrac{1}{2} = \dfrac{7}{12} \cdot \dfrac{2}{1} = \dfrac{7 \cdot 2}{12 \cdot 1} = \dfrac{7 \cdot 2}{2 \cdot 6 \cdot 1} = \dfrac{7}{6}$

26. $\dfrac{3}{5} \div \dfrac{9}{10} = \dfrac{3}{5} \cdot \dfrac{10}{9} = \dfrac{3 \cdot 10}{5 \cdot 9} = \dfrac{3 \cdot 2 \cdot 5}{5 \cdot 3 \cdot 3} = \dfrac{2}{3}$

28. $\dfrac{3}{35} \cdot \dfrac{10}{63} = \dfrac{3 \cdot 10}{35 \cdot 63} = \dfrac{3 \cdot 2 \cdot 5}{5 \cdot 7 \cdot 3 \cdot 3 \cdot 7} = \dfrac{2}{3 \cdot 7 \cdot 7} = \dfrac{2}{147}$

30. $\dfrac{1}{5} \cdot 5\dfrac{5}{6} = \dfrac{1}{4} \cdot \dfrac{35}{6} = \dfrac{1 \cdot 35}{4 \cdot 6} = \dfrac{35}{24} = 1\dfrac{11}{24}$

32. Area $= \dfrac{1}{2} \cdot 1\dfrac{1}{4} \cdot \dfrac{1}{2} = \dfrac{1}{2} \cdot \dfrac{5}{4} \cdot \dfrac{1}{2} = \dfrac{5}{2 \cdot 4 \cdot 2} = \dfrac{5}{16}$ sq m

34. $\dfrac{6}{7} - \dfrac{1}{7} = \dfrac{6-1}{7} = \dfrac{5}{7}$

36. $\dfrac{6}{7} + \dfrac{1}{7} = \dfrac{6+1}{7} = \dfrac{7}{7} = 1$

38. $\dfrac{18}{35} - \dfrac{11}{35} = \dfrac{18-11}{35} = \dfrac{7}{35} = \dfrac{7}{5 \cdot 7} = \dfrac{1}{5}$

40. $\dfrac{13}{132} + \dfrac{35}{132} = \dfrac{13+35}{132}$

$= \dfrac{48}{132}$

$= \dfrac{2 \cdot 2 \cdot 2 \cdot 2 \cdot 3}{2 \cdot 2 \cdot 3 \cdot 11}$

$= \dfrac{2 \cdot 2}{11}$

$= \dfrac{4}{11}$

42. $\dfrac{2}{3} = \dfrac{2 \cdot 3}{3 \cdot 3} = \dfrac{6}{9}$

44. $\dfrac{8}{7} = \dfrac{8 \cdot 8}{7 \cdot 8} = \dfrac{64}{56}$

46. $\dfrac{4}{5} = \dfrac{4\cdot5}{5\cdot5} = \dfrac{20}{25}$

48. $\dfrac{3}{4} + \dfrac{1}{6} = \dfrac{3\cdot3}{4\cdot3} + \dfrac{1\cdot2}{6\cdot2} = \dfrac{9}{12} + \dfrac{2}{12} = \dfrac{11}{12}$

50. $5\dfrac{2}{9} - 3\dfrac{1}{6} = \dfrac{47}{9} - \dfrac{19}{6}$

$= \dfrac{47\cdot2}{9\cdot2} - \dfrac{19\cdot3}{6\cdot3}$

$= \dfrac{94}{18} - \dfrac{57}{18}$

$= \dfrac{94-57}{18}$

$= \dfrac{37}{18}$

$= 2\dfrac{1}{18}$

52. $\dfrac{7}{10} - \dfrac{8}{15} = \dfrac{7\cdot3}{10\cdot3} - \dfrac{8\cdot2}{15\cdot2}$

$= \dfrac{21}{30} - \dfrac{16}{30}$

$= \dfrac{21-16}{30}$

$= \dfrac{5}{30}$

$= \dfrac{1}{6}$

54. $2 - \dfrac{3}{8} = \dfrac{16}{8} - \dfrac{3}{8} = \dfrac{16-3}{8} = \dfrac{13}{8}$

56. $1 - \dfrac{3}{11} - \dfrac{2}{11} = \dfrac{11}{11} - \dfrac{3}{11} - \dfrac{2}{11} = \dfrac{11-3-2}{11} = \dfrac{6}{11}$

The unknown part is $\dfrac{6}{11}$.

58. $1 - \dfrac{1}{10} - \dfrac{3}{5} = \dfrac{10}{10} - \dfrac{1}{10} - \dfrac{3\cdot2}{5\cdot2} = \dfrac{10-1-6}{10} = \dfrac{3}{10}$

The unknown part is $\dfrac{3}{10}$.

60. $1 - \dfrac{1}{6} - \dfrac{1}{3} - \dfrac{5}{12} = \dfrac{12}{12} - \dfrac{1\cdot2}{6\cdot2} - \dfrac{1\cdot4}{3\cdot4} - \dfrac{5}{12}$

$= \dfrac{12-2-4-5}{12}$

$= \dfrac{1}{12}$

The unknown part is $\dfrac{1}{12}$.

62. $\dfrac{11}{35} + \dfrac{3}{35} = \dfrac{11+3}{35} = \dfrac{14}{35} = \dfrac{2\cdot7}{5\cdot7} = \dfrac{2}{5}$

64. $\dfrac{11}{7} - \dfrac{3}{35} = \dfrac{11\cdot5}{7\cdot5} - \dfrac{3}{35} = \dfrac{55}{35} - \dfrac{3}{35} = \dfrac{52}{35}$

66. $\dfrac{2}{3} \div \dfrac{3}{5} = \dfrac{2}{3} \cdot \dfrac{5}{3} = \dfrac{2\cdot5}{3\cdot3} = \dfrac{10}{9}$

68. $\dfrac{3}{4} \cdot \dfrac{7}{12} = \dfrac{3\cdot7}{4\cdot12} = \dfrac{3\cdot7}{2\cdot2\cdot2\cdot2\cdot3} = \dfrac{7}{2\cdot2\cdot2\cdot2} = \dfrac{7}{16}$

70. $\dfrac{2}{7} + \dfrac{4}{7} = \dfrac{2+4}{7} = \dfrac{6}{7}$

72. $7 + \dfrac{1}{10} = \dfrac{70}{10} + \dfrac{1}{10} = \dfrac{70+1}{10} = \dfrac{71}{10}$

74. $3 \div \dfrac{3}{4} = 3 \cdot \dfrac{4}{3} = \dfrac{9}{3} \cdot \dfrac{4}{3} = \dfrac{9\cdot4}{3\cdot3} = \dfrac{36}{9} = 4$

76. $4\dfrac{3}{7} \div \dfrac{31}{7} = \dfrac{31}{7} \div \dfrac{31}{7} = \dfrac{31}{7} \cdot \dfrac{7}{31} = \dfrac{31\cdot7}{7\cdot31} = 1$

78. $\dfrac{57}{132} - \dfrac{13}{132} = \dfrac{57-13}{132} = \dfrac{44}{132} = \dfrac{4\cdot11}{3\cdot4\cdot11} = \dfrac{1}{3}$

80. $2\dfrac{3}{5} + 4\dfrac{7}{10} = \dfrac{13}{5} + \dfrac{47}{10}$

$= \dfrac{13\cdot2}{5\cdot2} + \dfrac{47}{10}$

$= \dfrac{26}{10} + \dfrac{47}{10}$

$= \dfrac{26+47}{10}$

$= \dfrac{73}{10}$

$= 7\dfrac{3}{10}$

82. $\dfrac{8}{11} - \dfrac{1}{4} + \dfrac{1}{2} = \dfrac{8 \cdot 4}{11 \cdot 4} - \dfrac{1 \cdot 11}{4 \cdot 11} + \dfrac{1 \cdot 22}{2 \cdot 22}$

$\qquad = \dfrac{32}{44} - \dfrac{11}{44} + \dfrac{22}{44}$

$\qquad = \dfrac{32 - 11 + 22}{44}$

$\qquad = \dfrac{43}{44}$

84. $2\left(16\dfrac{1}{2}\right) + 2\left(12\dfrac{3}{8}\right) = \dfrac{2}{1} \cdot \dfrac{33}{2} + \dfrac{2}{1} \cdot \dfrac{99}{8}$

$\qquad = \dfrac{33}{1} + \dfrac{99}{4}$

$\qquad = \dfrac{33 \cdot 4}{1 \cdot 4} + \dfrac{99}{4}$

$\qquad = \dfrac{132}{4} + \dfrac{99}{4}$

$\qquad = \dfrac{132 + 99}{4}$

$\qquad = \dfrac{231}{4}$

$\qquad = 57\dfrac{3}{4}$ feet

86. $1\dfrac{3}{16} + \dfrac{5}{16} = \dfrac{19}{16} + \dfrac{5}{16} = \dfrac{19 + 5}{16} = \dfrac{24}{16} = 1\dfrac{8}{16} = 1\dfrac{1}{2}$

The Belmont is a $1\dfrac{1}{2}$-mile race.

88. Answers may vary

90. $3\dfrac{1}{2} + 5\dfrac{1}{2} + 2\dfrac{1}{8} + 1\dfrac{3}{4} = \dfrac{7}{2} + \dfrac{11}{2} + \dfrac{17}{8} + \dfrac{7}{4}$

$\qquad = \dfrac{7 \cdot 4}{2 \cdot 4} + \dfrac{11 \cdot 4}{2 \cdot 4} + \dfrac{17}{8} + \dfrac{7 \cdot 2}{4 \cdot 2}$

$\qquad = \dfrac{28}{8} + \dfrac{44}{8} + \dfrac{17}{8} + \dfrac{14}{8}$

$\qquad = \dfrac{28 + 44 + 17 + 14}{8}$

$\qquad = \dfrac{103}{8}$

$\qquad = 12\dfrac{7}{8}$

The distance for all 4 trails is $12\dfrac{7}{8}$ mi.

92. $\dfrac{21}{100}$ are in engineering.

94. $\dfrac{4}{25} + \dfrac{7}{50} = \dfrac{4 \cdot 2}{25 \cdot 2} + \dfrac{7}{50}$

$\qquad = \dfrac{8}{50} + \dfrac{7}{50}$

$\qquad = \dfrac{8 + 7}{50}$

$\qquad = \dfrac{15}{50}$

$\qquad = \dfrac{3 \cdot 5}{10 \cdot 5}$

$\qquad = \dfrac{3}{10}$

$\dfrac{3}{10}$ are in the social sciences and psychology.

96. $\dfrac{1335}{3054} + \dfrac{256}{3054} + \dfrac{5}{3054} = \dfrac{1335 + 256 + 5}{3054}$

$\qquad = \dfrac{1596}{3054}$

$\qquad = \dfrac{266 \cdot 6}{509 \cdot 6}$

$\qquad = \dfrac{266}{509}$

$\dfrac{266}{509}$ stores were either domestic or international.

98. Area $= L \cdot W = \dfrac{2}{5} \cdot \dfrac{3}{11} = \dfrac{2 \cdot 3}{5 \cdot 11} = \dfrac{6}{55}$ square meters

Section 1.4

Practice Exercises

1. a. $1^3 = 1 \cdot 1 \cdot 1 = 1$

b. $5^2 = 5 \cdot 5 = 25$

c. $\left(\dfrac{1}{10}\right)^2 = \left(\dfrac{1}{10}\right)\left(\dfrac{1}{10}\right) = \dfrac{1}{100}$

d. $9^1 = 9$

e. $\left(\dfrac{2}{5}\right)^3 = \left(\dfrac{2}{5}\right)\left(\dfrac{2}{5}\right)\left(\dfrac{2}{5}\right) = \dfrac{8}{125}$

2. a. $6 + 3 \cdot 9 = 6 + 27 = 33$

b. $4^3 \div 8 + 3 = 64 \div 8 + 3 = 8 + 3 = 11$

c. $\left(\dfrac{2}{3}\right)^2 \cdot \left|-8\right| = \dfrac{4}{9} \cdot 8 = \dfrac{32}{9}$ or $3\dfrac{5}{9}$

d. $\dfrac{9(14-6)}{\left|-2\right|} = \dfrac{9(8)}{2} = \dfrac{72}{2} = 36$

e. $\dfrac{7}{4} \cdot \dfrac{1}{4} - \dfrac{1}{4} = \dfrac{7}{16} - \dfrac{4}{16} = \dfrac{3}{16}$

3. $\dfrac{6^2 - 5}{3 + \left|6 - 5\right| \cdot 8} = \dfrac{36 - 5}{3 + \left|1\right| \cdot 8} = \dfrac{31}{3 + 8} = \dfrac{31}{11}$

4. $4[25 - 3(5+3)] = 4[25 - 3(8)]$
$\qquad\qquad\qquad = 4[25 - 24]$
$\qquad\qquad\qquad = 4[1]$
$\qquad\qquad\qquad = 4$

5. $\dfrac{36 \div 9 + 5}{5^2 - 3} = \dfrac{4 + 5}{25 - 3} = \dfrac{9}{22}$

6. a. $2x + y = 2(2) + 5 = 4 + 5 = 9$

b. $\dfrac{4x}{3y} = \dfrac{4(2)}{3(5)} = \dfrac{8}{15}$

c. $\dfrac{3}{x} + \dfrac{x}{y} = \dfrac{3}{2} + \dfrac{2}{5} = \dfrac{15}{10} + \dfrac{4}{10} = \dfrac{19}{10}$

d. $x^3 + y^2 = 2^3 + 5^2 = 8 + 25 = 33$

7. $9x - 6 = 7x$
$9(4) - 6 \overset{?}{=} 7(4)$
$36 - 6 \overset{?}{=} 28$
$\qquad 30 = 28$ False
4 is not a solution of $9x - 6 = 7x$.

8. a. Six times a number is $6x$, since $6x$ denotes the product of 6 and x.

b. A number decreased by 8 is $x - 8$ because "decreased by" means subtract.

c. The product of a number and 9 is $x \cdot 9$ or $9x$.

d. Two times a number is $2x$, plus 3 is $2x + 3$.

e. The sum of 7 and a number x is $7 + x$.

9. a. A number x increased by 7 is $x + 7$, so $x + 7 = 13$.

b. Two less than a number x is $x - 2$, so $x - 2 = 11$.

c. Double a number x is $2x$, added to 9 is $2x + 9$, so $2x + 9 \neq 25$.

d. Five times 11 is $5(11)$, so $5(11) \geq x$, where x is an unknown number.

Calculator Explorations

1. $5^4 = 625$

2. $7^4 = 2401$

3. $9^5 = 59,049$

4. $8^6 = 262,144$

5. $2(20 - 5) = 30$

6. $3(14 - 7) + 21 = 3(7) + 21 = 21 + 21 = 42$

7. $24(862 - 455) + 89 = 9857$

8. $99 + (401 + 962) = 1462$

9. $\dfrac{4623 + 129}{36 - 34} = 2376$

10. $\dfrac{956 - 452}{89 - 86} = 168$

Vocabulary and Readiness Check

1. In the expression 5^2, the 5 is called the <u>base</u> and the 2 is called the <u>exponent</u>.

2. The symbols ( ), [ ], and { } are examples of <u>grouping</u> symbols.

3. A symbol that is used to represent a number is called a <u>variable</u>.

4. A collection of numbers, variables, operation symbols, and grouping symbols is called an <u>expression</u>.

5. A mathematical statement that two expressions are equal is called an <u>equation</u>.

6. A value for the variable that makes an equation a true statement is called a <u>solution</u>.

7. Deciding what values of a variable make an equation a true statement is called <u>solving</u> the equation.

8. To simplify the expression $1 + 3 \cdot 6$, first <u>multiply</u>.

9. To simplify the expression $(1 + 3) \cdot 6$, first <u>add</u>.

10. To simplify the expression $(20 - 4) \cdot 2$, first <u>subtract</u>.

11. To simplify the expression $20 - 4 \div 2$, first <u>divide</u>.

Exercise Set 1.4

2. $2^5 = 2 \cdot 2 \cdot 2 \cdot 2 \cdot 2 = 32$

4. $4^4 = 4 \cdot 4 \cdot 4 \cdot 4 = 256$

6. $1^8 = 1 \cdot 1 \cdot 1 \cdot 1 \cdot 1 \cdot 1 \cdot 1 \cdot 1 = 1$

8. $8^1 = 8$

10. $\left(\dfrac{6}{11}\right)^2 = \left(\dfrac{6}{11}\right)\left(\dfrac{6}{11}\right) = \dfrac{6 \cdot 6}{11 \cdot 11} = \dfrac{36}{121}$

12. $\left(\dfrac{1}{2}\right)^5 = \left(\dfrac{1}{2}\right)\left(\dfrac{1}{2}\right)\left(\dfrac{1}{2}\right)\left(\dfrac{1}{2}\right)\left(\dfrac{1}{2}\right)$
$= \dfrac{1 \cdot 1 \cdot 1 \cdot 1 \cdot 1}{2 \cdot 2 \cdot 2 \cdot 2 \cdot 2}$
$= \dfrac{1}{32}$

14. $9^2 = 9 \cdot 9 = 81$

16. $4^3 = 4 \cdot 4 \cdot 4 = 64$

18. $(0.07)^2 = (0.07)(0.07) = 0.0049$

20. $8 + 5 \cdot 3 = 8 + 15 = 23$

22. $12 \cdot 5 - 3 \cdot 6 = 60 - 18 = 42$

24. $5(6 - 2) = 5(4) = 20$

26. $6 - 2 \cdot 2 + 2^5 = 6 - 2 \cdot 2 + 32 = 6 - 4 + 32 = 34$

28. $2 \cdot 5^2 = 2 \cdot 25 = 50$

30. $\dfrac{3}{4} \cdot \dfrac{1}{2} + \dfrac{2}{3} = \dfrac{3}{8} + \dfrac{2}{3} = \dfrac{9}{24} + \dfrac{16}{24} = \dfrac{25}{24}$

32. $\dfrac{8-5}{24-20} = \dfrac{3}{4}$

34. $3[4 + 3(6 - 4)] = 3[4 + 3(2)]$
$= 3[4 + 6]$
$= 3[10]$
$= 30$

36. $\dfrac{4 \cdot 3 + 2}{4 + 3 \cdot 2} = \dfrac{12 + 2}{4 + 6} = \dfrac{14}{10} = \dfrac{7}{5}$

38. $\dfrac{15 - |3 - 1|}{12 - 3 \cdot 2} = \dfrac{15 - |2|}{12 - 6} = \dfrac{15 - 2}{6} = \dfrac{13}{6}$

40. $\dfrac{3 + 6(8 - 5)}{4^2 + 2} = \dfrac{3 + 6(3)}{4^2 + 2}$
$= \dfrac{3 + 6(3)}{16 + 2}$
$= \dfrac{3 + 18}{16 + 2}$
$= \dfrac{21}{18}$
$= \dfrac{7}{6}$

42. $\dfrac{16 + |13 - 5| + 4^2}{17 - 5} = \dfrac{16 + |8| + 4^2}{17 - 5}$
$= \dfrac{16 + 8 + 4^2}{17 - 5}$
$= \dfrac{16 + 8 + 16}{17 - 5}$
$= \dfrac{40}{12}$
$= \dfrac{4 \cdot 10}{4 \cdot 3}$
$= \dfrac{10}{3}$

44. Yes; since in the absence of grouping symbols we always perform multiplications or divisions before additions or subtractions in any expression.

46. **a.** $(1 + 4) \cdot 6 - 3 = 5 \cdot 6 - 3 = 30 - 3 = 27$

   b. $1 + 4 \cdot (6 - 3) = 1 + 4 \cdot 3 = 1 + 12 = 13$

c. $1 + 4 \cdot 6 - 3 = 1 + 24 - 3 = 22$

d. $(1 + 4) \cdot (6 - 3) = 5 \cdot 3 = 15$

48. Let $x = 1$.
$4x = 4(1) = 4$

50. Let $y = 3$ and $z = 5$.
$$\frac{y}{2z} = \frac{3}{2(5)} = \frac{3}{10}$$

52. Let $y = 3$.
$6y - 8 = 6(3) - 8 = 18 - 8 = 10$

54. Let $y = 3$ and $z = 5$.
$|5z - 2y| = |5(5) - 2(3)| = |25 - 6| = |19| = 19$

56. Let $z = 5$.
$2z^2 = 2(5)^2 = 2(25) = 50$

58. Let $x = 12$, $y = 8$ and $z = 4$.
$$\frac{y}{z} + 8x = \frac{8}{4} + 8(12) = 2 + 96 = 98$$

60. Let $x = 12$ and $y = 8$.
$y^2 - 3x + y = (8)^2 - 3(12) + 8 = 64 - 36 + 8 = 36$

62. Let $x = 12$ and $y = 8$.
$$\frac{y^2 + x}{x^2 + 3y} = \frac{(8)^2 + 12}{(12)^2 + 3(8)} = \frac{64 + 12}{144 + 24} = \frac{76}{168} = \frac{19}{42}$$

64. No; the distance fallen during each second increases from $64 - 16 = 48$ to $256 - 144 = 112$ because the distance varies with the square of the time.

66. Let $x = 6$.
$2x + 7 = 3x$
$2(6) + 7 \stackrel{?}{=} 3(6)$
$12 + 7 \stackrel{?}{=} 18$
$19 = 18$, false
6 is not a solution of the equation.

68. Let $x = 2$.
$4x + 2 = x + 8$
$4(2) + 2 \stackrel{?}{=} 2 + 8$
$8 + 2 \stackrel{?}{=} 10$
$10 = 10$, true
2 is a solution of the equation.

70. Let $x = 6$.
$3x - 10 = 8$
$3(6) - 10 \stackrel{?}{=} 8$
$18 - 10 \stackrel{?}{=} 8$
$8 = 8$, true
6 is a solution of the equation.

72. Let $x = 10$.
$x + 6 = x + 6$
$10 + 6 \stackrel{?}{=} 10 + 6$
$16 = 16$, true
16 is a solution of the equation.

74. Let $x = 1$.
$4 = 1 - x$
$4 \stackrel{?}{=} 1 - 1$
$4 = 0$, false
1 is not a solution of the equation.

76. One-half times a number is $\frac{1}{2}x$.

78. The quotient of a number and 9 is $\frac{x}{9}$.

80. The product means multiply and decreased by means subtract; $8x - 10$

82. Four subtracted from eight is equal to two squared is $8 - 4 = 2^2$.

84. The difference means subtract; $16 - 4 > 10$.

86. Twice a number is 17 is represented as $2x = 17$.

88. Seven subtracted from a number is 0 is represented by $x - 7 = 0$.

90. The sum of 8 and twice a number is 42 is represented by $8 + 2x = 42$.

92. a. expression because it does not have =

b. equation because it has =

c. equation because it has =

d. expression because it does not have =

94. $2 \cdot (5 + 3^2) = 2 \cdot (5 + 9) = 2(14) = 28$

96. $P = a + b + c$

$$= \frac{1}{7} + \frac{5}{14} + \frac{2}{7}$$

$$= \frac{1 \cdot 2}{7 \cdot 2} + \frac{5}{14} + \frac{2 \cdot 2}{7 \cdot 2}$$

$$= \frac{2 + 5 + 4}{14}$$

$$= \frac{11}{14}$$

The perimeter is $\frac{11}{14}$ yd.

98. $A = \frac{1}{2} h(B + b) = \frac{1}{2}(5)(15 + 7) = \frac{1}{2}(5)(22) = 55$

The area is 55 sq in.

100. $r = \frac{d}{t} = \frac{432}{8.5} = 51$

The rate is 51 mph.

102. Density $= \frac{M}{V} = \frac{29.76}{12} = 2.48$

The density is 2.48 g/ml.

Section 1.5

Practice Exercises

1.

$2 + 4 = 6$

2.

$-2 + (-3) = -5$

3. a. $-5 + (-8)$
Add the absolute values.
$5 + 8 = 13$
The common sign is negative, so
$-5 + (-8) = -13$.

b. $-31 + (-1)$
Add the absolute values.
$31 + 1 = 32$
The common sign is negative, so
$-31 + (-1) = -32$.

4.

$-3 + 8 = 5$

5. a. $15 + (-18)$
Subtract the absolute values.
$18 - 15 = 3$
Use the sign of the number with the largest absolute value.
$15 + (-18) = -3$

b. $-19 + 20 = 20 - 19 = 1$

c. $-0.6 + 0.4 = -(0.6 - 0.4) = -(0.2) = -0.2$

6. a. $-\frac{3}{5} + \left(-\frac{2}{5}\right) = -\frac{5}{5} = -1$

b. $3 + (-9) = -6$

c. $2.2 + (-1.7) = 0.5$

d. $-\frac{2}{7} + \frac{3}{10} = -\frac{20}{70} + \frac{21}{70} = \frac{1}{70}$

7. a. $8 + (-5) + (-9) = 3 + (-9) = -6$

b. $[-8 + 5] + \left[-5 + |-2|\right] = [-3] + [-5 + 2]$
$= -3 + [-3]$
$= -6$

8. $-5 + 8 + (-2) = 3 + (-2) = 1$
The overall gain is $1.

9. a. The opposite of $-\frac{5}{9}$ is $\frac{5}{9}$.

b. The opposite of 8 is -8.

c. The opposite of 6.2 is -6.2.

d. The opposite of -3 is 3.

10. a. Since $|-15| = 15$, $-|-15| = -15$.

b. $-\left(-\frac{3}{5}\right) = \frac{3}{5}$

c. $-(-5y) = 5y$

d. $-(-8) = 8$

Vocabulary and Readiness Check

1. Two numbers that are the same distance from 0 but lie on opposite sides of 0 are called <u>opposites</u>.

2. The sum of a number and its opposite is always <u>0</u>.

3. If n is a number, then $-(-n) = \underline{n}$.

4. $-80 + (-127) = $ <u>negative number</u>.

5. $-162 + 164 = $ <u>positive number</u>.

6. $-162 + 162 = \underline{0}$.

7. $-1.26 + (-8.3) = $ <u>negative number</u>.

8. $-3.68 + 0.27 = $ <u>negative number</u>.

9. $-\dfrac{2}{3} + \dfrac{2}{3} = \underline{0}$.

Exercise Set 1.5

2. $9 + (-12) = -3$

4. $-6 + (-14) = -20$

6. $6 + (-4) = 2$

8. $-10 + 5 = -5$

10. $-7 + (-4) = -11$

12. $7 + (-5) = 2$

14. $-5 + 9 = 4$

16. $8 + (-6) = 2$

18. $3 + (-6) = -3$

20. $23 + (-23) = 0$

22. $53 + (-37) = 16$

24. $-26 + 14 = -12$

26. $-18 + (-26) = -44$

28. $9.2 + (-11.4) = -2.2$

30. $|-6| + (-61) = 6 + (-61) = -55$

32. $144 + (-88) = 56$

34. $-6.7 + (-7.6) = -14.3$

36. $-\dfrac{5}{12} + \dfrac{7}{12} = \dfrac{2}{12} = \dfrac{1}{6}$

38. $-\dfrac{5}{9} + \dfrac{1}{3} = -\dfrac{5}{9} + \dfrac{1 \cdot 3}{3 \cdot 3} = -\dfrac{5}{9} + \dfrac{3}{9} = -\dfrac{2}{9}$

40. $-\dfrac{5}{6} + \left(-\dfrac{2}{3}\right) = -\dfrac{5}{6} + \left(-\dfrac{2 \cdot 2}{3 \cdot 2}\right)$
$= -\dfrac{5}{6} + \left(-\dfrac{4}{6}\right)$
$= -\dfrac{9}{6}$
$= -\dfrac{3}{2}$

42. $-9 + 15 + (-5) = 6 + (-5) = 1$

44. $-18 + (-6) + (-40) = -24 + (-40) = -64$

46. $-14 + (-3) + 11 = -17 + 11 = -6$

48. $|7 + (-17)| = |-10| = 10$

50. $8 + (-2) + 7 = 6 + 7 = 13$

52. $[-2 + (-7)] + [-11 + 22] = [-9] + [11] = 2$

54. $|43 + (-73)| + |-20| = |-30| + 20 = 30 + 20 = 50$

56. $-3.7 + [0.1 + (-0.6) + 8.1] = -3.7 + [-0.5 + 8.1]$
$= -3.7 + [7.6]$
$= 3.9$

58. $-4 + 49 = 45$
It rose to a temperature of 45°F.

60. $-512 + 658 = 146$
Your elevation is 146 feet.

62. $(-409) + (-68) + (343) = (-477) + (343) = -134$
The total net income was $-$134$ million.

64. $(-6) + (0) + (-3) + (-6) = (-6) + (-3) + (-6)$
$= (-9) + (-6)$
$= -15$
She was 15 under par.

66. The opposite of 4 is -4.

68. The opposite of -8 is 8.

70. The opposite of $-\dfrac{1}{4}$ is $\dfrac{1}{4}$.

72. Since $|-11|$ is 11, the opposite of $|-11|$ is -11.

74. Answers may vary

76. $-(-3) = 3$

78. $\left|-\dfrac{2}{3}\right| = \dfrac{2}{3}$

80. $-(-7) = 7$

82. Answers may vary

84. Let $x = 10$.
$7 = -x + 3$
$7 \overset{?}{=} -(10) + 3$
$7 = -7$, false
10 is not a solution of the equation.

86. Let $y = -6$.
$1 = y + 7$
$1 \overset{?}{=} -6 + 7$
$1 = 1$, true
-6 is a solution of the equation.

88. Look for the shortest bar. The month for which the temperature is the lowest is February.

90. Look for the bar whose length has a negative value closest to 0; November

92. $[(-19.3) + 27.0 + 8.8] \div 3 = [7.7 + 8.8] \div 3$
$\qquad\qquad\qquad\qquad = [16.5] \div 3$
$\qquad\qquad\qquad\qquad = 5.5$
The average was 5.5°F.

94. Since b is a negative number, $-b$ is a positive number.

96. Since b is a negative number, $b + b$ is a negative number.

Section 1.6

Practice Exercises

1. a. $-7 - 6 = -7 + (-6) = -13$

b. $-8 - (-1) = -8 + 1 = -7$

c. $9 - (-3) = 9 + 3 = 12$

d. $5 - 7 = 5 + (-7) = -2$

2. a. $8.4 - (-2.5) = 8.4 + 2.5 = 10.9$

b. $-\dfrac{5}{8} - \left(-\dfrac{1}{8}\right) = -\dfrac{5}{8} + \dfrac{1}{8} = -\dfrac{4}{8} = -\dfrac{1}{2}$

c. $-\dfrac{3}{4} - \dfrac{1}{5} = -\dfrac{3}{4} + \left(-\dfrac{1}{5}\right)$
$\qquad\qquad = -\dfrac{15}{20} + \left(-\dfrac{4}{20}\right)$
$\qquad\qquad = -\dfrac{19}{20}$

3. $-2 - 5 = -2 + (-5) = -7$

4. a. $-15 - 2 - (-4) + 7 = -15 + (-2) + 4 + 7 = -6$

b. $3.5 + (-4.1) - (-6.7) = 3.5 + (-4.1) + 6.7$
$\qquad\qquad\qquad\qquad = 6.1$

5. a. $-4 + [(-8 - 3) - 5] = -4 + [(-8 + (-3)) - 5]$
$\qquad\qquad\qquad\qquad = -4 + [(-11) - 5]$
$\qquad\qquad\qquad\qquad = -4 + [-11 + (-5)]$
$\qquad\qquad\qquad\qquad = -4 + [-16]$
$\qquad\qquad\qquad\qquad = -20$

b. $|-13| - 3^2 + [2 - (-7)] = 13 - 9 + [2 + 7]$
$\qquad\qquad\qquad\qquad\qquad = 13 - 9 + 9$
$\qquad\qquad\qquad\qquad\qquad = 13$

6. a. $\dfrac{7 - x}{2y + x} = \dfrac{7 - (-3)}{2(4) + (-3)} = \dfrac{7 + 3}{8 + (-3)} = \dfrac{10}{5} = 2$

b. $y^2 + x = (4)^2 + (-3) = 16 + (-3) = 13$

7. $282 - (-75) = 282 + 75 = \$357$

8. a. $x = 90° - 62° = 28°$

b. $y = 180° - 43° = 137°$

Vocabulary and Readiness Check

1. 7 minus a number $\underline{7 - x}$

2. 7 subtracted from a number $\underline{x - 7}$.

3. A number decreased by 7 $\underline{x - 7}$

4. 7 less a number $\underline{7-x}$

5. A number less than 7 $\underline{7-x}$

6. A number subtracted from 7 $\underline{7-x}$

Exercise Set 1.6

2. $-12 - 8 = -12 + (-8) = -20$

4. $8 - 11 = 8 + (-11) = -3$

6. $12 - (-5) = 12 + 5 = 17$

8. $\dfrac{3}{4} - \dfrac{7}{8} = \dfrac{3}{4} + \left(-\dfrac{7}{8}\right)$

     $= \dfrac{3 \cdot 2}{4 \cdot 2} + \left(-\dfrac{7}{8}\right)$

     $= \dfrac{6}{8} + \left(-\dfrac{7}{8}\right)$

     $= -\dfrac{1}{8}$

10. $-20 - (-48) = -20 + 48 = 28$

12. $-8 - 4 = -8 + (-4) = -12$

14. $3 - (-6) = 3 + 6 = 9$

16. $-4 - (-16) = -4 + 16 = 12$

18. $15 - (-33) = 15 + 33 = 48$

20. $8.3 - 11.2 = 8.3 + (-11.2) = -2.9$

22. $-36 - 51 = -36 + (-51) = -87$

24. $-17 - (-17) = -17 + 17 = 0$

26. $-6.1 - (-5.3) = -6.1 + 5.3 = -0.8$

28. $-\dfrac{4}{7} - \left(-\dfrac{1}{7}\right) = -\dfrac{4}{7} + \dfrac{1}{7} = -\dfrac{3}{7}$

30. $-\dfrac{1}{10} - \dfrac{7}{8} = -\dfrac{1}{10} + \left(-\dfrac{7}{8}\right)$

     $= -\dfrac{1 \cdot 4}{10 \cdot 4} + \left(-\dfrac{7 \cdot 5}{8 \cdot 5}\right)$

     $= -\dfrac{4}{40} + \left(-\dfrac{35}{40}\right)$

     $= -\dfrac{39}{40}$

32. $4.3 - (-0.87) = 4.3 + 0.87 = 5.17$

34. $-2 - 3 = -2 + (-3) = -5$

36. $1 - 17 = 1 + (-17) = -16$

38. $-4 - 9 = -4 + (-9) = -13$

40. $11 - (-14) = 11 + 14 = 25$

42. Answers may vary

44. $-16 - (-3) + (-11) - 14 = -16 + 3 + (-11) + (-14)$

     $= -13 + (-11) + (-14)$

     $= -24 + (-14)$

     $= -38$

46. $7 - 12 + (-5) - 2 + (-2)$

     $= 7 + (-12) + (-5) + (-2) + (-2)$

     $= -5 + (-5) + (-2) + (-2)$

     $= -10 + (-2) + (-2)$

     $= -12 + (-2)$

     $= -14$

48. $-9 - (3 - 8) = -9 - (-5) = -9 + 5 = -4$

50. $2^3 - 6 \cdot 3 = 8 - 6 \cdot 3 = 8 - 18 = 8 + (-18) = -10$

52. $4 - 6(7 - 3) = 4 - 6(4) = 4 - 24 = 4 + (-24) = -20$

54. $(2 - 3) + 5^2 = [2 + (-3)] + 5^2$

     $= [-1] + 5^2$

     $= [-1] + 25$

     $= 24$

56. $-5 + [(4 - 15) - (-6) - 8]$

     $= -5 + [(4 + (-15)) + 6 + (-8)]$

     $= -5 + [(-11) + 6 + (-8)]$

     $= -5 + [(-5) + (-8)]$

     $= -5 + [-13]$

     $= -18$

58. $|-2| + 6^2 + (-3 - 8) = 2 + 6^2 + [-3 + (-8)]$

     $= 2 + 6^2 + [-11]$

     $= 2 + 36 + [-11]$

     $= 38 + [-11]$

     $= 27$

60. Let $x = -5$ and $y = 4$.

     $y - x = 4 - (-5) = 4 + 5 = 9$

62. Let $x = -5$, $y = 4$, and $t = 10$.
$$\begin{aligned}
|x + t - 7y| &= |-5 + 10 - 7(4)| \\
&= |-5 + 10 - 28| \\
&= |-5 + 10 + (-28)| \\
&= |5 + (-28)| \\
&= |-23| \\
&= 23
\end{aligned}$$

64. Let $x = -5$ an $y = 4$.
$$\frac{15 - x}{y + 2} = \frac{15 - (-5)}{4 + 2} = \frac{15 + 5}{4 + 2} = \frac{20}{6} = \frac{2 \cdot 10}{2 \cdot 3} = \frac{10}{3}$$

66. Let $x = -5$ and $t = 10$.
$$t^2 - x = 10^2 - (-5) = 100 + 5 = 105$$

68. Let $x = -5$, $y = 4$ and $t = 10$.
$$\begin{aligned}
\frac{|5y - x|}{6t} &= \frac{|5(4) - (-5)|}{6(10)} \\
&= \frac{|20 + 5|}{6(10)} \\
&= \frac{|25|}{6(10)} \\
&= \frac{25}{60} \\
&= \frac{5 \cdot 5}{12 \cdot 5} \\
&= \frac{5}{12}
\end{aligned}$$

70. $5 + (-12) = -7$
The new elevation is 7 feet below sea level.

72. Beginning: $+15$
Loss: -24
$15 + (-24) = -9$
New score is -9 points.

74. $60 - 70 = 60 + (-70) = -10$
He was born in 10 B.C.

76. Drops: -1.625, -0.75
$-1.625 + (-0.75) = -2.375$
The overall change in the price of the stock was a drop of 2.375 points.

78. The difference in elevation is
the higher elevation − the lower elevation.
$4101 - (-226) = 4101 + 226 = 4327$
4327 feet higher

80. $x = 90 - 50 = 90 + (-50) = 40$
The complementary angle is $40°$.

82. $y = 180 - 105 = 180 + (-105) = 75$
The supplementary angle is $75°$.

84. Let $x = 3$.
$$\begin{aligned}
x - 10 &= -7 \\
3 - 10 &\overset{?}{=} -7 \\
-7 &= -7, \text{ true}
\end{aligned}$$
3 is a solution of the equation.

86. Let $x = -10$.
$$\begin{aligned}
-x - 6 &= -x - 1 \\
-(-10) - 6 &\overset{?}{=} -(-10) - 1 \\
10 + (-6) &\overset{?}{=} 10 + (-1) \\
4 &= 9, \text{ false}
\end{aligned}$$
-10 is not a solution of the equation.

88. Let $x = 5$.
$$\begin{aligned}
4 &= 1 - x \\
4 &\overset{?}{=} 1 - 5 \\
4 &\overset{?}{=} 1 + (-5) \\
4 &= -4, \text{ false}
\end{aligned}$$
5 is not a solution of the equation.

90. The change in temperature is the difference between the given month's temperature and the previous month's.
F: $-23.7 - (-19.3) = -23.7 + 19.3 = -4.4°$
Mr: $-21.1 - (-23.7) = -21.1 + 23.7 = 2.6°$
Ap: $-9.1 - (-21.1) = -9.1 + 21.1 = 12°$
Ma: $14.4 - (-9.1) = 14.4 + 9.1 = 23.5°$
Jn: $29.7 - 14.4 = 29.7 + (-14.4) = 15.3°$
Jy: $33.6 - 29.7 = 33.6 + (-29.7) = 3.9°$
Au: $33.3 - 33.6 = 33.3 + (-33.6) = -0.3°$
S: $27.0 - 33.3 = 27.0 + (-33.3) = -6.3°$
O: $8.8 - 27.0 = 8.8 + (-27.0) = -18.2°$
N: $-6.9 - 8.8 = -6.9 + (-8.8) = -15.7°$
D: $-17.2 - (-6.9) = -17.2 + 6.9 = -10.3°$
May showed the greatest increase.

92. True; answers may vary

94. False; answers may vary

96. Negative
$56,875 - 87,262 = -30,387$

Integrated Review

1. The opposite of a positive number is a <u>negative</u> number.

2. The sum of two negative numbers is a <u>negative</u> number.

3. The absolute value of a negative number is a <u>positive</u> number.

4. The absolute value of zero is <u>0</u>.

5. The reciprocal of a positive number is a <u>positive</u> number.

6. The sum of a number and its opposite is <u>0</u>.

7. The absolute value of a positive number is a <u>positive</u> number.

8. The opposite of a negative number is a <u>positive</u> number.

	Number	Opposite	Absolute Value
9.	$\frac{1}{7}$	$-\frac{1}{7}$	$\frac{1}{7}$
10.	$-\frac{12}{5}$	$\frac{12}{5}$	$\frac{12}{5}$
11.	3	-3	3
12.	$-\frac{9}{11}$	$\frac{9}{11}$	$\frac{9}{11}$

13. $-19 + (-23) = -42$

14. $7 - (-3) = 7 + 3 = 10$

15. $-15 + 17 = 2$

16. $-8 - 10 = -8 + (-10) = -18$

17. $18 + (-25) = -7$

18. $-2 + (-37) = -39$

19. $-14 - (-12) = -14 + 12 = -2$

20. $5 - 14 = 5 + (-14) = -9$

21. $4.5 - 7.9 = 4.5 + (-7.9) = -3.4$

22. $-8.6 - 1.2 = -8.6 + (-1.2) = -9.8$

23. $-\dfrac{3}{4} - \dfrac{1}{7} = -\dfrac{21}{28} - \dfrac{4}{28} = -\dfrac{21}{28} + \left(-\dfrac{4}{28}\right) = -\dfrac{25}{28}$

24. $\dfrac{2}{3} - \dfrac{7}{8} = \dfrac{16}{24} - \dfrac{21}{24} = \dfrac{16}{24} + \left(-\dfrac{21}{24}\right) = -\dfrac{5}{24}$

25. $\begin{aligned}-9 - (-7) + 4 - 6 &= -9 + 7 + 4 - 6 \\ &= -9 + 7 + 4 + (-6) \\ &= -4\end{aligned}$

26. $\begin{aligned}11 - 20 + (-3) - 12 &= 11 + (-20) + (-3) + (-12) \\ &= -9 + (-3) + (-12) \\ &= -12 + (-12) \\ &= -24\end{aligned}$

27. $\begin{aligned}24 - 6(14 - 11) &= 24 - 6[14 + (-11)] \\ &= 24 - 6(3) \\ &= 24 - 18 \\ &= 24 + (-18) \\ &= 6\end{aligned}$

28. $\begin{aligned}30 - 5(10 - 8) &= 30 - 5[10 + (-8)] \\ &= 30 - 5(2) \\ &= 30 - 10 \\ &= 30 + (-10) \\ &= 20\end{aligned}$

29. $(7 - 17) + 4^2 = [7 + (-17)] + 4^2 = (-10) + 16 = 6$

30. $\begin{aligned}9^2 + (10 - 30) &= 9^2 + [10 + (-30)] \\ &= 81 + (-20) \\ &= 61\end{aligned}$

31. $\begin{aligned}\left|-9\right| + 3^2 + (-4 - 20) &= 9 + 9 + [-4 + (-20)] \\ &= 9 + 9 + (-24) \\ &= 18 + (-24) \\ &= -6\end{aligned}$

32. $\begin{aligned}\left|-4 - 5\right| + 5^2 + (-50) &= \left|-4 + (-5)\right| + 5^2 + (-50) \\ &= \left|-9\right| + 25 + (-50) \\ &= 9 + 25 + (-50) \\ &= 34 + (-50) \\ &= -16\end{aligned}$

33. $\begin{aligned}-7 + [(1 - 2) + (-2 - 9)] &= -7 + [(-1) + (-11)] \\ &= -7 + [-12] \\ &= -19\end{aligned}$

34. $\begin{aligned}-6 + [(-3 + 7) + (4 - 15)] &= -6 + [(4) + (-11)] \\ &= -6 + (-7) \\ &= -13\end{aligned}$

35. $1 - 5 = 1 + (-5) = -4$

36. $-3-(-2) = -3+2 = -1$

37. $\dfrac{1}{4}-\left(-\dfrac{2}{5}\right) = \dfrac{1}{4}+\dfrac{2}{5} = \dfrac{5}{20}+\dfrac{8}{20} = \dfrac{13}{20}$

38. $-\dfrac{5}{8}-\left(\dfrac{1}{10}\right) = -\dfrac{25}{40}-\dfrac{4}{40} = -\dfrac{25}{40}+\left(-\dfrac{4}{40}\right) = -\dfrac{29}{40}$

39. $2(19-17)^3 - 3(-7+9)^2$
$= 2[19+(-17)]^3 - 3(-7+9)^2$
$= 2(2)^3 - 3(2)^2$
$= 2(8) - 3(4)$
$= 16 - 12$
$= 16 + (-12)$
$= 4$

40. $3(10-9)^2 + 6(20-19)^3$
$= 3[10+(-9)]^2 + 6[20+(-19)]^3$
$= 3(1)^2 + 6(1)^3$
$= 3 + 6$
$= 9$

41. $x-y = -2-(-1) = -2+1 = -1$

42. $x+y = -2+(-1) = -3$

43. $y+z = -1+9 = 8$

44. $z-y = 9-(-1) = 9+1 = 10$

45. $\dfrac{|5z-x|}{y-x} = \dfrac{|5(9)-(-2)|}{-1-(-2)} = \dfrac{|45+2|}{-1+2} = \dfrac{|47|}{1} = 47$

46. $\dfrac{|-x-y+z|}{2z} = \dfrac{|-(-2)-(-1)+9|}{2(9)}$
$= \dfrac{|2+1+9|}{18}$
$= \dfrac{|12|}{18}$
$= \dfrac{12}{18}$
$= \dfrac{2}{3}$

Section 1.7

Practice Exercises

1. a. $8(-5) = -40$

  b. $(-3)(-4) = 12$

  c. $(-6)(9) = -54$

2. a. $(-1)(-5)(-6) = 5(-6) = -30$

  b. $(-3)(-2)(4) = 6(4) = 24$

  c. $(-4)(0)(5) = 0(5) = 0$

  d. $(-2)(-3)-(-4)(5) = 6-(-20)$
$= 6+20$
$= 26$

3. a. $(0.23)(-0.2) = -[(0.23)(0.2)] = -0.046$

  b. $\left(-\dfrac{3}{5}\right)\cdot\left(\dfrac{4}{9}\right) = -\dfrac{3\cdot 4}{5\cdot 9} = -\dfrac{12}{45} = -\dfrac{4}{15}$

  c. $\left(-\dfrac{7}{12}\right)(-24) = \dfrac{7\cdot 24}{12\cdot 1} = 7\cdot 2 = 14$

4. a. $(-6)^2 = (-6)(-6) = 36$

  b. $-6^2 = -(6\cdot 6) = -(36) = -36$

  c. $(-4)^3 = (-4)(-4)(-4) = 16(-4) = -64$

  d. $-4^3 = -(4\cdot 4\cdot 4) = -[16(4)] = -64$

5. a. The reciprocal of $\dfrac{8}{3}$ is $\dfrac{3}{8}$ since $\dfrac{8}{3}\cdot\dfrac{3}{8} = 1$.

  b. The reciprocal of 15 is $\dfrac{1}{15}$ since $15\cdot\dfrac{1}{15} = 1$.

  c. The reciprocal of $-\dfrac{2}{7}$ is $-\dfrac{7}{2}$ since
$\left(-\dfrac{2}{7}\right)\left(-\dfrac{7}{2}\right) = 1$.

d. The reciprocal of -5 is $-\dfrac{1}{5}$ since

$$(-5)\left(-\frac{1}{5}\right) = 1.$$

6. a. $\dfrac{16}{-2} = 16\left(-\dfrac{1}{2}\right) = -8$

b. $24 \div (-6) = 24\left(-\dfrac{1}{6}\right) = -4$

c. $\dfrac{-35}{-7} = \dfrac{35}{7} = \dfrac{5 \cdot 7}{7} = 5$

7. a. $\dfrac{-18}{-6} = \dfrac{18}{6} = \dfrac{3 \cdot 6}{6} = 3$

b. $\dfrac{-48}{3} = -\dfrac{48}{3} = -\dfrac{3 \cdot 16}{3} = -16$

c. $\dfrac{3}{5} \div \left(-\dfrac{1}{2}\right) = \dfrac{3}{5} \cdot (-2) = -\dfrac{6}{5}$

d. $-\dfrac{4}{9} \div 8 = -\dfrac{4}{9} \cdot \dfrac{1}{8} = -\dfrac{4}{9 \cdot 4 \cdot 2} = -\dfrac{1}{9 \cdot 2} = -\dfrac{1}{18}$

8. a. $\dfrac{0}{-2} = 0$

b. $\dfrac{-4}{0}$ is undefined.

c. $\dfrac{-5}{6(0)} = \dfrac{-5}{0}$ is undefined.

9. a. $\dfrac{(-8)(-11) - 4}{-9 - (-4)} = \dfrac{88 - 4}{-9 + 4} = \dfrac{84}{-5} = -\dfrac{84}{5}$

b. $\dfrac{3(-2)^3 - 9}{-6 + 3} = \dfrac{3(-8) - 9}{-3}$

$\qquad = \dfrac{-24 - 9}{-3}$

$\qquad = \dfrac{-33}{-3}$

$\qquad = 11$

10. a. $7y - x = 7(-2) - (-5) = -14 + 5 = -9$

b. $\begin{aligned} x^2 - y^3 &= (-5)^2 - (-2)^3 \\ &= 25 - (-8) \\ &= 25 + 8 \\ &= 33 \end{aligned}$

c. $\dfrac{2x}{3y} = \dfrac{2(-5)}{3(-2)} = \dfrac{-10}{-6} = \dfrac{5}{3}$

Calculator Explorations

1. $-38(26 - 27) = 38$

2. $-59(-8) + 1726 = 2198$

3. $134 + 25(68 - 91) = -441$

4. $45(32) - 8(218) = -304$

5. $\dfrac{-50(294)}{175 - 265} = 163.\overline{3}$

6. $\dfrac{-444 - 444.8}{-181 - 324} = 1.76$

7. $9^5 - 4550 = 54,499$

8. $5^8 - 6259 = 384,366$

9. $(-125)^2 = 15,625$

10. $-125^2 = -15,625$

Vocabulary and Readiness Check

1. If n is a real number, then $n \cdot 0 = \underline{0}$ and $0 \cdot n = \underline{0}$.

2. If n is a real number, but not 0, then $\dfrac{0}{n} = \underline{0}$ and

we say $\dfrac{n}{0}$ is <u>undefined</u>.

3. The product of two negative numbers is a <u>positive</u> number.

4. The quotient of two negative numbers is a <u>positive</u> number.

5. The quotient of a positive number and a negative number is a <u>negative</u> number.

6. The product of a positive number and a negative number is a <u>negative</u> number.

7. The reciprocal of a positive number is a <u>positive</u> number.

8. The opposite of a positive number is a <u>negative</u> number.

Exercise Set 1.7

2. $-8(5) = -40$

4. $7(-4) = -28$

6. $-6(-11) = 66$

8. $-2 \cdot 8 = -16$

10. $-6 \cdot 0 = 0$

12. $3(-5) = -15$

14. $-\dfrac{1}{8}\left(-\dfrac{1}{3}\right) = \dfrac{1 \cdot 1}{8 \cdot 3} = \dfrac{1}{24}$

16. $-\dfrac{5}{6}\left(-\dfrac{3}{10}\right) = \dfrac{5 \cdot 3}{6 \cdot 10} = \dfrac{15}{60} = \dfrac{15}{15 \cdot 4} = \dfrac{1}{4}$

18. $6(-2.5) = -15$

20. $-0.5(-0.3) = 0.15$

22. $-20(60) = -1200$

24. $5(-9) = -45$

26. $(-7)(-7) = 49$

28. $\dfrac{2}{7}\left(-\dfrac{2}{11}\right) = -\dfrac{2 \cdot 2}{7 \cdot 11} = -\dfrac{4}{77}$

30. $-12(12) = -144$

32. $-\dfrac{25}{36}\left(\dfrac{6}{15}\right) = -\dfrac{25 \cdot 6}{36 \cdot 15} = -\dfrac{150}{480} = -\dfrac{5}{18}$

34. $(-2)(-3)(-4)(-2) = 6(-4)(-2) = -24(-2) = 48$

36. $8(-3) - 4(-5) = -24 - (-20) = -24 + 20 = -4$

38. $20 - (-4)(3)(-2) = 20 - (24) = 20 + (-24) = -4$

40. True; example: $2 \cdot 2 \cdot 2 = 8$

42. True; example: $2 \cdot 2 \cdot 2 \cdot 2 = 16$

44. $-2^4 = -(2 \cdot 2 \cdot 2 \cdot 2) = -16$

46. $(-1)^5 = (-1)(-1)(-1)(-1)(-1) = -1$

48. $-5^2 = -(5 \cdot 5) = -25$

50. $(-7)^2 = (-7)(-7) = 49$

52. Reciprocal of 100 is $\dfrac{1}{100}$ since $100 \cdot \dfrac{1}{100} = 1$.

54. Reciprocal of $\dfrac{1}{7}$ is 7 since $\dfrac{1}{7} \cdot 7 = 1$.

56. Reciprocal of -8 is $-\dfrac{1}{8}$ since $-8 \cdot -\dfrac{1}{8} = 1$.

58. Reciprocal of $-\dfrac{6}{13}$ is $-\dfrac{13}{6}$ since $-\dfrac{6}{13} \cdot -\dfrac{13}{6} = 1$.

60. Reciprocal of 1.5 is $\dfrac{1}{1.5}$ since $1.5 \cdot \dfrac{1}{1.5} = 1$.

62. Reciprocal of $\dfrac{1}{-8.9}$ is -8.9 since
$\dfrac{1}{-8.9} \cdot -8.9 = 1$.

64. $\dfrac{20}{-10} = 20 \cdot -\dfrac{1}{10} = -2$

66. $\dfrac{-18}{-6} = -18 \cdot -\dfrac{1}{6} = 3$

68. $\dfrac{-60}{5} = -60 \cdot \dfrac{1}{5} = -12$

70. $\dfrac{0}{-9} = 0 \cdot -\dfrac{1}{9} = 0$

72. $-\dfrac{24}{8} = -24 \cdot \dfrac{1}{8} = -3$

74. $\dfrac{3}{0}$ is undefined.

76. $\dfrac{-45}{-9} = -45 \cdot -\dfrac{1}{9} = 5$

78. $\dfrac{14}{-2} = 14 \cdot -\dfrac{1}{2} = -7$

80. $\dfrac{4}{5} \div \left(-\dfrac{1}{2}\right) = \dfrac{4}{5} \cdot \left(-\dfrac{2}{1}\right) = -\dfrac{4 \cdot 2}{5 \cdot 1} = -\dfrac{8}{5}$

82. $-\dfrac{1}{10} \div \left(-\dfrac{8}{11}\right) = -\dfrac{1}{10} \cdot \left(-\dfrac{11}{8}\right) = \dfrac{1 \cdot 11}{10 \cdot 8} = \dfrac{11}{80}$

84. $-\dfrac{5}{12} \div \dfrac{5}{12} = -\dfrac{5}{12} \cdot \dfrac{12}{5} = -\dfrac{5 \cdot 12}{12 \cdot 5} = -1$

86. $\dfrac{-6(-3)}{-4} = \dfrac{18}{-4} = -\dfrac{9}{2}$

88. $\dfrac{-15}{1-4} = \dfrac{-15}{-3} = 5$

90. $\dfrac{3^2 + 4}{5} = \dfrac{9 + 4}{5} = \dfrac{13}{5}$

92. $\dfrac{6 + (-2)^2}{4 - 9} = \dfrac{6 + 4}{4 - 9} = \dfrac{10}{-5} = -2$

94. $\dfrac{-20 + (-4)(3)}{1 - 5} = \dfrac{-20 + (-12)}{1 - 5} = \dfrac{-32}{-4} = 8$

96. $\dfrac{-2 - 4^2}{3(-6)} = \dfrac{-2 - 16}{3(-6)} = \dfrac{-2 + (-16)}{-18} = \dfrac{-18}{-18} = 1$

98. $\dfrac{8 - 3(-2)}{2 - 5(-4)} = \dfrac{8 - (-6)}{2 - (-20)} = \dfrac{8 + 6}{2 + 20} = \dfrac{14}{22} = \dfrac{7}{11}$

100. $\dfrac{-4 - 8(-2)}{-9 - 2(-3)} = \dfrac{-4 - (-16)}{-9 - (-6)} = \dfrac{-4 + 16}{-9 + 6} = \dfrac{12}{-3} = -4$

102. $\dfrac{|-3 + 6| + |-2 + 7|}{|-2 \cdot 2|} = \dfrac{|3| + |5|}{|-4|} = \dfrac{3 + 5}{4} = \dfrac{8}{4} = 2$

104. Let $x = -5$ and $y = -3$.
$4x + 5y = 4(-5) + 5(-3) = -20 + (-15) = -35$

106. Let $x = -5$ and $y = -3$.
$$\begin{aligned} x^2 - 2y^2 &= (-5)^2 - 2(-3)^2 \\ &= 25 - 2(9) \\ &= 25 + (-18) \\ &= 7 \end{aligned}$$

108. Let $x = -5$ and $y = -3$.
$y^3 + 3x = (-3)^3 + 3(-5) = -27 + (-15) = -42$

110. Let $x = -5$ and $y = -3$.
$\dfrac{2y - 12}{x - 4} = \dfrac{2(-3) - 12}{-5 - 4} = \dfrac{-6 - 12}{-5 - 4} = \dfrac{-18}{-9} = 2$

112. Let $x = -5$ and $y = -3$.
$\dfrac{4 - 2x}{y + 3} = \dfrac{4 - 2(-5)}{-3 + 3} = \dfrac{4 + 10}{0}$ is undefined.

114. $4(-115) = -460$
The income would be –$460 million.

116. Let $x = -4$.
$$\begin{aligned} 2x &= x - 1 \\ 2(-4) &\overset{?}{=} -4 - 1 \\ -8 &= -5, \text{ false} \end{aligned}$$
–4 is not a solution of the equation.

118. Let $x = -3$.
$$\begin{aligned} \dfrac{45}{x} &= -15 \\ \dfrac{45}{-3} &\overset{?}{=} -15 \\ -15 &= -15, \text{ true} \end{aligned}$$
–3 is a solution of the equation.

120. Let $x = -4$.
$$\begin{aligned} 2x + 4 &= x + 8 \\ 2(-4) + 4 &\overset{?}{=} -4 + 8 \\ -8 + 4 &\overset{?}{=} 4 \\ -4 &= 4, \text{ false} \end{aligned}$$
–4 is not a solution of the equation.

122. Yes; multiplication is commutative.

124. Answers may vary

126. Since q is negative, r is negative, and t is positive, then $q^2 \cdot r \cdot t$ is negative.

128. Not possible to determine whether $t + r$ is positive or negative.

130. Since q is negative, r is negative, and t is positive, then $r(q - t)$ is positive.

132. $1 + (-8)(-5) = 1 + 40 = 41$

134. $\dfrac{0}{5} - 7 = 0 - 7 = -7$

The Bigger Picture

1. $-0.2(25) - 5$

2. $86 - 100 = -14$

3. $-\dfrac{1}{7} + \left(-\dfrac{3}{5}\right) = -\dfrac{5}{35} - \dfrac{21}{35} = -\dfrac{26}{35}$

4. $\dfrac{-40}{-5} = 8$

5. $(-7)^2 = (-7)(-7) = 49$

6. $-7^2 = -(7 \cdot 7) = -49$

7. $\dfrac{|-42|}{-|-2|} = \dfrac{42}{-2} = -21$

8. $\dfrac{8.6}{0}$ is undefined.

9. $\dfrac{0}{8.6} = 0$

10. $-25 - (-13) = -25 + 13 = -12$

11. $-8.3 - 8.3 = -16.6$

12. $-\dfrac{8}{9}\left(-\dfrac{3}{16}\right) = \dfrac{3 \cdot 8}{9 \cdot 16} = \dfrac{1 \cdot 1}{3 \cdot 2} = \dfrac{1}{6}$

13. $2 + 3(8 - 11)^3 = 2 + 3(-3)^3$
$= 2 + 3(-27)$
$= 2 + (-81)$
$= -79$

14. $-2\dfrac{1}{2} \div \left(-3\dfrac{1}{4}\right) = -\dfrac{5}{2} \div \left(-\dfrac{13}{4}\right)$
$= -\dfrac{5}{2}\left(-\dfrac{4}{13}\right)$
$= \dfrac{4 \cdot 5}{2 \cdot 13}$
$= \dfrac{2 \cdot 5}{13}$
$= \dfrac{10}{13}$

15. $20 \div 2 \cdot 5 = 10 \cdot 5 = 50$

16. $-2[(1 - 5) - (7 - 17)] = -2[(-4) - (-10)]$
$= -2[-4 + 10]$
$= -2[6]$
$= -12$

Section 1.8

Practice Exercises

1. **a.** $x \cdot 8 = \underline{8 \cdot x}$

   b. $x + 17 = \underline{17 + x}$

2. **a.** $(2 + 9) + 7 = \underline{2 + (9 + 7)}$

   b. $-4 \cdot (2 \cdot 7) = \underline{(-4 \cdot 2) \cdot 7}$

3. **a.** $(5 + x) + 9 = (x + 5) + 9 = x + (5 + 9) = x + 14$

   b. $5(-6x) = [5 \cdot (-6)]x = -30x$

4. **a.** $5(x - y) = 5(x) - 5(y) = 5x - 5y$

   b. $-6(4 + 2t) = -6(4) + (-6)(2t) = -24 - 12t$

   c. $2(3x - 4y - z) = 2(3x) + 2(-4y) + 2(-z)$
$= 6x - 8y - 2z$

   d. $(3 - y) \cdot (-1) = 3(-1) + (-y)(-1) = -3 + y$

   e. $-(x - 7 + 2s) = (-1)(x - 7 + 2s)$
$= (-1)x + (-1)(-7) + (-1)(2s)$
$= -x + 7 - 2s$

   f. $2(7x + 4) + 6 = 2(7x) + 2(4) + 6$
$= 14x + 8 + 6$
$= 14x + 14$

5. **a.** $5 \cdot w + 5 \cdot 3 = 5(w + 3)$

b. $9w + 9z = 9 \cdot w + 9 \cdot z = 9(w + z)$

6. a. $(7 \cdot 3x) \cdot 4 = (3x \cdot 7) \cdot 4$; commutative property of multiplication

b. $6 + (3 + y) = (6 + 3) + y$; associative property of addition

c. $8 + (t + 0) = 8 + t$; identity element for addition

d. $-\dfrac{3}{4} \cdot \left(-\dfrac{4}{3}\right) = 1$; multiplicative inverse property

e. $(2 + x) + 5 = 5 + (2 + x)$; commutative property of addition

f. $3 + (-3) = 0$; additive inverse property

g. $(-3b) \cdot 7 = (-3 \cdot 7) \cdot b$; commutative and associative properties of multiplication

Vocabulary and Readiness Check

1. $x + 5 = 5 + x$ is a true statement by the <u>commutative property of addition</u>.

2. $x \cdot 5 = 5 \cdot x$ is a true statement by the <u>commutative property of multiplication</u>.

3. $3(y + 6) = 3 \cdot y + 3 \cdot 6$ is true by the <u>distributive property</u>.

4. $2 \cdot (x \cdot y) = (2 \cdot x) \cdot y$ is a true statement by the <u>associative property of multiplication</u>.

5. $x + (7 + y) = (x + 7) + y$ is a true statement by the <u>associative property of addition</u>.

6. The numbers $-\dfrac{2}{3}$ and $-\dfrac{3}{2}$ are called <u>reciprocals or multiplicative inverses</u>.

7. The numbers $-\dfrac{2}{3}$ and $\dfrac{2}{3}$ are called <u>opposites or additive inverses</u>.

Exercise Set 1.8

2. $4 + y = y + 4$

4. $-2 \cdot x = x \cdot (-2)$

6. $ab = ba$

8. $19 + 3y = 3y + 19$

10. $3 \cdot (xy) = (3x) \cdot y$

12. $(y + 4) + z = y + (4 + z)$

14. $(-3y) \cdot z = -3 \cdot (yz)$

16. $6 + (r + s) = (6 + r) + s$

18. $(r + 3) + 11 = r + (3 + 11) = r + 14$

20. $2(42x) = (2 \cdot 42)x = 84x$

22. $\dfrac{1}{8}(8z) = \left(\dfrac{1}{8} \cdot 8\right)z = 1 \cdot z = z$

24. $7 + (x + 4) = 7 + (4 + x) = (7 + 4) + x = 11 + x$

26. $-3(12y) = (-3 \cdot 12)y = -36y$

28. $\dfrac{2}{7}\left(\dfrac{7}{2}r\right) = \left(\dfrac{2}{7} \cdot \dfrac{7}{2}\right)r = 1r = r$

30. Answers may vary

32. $7(a + b) = 7a + 7b$

34. $11(y - 4) = 11y - 11 \cdot 4 = 11y - 44$

36. $5(7 + 8y) = 5(7) + 5(8y) = 35 + 40y$

38. $3(8x - 1) = 3(8x) - 3(1) = 24x - 3$

40. $2(x + 5) = 2(x) + 2(5) = 2x + 10$

42. $-3(z - y) = -3z - (-3)y = -3z + 3y$

44. $-5(2r + 11) = -5(2r) + (-5)(11) = -10r - 55$

46. $8(3y + z - 6) = 8(3y) + 8z - 8(6) = 24y + 8z - 48$

48. $-4(4 + 2p + 5) = -4(4) + (-4)(2p) + (-4)(5)$
$$= -16 - 8p - 20$$

50. $-(9r + 5) = -1(9r + 5)$
$$= -1(9r) + (-1)(5)$$
$$= -9r - 5$$

52. $-(q - 2 + 6r) = -1(q - 2 + 6r)$
$$= -1q - (-1)(2) + (-1)(6r)$$
$$= -q + 2 - 6r$$

54. $\frac{1}{4}(4x-2) = \frac{1}{4}(4x) - \frac{1}{4}(2)$

$\qquad = \left(\frac{1}{4} \cdot 4\right)x - \left(\frac{1}{4} \cdot 2\right)$

$\qquad = x - \frac{1}{2}$

56. $-\frac{1}{5}(10a - 25b) = -\frac{1}{5}(10a) - \left(-\frac{1}{5}\right)(25b)$

$\qquad = \left(-\frac{1}{5} \cdot 10\right)a - \left(-\frac{1}{5} \cdot 25\right)b$

$\qquad = -2 \cdot a + 5 \cdot b$

$\qquad = -2a + 5b$

58. $10(4s + 6) - 40 = 10(4s) + 10(6) - 40$

$\qquad = 40s + 60 + (-40)$

$\qquad = 40s + 20$

60. $-11(5x + 3) + 10 = -11(5x) + (-11)(3) + 10$

$\qquad = -55x - 33 + 10$

$\qquad = -55x - 23$

62. $-6(2x + 1) - 1 = -6(2x) + (-6)(1) - 1$

$\qquad = -12x + (-6) - 1$

$\qquad = -12x - 7$

64. $14 \cdot z + 14 \cdot 5 = 14(z + 5)$

66. $9a + 9b = 9(a + b)$

68. $(-3)a + (-3)b = -3(a + b)$

70. $25x + 25y = 25(x + y)$

72. $4(3 + 8) = 4 \cdot 3 + 4 \cdot 8$; distributive property

74. $(x + 9) + 3 = (9 + x) + 3$; commutative property of addition

76. $1 \cdot 9 = 9$; identity element of multiplication

78. $6 \cdot \frac{1}{6} = 1$; multiplicative inverse property

80. $(a + 9) + 6 = a + (9 + 6)$; associative property of addition

82. $(11 + r) + 8 = (r + 11) + 8$; commutative property of addition

84. $r + 0 = r$; identity element of addition

86.

Expression	Opposite	Reciprocal
$-\frac{2}{3}$	$\frac{2}{3}$	$-\frac{3}{2}$

88.

Expression	Opposite	Reciprocal
$4y$	$-4y$	$\frac{1}{4y}$

90.

Expression	Opposite	Reciprocal
$-7x$	$7x$	$-\frac{1}{7x}$

92. No

94. Yes

96. Answers may vary

Chapter 1 Vocabulary Check

1. The symbols $\neq$, $<$, and $>$ are called <u>inequality symbols</u>.

2. A mathematical statement that two expressions are equal is called an <u>equation</u>.

3. The <u>absolute value</u> of a number is the distance between that number and 0 on the number line.

4. A symbol used to represent a number is called a <u>variable</u>.

5. Two numbers that are the same distance from 0 but lie on opposite sides of 0 are called <u>opposites</u>.

6. The number in a fraction above the fraction bar is called the <u>numerator</u>.

7. A <u>solution</u> of an equation is a value for the variable that makes the equation a true statement.

8. Two numbers whose product is 1 are called <u>reciprocals</u>.

9. In 2^3, the 2 is called the <u>base</u> and the 3 is called the <u>exponent</u>.

10. The number in a fraction below the fraction bar is called the <u>denominator</u>.

11. Parentheses and brackets are examples of <u>grouping symbols</u>.

12. A <u>set</u> is a collection of objects.

Chapter 1 Review

1. $8 < 10$ since 8 is to the left of 10 on the number line.

2. $7 > 2$ since 7 is to the right of 2 on the number line.

3. $-4 > -5$ since -4 is to the right of -5 on the number line.

4. $\dfrac{12}{2} > -8$ since $6 > -8$.

5. $|-7| < |-8|$ since $7 < 8$.

6. $|-9| > -9$ since $9 > -9$.

7. $-|-1| = -1$ since $-1 = -1$.

8. $|-14| = -(-14)$ since $14 = 14$.

9. $1.2 > 1.02$ since 1.2 is to the right of 1.02 on the number line.

10. $-\dfrac{3}{2} < -\dfrac{3}{4}$ since $-\dfrac{3}{2}$ is to the left of $-\dfrac{3}{4}$ on the number line.

11. Four is greater than or equal to negative three is written as $4 \geq -3$.

12. Six is not equal to five is written as $6 \neq 5$.

13. 0.03 is less than 0.3 is written as $0.03 < 0.3$.

14. $400 > 155$ or $155 < 400$

15. a. The natural numbers are 1 and 3.

    b. The whole numbers are 0, 1, and 3.

    c. The integers are -6, 0, 1, and 3.

    d. The rational numbers are -6, 0, 1, $1\dfrac{1}{2}$, 3, and 9.62.

    e. The irrational number is π.

    f. The real numbers are all numbers in the given set.

16. a. The natural numbers are 2 and 5.

    b. The whole numbers are 2 and 5.

    c. The integers are -3, 2, and 5.

    d. The rational numbers are -3, -1.6, 2, 5, $\dfrac{11}{2}$, and 15.1.

    e. The irrational numbers are $\sqrt{5}$ and 2π.

    f. The real numbers are all numbers in the given set.

17. Look for the negative number with the greatest absolute value. The greatest loss was on Friday.

18. Look for the largest positive number. The greatest gain was on Wednesday.

19. $36 = 4 \cdot 9 = 2 \cdot 2 \cdot 3 \cdot 3$

20. $120 = 8 \cdot 15 = 2 \cdot 2 \cdot 2 \cdot 3 \cdot 5$

21. $\dfrac{8}{15} \cdot \dfrac{27}{30} = \dfrac{8 \cdot 27}{15 \cdot 30} = \dfrac{2 \cdot 4 \cdot 3 \cdot 3 \cdot 3}{3 \cdot 5 \cdot 2 \cdot 3 \cdot 5} = \dfrac{12}{25}$

22. $\dfrac{7}{8} \div \dfrac{21}{32} = \dfrac{7}{8} \cdot \dfrac{32}{21} = \dfrac{7 \cdot 32}{8 \cdot 21} = \dfrac{7 \cdot 8 \cdot 4}{8 \cdot 3 \cdot 7} = \dfrac{4}{3}$

23. $\dfrac{7}{15} + \dfrac{5}{6} = \dfrac{7 \cdot 2}{15 \cdot 2} + \dfrac{5 \cdot 5}{6 \cdot 5}$

$= \dfrac{14}{30} + \dfrac{25}{30}$

$= \dfrac{14 + 25}{30}$

$= \dfrac{39}{30}$

$= \dfrac{3 \cdot 13}{3 \cdot 10}$

$= \dfrac{13}{10}$

24. $\dfrac{3}{4} - \dfrac{3}{20} = \dfrac{3 \cdot 5}{4 \cdot 5} - \dfrac{3}{20}$

$= \dfrac{15}{20} - \dfrac{3}{20}$

$= \dfrac{15 - 3}{20}$

$= \dfrac{12}{20}$

$= \dfrac{3 \cdot 4}{5 \cdot 4}$

$= \dfrac{3}{5}$

25. $2\dfrac{3}{4} + 6\dfrac{5}{8} = \dfrac{11}{4} + \dfrac{53}{8}$

$= \dfrac{11 \cdot 2}{4 \cdot 2} + \dfrac{53}{8}$

$= \dfrac{22}{8} + \dfrac{53}{8}$

$= \dfrac{22 + 53}{8}$

$= \dfrac{75}{8}$

$= 9\dfrac{3}{8}$

26. $7\dfrac{1}{6} - 2\dfrac{2}{3} = \dfrac{43}{6} - \dfrac{8}{3}$

$= \dfrac{43}{6} - \dfrac{8 \cdot 2}{3 \cdot 2}$

$= \dfrac{43}{6} - \dfrac{16}{6}$

$= \dfrac{43 - 16}{6}$

$= \dfrac{27}{6}$

$= \dfrac{9 \cdot 3}{2 \cdot 3}$

$= \dfrac{9}{2}$

$= 4\dfrac{1}{2}$

27. $5 \div \dfrac{1}{3} = 5 \cdot \dfrac{3}{1} = 15$

28. $2 \cdot 8\dfrac{3}{4} = 2 \cdot \dfrac{35}{4} = \dfrac{2 \cdot 35}{2 \cdot 2} = \dfrac{35}{2} = 17\dfrac{1}{2}$

29. $1 - \dfrac{1}{6} - \dfrac{1}{4} = \dfrac{12}{12} - \dfrac{1 \cdot 2}{6 \cdot 2} - \dfrac{1 \cdot 3}{4 \cdot 3}$

$= \dfrac{12}{12} - \dfrac{2}{12} - \dfrac{3}{12}$

$= \dfrac{12 - 2 - 3}{12}$

$= \dfrac{7}{12}$

The unknown part is $\dfrac{7}{12}$.

30. $P = 2l + 2w$

$P = 2\left(1\dfrac{1}{3}\right) + 2\left(\dfrac{7}{8}\right)$

$= \dfrac{2}{1} \cdot \dfrac{4}{3} + \dfrac{2}{1} \cdot \dfrac{7}{8}$

$= \dfrac{8}{3} + \dfrac{14}{8}$

$= \dfrac{8 \cdot 8}{3 \cdot 8} + \dfrac{14 \cdot 3}{8 \cdot 3}$

$= \dfrac{64}{24} + \dfrac{42}{24}$

$= \dfrac{64 + 42}{24}$

$= \dfrac{106}{24}$

$= 4\dfrac{10}{24}$

$= 4\dfrac{5}{12}$ meters

$A = lw$

$A = 1\dfrac{1}{3} \cdot \dfrac{7}{8}$

$= \dfrac{4}{3} \cdot \dfrac{7}{8}$

$= \dfrac{4 \cdot 7}{3 \cdot 2 \cdot 4}$

$= \dfrac{7}{6}$

$= 1\dfrac{1}{6}$ sq meters

31. $P = $ the sum of the lengths of the sides

$P = \dfrac{5}{11} + \dfrac{8}{11} + \dfrac{3}{11} + \dfrac{3}{11} + \dfrac{2}{11} + \dfrac{5}{11} = \dfrac{26}{11} = 2\dfrac{4}{11}$ in.

$A = $ the sum of the two areas, each given by lw

$A = \dfrac{5}{11} \cdot \dfrac{5}{11} + \dfrac{3}{11} \cdot \dfrac{3}{11} = \dfrac{25}{121} + \dfrac{9}{121} = \dfrac{34}{121}$ sq in.

32.
$$7\frac{1}{2} - 6\frac{1}{8} = \frac{15}{2} - \frac{49}{8}$$
$$= \frac{15 \cdot 4}{2 \cdot 4} - \frac{49}{8}$$
$$= \frac{60}{8} - \frac{49}{8}$$
$$= \frac{60 - 49}{8}$$
$$= \frac{11}{8}$$
$$= 1\frac{3}{8} \text{ ft}$$

33.
$$1\frac{1}{8} + 1\frac{13}{16} = \frac{9}{8} + \frac{29}{16}$$
$$= \frac{9 \cdot 2}{8 \cdot 2} + \frac{29}{16}$$
$$= \frac{18}{16} + \frac{29}{16}$$
$$= \frac{18 + 29}{16}$$
$$= \frac{47}{16}$$
$$= 2\frac{15}{16} \text{ lb}$$

34.
$$1\frac{1}{2} + 1\frac{11}{16} + 1\frac{3}{4} + 1\frac{5}{8} + \frac{11}{16} + 1\frac{1}{8}$$
$$= \frac{3}{2} + \frac{27}{16} + \frac{7}{4} + \frac{13}{8} + \frac{11}{16} + \frac{9}{8}$$
$$= \frac{3 \cdot 8}{2 \cdot 8} + \frac{27}{16} + \frac{7 \cdot 4}{4 \cdot 4} + \frac{13 \cdot 2}{8 \cdot 2} + \frac{11}{16} + \frac{9 \cdot 2}{8 \cdot 2}$$
$$= \frac{24 + 27 + 28 + 26 + 11 + 18}{16}$$
$$= \frac{134}{16}$$
$$= 8\frac{3}{8} \text{ lb}$$

35. Total weight = weight of girls + weight of boys
$$8\frac{3}{8} + 2\frac{15}{16} = \frac{67}{8} + \frac{47}{16}$$
$$= \frac{67 \cdot 2}{8 \cdot 2} + \frac{47}{16}$$
$$= \frac{134 + 47}{16}$$
$$= \frac{181}{16}$$
$$= 11\frac{5}{16} \text{ lb}$$

36. Look for the largest number. Jioke weighed the most.

37. Look for the smallest number. Odera weighed the least.

38.
$$1\frac{13}{16} - \frac{11}{16} = \frac{29}{16} - \frac{11}{16}$$
$$= \frac{29 - 11}{16}$$
$$= \frac{18}{16}$$
$$= 1\frac{2}{16}$$
$$= 1\frac{1}{8} \text{ lb}$$

39.
$$5\frac{1}{2} - 1\frac{5}{8} = \frac{11}{2} - \frac{13}{8}$$
$$= \frac{11 \cdot 4}{2 \cdot 4} - \frac{13}{8}$$
$$= \frac{44 - 13}{8}$$
$$= \frac{31}{8}$$
$$= 3\frac{7}{8} \text{ lb}$$

40.
$$4\frac{5}{32} - 1\frac{1}{8} = \frac{133}{32} - \frac{9}{8}$$
$$= \frac{133}{32} - \frac{9 \cdot 4}{8 \cdot 4}$$
$$= \frac{133 - 36}{32}$$
$$= \frac{97}{32}$$
$$= 3\frac{1}{32} \text{ lb}$$

41. $2^4 = 2 \cdot 2 \cdot 2 \cdot 2 = 16$

42. $5^2 = 5 \cdot 5 = 25$

43. $\left(\frac{2}{7}\right)^2 = \frac{2}{7} \cdot \frac{2}{7} = \frac{4}{49}$

44. $\left(\frac{3}{4}\right)^3 = \frac{3}{4} \cdot \frac{3}{4} \cdot \frac{3}{4} = \frac{27}{64}$

45. $6 \cdot 3^2 + 2 \cdot 8 = 6 \cdot 9 + 2 \cdot 8 = 54 + 16 = 70$

46. $68 - 5 \cdot 2^3 = 68 - 5 \cdot 8 = 68 - 40 = 28$

47. $3(1 + 2 \cdot 5) + 4 = 3(1 + 10) + 4$
$$= 3(11) + 4$$
$$= 33 + 4$$
$$= 37$$

48. $8 + 3(2 \cdot 6 - 1) = 8 + 3(12 - 1)$
$$= 8 + 3(11)$$
$$= 8 + 33$$
$$= 41$$

49. $\dfrac{4 + |6 - 2| + 8^2}{4 + 6 \cdot 4} = \dfrac{4 + |4| + 64}{4 + 24}$
$$= \dfrac{4 + 4 + 64}{4 + 24}$$
$$= \dfrac{72}{28}$$
$$= \dfrac{4 \cdot 18}{4 \cdot 7}$$
$$= \dfrac{18}{7}$$

50. $5[3(2 + 5) - 5] = 5[3(7) - 5]$
$$= 5[21 - 5]$$
$$= 5[16]$$
$$= 80$$

51. The difference of twenty and twelve is equal to the product of two and four is written as $20 - 12 = 2 \cdot 4$.

52. The quotient of nine and two is greater than negative five is written as $\dfrac{9}{2} > -5$.

53. Let $x = 6$ and $y = 2$.
$2x + 3y = 2(6) + 3(2) = 12 + 6 = 18$

54. Let $x = 6$, $y = 2$, and $z = 8$.
$x(y + 2z) = 6[2 + 2(8)] = 6[2 + 16] = 6[18] = 108$

55. Let $x = 6$, $y = 2$, and $z = 8$.
$\dfrac{x}{y} + \dfrac{z}{2y} = \dfrac{6}{2} + \dfrac{8}{2(2)} = \dfrac{6}{2} + \dfrac{8}{4} = 3 + 2 = 5$

56. Let $x = 6$ and $y = 2$.
$x^2 - 3y^2 = (6)^2 - 3(2)^2$
$$= 36 - 3(4)$$
$$= 36 - 12$$
$$= 36 + (-12)$$
$$= 24$$

57. Let $a = 37$ and $b = 80$.
$180 - a - b = 180 - 37 - 80$
$$= 180 + (-37) + (-80)$$
$$= 143 + (-80)$$
$$= 63°$$

58. Let $x = 3$.
$7x - 3 = 18$
$7(3) - 3 \stackrel{?}{=} 18$
$21 - 3 \stackrel{?}{=} 18$
$18 = 18$, true
3 is a solution to the equation.

59. Let $x = 1$.
$3x^2 + 4 = x - 1$
$3(1)^2 + 4 \stackrel{?}{=} 1 - 1$
$3 + 4 \stackrel{?}{=} 0$
$7 = 0$, false
1 is not a solution to the equation.

60. The additive inverse of -9 is 9.

61. The additive inverse of $\dfrac{2}{3}$ is $-\dfrac{2}{3}$.

62. The additive inverse of $|-2|$ is -2 since $|-2| = 2$.

63. The additive inverse of $-|-7|$ is 7 since $-|-7| = -7$.

64. $-15 + 4 = -11$

65. $-6 + (-11) = -17$

66. $\dfrac{1}{16} + \left(-\dfrac{1}{4}\right) = \dfrac{1}{16} + \left(-\dfrac{1 \cdot 4}{4 \cdot 4}\right)$
$$= \dfrac{1}{16} + \left(-\dfrac{4}{16}\right)$$
$$= -\dfrac{3}{16}$$

67. $-8 + |-3| = -8 + 3 = -5$

68. $-4.6 + (-9.3) = -13.9$

69. $-2.8 + 6.7 = 3.9$

70. $-282 + 728 = 446$ feet

71. $6 - 20 = 6 + (-20) = -14$

72. $-3.1 - 8.4 = -3.1 + (-8.4) = -11.5$

73. $-6 - (-11) = -6 + 11 = 5$

74. $4 - 15 = 4 + (-15) = -11$

75. $\begin{aligned} -21 - 16 + 3(8 - 2) &= -21 + (-16) + 3[8 + (-2)] \\ &= -21 + (-16) + 3[6] \\ &= -21 + (-16) + 18 \\ &= -37 + 18 \\ &= -19 \end{aligned}$

76. $\begin{aligned} \dfrac{11 - (-9) + 6(8 - 2)}{2 + 3 \cdot 4} &= \dfrac{11 + 9 + 6[8 + (-2)]}{2 + 3 \cdot 4} \\ &= \dfrac{11 + 9 + 6[6]}{2 + 3 \cdot 4} \\ &= \dfrac{11 + 9 + 36}{2 + 12} \\ &= \dfrac{56}{14} \\ &= 4 \end{aligned}$

77. Let $x = 3$, $y = -6$, and $z = -9$.
$$\begin{aligned} 2x^2 - y + z &= 2(3)^2 - (-6) + (-9) \\ &= 2(9) + 6 + (-9) \\ &= 18 + 6 + (-9) \\ &= 24 + (-9) \\ &= 15 \end{aligned}$$

78. Let $x = 3$ and $y = -6$.
$$\begin{aligned} \dfrac{y - x + 5x}{2x} &= \dfrac{y + 4x}{2x} \\ &= \dfrac{-6 + 4(3)}{2(3)} \\ &= \dfrac{-6 + 12}{6} \\ &= \dfrac{6}{6} \\ &= 1 \end{aligned}$$

79. The multiplicative inverse of -6 is $-\dfrac{1}{6}$ since
$$-6 \cdot -\dfrac{1}{6} = 1.$$

80. The multiplicative inverse of $\dfrac{3}{5}$ is $\dfrac{5}{3}$ since
$$\dfrac{3}{5} \cdot \dfrac{5}{3} = 1.$$

81. $6(-8) = -48$

82. $(-2)(-14) = 28$

83. $\dfrac{-18}{-6} = 3$

84. $\dfrac{42}{-3} = -14$

85. $\dfrac{4 \cdot (-3) + (-8)}{2 + (-2)} = \dfrac{-12 + (-8)}{2 + (-2)} = \dfrac{-20}{0}$
The expression is undefined.

86. $\dfrac{3(-2)^2 - 5}{-14} = \dfrac{3(4) - 5}{-14} = \dfrac{12 - 5}{-14} = \dfrac{7}{-14} = -\dfrac{1}{2}$

87. $\dfrac{-6}{0}$ is undefined.

88. $\dfrac{0}{-2} = 0$

89. $\begin{aligned} -4^2 - (-3 + 5) \div (-1) \cdot 2 &= -16 - (2) \div (-1) \cdot 2 \\ &= -16 + 2 \cdot 2 \\ &= -16 + 4 \\ &= -12 \end{aligned}$

90. $\begin{aligned} -5^2 - (2 - 20) \div (-3) \cdot 3 &= -25 - (-18) \div (-3) \cdot 3 \\ &= -25 - 6 \cdot 3 \\ &= -25 - 18 \\ &= -43 \end{aligned}$

91. Let $x = -5$ and $y = -2$.
$$x^2 - y^4 = (-5)^2 - (-2)^4 = 25 - 16 = 9$$

92. Let $x = -5$ and $y = -2$.
$$x^2 - y^3 = (-5)^2 - (-2)^3 = 25 - (-8) = 25 + 8 = 33$$

93. $\dfrac{-9 + (-7) + 1}{3} = \dfrac{-15}{3} = -5$
Her average score per round was 5 under par.

94. $\dfrac{-1+0+(-3)+0}{4} = \dfrac{-4}{4} = -1$

His average score per round was 1 under par.

95. $-6 + 5 = 5 + (-6)$; commutative property of addition

96. $6 \cdot 1 = 6$; multiplicative identity property

97. $3(8 - 5) = 3 \cdot 8 + 3 \cdot (-5)$; distributive property

98. $4 + (-4) = 0$; additive inverse property

99. $2 + (3 + 9) = (2 + 3) + 9$; associative property of addition

100. $2 \cdot 8 = 8 \cdot 2$; commutative property of multiplication

101. $6(8 + 5) = 6 \cdot 8 + 6 \cdot 5$; distributive property

102. $(3 \cdot 8) \cdot 4 = 3 \cdot (8 \cdot 4)$; associative property of multiplication

103. $4 \cdot \dfrac{1}{4} = 1$; multiplicative inverse property

104. $8 + 0 = 8$; additive identity property

105. $5(y - 2) = 5(y) + 5(-2) = 5y - 10$

106. $-3(z + y) = -3(z) + (-3)(y) = -3z - 3y$

107. $-(7 - x + 4z) = (-1)(7) + (-1)(-x) + (-1)(4z)$
$= -7 + x - 4z$

108. $\dfrac{1}{2}(6z - 10) = \dfrac{1}{2}(6z) + \dfrac{1}{2}(-10) = 3z - 5$

109. $-4(3x + 5) - 7 = -4(3x) + (-4)(5) - 7$
$= -12x - 20 - 7$
$= -12x - 27$

110. $-8(2y + 9) - 1 = -8(2y) + (-8)(9) - 1$
$= -16y - 72 - 1$
$= -16y - 73$

111. $-|-11| < |11.4|$ since $-|-11| = -11$ and $|11.4| = 11.4$.

112. $-1\dfrac{1}{2} > -2\dfrac{1}{2}$ since $-1\dfrac{1}{2}$ is to the right of $-2\dfrac{1}{2}$ on the number line.

113. $-7.2 + (-8.1) = -15.3$

114. $14 - 20 = 14 + (-20) = -6$

115. $4(-20) = -80$

116. $\dfrac{-20}{4} = -5$

117. $-\dfrac{4}{5}\left(\dfrac{5}{16}\right) = -\dfrac{4}{16} = -\dfrac{1}{4}$

118. $-0.5(-0.3) = 0.15$

119. $8 \div 2 \cdot 4 = 4 \cdot 4 = 16$

120. $(-2)^4 = (-2)(-2)(-2)(-2) = 16$

121. $\dfrac{-3 - 2(-9)}{-15 - 3(-4)} = \dfrac{-3 + 18}{-15 + 12} = \dfrac{15}{-3} = -5$

122. $5 + 2[(7 - 5)^2 + (1 - 3)] = 5 + 2[2^2 + (-2)]$
$= 5 + 2[4 + (-2)]$
$= 5 + 2[2]$
$= 5 + 4$
$= 9$

123. $-\dfrac{5}{8} \div \dfrac{3}{4} = -\dfrac{5}{8} \cdot \dfrac{4}{3} = -\dfrac{20}{24} = -\dfrac{5}{6}$

124. $\dfrac{-15 + (-4)^2 + |-9|}{10 - 2 \cdot 5} = \dfrac{-15 + 16 + 9}{10 - 10} = \dfrac{1 + 9}{0}$ is undefined.

Chapter 1 Test

1. The absolute value of negative seven is greater than five is written as $|-7| > 5$.

2. The sum of nine and five is greater than or equal to four is written as $(9 + 5) \geq 4$.

3. $-13 + 8 = -5$

4. $-13 - (-2) = -13 + 2 = -11$

5. $12 \div 4 \cdot 3 - 6 \cdot 2 = 3 \cdot 3 - 6 \cdot 2 = 9 - 12 = -3$

6. $(13)(-3) = -39$

7. $(-6)(-2) = 12$

8. $\dfrac{\left|-16\right|}{-8} = \dfrac{16}{-8} = -2$

9. $\dfrac{-8}{0}$ is undefined.

10. $\dfrac{\left|-6\right| + 2}{5-6} = \dfrac{6+2}{5+(-6)} = \dfrac{8}{-1} = -8$

11. $\dfrac{1}{2} - \dfrac{5}{6} = \dfrac{1 \cdot 3}{2 \cdot 3} - \dfrac{5}{6} = \dfrac{3}{6} - \dfrac{5}{6} = \dfrac{3-5}{6} = \dfrac{-2}{6} = -\dfrac{1}{3}$

12. $-1\dfrac{1}{8} + 5\dfrac{3}{4} = -\dfrac{9}{8} + \dfrac{23}{4}$

$= -\dfrac{9}{8} + \dfrac{2 \cdot 23}{2 \cdot 4}$

$= -\dfrac{9}{8} + \dfrac{46}{8}$

$= \dfrac{-9 + 46}{8}$

$= \dfrac{37}{8}$

$= 4\dfrac{5}{8}$

13. $(2-6) \div \dfrac{-2-6}{-3-1} - \dfrac{1}{2} = (2-6) \div \dfrac{-8}{-4} - \dfrac{1}{2}$

$= -4 \div 2 - \dfrac{1}{2}$

$= -2 - \dfrac{1}{2}$

$= -2\dfrac{1}{2}$

14. $3(-4)^2 - 80 = 3(16) - 80 = 48 + (-80) = -32$

15. $6[5 + 2(3-8) - 3] = 6\{5 + 2[3 + (-8)] + (-3)\}$

$= 6\{5 + 2[-5] + (-3)\}$

$= 6\{5 + (-10) + (-3)\}$

$= 6\{-5 + (-3)\}$

$= 6\{-8\}$

$= -48$

16. $\dfrac{-12 + 3 \cdot 8}{4} = \dfrac{-12 + 24}{4} = \dfrac{12}{4} = 3$

17. $\dfrac{(-2)(0)(-3)}{-6} = \dfrac{0(-3)}{-6} = \dfrac{0}{-6} = 0$

18. $-3 > -7$ since -3 is to the right of -7 on the number line.

19. $4 > -8$ since 4 is to the right of -8 on the number line.

20. $2 < \left|-3\right|$ since $2 < 3$.

21. $\left|-2\right| = -1 - (-3)$ since $\left|-2\right| = 2$ and $-1 - (-3) = -1 + 3 = 2$.

22. $2221 < 10{,}993$ or $10{,}993 > 2221$

23. a. The natural numbers are 1 and 7.

    b. The whole numbers are 0, 1 and 7.

    c. The integers are $-5, -1, 0, 1$, and 7.

    d. The rational numbers are $-5, -1, \dfrac{1}{4}, 0, 1, 7$, and 11.6.

    e. The irrational numbers are $\sqrt{7}$ and 3π.

    f. The real numbers are all numbers in the given set.

24. Let $x = 6$ and $y = -2$.
$x^2 + y^2 = (6)^2 + (-2)^2 = 36 + 4 = 40$

25. Let $x = 6$, $y = -2$ and $z = -3$.
$x + yz = 6 + (-2)(-3) = 6 + 6 = 12$

26. Let $x = 6$ and $y = -2$.
$2 + 3x - y = 2 + 3(6) - (-2)$
$= 2 + 18 + 2$
$= 20 + 2$
$= 22$

27. Let $x = 6$, $y = -2$ and $z = -3$.
$\dfrac{y + z - 1}{x} = \dfrac{-2 + (-3) - 1}{6} = \dfrac{-5 + (-1)}{6} = \dfrac{-6}{6} = -1$

28. $8 + (9 + 3) = (8 + 9) + 3$; associative property of addition

29. $6 \cdot 8 = 8 \cdot 6$; commutative property of multiplication

30. $-6(2 + 4) = -6 \cdot 2 + (-6) \cdot 4$; distributive property

31. $\frac{1}{6}(6) = 1$; multiplicative inverse property

32. The opposite of -9 is 9.

33. The reciprocal of $-\frac{1}{3}$ is -3.

34. Look for the negative number that has the greatest absolute value. The second down had the greatest loss of yardage.

35. Gains: 5, 29
Losses: $-10, -2$
$$\begin{aligned} \text{Total gain or loss} &= 5 + (-10) + (-2) + 29 \\ &= (-5) + (-2) + 29 \\ &= -7 + 29 \\ &= 22 \text{ yards gained} \end{aligned}$$
Yes, they scored a touchdown.

36. Since $-14 + 31 = 17$, the temperature at noon was $17°$.

37. $356 + 460 + (-166) = 650$
The net income was \$650 million.

38. Change in value per share $= -1.50$
Change in total value $= 280(-1.50) = -420$
Total loss of \$420

Chapter 2

Section 2.1

Practice Exercises

1. **a.** The numerical coefficient of t is 1, since t is $1t$.

    b. The numerical coefficient of $-7x$ is -7.

    c. The numerical coefficient of $-\dfrac{w}{5}$ is $-\dfrac{1}{5}$, since $-\dfrac{w}{5}$ means $-\dfrac{1}{5} \cdot w$.

    d. The numerical coefficient of $43x^4$ is 43.

    e. The numerical coefficient of $-b$ is -1, since $-b$ is $-1b$.

2. **a.** $-4xy$ and $5yx$ are like terms, since $xy = yx$ by the commutative property.

    b. $5q$ and $-3q^2$ are unlike terms, since the exponents on q are not the same.

    c. $3ab^2$, $-2ab^2$, and $43ab^2$ are like terms, since each variable and its exponent match.

    d. y^5 and $\dfrac{y^5}{2}$ are like terms, since the exponents on y are the same.

3. **a.** $4x^2 + 3x^2 = (4+3)x^2 = 7x^2$

    b. $-3y + y = -3y + 1y = (-3+1)y = -2y$

    c. $5x - 3x^2 + 8x^2 = 5x + (-3+8)x^2 = 5x + 5x^2$

4. **a.** $3y + 8y - 7 + 2 = (3+8)y + (-7+2) = 11y - 5$

    b. $6x - 3 - x - 3 = 6x - 1x + (-3-3)$
    $= (6-1)x + (-3-3)$
    $= 5x - 6$

    c. $\dfrac{3}{4}t - t = \dfrac{3}{4}t - 1t = \left(\dfrac{3}{4} - 1\right)t = -\dfrac{1}{4}t$

    d. $9y + 3.2y + 10 + 3 = (9+3.2)y + (10+3)$
    $= 12.2y + 13$

    e. $5z - 3z^4$
    These two terms cannot be combined because they are unlike terms.

5. **a.** $3(2x - 7) = 3(2x) + 3(-7) = 6x - 21$

    b. $-5(3x - 4z - 5)$
    $= -5(3x) + (-5)(-4z) + (-5)(-5)$
    $= -15x + 20z + 25$

    c. $-(2x - y + z - 2)$
    $= -1(2x - y + z - 2)$
    $= -1(2x) - 1(-y) - 1(z) - 1(-2)$
    $= -2x + y - z + 2$

6. **a.** $4(9x + 1) + 6 = 36x + 4 + 6 = 36x + 10$

    b. $-7(2x - 1) - (6 - 3x) = -14x + 7 - 6 + 3x$
    $= -11x + 1$

    c. $8 - 5(6x + 5) = 8 - 30x - 25 = -30x - 17$

7. "Subtract $7x - 1$ from $2x + 3$" translates to
    $(2x + 3) - (7x - 1) = 2x + 3 - 7x + 1 = -5x + 4$

8. **a.**

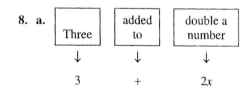

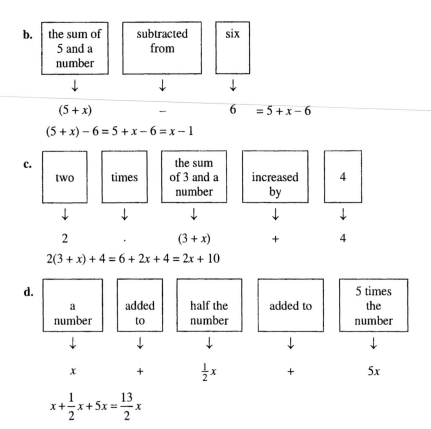

b.

the sum of 5 and a number	subtracted from	six

$(5 + x)$ $-$ 6 $= 5 + x - 6$

$(5 + x) - 6 = 5 + x - 6 = x - 1$

c.

two	times	the sum of 3 and a number	increased by	4

2 $\cdot$ $(3 + x)$ $+$ 4

$2(3 + x) + 4 = 6 + 2x + 4 = 2x + 10$

d.

a number	added to	half the number	added to	5 times the number

x $+$ $\frac{1}{2}x$ $+$ $5x$

$x + \dfrac{1}{2}x + 5x = \dfrac{13}{2}x$

Vocabulary and Readiness Check

1. $23y^2 + 10y - 6$ is called an <u>expression</u> while $23y^2$, $10y$, and -6 are each called a <u>term</u>.

2. To simplify $x + 4x$, we <u>combine like terms</u>.

3. The term y has an understood <u>numerical coefficient</u> of 1.

4. The terms $7z$ and $7y$ are <u>unlike</u> terms and the terms $7z$ and $-z$ are <u>like</u> terms.

5. For the term $-\dfrac{1}{2}xy^2$, the number $-\dfrac{1}{2}$ is the <u>numerical coefficient</u>.

6. $5(3x - y)$ equals $15x - 5y$ by the <u>distributive property</u>.

7. The numerical coefficient of $-7y$ is -7.

8. The numerical coefficient of $3x$ is 3.

9. The numerical coefficient of x is 1.

10. The numerical coefficient of $-y$ is -1.

11. The numerical coefficient of $-\dfrac{5y}{3}$ is $-\dfrac{5}{3}$.

12. The numerical coefficient of $-\dfrac{2}{3}z$ is $-\dfrac{2}{3}$.

13. $5y$ and y are like terms.

14. $-2x^2 y$ and $6xy$ are unlike terms.

15. $2z$ and $3z^2$ are unlike terms.

16. $b^2 a$ and $-\dfrac{7}{8}ab^2$ are like terms.

Exercise Set 2.1

2. $3x + 2x = (3 + 2)x = 5x$

4. $c - 7c + 2c = (1 - 7 + 2)c = -4c$

6. $6g + 5 - 3g - 7 = 6g - 3g + 5 - 7$
$$= (6 - 3)g - 2$$
$$= 3g - 2$$

8. $a + 3a - 2 - 7a = a + 3a - 7a - 2$
$$= (1 + 3 - 7)a - 2$$
$$= -3a - 2$$

10. $8p + 4 - 8p - 15 = (8p - 8p) + (4 - 15)$
$$= (8 - 8)p + (-11)$$
$$= 0p - 11$$
$$= -11$$

12. $7.9y - 0.7 - y + 0.2 = 7.9y - y - 0.7 + 0.2$
$$= (7.9 - 1)y - 0.5$$
$$= 6.9y - 0.5$$

14. $8h + 13h - 6 + 7h - h = 8h + 13h + 7h - h - 6$
$$= (8 + 13 + 7 - 1)h - 6$$
$$= 27h - 6$$

16. $8x^3 + x^3 - 11x^3 = (8 + 1 - 11)x^3 = -2x^3$

18. $0.4y - 6.7 + y - 0.3 - 2.6y$
$$= 0.4y + y - 2.6y - 6.7 - 0.3$$
$$= (0.4 + 1 - 2.6)y - 7.0$$
$$= -1.2y - 7$$

20. Answers may vary

22. $7(r - 3) = 7(r) - 7(3) = 7r - 21$

24. $-4(y + 6) = -4(y) + (-4)(6) = -4y - 24$

26. $9(z + 7) - 15 = 9z + 63 - 15 = 9z + 48$

28. $-2(4x - 3z - 1) = -2(4x) - (-2)(3z) - (-2)(1)$
$$= -8x + 6z + 2$$

30. $-(y + 5z - 7) = -y - 5z + 7$

32. $4(2x - 3) - 2(x + 1) = 8x - 12 - 2x - 2$
$$= 6x - 14$$

34.

$3y - 5$	added to	$y + 16$
↓	↓	↓
$(3y - 5)$	$+$	$(y + 16) = 3y + y - 5 + 16$

$$= 4y + 11$$

36.

$12 + x$	minus	$4x - 7$
↓	↓	↓
$(12 + x)$	$-$	$(4x - 7) = 12 + x - 4x + 7$

$$= 12 + 7 + x - 4x$$
$$= 19 - 3x$$

38.

$2m - 6$	minus	$m - 3$
↓	↓	↓
$(2m - 6)$	$-$	$(m - 3) = 2m - 6 - m + 3$

$$= 2m - m - 6 + 3$$
$$= m - 3$$

40. $7c - 8 - c = 7c - c - 8 = (7 - 1)c - 8 = 6c - 8$

42. $5y - 14 + 7y - 20y = 5y + 7y - 20y - 14$
$$= (5 + 7 - 20)y - 14$$
$$= -8y - 14$$

44. $-3(2x + 5) - 6x = -3(2x) + (-3)(5) - 6x$
$$= -6x - 15 - 6x$$
$$= -6x - 6x - 15$$
$$= -12x - 15$$

46. $2(6x - 1) - (x - 7) = 12x - 2 - x + 7$
$$= 11x + 5$$

48. $8y - 2 - 3(y + 4) = 8y - 2 - 3y - 12 = 5y - 14$

50. $-11c - (4 - 2c) = -11c - 4 + 2c = -9c - 4$

52. $(8 - 5y) - (4 + 3y) = 8 - 5y - 4 - 3y = -8y + 4$

54. $2.8w - 0.9 - 0.5 - 2.8w = 2.8w - 2.8w - 0.9 - 0.5$
$$= -1.4$$

56. $\dfrac{1}{5}(9y+2)+\dfrac{1}{10}(2y-1)=\dfrac{9}{5}y+\dfrac{2}{5}+\dfrac{2}{10}y-\dfrac{1}{10}$

$\qquad\qquad\qquad\qquad=\dfrac{9}{5}y+\dfrac{1}{5}y+\dfrac{2}{5}-\dfrac{1}{10}$

$\qquad\qquad\qquad\qquad=\dfrac{10}{5}y+\dfrac{4}{10}-\dfrac{1}{10}$

$\qquad\qquad\qquad\qquad=2y+\dfrac{3}{10}$

58. $8+4(3x-4)=8+12x-16=-8+12x$

60. $0.2(k+8)-0.1k=0.2k+1.6-0.1k=0.1k+1.6$

62. $14-11(5m+3n)=14-55m-33n$

64. $7(2x+5)-4(x+2)-20x=14x+35-4x-8-20x$

$\qquad\qquad\qquad\qquad\qquad=14x-4x-20x+35-8$

$\qquad\qquad\qquad\qquad\qquad=-10x+27$

66. $\dfrac{1}{3}(9x-6)-(x-2)=3x-2-x+2$

$\qquad\qquad\qquad\qquad=2x$

68.

The difference of a number and 2	divided by	5
↓	↓	↓
$(x-2)$	$\div$	$5=\dfrac{x-2}{5}$

70.

8	more than	triple a number
↓	↓	↓
8	+	$3x$

72.

eleven	increased by	two-thirds of a number
↓	↓	↓
11	+	$\dfrac{2}{3}x$

74.

9 times a number	subtract	3 times a number and 10
↓	↓	↓
$9x$	−	$(3x+10)$

$9x-(3x+10)=9x-3x-10=6x-10$

76.

Six	times	the difference of a number and 5
↓	↓	↓
6	·	$(x-5)$

$6(x-5) = 6x - 30$

78.

half a number	minus	the product of the number and 8
↓	↓	↓
$\dfrac{1}{2}x$	–	$8x$

$\dfrac{1}{2}x - 8x = -7.5x$

80.

the product of a number and 10	less	20
↓	↓	↓
$10x$	–	20

82.

twice a number	added to	-1	added to	5 times a number	added to	-12
↓	↓	↓	↓	↓	↓	↓
$2x$	+	-1	+	$5x$	+	-12

$2x + (-1) + 5x + (-12) = 7x - 13$

84. $gh - h^2 = 0(-4) - (-4)^2 = 0 - 16 = -16$

86. $x^3 - x^2 + 4 = (-3)^3 - (-3)^2 + 4$
$ = -27 - 9 + 4$
$ = -32$

88. $x^3 - x^2 - x = (-2)^3 - (-2)^2 - (-2)$
$ = -8 - 4 + 2$
$ = -10$

90. $5 + (3x - 1) + (2x + 5) = 5 + 3x - 1 + 2x + 5$
$ = 5x + 9$
The perimeter is $(5x + 9)$ centimeters.

92.   2 cylinders $\overset{?}{=}$ 3 cubes
2 cubes + 2 cubes $\overset{?}{=}$ 3 cubes
4 cubes = 3 cubes: Not balanced

94. 1 cylinder $\overset{?}{=}$ 1 cone + 1 cube
2 cubes $\overset{?}{=}$ 1 cube + 1 cube
2 cubes = 2 cubes: Balanced

96. Answers may vary

98. $5x + 10(3x) + 25(30x - 1) = 5x + 30x + 750x - 25$
$$= 785x - 25$$
The total value is $(785x - 25)\cancel{c}$.

100. $4m^4 p^2 + m^4 p^2 - 5m^2 p^4 = 5m^4 p^2 - 5m^2 p^4$

102. $9y^2 - (6xy^2 - 5y^2) - 8xy^2$
$$= 9y^2 - 6xy^2 + 5y^2 - 8xy^2$$
$$= 14y^2 - 14xy^2$$

104. $-(7c^3 d - 8c) - 5c - 4c^3 d$
$$= -7c^3 d + 8c - 5c - 4c^3 d$$
$$= -11c^3 d + 3c$$

Section 2.2

Practice Exercises

1. $x + 3 = -5$
$$x + 3 - 3 = -5 - 3$$
$$x = -8$$
Check: $x + 3 = -5$
$$-8 + 3 \overset{?}{=} -5$$
$$-5 = -5$$
The solution is -8.

2. $y - 0.3 = -2.1$
$$y - 0.3 + 0.3 = -2.1 + 0.3$$
$$y = -1.8$$
Check: $y - 0.3 = -2.1$
$$-1.8 - 0.3 \overset{?}{=} -2.1$$
$$-2.1 = -2.1$$
The solution is -1.8.

3. $8x - 5x - 3 + 9 = x + x + 3 - 7$
$$3x + 6 = 2x - 4$$
$$3x + 6 - 2x = 2x - 4 - 2x$$
$$x + 6 = -4$$
$$x + 6 - 6 = -4 - 6$$
$$x = -10$$
Check:
$$8x - 5x - 3 + 9 = x + x + 3 - 7$$
$$8(-10) - 5(-10) - 3 + 9 \overset{?}{=} -10 + (-10) + 3 - 7$$
$$-80 + 50 - 3 + 9 \overset{?}{=} -10 + (-10) + 3 - 7$$
$$-24 = -24$$
The solution is -10.

4. $2 = 4(2a - 3) - (7a + 4)$
$$2 = 4(2a) + 4(-3) - 7a - 4$$
$$2 = 8a - 12 - 7a - 4$$
$$2 = a - 16$$
$$2 + 16 = a - 16 + 16$$
$$18 = a$$
Check by replacing a with 18 in the original equation.

5. $\dfrac{4}{5}x = 16$
$$\frac{5}{4} \cdot \frac{4}{5}x = \frac{5}{4} \cdot 16$$
$$\left(\frac{5}{4} \cdot \frac{4}{5}\right)x = \frac{5}{4} \cdot 16$$
$$1x = 20$$
$$x = 20$$

Check: $\dfrac{4}{5}x = 16$
$$\frac{4}{5} \cdot 20 \overset{?}{=} 16$$
$$16 = 16$$
The solution is 20.

6. $8x = -96$
$$\frac{8x}{8} = \frac{-96}{8}$$
$$x = -12$$
Check: $8x = -96$
$$8(-12) \overset{?}{=} -96$$
$$-96 = -96$$
The solution is -12.

7. $\dfrac{x}{5} = 13$
$$5 \cdot \frac{x}{5} = 5 \cdot 13$$
$$x = 65$$
Check: $\dfrac{x}{5} = 13$
$$\frac{65}{5} \overset{?}{=} 13$$
$$13 = 13$$
The solution is 65.

8. $6b - 11b = 18 + 2b - 6 + 9$
$-5b = 21 + 2b$
$-5b - 2b = 21 + 2b - 2b$
$-7b = 21$
$\dfrac{-7b}{-7} = \dfrac{21}{-7}$
$b = -3$

Check by replacing b with -3 in the original equation. The solution is -3.

9. a. The other number is $9 - 2 = 7$.

b. The other number is $9 - x$.

c. The other piece has length $(9 - x)$ feet.

10. Let $x =$ first integer.
$x + 2 =$ second even integer.
$x + 4 =$ third even integer.
$x + (x + 2) + (x + 4) = 3x + 6$

Vocabulary and Readiness Check

1. The difference between an equation and an expression is that an <u>equation</u> contains an equal sign, whereas an <u>expression</u> does not.

2. <u>Equivalent</u> equations are equations that have the same solution.

3. A value of the variable that makes the equation a true statement is called a <u>solution</u> of the equation.

4. The process of finding the solution of an equation is called <u>solving</u> the equation for the variable.

5. By the <u>addition</u> property of equality, $x = -2$ and $x + 10 = -2 + 10$ are equivalent equations.

6. The equations $x = \dfrac{1}{2}$ and $\dfrac{1}{2} = x$ are equivalent equations. The statement is true.

7. By the <u>multiplication</u> property of equality,
$y = \dfrac{1}{2}$ and $5 \cdot y = 5 \cdot \dfrac{1}{2}$ are equivalent equations.

8. The equations $\dfrac{z}{4} = 10$ and $4 \cdot \dfrac{z}{4} = 10$ are not equivalent equations. The statement is false.

9. The equations $-7x = 30$ and $\dfrac{-7x}{-7} = \dfrac{30}{7}$ are not equivalent equations. The statement is false.

10. By the <u>multiplication</u> property of equality, $9x = -63$ and $\dfrac{9x}{9} = \dfrac{-63}{9}$ are equivalent equations.

11. $3a = 27$
$a = \dfrac{27}{3} = 9$

12. $9c = 54$
$c = \dfrac{54}{9} = 6$

13. $5b = 10$
$b = \dfrac{10}{5} = 2$

14. $7t = 14$
$t = \dfrac{14}{7} = 2$

Exercise Set 2.2

2. $x + 14 = 25$
$x + 14 - 14 = 25 - 14$
$x = 11$
Check: $x + 14 = 25$
$11 + 14 \stackrel{?}{=} 25$
$25 = 25$
The solution is 11.

4. $y - 9 = 1$
$y - 9 + 9 = 1 + 9$
$y = 10$
Check: $y - 9 = 1$
$10 - 9 \stackrel{?}{=} 1$
$1 = 1$
The solution is 10.

6. $8 + z = -8$
$8 - 8 + z = -8 - 8$
$z = -16$
Check: $8 + z = -8$
$8 + (-16) \stackrel{?}{=} -8$
$-8 = -8$
The solution is -16.

8.
$$t - 9.2 = -6.8$$
$$5 - 9.2 + 9.2 = -6.8 + 9.2$$
$$t = 2.4$$
Check: $\quad t - 9.2 = -6.8$
$$2.4 - 9.2 \overset{?}{=} -6.8$$
$$-6.8 = -6.8$$
The solution is 2.4.

10.
$$2x = x - 5$$
$$2x - x = x - x - 5$$
$$x = -5$$
Check: $\quad 2x = x - 5$
$$2(-5) \overset{?}{=} -5 - 5$$
$$-10 = -10$$
The solution is -5.

12.
$$9x + 5.5 = 10x$$
$$9x - 9x + 5.5 = 10x - 9x$$
$$5.5 = x$$
Check: $\quad 9x + 5.5 = 10x$
$$9(5.5) + 5.5 \overset{?}{=} 10(5.5)$$
$$49.5 + 5.5 \overset{?}{=} 55$$
$$55 = 55$$
The solution is 5.5.

14.
$$18x - 9 = 19x$$
$$18x - 18x - 9 = 19x - 18x$$
$$-9 = x$$
Check: $\quad 18x - 9 = 19x$
$$18(-9) - 9 \overset{?}{=} 19(-9)$$
$$-162 - 9 \overset{?}{=} -171$$
$$-171 = 171$$
The solution is -9.

16.
$$7y + 2 = 6y + 2$$
$$7y - 6y + 2 = 6y - 6y + 2$$
$$y + 2 = 2$$
$$y + 2 - 2 = 2 - 2$$
$$y = 0$$
The solution is 0.

18.
$$4c + 8 - c = 8 + 2c$$
$$3c + 8 = 8 + 2c$$
$$3c - 2c + 8 = 8 + 2c - 2c$$
$$c + 8 = 8$$
$$c + 8 - 8 = 8 - 8$$
$$c = 0$$
The solution is 0.

20.
$$3n + 2n = 7 + 4n$$
$$5n = 7 + 4n$$
$$5n - 4n = 7 + 4n - 4n$$
$$n = 7$$
The solution is 7.

22.
$$10 = 8(3y - 4) - 23y + 20$$
$$10 = 24y - 32 - 23y + 20$$
$$10 = y - 12$$
$$10 + 12 = y - 12 + 12$$
$$22 = y$$
The solution is 22.

24.
$$-7x = -49$$
$$\frac{-7x}{-7} = \frac{-49}{-7}$$
$$x = 7$$
The solution is 7.

26.
$$-2x = 0$$
$$\frac{-2x}{-2} = \frac{0}{-2}$$
$$x = 0$$
The solution is 0.

28.
$$-y = 8$$
$$\frac{-y}{-1} = \frac{8}{-1}$$
$$y = -8$$
The solution is -8.

30.
$$-y + 4y = 33$$
$$3y = 33$$
$$\frac{3y}{3} = \frac{33}{3}$$
$$y = 11$$
The solution is 11.

32.
$$\frac{3}{4}n = -15$$
$$\frac{4}{3}\left(\frac{3}{4}n\right) = \frac{4}{3}(-15)$$
$$n = -20$$
The solution is -20.

34.
$$\frac{1}{8}v = \frac{1}{4}$$
$$8\left(\frac{1}{8}v\right) = 8\left(\frac{1}{4}\right)$$
$$v = 2$$
The solution is 2.

36.

$$\frac{d}{15} = 2$$
$$15\left(\frac{d}{15}\right) = 15(2)$$
$$d = 30$$

The solution is 30.

38.

$$\frac{f}{-5} = 0$$
$$-5\left(\frac{f}{-5}\right) = -5(0)$$
$$f = 0$$

The solution is 0.

40. Answers may vary

42.

$$3x - 1 = 26$$
$$3x - 1 + 1 = 26 + 1$$
$$3x = 27$$
$$\frac{3x}{3} = \frac{27}{3}$$
$$x = 9$$

Check: $3x - 1 = 26$
$$3(9) - 1 \stackrel{?}{=} 26$$
$$27 - 1 \stackrel{?}{=} 26$$
$$26 = 26$$

The solution is 9.

44.

$$-x + 4 = -24$$
$$-x + 4 - 4 = -24 - 4$$
$$-x = -28$$
$$x = 28$$

Check: $-x + 4 = -24$
$$-(28) + 4 \stackrel{?}{=} -24$$
$$-28 + 4 \stackrel{?}{=} -24$$
$$-24 = -24$$

The solution is 28.

46.

$$8t + 5 = 5$$
$$8t + 5 - 5 = 5 - 5$$
$$8t = 0$$
$$\frac{8t}{8} = \frac{0}{8}$$
$$t = 0$$

Check: $8t + 5 = 5$
$$8(0) + 5 \stackrel{?}{=} 5$$
$$0 + 5 \stackrel{?}{=} 5$$
$$5 = 5$$

The solution is 0.

48.

$$-10y + 15 = 5$$
$$-10y + 15 - 15 = 5 - 15$$
$$-10y = -10$$
$$\frac{-10y}{-10} = \frac{-10}{-10}$$
$$y = 1$$

Check: $-10y + 15 = 5$
$$-10 \cdot 1 + 15 \stackrel{?}{=} 5$$
$$-10 + 15 \stackrel{?}{=} 5$$
$$5 = 5$$

The solution is 1.

50.

$$2 + 0.4p = 2$$
$$2 - 2 + 0.4p = 2 - 2$$
$$0.4p = 0$$
$$\frac{0.4p}{0.4} = \frac{0}{0.4}$$
$$p = 0$$

Check: $2 + 0.4p = 2$
$$2 + 0.4 \cdot 0 \stackrel{?}{=} 2$$
$$2 + 0 \stackrel{?}{=} 2$$
$$2 = 2$$

The solution is 0.

52.

$$-3n - \frac{1}{3} = \frac{8}{3}$$
$$-3n - \frac{1}{3} + \frac{1}{3} = \frac{8}{3} + \frac{1}{3}$$
$$-3n = \frac{9}{3}$$
$$-3n = 3$$
$$\frac{-3n}{-3} = \frac{3}{-3}$$
$$n = -1$$

Check: $-3n - \dfrac{1}{3} = \dfrac{8}{3}$
$$-3(-1) - \frac{1}{3} \stackrel{?}{=} \frac{8}{3}$$
$$3 - \frac{1}{3} \stackrel{?}{=} \frac{8}{3}$$
$$\frac{9}{3} - \frac{1}{3} \stackrel{?}{=} \frac{8}{3}$$
$$\frac{8}{3} = \frac{8}{3}$$

The solution is -1.

54. $\dfrac{b}{4} - 1 = -7$

$\dfrac{b}{4} - 1 + 1 = -7 + 1$

$\dfrac{b}{4} = -6$

$4\left(\dfrac{b}{4}\right) = 4(-6)$

$b = -24$

Check: $\dfrac{b}{4} - 1 = -7$

$\dfrac{-24}{4} - 1 \overset{?}{=} -7$

$-6 - 1 \overset{?}{=} -7$

$-7 = -7$

The solution is -24.

56. $12 = 3j - 4$

$12 + 4 = 3j - 4 + 4$

$16 = 3j$

$\dfrac{16}{3} = \dfrac{3j}{3}$

$\dfrac{16}{3} = j$

Check: $12 = 3j - 4$

$12 \overset{?}{=} 3 \cdot \dfrac{16}{3} - 4$

$12 \overset{?}{=} 16 - 4$

$12 = 12$

The solution is $\dfrac{16}{3}$.

58. $4a + 1 + a - 11 = 0$

$5a - 10 = 0$

$5a - 10 + 10 = 0 + 10$

$5a = 10$

$\dfrac{5a}{5} = \dfrac{10}{5}$

$a = 2$

Check: $4a + 1 + a - 11 = 0$

$4 \cdot 2 + 1 + 2 - 11 \overset{?}{=} 0$

$8 + 1 + 2 - 11 \overset{?}{=} 0$

$0 = 0$

The solution is 2.

60. $12x + 30 + 8x - 6 = 10$

$20x + 24 = 10$

$20x + 24 - 24 = 10 - 24$

$20x = -14$

$\dfrac{20x}{20} = \dfrac{-14}{20}$

$x = -\dfrac{7}{10}$

Check: $12x + 30 + 8x - 6 = 10$

$12\left(-\dfrac{7}{10}\right) + 30 + 8\left(-\dfrac{7}{10}\right) - 6 \overset{?}{=} 10$

$-\dfrac{84}{10} + 24 - \dfrac{56}{10} \overset{?}{=} 10$

$-\dfrac{140}{10} + 24 \overset{?}{=} 10$

$-14 + 24 \overset{?}{=} 10$

$10 = 10$

The solution is $-\dfrac{7}{10}$.

62. $-\dfrac{3}{4}x = 9$

$-\dfrac{4}{3}\left(-\dfrac{3}{4}x\right) = -\dfrac{4}{3} \cdot 9$

$x = -12$

Check: $-\dfrac{3}{4}x = 9$

$-\dfrac{3}{4}(-12) \overset{?}{=} 9$

$9 = 9$

The solution is -12.

64. $19 = 0.4x - 0.9x - 6$

$19 = -0.5x - 6$

$19 + 6 = -0.5x - 6 + 6$

$25 = -0.5x$

$\dfrac{25}{-0.5} = \dfrac{-0.5x}{-0.5}$

$-50 = x$

Check: $19 = 0.4x - 0.9x - 6$

$19 \overset{?}{=} 0.4(-50) - 0.9(-50) - 6$

$19 \overset{?}{=} -20 + 45 - 6$

$19 = 19$

The solution is -50.

66.
$$t - 6t = -13 + t - 3t$$
$$-5t = -2t - 13$$
$$-5t + 2t = -2t + 2t - 13$$
$$-3t = -13$$
$$\frac{-3t}{-3} = \frac{-13}{-3}$$
$$t = \frac{13}{3}$$

Check: $t - 6t = -13 + t - 3t$
$$\frac{13}{3} - 6 \cdot \frac{13}{3} \overset{?}{=} -13 + \frac{13}{3} - 3 \cdot \frac{13}{3}$$
$$\frac{13}{3} - \frac{78}{3} \overset{?}{=} -\frac{39}{3} + \frac{13}{3} - \frac{39}{3}$$
$$-\frac{65}{3} = -\frac{65}{3}$$

The solution is $\frac{13}{3}$.

68.
$$0.4x - 0.9x - 6 = 19$$
$$-0.5x - 6 = 19$$
$$-0.5x - 6 + 6 = 19 + 6$$
$$-0.5x = 25$$
$$\frac{-0.5x}{-0.5} = \frac{25}{-0.5}$$
$$x = -50$$

Check: $0.4x - 0.9x - 6 = 19$
$$0.4(-50) - 0.9(-50) - 6 \overset{?}{=} 19$$
$$-20 + 45 - 6 \overset{?}{=} 19$$
$$19 = 19$$

The solution is -50.

70.
$$-5 - 6y + 6 = 19$$
$$-6y + 1 = 19$$
$$-6y + 1 - 1 = 19 - 1$$
$$-6y = 18$$
$$\frac{-6y}{-6} = \frac{18}{-6}$$
$$y = -3$$

Check: $-5 - 6y + 6 = 19$
$$-5 - 6(-3) + 6 \overset{?}{=} 19$$
$$-5 + 18 + 6 \overset{?}{=} 19$$
$$19 = 19$$

The solution is -3.

72.
$$4b - 8 - b = 10b - 3b$$
$$3b - 8 = 7b$$
$$3b - 3b - 8 = 7b - 3b$$
$$-8 = 4b$$
$$\frac{-8}{4} = \frac{4b}{4}$$
$$-2 = b$$

Check: $4b - 8 - b = 10b - 3b$
$$4(-2) - 8 - (-2) \overset{?}{=} 10(-2) - 3(-2)$$
$$-8 - 8 + 2 \overset{?}{=} -20 + 6$$
$$-14 = -14$$

The solution is -2.

74.
$$-3 = -5(4x + 3) + 21x$$
$$-3 = -20x - 15 + 21x$$
$$-3 = x - 15$$
$$-3 + 15 = x - 15 + 15$$
$$12 = x$$

Check: $-3 = -5(4x + 3) + 21x$
$$-3 \overset{?}{=} -5(4 \cdot 12 + 3) + 21 \cdot 12$$
$$-3 \overset{?}{=} -5(48 + 3) + 252$$
$$-3 \overset{?}{=} -5(51) + 252$$
$$-3 \overset{?}{=} -255 + 252$$
$$-3 = -3$$

The solution is 12.

76. The other number is $13 - y$.

78. The length of the other piece is $(5 - x)$ feet.

80. The complement of the angle $x°$ is $(90 - x)°$.

82. The length of the computer desk is $\left(m + 1\frac{1}{2} \right)$ feet.

84. The length of I-90 is $(m + 178.5)$ miles.

86. Susan received $(n + 30,898)$ votes.

88. The weight of the Hoba West meteorite is $3y$ kilograms.

90. Sum = first integer + second integer + third integer + fourth integer.
$$\text{Sum} = x + (x + 2) + (x + 4) + (x + 6)$$
$$= x + x + 2 + x + 4 + x + 6$$
$$= 4x + 12$$

92. Sum = 20 + second integer.
$$\text{Sum} = 20 + (x+1)$$
$$= 20 + x + 1$$
$$= x + 21$$

94. Let x be an odd integer.
Then $x + 2$ is the next odd integer.
$$x + (x+2) + x + (x+2) = 4x + 4$$

96. $-7y + 2y - 3(y+1) = -7y + 2y - 3y - 3 = -8y - 3$

98. $-(3a - 3) + 2a - 6 = -3a + 3 + 2a - 6 = -a - 3$

100. $(-2)^4 = (-2)(-2)(-2)(-2) = 16$
$-2^4 = -2 \cdot 2 \cdot 2 \cdot 2 = -16$
$(-2)^4 > -2^4$

102. $(-4)^3 = (-4)(-4)(-4) = -64$
$-4^3 = -4 \cdot 4 \cdot 4 = -64$
$(-4)^3 = -4^3$

104. $360 - (x + 3x + 5x) = 360 - (9x) = 360 - 9x$
The fourth angle is $(360 - 9x)°$.

106. Answers may vary

108. $$a + 9 = 15$$
$$a + 9 + (-9) = 15 + (-9)$$
$$a = 6$$
The answer is -9.

110. Answers may vary

112. Answers may vary

114.
$$x = 10$$
$$\frac{}{\frac{1}{2}} = 10$$
$$\frac{}{\frac{1}{2}} \cdot 2 = 10 \cdot 2$$
$$= 20$$

116. $9x = 13.5$
$$\frac{9x}{9} = \frac{13.5}{9}$$
$$x = 1.5$$
Each dose should be 1.5 milliliters.

118. Check $a = 6.3$.
$$3(a + 4.6) = 5a + 2.5$$
$$3(6.3 + 4.6) \stackrel{?}{=} 5(6.3) + 2.5$$
$$3(10.9) \stackrel{?}{=} 31.5 + 2.5$$
$$32.7 = 34$$
Not a solution

120. $4.95y = -31.185$
$$\frac{4.95y}{4.95} = \frac{-31.185}{4.95}$$
$$y = -6.3$$

122.
$$0.06y + 2.63 = 2.5562$$
$$0.06y + 2.63 - 2.63 = 2.5562 - 2.63$$
$$0.06y = -0.0738$$
$$\frac{0.06y}{0.06} = \frac{-0.0738}{0.06}$$
$$y = -1.23$$

Section 2.3

Practice Exercises

1. $2(4a - 9) + 3 = 5a - 6$
$$8a - 18 + 3 = 5a - 6$$
$$8a - 15 = 5a - 6$$
$$8a - 15 - 5a = 5a - 6 - 5a$$
$$3a - 15 = -6$$
$$3a - 15 + 15 = -6 + 15$$
$$3a = 9$$
$$\frac{3a}{3} = \frac{9}{3}$$
$$a = 3$$
Check: $2(4a - 9) + 3 = 5a - 6$
$$2[4(3) - 9] + 3 \stackrel{?}{=} 5(3) - 6$$
$$2(12 - 9) + 3 \stackrel{?}{=} 15 - 6$$
$$2(3) + 3 \stackrel{?}{=} 9$$
$$6 + 3 \stackrel{?}{=} 9$$
$$9 = 1$$
The solution is 3 or the solution set is {3}.

2. $7(x - 3) = -6x$
$$7x - 21 = -6x$$
$$7x - 21 - 7x = -6x - 7x$$
$$-21 = -13x$$
$$\frac{-21}{-13} = \frac{-13x}{-13}$$
$$\frac{21}{13} = x$$

Check: $7(x-3) = -6x$

$$7\left(\frac{21}{13} - 3\right) \stackrel{?}{=} -6\left(\frac{21}{13}\right)$$

$$7\left(\frac{21}{13} - \frac{39}{13}\right) \stackrel{?}{=} -\frac{126}{13}$$

$$7\left(-\frac{18}{13}\right) \stackrel{?}{=} -\frac{126}{13}$$

$$-\frac{126}{13} = -\frac{126}{13}$$

The solution is $\frac{21}{13}$.

3.
$$\frac{3}{5}x - 2 = \frac{2}{3}x - 1$$

$$15\left(\frac{3}{5}x - 2\right) = 15\left(\frac{2}{3}x - 1\right)$$

$$15\left(\frac{3}{5}x\right) - 15(2) = 15\left(\frac{2}{3}x\right) - 15(1)$$

$$9x - 30 = 10x - 15$$

$$9x - 30 - 9x = 10x - 15 - 9x$$

$$-30 = x - 15$$

$$-30 + 15 = x - 15 + 15$$

$$-15 = x$$

Check: $\frac{3}{5}x - 2 = \frac{2}{3}x - 1$

$$\frac{3}{5} \cdot -15 - 2 \stackrel{?}{=} \frac{2}{3} \cdot -15 - 1$$

$$-9 - 2 \stackrel{?}{=} -10 - 1$$

$$-11 = -11$$

The solution is -15.

4.
$$\frac{4(y+3)}{3} = 5y - 7$$

$$3 \cdot \frac{4(y+3)}{3} = 3 \cdot (5y - 7)$$

$$4(y+3) = 3(5y - 7)$$

$$4y + 12 = 15y - 21$$

$$4y + 12 - 4y = 15y - 21 - 4y$$

$$12 = 11y - 21$$

$$12 + 21 = 11y - 21 + 21$$

$$33 = 11y$$

$$\frac{33}{11} = \frac{11y}{11}$$

$$3 = y$$

To check, replace y with 3 in the original equation. The solution is 3.

5.
$$0.35x + 0.09(x + 4) = 0.30(12)$$

$$100[0.35x + 0.09(x + 4)] = 100[0.03(12)]$$

$$35x + 9(x + 4) = 3(12)$$

$$35x + 9x + 36 = 36$$

$$44x + 36 = 36$$

$$44x + 36 - 36 = 36 - 36$$

$$44x = 0$$

$$\frac{44x}{44} = \frac{0}{44}$$

$$x = 0$$

To check, replace x with 0 in the original equation. The solution is 0.

6.
$$4(x + 4) - x = 2(x + 11) + x$$

$$4x + 16 - x = 2x + 22 + x$$

$$3x + 16 = 3x + 22$$

$$3x + 16 - 3x = 3x + 22 - 3x$$

$$16 = 22$$

There is no solution.

7.
$$12x - 18 = 9(x - 2) + 3x$$

$$12x - 18 = 9x - 18 + 3x$$

$$12x - 18 = 12x - 18$$

$$12x - 18 + 18 = 12x - 18 + 18$$

$$12x = 12x$$

$$12x - 12x = 12x - 12x$$

$$0 = 0$$

The solution is all real numbers.

Calculator Explorations

1. Solution $(-24 = -24)$

2. Solution $(-4 = -4)$

3. Not a solution $(19.4 \neq 10.4)$

4. Not a solution $(-11.9 \neq -60.1)$

5. Solution $(17{,}061 = 17{,}061)$

6. Solution $(-316 = -316)$

Vocabulary and Readiness Check

1. $x = -7$ is an equation.

2. $x - 7$ is an expression.

3. $4y - 6 + 9y + 1$ is an expression.

4. $4y - 6 = 9y + 1$ is an equation.

5. $\dfrac{1}{x} - \dfrac{x-1}{8}$ is an expression.

6. $\dfrac{1}{x} - \dfrac{x-1}{8} = 6$ is an equation.

7. $0.1x + 9 = 0.2x$ is an equation.

8. $0.1x^2 + 9y - 0.2x^2$ is an expression.

Exercise Set 2.3

2.
$$-3x + 1 = -2(4x + 2)$$
$$-3x + 1 = -8x - 4$$
$$-3x + 1 - 1 = -8x - 4 - 1$$
$$-3x = -8x - 5$$
$$-3x + 8x = -8x - 5 + 8x$$
$$5x = -5$$
$$\frac{5x}{5} = \frac{-5}{5}$$
$$x = -1$$

4.
$$15x - 5 = 7 + 12x$$
$$15x - 5 + 5 = 7 + 12x + 5$$
$$15x = 12 + 12x$$
$$15x - 12x = 12 + 12x - 12x$$
$$3x = 12$$
$$\frac{3x}{3} = \frac{12}{3}$$
$$x = 4$$

6.
$$-(5x - 10) = 5x$$
$$-5x + 10 = 5x$$
$$-5x + 10 + 5x = 5x + 5x$$
$$10 = 10x$$
$$\frac{10}{10} = \frac{10x}{10}$$
$$1 = x$$

8.
$$3(2 - 5x) + 4(6x) = 12$$
$$6 - 15x + 24x = 12$$
$$6 + 9x = 12$$
$$6 - 6 + 9x = 12 - 6$$
$$9x = 6$$
$$\frac{9x}{9} = \frac{6}{9}$$
$$x = \frac{2}{3}$$

10.
$$-4(n - 4) - 23 = -7$$
$$-4n + 16 - 23 = -7$$
$$-4n - 7 = -7$$
$$-4n - 7 + 7 = -7 + 7$$
$$-4n = 0$$
$$\frac{-4n}{-4} = \frac{0}{-4}$$
$$n = 0$$

12.
$$5 - 6(2 + b) = b - 14$$
$$5 - 12 - 6b = b - 14$$
$$-7 - 6b = b - 14$$
$$-7 - 6b - b = b - b - 14$$
$$-7 - 7b = -14$$
$$-7 + 7 - 7b = -14 + 7$$
$$-7b = -7$$
$$\frac{-7b}{-7} = \frac{-7}{-7}$$
$$b = 1$$

14.
$$6y - 8 = -6 + 3y + 13$$
$$6y - 8 = 3y + 7$$
$$6y - 3y - 8 = 3y - 3y + 7$$
$$3y - 8 = 7$$
$$3y - 8 + 8 = 7 + 8$$
$$3y = 15$$
$$\frac{3y}{3} = \frac{15}{3}$$
$$y = 5$$

16.
$$-7n + 5 = 8n - 10$$
$$-7n + 5 - 5 = 8n - 10 - 5$$
$$-7n = 8n - 15$$
$$-7n - 8n = 8n - 15 - 8n$$
$$-15n = -15$$
$$\frac{-15n}{-15} = \frac{-15}{-15}$$
$$n = 1$$

18.
$$\frac{4}{5}x - \frac{8}{5} = -\frac{16}{5}$$
$$5\left(\frac{4}{5}x - \frac{8}{5}\right) = 5\left(-\frac{16}{5}\right)$$
$$4x - 8 = -16$$
$$4x - 8 + 8 = -16 + 8$$
$$4x = -8$$
$$\frac{4x}{4} = \frac{-8}{4}$$
$$x = -2$$

20.
$$\frac{2}{9}x - \frac{1}{3} = 1$$
$$9\left(\frac{2}{9}x - \frac{1}{3}\right) = 9(1)$$
$$2x - 3 = 9$$
$$2x - 3 + 3 = 9 + 3$$
$$2x = 12$$
$$\frac{2x}{2} = \frac{12}{2}$$
$$x = 6$$

22.
$$0.40x + 0.06(30) = 9.8$$
$$100[0.40x + 0.06(30)] = 100(9.8)$$
$$40x + 6(30) = 980$$
$$40x + 180 = 980$$
$$40x + 180 - 180 = 980 - 180$$
$$40x = 800$$
$$\frac{40x}{40} = \frac{800}{40}$$
$$x = 20$$

24.
$$\frac{3(y+3)}{5} = 2y + 6$$
$$5\left[\frac{3(y+3)}{5}\right] = 5[2y+6]$$
$$3(y+3) = 10y + 30$$
$$3y + 9 = 10y + 30$$
$$3y - 10y + 9 = 10y - 10y + 30$$
$$-7y + 9 = 30$$
$$-7y + 9 - 9 = 30 - 9$$
$$-7y = 21$$
$$\frac{-7y}{-7} = \frac{21}{-7}$$
$$y = -3$$

26.
$$\frac{5}{2}x - 1 = x + \frac{1}{4}$$
$$4\left(\frac{5}{2}x - 1\right) = 4\left(x + \frac{1}{4}\right)$$
$$10x - 4 = 4x + 1$$
$$10x - 4 - 4 = 4x - 4x + 1$$
$$6x - 4 = 1$$
$$6x - 4 + 4 = 1 + 4$$
$$6x = 5$$
$$\frac{6x}{6} = \frac{5}{6}$$
$$x = \frac{5}{6}$$

28.
$$0.60(z - 300) + 0.05z = 0.70z - 205$$
$$100[0.60(z-300)+0.05z] = 100[0.70z - 205]$$
$$60(z - 300) + 5z = 70z - 20{,}500$$
$$60z - 18{,}000 + 5z = 70z - 20{,}500$$
$$65z - 18{,}000 = 70z - 20{,}500$$
$$65z - 70z - 18{,}000 = 70z - 70z - 20{,}500$$
$$-5z - 18{,}000 = -20{,}500$$
$$-5z - 18{,}000 + 18{,}000 = -20{,}500 + 18{,}000$$
$$-5z = -2500$$
$$\frac{-5z}{-5} = \frac{-2500}{-5}$$
$$z = 500$$

30.
$$14x + 7 = 7(2x + 1)$$
$$14x + 7 = 14x + 7$$
$$14x + 7 - 14x = 14x + 7 - 14x$$
$$7 = 7$$
All real numbers are solutions.

32.
$$\frac{x}{3} - 2 = \frac{x}{3}$$
$$3\left(\frac{x}{3} - 2\right) = 3\left(\frac{x}{3}\right)$$
$$x - 6 = x$$
$$x - x - 6 = x - x$$
$$-6 = 0$$
There is no solution.

34.
$$2(x - 5) = 2x + 10$$
$$2x - 10 = 2x + 10$$
$$2x - 2x - 10 = 2x - 2x + 10$$
$$-10 = 10$$
There is no solution.

36.
$$-5(4y - 3) + 2 = -20y + 17$$
$$-20y + 15 + 2 = -20y + 17$$
$$-20y + 17 = -20y + 17$$
$$-20y + 17 + 20y = -20y + 17 + 20y$$
$$17 = 17$$
All real numbers are solutions.

38.
$$\frac{4(5 - w)}{3} = -w$$
$$3\left[\frac{4(5 - w)}{3}\right] = 3(-w)$$
$$4(5 - w) = -3w$$
$$20 - 4w = -3w$$
$$20 - 4w + 4w = -3w + 4w$$
$$20 = w$$

40.
$$-(4a-7)-5a = 10+a$$
$$-4a+7-5a = 10+a$$
$$-9a+7 = 10+a$$
$$-9a-a+7 = 10+a-a$$
$$-10a+7 = 10$$
$$-10a+7-7 = 10-7$$
$$-10a = 3$$
$$\frac{-10a}{-10} = \frac{3}{-10}$$
$$a = -\frac{3}{10}$$

42.
$$9x+3(x-4) = 10(x-5)+7$$
$$9x+3x-12 = 10x-50+7$$
$$12x-12 = 10x-43$$
$$12x-12+12 = 10x-43+12$$
$$12x = 10x-31$$
$$12x-10x = 10x-31-10x$$
$$2x = -31$$
$$\frac{2x}{2} = \frac{-31}{2}$$
$$x = -\frac{31}{2}$$

44.
$$\frac{5(x-1)}{4} = \frac{3(x+1)}{2}$$
$$4\left[\frac{5(x-1)}{4}\right] = 4\left[\frac{3(x+1)}{2}\right]$$
$$5(x-1) = 6(x+1)$$
$$5x-5 = 6x+6$$
$$5x-6x-5 = 6x-6x+6$$
$$-x-5 = 6$$
$$-x-5+5 = 6+5$$
$$-x = 11$$
$$\frac{-x}{-1} = \frac{11}{-1}$$
$$x = -11$$

46.
$$0.9x-4.1 = 0.4$$
$$10(0.9x-4.1) = 10(0.4)$$
$$9x-41 = 4$$
$$9x-41+41 = 4+41$$
$$9x = 45$$
$$\frac{9x}{9} = \frac{45}{9}$$
$$x = 5$$

48.
$$3(2x-1)+5 = 6x+2$$
$$6x-3+5 = 6x+2$$
$$6x+2 = 6x+2$$
$$6x-6x+2 = 6x-6x+2$$
$$2 = 2$$
All real numbers are solutions.

50.
$$4(4y+2) = 2(1+6y)+8$$
$$16y+8 = 2+12y+8$$
$$16y+8 = 10+12y$$
$$16y+8-8 = 10+12y-8$$
$$16y = 2+12y$$
$$16y-12y = 2+12y-12y$$
$$4y = 2$$
$$\frac{4y}{4} = \frac{2}{4}$$
$$y = \frac{1}{2}$$

52.
$$\frac{7}{8}x+\frac{1}{4} = \frac{3}{4}x$$
$$8\left(\frac{7}{8}x+\frac{1}{4}\right) = 8\left(\frac{3}{4}x\right)$$
$$7x+2 = 6x$$
$$7x+2-7x = 6x-7x$$
$$2 = -x$$
$$\frac{2}{-1} = \frac{-x}{-1}$$
$$-2 = x$$

54.
$$\frac{x}{5}-7 = \frac{x}{3}-5$$
$$15\left(\frac{x}{5}-7\right) = 15\left(\frac{x}{3}-5\right)$$
$$3x-105 = 5x-75$$
$$3x-105-3x = 5x-75-3x$$
$$-105 = 2x-75$$
$$-105+75 = 2x-75+75$$
$$-30 = 2x$$
$$\frac{-30}{2} = \frac{2x}{2}$$
$$-15 = x$$

56.
$$4(2+x)+1 = 7x-3(x-2)$$
$$8+4x+1 = 7x-3x+6$$
$$9+4x = 4x+6$$
$$9+4x-4x = 4x-4x+6$$
$$9 = 6$$
There is no solution.

58.
$$-0.01(5x+4) = 0.04 - 0.01(x+4)$$
$$100[-0.01(5x+4)] = 100[0.04 - 0.01(x+4)]$$
$$-(5x+4) = 4 - 1(x+4)$$
$$-5x - 4 = 4 - x - 4$$
$$-5x - 4 = -x$$
$$-5x + x - 4 = -x + x$$
$$-4x - 4 = 0$$
$$-4x - 4 + 4 = 0 + 4$$
$$-4x = 4$$
$$\frac{-4x}{-4} = \frac{4}{-4}$$
$$x = -1$$

60.
$$3 - \frac{1}{2}x = 5x - 8$$
$$2\left(3 - \frac{1}{2}x\right) = 2(5x - 8)$$
$$6 - x = 10x - 16$$
$$6 - x + x = 10x - 16 + x$$
$$6 = 11x - 16$$
$$6 + 16 = 11x - 16 + 16$$
$$22 = 11x$$
$$\frac{22}{11} = \frac{11x}{11}$$
$$2 = x$$

62.
$$7n + 5 = 10n - 10$$
$$7n + 5 - 5 = 10n - 10 - 5$$
$$7n = 10n - 15$$
$$7n - 10n = 10n - 15 - 10n$$
$$-3n = -15$$
$$\frac{-3n}{-3} = \frac{-15}{-3}$$
$$n = 5$$

64.
$$0.2x - 0.1 = 0.6x - 2.1$$
$$10(0.2x - 0.1) = 10(0.6x - 2.1)$$
$$2x - 1 = 6x - 21$$
$$2x - 6x - 1 = 6x - 6x - 21$$
$$-4x - 1 = -21$$
$$-4x - 1 + 1 = -21 + 1$$
$$-4x = -20$$
$$\frac{-4x}{-4} = \frac{-20}{-4}$$
$$x = 5$$

66.
$$0.03(2m + 7) = 0.06(5 + m) - 0.09$$
$$100[0.03(2m + 7)] = 100[0.06(5 + m) - 0.09]$$
$$3(2m + 7) = 6(5 + m) - 9$$
$$6m + 21 = 30 + 6m - 9$$
$$6m + 21 = 21 + 6m$$
$$6m - 6m + 21 = 21 + 6m - 6m$$
$$21 = 21$$
All real numbers are solutions.

68.

3	times	a number
↓	↓	↓
3	·	x = $3x$

70.

8	minus	twice a number
↓	↓	↓
8	−	$2x$

72.

the quotient of -12	and	the difference of a number and 3		
↓	↓	↓		
-12	÷	$(x-3)$	=	$\dfrac{-12}{x-3}$

74. $x + (7x - 9) = x + 7x - 9 = 8x - 9$
The total length is $(8x - 9)$ feet.

76. a.
$$x + 3 = x + 5$$
$$x + 3 - x = x + 5 - x$$
$$3 = 5$$
There is no solution.

b. Answers may vary

c. Answers may vary

78.
$$3x + 1 = 3x + 2$$
$$3x + 1 - 3x = 3x + 2 - 3x$$
$$1 = 2$$
There is no solution. The answer is b.

80.
$$x - 11x - 3 = -10x - 1 - 2$$
$$-10x - 3 = -10x - 3$$
$$-10x - 3 + 10x = -10x - 3 + 10x$$
$$-3 = -3$$
All real numbers are solutions. The answer is a.

82. $-x + 15 = x + 15$

$-x + 15 + x = x + 15 + x$

$15 = 2x + 15$

$15 - 15 = 2x + 15 - 15$

$0 = 2x$

$\dfrac{0}{2} = \dfrac{2x}{2}$

$0 = x$

The answer is c.

84. Answers may vary

86. a. Since the perimeter is the sum of the lengths of the sides, $x + 2x + 1 + 3x - 2 = 35$.

b. $6x - 1 = 35$

$6x - 1 + 1 = 35 + 1$

$6x = 36$

$\dfrac{6x}{6} = \dfrac{36}{6}$

$x = 6$

c. $2x + 1 = 2(6) + 1 = 13$

$3x - 2 = 3(6) - 2 = 16$

The lengths are $x = 6$ meters,

$2x + 1 = 13$ meters and $3x - 2 = 16$ meters.

88. Answers may vary

90. $1000(x + 40) = 100(16 + 7x)$

$1000x + 40{,}000 = 1600 + 700x$

$1000x + 40{,}000 - 700x = 1600 + 700x - 700x$

$300x + 40{,}000 = 1600$

$300x + 40{,}000 - 40{,}000 = 1600 - 40{,}000$

$300x = -38{,}400$

$\dfrac{300x}{300} = \dfrac{-38{,}400}{300}$

$x = -128$

92. $0.127x - 2.685 = 0.027x - 2.38$

$1000(0.127x - 2.685) = 1000(0.027x - 2.38)$

$127x - 2685 = 27x - 2380$

$127x - 27x - 2685 = 27x - 27x - 2380$

$100x - 2685 = -2380$

$100x - 2685 + 2685 = -2380 + 2685$

$100x = 305$

$\dfrac{100x}{100} = \dfrac{305}{100}$

$x = 3.05$

94. $t^2 - 6t = t(8 + t)$

$t^2 - 6t = 8t + t^2$

$t^2 - t^2 - 6t = 8t + t^2 - t^2$

$-6t = 8t$

$-6t + 6t = 8t + 6t$

$0 = 14t$

$\dfrac{0}{14} = \dfrac{14t}{14}$

$0 = t$

96. $y^2 - 4y + 10 = y(y - 5)$

$y^2 - 4y + 10 = y^2 - 5y$

$y^2 - y^2 - 4y + 10 = y^2 - y^2 - 5y$

$-4y + 10 = -5y$

$-4y + 5y + 10 = -5y + 5y$

$y + 10 = 0$

$y + 10 - 10 = -10$

$y = -10$

The Bigger Picture

1. $3x - 4 = 3(2x - 1) + 7$

$3x - 4 = 6x - 3 + 7$

$3x - 4 = 6x + 4$

$3x - 4 - 6x = 6x + 4 - 6x$

$-3x - 4 = 4$

$-3x - 4 + 4 = 4 + 4$

$-3x = 8$

$\dfrac{-3x}{-3} = \dfrac{8}{-3}$

$x = -\dfrac{8}{3}$

2. $5 + 2x = 5(x + 1)$

$5 + 2x = 5x + 5$

$5 + 2x - 5x = 5x + 5 - 5x$

$5 - 3x = 5$

$5 - 3x - 5 = 5 - 5$

$-3x = 0$

$\dfrac{-3x}{-3} = \dfrac{0}{-3}$

$x = 0$

3.
$$\frac{x+3}{2} = 1$$
$$2\left(\frac{x+3}{2}\right) = 2(1)$$
$$x + 3 = 2$$
$$x + 3 - 3 = 2 - 3$$
$$x = -1$$

4.
$$\frac{x-2}{2} - \frac{x-4}{3} = \frac{5}{6}$$
$$6\left(\frac{x-2}{2} - \frac{x-4}{3}\right) = 6\left(\frac{5}{6}\right)$$
$$3(x-2) - 2(x-4) = 5$$
$$3x - 6 - 2x + 8 = 5$$
$$x + 2 = 5$$
$$x + 2 - 2 = 5 - 2$$
$$x = 3$$

5.
$$\frac{7}{5} + \frac{y}{10} = 2$$
$$10\left(\frac{7}{5} + \frac{y}{10}\right) = 10(2)$$
$$2(7) + y = 20$$
$$14 + y = 20$$
$$14 + y - 14 = 20 - 14$$
$$y = 6$$

6.
$$5 + 2x = 2(x+1)$$
$$5 + 2x = 2x + 2$$
$$5 + 2x - 2x = 2x + 2 - 2x$$
$$5 = 2 \quad \text{False}$$
This false statement indicates that there is no solution.

7.
$$4(x-2) + 3x = 9(x-1) - 2$$
$$4x - 8 + 3x = 9x - 9 - 2$$
$$7x - 8 = 9x - 11$$
$$7x - 8 - 9x = 9x - 11 - 9x$$
$$-2x - 8 = -11$$
$$-2x - 8 + 8 = -11 + 8$$
$$-2x = -3$$
$$\frac{-2x}{-2} = \frac{-3}{-2}$$
$$x = \frac{3}{2}$$

8.
$$6(x+1) - 2 = 6x + 4$$
$$6x + 6 - 2 = 6x + 4$$
$$6x + 4 = 6x + 4$$
$$6x + 4 - 6x = 6x + 4 - 6x$$
$$4 = 4 \quad \text{True}$$
This true statement indicates that all real numbers are solutions of the equation.

Integrated Review

1.
$$x - 10 = -4$$
$$x - 10 + 10 = -4 + 10$$
$$x = 6$$

2.
$$y + 14 = -3$$
$$y + 14 - 14 = -3 - 14$$
$$y = -17$$

3.
$$9y = 108$$
$$\frac{9y}{9} = \frac{108}{9}$$
$$y = 12$$

4.
$$-3x = 78$$
$$\frac{-3x}{-3} = \frac{78}{-3}$$
$$x = -26$$

5.
$$-6x + 7 = 25$$
$$-6x + 7 - 7 = 25 - 7$$
$$-6x = 18$$
$$\frac{-6x}{-6} = \frac{18}{-6}$$
$$x = -3$$

6.
$$5y - 42 = -47$$
$$5y - 42 + 42 = -47 + 42$$
$$5y = -5$$
$$\frac{5y}{5} = \frac{-5}{5}$$
$$y = -1$$

7.
$$\frac{2}{3}x = 9$$
$$\frac{3}{2}\left(\frac{2}{3}x\right) = \frac{3}{2}(9)$$
$$x = \frac{27}{2}$$

8. $\dfrac{4}{5}z = 10$

$\dfrac{5}{4}\left(\dfrac{4}{5}z\right) = \dfrac{5}{4}(10)$

$z = \dfrac{25}{2}$

9. $\dfrac{r}{-4} = -2$

$-4\left(\dfrac{r}{-4}\right) = -4(-2)$

$r = 8$

10. $\dfrac{y}{-8} = 8$

$-8\left(\dfrac{y}{-8}\right) = -8(8)$

$y = -64$

11. $6 - 2x + 8 = 10$

$-2x + 14 = 10$

$-2x + 14 - 14 = 10 - 14$

$-2x = -4$

$\dfrac{-2x}{-2} = \dfrac{-4}{-2}$

$x = 2$

12. $-5 - 6y + 6 = 19$

$-6y + 1 = 19$

$-6y + 1 - 1 = 19 - 1$

$-6y = 18$

$\dfrac{-6y}{-6} = \dfrac{18}{-6}$

$y = -3$

13. $2x - 7 = 2x - 27$

$2x - 2x - 7 = 2x - 2x - 27$

$-7 = -27$

There is no solution.

14. $3 + 8y = 8y - 2$

$3 + 8y - 8y = 8y - 8y - 2$

$3 = -2$

There is no solution.

15. $-3a + 6 + 5a = 7a - 8a$

$2a + 6 = -a$

$2a - 2a + 6 = -a - 2a$

$6 = -3a$

$\dfrac{6}{-3} = \dfrac{-3a}{-3}$

$-2 = a$

16. $4b - 8 - b = 10b - 3b$

$3b - 8 = 7b$

$3b - 3b - 8 = 7b - 3b$

$-8 = 4b$

$\dfrac{-8}{4} = \dfrac{4b}{4}$

$-2 = b$

17. $-\dfrac{2}{3}x = \dfrac{5}{9}$

$-\dfrac{3}{2}\left(-\dfrac{2}{3}x\right) = -\dfrac{3}{2}\left(\dfrac{5}{9}\right)$

$x = -\dfrac{5}{6}$

18. $-\dfrac{3}{8}y = -\dfrac{1}{16}$

$-\dfrac{8}{3}\left(-\dfrac{3}{8}y\right) = -\dfrac{8}{3}\left(-\dfrac{1}{16}\right)$

$y = \dfrac{1}{6}$

19. $10 = -6n + 16$

$10 - 16 = -6n + 16 - 16$

$-6 = -6n$

$\dfrac{-6}{-6} = \dfrac{-6n}{-6}$

$1 = n$

20. $-5 = -2m + 7$

$-5 - 7 = -2m + 7 - 7$

$-12 = -2m$

$\dfrac{-12}{-2} = \dfrac{-2m}{-2}$

$6 = m$

21.
$$3(5c-1)-2=13c+3$$
$$15c-3-2=13c+3$$
$$15c-5=13c+3$$
$$15c-13c-5=13c-13c+3$$
$$2c-5=3$$
$$2c-5+5=3+5$$
$$2c=8$$
$$\frac{2c}{2}=\frac{8}{2}$$
$$c=4$$

22.
$$4(3t+4)-20=3+5t$$
$$12t+16-20=3+5t$$
$$12t-4=3+5t$$
$$12t-5t-4=3+5t-5t$$
$$7t-4=3$$
$$7t-4+4=3+4$$
$$7t=7$$
$$\frac{7t}{7}=\frac{7}{7}$$
$$t=1$$

23.
$$\frac{2(z+3)}{3}=5-z$$
$$3\left[\frac{2(z+3)}{3}\right]=3(5-z)$$
$$2z+6=15-3z$$
$$2z+3z+6=15-3z+3z$$
$$5z+6=15$$
$$5z+6-6=15-6$$
$$5z=9$$
$$\frac{5z}{5}=\frac{9}{5}$$
$$z=\frac{9}{5}$$

24.
$$\frac{3(w+2)}{4}=2w+3$$
$$4\left[\frac{3(w+2)}{4}\right]=4(2w+3)$$
$$3w+6=8w+12$$
$$3w-8w+6=8w-8w+12$$
$$-5w+6=12$$
$$-5w+6-6=12-6$$
$$-5w=6$$
$$\frac{-5w}{-5}=\frac{6}{-5}$$
$$w=-\frac{6}{5}$$

25.
$$-2(2x-5)=-3x+7-x+3$$
$$-4x+10=-4x+10$$
$$-4x+4x+10=-4x+4x+10$$
$$10=10$$
All real numbers are solutions.

26.
$$-4(5x-2)=-12x+4-8x+4$$
$$-20x+8=-20x+8$$
$$-20x+20x+8=-20x+20x+8$$
$$8=8$$
All real numbers are solutions.

27.
$$0.02(6t-3)=0.04(t-2)+0.02$$
$$100[0.02(6t-3)]=100[0.04(t-2)+0.02]$$
$$2(6t-3)=4(t-2)+2$$
$$12t-6=4t-8+2$$
$$12t-6=4t-6$$
$$12t-4t-6=4t-4t-6$$
$$8t-6=-6$$
$$8t-6+6=-6+6$$
$$8t=0$$
$$\frac{8t}{8}=\frac{0}{8}$$
$$t=0$$

28.
$$0.03(m+7)=0.02(5-m)+0.03$$
$$100[0.03(m+7)]=100[0.02(5-m)+0.03]$$
$$3(m+7)=2(5-m)+3$$
$$3m+21=10-2m+3$$
$$3m+21=13-2m$$
$$3m+2m+21=13-2m+2m$$
$$5m+21=13$$
$$5m+21-21=13-21$$
$$5m=-8$$
$$\frac{5m}{5}=\frac{-8}{5}$$
$$m=-\frac{8}{5}=-1.6$$

29.
$$-3y=\frac{4(y-1)}{5}$$
$$5(-3y)=5\left[\frac{4(y-1)}{5}\right]$$
$$-15y=4y-4$$
$$-15y-4y=4y-4y-4$$
$$-19y=-4$$
$$\frac{-19y}{-19}=\frac{-4}{-19}$$
$$y=\frac{4}{19}$$

30.
$$-4x = \frac{5(1-x)}{6}$$
$$6(-4x) = 6\left[\frac{5(1-x)}{6}\right]$$
$$-24x = 5 - 5x$$
$$-24x + 5x = 5 - 5x + 5x$$
$$-19x = 5$$
$$\frac{-19x}{-19} = \frac{5}{-19}$$
$$x = -\frac{5}{19}$$

31.
$$\frac{5}{3}x - \frac{7}{3} = x$$
$$3\left(\frac{5}{3}x - \frac{7}{3}\right) = 3(x)$$
$$5x - 7 = 3x$$
$$5x - 5x - 7 = 3x - 5x$$
$$-7 = -2x$$
$$\frac{-7}{-2} = \frac{-2x}{-2}$$
$$\frac{7}{2} = x$$

32.
$$\frac{7}{5}n + \frac{3}{5} = -n$$
$$5\left(\frac{7}{5}n + \frac{3}{5}\right) = 5(-n)$$
$$7n + 3 = -5n$$
$$7n - 7n + 3 = -5n - 7n$$
$$3 = -12n$$
$$\frac{3}{-12} = \frac{-12n}{-12}$$
$$-\frac{1}{4} = n$$

33.
$$\frac{1}{10}(3x - 7) = \frac{3}{10}x + 5$$
$$10\left[\frac{1}{10}(3x-7)\right] = 10\left(\frac{3}{10}x + 5\right)$$
$$3x - 7 = 3x + 50$$
$$3x - 7 - 3x = 3x + 50 - 3x$$
$$-7 = 50$$
There is no solution.

34.
$$\frac{1}{7}(2x - 5) = \frac{2}{7}x + 1$$
$$7\left[\frac{1}{7}(2x-5)\right] = 7\left(\frac{2}{7}x + 1\right)$$
$$2x - 5 = 2x + 7$$
$$2x - 5 - 2x = 2x + 7 - 2x$$
$$-5 = 7$$
There is no solution.

35.
$$5 + 2(3x - 6) = -4(6x - 7)$$
$$5 + 6x - 12 = -24x + 28$$
$$6x - 7 = -24x + 28$$
$$6x - 7 + 24x = -24x + 28 + 24x$$
$$30x - 7 = 28$$
$$30x - 7 + 7 = 28 + 7$$
$$30x = 35$$
$$\frac{30x}{30} = \frac{35}{30}$$
$$x = \frac{7}{6}$$

36.
$$3 + 5(2x - 4) = -7(5x + 2)$$
$$3 + 10x - 20 = -35x - 14$$
$$10x - 17 = -35x - 14$$
$$10x - 17 + 35x = -35x - 14 + 35x$$
$$45x - 17 = -14$$
$$45x - 17 + 17 = -14 + 17$$
$$45x = 3$$
$$\frac{45x}{45} = \frac{3}{45}$$
$$x = \frac{1}{15}$$

Section 2.4

Practice Exercises

1. Let x = the number.
$$3x - 6 = 2x + 3$$
$$3x - 6 - 2x = 2x + 3 - 2x$$
$$x - 6 = 3$$
$$x - 6 + 6 = 3 + 6$$
$$x = 9$$
The number is 9.

2. Let x = the number.
$$3x - 4 = 2(x - 1)$$
$$3x - 4 = 2x - 2$$
$$3x - 4 - 2x = 2x - 2 - 2x$$
$$x - 4 = -2$$
$$x - 4 + 4 = -2 + 4$$
$$x = 2$$
The number is 2.

3. Let x = the length of short piece,
then $4x$ = the length of long piece.
$$x + 4x = 45$$
$$5x = 45$$
$$\frac{5x}{5} = \frac{45}{5}$$
$$x = 9$$
$$4x = 4(9) = 36$$
The short piece is 9 inches and the long piece is 36 inches.

4. Let x = number of Republicans, then
$x + 6$ = number of Democrats.
$$x + x + 6 = 50$$
$$2x + 6 = 50$$
$$2x + 6 - 6 = 50 - 6$$
$$2x = 44$$
$$\frac{2x}{2} = \frac{44}{2}$$
$$x = 22$$
$$x + 6 = 22 + 6 = 28$$
There were 22 Republican and 28 Democratic Governors.

5. x = degree measure of first angle
$3x$ = degree measure of second angle
$x + 55$ = degree measure of third angle
$$x + 3x + (x + 55) = 180$$
$$5x + 55 = 180$$
$$5x + 55 - 55 = 180 - 55$$
$$5x = 125$$
$$\frac{5x}{5} = \frac{125}{5}$$
$$x = 25$$
$$3x = 3(25) = 75$$
$$x + 55 = 25 + 55 = 80$$
The measures of the angles are 25°, 75°, and 80°.

6. Let x = the first even integer, then
$x + 2$ = the second even integer, and
$x + 4$ = the third even integer.
$$x + (x + 2) + (x + 4) = 144$$
$$3x + 6 = 144$$
$$3x + 6 - 6 = 144 - 6$$
$$3x = 138$$
$$\frac{3x}{3} = \frac{138}{3}$$
$$x = 46$$
$$x + 2 = 46 + 2 = 48$$
$$x + 4 = 46 + 4 = 50$$
The integers are 46, 48, and 50.

Vocabulary and Readiness Check

1. $2x$; $2x - 31$

2. $3x$; $3x + 17$

3. $x + 5$; $2(x + 5)$

4. $x - 11$; $7(x - 11)$

5. $20 - y$; $\dfrac{20 - y}{3}$ or $(20 - y) \div 3$

6. $-10 + y$; $\dfrac{-10 + y}{9}$ or $(-10 + y) \div 9$

Exercise Set 2.4

2. Let x = the number.
$$3x - 1 = 2x$$
$$3x - 1 - 3x = 2x - 3x$$
$$3x - 1 - 3x = 2x - 3x$$
$$-1 = -x$$
$$\frac{-1}{-1} = \frac{-x}{-1}$$
$$1 = x$$
The number is 1.

4. Let x = the number.
$$4x + (-2) = 5x + (-2)$$
$$4x - 2 = 5x - 2$$
$$4x - 2 + 2 = 5x - 2 + 2$$
$$4x = 5x$$
$$4x - 4x = 5x - 4x$$
$$0 = x$$
The number is 0.

6. Let x = the number.
$$5[x+(-1)] = 6x$$
$$5x + 5(-1) = 6x$$
$$5x - 5 = 6x$$
$$5x - 5x - 5 = 6x - 5x$$
$$-5 = x$$
The number is -5.

8. Let x = the number.
$$2(x-4) = x - \frac{1}{4}$$
$$2x - 8 = x - \frac{1}{4}$$
$$4(2x-8) = 4\left(x - \frac{1}{4}\right)$$
$$8x - 32 = 4x - 1$$
$$8x - 4x - 32 = 4x - 4x - 1$$
$$4x - 32 = -1$$
$$4x - 32 + 32 = -1 + 32$$
$$4x = 31$$
$$\frac{4x}{4} = \frac{31}{4}$$
The number is $\frac{31}{4}$.

10. Let x = length of shorter piece,
then $5x + 1$ = length of longer piece.
$$x + (5x+1) = 25$$
$$6x + 1 = 25$$
$$6x + 1 - 1 = 25 - 1$$
$$6x = 24$$
$$\frac{6x}{6} = \frac{24}{6}$$
$$x = 4$$
$5x + 1 = 5(4) + 1 = 21$
The shorter piece is 4 feet and the longer piece is 21 feet.

12. Let x = area of Gobi Desert,
then $7x$ = area of Sahara Desert.
$$x + 7x = 4,000,000$$
$$8x = 4,000,000$$
$$\frac{8x}{8} = \frac{4,000,000}{8}$$
$$x = 500,000$$
$7x = 7(500,000) = 3,500,000$
The area of the Gobi Desert is 500,000 square miles, and the area of the Sahara Desert is 3,500,000 miles.

14. Let x = number of television stations in China, then $x + 4066$ = number of television stations in Russia.
$$x + x + 4066 = 10,546$$
$$2x + 4066 = 10,546$$
$$2x + 4066 - 4066 = 10,546 - 4066$$
$$2x = 6480$$
$$\frac{2x}{2} = \frac{6480}{2}$$
$$x = 3240$$
$x + 4066 = 3240 + 4066 = 7306$
China has 3240 television stations and Russia has 7306.

16. Let x = the measure of angles B and C, and $x - 42$ = the measure of A.
$$x + x + x - 42 = 180$$
$$3x - 42 = 180$$
$$3x - 42 + 42 = 180 + 42$$
$$3x = 222$$
$$\frac{3x}{3} = \frac{222}{3}$$
$$x = 74$$
$x - 42 = 74 - 42 = 32$
The angles are $B = 74°$, $C = 74°$, and $A = 32°$.

18. Three consecutive integers:
Integer: x
Next integers: $x + 1$, $x + 2$
Sum of the second and third consecutive integers, simplified: $(x + 1) + (x + 2) = 2x + 3$

20. Three consecutive odd integers:
Odd integer: x
Next integers: $x + 2$, $x + 4$
Sum of the three consecutive odd integers, simplified: $x + (x + 2) + (x + 4) = 3x + 6$

22. Four consecutive integers:
Integer: x
Next integers: $x + 1$, $x + 2$, $x + 3$
Sum of the first and fourth consecutive integers, simplified: $x + (x + 3) = 2x + 3$

24. Three consecutive even integers:
Even integer: x
Next integers: $x + 2$, $x + 4$
Sum of the three consecutive even integers, simplified: $x + (x + 2) + (x + 4) = 3x + 6$

26. Let x = the number of one room
and $x + 2$ = the number of the other.
$$x + x + 2 = 654$$
$$2x + 2 = 654$$
$$2x + 2 - 2 = 654 - 2$$
$$2x = 652$$
$$\frac{2x}{2} = \frac{652}{2}$$
$$x = 326$$
$$x + 2 = 326 + 2 = 328$$
The room numbers are 326 and 328.

28. Let x = code for Mali Republic,
$x + 2$ = code for Cote d'Ivoire,
and $x + 4$ = code for Niger.
$$x + x + 2 + x + 4 = 675$$
$$3x + 6 = 675$$
$$3x + 6 - 6 = 675 - 6$$
$$3x = 669$$
$$\frac{3x}{3} = \frac{669}{3}$$
$$x = 223$$
$$x + 2 = 223 + 2 = 225$$
$$x + 4 = 223 + 4 = 227$$
The codes are: 223 for Mali, 225 for Cote
d'Ivoire, 227 for Niger.

30. $x + 3x + (2 + 7x) = 46$
$$11x + 2 = 46$$
$$11x + 2 - 2 = 46 - 2$$
$$11x = 44$$
$$\frac{11x}{11} = \frac{44}{11}$$
$$x = 4$$
$$3x = 3(4) = 12$$
$$2 + 7x = 2 + 7(4) = 30$$
The lengths of the pieces are 4 feet, 12 feet, and
30 feet.

32. Let x = the number.
$$9 = 2x - 10$$
$$9 + 10 = 2x - 10 + 10$$
$$19 = 2x$$
$$\frac{19}{2} = \frac{2x}{2}$$
$$\frac{19}{2} = x$$

The number is $\frac{19}{2}$.

34. Let x = species of grasshoppers,
then $20x$ = species of beetles.
$$x + 20x = 420,000$$
$$21x = 420,000$$
$$\frac{21x}{21} = \frac{420,000}{21}$$
$$x = 20,000$$
$$20x = 20(20,000) = 400,000$$
There are 400,000 species of beetles and
20,000 species of grasshoppers.

36. Let x = the measure of the smallest angle,
$x + 2$ = the measure of the second,
$x + 4$ = the measure of the third, and
$x + 6$ = the measure of the fourth.
$$x + x + 2 + x + 4 + x + 6 = 360$$
$$4x + 12 = 360$$
$$4x + 12 - 12 = 360 - 12$$
$$4x = 348$$
$$\frac{4x}{4} = \frac{348}{4}$$
$$x = 87$$
$$x + 2 = 87 + 2 = 89$$
$$x + 4 = 87 + 4 = 91$$
$$x + 6 = 87 + 6 = 93$$
The angles are $87°$, $89°$, $91°$, and $93°$.

38. Let x = first odd integer,
then $x + 2$ = next odd integer,
and $x + 4$ = third consecutive odd integer.
$$x + (x + 2) + (x + 4) = 51$$
$$3x + 6 = 51$$
$$3x + 6 - 6 = 51 - 6$$
$$3x = 45$$
$$\frac{3x}{3} = \frac{45}{3}$$
$$x = 15$$
$$x + 2 = 15 + 2 = 17$$
$$x + 4 = 15 + 4 = 19$$
The code is 15, 17, 19.

40. Let x = the number.
$$2(x + 6) = 3(x + 4)$$
$$2x + 12 = 3x + 12$$
$$2x + 12 - 12 = 3x + 12 - 12$$
$$2x = 3x$$
$$2x - 2x = 3x - 2x$$
$$0 = x$$
The number is 0.

42. Let x = votes for Zanzi,
then $x + 35{,}650$ = votes for Bishop.
$$x + x + 35{,}650 = 158{,}192$$
$$2x + 35{,}650 = 158{,}192$$
$$2x + 35{,}650 - 35{,}650 = 158{,}192 - 35{,}650$$
$$2x = 122{,}542$$
$$\frac{2x}{2} = \frac{122{,}542}{2}$$
$$x = 61{,}271$$
$x + 35{,}650 = 61{,}271 + 35{,}650 = 96{,}921$
Zanzi received 61,271 votes and Bishop received 96,921 votes.

44. Let x = the measure of the first angle
then $2x - 3$ = the measure of the other.
$$x + 2x - 3 = 90$$
$$3x - 3 = 90$$
$$3x - 3 + 3 = 90 + 3$$
$$3x = 93$$
$$\frac{3x}{3} = \frac{93}{3}$$
$$x = 31$$
$2x - 3 = 2(31) - 3 = 59$
The angles are 31° and 59°.

46. Let x = the number.
$$\frac{3}{4} + 3x = 2x - \frac{1}{2}$$
$$4\left(\frac{3}{4} + 3x\right) = 4\left(2x - \frac{1}{2}\right)$$
$$3 + 12x = 8x - 2$$
$$3 + 12x - 8x = 8x - 2 - 8x$$
$$3 + 4x = -2$$
$$3 + 4x - 3 = -2 - 3$$
$$4x = -5$$
$$\frac{4x}{4} = \frac{-5}{4}$$
$$x = -\frac{5}{4}$$
The number is $-\dfrac{5}{4}$.

48. Let x = the measure of each of the two equal angles A and D,
and $2x$ = the measure of each of the other two equal angles C and B.
$$x + x + 2x + 2x = 360$$
$$6x = 360$$
$$\frac{6x}{6} = \frac{360}{6}$$
$$x = 60$$

$2x = 2(60) = 120$
The angles are $A = 60°$, $D = 60°$, $C = 120°$, $B = 120°$.

50. Let x = floor space of Empire State Building,
then $3x$ = floor space of the Pentagon.
$$x + 3x = 8700$$
$$4x = 8700$$
$$\frac{4x}{4} = \frac{8700}{4}$$
$$x = 2175$$
$3x = 3(2175) = 6525$
The Empire State Building has 2175 thousand square feet and the Pentagon has 6525 thousand square feet.

52. Let x = the number.
$$\frac{7}{8} \cdot x = \frac{1}{2}$$
$$\frac{8}{7} \cdot \frac{7}{8} x = \frac{8}{7} \cdot \frac{1}{2}$$
$$x = \frac{4}{7}$$
The number is $\dfrac{4}{7}$.

54. Let x = first integer (smallest piece)
then $x + 2$ = second integer (middle piece)
and $x + 4$ = third integer (longest piece)
$$x + (x + 2) + (x + 4) = 48$$
$$3x + 6 = 48$$
$$3x + 6 - 6 = 48 - 6$$
$$3x = 42$$
$$\frac{3x}{3} = \frac{42}{3}$$
$$x = 14$$
$x + 2 = 14 + 2 = 16$
$x + 4 = 14 + 4 = 18$
The pieces measure 14 inches, 16 inches, and 18 inches.

56. Let x = points for Michigan,
and $x + 14$ = points for USC.
$$x + (x + 14) = 50$$
$$2x + 14 = 50$$
$$2x + 14 - 14 = 50 - 14$$
$$2x = 36$$
$$\frac{2x}{2} = \frac{36}{2}$$
$$x = 18$$
$x + 14 = 18 + 14 = 32$
Michigan scored 18 points and USC scored 32 points.

58. Let x = smallest angle, then $4x$ = largest angles.
$$x + 4x + 4x = 180$$
$$9x = 180$$
$$\frac{9x}{9} = \frac{180}{9}$$
$$x = 20$$
$$4x = 4(20) = 80$$
The angles measure 20°, 80°, and 80°.

60. Let x = length of first piece,
then $4x$ = length of second piece,
and $5x$ = length of third piece.
$$x + 4x + 5x = 30$$
$$10x = 30$$
$$\frac{10x}{10} = \frac{30}{10}$$
$$x = 3$$
$$4x = 4(3) = 12$$
$$5x = 5(3) = 15$$
The first piece is 3 feet, the second piece is 12 feet, and the third piece is 15 feet.

62. The heights of the bars representing Texas and Pennsylvania are between 30 and 40. Therefore, Texas and Pennsylvania spend between $30 million and $40 million on tourism.

64. Let x = amount spent by Pennsylvania,
then $2x - 14.2$ = amount spent by Hawaii.
$$x + (2x - 14.2) = 91.1$$
$$3x - 14.2 = 91.1$$
$$3x - 14.2 + 14.2 = 91.1 + 14.2$$
$$3x = 105.3$$
$$\frac{3x}{3} = \frac{105.3}{3}$$
$$x = 35.1$$
$$2x - 14.2 = 2(35.1) - 14.2 = 56$$
Pennsylvania spends $35.1 million and Hawaii spends $56 million.

66. Answers may vary.

68. $\frac{1}{2} Bh = \frac{1}{2}(14)(22) = 7 \cdot 22 = 154$

70. $r \cdot t = 15 \cdot 2 = 30$

72. Answers may vary

Section 2.5

Practice Exercises

1. Let $d = 580$ and $r = 5$.
$$d = r \cdot t$$
$$580 = 5t$$
$$\frac{580}{5} = \frac{5t}{5}$$
$$116 = t$$
It takes 116 seconds or 1 minute 56 seconds.

2. Let $l = 40$ and $P = 98$.
$$P = 2l + 2w$$
$$98 = 2 \cdot 40 + 2w$$
$$98 = 80 + 2w$$
$$98 - 80 = 80 + 2w - 80$$
$$18 = 2w$$
$$\frac{18}{2} = \frac{2w}{2}$$
$$9 = w$$
The dog run is 9 feet wide.

3. Let $C = 8$.
$$F = \frac{9}{5}C + 32$$
$$F = \frac{9}{5} \cdot 8 + 32$$
$$F = \frac{72}{5} + \frac{160}{5}$$
$$F = \frac{232}{5} = 46.4$$
The equivalent temperature is 46.4°F.

4. Let w = width of sign, then
$5w + 3$ = length of sign.
$$P = 2l + 2w$$
$$66 = 2(5w + 3) + 2w$$
$$66 = 10w + 6 + 2w$$
$$66 = 12w + 6$$
$$66 - 6 = 12w + 6 - 6$$
$$60 = 12w$$
$$\frac{60}{12} = \frac{12w}{12}$$
$$5 = w$$
$$5w + 3 = 5(5) + 3 = 28$$
The sign has length 28 inches and width 5 inches.

5.
$$I = Prt$$
$$\frac{I}{Pt} = \frac{Prt}{Pt}$$
$$\frac{I}{Pt} = r \text{ or } r = \frac{I}{Pt}$$

6.
$$H = 5as + 10a$$
$$H - 10a = 5as + 10a - 10a$$
$$H - 10a = 5as$$
$$\frac{H - 10a}{5a} = \frac{5as}{5a}$$
$$\frac{H - 10a}{5a} = s \text{ or } s = \frac{H - 10a}{5a}$$

7.
$$N = F + d(n-1)$$
$$N - F = F + d(n-1) - F$$
$$N - F = d(n-1)$$
$$\frac{N - F}{n-1} = \frac{d(n-1)}{n-1}$$
$$\frac{N - F}{n-1} = d \text{ or } d = \frac{N - F}{n-1}$$

8.
$$A = \frac{1}{2}a(b+B)$$
$$2 \cdot A = 2 \cdot \frac{1}{2}a(b+B)$$
$$2A = a(b+B)$$
$$2A = ab + aB$$
$$2A - ab = ab + aB - ab$$
$$2A - ab = aB$$
$$\frac{2A - ab}{a} = \frac{aB}{a}$$
$$\frac{2A - ab}{a} = B \text{ or } B = \frac{2A - ab}{a}$$

Exercise Set 2.5

2. Let $d = 195$ and $t = 3$.
$$d = rt$$
$$195 = r(3)$$
$$\frac{195}{3} = \frac{3r}{3}$$
$$65 = r$$

4. Let $l = 14$, $w = 8$, and $h = 3$.
$$V = lwh$$
$$V = 14(8)(3)$$
$$V = 336$$

6. Let $A = 60$, $B = 7$, and $b = 3$.
$$A = \frac{1}{2}h(B+b)$$
$$60 = \frac{1}{2}h(7+3)$$
$$2(60) = 2\left[\frac{1}{2}h(10)\right]$$
$$120 = 10h$$
$$\frac{120}{10} = \frac{10h}{10}$$
$$12 = h$$

8. Let $V = 45$, and $h = 5$.
$$V = \frac{1}{3}Ah$$
$$45 = \frac{1}{3}A(5)$$
$$3(45) = 3\left[\frac{1}{3}(5A)\right]$$
$$135 = 5A$$
$$\frac{135}{5} = \frac{5A}{5}$$
$$27 = A$$

10. Let $r = 4.5$, and $\pi \approx 3.14$.
$$A = \pi r^2$$
$$A \approx 3.14(4.5)^2$$
$$A \approx 3.14(20.25)$$
$$A \approx 63.6$$

12. Let $I = 1{,}056{,}000$, $R = 0.055$, and $T = 6$.
$$I = PRT$$
$$1{,}056{,}000 = P(0.055)(6)$$
$$1{,}056{,}000 = 0.33P$$
$$\frac{1{,}056{,}000}{0.33} = \frac{0.33P}{0.33}$$
$$3{,}200{,}000 = P$$

14. Let $r = 3$ and $\pi \approx 3.14$.
$$V = \frac{4}{3}\pi r^3$$
$$V \approx \frac{4}{3}(3.14)(3)^3$$
$$V \approx \frac{4}{3}(3.14)(27)$$
$$V \approx \frac{4}{3}(84.78)$$
$$V \approx 113.0$$
$$(V \approx 113.1 \text{ using a calculator.})$$

16. $A = \pi ab$

$\dfrac{A}{\pi a} = \dfrac{\pi ab}{\pi a}$

$\dfrac{A}{\pi a} = b$

18. $T = mnr$

$\dfrac{T}{mr} = \dfrac{mnr}{mr}$

$\dfrac{T}{mr} = n$

20. $-x + y = 13$

$-x + x + y = 13 + x$

$y = 13 + x$

22. $A = P + PRT$

$A - P = P - P + PRT$

$A - P = PRT$

$\dfrac{A - P}{PR} = \dfrac{PRT}{PR}$

$\dfrac{A - P}{PR} = T$

24. $D = \dfrac{1}{4} fk$

$4D = 4\left(\dfrac{1}{4} fk\right)$

$4D = fk$

$\dfrac{4D}{f} = \dfrac{fk}{f}$

$\dfrac{4D}{f} = k$

26. $PR = x + y + z + w$

$PR - (x + y + w) = x + y + z + w - (x + y + w)$

$PR - x - y - w = x + y + z + w - x - y - w$

$PR - x - y - w = z$

28. $S = 4lw + 2wh$

$S - 4lw = 4lw - 4lw + 2wh$

$S - 4lw = 2wh$

$\dfrac{S - 4lw}{2w} = \dfrac{2wh}{2w}$

$\dfrac{S - 4lw}{2w} = h$

30. a. $A = \dfrac{1}{2} bh$ $P = l_1 + l_2 + l_3$

$A = \dfrac{1}{2} \cdot 36 \cdot 27$ $P = 27 + 36 + 45$

$A = 486$ $P = 108$

The area is 486 square feet and the perimeter is 108 feet.

b. The fence has to do with perimeter because it is located around the edge of the property. The grass seed has to do with area because it is located in the middle of the property.

32. a. $A = bh$ $P = 2l_1 + 2l_2$

$A = 9.3(7)$ $P = 2(11.7) + 2(9.3)$

$A = 65.1$ $P = 23.4 + 18.6$

          $P = 42$

The area is 65.1 square feet and the perimeter is 42 feet.

b. The border has to do with the perimeter because it surrounds the edge. The paint has to do with the area because it covers the wall.

34. Let $A = 52,400$ and $l = 400$.

$A = lw$

$52,400 = 400w$

$\dfrac{52,400}{400} = \dfrac{400w}{400}$

$131 = w$

The width is 131 feet.

36. Let $C = -5$.

$F = \dfrac{9}{5}(-5) + 32 = -9 + 32 = 23$

The equivalent temperature is 23°F.

38. Let $d = 303$ and $t = 8\dfrac{1}{2}$.

$d = rt$

$303 = r\left(8\dfrac{1}{2}\right)$

$303 = \dfrac{17}{2} r$

$2(303) = 2\left(\dfrac{17}{2} r\right)$

$606 = 17r$

$\dfrac{606}{17} = \dfrac{17r}{17}$

$\dfrac{606}{17} = r$

$$r = \frac{606}{17} = 35\frac{11}{17}$$

The average rate was $35\frac{11}{17}$ mph.

---

40. Let $P = 400$ and $l = 2w - 10$.

$$P = 2l + 2w$$
$$400 = 2(2w - 10) + 2w$$
$$400 = 4w - 20 + 2w$$
$$400 = 6w - 20$$
$$400 + 20 = 6w - 20 + 20$$
$$420 = 6w$$
$$\frac{420}{6} = \frac{6w}{6}$$
$$70 = w$$
$$l = 2w - 10 = 2(70) - 10 = 140 - 10 = 130$$

The length is 130 meters.

42. Let $x =$ the measure of each of the two equal sides, and $x - 2 =$ the measure of the third.

$$x + x + x - 2 = 22$$
$$3x - 2 = 22$$
$$3x - 2 + 2 = 22 + 2$$
$$3x = 24$$
$$\frac{3x}{3} = \frac{24}{3}$$
$$x = 8$$
$$x - 2 = 8 - 2 = 6$$

The shortest side is 6 feet.

44. Let $d = 700$ and $r = 55$.

$$d = rt$$
$$700 = 55t$$
$$\frac{700}{55} = \frac{55t}{55}$$
$$\frac{700}{55} = t$$
$$t = \frac{700}{55} = \frac{140}{11} = 12\frac{8}{11}$$

The trip will take $12\frac{8}{11}$ hours.

46. Let $r = 4$ and $h = 3$. Use $\pi \approx 3.14$.

$$V = \pi r^2 h$$
$$V \approx (3.14)(4)^2(3)$$
$$\approx (3.14)(16)(3)$$
$$\approx 150.72$$

Let $x =$ number of goldfish and volume per fish $= 2$.

$$150.72 = 2x$$
$$\frac{150.72}{2} = \frac{2x}{2}$$
$$75.36 = x$$

75 goldfish can be placed in the tank.

48. Let $A = 20$, and $b = 5$.

$$A = \frac{1}{2}bh$$
$$20 = \frac{1}{2}(5)h$$
$$2(20) = 2\left(\frac{5}{2}h\right)$$
$$40 = 5h$$
$$\frac{40}{5} = \frac{5h}{5}$$
$$8 = h$$

The height is 8 feet.

50. Let $r = 4000$. Use $\pi \approx 3.14$.

$$C = 2\pi r \approx 2(3.14)(4000)$$
$$C \approx 25{,}120$$

The length of rope is 25,120 miles.

52.
$$x + (2x - 8) + (3x - 12) = 82$$
$$6x - 20 = 82$$
$$6x - 20 + 20 = 82 + 20$$
$$6x = 102$$
$$\frac{6x}{6} = \frac{102}{6}$$
$$x = 17$$
$$2x - 8 = 2(17) - 8 = 26$$
$$3x - 12 = 3(17) - 12 = 39$$

The lengths are 17 feet, 26 feet, and 39 feet.

54. Let $d = 6$ and $r = 0.5$.

$$d = rt$$
$$6 = 0.5t$$
$$\frac{6}{0.5} = \frac{0.5t}{0.5}$$
$$\frac{6}{0.5} = t$$
$$12 = t$$

It took about 12 hours.

56. Let x = the length of a side of the square and
$2x - 15$ = the length of a side of the triangle.

$P(\text{triangle}) = P(\text{square})$

$3(2x - 15) = 4x$

$6x - 45 = 4x$

$6x - 4x - 45 = 4x - 4x$

$2x - 45 = 0$

$2x - 45 + 45 = 45$

$2x = 45$

$\dfrac{2x}{2} = \dfrac{45}{2}$

$x = 22.5$

$2x - 15 = 2(22.5) - 15 = 45 - 15 = 30$

The side of the triangle is 30 units and the side of the square is 22.5 units.

58. Let $d = 150$ and $r = 45$.

$d = rt$

$150 = 45t$

$\dfrac{150}{45} = \dfrac{45t}{45}$

$\dfrac{150}{45} = t$

$t = \dfrac{150}{45} = \dfrac{10}{3}$

The trip will take $\dfrac{10}{3} = 3\dfrac{1}{3}$ hours or 3 hours

20 minutes.

He should arrive at 7:20 A.M.

60. Let $F = 78$.

$F = \dfrac{9}{5}C + 32$

$78 = \dfrac{9}{5}C + 32$

$5(78) = 5\left(\dfrac{9}{5}C + 32\right)$

$390 = 9C + 160$

$390 - 160 = 9C + 160 - 160$

$230 = 9C$

$\dfrac{230}{9} = \dfrac{9C}{9}$

$\dfrac{230}{9} = C$

$C = \dfrac{230}{9} = 25\dfrac{5}{9}$

The equivalent temperature is $25\dfrac{5}{9}°C$.

62. Let $C = -10$.

$F = \dfrac{9}{5}C + 32$

$= \dfrac{9}{5}(-10) + 32$

$= -18 + 32$

$= 14$

The equivalent temperature is 14°F

64. Let $d = 2810$ and $r = 105$.

$d = rt$

$2810 = 105t$

$\dfrac{2810}{105} = \dfrac{105t}{105}$

$\dfrac{2810}{105} = t$

$t = \dfrac{2810}{105} \approx 26.8$

The trip will take 26.8 hours.

66. Let $\pi \approx 3.14$ and $d = 30$ so $r = 15$.

$V = \dfrac{4}{3}\pi r^3 \approx \dfrac{4}{3}(3.14)(15)^3 = 14{,}130$

The volume is 14,130 cubic inches.

68. Let $F = -227$.

$C = \dfrac{5}{9}(F - 32)$

$C = \dfrac{5}{9}(-227 - 32) \approx -144$

The equivalent temperature is −144°C.

70. Half the product of a number and five is $\dfrac{1}{2}(5x)$.

72. Double the sum of ten and four times a number is $2(10 + 4x)$.

74. A number minus the sum of the number and six is $x - (x + 6)$.

76. $\bigcirc \cdot \square + \triangle = \bigcirc$

$\bigcirc \cdot \square = \bigcirc - \triangle$

$\square = \dfrac{\bigcirc - \triangle}{\bigcirc}$

78. Let $F = 50{,}000$.

$C = \dfrac{5}{9}(F - 32)$

$C = \dfrac{5}{9}(50{,}000 - 32) = 27{,}760$

The equivalent temperature is 27,760°C.

80. Let $d = 238{,}860$ and $r = 186{,}000$.
$$d = rt$$
$$238{,}860 = 186{,}000t$$
$$\frac{238{,}860}{186{,}000} = \frac{186{,}000t}{186{,}000}$$
$$1.3 \approx t$$
It will take 1.3 seconds.

82. $20 \dfrac{\text{miles}}{\text{hour}}$
$$= 20 \ \frac{\text{miles}}{\text{hour}} \left(\frac{5280 \text{ feet}}{1 \text{ mile}} \right) \left(\frac{1 \text{ hour}}{3600 \text{ seconds}} \right)$$
$$= \frac{88}{3} \text{ feet/second}$$

Let $d = 1300$ and $r = \dfrac{88}{3}$.
$$d = rt$$
$$1300 = \frac{88}{3} t$$
$$\frac{3}{88}(1300) = \frac{3}{88}\left(\frac{88}{3} \right) t$$
$$44.3 \approx t$$
It will take about 44.3 seconds.

84. Let $C = F$.
$$F = \frac{9}{5} C + 32$$
$$F = \frac{9}{5} F + 32$$
$$F - \frac{9}{5} F = \frac{9}{5} F - \frac{9}{5} F + 32$$
$$-\frac{4}{5} F = 32$$
$$-\frac{5}{4}\left(-\frac{4}{5} F \right) = -\frac{5}{4}(32)$$
$$F = -40$$
The measurements are the same number at $-40°$.

86. The original box has a volume $V = LWH$.
The altered box, has a length $2L$, a width $2W$, a height $2H$ and a new volume
$V = 2L(2W)(2H) = 8LWH$.
The volume is multiplied by 8.

Section 2.6

Practice Exercises

1. Let $x =$ the unknown percent.
$$35 = x \cdot 56$$
$$\frac{35}{56} = \frac{56x}{56}$$
$$0.625 = x$$
The number 35 is 62.5% of 56.

2. Let $x =$ the unknown number.
$$198 = 55\% \cdot x$$
$$198 = 0.55x$$
$$\frac{198}{0.55} = \frac{0.55x}{0.55}$$
$$360 = x$$
The number 198 is 55% of 360.

3. a. From the circle graph, 4% of trips made by American travelers are for combined business/pleasure.

b. From the circle graph,
$17\% + 66\% + 4\% = 87\%$ of trips are for business, pleasure, or combined business/pleasure.

c. Since 4% are trips for business/pleasure, find 4% of 325.
$0.04 \cdot 325 = 13$
We can expect 13 of the Americans to be traveling for business/pleasure.

4. Let $x =$ discount.
$x = 85\% \cdot 480$
$x = 0.85 \cdot 480$
$x = 408$
The discount is $408.
New price = $480 − $408 = $72

5. Increase = $299{,}800 − 198{,}900 = 100{,}900$
Let $x =$ percent increase.
$$100{,}900 = x \cdot 198{,}900$$
$$\frac{100{,}900}{198{,}900} = \frac{198{,}900x}{198{,}900}$$
$$0.507 \approx x$$
The percent increase is 50.7%.

6. Let x = number of new films in 2004.
$$x + 0.028x = 535$$
$$1.028x = 535$$
$$\frac{1.028x}{1.028} = \frac{535}{1.028}$$
$$x \approx 520$$
There were 520 new feature films released in 2004.

7. Let x = number of liters of 2% solution.

Eyewash	No. of gallons	·	Acid Strength	=	Amt. of Acid
2%	x		2%		$0.02x$
5%	$6 - x$		5%		$0.05(6 - x)$
Mix: 3%	6		3%		$0.03(6)$

$$0.02x + 0.05(6 - x) = 0.03(6)$$
$$0.02x + 0.3 - 0.05x = 0.18$$
$$-0.03x + 0.3 = 0.18$$
$$-0.03x + 0.3 - 0.3 = 0.18 - 0.3$$
$$-0.03x = -0.12$$
$$\frac{-0.03x}{-0.03} = \frac{-0.12}{-0.03}$$
$$x = 4$$
$6 - x = 6 - 4 = 2$
She should mix 4 liters of 2% eyewash with 2 liters of 5% eyewash.

Vocabulary and Readiness Check

1. No, 25% + 25% + 40% = 90% ≠ 100%.

2. No, 30% + 30% + 30% = 90% ≠ 100%.

3. Yes, 25% + 25% + 25% + 25% = 100%.

4. Yes, 40% + 50% + 10% = 100%.

Exercise Set 2.6

2. Let x = the number.
$$x = 88\% \cdot 1000$$
$$x = 0.88 \cdot 1000$$
$$x = 880$$
880 is 88% of 1000.

4. Let x = the percent.
$$87.2 = x \cdot 436$$
$$\frac{87.2}{436} = \frac{436x}{436}$$
$$0.2 = x$$
87.2 is 20% of 436.

6. Let $x =$ the number.
$$126 = 35\% \cdot x$$
$$126 = 0.35x$$
$$\frac{126}{0.35} = \frac{0.35x}{0.35}$$
$$360 = x$$
126 is 35% of 360.

8. Exports = 19%
Not Exports = 100% − 19% = 81%
81% of corn production is not used for exports.

10. 12% of 10,535 = 0.12 · 10,535 = 1264.2
1264.2 million bushels or 1,264,200,000 bushels were used for food, seed, or other.

12. Let $x =$ amount of discount.
$$x = 25\% \cdot 12.50$$
$$x = 0.25 \cdot 12.50$$
$$x = 3.125 \approx 3.13$$
New price = 12.50 − 3.13 = 9.37
The discount was $3.13 and the new price is $9.37.

14. Let $x =$ tip.
$$x = 20\% \cdot 65.40$$
$$x = 0.2 \cdot 65.4$$
$$x = 13.08$$
Total = 65.40 + 13.08 = 78.48
The total cost is $78.48.

16. Increase = 22,200 − 19,000 = 3200
Let $x =$ percent.
$$3200 = x \cdot 19,000$$
$$\frac{3200}{19,000} = \frac{19,000x}{19,000}$$
$$17 \approx x$$
The percent increase is 17%.

18. Decrease = 100 − 81 = 11
Let $x =$ percent.
$$11 = x \cdot 100$$
$$\frac{11}{100} = \frac{100x}{100}$$
$$0.11 = x$$
The percent decrease is 11%.

20. Let $x =$ original price and $0.25x =$ increase.
$$x + 0.25x = 80$$
$$1.25x = 80$$
$$\frac{1.25x}{1.25} = \frac{80}{1.25}$$
$$x = 64$$
The original price was $64.

22. Let $x =$ last year's salary, and $0.03x =$ increase.
$$x + 0.03x = 55,620$$
$$1.03x = 55,620$$
$$\frac{1.03x}{1.03} = \frac{55,620}{1.03}$$
$$x = 54,000$$
Last year's salary was $54,000.

24. Let $x =$ the amount of 25% solution.

	No. of cu cm	· Strength =	Amt. of Antibiotic
25%	x	0.25	$0.25x$
60%	10	0.6	$10(0.6)$
30%	$x + 10$	0.3	$0.3(x + 10)$

$$0.25x + 10(0.6) = 0.3(x + 10)$$
$$0.25x + 6 = 0.3x + 3$$
$$0.25x - 0.25x + 6 = 0.3x - 0.25x + 3$$
$$6 = 0.05x + 3$$
$$6 - 3 = 0.05x + 3 - 3$$
$$3 = 0.05x$$
$$\frac{3}{0.05} = \frac{0.05x}{0.05}$$
$$60 = x$$
Add 60 cc of 25% solution.

26. Let $x =$ the pounds of cashew nuts.

	No. of lb	Cost/lb	= Value
Peanuts	20	3	3(20)
Cashews	x	5	$5x$
Mix	$x + 20$	3.50	$3.50(x + 20)$

$$3(20) + 5x = 3.50(x + 20)$$
$$60 + 5x = 3.5x + 70$$
$$60 + 5x - 3.5x = 3.5x - 3.5x + 70$$
$$60 + 1.5x = 70$$
$$60 - 60 + 1.5x = 70 - 60$$
$$1.5x = 10$$
$$\frac{1.5x}{1.5} = \frac{10}{1.5}$$
$$x = 6\frac{2}{3}$$

Add $6\frac{2}{3}$ pounds of cashews.

28. Let $x =$ the number.
$$x = 140\% \cdot 86$$
$$x = 1.4 \cdot 86$$
$$x = 120.4$$
140% of 86 is 120.4.

30. Let $x =$ the number.
$$56.25 = 45\% \cdot x$$
$$56.25 = 0.45x$$
$$\frac{56.25}{0.45} = \frac{0.45x}{0.45}$$
$$125 = x$$
56.25 is 45% of 125.

32. Let $x =$ the percent.
$$42 = x \cdot 35$$
$$\frac{42}{35} = \frac{35x}{35}$$
$$1.2 = x$$
42 is 120% of 35.

34. From the graph, the height of the bar is 65. Therefore, 65% of the population in Charlottesville, Virginia, shop by catalog.

36. 81% of 30,987 $= 0.81 \cdot 30,987 \approx 25,099$
We predict 25,099 catalog shoppers live in Juneau.

38.

Kraft Foods North America **Volume Food Produced in a Year**		
Food Group	*Volume (in pounds)*	*Percent (Round to Nearest Percent)*
Cheese, Meals, and Enhancers	6183	$\frac{6183}{13,741} \approx 45\%$
Biscuits, Snacks, and Confectionaries	2083	Example: $\frac{2083}{13,741} \approx 15\%$
Beverages, Desserts, and Cereals	3905	$\frac{3905}{13,741} \approx 28\%$
Oscar Mayer and Pizza	1570	$\frac{1570}{13,741} \approx 11\%$
Total	13,741	99% due to rounding
Source: Kraft Foods, North America		

40. Let x = the decrease in price.
$x = 0.15(0.95) = 0.1425 \approx 0.14$
The decrease in price is $0.14.
The new price is $0.95 - 0.14 = \$0.81$.

42. Decrease = $25.6 - 22.4 = 3.2$
Let x = the percent.
$3.2 = x \cdot 25.6$
$\dfrac{3.2}{25.6} = \dfrac{25.6x}{25.6}$
$0.125 = x$
The percent decrease is 12.5%.

44. Let x = amount produced in 2007, and
$0.44x$ = amount of increase.
$x + 0.44x = 10,800$
$1.44x = 10,800$
$\dfrac{1.44x}{1.44} = \dfrac{10,800}{1.44}$
$x = 7500$
There were 7500 million gallons produced in 2007.

46. Let x = the gallons of water.
No. of Gal. $\cdot$ Strength = Amt. of Antifreeze

Water	x	0	0
70%	30	0.7	0.7(30)
60%	$x + 30$	0.6	0.6(x + 30)

$0.7(30) = 0.6(x + 30)$
$21 = 0.6x + 18$
$21 - 18 = 0.6x + 18 - 18$
$3 = 0.6x$
$\dfrac{3}{0.6} = \dfrac{0.6x}{0.6}$
$5 = x$
Add 5 gallons of water.

48. Let x = mark-up.
$x = 10\% \cdot 99.90$
$x = 0.1 \cdot 99.9$
$x = 9.99$
New price = $99.90 + 9.99 = 109.89$
The mark-up is $9.99 and the new price is $109.89.

50. Increase = $24 - 6 = 18$
Let x = percent.
$18 = x \cdot 6$
$\dfrac{18}{6} = \dfrac{6x}{6}$
$3 = x$
The percent increase is 300%.

52. Let x = average in 1920,
then $0.44x$ = decrease.
$x - 0.44x = 1.9$
$0.56x = 1.9$
$\dfrac{0.56x}{0.56} = \dfrac{1.9}{0.56}$
$x \approx 3.4$
In 1920, there were 3.4 children per woman.

54. Let x = ounces of self-tanning lotion.

	ounces	$ per ounce	$
self-tanning lotion	x	3.00	$3x$
everyday lotion	800	0.30	0.3(800)
experimental lotion	$x + 800$	1.20	1.2($x + 800$)

$$3x + 0.3(800) = 1.2(x + 800)$$
$$3x + 240 = 1.2x + 960$$
$$3x + 240 - 1.2x = 1.2x + 960 - 1.2x$$
$$1.8x + 240 = 960$$
$$1.8x + 240 - 240 = 960 - 240$$
$$1.8x = 720$$
$$\frac{1.8x}{1.8} = \frac{720}{1.8}$$
$$x = 400$$

Therefore, 400 ounces of self-tanning lotion should be mixed.

56. Increase = $444 - 436 = 8$
Let x = percent.
$$8 = x \cdot 436$$
$$\frac{8}{436} = \frac{436x}{436}$$
$$0.018 \approx x$$
The percent increase is 1.8%.

58. Let x = movie screens in 2000,
then $0.043x$ = increase.
$$x + 0.043x = 37,092$$
$$\frac{1.043x}{1.043} = \frac{37,092}{1.043}$$
$$x \approx 35,563$$
There were 35,563 movie screens operating in 2000.

60. Let x = increase.
$$x = 80.4\% \cdot 138.56$$
$$x = 0.804 \cdot 138.56$$
$$x \approx 111.40$$
His throw = $138.56 + 111.40 \approx 250$
Christian Sandstrom's throw was 250 meters.

62. 64% of $9800 = 0.64 \cdot 9800 = 6272$
We would expect 6272 U.S. colleges to have Internet access in their classrooms.

64. $\dfrac{12}{3} = 2^2$

66. $-3^3 = (-3)^3$

68. $|-2| = 2; -|-2| = -2$
$|-2| > -|-2|$

70. Answers may vary

72. a. Yes; answers may vary

   b. No; answers may vary

74. 23 is y percent of 300.
$y(300) = 23$
$$y = \frac{23}{300} \approx 0.077 = 7.7\%$$
This is about 7.7% of the daily value.

76. Let x = percent of calories from fat.
$x(280) = 9(6)$
$$x = \frac{54}{280} \approx 0.193 = 19.3\%$$
19.3% of the calories in one serving are from fat.

78. Answers may vary

Section 2.7

Practice Exercises

1. Let x = time down, then $x + 1$ = time up.

	Rate ·	Time =	Distance
Up	1.5	$x+1$	$1.5(x+1)$
Down	4	x	$4x$

$$d = d$$
$$1.5(x+1) = 4x$$
$$1.5x + 1.5 = 4x$$
$$1.5 = 2.5x$$
$$\frac{1.5}{2.5} = \frac{2.5x}{2.5}$$
$$0.6 = x$$
Total Time = $x + 1 + x = 0.6 + 1 + 0.6 = 2.2$
The entire hike took 2.2 hours.

2. Let x = speed of eastbound train, then
$x - 10$ = speed of westbound train.

	r ·	t =	d
East	x	1.5	$1.5x$
West	$x-10$	1.5	$1.5(x-10)$

$$1.5x + 1.5(x-10) = 171$$
$$1.5x + 1.5x - 15 = 171$$
$$3x - 15 = 171$$
$$3x = 186$$
$$\frac{3x}{3} = \frac{186}{3}$$
$$x = 62$$
$x - 10 = 62 - 10 = 52$
The eastbound train is traveling at 62 mph and the westbound train is traveling at 52 mph.

3. Let x = the number of $20 bills, then
$x + 47$ = number of $5 bills.

Denomination	Number	Value
$5 bills	$x+47$	$5(x+47)$
$20 bills	x	$20x$

$$5(x+47) + 20x = 1710$$
$$5x + 235 + 20x = 1710$$
$$235 + 25x = 1710$$
$$25x = 1475$$
$$x = 59$$
$x + 47 = 59 + 47 = 106$
There are 106 $5 bills and 59 $20 bills.

4. Let $x =$ amount invested at 11.5%, then
$30,000 - x =$ amount invested at 6%.

	Principal ·	Rate ·	Time =	Interest
11.5%	x	0.115	1	$x(0.115)(1)$
6%	$30,000 - x$	0.06	1	$0.06(30,000 - x)(1)$
Total	30,000			2790

$$0.115x + 0.06(30,000 - x) = 2790$$
$$0.115x + 1800 - 0.06x = 2790$$
$$1800 + 0.055x = 2790$$
$$0.055x = 990$$
$$\frac{0.055x}{0.055} = \frac{990}{0.055}$$
$$x = 18,000$$

$30,000 - x = 30,000 - 18,000 = 12,000$
She invested \$18,000 at 11.5% and \$12,000 at 6%.

Exercise Set 2.7

2. Let $x =$ the time traveled by the bus.

	Rate ·	Time =	Distance
Bus	60	x	$60x$
Car	40	$x + 1.5$	$40(x + 1.5)$

$$d = d$$
$$60x = 40(x + 1.5)$$
$$60x = 40x + 60$$
$$20x = 60$$
$$\frac{20x}{20} = \frac{60}{20}$$
$$x = 3$$

It will take the bus 3 hours to overtake the car.

4. Let $x =$ the time to get to Disneyland
and $7.2 - x =$ the time to return

	Rate ·	Time =	Distance
Going	50	x	$50x$
Returning	40	$7.2 - x$	$40(7.2 - x)$

$$d = d$$
$$50x = 40(7.2 - x)$$
$$50x = 288 - 40x$$
$$90x = 288$$
$$\frac{90x}{90} = \frac{288}{90}$$
$$x = 3.2$$

It took 3.2 hours to get to Disneyland.

$$d = rt$$
$$d = 50(3.2) = 160$$

The distance to Disneyland is 160 miles.

6. The value of z quarters is $0.25z$.

8. The value of $20 - z$ half-dollars is $0.50(20 - z)$.

10. The value of $97z$ $100 bills is $100(97z)$ or $9700z$.

12. The value of $15 - y$ $10 bills is $10(15 - y)$.

14. Let x = number of $50 bills, then
$6x$ = number of $20 bills.

	Number of Bills	Value of Bills
$20 bills	$6x$	$20(6x)$
$50 bills	x	$50x$
Total		3910

$$20(6x) + 50x = 3910$$
$$120x + 50x = 3910$$
$$170x = 3910$$
$$x = 23$$
$$6x = 6(23) = 138$$

There are 138 $20 bills and 23 $50 bills.

16. Let x = the amount invested at 9% for one year.

	Principal ·	Rate	=	Interest
9%	x	0.09		$0.09x$
10%	$x + 250$	0.10		$0.10(x + 250)$
Total				101

$$0.09x + 0.10(x + 250) = 101$$
$$0.09x + 0.10x + 25 = 101$$
$$0.19x + 25 = 101$$
$$0.19x = 76$$
$$\frac{0.19x}{0.19} = \frac{76}{0.19}$$
$$x = 400$$
$$x + 250 = 400 + 250 = 650$$

She invested $650 at 10% and $400 at 9%.

18. Let x = the amount invested at 10% for one year.

	Principal ·	Rate	=	Interest
10%	x	0.10		$0.10x$
12%	$2x$	0.12		$0.12(2x)$
Total				2890

$$0.10x + 0.12(2x) = 2890$$
$$0.10x + 0.24x = 2890$$
$$0.34x = 2890$$
$$\frac{0.34x}{0.34} = \frac{2890}{0.34}$$
$$x = 8500$$
$$2x = 2(8500) = 17,000$$

He invested $17,000 at 12% and $8500 at 10%.

20. Let x = number of adult tickets, then
$732 - x$ = number of child tickets.

	Number ·	Rate	=	Cost
Adult	x	22		$22x$
Child	$732 - x$	15		$15(732 - x)$
Total	732			12,912

$$22x + 15(732 - x) = 12,912$$
$$22x + 10,980 - 15x = 12,912$$
$$10,980 + 7x = 12,912$$
$$7x = 1932$$
$$x = 276$$
$$732 - x = 732 - 276 = 456$$

Sales included 276 adult tickets and 456 child tickets.

22. Let $x =$ the amount invested at 12% for one year.

	Principal	Rate	= Interest
12%	x	0.12	$0.12x$
4%	$20{,}000 - x$	-0.04	$-0.04(20{,}000 - x)$

$$0.12x - 0.04(20{,}000 - x) = 0$$
$$0.12x - 800 + 0.04x = 0$$
$$0.16x - 800 = 0$$
$$0.16x = 800$$
$$\frac{0.16x}{0.16} = \frac{800}{0.16}$$
$$x = 5000$$
$$20{,}000 - x = 20{,}000 - 5000 = 15{,}000$$
She invested \$15,000 at 4% and \$5000 at 12%.

24. Let $x =$ the time they are able to talk.

	Rate	· Time	= Distance
Cade	5	x	$5x$
Kathleen	4	x	$4x$
Total			20

$$5x + 4x = 20$$
$$9x = 20$$
$$\frac{9x}{9} = \frac{20}{9}$$
$$x = 2\frac{2}{9}$$

They can talk for $2\frac{2}{9}$ hours.

26. Let $x =$ number of quarters, then
$5x =$ number of dimes.

	Number	Value
Quarters	x	$0.25x$
Dimes	$5x$	$0.10(5x)$
Total		27.75

$$0.25x + 0.10(5x) = 27.75$$
$$0.25x + 0.5x = 27.75$$
$$0.75x = 27.75$$
$$x = 37$$
$$5x = 5(37) = 185$$
The collection has 37 quarters and 185 dimes.

28. Let x = the amount invested at 9% for one year.

	Principal ·	Rate	=	Interest
9%	x	0.09		$0.09x$
10%	$2x$	0.10		$0.1(2x)$
11%	$3x$	0.11		$0.11(3x)$
Total				2790

$$0.09x + 0.1(2x) + 0.11(3x) = 2790$$
$$0.09x + 0.2x + 0.33x = 2790$$
$$0.62x = 2790$$
$$\frac{0.62x}{0.62} = \frac{2790}{0.62}$$
$$x = 4500$$

$2x = 2(4500) = 9000$
$3x = 3(4500) = 13{,}500$
She invested \$4500 at 9%, \$9000 at 10% and \$13,500 at 11%.

30. Let x = the time it takes them to meet.

	Rate	· Time	= Distance
Nedra	3	x	$3x$
Latonya	4	x	$4x$
Total			12

$$3x + 4x = 12$$
$$7x = 12$$
$$\frac{7x}{7} = \frac{12}{7}$$
$$x = 1\frac{5}{7}$$

They meet in $1\frac{5}{7}$ hours.

32. Let x = the time before getting stopped.

	Rate ·	Time	= Distance
Before	70	x	$70x$
After	60	$4 - x$	$60(4 - x)$
Total			255

$$70x + 60(4 - x) = 255$$
$$70x + 240 - 60x = 255$$
$$10x + 240 = 255$$
$$10x = 15$$
$$\frac{10x}{10} = \frac{15}{10}$$
$$x = 1.5$$

He drove 1.5 hours before getting stopped.

34. $(-2) + (-8) = -10$

36. $-11 + 2.9 = -8.1$

38. $-12 - 3 = -12 + (-3) = -15$

40. Let x = number of quarters, then
$136 + x$ = number of dimes,
$8x$ = number of nickels,
$16x + 32$ = number of pennies.

	Number	Value
Quarters	x	$0.25x$
Dimes	$136 + x$	$0.10(136 + x)$
Nickels	$8x$	$0.05(8x)$
Pennies	$16x + 32$	$0.01(16x + 32)$
Total		44.86

$$0.25x + 0.10(136 + x) + 0.05(8x) + 0.01(16x + 32) = 44.86$$
$$0.25x + 13.6 + 0.1x + 0.4x + 0.16x + 0.32 = 44.86$$
$$0.91x + 13.92 = 44.86$$
$$0.91x = 30.94$$
$$x = 34$$

$136 + x = 136 + 34 = 170$
$8x = 8(34) = 272$
$16x + 32 = 16(34) + 32 = 576$
There were 34 quarters, 170 dimes, 272 nickels, and 576 pennies.

42. $R = C$
$$60x = 50x + 5000$$
$$10x = 5000$$
$$\frac{10x}{10} = \frac{5000}{10}$$
$$x = 500$$
Should sell 500 boards to break even.
$C = R = 60x = 60(500) = 30,000$
It costs \$30,000 to produce the break-even number of boards.

44.
$$R = C$$
$$105x = 870 + 70x$$
$$105x - 70x = 870 + 70x - 70x$$
$$35x = 870$$
$$\frac{35x}{35} = \frac{870}{35}$$
$$x \approx 24.857$$
Should sell 25 monitors to break even.

Section 2.8

Practice Exercises

1. $x < 5$

Place a parenthesis at 5 since the inequality symbol is $<$. Shade to the left of 5. The solution set is $(-\infty, 5)$.

2.
$$x + 11 \geq 6$$
$$x + 11 - 11 \geq 6 - 11$$
$$x \geq -5$$
The solution set is $[-5, \infty)$.

3.
$$-5x \geq -15$$
$$\frac{-5x}{-5} \leq \frac{-15}{-5}$$
$$x \leq 3$$
The solution set is $(-\infty, 3]$.

4. $3x > -9$
$$\frac{3x}{3} > \frac{-9}{3}$$
$$x > -3$$
The solution set is $(-3, \infty)$.

5.
$$45 - 7x \leq -4$$
$$45 - 7x - 45 \leq -4 - 45$$
$$-7x \leq -49$$
$$\frac{-7x}{-7} \geq \frac{-49}{-7}$$
$$x \geq 7$$
The solution set is $[7, \infty)$.

6.
$$3x + 20 \leq 2x + 13$$
$$3x + 20 - 2x \leq 2x + 13 - 2x$$
$$x + 20 \leq 13$$
$$x + 20 - 20 \leq 13 - 20$$
$$x \leq -7$$
The solution set is $(-\infty, -7]$.

7.
$$6 - 5x > 3(x - 4)$$
$$6 - 5x > 3x - 12$$
$$6 - 5x - 3x > 3x - 12 - 3x$$
$$6 - 8x > -12$$
$$6 - 8x - 6 > -12 - 6$$
$$-8x > -18$$
$$\frac{-8x}{-8} < \frac{-18}{-8}$$
$$x < \frac{9}{4}$$
The solution set is $\left(-\infty, \frac{9}{4}\right)$.

8.
$$3(x - 4) - 5 \leq 5(x - 1) - 12$$
$$3x - 12 - 5 \leq 5x - 5 - 12$$
$$3x - 17 \leq 5x - 17$$
$$3x - 17 - 5x \leq 5x - 17 - 5x$$
$$-2x - 17 \leq -17$$
$$-2x - 17 + 17 \leq -17 + 17$$
$$-2x \leq 0$$
$$\frac{-2x}{-2} \geq \frac{0}{-2}$$
$$x \geq 0$$
The solution set is $[0, \infty)$.

9. $-3 \leq x < 1$

Graph all numbers greater than or equal to -3 and less than 1. Place a bracket at -3 and a parenthesis at 1.

The solution set is $[-3, 1)$.

10.
$$-4 < 3x + 2 \le 8$$
$$-4 - 2 < 3x + 2 - 2 \le 8 - 2$$
$$-6 < 3x \le 6$$
$$\frac{-6}{3} < \frac{3x}{3} \le \frac{6}{3}$$
$$-2 < x \le 2$$
The solution set is $(-2, 2]$.

11.
$$1 < \frac{3}{4}x + 5 < 6$$
$$4(1) < 4\left(\frac{3}{4}x + 5\right) < 4(6)$$
$$4 < 3x + 20 < 24$$
$$4 - 20 < 3x + 20 - 20 < 24 - 20$$
$$-16 < 3x < 4$$
$$\frac{-16}{3} < \frac{3x}{3} < \frac{4}{3}$$
$$-\frac{16}{3} < x < \frac{4}{3}$$
The solution set is $\left(-\frac{16}{3}, \frac{4}{3}\right)$.

12. Let x = number of classes.
$$300 + 375x \le 1500$$
$$300 + 375x - 300 \le 1500 - 300$$
$$375x \le 1200$$
$$\frac{375x}{375} \le \frac{1200}{375}$$
$$x \le 3.2$$
Kasonga can afford at most 3 community college classes this semester.

Vocabulary and Readiness Check

1. $6x - 7(x + 9)$ is an expression.

2. $6x = 7(x + 9)$ is an equation.

3. $6x < 7(x + 9)$ is an inequality.

4. $5y - 2 \ge -38$ is an inequality.

5. $\frac{9}{7} = \frac{x+2}{14}$ is an equation.

6. $\frac{9}{7} - \frac{x+2}{14}$ is an expression.

7. -5 is not a solution to $x \ge -3$.

8. $|-6| = 6$ is not a solution to $x < 6$.

9. 4.1 is not a solution to $x < 4.01$.

10. -4 is not a solution to $x \ge -3$.

Exercise Set 2.8

2. $(-3, \infty)$, $x > -3$

4. $(-\infty, 4]$, $x \le 4$

6. $y < 0$, $(-\infty, 0)$

8. $z < -\frac{2}{3}$, $\left(-\infty, -\frac{2}{3}\right)$

10. $x > 3$, $(3, \infty)$

12. $3x > -9$
$$x > -3, (-3, \infty)$$

14. $x + 4 \le 1$
$$x \le -3, (-\infty, -3]$$

16. $-5x < 20$
$$\frac{-5x}{-5} > \frac{20}{-5}$$
$$x > -4, (-4, \infty)$$

18. $3 - 7x \ge 10 - 8x$
$$3 + x \ge 10$$
$$x \ge 7, [7, \infty)$$

20. $7x + 3 < 9x - 3x$
$7x + 3 < 6x$
$x + 3 < 0$
$x < -3, \ (-\infty, -3)$

![number line with open circle at -3, shaded left]

22. $3x + 9 \le 5(x - 1)$
$3x + 9 \le 5x - 5$
$-2x + 9 \le -5$
$-2x \le -14$
$\dfrac{-2x}{-2} \ge \dfrac{-14}{-2}$
$x \ge 7, \ [7, \infty)$

![number line with bracket at -7, shaded right]

24. $-7x + 4 > 3(4 - x)$
$-7x + 4 > 12 - 3x$
$-4x + 4 > 12$
$-4x > 8$
$\dfrac{-4x}{-4} < \dfrac{8}{-4}$
$x < -2, \ (-\infty, -2)$

![number line with open circle at -2, shaded left]

26. $3(5x - 4) \le 4(3x - 2)$
$15x - 12 \le 12x - 8$
$3x - 12 \le -8$
$3x \le 4$
$x \le \dfrac{4}{3}, \ \left(-\infty, \dfrac{4}{3}\right]$

![number line with bracket at 4/3, shaded left]

28. $7(x - 2) + x \le -4(5 - x) - 12$
$7x - 14 + x \le -20 + 4x - 12$
$8x - 14 \le -32 + 4x$
$4x - 14 \le -32$
$4x \le -18$
$x \le -\dfrac{9}{2}, \ \left(-\infty, -\dfrac{9}{2}\right]$

![number line with bracket at -9/2, shaded left]

30. $-7x > 21$
$\dfrac{-7x}{-7} < \dfrac{21}{-7}$
$x < -3, \ (-\infty, -3)$

![number line with open circle at -3, shaded left]

32. $y - 4 \le 1$
$y \le 5, \ (-\infty, 5]$

![number line with bracket at 5, shaded left]

34. $2x - 1 \ge 4x - 5$
$-2x - 1 \ge -5$
$-2x \ge -4$
$\dfrac{-2x}{-2} \le \dfrac{-4}{-2}$
$x \le 2, \ (-\infty, 2]$

![number line with bracket at 2, shaded left]

36. $4 - x < 8x + 2x$
$4 - x < 10x$
$4 - 11x < 0$
$-11x < -4$
$\dfrac{-11x}{-11} > \dfrac{-4}{-11}$
$x > \dfrac{4}{11}, \ \left(\dfrac{4}{11}, \infty\right)$

![number line with open circle at 4/11, shaded right]

38. $\dfrac{5}{6}x \ge -8$
$x \ge -\dfrac{48}{5}, \ \left[-\dfrac{48}{5}, \infty\right)$

![number line with bracket at -48/5, shaded right]

40. $5(x + 4) < 4(2x + 3)$
$5x + 20 < 8x + 12$
$-3x + 20 < 12$
$-3x < -8$
$\dfrac{-3x}{-3} > \dfrac{-8}{-3}$
$x > \dfrac{8}{3}, \ \left(\dfrac{8}{3}, \infty\right)$

![number line with open circle at 8/3, shaded right]

42. $6(2-x) \geq 12$

$12 - 6x \geq 12$

$-6x \geq 0$

$\dfrac{-6x}{-6} \leq \dfrac{0}{-6}$

$x \leq 0, \, (\infty, 0]$

44. $-6x + 2 < -3(x+4)$

$-6x + 2 < -3x - 12$

$-3x + 2 < -12$

$-3x < -14$

$\dfrac{-3x}{-3} > \dfrac{-14}{-3}$

$x > \dfrac{14}{3}, \, \left(\dfrac{14}{3}, \infty\right)$

46. $-5(1-x) + x \leq -(6-2x) + 6$

$-5 + 5x + x \leq -6 + 2x + 6$

$-5 + 6x \leq 2x$

$-5 + 4x \leq 0$

$4x \leq 5$

$x \leq \dfrac{5}{4}, \, \left(-\infty, \dfrac{5}{4}\right]$

48. $-(x-4) < 4$

$-x + 4 < 4$

$-x < 0$

$\dfrac{-x}{-1} > \dfrac{0}{-1}$

$x > 0, \, (0, \infty)$

50. Answers may vary

52. $2 \leq y \leq 3, \, [2, 3]$

54. $-1 \leq x \leq 4, \, [-1, 4]$

56. $-5 < 2x < -2$

$-\dfrac{5}{2} < x < -1, \, \left(-\dfrac{5}{2}, -1\right)$

58. $4 \leq 5x - 6 \leq 19$

$10 \leq 5x \leq 25$

$2 \leq x \leq 5, \, [2, 5]$

60. $0 < 4(x+5) \leq 8$

$0 < 4x + 20 \leq 8$

$-20 < 4x \leq -12$

$-5 < x \leq -3, \, (-5, -3]$

62. $1 < 4 + 2x \leq 7$

$-3 < 2x \leq 3$

$-\dfrac{3}{2} < x \leq \dfrac{3}{2}, \, \left(-\dfrac{3}{2}, \dfrac{3}{2}\right]$

64. $-5 \leq 2(x+4) < 8$

$-5 \leq 2x + 8 < 8$

$-13 \leq 2x < 0$

$-\dfrac{13}{2} \leq x < 0, \, \left[-\dfrac{13}{2}, 0\right)$

66. Answers may vary

68. $5x + 1 \leq 10$

$5x \leq 9$

$x \leq \dfrac{9}{5}$

70. Let x = the number of people invited.

$15x + 40 \leq 860$

$15x \leq 820$

$x \leq 54.67$

They may invite 54 people.

72. $4x + x + 12 \le 87$

$\qquad 5x + 12 \le 87$

$\qquad\qquad 5x \le 75$

$\qquad\qquad\quad x \le 15$

x can be no greater than 15.

74. Let x = the sales per month and

$x - 1000$ = sales over 1000.

$600 + 0.04(x - 1000) \ge 3000$

$\qquad 600 + 0.04x - 40 \ge 3000$

$\qquad\qquad 0.04x + 560 \ge 3000$

$\qquad\qquad\qquad 0.04x \ge 2440$

$\qquad\qquad\qquad\quad x \ge 61,000$

He must sell $61,000 or more per month.

76. Let x = the height of the center in inches.

$$\frac{80 + 78 + 72 + 69 + x}{5} \ge 77$$

$$5\left(\frac{80 + 78 + 72 + 69 + x}{5}\right) \ge 5(77)$$

$$299 + x \ge 385$$

$$x \ge 86$$

He must be at least 86 in. = 7'2" tall.

78. EF-0 $65 \le y \le 85$

EF-1 $86 \le y \le 110$

EF-2 $111 \le y \le 135$

EF-3 $136 \le y \le 165$

EF-4 $166 \le y \le 200$

EF-5 $y \ge 201$

80. Let x = the unknown number.

$$2 < \frac{1}{2}x - 4 < 3$$

$$6 < \frac{1}{2}x < 7$$

$$12 < x < 14$$

All numbers between 12 and 14

82. Let x = score needed on the final exam.

$$90 \le \frac{85 + 95 + 92 + 3x}{6} \le 100$$

$$6(90) \le 6\left(\frac{85 + 95 + 92 + 3x}{6}\right) \le 6(100)$$

$$540 \le 272 + 3x \le 600$$

$$268 \le 3 \le 328$$

$$89.3 \le x \le 109.3$$

He must make between 89.3 and 100.

84. $(3)^3 = (3)(3)(3) = 27$

86. $0^5 = (0)(0)(0)(0)(0) = 0$

88. $\left(\dfrac{2}{3}\right)^3 = \left(\dfrac{2}{3}\right)\left(\dfrac{2}{3}\right)\left(\dfrac{2}{3}\right) = \dfrac{8}{27}$

90. Read the value on the vertical axis corresponding to 2005; $50.20

92. Find the points on the graph greater than $52. The years are 2001, 2002, 2003.

94. $C = 3.14d$

$\qquad 118 \le 3.14d \le 122$

$\qquad 37.58 \le d \le 38.85$

The diameter must be between 37.58 mm and 38.85 mm.

96. $x(x - 3) \ge x^2 - 5x - 8$

$\qquad x^2 - 3x \ge x^2 - 5x - 8$

$\qquad\qquad -3x \ge -5x - 8$

$\qquad\qquad\quad 2x \ge -8$

$\qquad\qquad\quad\quad x \ge -4, \; [-4, \infty)$

98. $x^2 - 4x + 8 < x(x + 8)$

$\qquad x^2 - 4x + 8 < x^2 + 8x$

$\qquad\qquad -4x + 8 < 8x$

$\qquad\qquad -12x + 8 < 0$

$\qquad\qquad\qquad -12x < -8$

$$\frac{-12x}{-12} > \frac{-8}{-12}$$

$$x > \frac{2}{3}, \; \left(\frac{2}{3}, \infty\right)$$

The Bigger Picture

1. $-5x = 15$

$$\frac{-5x}{-5} = \frac{15}{-5}$$

$$x = -3$$

The solution is -3.

2. $-5x > 15$

$$\frac{-5x}{-5} < \frac{15}{-5}$$

$$x < -3$$

The solution set is $(-\infty, -3)$.

3.
$$9y - 14 = -12$$
$$9y - 14 + 14 = -12 + 14$$
$$9y = 2$$
$$\frac{9y}{9} = \frac{2}{9}$$
$$y = \frac{2}{9}$$

The solution is $\frac{2}{9}$.

4.
$$9x - 3 = 5x - 4$$
$$9x - 3 - 5x = 5x - 4 - 5x$$
$$4x - 3 = -4$$
$$4x - 3 + 3 = -4 + 3$$
$$4x = -1$$
$$\frac{4x}{4} = \frac{-1}{4}$$
$$x = -\frac{1}{4}$$

The solution is $-\frac{1}{4}$.

5.
$$4(x - 2) \le 5x + 7$$
$$4x - 8 \le 5x + 7$$
$$4x - 8 - 5x \le 5x + 7 - 5x$$
$$-x - 8 \le 7$$
$$-x - 8 + 8 \le 7 + 8$$
$$-x \le 15$$
$$\frac{-x}{-1} \ge \frac{15}{-1}$$
$$x \ge -15$$

The solution set is $[-15, \infty)$.

6.
$$5(4x - 1) = 2(10x - 1)$$
$$20x - 5 = 20x - 2$$
$$20x - 5 - 20x = 20x - 2 - 20x$$
$$-5 = -2$$

Since this is a false statement, there is no solution.

7.
$$-5.4 = 0.6x - 9.6$$
$$-5.4 + 9.6 = 0.6x - 9.6 + 9.6$$
$$4.2 = 0.6x$$
$$\frac{4.2}{0.6} = \frac{0.6x}{0.6}$$
$$7 = x$$

The solution is 7.

8.
$$\frac{1}{3}(x - 4) < \frac{1}{4}(x + 7)$$
$$12\left[\frac{1}{3}(x - 4)\right] < 12\left[\frac{1}{4}(x + 7)\right]$$
$$4(x - 4) < 3(x + 7)$$
$$4x - 16 < 3x + 21$$
$$4x - 16 - 3x < 3x + 21 - 3x$$
$$x - 16 < 21$$
$$x - 16 + 16 < 21 + 16$$
$$x < 37$$

The solution set is $(-\infty, 37)$.

9.
$$3y - 5(y - 4) = -2(y - 10)$$
$$3y - 5y + 20 = -2y + 20$$
$$-2y + 20 = -2y + 20$$
$$-2y + 20 + 2y = -2y + 20 + 2y$$
$$20 = 20$$

All real numbers are solutions.

10.
$$\frac{7(x - 1)}{3} = \frac{2(x + 1)}{5}$$
$$15\left[\frac{7(x - 1)}{3}\right] = 15\left[\frac{2(x + 1)}{5}\right]$$
$$35(x - 1) = 6(x + 1)$$
$$35x - 35 = 6x + 6$$
$$35x - 35 - 6x = 6x + 6 - 6x$$
$$29x - 35 = 6$$
$$29x - 35 + 35 = 6 + 35$$
$$29x = 41$$
$$\frac{29x}{29} = \frac{41}{29}$$
$$x = \frac{41}{29}$$

The solution is $\frac{41}{29}$.

Chapter 2 Vocabulary Check

1. Terms with the same variables raised to exactly the same powers are called <u>like terms</u>.

2. A <u>linear equation in one variable</u> can be written in the form $ax + b = c$.

3. Equations that have the same solution are called <u>equivalent equations</u>.

4. Inequalities containing two inequality symbols are called <u>compound inequalities</u>.

5. An equation that describes a known relationship among quantities is called a <u>formula</u>.

6. A <u>linear inequality in one variable</u> can be written in the form $ax + b < c$, (or $>$, $\leq$, $\geq$).

7. The <u>numerical coefficient</u> of a term is its numerical factor.

Chapter 2 Review

1. $5x - x + 2x = 6x$

2. $0.2z - 4.6x - 7.4z = -4.6x - 7.2z$

3. $\dfrac{1}{2}x + 3 + \dfrac{7}{2}x - 5 = \dfrac{8}{2}x - 2 = 4x - 2$

4. $\dfrac{4}{5}y + 1 + \dfrac{6}{5}y + 2 = \dfrac{10}{5}y + 3 = 2y + 3$

5. $2(n - 4) + n - 10 = 2n - 8 + n - 10 = 3n - 18$

6. $3(w + 2) - (12 - w) = 3w + 6 - 12 + w = 4w - 6$

7. $(x + 5) - (7x - 2) = x + 5 - 7x + 2 = -6x + 7$

8. $(y - 0.7) - (1.4y - 3) = y - 0.7 - 1.4y + 3$
$$= -0.4y + 2.3$$

9. Three times a number decreased by 7 is $3x - 7$.

10. Twice the sum of a number and 2.8 added to 3 times a number is $2(x + 2.8) + 3x$.

11.
$$8x + 4 = 9x$$
$$8x + 4 - 8x = 9x - 8x$$
$$4 = x$$

12.
$$5y - 3 = 6y$$
$$5y - 3 - 5y = 6y - 5y$$
$$-3 = y$$

13. $\dfrac{2}{7}x + \dfrac{5}{7}x = 6$
$$\dfrac{7}{7}x = 6$$
$$x = 6$$

14. $3x - 5 = 4x + 1$
$$-5 = x + 1$$
$$-6 = x$$

15. $2x - 6 = x - 6$
$$x - 6 = -6$$
$$x = 0$$

16. $4(x + 3) = 3(1 + x)$
$$4x + 12 = 3 + 3x$$
$$x + 12 = 3$$
$$x = -9$$

17. $6(3 + n) = 5(n - 1)$
$$18 + 6n = 5n - 5$$
$$18 + n = -5$$
$$n = -23$$

18. $5(2 + x) - 3(3x + 2) = -5(x - 6) + 2$
$$10 + 5x - 9x - 6 = -5x + 30 + 2$$
$$-4x + 4 = -5x + 32$$
$$x + 4 = 32$$
$$x = 28$$

19. $x - 5 = 3$
$$x - 5 + \underline{5} = 3 + \underline{5}$$
$$x = 8$$

20. $x + 9 = -2$
$$x + 9 - \underline{9} = -2 - \underline{9}$$
$$x = -11$$

21. $10 - x$; choice b.

22. $x - 5$; choice a.

23. Complementary angles sum to $90°$.
$(90 - x)°$; choice b.

24. Supplementary angles sum to $180°$.
$180 - (x + 5) = 180 - x - 5 = 175 - x$
$(175 - x)°$; choice c.

25. $\dfrac{3}{4}x = -9$
$$\dfrac{4}{3}\left(\dfrac{3}{4}x\right) = \dfrac{4}{3}(-9)$$
$$x = -12$$

26. $\dfrac{x}{6} = \dfrac{2}{3}$
$$6 \cdot \dfrac{x}{6} = 6 \cdot \dfrac{2}{3}$$
$$x = 4$$

27. $-5x = 0$
$$\dfrac{-5x}{-5} = \dfrac{0}{-5}$$
$$x = 0$$

28. $-y = 7$

$$\frac{-y}{-1} = \frac{7}{-1}$$
$$y = -7$$

29. $0.2x = 0.15$

$$\frac{0.2x}{0.2} = \frac{0.15}{0.2}$$
$$x = 0.75$$

30. $\dfrac{-x}{3} = 1$

$$-3 \cdot \frac{-x}{3} = -3 \cdot 1$$
$$x = -3$$

31. $-3x + 1 = 19$

$$-3x = 18$$
$$\frac{-3x}{-3} = \frac{18}{-3}$$
$$x = -6$$

32. $5x + 25 = 20$

$$5x = -5$$
$$\frac{5x}{5} = \frac{-5}{5}$$
$$x = -1$$

33. $7(x - 1) + 9 = 5x$

$$7x - 7 + 9 = 5x$$
$$7x + 2 = 5x$$
$$2 = -2x$$
$$\frac{2}{-2} = \frac{-2x}{-2}$$
$$-1 = x$$

34. $7x - 6 = 5x - 3$

$$2x - 6 = -3$$
$$2x = 3$$
$$\frac{2x}{2} = \frac{3}{2}$$
$$x = \frac{3}{2}$$

35. $-5x + \dfrac{3}{7} = \dfrac{10}{7}$

$$7\left(-5x + \frac{3}{7}\right) = 7 \cdot \frac{10}{7}$$
$$-35x + 3 = 10$$
$$-35x = 7$$
$$x = -\frac{7}{35}$$
$$x = -\frac{1}{5}$$

36. $5x + x = 9 + 4x - 1 + 6$

$$6x = 4x + 14$$
$$2x = 14$$
$$x = 7$$

37. Let x = the first integer, then
    $x + 1$ = the second integer, and
    $x + 2$ = the third integer.
    sum = $x + (x + 1) + (x + 2) = 3x + 3$

38. Let x = the first integer, then
    $x + 2$ = the second integer
    $x + 4$ = the third integer
    $x + 6$ = the fourth integer.
    sum = $x + (x + 6) = 2x + 6$

39. $\dfrac{5}{3}x + 4 = \dfrac{2}{3}x$

$$3\left(\frac{5}{3}x + 4\right) = 3\left(\frac{2}{3}x\right)$$
$$5x + 12 = 2x$$
$$12 = -3x$$
$$-4 = x$$

40. $\dfrac{7}{8}x + 1 = \dfrac{5}{8}x$

$$8\left(\frac{7}{8}x + 1\right) = 8\left(\frac{5}{8}x\right)$$
$$7x + 8 = 5x$$
$$8 = -2x$$
$$-4 = x$$

41. $-(5x + 1) = -7x + 3$

$$-5x - 1 = -7x + 3$$
$$2x - 1 = 3$$
$$2x = 4$$
$$x = 2$$

42.
$$-4(2x+1) = -5x+5$$
$$-8x-4 = -5x+5$$
$$-3x-4 = 5$$
$$-3x = 9$$
$$x = -3$$

43.
$$-6(2x-5) = -3(9+4x)$$
$$-12x+30 = -27-12x$$
$$30 = -27$$
There is no solution.

44.
$$3(8y-1) = 6(5+4y)$$
$$24y-3 = 30+24y$$
$$-3 = 30$$
There is no solution.

45.
$$\frac{3(2-z)}{5} = z$$
$$3(2-z) = 5z$$
$$6-3z = 5z$$
$$6 = 8z$$
$$\frac{6}{8} = z$$
$$\frac{3}{4} = z$$

46.
$$\frac{4(n+2)}{5} = -n$$
$$4(n+2) = -5n$$
$$4n+8 = -5n$$
$$8 = -9n$$
$$-\frac{8}{9} = n$$

47.
$$0.5(2n-3)-0.1 = 0.4(6+2n)$$
$$10[0.5(2n-3)-0.1] = 10[0.4(6+2n)]$$
$$5(2n-3)-1 = 4(6+2n)$$
$$10n-15-1 = 24+8n$$
$$10n-16 = 24+8n$$
$$2n-16 = 24$$
$$2n = 40$$
$$n = 20$$

48.
$$-9-5a = 3(6a-1)$$
$$-9-5a = 18a-3$$
$$-9 = 23a-3$$
$$-6 = 23a$$
$$-\frac{6}{23} = a$$

49.
$$\frac{5(c+1)}{6} = 2c-3$$
$$5(c+1) = 6(2c-3)$$
$$5c+5 = 12c-18$$
$$-7c+5 = -18$$
$$-7c = -23$$
$$c = \frac{23}{7}$$

50.
$$\frac{2(8-a)}{3} = 4-4a$$
$$2(8-a) = 3(4-4a)$$
$$16-2a = 12-12a$$
$$10a+16 = 12$$
$$10a = -4$$
$$a = \frac{-4}{10}$$
$$a = -\frac{2}{5}$$

51.
$$200(70x-3560) = -179(150x-19,300)$$
$$14,000x-712,000 = -26,850x+3,454,700$$
$$40,850x-712,000 = 3,454,700$$
$$40,850x = 4,166,700$$
$$x = 102$$

52.
$$1.72y-0.04y = 0.42$$
$$1.68y = 0.42$$
$$y = 0.25$$

53. Let x = length of a side of the square, then $50.5 + 10x$ = the height.
$$x+(50.5+10x) = 7327$$
$$11x+50.5 = 7327$$
$$11x = 7276.5$$
$$x = 661.5$$
$$50.5+10x = 50.5+10(661.5) = 6665.5$$
The height is 6665.5 inches.

54. Let x = the length of the shorter piece and $2x$ = the length of the other.
$$x+2x = 12$$
$$3x = 12$$
$$x = 4$$
$$2x = 2(4) = 8$$
The lengths are 4 feet and 8 feet.

55. Let x = number of Keebler plants, then
$2x - 1$ = number of Kellogg plants.
$$x + (2x - 1) = 53$$
$$3x - 1 = 53$$
$$3x = 54$$
$$x = 18$$
$2x - 1 = 2(18) - 1 = 35$
There were 18 Keebler plants and 35 Kellogg plants.

56. Let x = first integer, then
$x + 1$ = second integer, and
$x + 2$ = third integer.
$$x + (x + 1) + (x + 2) = -114$$
$$3x + 3 = -114$$
$$3x = -117$$
$$x = -39$$
$x + 1 = -39 + 1 = -38$
$x + 2 = -39 + 2 = -37$
The integers are $-39, -38, -37$.

57. Let x = the unknown number.
$$\frac{x}{3} = x - 2$$
$$3 \cdot \frac{x}{3} = 3(x - 2)$$
$$x = 3x - 6$$
$$-2x = -6$$
$$x = 3$$
The number is 3.

58. Let x = the unknown number.
$$2(x + 6) = -x$$
$$2x + 12 = -x$$
$$12 = -3x$$
$$-4 = x$$
The number is -4.

59. Let $P = 46$ and $l = 14$.
$$P = 2l + 2w$$
$$46 = 2(14) + 2w$$
$$46 = 28 + 2w$$
$$18 = 2w$$
$$9 = w$$

60. Let $V = 192$, $l = 8$, and $w = 6$.
$$V = lwh$$
$$192 = 8(6)h$$
$$192 = 48h$$
$$4 = h$$

61.
$$y = mx + b$$
$$y - b = mx$$
$$\frac{y - b}{x} = m$$

62.
$$r = vst - 5$$
$$r + 5 = vst$$
$$\frac{r + 5}{vt} = s$$

63. $2y - 5x = 7$
$$-5x = -2y + 7$$
$$x = \frac{-2y + 7}{-5}$$
$$x = \frac{2y - 7}{5}$$

64. $3x - 6y = -2$
$$-6y = -3x - 2$$
$$y = \frac{-3x - 2}{-6}$$
$$y = \frac{3x + 2}{6}$$

65. $C = \pi D$
$$\frac{C}{D} = \pi$$

66. $C = 2\pi r$
$$\frac{C}{2r} = \pi$$

67. Let $V = 900$, $l = 20$, and $h = 3$.
$$V = lwh$$
$$900 = 20w(3)$$
$$900 = 60w$$
$$15 = w$$
The width is 15 meters.

68. Let x = width, then $x + 6$ = length.
$$60 = 2x + 2(x + 6)$$
$$60 = 2x + 2x + 12$$
$$60 = 4x + 12$$
$$48 = 4x$$
$$12 = x$$
$x + 6 = 12 + 6 = 18$
The dimensions are 18 feet by 12 feet.

69. Let $d = 10{,}000$ and $r = 125$.
$$d = rt$$
$$10{,}000 = 125t$$
$$80 = t$$
It will take 80 minutes or 1 hour and 20 minutes.

70. Let $F = 104$.
$$C = \frac{5}{9}(F - 32)$$
$$= \frac{5}{9}(104 - 32)$$
$$= \frac{5}{9}(72)$$
$$= 40$$
The temperature was 40°C.

71. Let $x =$ the percent.
$$9 = x \cdot 45$$
$$\frac{9}{45} = \frac{45x}{45}$$
$$0.2 = x$$
9 is 20% of 45.

72. Let $x =$ the percent.
$$59.5 = x \cdot 85$$
$$\frac{59.5}{85} = \frac{85x}{85}$$
$$0.7 = x$$
59.5 is 70% of 85.

73. Let $x =$ the number.
$$137.5 = 125\% \cdot x$$
$$137.5 = 1.25x$$
$$\frac{137.5}{1.25} = \frac{1.25x}{1.25}$$
$$110 = x$$
137.5 is 125% of 110.

74. Let $x =$ the number.
$$768 = 60\% \cdot x$$
$$768 = 0.6x$$
$$\frac{768}{0.6} = \frac{0.6x}{0.6}$$
$$1280 = x$$
768 is 60% of 1280.

75. Let $x =$ mark-up.
$$x = 11\% \cdot 1900$$
$$x = 0.11 \cdot 1900$$
$$x = 209$$
New price = $1900 + 209 = 2109$
The mark-up is $209 and the new price is $2109.

76. Find 66.9% of 76,000.
$0.669 \cdot 76,000 = 50,844$
We would expect 50,844 people to use the Internet.

77. Let x = gallons of 40% solution.

Strength	gallons	Concentration	
40%	x	0.4	$0.4x$
10%	$30 - x$	0.1	$0.1(30 - x)$
20%	30	0.2	$0.2(30)$

$$0.4x + 0.1(30 - x) = 0.2(30)$$
$$0.4x + 3 - 0.1x = 6$$
$$0.3x + 3 = 6$$
$$0.3x = 3$$
$$x = 10$$
$30 - x = 30 - 10 = 20$
Mix 10 gallons of 40% acid solution with 20 gallons of 10% acid solution.

78. Increase $= 21.0 - 20.7 = 0.3$
Let x = percent.
$$0.3 = x \cdot 20.7$$
$$\frac{0.3}{20.7} = \frac{20.7x}{20.7}$$
$$0.0145 \approx x$$
The percent increase is 1.45%.

79. From the graph, the height of 'Almost hit a car' is 18%.

80. Choose the tallest graph. The most common effect is swerving into another lane.

81. Find 21% of 4600.
$0.21 \cdot 4600 = 966$
We would expect 966 customers to have cut someone off.

82. $46\% + 41\% + 21\% + 18\% = 126\%$
No; answers may vary

83. Let x = time up, then $3 - x$ = time down.

Rate · Time = Distance

	Rate	Time	Distance
Up	10	x	$10x$
Down	50	$3 - x$	$50(3 - x)$

$$d = d$$
$$10x = 50(3 - x)$$
$$10x = 150 - 50x$$
$$60x = 150$$
$$x = 2.5$$

$$\begin{aligned}
\text{Total distance} &= 10x + 50(3 - x) \\
&= 10(2.5) + 50(3 - 2.5) \\
&= 25 + 50(0.5) \\
&= 25 + 25 \\
&= 50
\end{aligned}$$

The distance traveled was 50 km.

84. Let x = the amount invested at 10.5% for one year.

	Principal ·	Rate =	Interest
10.5%	x	0.105	0.105
8.5%	$50,000 - x$	0.085	$0.085(50,000 - x)$
Total	50,000		4550

$$\begin{aligned}
0.105x + 0.085(50,000 - x) &= 4550 \\
0.105x + 4250 - 0.085x &= 4550 \\
0.02x + 4250 &= 4550 \\
0.02x &= 300 \\
x &= 15,000
\end{aligned}$$

$50,000 - x = 50,000 - 15,000 = 35,000$
Invest $35,000 at 8.5% and $15,000 at 10.5%.

85. Let x = the number of dimes,
$2x$ = the number of quarters, and
$500 - x - 2x$ the number of nickels.

	No. of Coins	· Value	= Amt. of Money
Dimes	x	0.1 ·	$0.1x$
Quarters	$2x$	0.25	$0.25(2x)$
Nickels	$500 - 3x$	0.05	$0.05(500 - 3x)$
Total	500		88

$$\begin{aligned}
0.1x + 0.25(2x) + 0.05(500 - 3x) &= 88 \\
0.1x + 0.5x + 25 - 0.15x &= 88 \\
0.45x + 25 &= 88 \\
0.45x &= 63 \\
x &= 140
\end{aligned}$$

$500 - 3x = 500 - 3(140) = 500 - 420 = 80$
There were 80 nickels in the pay phone.

86. Let x = the time traveled by the Amtrak train.

	Rate ·	Time	=	Distance
Amtrak	60	x		$60x$
Freight	45	$x + 1.5$		$45(x + 1.5)$

$$d = d$$
$$60x = 45(x + 1.5)$$
$$60x = 45x + 67.5$$
$$15x = 67.5$$
$$x = 4.5$$

It will take 4.5 hours.

87. $x > 0, (0, \infty)$

88. $x \le -2, (-\infty, -2]$

89. $0.5 \le y < 1.5, [0.5, 1.5)$

90. $-1 < x < 1, (-1, 1)$

91. $-3x > 12$
$$\frac{-3x}{-3} < \frac{12}{-3}$$
$$x < -4, (-\infty, -4)$$

92. $-2x \ge -20$
$$\frac{-2x}{-2} \le \frac{-20}{-2}$$
$$x \le 10, (-\infty, 10]$$

93. $x + 4 \ge 6x - 16$
$$-5x + 4 \ge -16$$
$$-5x \ge -20$$
$$\frac{-5x}{-5} \le \frac{-20}{-5}$$
$$x \le 4, (-\infty, 4]$$

94. $5x - 7 > 8x + 5$
$$-3x - 7 > 5$$
$$-3x > 12$$
$$\frac{-3x}{-3} < \frac{12}{-3}$$
$$x < -4, (-\infty, -4)$$

95. $-3 < 4x - 1 < 2$
$$-2 < 4x < 3$$
$$-\frac{1}{2} < x < \frac{3}{4}, \left(-\frac{1}{2}, \frac{3}{4}\right)$$

96. $2 \le 3x - 4 < 6$
$$6 \le 3x < 10$$
$$2 \le x < \frac{10}{3}, \left[2, \frac{10}{3}\right)$$

97. $4(2x - 5) \le 5x - 1$
$$8x - 20 \le 5x - 1$$
$$3x - 20 \le -1$$
$$3x \le 19$$
$$x \le \frac{19}{3}, \left(-\infty, \frac{19}{3}\right]$$

98. $-2(x - 5) > 2(3x - 2)$
$$-2x + 10 > 6x - 4$$
$$-8x + 10 > -4$$
$$-8x > -14$$
$$\frac{-8x}{-8} < \frac{-14}{-8}$$
$$x < \frac{7}{4}, \left(-\infty, \frac{7}{4}\right)$$

99. Let x = the amount of sales then
$0.05x$ = her commission.
$$175 + 0.05x \geq 300$$
$$0.05x \geq 125$$
$$x \geq 2500$$
Sales must be at least $2500.

100. Let x = her score on the fourth round.
$$\frac{76 + 82 + 79 + x}{4} < 80$$
$$237 + x < 320$$
$$x < 83$$
Her score must be less than 83.

101. $6x + 2x - 1 = 5x + 11$
$$8x - 1 = 5x + 11$$
$$3x - 1 = 11$$
$$3x = 12$$
$$x = 4$$

102. $2(3y - 4) = 6 + 7y$
$$6y - 8 = 6 + 7y$$
$$-8 = 6 + y$$
$$-14 = y$$

103. $4(3 - a) - (6a + 9) = -12a$
$$12 - 4a - 6a - 9 = -12a$$
$$3 - 10a = -12a$$
$$3 = -2a$$
$$-\frac{3}{2} = a$$

104. $\dfrac{x}{3} - 2 = 5$
$$\frac{x}{3} = 7$$
$$3 \cdot \frac{x}{3} = 3 \cdot 7$$
$$x = 21$$

105. $2(y + 5) = 2y + 10$
$$2y + 10 = 2y + 10$$
$$10 = 10$$
All real numbers are solutions.

106. $7x - 3x + 2 = 2(2x - 1)$
$$4x + 2 = 4x - 2$$
$$2 = -2$$
There is no solution.

107. Let x = the number.
$$6 + 2x = x - 7$$
$$6 + x = -7$$
$$x = -13$$
The number is -13.

108. Let x = length of shorter piece, then
$4x + 3$ = length of longer piece.
$$x + (4x + 3) = 23$$
$$5x + 3 = 23$$
$$5x = 20$$
$$x = 4$$
$$4x + 3 = 4(4) + 3 = 19$$
The shorter piece is 4 inches and the longer piece is 19 inches.

109. $V = \dfrac{1}{3} Ah$
$$3 \cdot V = 3 \cdot \frac{1}{3} Ah$$
$$3V = Ah$$
$$\frac{3V}{A} = \frac{Ah}{A}$$
$$\frac{3V}{A} = h$$

110. Let x = the number.
$$x = 26\% \cdot 85$$
$$x = 0.26 \cdot 85$$
$$x = 22.1$$
22.1 is 26% of 85.

111. Let x = the number.
$$72 = 45\% \cdot x$$
$$72 = 0.45x$$
$$\frac{72}{0.45} = \frac{0.45x}{0.45}$$
$$160 = x$$
72 is 45% of 160.

112. Increase $= 282 - 235 = 47$
Let x = percent.
$$47 = x \cdot 235$$
$$\frac{47}{235} = \frac{235x}{235}$$
$$0.2 = x$$
The percent increase is 20%.

113. $4x - 7 > 3x + 2$
$$x - 7 > 2$$
$$x > 9, \ (9, \infty)$$

114. $-5x < 20$

$$\frac{-5x}{-5} > \frac{20}{-5}$$

$$x > -4, \ (-4, \infty)$$

115. $-3(1+2x)+x \geq -(3-x)$

$$-3-6x+x \geq -3+x$$

$$-3-5x \geq -3+x$$

$$-5x \geq x$$

$$-6x \geq 0$$

$$\frac{-6x}{-6} \leq \frac{0}{-6}$$

$$x \leq 0, \ (-\infty, 0]$$

Chapter 2 Test

1. $2y - 6 - y - 4 = y - 10$

2. $2.7x + 6.1 + 3.2x - 4.9 = 5.9x + 1.2$

3. $4(x-2) - 3(2x-6) = 4x - 8 - 6x + 18$
$$= -2x + 10$$

4. $7 + 2(5y-3) = 7 + 10y - 6 = 10y + 1$

5.
$$-\frac{4}{5}x = 4$$

$$-\frac{5}{4} \cdot \left(-\frac{4}{5}x\right) = -\frac{5}{4} \cdot 4$$

$$x = -5$$

6. $4(n-5) = -(4-2n)$

$$4n - 20 = -4 + 2n$$

$$2n - 20 = -4$$

$$2n = 16$$

$$n = 8$$

7. $5y - 7 + y = -(y + 3y)$

$$6y - 7 = -4y$$

$$-7 = -10y$$

$$\frac{7}{10} = y$$

8. $4z + 1 - z = 1 + z$

$$3z + 1 = 1 + z$$

$$2z + 1 = 1$$

$$2z = 0$$

$$z = 0$$

9. $\dfrac{2(x+6)}{3} = x - 5$

$$2(x+6) = 3(x-5)$$

$$2x + 12 = 3x - 15$$

$$12 = x - 15$$

$$27 = x$$

10. $\dfrac{1}{2} - x + \dfrac{3}{2} = x - 4$

$$2\left(\frac{1}{2} - x + \frac{3}{2}\right) = 2(x-4)$$

$$1 - 2x + 3 = 2x - 8$$

$$-2x + 4 = 2x - 8$$

$$-4x + 4 = -8$$

$$-4x = -12$$

$$x = 3$$

11. $-0.3(x-4) + x = 0.5(3-x)$

$$10[-0.3(x-4)+x] = 10[0.5(3-x)]$$

$$-3(x-4) + 10x = 5(3-x)$$

$$-3x + 12 + 10x = 15 - 5x$$

$$7x + 12 = 15 - 5x$$

$$12x + 12 = 15$$

$$12x = 3$$

$$x = \frac{3}{12} = \frac{1}{4} = 0.25$$

12. $-4(a+1) - 3a = -7(2a-3)$

$$-4a - 4 - 3a = -14a + 21$$

$$-7a - 4 = -14a + 21$$

$$7a - 4 = 21$$

$$7a = 25$$

$$a = \frac{25}{7}$$

13. $-2(x-3) = x + 5 - 3x$

$$-2x + 6 = -2x + 5$$

$$6 = 5$$

There is no solution.

14. Let x = the number.

$$x + \frac{2}{3}x = 35$$

$$3\left(x + \frac{2}{3}x\right) = 3(35)$$

$$3x + 2x = 105$$

$$5x = 105$$

$$x = 21$$

The number is 21.

15. Let $l = 35$, and $w = 20$.
$2A = 2lw = 2(35)(20) = 1400$
Let $x =$ the number of gallons needed at
200 square feet per gallon.
$1400 = 200x$
$\quad 7 = x$
7 gallons are needed.

16. Let $x =$ one area code, then
$2x =$ other area code.
$x + 2x = 1203$
$\quad 3x = 1203$
$\quad \dfrac{3x}{3} = \dfrac{1203}{3}$
$\quad\quad x = 401$
$2x = 2(401) = 802$
The area codes are 401 and 802.

17. Let $x =$ the amount invested at 10% for one year.

Principal $\cdot$ Rate $=$ Interest

10%	x	0.10	$0.1x$
12%	$2x$	0.12	$0.12(2x)$
Total			2890

$0.1x + 0.12(2x) = 2890$
$\quad 0.1x + 0.24x = 2890$
$\quad\quad\quad 0.34x = 2890$
$\quad\quad\quad\quad x = 8500$
$2x = 2(8500) = 17,000$
He invested \$8500 at 10% and \$17,000 at 12%.

18. Let $x =$ the time they travel.

Rate $\cdot$ Time $=$ Distance

Train 1	50	x	$50x$
Train 2	64	x	$64x$
Total			285

$50x + 64x = 285$
$\quad 114x = 285$
$\quad\quad x = 2\dfrac{1}{2}$

They must travel for $2\dfrac{1}{2}$ hours.

19. Let $y = -14$, $m = -2$, and $b = -2$.
$\quad y = mx + b$
$-14 = -2x - 2$
$-12 = -2x$
$\quad 6 = x$

20. $\quad V = \pi r^2 h$
$\quad \dfrac{V}{\pi r^2} = \dfrac{\pi r^2 h}{\pi r^2}$
$\quad \dfrac{V}{\pi r^2} = h$

21. $3x - 4y = 10$
$\quad -4y = -3x + 10$
$\quad\quad y = \dfrac{-3x + 10}{-4}$
$\quad\quad y = \dfrac{3x - 10}{4}$

22. $\quad 3x - 5 \geq 7x + 3$
$\quad -4x - 5 \geq 3$
$\quad\quad -4x \geq 8$
$\quad\quad \dfrac{-4x}{-4} \leq \dfrac{8}{-4}$
$\quad\quad x \leq -2, \ (-\infty, -2]$

23. $\quad x + 6 > 4x - 6$
$\quad -3x + 6 > -6$
$\quad\quad -3x > -12$
$\quad\quad \dfrac{-3x}{-3} < \dfrac{-12}{-3}$
$\quad\quad x < 4, \ (-\infty, 4)$

24. $-2 < 3x + 1 < 8$
$\quad -3 < 3x < 7$
$\quad -1 < x < \dfrac{7}{3}, \ \left(-1, \dfrac{7}{3}\right)$

25. $\dfrac{2(5x+1)}{3} > 2$

$2(5x+1) > 6$

$10x + 2 > 6$

$10x > 4$

$x > \dfrac{4}{10} = \dfrac{2}{5}, \left(\dfrac{2}{5}, \infty\right)$

$\dfrac{2}{5}$

Chapter 2 Cumulative Review

1. a. the natural numbers are 11 and 112.

   b. The whole numbers are 0, 11, and 112.

   c. The integers are $-3, -2, 0, 11,$ and 112.

   d. The rational numbers are $-3, -2, -1.5, 0,$ $\dfrac{1}{4}, 11,$ and 112.

   e. The irrational number is $\sqrt{2}$.

   f. All the numbers in the given set are real numbers.

2. a. The natural numbers are 2, 7, and 8.

   b. The whole numbers are 0, 2, 7, and 8.

   c. The integers are $-185, 0, 2, 7,$ and 8.

   d. The rational numbers are $-185, -\dfrac{1}{5}, 0, 2, 7,$ and 8.

   e. The irrational number is $\sqrt{3}$.

   f. All the numbers in the given set are real numbers.

3. a. $|4| = 4$

   b. $|-5| = 5$

   c. $|0| = 0$

   d. $\left|-\dfrac{1}{2}\right| = \dfrac{1}{2}$

   e. $|5.6| = 5.6$

4. a. $|5| = 5$

   b. $|-8| = 8$

   c. $\left|-\dfrac{2}{3}\right| = \dfrac{2}{3}$

5. a. $40 = 2 \cdot 2 \cdot 2 \cdot 5$

   b. $63 = 3 \cdot 3 \cdot 7$

6. a. $44 = 2 \cdot 2 \cdot 11$

   b. $90 = 2 \cdot 3 \cdot 3 \cdot 5$

7. $\dfrac{2}{5} = \dfrac{2}{5} \cdot \dfrac{4}{4} = \dfrac{8}{20}$

8. $\dfrac{2}{3} = \dfrac{2}{3} \cdot \dfrac{8}{8} = \dfrac{16}{24}$

9. $3[4 + 2(10 - 1)] = 3[4 + 2(9)]$
$= 3[4 + 18]$
$= 3[22]$
$= 66$

10. $5[16 - 4(2 + 1)] = 5[16 - 4(3)]$
$= 5[16 - 12]$
$= 5[4]$
$= 20$

11. Let $x = 2$.
$3x + 10 = 8x$
$3(2) + 10 \overset{?}{=} 8(2)$
$6 + 10 \overset{?}{=} 16$
$16 = 16$
2 is a solution of the equation.

12. Let $x = 3$.
$5x - 2 = 4x$
$5(3) - 2 \overset{?}{=} 4(3)$
$15 - 2 \overset{?}{=} 12$
$13 \neq 12$
3 is not a solution of the equation.

13. $-1 + (-2) = -3$

14. $(-2) + (-8) = -10$

15. $-4 + 6 = 2$

16. $-3 + 10 = 7$

17. a. $-(-10) = 10$

   b. $-\left(-\dfrac{1}{2}\right) = \dfrac{1}{2}$

   c. $-(-2x) = 2x$

   d. $-|-6| = -(6) = -6$

18. a. $-(-5) = 5$

   b. $-\left(-\dfrac{2}{3}\right) = \dfrac{2}{3}$

   c. $-(-a) = a$

   d. $-|-3| = -(3) = -3$

19. a. $5.3 - (-4.6) = 5.3 + 4.6 = 9.9$

   b. $-\dfrac{3}{10} - \dfrac{5}{10} = -\dfrac{3}{10} + \left(-\dfrac{5}{10}\right)$
$$= \dfrac{-3-5}{10}$$
$$= -\dfrac{8}{10}$$
$$= -\dfrac{4}{5}$$

   c. $-\dfrac{2}{3} - \left(-\dfrac{4}{5}\right) = -\dfrac{2}{3} \cdot \dfrac{5}{5} + \dfrac{4}{5} \cdot \dfrac{3}{3}$
$$= -\dfrac{10}{15} + \dfrac{12}{15}$$
$$= \dfrac{2}{15}$$

20. a. $-2.7 - 8.4 = -2.7 + (-8.4) = -11.1$

   b. $-\dfrac{4}{5} - \left(-\dfrac{3}{5}\right) = -\dfrac{4}{5} + \dfrac{3}{5} = \dfrac{-4+3}{5} = -\dfrac{1}{5}$

   c. $\dfrac{1}{4} - \left(-\dfrac{1}{2}\right) = \dfrac{1}{4} + \dfrac{1}{2} \cdot \dfrac{2}{2} = \dfrac{1}{4} + \dfrac{2}{4} = \dfrac{3}{4}$

21. a. $x = 90 - 38 = 90 + (-38) = 52$
The complementary angle is 52°.

   b. $y = 180 - 62 = 180 + (-62) = 118$
The supplementary angle is 118°.

22. a. $x = 90 - 72 = 90 + (-72) = 18$
The complementary angle is 18°.

   b. $y = 180 - 47 = 180 + (-47) = 133$
The supplementary angle is 133°.

23. a. $(-1.2)(0.05) = -0.06$

   b. $\dfrac{2}{3} \cdot \left(-\dfrac{7}{10}\right) = -\dfrac{2 \cdot 7}{3 \cdot 10} = -\dfrac{14}{30} = -\dfrac{7}{15}$

   c. $\left(-\dfrac{4}{5}\right)(-20) = \dfrac{4 \cdot 20}{5} = \dfrac{80}{5} = 16$

24. a. $(4.5)(-0.08) = -0.36$

   b. $-\dfrac{3}{4} \cdot -\dfrac{8}{17} = \dfrac{3 \cdot 8}{4 \cdot 17} = \dfrac{24}{68} = \dfrac{6}{17}$

25. a. $\dfrac{-24}{-4} = 6$

   b. $\dfrac{-36}{3} = -12$

   c. $\dfrac{2}{3} \div \left(-\dfrac{5}{4}\right) = \dfrac{2}{3}\left(-\dfrac{4}{5}\right) = -\dfrac{8}{15}$

   d. $-\dfrac{3}{2} \div 9 = -\dfrac{3}{2} \div \dfrac{9}{1} = -\dfrac{3}{2} \cdot \dfrac{1}{9} = -\dfrac{3}{18} = -\dfrac{1}{6}$

26. a. $\dfrac{-32}{8} = -4$

   b. $\dfrac{-108}{-12} = 9$

   c. $-\dfrac{5}{7} \div \left(\dfrac{-9}{2}\right) = -\dfrac{5}{7}\left(-\dfrac{2}{9}\right) = \dfrac{10}{63}$

27. a. $x + 5 = 5 + x$

   b. $3 \cdot x = x \cdot 3$

28. a. $y + 1 = 1 + y$

   b. $y \cdot 4 = 4 \cdot y$

29. a. $8 \cdot 2 + 8 \cdot x = 8(2 + x)$

   b. $7s + 7t = 7(s + t)$

30. a. $4 \cdot y + 4 \cdot \dfrac{1}{3} = 4\left(y + \dfrac{1}{3}\right)$

    b. $0.10x + 0.10y = 0.10(x + y)$

31. $(2x - 3) - (4x - 2) = 2x - 3 - 4x + 2 = -2x - 1$

32. $(-5x + 1) - (10x + 3) = -5x + 1 - 10x - 3$
$$= -15x - 2$$

33. $\quad\;\; y + 0.6 = -1.0$
$$y + 0.6 - 0.6 = -1.0 - 0.6$$
$$y = -1.6$$

34. $\qquad \dfrac{5}{6} + x = \dfrac{2}{3}$
$$6\left(\dfrac{5}{6}\right) + 6(x) = 6\left(\dfrac{2}{3}\right)$$
$$5 + 6x = 4$$
$$6x = -1$$
$$x = -\dfrac{1}{6}$$

35. $\quad\;\; 7 = -5(2a - 1) - (-11a + 6)$
$$7 = -10a + 5 + 11a - 6$$
$$7 = a - 1$$
$$7 + 1 = a - 1 + 1$$
$$8 = a$$

36. $\;\; -3x + 1 - (-4x - 6) = 10$
$$-3x + 1 + 4x + 6 = 10$$
$$x + 7 = 10$$
$$x = 3$$

37. $\dfrac{y}{7} = 20$
$$y = 140$$

38. $\dfrac{x}{4} = 18$
$$x = 72$$

39. $4(2x - 3) + 7 = 3x + 5$
$$8x - 12 + 7 = 3x + 5$$
$$8x - 5 = 3x + 5$$
$$5x - 5 = 5$$
$$5x = 10$$
$$x = 2$$

40. $\quad 6x + 5 = 4(x + 4) - 1$
$$6x + 5 = 4x + 16 - 1$$
$$6x + 5 = 4x + 15$$
$$2x + 5 = 15$$
$$2x = 10$$
$$x = 5$$

41. Let $x =$ a number.
$$2(x + 4) = 4x - 12$$
$$2x + 8 = 4x - 12$$
$$8 = 2x - 12$$
$$20 = 2x$$
$$10 = x$$
The number is 10.

42. Let $x =$ a number.
$$x + 4 = 3x - 8$$
$$4 = 2x - 8$$
$$12 = 2x$$
$$6 = x$$
The number is 6.

43. $\quad V = lwh$
$$\dfrac{V}{wh} = \dfrac{lwh}{wh}$$
$$\dfrac{V}{wh} = l$$

44. $\quad C = 2\pi r$
$$\dfrac{C}{2\pi} = \dfrac{2\pi r}{2\pi}$$
$$\dfrac{C}{2\pi} = r$$

45. $x + 4 \leq -6$
$$x \leq -10, \; (-\infty, -10]$$

46. $x - 3 > 2$
$$x > 5, \; (5, \infty)$$

Chapter 3

Practice Exercises

1. a. We look for the shortest bar, which is the bar representing Germany. We move from the right edge of this bar vertically downward to the Internet user axis. Germany has approximately 45 million Internet users.

b. India has approximately 50 million Internet users. Germany has approximately 45 million Internet users. We subtract $50 - 45 = 5$ or 5 million. India has 5 million more Internet users than Germany.

2. a. We locate the number 40 along the time axis and move vertically upward until the line is reached. From this point on the line, we move horizontally to the left until the pulse rate axis is reached. Reading the number of beats per minute, we find that the pulse rate is 70 beats per minute 40 minutes after a cigarette is lit.

b. The number 0 on the time axis corresponds to the time when the cigarette is being lit. We move vertically upward to the point on the line and then horizontally to the left to the pulse rate axis. The pulse rate is 60 beats per minute when the cigarette is being lit.

c. We find the highest point of the line graph, which represents the highest pulse rate. From this point, we move vertically downward to the time axis. We find the pulse rate is the highest at 5 minutes, which means 5 minutes after lighting a cigarette.

3. a. Point $(4, -3)$ lies in quadrant IV.

b. Point $(-3, 5)$ lies in quadrant II.

c. Point $(0, 4)$ lies on an axis, so it is not in any quadrant.

d. Point $(-6, 1)$ lies in quadrant II.

e. Point $(-2, 0)$ lies on an axis, so it is not in any quadrant.

f. Point $(5, 5)$ lies in quadrant I.

g. Point $\left(3\frac{1}{2}, 1\frac{1}{2}\right)$ lies in quadrant I.

h. Point $(-4, -5)$ lies in quadrant III.

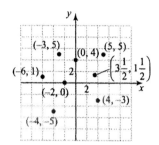

4. a. The ordered pairs are $(2000, 92)$, $(2001, 84)$, $(2002, 73)$, $(2003, 64)$, $(2004, 65)$, $(2005, 67)$, and $(2006, 96)$.

b. We plot the ordered pairs. We label the horizontal axis "Year" and the vertical axis "Wildfires (in thousands)."

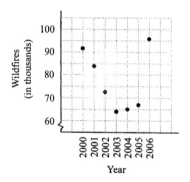

5. a. Let $x = 3$ and $y = 1$.
$$x + 3y = 6$$
$$3 + 3(1) = 6$$
$$3 + 3 = 6$$
$$6 = 6 \quad \text{true}$$
$(3, 1)$ is a solution.

b. Let $x = 6$ and $y = 0$.
$$x + 3y = 6$$
$$6 + 3(0) = 6$$
$$6 + 0 = 6$$
$$6 = 6 \quad \text{true}$$
$(6, 0)$ is a solution.

c. Let $x = -2$ and $y = \dfrac{2}{3}$.

$$x + 3y = 6$$
$$-2 + 3\left(\dfrac{2}{3}\right) = 6$$
$$-2 + 2 = 6$$
$$0 = 6 \quad \text{false}$$

$\left(-2, \dfrac{2}{3}\right)$ is not a solution.

6. a. Let $x = 0$ and solve for y.
$$2x - y = 8$$
$$2(0) - y = 8$$
$$0 - y = 8$$
$$-y = 8$$
$$y = -8$$
The ordered pair is $(0, -8)$.

b. Let $y = 4$ and solve for x.
$$2x - y = 8$$
$$2x - 4 = 8$$
$$2x = 12$$
$$x = 6$$
The ordered pair is $(6, 4)$.

c. Let $x = -3$ and solve for y.
$$2x - y = 8$$
$$2(-3) - y = 8$$
$$-6 - y = 8$$
$$-y = 14$$
$$y = -14$$
The ordered pair is $(-3, -14)$.

7. a. Replace x with -2 in the equation and solve for y.
$$y = -4x$$
$$y = -4(-2)$$
$$y = 8$$
The ordered pair is $(-2, 8)$.

b. Replace y with -12 in the equation and solve for x.
$$y = -4x$$
$$-12 = -4x$$
$$3 = x$$
The ordered pair is $(3, -12)$.

c. Replace x with 0 in the equation and solve for y.
$$y = -4x$$
$$y = -4(0)$$
$$y = 0$$
The ordered pair is $(0, 0)$.

The completed table is shown below.

x	y
-2	8
3	-12
0	0

8. a. Let $x = -10$.
$$y = \dfrac{1}{5}x - 2$$
$$y = \dfrac{1}{5}(-10) - 2$$
$$y = -2 - 2$$
$$y = -4$$
Ordered pair: $(-10, -4)$

b. Let $x = 0$.
$$y = \dfrac{1}{5}x - 2$$
$$y = \dfrac{1}{5}(0) - 2$$
$$y = 0 - 2$$
$$y = -2$$
Ordered pair: $(0, -2)$

c. Let $y = 0$.
$$y = \dfrac{1}{5}x - 2$$
$$0 = \dfrac{1}{5}x - 2$$
$$2 = \dfrac{1}{5}x$$
$$10 = x$$
Ordered pair: $(10, 0)$

The completed table is shown below.

x	y
-10	-4
0	-2
10	0

9. When $x = 0$,
$$y = -1800x + 12,000$$
$$y = -1800 \cdot 0 + 12,000$$
$$y = 0 + 12,000$$
$$y = 12,000$$

When $x = 1$,
$$y = -1800x + 12,000$$
$$y = -1800 \cdot 1 + 12,000$$
$$y = -1800 + 12,000$$
$$y = 10,200$$

When $x = 2$,
$$y = -1800x + 12,000$$
$$y = -1800 \cdot 2 + 12,000$$
$$y = -3600 + 12,000$$
$$y = 8400$$

When $x = 3$,
$$y = -1800x + 12,000$$
$$y = -1800 \cdot 3 + 12,000$$
$$y = -5400 + 12,000$$
$$y = 6600$$

When $x = 4$,
$$y = -1800x + 12,000$$
$$y = -1800 \cdot 4 + 12,000$$
$$y = -7200 + 12,000$$
$$y = 4800$$

The completed table is shown below.

x	0	1	2	3	4
y	12,000	10,200	8400	6600	4800

Vocabulary and Readiness Check

1. The horizontal axis is called the <u>x-axis</u>.

2. The vertical axis is called the <u>y-axis</u>.

3. The intersection of the horizontal axis and the vertical axis is a point called the <u>origin</u>.

4. The axes divide the plane into regions, called <u>quadrants</u>. There are <u>four</u> of these regions.

5. In the ordered pair of numbers $(-2, 5)$, the number -2 is called the <u>x-coordinate</u> and the number 5 is called the <u>y-coordinate</u>.

6. Each ordered pair of numbers corresponds to <u>one</u> point in the plane.

7. An ordered pair is a <u>solution</u> of an equation in two variables if replacing the variables by the coordinates of the ordered pair results in a true statement.

Exercise Set 3.1

2. We look for the shortest bar. The bars representing Austria and Turkey appear to be the same height and are shorter than the rest of the bars. Austria and Turkey are the least popular tourist destinations shown.

4. We look for bars ending between the horizontal line at 40 on the vertical axis and the horizontal line at 50 on the vertical axis, which are the bars representing the U.S. and China. These two countries have between 40 and 50 million tourists per year.

6. The bar for Turkey extends to the horizontal line at 20 on the vertical axis. Turkey has approximately 20 million tourists per year.

8. From 2004 on the year axis, we move vertically up to the point on the line graph. Then we move horizontally to the attendance axis. The Super Bowl attendance in 2004 was approximately 71,500.

10. We find the lowest point on the line graph and move vertically downward to the year axis. The year with the least Super Bowl attendance was 2003. From the lowest point on the graph, we move horizontally to the attendance axis. The least attendance was approximately 67,600.

12. From 2010 on the year axis, we move vertically up to the point on the line graph. Then we move horizontally to the vertical axis. The number of students per teacher is projected to be approximately 15 in 2010.

14. The points on the line graph for 1994 and 1996 lie above the horizontal line at 17 on the vertical axis. The point for 1998 is the first that lies below this horizontal line. The first year shown that the number of students per teacher fell below 17 was 1998.

16. Answers may vary.

18. **a.** Point $(2, 4)$ lies in quadrant I.

   b. Point $(0, 2)$ lies on the y-axis, so it is not in any quadrant.

c. Point $(-2, 1)$ lies in quadrant II.

d. Point $(-3, -3)$ lies in quadrant III.

e. Point $\left(3\frac{3}{4}, 0\right)$ lies on the x-axis, so it is not in any quadrant.

f. Point $(5, -4)$ lies in quadrant IV.

g. Point $(-3.4, 4.8)$ lies in quadrant II.

h. Point $\left(\frac{1}{3}, -5\right)$ lies in quadrant IV.

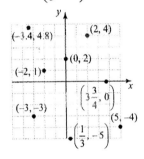

20. Point B lies on the x-axis $3\frac{1}{2}$ units to the right of the origin. Its coordinates are given by the ordered pair $\left(3\frac{1}{2}, 0\right)$.

22. Point D lies one unit to the left and three units above the origin. Its coordinates are given by the ordered pair $(-1, 3)$.

24. Point F lies on the y-axis one unit below the origin. Its coordinates are given by the ordered pair $(0, -1)$.

26. Point A lies on the x-axis two units to the right of the origin. Its coordinates are given by the ordered pair $(2, 0)$.

28. Point C lies two units to the left and three units above the origin. Its coordinates are given by the ordered pair $(-2, 3)$.

30. Point E lies one unit to the right and one unit below the origin. Its coordinates are given by the ordered pair $(1, -1)$.

32. Point G lies on the x-axis two units to the left of the origin. Its coordinates are given by the ordered pair $(-2, 0)$.

34. a. The ordered pairs are $(2001, 1.38)$, $(2002, 1.31)$, $(2003, 1.52)$, $(2004, 1.81)$, $(2005, 2.24)$, and $(2006, 2.53)$.

    b. We plot the ordered pairs. We label the horizontal axis "Year" and the vertical axis "Price per Gallon of Unleaded Gasoline (in dollars)."

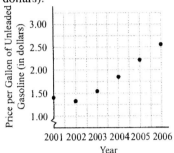

36. a. The ordered pairs are $(1970, 8.6)$, $(1980, 12.1)$, $(1990, 13.8)$, $(2000, 15.3)$, and $(2010, 18.7)$.

    b. We plot the ordered pairs. We label the horizontal axis "Year" and the vertical axis "Enrollment in College (in millions)."

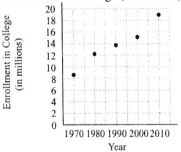

    c. The trend is increasing enrollment every year.

38. a. The ordered pairs are $(2001, 438)$, $(2002, 440)$, $(2003, 441)$, $(2004, 443)$, $(2005, 445)$, and $(2006, 446)$.

    b. We plot the ordered pairs. We label the horizontal axis "Year" and the vertical axis "Average Farm Size (in acres)."

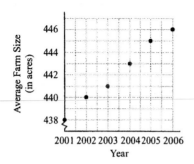

40. For (2, 3), let $x = 2$ and $y = 3$.
$$3x + y = 8$$
$$3(2) + 3 = 8$$
$$6 + 3 = 8$$
$$9 = 8 \quad \text{false}$$
No, (2, 3) is not a solution.

For (0, 8), let $x = 0$ and $y = 8$.
$$3x + y = 8$$
$$3(0) + 8 = 8$$
$$0 + 8 = 8$$
$$8 = 8 \quad \text{true}$$
Yes, (0, 8) is a solution.

For (8, 0), let $x = 8$ and $y = 0$.
$$3x + y = 8$$
$$3(8) + 0 = 8$$
$$24 + 0 = 8$$
$$24 = 8 \quad \text{false}$$
No, (8, 0) is not a solution.

42. For (0, 0), let $x = 0$ and $y = 0$.
$$y = -\frac{1}{2}x$$
$$0 = -\frac{1}{2}(0)$$
$$0 = 0 \quad \text{true}$$
Yes, (0, 0) is a solution.

For (4, 2), let $x = 4$ and $y = 2$.
$$y = -\frac{1}{2}x$$
$$2 = -\frac{1}{2}(4)$$
$$2 = -2 \quad \text{false}$$
No, (4, 2) is not a solution.

44. For (-2, 2), let $x = -2$ and $y = 2$.
$$y = -2$$
$$2 = -2 \quad \text{false}$$
No, (-2, 2) is not a solution.

For (2, -2), let $x = 2$ and $y = -2$.
$$y = -2$$
$$-2 = -2 \quad \text{true}$$
Yes, (2, -2) is a solution.

For (0, -2), let $x = 0$ and $y = -2$.
$$y = -2$$
$$-2 = -2 \quad \text{true}$$
Yes, (0, -2) is a solution.

46. Replace y with -2 and solve for x.
$$x - 5y = -1$$
$$x - 5(-2) = -1$$
$$x + 10 = -1$$
$$x = -11$$
The ordered pair is (-11, -2).

Replace x with 4 and solve for y.
$$x - 5y = -1$$
$$4 - 5y = -1$$
$$-5y = -5$$
$$y = 1$$
The ordered pair is (4, 1).

48. Replace x with -10 and solve for y.
$$y = \frac{1}{5}x - 2$$
$$y = \frac{1}{5}(-10) - 2$$
$$y = -2 - 2$$
$$y = -4$$
The ordered pair is (-10, -4).

Replace y with 1 and solve for x.
$$y = \frac{1}{5}x - 2$$
$$1 = \frac{1}{5}x - 2$$
$$3 = \frac{1}{5}x$$
$$15 = x$$
The ordered pair is (15, 1).

50. Replace x with 0 and solve for y.
$$y = -9x$$
$$y = -9(0)$$
$$y = 0$$
The ordered pair is (0, 0).

Replace x with -3 and solve for y.

$y = -9x$

$y = -9(-3)$

$y = 27$

The ordered pair is $(-3, 27)$.

Replace y with 2 and solve for x.

$y = -9x$

$2 = -9x$

$-\dfrac{2}{9} = x$

The ordered pair is $\left(-\dfrac{2}{9}, 2\right)$.

The completed table is shown below.

x	y
0	0
-3	27
$-\dfrac{2}{9}$	2

52. Replace y with 0 and solve for x.

$x = -y + 4$

$x = -0 + 4$

$x = 4$

The ordered pair is $(4, 0)$.

Replace x with 0 and solve for y.

$x = -y + 4$

$0 = -y + 4$

$y = 4$

The ordered pair is $(0, 4)$.

Replace y with -3 and solve for x.

$x = -y + 4$

$x = -(-3) + 4$

$x = 3 + 4$

$x = 7$

The ordered pair is $(7, -3)$.

The completed table is shown below.

x	y
4	0
0	4
7	-3

54. Replace x with 0 and solve for y.

$y = \dfrac{1}{3}x$

$y = \dfrac{1}{3}(0)$

$y = 0$

The ordered pair is $(0, 0)$.

Replace x with -6 and solve for y.

$y = \dfrac{1}{3}x$

$y = \dfrac{1}{3}(-6)$

$y = -2$

The ordered pair is $(-6, -2)$.

Replace y with 1 and solve for x.

$y = \dfrac{1}{3}x$

$1 = \dfrac{1}{3}x$

$3 = x$

The ordered pair is $(3, 1)$.

The completed table is shown below.

x	y
0	0
-6	-2
3	1

56. Replace y with 4 and solve for x.

$2x + y = 4$

$2x + 4 = 4$

$2x = 0$

$x = 0$

The ordered pair is $(0, 4)$.

Replace x with 2 and solve for y.

$2x + y = 4$

$2(2) + y = 4$

$4 + y = 4$

$y = 0$

The ordered pair is $(2, 0)$.

Replace y with 2 and solve for x.

$2x + y = 4$

$2x + 2 = 4$

$2x = 2$

$x = 1$

The ordered pair is (1, 2).
The completed table is shown below.

x	y
0	4
2	0
1	2

58. Replace y with 0 and solve for x.
$$y = 5x + 10$$
$$0 = 5x + 10$$
$$-5x = 10$$
$$x = -2$$
The ordered pair is (−2, 0).

Replace y with 5 and solve for x.
$$y = 5x + 10$$
$$5 = 5x + 10$$
$$-5 = 5x$$
$$-1 = x$$
The ordered pair is (−1, 5).

Replace x with 0 and solve for y.
$$y = 5x + 10$$
$$y = 5(0) + 10$$
$$y = 0 + 10$$
$$y = 10$$
The ordered pair is (0, 10).
The completed table is shown below.

x	y
−2	0
−1	5
0	10

60. Replace x with 0 and solve for y.
$$x - 6y = 3$$
$$0 - 6y = 3$$
$$-6y = 3$$
$$y = -\frac{3}{6} = -\frac{1}{2}$$
The ordered pair is $\left(0, -\frac{1}{2}\right)$.

Replace x with 1 and solve for y.
$$x - 6y = 3$$
$$1 - 6y = 3$$
$$-6y = 2$$
$$y = -\frac{2}{6} = -\frac{1}{3}$$
The ordered pair is $\left(1, -\frac{1}{3}\right)$.

Replace y with −1 and solve for x.
$$x - 6y = 3$$
$$x - 6(-1) = 3$$
$$x + 6 = 3$$
$$x = -3$$
The ordered pair is (−3, −1).
The completed table is shown below.

x	y
0	$-\frac{1}{2}$
1	$-\frac{1}{3}$
−3	−1

62. Replace x with 0 and solve for y.
$$y = -3x$$
$$y = -3(0)$$
$$y = 0$$
The ordered pair is (0, 0).

Replace x with −2 and solve for y.
$$y = -3x$$
$$y = -3(-2)$$
$$y = 6$$
The ordered pair is (−2, 6).

Replace y with 9 and solve for x.
$$y = -3x$$
$$9 = -3x$$
$$-3 = x$$
The ordered pair is (−3, 9).
The completed table is shown below.

x	y
0	0
−2	6
−3	9

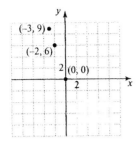

64. Replace x with 0 and solve for y.

$y = \dfrac{1}{2}x + 3$

$y = \dfrac{1}{2}(0) + 3$

$y = 3$

The ordered pair is (0, 3).

Replace x with –4 and solve for y.

$y = \dfrac{1}{2}x + 3$

$y = \dfrac{1}{2}(-4) + 3$

$y = -2 + 3$

$y = 1$

The ordered pair is (–4, 1).

Replace y with 0 and solve for x.

$y = \dfrac{1}{2}x + 3$

$0 = \dfrac{1}{2}x + 3$

$-\dfrac{1}{2}x = 3$

$x = -6$

The ordered pair is (–6, 0).
The completed table is shown below.

x	y
0	3
–4	1
–6	0

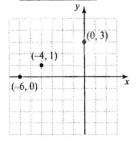

66. a. When $x = 0$,

$y = 0.25x + 9$

$y = 0.25(0) + 9$

$y = 9$

When $x = 1$,

$y = 0.25x + 9$

$y = 0.25(1) + 9$

$y = 0.25 + 9$

$y = 9.25$

When $x = 5$,

$y = 0.25x + 9$

$y = 0.25(5) + 9$

$y = 1.25 + 9$

$y = 10.25$

When $x = 10$,

$y = 0.25x + 9$

$y = 0.25(10) + 9$

$y = 2.50 + 9$

$y = 11.50$

The completed table is shown below.

x	0	1	5	10
y	9	9.25	10.25	11.50

b. Replace y with 12.25 and solve for x.

$y = 0.25x + 9$

$12.25 = 0.25x + 9$

$3.25 = 0.25x$

$13 = x$

An employee must produce 13 units each hour to earn an hourly wage of \$12.25.

68. a. When $x = 2$,

$y = -2.18x + 944.68$

$y = -2.18(2) + 944.68$

$y = -4.36 + 944.68$

$y = 940.32$

When $x = 4$,

$y = -2.18x + 944.68$

$y = -2.18(4) + 944.68$

$y = -8.72 + 944.68$

$y = 935.96$

When $x = 6$,

$y = -2.18x + 944.68$

$y = -2.18(6) + 944.68$

$y = -13.08 + 944.68$

$y = 931.60$

The completed table is shown below.

x	2	4	6
y	940.32	935.96	931.6

b. Replace y with 933 and solve for x.

$$933 = -2.18x + 944.68$$
$$-11.68 = -2.18x$$
$$5 \approx x$$

There were approximately 933 million acres of land operated by farms in year 5 or 2005.

70. Six years after 2000, or in 2006, there were 1488 Target stores.

72.

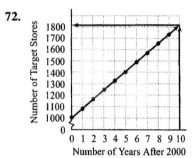

Source: Target

By drawing a line that passes through or near the given points, we can predict that there will be approximately 1730 Target stores in 2009.

74. Answers may vary

76. Subtract x from each side. Then multiply each side by -1.

$$x - y = 3$$
$$-y = -x + 3$$
$$y = x - 3$$

78. Subtract $5x$ from each side. Then divide each side by 2.

$$5x + 2y = 7$$
$$2y = -5x + 7$$
$$y = -\frac{5}{2}x + \frac{7}{2}$$

80. Divide each side by 4.

$$4y = -8x$$
$$y = -2x$$

82. Subtract $2x$ from each side. Then divide each side by -9.

$$2x - 9y = -20$$
$$-9y = -2x - 20$$
$$y = \frac{2}{9}x + \frac{20}{9}$$

84. False; the point $(3, 0)$ lies on the x-axis.

86. False

88. In quadrant I, both coordinates are positive: (positive, positive).

90. In quadrant II, the x-coordinate is negative and the y-coordinate is positive: (negative, positive).

92. A point of the form (number, 0) is located on the x-axis.

94. Answers may vary

96. Answers may vary

98. Answers may vary

100. The point three units to the left of the origin has ordered pair $(-3, 0)$.

102.

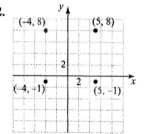

a. The fourth vertex is $(5, -1)$. The square is 9 units by 9 units.

b. The perimeter is $9 + 9 + 9 + 9 = 36$ units.

c. The area is $9 \times 9 = 81$ square units.

Section 3.2

Practice Exercises

1. a. $3x + 2.7y = -5.3$ is a linear equation in two variables because it is written in the form $Ax + By = C$ with $A = 3$, $B = 2.7$, and $C = -5.3$.

b. $x^2 + y = 8$ is not a linear equation in two variables because x is squared.

c. $y = 12$ is a linear equation in two variables because it can be written in the form $Ax + By = C$: $0x + y = 12$.

d. $5x = -3y$ is a linear equation in two variables because it can be written in the form $Ax + By = C$: $5x + 3y = 0$.

2. Find three ordered pair solutions.
Let $x = 0$.
$x + 3y = 9$
$0 + 3y = 9$
$3y = 9$
$y = 3$

Let $x = 3$.
$x + 3y = 9$
$3 + 3y = 9$
$3y = 6$
$y = 2$

Let $y = 1$.
$x + 3y = 9$
$x + 3(1) = 9$
$x + 3 = 9$
$x = 6$
The ordered pairs are $(0, 3)$, $(3, 2)$, and $(6, 1)$.

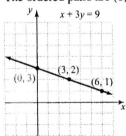

3. Find three ordered pair solutions.
Let $x = 0$.
$3x - 4y = 12$
$3(0) - 4y = 12$
$-4y = 12$
$y = -3$

Let $y = 0$.
$3x - 4y = 12$
$3x - 4(0) = 12$
$3x = 12$
$x = 4$

Let $x = 2$.
$3x - 4y = 12$
$3(2) - 4y = 12$
$6 - 4y = 12$
$-4y = 6$
$y = -\dfrac{6}{4} = -\dfrac{3}{2}$
The ordered pairs are $(0, -3)$, $(4, 0)$, and $\left(2, -\dfrac{3}{2}\right)$.

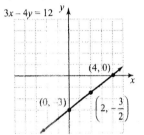

4. Find three ordered pair solutions.
If $x = 1$, $y = -2(1) = -2$.
If $x = 0$, $y = -2(0) = 0$.
If $x = -1$, $y = -2(-1) = 2$.

x	y
1	-2
0	0
-1	2

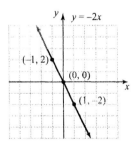

5. Find three ordered pair solutions.
If $x = 2$, $y = \dfrac{1}{2}(2) + 3 = 1 + 3 = 4$.

If $x = 0$, $y = \dfrac{1}{2}(0) + 3 = 0 + 3 = 3$.

If $x = -4$, $y = \dfrac{1}{2}(-4) + 3 = -2 + 3 = 1$.

x	y
2	4
0	3
–4	1

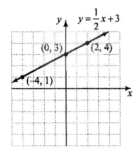

6. Find three ordered pair solutions.
   If $x = 1$, $y = -2(1) + 3 = -2 + 3 = 1$.
   If $x = 0$, $y = -2(0) + 3 = 0 + 3 = 3$.
   If $x = 3$, $y = -2(3) + 3 = -6 + 3 = -3$.

x	y
1	1
0	0
3	–3

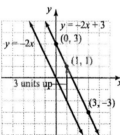

The graph of $y = -2x + 3$ is the same as the graph of $y = -2x$ except that the graph of $y = -2x + 3$ is moved three units upward.

7. **a.** Find three ordered pair solutions.
   If $x = 0$, $y = 22.2(0) + 371 = 0 + 371 = 371$.
   If $x = 6$,
   $y = 22.2(6) + 371 = 133.2 + 371 = 504.2$.
   If $x = 9$,
   $y = 22.2(9) + 371 = 199.8 + 371 = 570.8$.

x	y
0	371
6	504.2
9	570.8

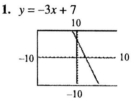

b. The graph shows that we predict approximately 700 thousand computer software application engineers in the year 2015.

Calculator Explorations

1. $y = -3x + 7$

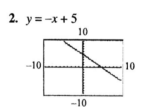

2. $y = -x + 5$

3. $y = 2.5x - 7.9$

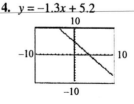

4. $y = -1.3x + 5.2$

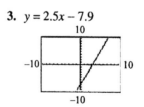

5. $y = -\dfrac{3}{10}x + \dfrac{32}{5}$

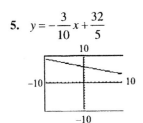

6. $y = \dfrac{2}{9}x - \dfrac{22}{3}$

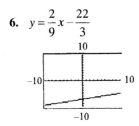

Exercise Set 3.2

2. Yes; it can be written in the form
$Ax + By = C$.

4. No; y is cubed.

6. Yes; it can be written in the form $Ax + By = C$.

8. Yes; it can be written in the form $Ax + By = C$.

10. Let $x = 0$.   Let $y = 2$.
$\quad x - y = 4$ $x - y = 4$
$\quad 0 - y = 4$ $x - 2 = 4$
$\quad\ \ -y = 4$ $x = 6$
$\qquad\ y = -4$

Let $x = -1$.
$\quad x - y = 4$
$-1 - y = 4$
$\quad\ \ -y = 4$
$\qquad\ y = -5$

x	y
0	−4
6	2
−1	−5

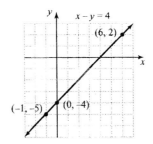

12. $y = -5x$
If $x = 1$, $y = -5(1) = -5$.
If $x = 0$, $y = -5(0) = 0$.
If $x = -1$, $y = -5(-1) = 5$.

x	y
1	−5
0	0
−1	5

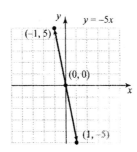

14. $y = \dfrac{1}{2}x$

If $x = 0$, $y = \dfrac{1}{2}(0) = 0$.

If $x = -4$, $y = \dfrac{1}{2}(-4) = -2$.

If $x = 2$, $y = \dfrac{1}{2}(2) = 1$.

x	y
0	0
−4	−2
2	1

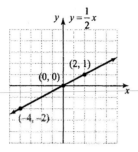

16. $y = -5x + 2$

If $x = 0$, $y = -5(0) + 2 = 0 + 2 = 2$.
If $x = 1$, $y = -5(1) + 2 = -5 + 2 = -3$.
If $x = 2$, $y = -5(2) + 2 = -10 + 2 = -8$.

x	y
0	2
1	−3
2	−8

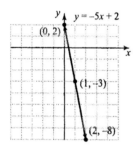

18. $x + y = 7$

x	y
0	7
−2	9
2	5

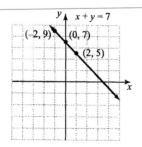

20. $-x + y = 6$

x	y
−6	0
0	6
−2	4

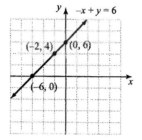

22. $-x + 5y = 5$

x	y
−5	0
0	1
5	2

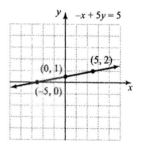

24. $y = -2x + 7$

x	y
0	7
2	3
4	−1

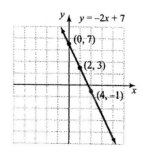

26. $y = 5$

x	y
-1	5
0	5
2	5

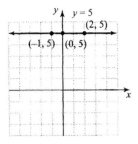

28. $x = -1$

x	y
-1	-1
-1	0
-1	2

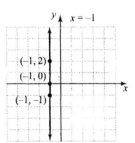

30. $y = -x$

x	y
-4	4
0	0
4	-4

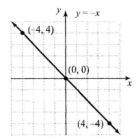

32. $x = -5y$

x	y
-5	1
0	0
5	-1

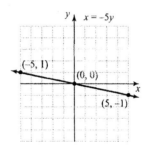

34. $2x + y = 2$

x	y
0	2
1	0
2	-2

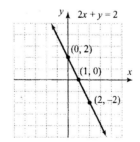

36. $y = \dfrac{1}{4}x + 3$

x	y
-4	2
0	3
4	4

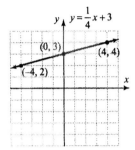

38. $2x - 7y = 14$

x	y
0	-2
$\dfrac{7}{2}$	-1
7	0

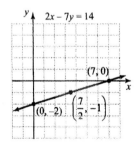

40. $y = -1.5x - 3$

x	y
-4	3
-2	0
0	-3

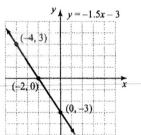

42.

$y = 2x$	
x	y
-2	-4
0	0
2	4

$y = 2x + 5$	
x	y
-2	1
0	5
2	9

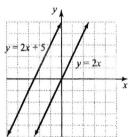

Answers may vary; possible answer: The graph of $y = 2x + 5$ is the same as the graph of $y = 2x$ except that it is moved 5 units upward.

44.

$y = x$	
x	y
-2	-2
0	0
2	2

$y = x - 7$	
x	y
-2	-9
0	-7
2	-5

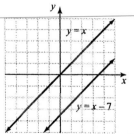

Answers may vary; possible answer: The graph of $y = x - 7$ is the same as the graph of $y = x$ except that it is moved 7 units downward.

46.

$y = -\frac{1}{4}x$

x	y
-4	1
0	0
4	-1

$y = -\frac{1}{4}x + 3$

x	y
-4	4
0	3
4	2

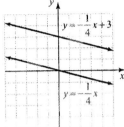

Answers may vary; possible answer: The graph of $y = -\frac{1}{4}x + 3$ is the same as the graph of $y = -\frac{1}{4}x$ except that it is moved 3 units upward.

48. Comparing $y = 5x - 4$ to $y = mx + b$, we see that $b = -4$. We see that graph b crosses the y-axis at $(0, -4)$.

50. Comparing $y = 5x + 2$ to $y = mx + b$, we see that $b = 2$. We see that graph a crosses the y-axis at $(0, 2)$.

52. a. Using the equation, let $x = 5$.
$y = 7x + 45$
$y = 7(5) + 45 = 35 + 45 = 80$
The ordered pair is $(5, 80)$.

  b. Five years after 2000, in 2005, the revenue for Home Depot stores was $80 billion.

  c. The year 2015 is 15 years after 2000, so let $x = 15$.
$y = 7x + 45$
$y = 7(15) + 45 = 105 + 45 = 150$
If the trend continues, Home Depot's revenue will be $150 billion in 2015.

54. Let $x = 9$.
$y = -196x + 1904$
$y = -196(9) + 1904 = -1764 + 1904 = 140$
The U.S. silver production is estimated to be 140 metric tons in 2009.

56.

The third and fourth vertices are either at $(-3, 4)$ and $(2, 4)$ or at $(-3, -6)$ and $(2, -6)$.

58. $5 + 7(x + 1) = 12 + 10x$
$5 + 7x + 7 = 12 + 10x$
$7x + 12 = 12 + 10x$
$-3x + 12 = 12$
$-3x = 0$
$x = 0$

60. $\frac{1}{6} + 2x = \frac{2}{3}$
$6\left(\frac{1}{6}\right) + 6(2x) = 6\left(\frac{2}{3}\right)$
$1 + 12x = 4$
$12x = 3$
$x = \frac{1}{4}$

62. The equation is $y = 2x$.

x	y
-2	-4
0	0
2	4

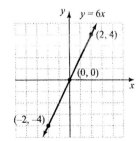

64. The equation is $5x + 2y = -10$.

x	y
-2	0
0	-5
-4	5

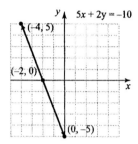

66. $x + y + x + y = 50$

$2x + 2y = 50$

When $y = 20$ miles,

$2x + 2(20) = 50$

$2x + 40 = 50$

$2x = 10$

$x = 5$ miles

68. If (a, b) is a solution of $x + y = 5$, then (b, a) is also a solution. Explanations may vary.

70. $y = |x|$

x	y
0	0
1	1
-1	1
2	2
-2	2

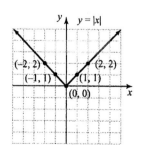

Section 3.3

Practice Exercises

1. The graph crosses the x-axis at the point $(-4, 0)$. The x-intercept is $(-4, 0)$. The graph crosses the y-axis at the point $(0, -6)$. The y-intercept is $(0, -6)$.

2. The graph crosses the x-axis at the point $(-1, 0)$ and at the point $(-0.5, 0)$. The x-intercepts are $(-1, 0)$ and $(-0.5, 0)$. The graph crosses the y-axis at the point $(0, 1)$. The y-intercept is $(0, 1)$.

3. The graph crosses both the x-axis and the y-axis at the point $(0, 0)$. The x-intercept is $(0, 0)$, and the y-intercept is $(0, 0)$.

4. The graph does not cross the x-axis. There is no x-intercept. The graph crosses the y-axis at the point $(0, 3)$. The y-intercept is $(0, 3)$.

5. The graph crosses the x-axis at the point $(-1, 0)$ and at the point $(5, 0)$. The x-intercepts are $(-1, 0)$ and $(5, 0)$. The graph crosses the y-axis at the point $(0, -2)$ and at the point $(0, 2)$. The y-intercepts are $(0, -2)$ and $(0, 2)$.

6. Let $y = 0$.　　　　　　Let $x = 0$.

　$x + 2y = -4$　　　　$x + 2y = -4$

　$x + 2(0) = -4$　　　$0 + 2y = -4$

　$x + 0 = -4$　　　　　$2y = -4$

　　$x = -4$　　　　　　$y = -2$

The x-intercept is $(-4, 0)$, and the y-intercept is $(0, -2)$.

Let $x = 2$.

$x + 2y = -4$

$2 + 2y = -4$

$2y = -6$

$y = -3$

x	y
-4	0
0	-2
2	-3

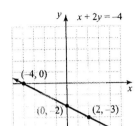

7. Let $y = 0$.   Let $x = 0$.
   $x = 3y$ $x = 3y$
   $x = 3(0)$ $0 = 3y$
   $x = 0$ $0 = y$

   Both the x-intercept and the y-intercept are
   $(0, 0)$.

   Let $y = -1$ Let $y = 1$.
   $x = 3(-1)$ $x = 3(1)$
   $x = -3$ $x = 3$

x	y
0	0
3	1
-3	-1

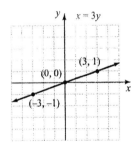

8. Let $y = 0$.   Let $x = 0$.
   $3x = 2y + 4$ $3x = 2y + 4$
   $3x = 2(0) + 4$ $3(0) = 2y + 4$
   $3x = 4$ $-4 = 2y$
   $x = \dfrac{4}{3}$ $-2 = y$

   Let $x = 2$.
   $3x = 2y + 4$
   $3(2) = 2y + 4$
   $6 = 2y + 4$
   $2 = 2y$
   $1 = y$

x	y
0	-2
$\dfrac{4}{3}$	0
2	1

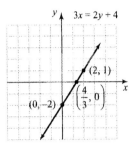

9. For any x-value chosen, notice that y is 2.

x	y
-5	2
0	2
5	2

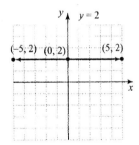

10. For any y-value chosen, notice that x is -2.

x	y
-2	-4
-2	0
-2	4

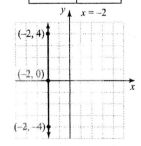

Calculator Explorations

1. $x = 3.78y$

$$y = \frac{x}{3.78}$$

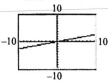

2. $-2.61y = x$

$$y = \frac{x}{-2.61}$$

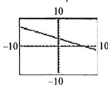

3. $3x + 7y = 21$

$$7y = -3x + 21$$

$$y = -\frac{3}{7}x + 3$$

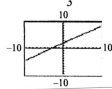

4. $-4x + 6y = 12$

$$6y = 4x + 12$$

$$y = \frac{2}{3}x + 2$$

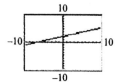

5. $-2.2x + 6.8y = 15.5$

$$6.8y = 2.2x + 15.5$$

$$y = \frac{2.2}{6.8}x + \frac{15.5}{6.8}$$

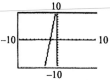

6. $5.9x - 0.8y = -10.4$

$$-0.8y = -5.9x - 10.4$$

$$y = \frac{5.9}{0.8}x + \frac{10.4}{0.8}$$

Vocabulary and Readiness Check

1. An equation that can be written in the form $Ax + By = C$ is called a <u>linear</u> equation in two variables.

2. The form $Ax + By = C$ is called <u>standard</u> form.

3. The graph of the equation $y = -1$ is a <u>horizontal</u> line.

4. The graph of the equation $x = 5$ is a <u>vertical</u> line.

5. A point where a graph crosses the y-axis is called a <u>y-intercept</u>.

6. A point where a graph crosses the x-axis is called a <u>x-intercept</u>.

7. Given an equation of a line, to find the x-intercept (if there is one), let <u>y</u> = 0 and solve for <u>x</u>.

8. Given an equation of a line, to find the y-intercept (if there is one), let <u>x</u> = 0 and solve for <u>y</u>.

9. False; for example, the horizontal line $y = 2$ does not have an x-intercept.

10. True

11. True

12. False; the graph of $y = 5x$ contains the point $(1, 5)$ but not the point $(5, 1)$.

Exercise Set 3.3

2. x-intercept: $(-4, 0)$
y-intercept: $(0, 3)$

4. x-intercepts: $(-3, 0)$, $(3, 0)$
y-intercept: $(0, 5)$

6. *x*-intercepts: $(-4, 0)$, $(-1, 0)$, $(1, 0)$
   y-intercept: $(0, 4)$

8. *x*-intercepts: $(-3, 0)$, $(3, 0)$
   y-intercepts: $(0, 2)$, $(0, -2)$

10. 1; because the line must either cross the *x*-axis or the *y*-axis.

12. 4; because the circle could cross each axis two times.

14. $x - y = -4$
   $y = 0$, $x - 0 = -4$, $x = -4$
   $x = 0$, $0 - y = -4$, $y = 4$
   x-intercept: $(-4, 0)$; *y*-intercept: $(0, 4)$

x	*y*
-4	0
0	4

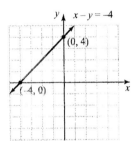

16. $x = 2y$
   $y = 0$, $x = 2(0)$, $x = 0$
   $x = 0$, $0 = 2y$, $y = 0$
   x-intercept: $(0, 0)$; *y*-intercept: $(0, 0)$
   $y = 2$, $x = 2(2)$, $x = 4$

x	*y*
0	0
4	2

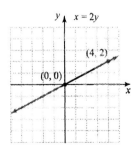

18. $x - 2y = -8$
   $y = 0$, $x - 2(0) = -8$, $x = -8$
   $x = 0$, $0 - 2y = -8$, $y = 4$
   x-intercept: $(-8, 0)$; *y*-intercept: $(0, 4)$

x	*y*
-8	0
0	4

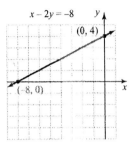

20. $2x + 3y = 6$
   $y = 0$, $2x + 3(0) = 6$, $x = 3$
   $x = 0$, $2(0) + 3y = 6$, $y = 2$
   x-intercept: $(3, 0)$; *y*-intercept: $(0, 2)$

x	*y*
3	0
0	2

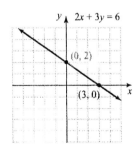

22. $y = -2x$
   $y = 0$, $0 = -2x$, $0 = x$
   $x = 0$, $y = -2(0)$, $y = 0$
   $x = 2$, $y = -2(2)$, $y = -4$
   x-intercept: $(0, 0)$; *y*-intercept: $(0, 0)$

x	*y*
0	0
2	-4

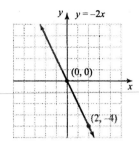

24. $y = 2x + 10$
$y = 0, 0 = 2x + 10, -10 = 2x, -5 = x$
$x = 0, y = 2(0) + 10, y = 10$
x-intercept: $(-5, 0)$; y-intercept: $(0, 10)$

x	y
-5	0
0	10

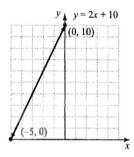

26. $y = 5$ for all values of x.

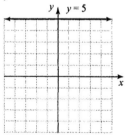

28. $x = 0$ for all values of y.

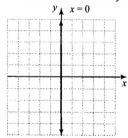

30. $x - 2 = 0$
$x = 2$ for all values of y.

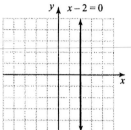

32. $y - 6 = 0$
$y = 6$ for all values of x.

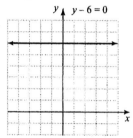

34. $x = -y$
x-intercept: $(0, 0)$; y-intercept: $(0, 0)$
Second point: $(5, -5)$

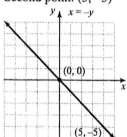

36. $x + 3y = 9$
x-intercept: $(9, 0)$; y-intercept: $(0, 3)$

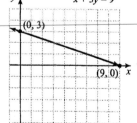

38. $4 = x - 3y$

x-intercept: $(4, 0)$; *y*-intercept: $\left(0, -\dfrac{4}{3}\right)$

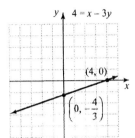

40. $-x + 9y = 10$

x-intercept: $(-10, 0)$; *y*-intercept: $\left(0, \dfrac{10}{9}\right)$

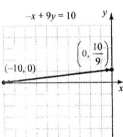

42. $x = -1\dfrac{3}{4}$ for all values of *y*.

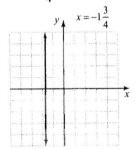

44. $y = 2\dfrac{1}{2}$ for all values of *x*.

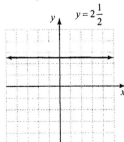

46. $y = -\dfrac{3}{5}x + 3$

x-intercept: $(5, 0)$; *y*-intercept: $(0, 3)$

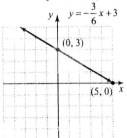

48. $9x - 6y + 3 = 0$

x-intercept: $\left(-\dfrac{1}{3}, 0\right)$; *y*-intercept: $\left(0, \dfrac{1}{2}\right)$

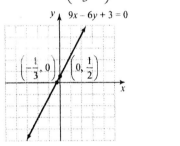

50. $y = 2x + 2$
The *y*-intercept is $(0, 2)$.
F

52. $x = 3$
This is a vertical line with an *x*-intercept of $(0, 3)$.
A

54. $y = -2x$
The *x*-intercept is $(0, 0)$ and the *y*-intercept is $(0, 0)$.
D

56. $\dfrac{4 - 5}{-1 - 0} = \dfrac{-1}{-1} = 1$

58. $\dfrac{12 - 3}{10 - 9} = \dfrac{9}{1} = 9$

60. $\dfrac{2 - 2}{3 - 5} = \dfrac{0}{-2} = 0$

62. $y = -78.1x + 491.8$

    a. Let $x = 0$ and solve for y.
$$y = -78.1(0) + 491.8 = 491.8$$
The y-intercept is $(0, 491.8)$.

    b. In 2000, the average price of a digital camera was $491.80.

64. $y = 0.2x + 5.42$

    a. $y = 0$
$$0 = 0.2x + 5.42$$
$$-5.42 = 0.2x$$
$$-27.1 = x$$
The x-intercept is $(-27.1, 0)$.

    b. 27 years before 2000, admission to movie theaters was free.

    c. Answers may vary

66. Parallel to $x = 5$ is vertical.
x-intercept is $(1, 0)$, so $x = 1$ for all values of y.
$x = 1$

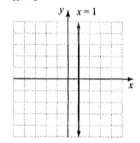

68. Answers may vary

70. Answers may vary

Section 3.4

Practice Exercises

1. If we let (x_1, y_1) be $(-4, 11)$, then $x_1 = -4$ and $y_1 = 11$. Also, let (x_2, y_2) be $(2, 5)$ so that $x_2 = 2$ and $y_2 = 5$.
$$m = \frac{y_2 - y_1}{x_2 - x_1} = \frac{5 - 11}{2 - (-4)} = \frac{-6}{6} = -1$$
The slope of the line is -1.

2. Let (x_1, y_1) be $(3, 1)$ and (x_2, y_2) be $(-3, -1)$.
$$m = \frac{y_2 - y_1}{x_2 - x_1} = \frac{-1 - 1}{-3 - 3} = \frac{-2}{-6} = \frac{1}{3}$$

3. $y = \dfrac{2}{3}x - 2$

The equation is in slope-intercept form,

$y = mx + b$. The coefficient of x, $\dfrac{2}{3}$, is the slope.

The constant term, -2, is the y-value of the y-intercept, $(0, -2)$.

4. Write the equation in slope-intercept form by solving the equation for y.
$$6x - y = 5$$
$$-y = -6x + 5$$
$$y = 6x - 5$$
The coefficient of x, 6, is the slope. The constant term, -5, is the y-value of the y-intercept, $(0, -5)$.

5. Write the equation in slope-intercept form by solving the equation for y.
$$5x + 2y = 8$$
$$2y = -5x + 8$$
$$\frac{2y}{2} = \frac{-5x}{2} + \frac{8}{2}$$
$$y = -\frac{5}{2}x + 4$$

The coefficient of x, $-\dfrac{5}{2}$, is the slope, and the y-intercept is $(0, 4)$.

6. Recall that $y = 3$ is a horizontal line. Two ordered pair solutions of $y = 3$ and $(1, 3)$ and $(3, 3)$.
$$m = \frac{y_2 - y_1}{x_2 - x_1} = \frac{3 - 3}{3 - 1} = \frac{0}{2} = 0$$
The slope of the line $y = 3$ is 0.

7. Recall that the graph of $x = -4$ is a vertical line. Two ordered pair solutions of $x = -4$ and $(-4, 1)$ and $(-4, 3)$.
$$m = \frac{y_2 - y_1}{x_2 - x_1} = \frac{3 - 1}{-4 - (-4)} = \frac{2}{0}$$
The slope of the vertical line $x = -4$ is undefined.

8. a. The slope of the line $y = -5x + 1$ is -5. We solve the second equation for y.

$$x - 5y = 10$$
$$-5y = -x + 10$$
$$\frac{-5y}{-5} = \frac{-x}{-5} + \frac{10}{-5}$$
$$y = \frac{1}{5}x - 2$$

The slope of the second line is $\frac{1}{5}$. Since the product of the slopes is $\frac{1}{5}(-5) = -1$, the lines are perpendicular.

b. Solve each equation for y.

$$x + y = 11 \qquad\qquad 2x + y = 11$$
$$y = -x + 11 \qquad\qquad y = -2x + 11$$

The slopes are -1 and -2. The slopes are not the same, and their product is not -1. Thus, the lines are neither parallel nor perpendicular.

c. Solve each equation for y.

$$2x + 3y = 21 \qquad\qquad 6y = -4x - 2$$
$$3y = -2x + 21 \qquad\qquad \frac{6y}{6} = \frac{-4x}{6} - \frac{2}{6}$$
$$\frac{3y}{3} = \frac{-2x}{3} + \frac{21}{3} \qquad\qquad y = -\frac{2}{3}x - \frac{1}{3}$$
$$y = -\frac{2}{3}x + 7$$

The slopes are $-\frac{2}{3}$ and $-\frac{2}{3}$. Since the lines have the same slope and different y-intercepts, they are parallel.

9. $\text{grade} = \dfrac{\text{rise}}{\text{run}} = \dfrac{1794}{7176} = 0.25 = 25\%$

The grade is 25%.

10. Use $(2, 2)$ and $(6, 5)$ to calculate slope.

$$m = \frac{5-2}{6-2} = \frac{3}{4} = \frac{0.75 \text{ dollar}}{1 \text{ pound}}$$

The Wash-n-Fold charges $0.75 per pound of laundry.

Calculator Explorations

1. $y_1 = 3.8x$
$y_2 = 3.8x - 3$
$y_3 = 3.8x + 9$

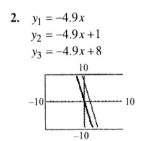

2. $y_1 = -4.9x$
$y_2 = -4.9x + 1$
$y_3 = -4.9x + 8$

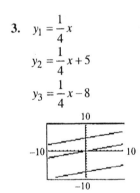

3. $y_1 = \dfrac{1}{4}x$
$y_2 = \dfrac{1}{4}x + 5$
$y_3 = \dfrac{1}{4}x - 8$

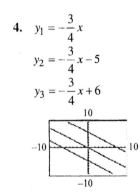

4. $y_1 = -\dfrac{3}{4}x$
$y_2 = -\dfrac{3}{4}x - 5$
$y_3 = -\dfrac{3}{4}x + 6$

Vocabulary and Readiness Check

1. The measure of the steepness or tilt of a line is called <u>slope</u>.

2. If an equation is written in the form $y = mx + b$, the value of the letter m is the value of the slope of the graph.

3. The slope of a horizontal line is $\underline{0}$.

4. The slope of a vertical line is <u>undefined</u>.

5. If the graph of a line moves upward from left to right, the line has <u>positive</u> slope.

6. If the graph of a line moves downward from left to right, the line has <u>negative</u> slope.

7. Given two points of a line, slope $= \dfrac{\text{change in } \underline{y}}{\text{change in } \underline{x}}$.

8. The line goes down. The slope is negative.

9. The line goes up. The slope is positive.

10. The line is vertical. The slope is undefined.

11. The line is horizontal. The slope is 0.

12. The slope is positive. The line is "upward."

13. The slope is negative. The line is "downward."

14. The slope is 0. The line is horizontal.

15. The slope is undefined. The line is vertical.

Exercise Set 3.4

2. $(3, 1)$ and $(2, 6)$
$$m = \frac{y_2 - y_1}{x_2 - x_1} = \frac{6-1}{2-3} = \frac{5}{-1} = -5$$

4. $(6, -6)$ and $(6, 2)$
$$m = \frac{y_2 - y_1}{x_2 - x_1} = \frac{2-(-6)}{6-6} = \frac{8}{0} \text{ is undefined.}$$

6. $(4, -3)$ and $(2, 2)$
$$m = \frac{y_2 - y_1}{x_2 - x_1} = \frac{2-(-3)}{2-4} = -\frac{5}{2}$$

8. $(0, 13)$ and $(-4, 13)$
$$m = \frac{y_2 - y_1}{x_2 - x_1} = \frac{13-13}{-4-0} = \frac{0}{-4} = 0$$

10. $(1, -2)$ and $(3, 3)$
$$m = \frac{y_2 - y_1}{x_2 - x_1} = \frac{3-(-2)}{3-1} = \frac{5}{2}$$

12. $(-2, -1)$ and $(1, -1)$
$$m = \frac{y_2 - y_1}{x_2 - x_1} = \frac{-1-(-1)}{1-(-2)} = \frac{0}{3} = 0$$

14. $(-3, 3)$ and $(1, -4)$
$$m = \frac{y_2 - y_1}{x_2 - x_1} = \frac{-4-3}{1-(-3)} = -\frac{7}{4}$$

16. The slope of line 1 is positive, and the slope of line 2 is negative. Thus, line 1 has the greater slope.

18. Line 1 has a positive slope and line 2 has a slope of 0, so line 1 has the greater slope.

20. A horizontal line has $m = 0$.
A

22. $(0, 0)$ and $(1, 3)$
$$m = \frac{y_2 - y_1}{x_2 - x_1} = \frac{3-0}{1-0} = \frac{3}{1} = 3$$
C

24. $(-2, 1)$ and $(2, -2)$
$$m = \frac{y_2 - y_1}{x_2 - x_1} = \frac{-2-1}{2-(-2)} = \frac{-3}{4} = -\frac{3}{4}$$
F

26. $y = 4$ is a horizontal line, so it has a slope $m = 0$.

28. $x = 2$ is a vertical line, so it has an undefined slope.

30. $y = -11$ is a horizontal line, so it has a slope $m = 0$.

32. $x = 0$ is a vertical line, so it has an undefined slope.

34. $y = -2x + 6$
The equation is in slope-intercept form. The coefficient of x, -2, is the slope.

36. $y = -7.6x - 0.1$
The equation is in slope-intercept form. The coefficient of x, -7.6, is the slope.

38. Solve for y.

$-5x + y = 10$

$\qquad y = 5x + 10$

The coefficient of x, 5, is the slope.

40. Solve for y.

$3x - 5y = 1$

$\qquad -5y = -3x + 1$

$\qquad \dfrac{-5y}{-5} = \dfrac{-3x}{-5} + \dfrac{1}{-5}$

$\qquad y = \dfrac{3}{5}x - \dfrac{1}{5}$

The coefficient of x, $\dfrac{3}{5}$, is the slope.

42. The graph of $y = -2$ is a horizontal line. The slope is 0.

44. Solve for y.

$\qquad x = -4y$

$-\dfrac{1}{4}x = y$ or $y = -\dfrac{1}{4}x$

The coefficient of x, $-\dfrac{1}{4}$, is the slope.

46. The graph of $x = 5$ is a vertical line. The slope is undefined.

48. Solve for y.

$-4x - 7y = 9$

$\qquad -7y = 4x + 9$

$\qquad \dfrac{-7y}{-7} = \dfrac{4x}{-7} + \dfrac{9}{-7}$

$\qquad y = -\dfrac{4}{7}x - \dfrac{9}{7}$

The coefficient of x, $-\dfrac{4}{7}$, is the slope.

50. Solve for y.

$24x - 3y = 5.7$

$\qquad -3y = -24x + 5.7$

$\qquad \dfrac{-3y}{-3} = \dfrac{-24x}{-3} + \dfrac{5.7}{-3}$

$\qquad y = 8x - 1.9$

The coefficient of x, 8, is the slope.

52. $y = \dfrac{1}{5}x + 20,\ y = -\dfrac{1}{5}x$

The slopes are $\dfrac{1}{5}$ and $-\dfrac{1}{5}$. The slopes are not the same, and their product is not -1. The lines are neither parallel nor perpendicular.

54. The slope of $y = 4x - 2$ is 4. Solve the second equation for y.

$4x + y = 5$

$\qquad y = -4x + 5$

The slope is -4. The slopes are not the same, and their product is not -1. The lines are neither parallel nor perpendicular.

56. Solve the equations for y.

$\begin{aligned} -x + 2y &= -2 & 2x &= 4y + 3 \\ 2y &= x - 2 & 2x - 3 &= 4y \\ \dfrac{2y}{2} &= \dfrac{x}{2} - \dfrac{2}{2} & \dfrac{2x}{4} - \dfrac{3}{4} &= \dfrac{4y}{4} \\ y &= \dfrac{1}{2}x - 1 & y &= \dfrac{1}{2}x - \dfrac{3}{4} \end{aligned}$

The lines have the same slope, $\dfrac{1}{2}$, but different y-intercepts. The lines are parallel.

58. Solve the equations for y.

$\begin{aligned} 10 + 3x &= 5y & 5x + 3y &= 1 \\ \dfrac{10}{5} + \dfrac{3x}{5} &= \dfrac{5y}{5} & 3y &= -5x + 1 \\ y &= \dfrac{3}{5}x + 2 & \dfrac{3y}{3} &= -\dfrac{5x}{3} + \dfrac{1}{3} \\ & & y &= -\dfrac{5}{3}x + \dfrac{1}{3} \end{aligned}$

The slopes are $\dfrac{3}{5}$ and $-\dfrac{5}{3}$. Their product is -1, so the lines are perpendicular.

60. $\text{pitch} = \dfrac{5}{10} = \dfrac{1}{2}$

62. $\text{grade} = \dfrac{\text{rise}}{\text{run}} = \dfrac{16}{100} = 0.16 = 16\%$

64. $\text{slope} = \dfrac{\text{rise}}{\text{run}} = \dfrac{0.25}{12} \approx 0.02$

66. $\text{slope} = \dfrac{\text{rise}}{\text{run}} = \dfrac{1}{12} = 0.0825 \approx 8.3\%$

68. Use (1996, 4) and (2004, 8.8) to calculate slope.

$$m = \frac{8.8 - 4}{2004 - 1996} = \frac{4.8}{8} = \frac{0.6 \text{ prescription}}{1 \text{ year}}$$

Every year there is 0.6 more prescription for ADHD written per 100 population under 18 years of age.

70. Use (10,000, 4800) and (40,000, 19,200) to calculate slope.

$$ml = \frac{19,200 - 4800}{40,000 - 10,000} = \frac{14,400}{30,000} = \frac{0.48 \text{ dollar}}{1 \text{ mile}}$$

It costs $0.48 per 1 mile to own and operate a standard pickup truck.

72. $y - 7 = -9(x - 6)$
$y - 7 = -9x + 54$
$y = -9x + 61$

74. $y - (-3) = 4(x - (-5))$
$y + 3 = 4(x + 5)$
$y + 3 = 4x + 20$
$y = 4x + 17$

76. (6, −2) and (1, 4)

$$m = \frac{y_2 - y_1}{x_2 - x_1} = \frac{4 - (-2)}{1 - 6} = \frac{6}{-5} = -\frac{6}{5}$$

  a. $m = -\dfrac{6}{5}$

  b. $m = \dfrac{5}{6}$

78. (6, −1) and (−4, −10)

$$m = \frac{y_2 - y_1}{x_2 - x_1} = \frac{-10 - (-1)}{-4 - 6} = \frac{-9}{-10} = \frac{9}{10}$$

  a. $m = \dfrac{9}{10}$

  b. $m = -\dfrac{10}{9}$

80. No; answers may vary

82. Answers may vary

84. In 2003, the average fuel economy was approximately 29.0 miles per gallon. In 2004, it was approximately 28.7 miles per gallon. The change was 28.7 − 29.0 or −0.3 mile per gallon. This is a decrease of 0.3 mile per gallon.

86. The highest point on the graph corresponds to the year 2003. The average fuel economy was approximately 29.0 miles per gallon.

88. The line segments from 1996 to 1997 and from 1997 to 1998 appear to have the same slope and are less steep than any other segment with positive slope.

90. $\text{pitch} = \dfrac{\text{rise}}{\text{run}}$

$$\frac{2}{5} = \frac{4}{\frac{x}{2}}$$

$$2\left(\frac{x}{2}\right) = 20$$

$$x = 20$$

92. a. (2006, 15,722) and (2002, 14,774)

  b.
$$m = \frac{y_2 - y_1}{x_2 - x_1}$$
$$= \frac{14,774 - 15,722}{2002 - 2006}$$
$$= \frac{-948}{-4}$$
$$= 237$$

  c. For the years 2002 through 2006, the number of kidney transplants increased at a rate of 237 per year.

94. (1, 3), (2, 1), (−4, 0) and (−3, −2)

$$m_1 = \frac{1 - 3}{2 - 1} = -2, \quad m_2 = \frac{1 - (-2)}{2 - (-3)} = \frac{3}{5}$$

$$m_3 = \frac{-2 - 0}{-3 - (-4)} = -2, \quad m_4 = \frac{3 - 0}{1 - (-4)} = \frac{3}{5}$$

$m_1 = m_3$ and $m_2 = m_4$, so the opposite sides are parallel. Therefore the quadrilateral is a parallelogram.

96. (−3.8, 1.2) and (−2.2, 4.5)

$$m = \frac{4.5 - 1.2}{-2.2 - (-3.8)} = \frac{3.3}{1.6} = 2.0625$$

98. $(14.3, -10.1)$ and $(9.8, -2.9)$

$$m = \frac{-2.9 - (-10.1)}{9.8 - 14.3} = \frac{7.2}{-4.5} = -1.6$$

100. $y = \frac{1}{2}x$

$y = 3x$

$y = 5x$

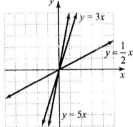

The line becomes steeper.

Integrated Review

1. $(0, 0)$ and $(2, 4)$

$$m = \frac{y_2 - y_1}{x_2 - x_1} = \frac{4 - 0}{2 - 0} = \frac{4}{2} = 2$$

2. Horizontal line, $m = 0$

3. $(0, 1)$ and $(3, -1)$

$$m = \frac{y_2 - y_1}{x_2 - x_1} = \frac{-1 - 1}{3 - 0} = -\frac{2}{3}$$

4. Vertical line, slope is undefined.

5. $y = -2x$

$m = -2, b = 0$

x	y
0	0
1	-2
-1	2

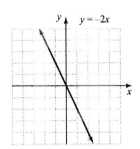

6. $x + y = 3$

$y = -x + 3$

$m = -1, b = 3$

x	y
0	3
3	0
1	2

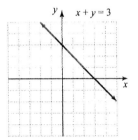

7. $x = -1$ for all values of y.
Vertical line; slope is undefined.

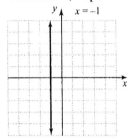

8. $y = 4$ for all values of x.
Horizontal line; $m = 0$

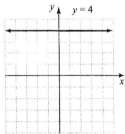

9. $x - 2y = 6$

$-2y = -x + 6$

$y = \frac{1}{2}x - 3$

$m = \frac{1}{2}, b = -3$

x	y
0	−3
2	−2
4	−1

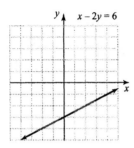

10. $y = 3x + 2$
$m = 3, b = 2$

x	y
0	2
−1	−1
−2	−4

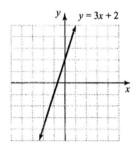

11. $5x + 3y = 15$

x	y
0	5
3	0

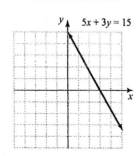

12. $2x - 4y = 8$

x	y
0	−2
4	0

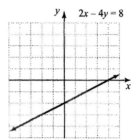

13. The slope of the first line is $-\dfrac{1}{5}$. Solve the second equation for y.
$$3x = -15y$$
$$\frac{3x}{-15} = \frac{-15y}{-15}$$
$$y = -\frac{1}{5}x$$

The slope of the second line is also $-\dfrac{1}{5}$. Since the lines have the same slope but different y-intercepts, the lines are parallel.

14. Solve the equations for y.

$$x - y = \frac{1}{2} \qquad\qquad 3x - y = \frac{1}{2}$$
$$-y = -x + \frac{1}{2} \qquad -y = -3x + \frac{1}{2}$$
$$y = x - \frac{1}{2} \qquad\qquad y = 3x - \frac{1}{2}$$

The slopes are 1 and 3. Since the slopes are not equal and their product is not −1, the lines are neither parallel nor perpendicular.

15. a. Let $x = 0$.
$y = -75(0) + 1650 = 1650$
The y-intercept is (0, 1650).

b. In 2002, there were 1650 million admissions to movie theaters in the United States.

c. The equation is in slope-intercept form. The coefficient of x, −75, is the slope.

d. For the years 2002 through 2005, the number of movie theater admissions decreased at a rate of 75 million per year.

16. a. Let $x = 9$.
$$y = 3.3(9) - 3.1 = 29.7 - 3.1 = 26.6$$
The ordered pair is (9, 26.6).

b. In 2009, the predicted revenue for online advertising is $26.6 billion.

Section 3.5

Practice Exercises

1. y-intercept: (0, 7); slope: $\dfrac{1}{2}$

Let $m = \dfrac{1}{2}$ and $b = 7$.
$$y = mx + b$$
$$y = \dfrac{1}{2}x + 7$$

2. $y = \dfrac{2}{3}x - 5$

The slope is $\dfrac{2}{3}$, and the y-intercept is (0, −5).

We plot (0, −5). From this point, we move up 2 units and then right 3 units. We stop at the point (3, −3).

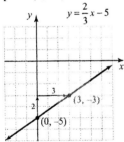

3. Solve the equation for y.
$$3x - y = 2$$
$$-y = -3x + 2$$
$$y = 3x - 2$$

The slope is 3, and the y-intercept is (0, −2). We plot (0, −2). From this point, we move up 3 units and then right 1 unit. We stop at the point (1, 1).

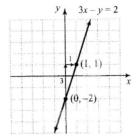

4. Line passing through (2, 3) with slope 4
$$y - y_1 = m(x - x_1)$$
$$y - 3 = 4(x - 2)$$
$$y - 3 = 4x - 8$$
$$-4x + y = -5$$
$$4x - y = 5$$

5. Line through (−1, 6) and (3, 1)
$$m = \frac{1 - 6}{3 - (-1)} = \frac{-5}{4} = -\frac{5}{4}$$

Use the slope $-\dfrac{5}{4}$ and the point (3, 1).
$$y - y_1 = m(x - x_1)$$
$$y - 1 = -\frac{5}{4}(x - 3)$$
$$4(y - 1) = 4\left(-\frac{5}{4}\right)(x - 3)$$
$$4y - 4 = -5(x - 3)$$
$$4y - 4 = -5x + 15$$
$$5x + 4y = 19$$

6. The equation of a vertical line can be written in the form $x = c$, so an equation for a vertical line passing through (3, −2) is $x = 3$.

7. Since the graph of $y = -2$ is a horizontal line, any line parallel to it is also vertical. The equation of a horizontal line can be written in the form $y = c$. An equation for the horizontal line passing through (4, 3) is $y = 3$.

8. a. Write two ordered pairs, (30, 150,000) and (50, 120,000).
$$m = \frac{120,000 - 150,000}{50 - 30}$$
$$= \frac{-30,000}{20}$$
$$= -1500$$

Use the slope −1500 and the point (30, 150,000).

$$y - y_1 = m(x - x_1)$$
$$y - 150,000 = -1500(x - 30)$$
$$y - 150,000 = -1500x + 45,000$$
$$y = -1500x + 195,000$$

b. Find y when $x = 60$.
$y = -1500x + 195,000$
$y = -1500(60) + 195,000$
$y = -90,000 + 195,000$
$y = 105,000$
To sell 60 condos per month, the price should be $105,000.

Calculator Explorations

1. $y_1 = x, \ y_2 = 6x, \ y_3 = -6x$

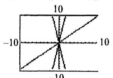

2. $y_1 = -x, \ y_2 = -5x, \ y_3 = -10x$

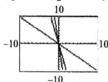

3. $y_1 = \dfrac{1}{2}x + 2, \ y_2 = \dfrac{3}{4}x + 2, \ y_3 = x + 2$

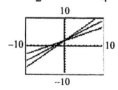

4. $y_1 = x + 1, \ y_2 = \dfrac{5}{4}x + 1, \ y_3 = \dfrac{5}{2}x + 1$

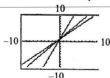

5. $y_1 = -7x + 5, \ y_2 = 7x + 5$

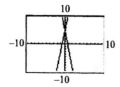

6. $y_1 = 3x - 1, \ y_2 = -3x - 1$

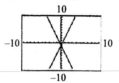

Vocabulary and Readiness Check

1. The form $y = mx + b$ is called <u>slope-intercept</u> form. When a linear equation in two variables is written in this form, <u>m</u> is the slope of its graph and $(0, \underline{b})$ is its y-intercept.

2. The form $y - y_1 = m(x - x_1)$ is called <u>point-slope</u> form. When a linear equation in two variables is written in this form, <u>m</u> is the slope of its graph and $\underline{(x_1, \ y_1)}$ is a point on the graph.

3. $y - 7 = 4(x + 3)$; <u>point-slope</u> form

4. $5x - 9y = 11$; <u>standard</u> form

5. $y = \dfrac{1}{2}$; <u>horizontal</u> line

6. $x = -17$; <u>vertical</u> line

7. $y = \dfrac{3}{4}x - \dfrac{1}{3}$; <u>slope-intercept</u> form

Exercise Set 3.5

2. $m = -3, \ b = -3$
$y = mx + b$
$y = -3x + (-3)$
$y = -3x - 3$

4. $m = 2, \ b = \dfrac{3}{4}$
$y = mx + b$
$y = 2x + \dfrac{3}{4}$

6. $m = -\dfrac{4}{5}, \ b = 0$
$y = mx + b$
$y = -\dfrac{4}{5}x + 0$
$y = -\dfrac{4}{5}x$

8. $m = 0, b = -2$
$y = mx + b$
$y = 0x + (-2)$
$y = -2$

10. $m = \dfrac{1}{2}, b = -\dfrac{1}{3}$
$y = mx + b$
$y = \dfrac{1}{2}x + \left(-\dfrac{1}{3}\right)$
$y = \dfrac{1}{2}x - \dfrac{1}{3}$

12. $y = -4x - 1$

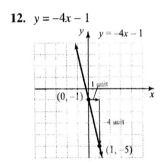

14. $y = \dfrac{1}{4}x - 3$

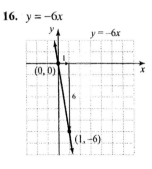

16. $y = -6x$

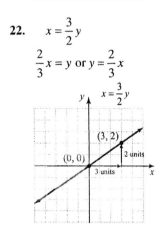

18. $-3x + y = 2$
$y = 3x + 2$

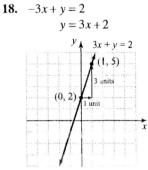

20. $3x - 4y = 4$
$-4y = -3x + 4$
$y = \dfrac{3}{4}x - 1$

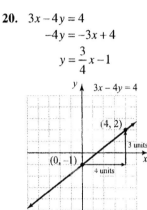

22. $x = \dfrac{3}{2}y$
$\dfrac{2}{3}x = y$ or $y = \dfrac{2}{3}x$

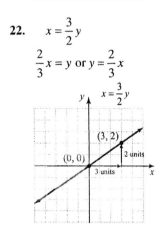

24. $m = 4; (1, 3)$
$y - y_1 = m(x - x_1)$
$y - 3 = 4(x - 1)$
$y - 3 = 4x - 4$
$-4x + y = -1$
$4x - y = 1$

26. $m = -2; (-11, -12)$
$y - y_1 = m(x - x_1)$
$y - (-12) = -2(x - (-11))$
$y + 12 = -2x - 22$
$2x + y = -34$

28. $m = \dfrac{2}{3}$; $(-8, 9)$

$$y - y_1 = m(x - x_1)$$
$$y - 9 = \dfrac{2}{3}(x - (-8))$$
$$3(y - 9) = 2(x + 8)$$
$$3y - 27 = 2x + 16$$
$$-2x + 3y = 43$$
$$2x - 3y = -43$$

30. $m = -\dfrac{1}{5}$; $(4, 0)$

$$y - y_1 = m(x - x_1)$$
$$y - 0 = -\dfrac{1}{5}(x - 4)$$
$$5y = -1(x - 4)$$
$$5y = -x + 4$$
$$x + 5y = 4$$

32. $(6, 2)$ and $(8, 8)$

$$m = \dfrac{y_2 - y_1}{x_2 - x_1} = \dfrac{8 - 2}{8 - 6} = \dfrac{6}{2} = 3$$
$$m = 3; \ (6, 2)$$
$$y - y_1 = m(x - x_1)$$
$$y - 2 = 3(x - 6)$$
$$y - 2 = 3x - 18$$
$$-3x + y = -16$$
$$3x - y = 16$$

34. $(-4, 0)$ and $(6, -1)$

$$m = \dfrac{y_2 - y_1}{x_2 - x_1} = \dfrac{-1 - 0}{6 - (-4)} = \dfrac{-1}{10}$$
$$m = -\dfrac{1}{10}; \ (-4, 0)$$
$$y - y_1 = m(x - x_1)$$
$$y - 0 = -\dfrac{1}{10}(x - (-4))$$
$$10y = -x - 4$$
$$x + 10y = -4$$

36. $(7, 10)$ and $(-1, -1)$

$$m = \dfrac{y_2 - y_1}{x_2 - x_1} = \dfrac{-1 - 10}{-1 - 7} = \dfrac{-11}{-8} = \dfrac{11}{8}$$
$$m = \dfrac{11}{8}; \ (7, 10)$$

$$y - y_1 = m(x - x_1)$$
$$y - 10 = \dfrac{11}{8}(x - 7)$$
$$8(y - 10) = 11(x - 7)$$
$$8y - 80 = 11x - 77$$
$$-11x + 8y = 3$$
$$11x - 8y = -3$$

38. $(0, 0)$ and $\left(-\dfrac{1}{2}, \dfrac{1}{3}\right)$

$$m = \dfrac{y_2 - y_1}{x_2 - x_1} = \dfrac{\frac{1}{3} - 0}{-\frac{1}{2} - 0} = \dfrac{1}{3}\left(-\dfrac{2}{1}\right) = -\dfrac{2}{3}$$
$$m = -\dfrac{2}{3}; \ (0, 0)$$
$$y - y_1 = m(x - x_1)$$
$$y - 0 = -\dfrac{2}{3}(x - 0)$$
$$3y = -2x$$
$$2x + 3y = 0$$

40. Horizontal line, point $(1, 4)$
$$y = c$$
$$y = 4$$

42. Vertical line, point $(-1, 3)$
$$x = c$$
$$x = -1$$

44. Horizontal line, point $\left(\dfrac{2}{7}, 0\right)$

$$y = c$$
$$y = 0$$

46. $y = 5$ is horizontal.
Perpendicular to $y = 5$ is vertical; $x = c$.
Point $(1, 2)$
$$x = 1$$

48. $y = -4$ is horizontal.
Parallel to $y = -4$ is horizontal; $y = c$.
Point $(0, -3)$
$$y = -3$$

50. $x = 7$ is vertical.
Perpendicular to $x = 7$ is horizontal; $y = c$.
Point $(-5, 0)$
$$y = 0$$

52. $m = \frac{5}{7}$; $(0, -3)$

$y = mx + b$

$y = \frac{5}{7}x - 3$

54. $(5, -6)$ and $(-6, 5)$

$m = \frac{y_2 - y_1}{x_2 - x_1} = \frac{5 - (-6)}{-6 - 5} = \frac{11}{-11} = -1$

$m = -1$; $(5, -6)$

$y - y_1 = m(x - x_1)$

$y - (-6) = -1(x - 5)$

$y + 6 = -x + 5$

$y = -x - 1$

56. Slope 0 is horizontal, point $(6.7, 12.1)$

$y = c$

$y = 12.1$

58. $m = 5$; $(6, -8)$

$y - y_1 = m(x - x_1)$

$y - (-8) = 5(x - 6)$

$y + 8 = 5x - 30$

$y = 5x - 38$

60. $m = -2$, $b = -4$

$y = mx + b$

$y = -2x - 4$

62. y-axis is vertical.

Parallel to y-axis is vertical; $x = c$.

Point $(1, -5)$

$x = 1$

64. $(4, 7)$ and $(0, 0)$

$m = \frac{y_2 - y_1}{x_2 - x_1} = \frac{0 - 7}{0 - 4} = \frac{-7}{-4} = \frac{7}{4}$

$m = \frac{7}{4}$; $(0, 0)$

$y - y_1 = m(x - x_1)$

$y - 0 = \frac{7}{4}(x - 0)$

$y = \frac{7}{4}x$

66. x-axis is horizontal.

Perpendicular to x-axis is vertical; $x = c$.

Point $(0, 12)$

$x = 0$

68. $m = -\frac{3}{5}$; $(4, 4)$

$y - y_1 = m(x - x_1)$

$y - 4 = -\frac{3}{5}(x - 4)$

$y - 4 = -\frac{3}{5}x + \frac{12}{5}$

$y = -\frac{3}{5}x + \frac{12}{5} + 4$

$y = -\frac{3}{5}x + \frac{32}{5}$

70. a. $(1, 30{,}000)$ and $(4, 66{,}000)$

$m = \frac{y_2 - y_1}{x_2 - x_1}$

$= \frac{66{,}000 - 30{,}000}{4 - 1}$

$= \frac{36{,}000}{3}$

$= 12{,}000$

$m = 12{,}000$; $(1, 30{,}000)$

$p - p_1 = m(t - t_1)$

$p - 30{,}000 = 12{,}000(t - 1)$

$p - 30{,}000 = 12{,}000t - 12{,}000$

$p = 12{,}000t + 18{,}000$

b. If $t = 7$, then

$p = 12{,}000(7) + 18{,}000 = \$102{,}000$.

72. a. Use $(0, 457)$ and $(10, 935)$.

$m = \frac{935 - 457}{10 - 0} = \frac{478}{10} = 47.8$

$b = 457$

$y = mx + b$

$y = 47.8x + 457$

b. Let $x = 2010 - 1996 = 14$.

$y = 47.8(14) + 457 = 669.2 + 457 = 1126.2$

We predict there will be 1126.2 thousand, or 1,126,200, eating establishments in 2010.

74. a. Use $(0, 152)$ and $(4, 150)$.

$m = \frac{150 - 152}{4 - 0} = \frac{-2}{4} = -0.5$

$b = 152$

$y = mx + b$

$y = -0.5x + 152$

b. Let $x = 2011 - 2001 = 10$.
$y = -0.5(10) + 152 = -5 + 152 = 147$
We predict there will be 147 thousand apparel and accessory stores in 2011.

76. a. The ordered pairs are $(0, 28.7)$ and $(5, 34.5)$.

b. $m = \dfrac{34.5 - 28.7}{5 - 0} = \dfrac{5.8}{5} = 1.16$
$b = 28.7$
$y = mx + b$
$y = 1.16x + 28.7$

c. Let $x = 2004 - 2002 = 2$.
$y = 1.16(2) + 28.7 = 2.32 + 28.7 = 31.02$
We estimate that OPEC produced 31.02 million barrels of crude oil per day in 2004.

78. a. The ordered pairs are $(0, 9.9)$ and $(3, 26.9)$.

b. $m = \dfrac{26.9 - 9.9}{3 - 0} = \dfrac{17}{3}$
$b = 9.9$
$y = mx + b$
$y = \dfrac{17}{3}x + 9.9$

c. Let $x = 2011 - 2002 = 9$.
$y = \dfrac{17}{3}(9) + 9.9 = 51 + 9.9 = 60.9$

We predict that 60.9 million electronic bills will be delivered and paid in 2011.

80. If $x = 5$, then
$x^2 - 3x + 1 = (5)^2 - 3(5) + 1 = 25 - 15 + 1 = 11$

82. If $x = -3$, then
$x^2 - 3x + 1 = (-3)^2 - 3(-3) + 1 = 9 + 9 + 1 = 19$

84. No

86. Yes

88. Answers may vary

90. $y = -2x + 3$, $m_1 = -2$

a. Parallel: $m_2 = m_1 = -2$; $(4, 0)$
$y - y_1 = m_2(x - x_1)$
$y - 0 = -2(x - 4)$
$y - 0 = -2x + 8$
$2x + y = 8$

b. Perpendicular: $m_2 = -\dfrac{1}{m_1} = \dfrac{1}{2}$; $(4, 0)$
$y - y_1 = m_2(x - x_1)$
$y - 0 = \dfrac{1}{2}(x - 4)$
$2(y - 0) = 1(x - 4)$
$2y - 0 = x - 4$
$-x + 2y = -4$
$x - 2y = 4$

92. $x + 3y = 6 \Rightarrow y = -\dfrac{1}{3}x + 2$, $m_1 = -\dfrac{1}{3}$

a. Parallel: $m_2 = m_1 = -\dfrac{1}{3}$; $(-2, 4)$
$y - y_1 = m_2(x - x_1)$
$y - 4 = -\dfrac{1}{3}[x - (-2)]$
$3y - 12 = -x - 2$
$x + 3y = 10$

b. Perpendicular: $m_2 = -\dfrac{1}{m_1} = 3$; $(-2, 4)$
$y - y_1 = m_2(x - x_1)$
$y - 4 = 3[x - (-2)]$
$y - 4 = 3x + 6$
$3x - y = -10$

Section 3.6

Practice Exercises

1. The domain is the set of all x-values $\{0, 1, 5\}$.
The range is the set of all y-values: $\{-2, 0, 3, 4\}$.

2. a. $\{(4, 1), (3, -2), (8, 5), (-5, 3)\}$
Each x-value is assigned to only one y-value, so this set of ordered pairs is a function.

b. $\{(1, 2), (-4, 3), (0, 8), (1, 4)\}$
The x-value 1 is assigned to two y-values, 2 and 4, so this set of ordered pairs is not a function.

3. a. This is the graph of the relation $\{(-2, 1), (3, -3), (3, 2)\}$. The x-coordinate 3 is paired with two y-coordinates, -3 and 2, so this is not the graph of a function.

b. This is the graph of the relation $\{(-2, 1), (0, 1), (1, -3), (3, 2)\}$. Each x-coordinate has exactly one y-coordinate, so this is the graph of a function.

4. a. This is the graph of a function since no vertical line will intersect this graph more than once.

b. This is the graph of a function since no vertical line will intersect this graph more than once.

c. This is the graph of a function since no vertical line will intersect this graph more than once.

d. This is not the graph of a function. Vertical lines can be drawn that intersect the graph in two points. An example of one is shown.

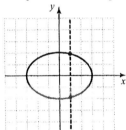

5. a. $y = 2x$ is a function because its graph is a nonvertical line.

b. $y = -3x - 1$ is a function because its graph is a nonvertical line.

c. $y = 8$ is a function because its graph is a nonvertical line.

d. $x = 2$ is not a function because its graph is a vertical line.

6. a. Since June is the sixth month, we look for 6 on the horizontal axis. From this point, we move vertically upward until the graph is reached. From the point on the graph, we move horizontally to the left to the vertical axis. The vertical axis there reads about 69°F.

b. We find 40°F on the temperature axis and move horizontally to the right. We eventually reach the point corresponding to 11, or November.

c. Yes, this is the graph of a function. It passes the vertical line test.

7. $h(x) = x^2 + 5$

a. $h(2) = 2^2 + 5 = 4 + 5 = 9$
$(2, 9)$

b. $h(-5) = (-5)^2 + 5 = 25 + 5 = 30$
$(-5, 30)$

c. $h(0) = 0^2 + 5 = 0 + 5 = 5$
$(0, 5)$

8. a. $h(x) = 6x + 3$
In this function, x can be any real number. The domain of $h(x)$ is the set of all real numbers, or $(-\infty, \infty)$ in interval notation.

b. $f(x) = \dfrac{1}{x^2}$
Recall that we cannot divide by 0 so that the domain of $f(x)$ is the set of all real numbers except 0. In interval notation, we write $(-\infty, 0) \cup (0, \infty)$.

9. a.

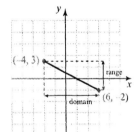

The domain is $[-4, 6]$.
The range is $[-2, 3]$.

b.

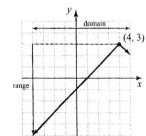

The domain is $(-\infty, \infty)$.
The range is $(-\infty, 3]$.

Vocabulary and Readiness Check

1. A set of ordered pairs is called a <u>relation</u>.

2. A set of ordered pairs that assigns to each
   x-value exactly one y-value is called a <u>function</u>.

3. The set of all y-coordinates of a relation is called
   the <u>range</u>.

4. The set of all x-coordinates of a relation is called
   the <u>domain</u>.

5. All linear equations are functions except those
   whose graphs are <u>vertical</u> lines.

6. All linear equations are functions except those
   whose equations are of the form <u>$x = c$</u>.

7. If $f(3) = 7$, the corresponding ordered pair is
   <u>(3, 7)</u>.

8. The domain of $f(x) = x + 5$ is <u>$(-\infty, \infty)$</u>.

Exercise Set 3.6

2. $\{(3, -6), (1, 4), (-2, -2)\}$
   Domain: $\{-2, 1, 3\}$
   Range: $\{-6, -2, 4\}$

4. $\{(5, 0), (5, -3), (5, 4), (5, 3)\}$
   Domain: $\{5\}$
   Range: $\{-3, 0, 3, 4\}$

6. Every point has a unique x-value: it is a function.

8. Two points have the same x-value: it is not a
   function.

10. Yes; no two points have the same x-coordinate.

12. No; two points have x-coordinate -2.

14. Yes; no vertical line can be drawn that intersects
    the graph more than once.

16. No; there are many vertical lines that intersect
    the graph twice, $x = -4$, for example.

18. Yes; $y = x - 1$ is a non-vertical line.

20. Yes; $2x - 3y = 9$ is a non-vertical line.

22. No; $x = 3$ is a vertical line.

24. Yes; $y = -9$ is a non-vertical line.

26. Yes; there is only one value of y for each value
    of x.

28. The point on the graph above November
    corresponds to approximately 3:45 P.M. on the
    time axis.

30. The sunset is at approximately 9 P.M. twice, in
    mid-May and in mid-July.

32. Yes; every location has exactly one sunset time
    per day.

34. $5.15 per hour; the year 2006 is included in the
    segment representing dates between September
    1997 and July 24, 2007, which corresponds to
    5.15 on the vertical axis.

36. $5.15 per hour; the segment representing dates
    between September 1997 and July 24, 2007 is
    the longest horizontal line segment in the graph.
    This segment corresponds to 5.15 on the vertical
    axis.

38. Answers may vary

40. $f(x) = 3 - 7x$
    $f(-2) = 3 - 7(-2) = 3 + 14 = 17$
    $f(0) = 3 - 7(0) = 3$
    $f(3) = 3 - 7(3) = 3 - 21 = -18$

42. $f(x) = x^2 - 4$
    $f(-2) = (-2)^2 - 4 = 4 - 4 = 0$
    $f(0) = (0)^2 - 4 = -4$
    $f(3) = (3)^2 - 4 = 9 - 4 = 5$

44. $f(x) = -3x$
    $f(-2) = -3(-2) = 6$
    $f(0) = -3(0) = 0$
    $f(3) = -3(3) = -9$

46. $f(x) = |2 - x|$
    $f(-2) = |2 - (-2)| = |4| = 4$
    $f(0) = |2 - 0| = |2| = 2$
    $f(3) = |2 - 3| = |-1| = 1$

48. $h(x) = -3x$
    $h(-1) = -3(-1) = 3$
    $h(0) = -3(0) = 0$
    $h(4) = -3(4) = -12$

50. $h(x) = 3x^2$

$h(-1) = 3(-1)^2 = 3(1) = 3$

$h(0) = 3(0)^2 = 3(0) = 0$

$h(4) = 3(4)^2 = 3(16) = 48$

52. $f(7) = -2$ corresponds to ordered pair $(7, -2)$.

54. $g(0) = -\dfrac{7}{8}$ corresponds to the ordered pair

$\left(0, -\dfrac{7}{8}\right)$.

56. $h(-10) = 1$ corresponds to the ordered pair $(-10, 1)$.

58. $(-\infty, \infty)$

60. $x - 6 \ne 0 \Rightarrow x \ne 6$, therefore $(-\infty, 6) \cup (6, \infty)$ or all real numbers except 6.

62. $(-\infty, \infty)$

64. D: $(-\infty, \infty)$, R: $x \le 5$, $(-\infty, 5]$

66. D: $(-\infty, \infty)$, R: $(-\infty, \infty)$

68. D: $\{3\}$, R: $(-\infty, \infty)$

70. $(3, 0)$

72. $(-3, -3)$

74. $g(9) = 20$

76. $f(3) = -4$

78. $f(-3) = 0$

80. $D(x) = \dfrac{136}{25} x$

    a. $D(35) = \dfrac{136}{25}(35) = 190.4$ mg

    b. $D(70) = \dfrac{136}{25}(70) = 380.8$ mg

82. Answers may vary

84. $f(x) = 2x + 7$

    a. $f(2) = 2(2) + 7 = 11$

    b. $f(a) = 2(a) + 7 = 2a + 7$

86. $h(x) = x^2 + 7$

    a. $h(3) = (3)^2 + 7 = 16$

    b. $h(a) = (a)^2 + 7 = a^2 + 7$

Chapter 3 Vocabulary Check

1. An ordered pair is a <u>solution</u> of an equation in two variables if replacing the variables by the coordinates of the ordered pair results in a true statement.

2. The vertical number line in the rectangle coordinate system is called the <u>y-axis</u>.

3. A <u>linear</u> equation can be written in the form $Ax + By = C$.

4. An <u>x-intercept</u> is a point of the graph where the graph crosses the x-axis.

5. The form $Ax + By = C$ is called <u>standard</u> form.

6. A <u>y-intercept</u> is a point of the graph where the graph crosses the y-axis.

7. The equation $y = 7x - 5$ is written in <u>slope-intercept</u> form.

8. The equation $y + 1 = 7(x - 2)$ is written in <u>point-slope</u> form.

9. To find an x-intercept of a graph, let <u>y</u> = 0.

10. The horizontal number line in the rectangular coordinate system is called the <u>x-axis</u>.

11. To find a y-intercept of a graph, let <u>x</u> = 0.

12. The <u>slope</u> of a line measures the steepness or tilt of a line.

13. A set of ordered pairs that assigns to each x-value exactly one y-value is called a <u>function</u>.

14. The set of all x-coordinates of a relation is called the <u>domain</u> of the relation.

15. The set of all y-coordinates of a relation is called the <u>range</u> of the relation.

16. A set of ordered pairs is called a <u>relation</u>.

Chapter 3 Review

1–6.

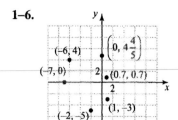

7. a. (8.00, 1), (7.50, 10), (6.50, 25), (5.00, 50), (2.00, 100)

   b.

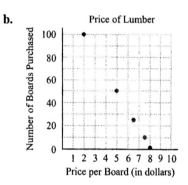

8. a. (2001, 9.8), (2002, 15.1), (2003, 14.6), (2004, 14.0), (2005, 13.8), (2006, 13.6)

   b.

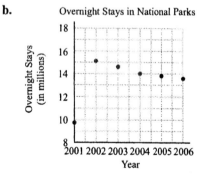

9. $7x - 8y = 56$
   (0, 56)
   $7(0) - 8(56) \stackrel{?}{=} 56$
   $-448 \neq 0$ No

   (8, 0)
   $7(8) - 8(0) \stackrel{?}{=} 56$
   $56 = 56$ Yes

10. $-2x + 5y = 10$
    (−5, 0)
    $-2(-5) + 5(0) \stackrel{?}{=} 10$
    $10 = 10$ Yes

    (1, 1)
    $-2(1) + 5(1) \stackrel{?}{=} 10$
    $3 \neq 10$ No

11. $x = 13$
    (13, 5)
    $(13) \stackrel{?}{=} 13$
    $13 = 13$ Yes

    (13, 13)
    $(13) \stackrel{?}{=} 13$
    $13 = 13$ Yes

12. $y = 2$
    (7, 2)
    $(2) \stackrel{?}{=} 2$
    $2 = 2$ Yes

    (2, 7)
    $(7) \stackrel{?}{=} 2$
    $7 \neq 2$ No

13. $-2 + y = 6x, \ x = 7$
    $-2 + y = 6(7)$
    $-2 + y = 42$
    $y = 44$
    (7, 44)

14. $y = 3x + 5, \ y = -8$
    $-8 = 3x + 5$
    $-13 = 3x$
    $-\dfrac{13}{3} = x$
    $\left(-\dfrac{13}{3}, -8\right)$

15. $9 = -3x + 4y$
    $y = 0$: $9 = -3x + 4(0)$, $9 = -3x$, $-3 = x$
    $y = 3$: $9 = -3x + 4(3)$, $9 = -3x + 12$, $-3 = -3x$,
         $1 = x$
    $x = 9$: $9 = -3(9) + 4y$, $9 = -27 + 4y$, $36 = 4y$,
         $9 = y$

x	y
−3	0
1	3
9	9

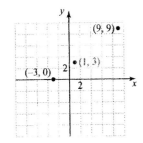

16. $y = 5$ for all values of x.

x	y
7	5
–7	5
0	5

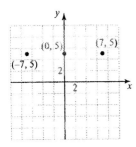

17. $x = 2y$

$y = 0$: $x = 2(0) = 0$
$y = 5$: $x = 2(5) = 10$
$y = -5$: $x = 2(-5) = -10$

x	y
0	0
10	5
–10	–5

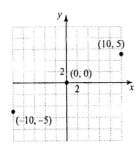

18. a. $y = 5x + 2000$
$x = 1$: $y = 5(1) + 2000 = 2005$
$x = 100$: $y = 5(100) + 2000 = 2500$
$x = 1000$: $y = 5(1000) + 2000 = 7000$

x	1	100	1000
y	2005	2500	7000

b. Let $y = 6430$.
$6430 = 5x + 2000$
$4430 = 5x$
$886 = x$
886 CD holders can be produced.

19. $x - y = 1$

x	y
1	0
0	–1

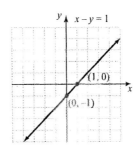

20. $x + y = 6$

x	y
6	0
0	6

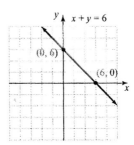

21. $x - 3y = 12$

x	y
12	0
0	–4

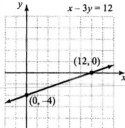

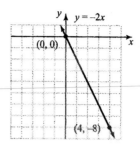

22. $5x - y = -8$

x	y
-2	-2
0	8

25. $2x - 3y = 6$

x	y
0	-2
3	0

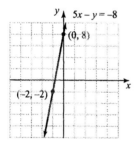

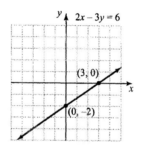

23. $x = 3y$

x	y
0	0
6	2

26. $4x - 3y = 12$

x	y
0	-4
3	0

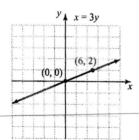

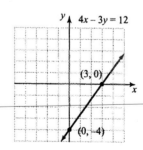

24. $y = -2x$

x	y
0	0
4	-8

27. $y = 3x + 111$

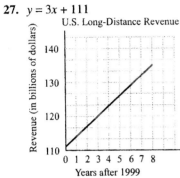

U.S. Long-Distance Revenue

Expect a revenue of $135 billion in 2007.

28. x-intercept: $(4, 0)$
    y-intercept: $(0, -2)$

29. y-intercept: $(0, -3)$

30. x-intercepts: $(-2, 0)$, $(2, 0)$
    y-intercepts: $(0, 2)$, $(0, -2)$

31. x-intercepts: $(-1, 0)$, $(2, 0)$, $(3, 0)$
    y-intercept: $(0, -2)$

32. $x - 3y = 12$

x	y
0	-4
12	0

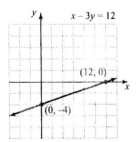

33. $-4x + y = 8$

x	y
0	8
-2	0

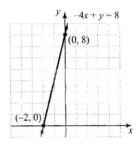

34. $y = -3$ for all x

x	y
0	-3

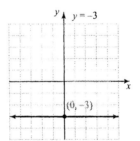

35. $x = 5$ for all y

x	y
5	0

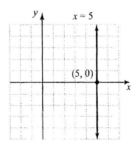

36. $y = -3x$
    Find a second point.

x	y
0	0
3	-9

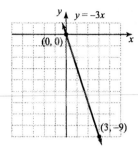

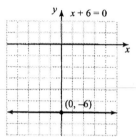

37. $x = 5y$

Find a second point.

x	y
0	0
5	1

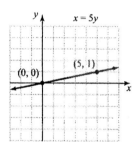

38. $x - 2 = 0$

$x = 2$ for all y

x	y
2	0

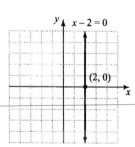

39. $y + 6 = 0$

$y = -6$ for all x

x	y
0	-6

40. $(-1, 2)$, and $(3, -1)$

$$m = \frac{y_2 - y_1}{x_2 - x_1} = \frac{-1 - 2}{3 - (-1)} = -\frac{3}{4}$$

41. $(-2, -2)$ and $(3, -1)$

$$m = \frac{y_2 - y_1}{x_2 - x_1} = \frac{-1 - (-2)}{3 - (-2)} = \frac{1}{5}$$

42. $m = 0$

d

43. $m = -1$

b

44. Slope is undefined.

c

45. $m = 3$

a

46. $m = \frac{2}{3}$

e

47. $(2, 5)$ and $(6, 8)$

$$m = \frac{y_2 - y_1}{x_2 - x_1} = \frac{8 - 5}{6 - 2} = \frac{3}{4}$$

48. $(4, 7)$ and $(1, 2)$

$$m = \frac{y_2 - y_1}{x_2 - x_1} = \frac{2 - 7}{1 - 4} = \frac{-5}{-3} = \frac{5}{3}$$

49. $(1, 3)$ and $(-2, -9)$

$$m = \frac{y_2 - y_1}{x_2 - x_1} = \frac{-9 - 3}{-2 - 1} = \frac{-12}{-3} = 4$$

50. $(-4, 1)$, and $(3, -6)$

$$m = \frac{y_2 - y_1}{x_2 - x_1} = \frac{-6 - 1}{3 - (-4)} = \frac{-7}{7} = -1$$

51. $y = 3x + 7$

The equation is in slope-intercept form. The slope is the coefficient of x, or 3.

52. Solve for y.

$x - 2y = 4$

$-2y = -x + 4$

$y = \dfrac{1}{2}x - 2$

The slope is $\dfrac{1}{2}$.

53. $y = -2$

This is the equation of a horizontal line. The slope is 0.

54. $x = 0$

This is the equation of a vertical line. The slope is undefined.

55. Solve the equations for y.

$\begin{aligned} x - y &= 6 \\ -y &= -x + 6 \\ y &= x - 6 \end{aligned} \qquad \begin{aligned} x + y &= 3 \\ y &= -x + 3 \end{aligned}$

The slopes are 1 and -1. Since their product is -1, the lines are perpendicular.

56. Solve the equations for y.

$\begin{aligned} 3x + y &= 7 \\ y &= -3x + 7 \end{aligned} \qquad \begin{aligned} -3x - y &= 10 \\ -y &= 3x + 10 \\ y &= -3x - 10 \end{aligned}$

The slopes are both -3. Since the lines have the same slope but different y-intercepts, they are parallel.

57. The first line, $y = 4x + \dfrac{1}{2}$, has slope 4. Solve the second equation for y.

$4x + 2y = 1$

$2y = -4x + 1$

$y = -2x + \dfrac{1}{2}$

The second line has slope -2. Since the slopes are not the same and their product is not -1, the lines are neither parallel nor perpendicular.

58. $x = 4, y = -2$

The first equation's graph is a vertical line, and the second equation's graph is a horizontal line. These lines are perpendicular.

59. Use the points (1985, 232) and (2006, 608).

$m = \dfrac{608 - 232}{2006 - 1985} = \dfrac{376}{21} \approx \dfrac{17.90 \text{ dollars}}{1 \text{ year}}$

Every 1 year, monthly daycare costs increase by $17.90.

60. Use the points (2004, 46) and (2009, 56.5).

$m = \dfrac{56.5 - 46}{2009 - 2004} = \dfrac{10.5}{5} \approx \dfrac{2.1 \text{ billion dollars}}{1 \text{ year}}$

Every 1 year, $2.1 billion more dollars are spent on technology.

61. $3x + y = 7$

$\qquad y = -3x + 7$

$y = mx + b$

$m = -3$, y-intercept $= (0, 7)$

62. $x - 6y = -1$

$\qquad -6y = -x - 1$

$\qquad\qquad y = \dfrac{1}{6}x + \dfrac{1}{6}$

$y = mx + b$

$\qquad m = \dfrac{1}{6}$, y-intercept $= \left(0, \dfrac{1}{6}\right)$

63. $y = 2$

$y = mx + b$

$m = 0$, y-intercept $= (0, 2)$

64. $x = -5$

$y = mx + b$

m is undefined.

There is no y-intercept.

65. $m = -5$, $b = \dfrac{1}{2}$

$y = mx + b$

$y = -5x + \dfrac{1}{2}$

66. $m = \dfrac{2}{3}$, $b = 6$

$y = mx + b$

$y = \dfrac{2}{3}x + 6$

67. $y = 3x - 1$
$y = mx + b$
$m = 3, b = -1$

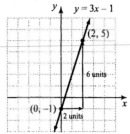

68. $y = -3x$
$y = mx + b$
$m = -3, b = 0$

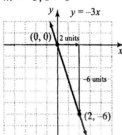

69. $5x - 3y = 15$
$-3y = -5x + 15$
$y = \dfrac{5}{3}x - 5$
$y = mx + b$
$m = \dfrac{5}{3}, b = -5$

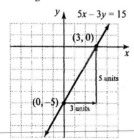

70. $-x + 2y = 8$
$2y = x + 8$
$y = \dfrac{1}{2}x + 4$
$y = mx + b$
$m = \dfrac{1}{2}, b = 4$

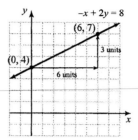

71. $y = -4x$
$m = -4, b = 0$
c

72. $y = -2x + 1$
$m = -2, b = 1$
d

73. $y = 2x - 1$
$m = 2, b = -1$
b

74. $y = 2x$
$m = 2, b = 0$
a

75. $m = -3; (0, -5)$
$y = mx + b$
$y = -3x - 5$
$3x + y = -5$

76. $m = \dfrac{1}{2}; \left(0, -\dfrac{7}{2}\right)$
$y = mx + b$
$y = \dfrac{1}{2}x - \dfrac{7}{2}$
$2y = x - 7$
$x - 2y = 7$

77. Horizontal line, point $(-2, -3)$
$y = c$
$y = -3$

78. Horizontal line, point $(0, 0)$
$y = c$
$y = 0$

79. $m = -6; (2, -1)$
$y - y_1 = m(x - x_1)$
$y - (-1) = -6(x - 2)$
$y + 1 = -6x + 12$
$6x + y = 11$

80. $m = 12; \left(\dfrac{1}{2}, 5\right)$

$$y - y_1 = m(x - x_1)$$
$$y - 5 = 12\left(x - \dfrac{1}{2}\right)$$
$$y - 5 = 12x - 6$$
$$12x - y = 1$$

81. $(0, 6)$ and $(6, 0)$

$$m = \dfrac{y_2 - y_1}{x_2 - x_1} = \dfrac{0 - 6}{6 - 0} = \dfrac{-6}{6} = -1$$
$$m = -1; (0, 6)$$
$$y - y_1 = m(x - x_1)$$
$$y - 6 = -1(x - 0)$$
$$y - 6 = -x$$
$$x + y = 6$$

82. $(0, -4)$ and $(-8, 0)$

$$m = \dfrac{y_2 - y_1}{x_2 - x_1} = \dfrac{0 - (-4)}{-8 - 0} = \dfrac{4}{-8} = -\dfrac{1}{2}$$
$$m = -\dfrac{1}{2}; (0, -4)$$
$$y - y_1 = m(x - x_1)$$
$$y - (-4) = -\dfrac{1}{2}(x - 0)$$
$$y + 4 = -\dfrac{1}{2}x$$
$$2y + 8 = -x$$
$$x + 2y = -8$$

83. Vertical line, point $(5, 7)$
$$x = c$$
$$x = 5$$

84. Horizontal line, point $(-6, 8)$
$$y = c$$
$$y = 8$$

85. $y = 8$ is horizontal.
Perpendicular to $y = 8$ is vertical; $x = c$.
Point $(6, 0)$
$$x = 6$$

86. $x = -2$ is vertical.
Perpendicular to $x = -2$ is horizontal; $y = c$,
point $(10, 12)$
$$y = 12$$

87. Two points have the same x-value: it is not a function.

88. Every point has a unique x-value: it is a function.

89. Yes; $7x - 6y = 1$ is a non-vertical line.

90. Yes; $y = 7$ is a non-vertical line.

91. No; $x = 2$ is a vertical line.

92. Yes; for each value of x there is only one value of y.

93. No; the graph does not pass the vertical line test.

94. Yes; the graph passes the vertical line test.

95. $f(x) = -2x + 6$

    a. $f(0) = -2(0) + 6 = 6$

    b. $f(-2) = -2(-2) + 6 = 4 + 6 = 10$

    c. $f\left(\dfrac{1}{2}\right) = -2\left(\dfrac{1}{2}\right) + 6 = -1 + 6 = 5$

96. $h(x) = -5 - 3x$

    a. $h(2) = -5 - 3(2) = -11$

    b. $h(-3) = -5 - 3(-3) = 4$

    c. $h(0) = -5 - 3(0) = -5$

97. $g(x) = x^2 + 12x$

    a. $g(3) = (3)^2 + 12(3) = 45$

    b. $g(-5) = (-5)^2 + 12(-5) = -35$

    c. $g(0) = (0)^2 + 12(0) = 0$

98. $h(x) = 6 - |x|$

    a. $h(-1) = 6 - |-1| = 6 - 1 = 5$

    b. $h(1) = 6 - |1| = 6 - 1 = 5$

    c. $h(-4) = 6 - |-4| = 6 - 4 = 2$

99. $(-\infty, \infty)$

100. $x - 2 \neq 0 \Rightarrow x \neq 2$, therefore $(-\infty, 2) \cup (2, \infty)$ or all real numbers except 2.

101. D: $[-3, 5]$, R: $[-4, 2]$

102. D: $(-\infty, \infty)$, R: $x \geq 0$, $[0, \infty)$

103. D: $\{3\}$, R: $(-\infty, \infty)$

104. D: $(-\infty, \infty)$, R: $x \leq 2$, $(-\infty, 2]$

105. $2x - 5y = 9$

Let $y = 1$.
$2x - 5(1) = 9$
$2x - 5 = 9$
$2x = 14$
$x = 7$

Let $x = 2$.
$2(2) - 5y = 9$
$4 - 5y = 9$
$-5y = 5$
$y = -1$

Let $y = -3$.
$2x - 5(-3) = 9$
$2x + 15 = 9$
$2x = -6$
$x = -3$

x	y
7	1
2	−1
−3	−3

106. $x = -3y$

Let $x = 0$.
$0 = -3y$
$0 = y$

Let $y = 1$.
$x = -3(1)$
$x = -3$

Let $x = 6$.
$6 = -3y$
$-2 = y$

x	y
0	0
−3	1
6	−2

107. $2x - 3y = 6$

Let $y = 0$.
$2x - 3(0) = 6$
$2x = 6$
$x = 3$

Let $x = 0$.
$2(0) - 3y = 6$
$-3y = 6$
$y = -2$

x-intercept: $(3, 0)$
y-intercept: $(0, -2)$

108. $-5x + y = 10$

Let $y = 0$.
$-5x + 0 = 10$
$-5x = 10$
$x = -2$

Let $x = 0$.
$-5(0) + y = 10$
$y = 10$

x-intercept: $(-2, 0)$
y-intercept: $(0, 10)$

109. $x - 5y = 10$

x	y
10	0
0	−2

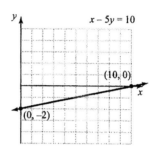

110. $x + y = 4$

x	y
4	0
0	4

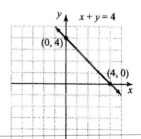

111. $y = -4x$

x	y
0	0
1	−4

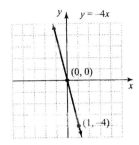

112. $2x + 3y = -6$

x	y
-3	0
0	-2

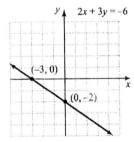

113. $x = 3$

This is the equation of a vertical line with x-intercept $(3, 0)$.

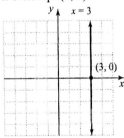

114. $y = -2$

This is the equation of a horizontal line with y-intercept $(0, -2)$.

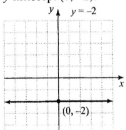

115. $(3, -5)$ and $(-4, 2)$

$$m = \frac{y_2 - y_1}{x_2 - x_1} = \frac{2 - (-5)}{-4 - 3} = \frac{7}{-7} = -1$$

116. $(1, 3)$ and $(-6, -8)$

$$m = \frac{y_2 - y_1}{x_2 - x_1} = \frac{-8 - 3}{-6 - 1} = \frac{-11}{-7} = \frac{11}{7}$$

117. $(0, -4)$ and $(2, 0)$

$$m = \frac{y_2 - y_1}{x_2 - x_1} = \frac{0 - (-4)}{2 - 0} = \frac{4}{2} = 2$$

118. $(0, 2)$ and $(6, 0)$

$$m = \frac{y_2 - y_1}{x_2 - x_1} = \frac{0 - 2}{6 - 0} = \frac{-2}{6} = -\frac{1}{3}$$

119. Solve for y.

$$-2x + 3y = -15$$
$$3y = 2x - 15$$
$$y = \frac{2}{3}x - 5$$

The slope is $\frac{2}{3}$. The y-intercept is $(0, -5)$.

120. Solve for y.

$$6x + y - 2 = 0$$
$$y = -6x + 2$$

The slope is -6. The y-intercept is $(0, 2)$.

121. $m = -5;\ (3, -7)$

$$y - y_1 = m(x - x_1)$$
$$y - (-7) = -5(x - 3)$$
$$y + 7 = -5x + 15$$
$$5x + y = 8$$

122. $m = 3;\ (0, 6)$

$$y = mx + b$$
$$y = 3x + 6$$
$$3x - y = -6$$

123. $(-3, 9)$ and $(-2, 5)$

$$m = \frac{y_2 - y_1}{x_2 - x_1} = \frac{5 - 9}{-2 - (-3)} = \frac{-4}{1} = -4$$

$m = -4;\ (-2, 5)$

$$y - y_1 = m(x - x_1)$$
$$y - 5 = -4(x - (-2))$$
$$y - 5 = -4(x + 2)$$
$$y - 5 = -4x - 8$$
$$4x + y = -3$$

124. (3, 1) and (5, −9)

$$m = \frac{y_2 - y_1}{x_2 - x_1} = \frac{-9 - 1}{5 - 3} = \frac{-10}{2} = -5$$

$m = -5; (3, 1)$

$$y - y_1 = m(x - x_1)$$
$$y - 1 = -5(x - 3)$$
$$y - 1 = -5x + 15$$
$$5x + y = 16$$

125. The highest point on the graph is above 2002 on the horizontal axis and corresponds to approximately 27.1 on the vertical axis, so the greatest beef production was 27.1 billion pounds in 2002.

126. The lowest point on the graph is above 2004 on the horizontal axis and corresponds to approximately 24.6 on the vertical axis, so the least beef production was 24.6 billion pounds in 2004.

127. The points for 2002, 2003, and 2006 lie above 25.0 on the vertical axis, so beef production was greater than 25 billion pounds in these years.

128. In 2003 and in 2004, there were decreases in beef production from the preceding years. In 2005 and in 2006, there were increases over the preceding years. The point for 2005 is only slightly higher than the point for 2004, denoting a small increase. However, the point for 2006 is much higher than the point for 2005, denoting a greater increase. The greatest increase occurred in 2006.

Chapter 3 Test

1. $y = \frac{1}{2}x$

$m = \frac{1}{2}; \ b = 0$

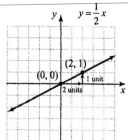

2. $2x + y = 8$

x	y
4	0
0	8

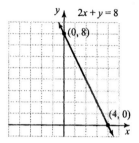

3. $5x - 7y = 10$

x	y
2	0
−5	−5

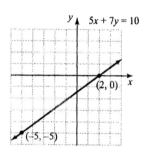

4. $y = -1$ for all values of x.

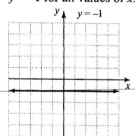

5. $x - 3 = 0$

$x = 3$ for all values of y.

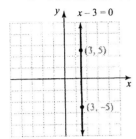

6. $(-1, -1)$ and $(4, 1)$

$$m = \frac{y_2 - y_1}{x_2 - x_1} = \frac{1 - (-1)}{4 - (-1)} = \frac{2}{5}$$

7. Horizontal line: $m = 0$

8. $(6, -5)$ and $(-1, 2)$

$$m = \frac{y_2 - y_1}{x_2 - x_1} = \frac{2 - (-5)}{-1 - 6} = \frac{7}{-7} = -1$$

9. $-3x + y = 5$

$\qquad y = 3x + 5$

$y = mx + b$

$m = 3$

10. $x = 6$ is a vertical line. The slope is undefined.

11. $7x - 3y = 2$

$\qquad -3y = -7x + 2$

$\qquad\quad y = \dfrac{7}{3}x - \dfrac{2}{3}$

$y = mx + b$

$m = \dfrac{7}{3},\ b = -\dfrac{2}{3},\ \left(0, -\dfrac{2}{3}\right)$

12. $y = 2x - 6,\ m_1 = 2$

$-4x = 2y,\ -2x = y$

$y = -2x,\ m_2 = -2$

$m_1 \neq m_2$ and $m_1 m_2 \neq -1$, neither

13. $m = -\dfrac{1}{4};\ (2, 2)$

$\qquad y - y_1 = m(x - x_1)$

$\qquad\quad y - 2 = -\dfrac{1}{4}(x - 2)$

$\quad 4(y - 2) = -(x - 2)$

$\quad 4y - 8 = -x + 2$

$\quad\ x + 4y = 10$

14. $(0, 0)$ and $(6, -7)$

$$m = \frac{y_2 - y_1}{x_2 - x_1} = \frac{-7 - 0}{6 - 0} = -\frac{7}{6}$$

$m = -\dfrac{7}{6};\ (0, 0)$

$\qquad y - y_1 = m(x - x_1)$

$\qquad\quad y - 0 = -\dfrac{7}{6}(x - 0)$

$\qquad\qquad 6y = -7x$

$\qquad 7x + 6y = 0$

15. $(2, -5)$ and $(1, 3)$

$$m = \frac{y_2 - y_1}{x_2 - x_1} = \frac{3 - (-5)}{1 - 2} = \frac{8}{-1} = -8$$

$m = -8;\ (1, 3)$

$\qquad y - y_1 = m(x - x_1)$

$\qquad\quad y - 3 = -8(x - 1)$

$\qquad\quad y - 3 = -8x + 8$

$\qquad 8x + y = 11$

16. $x = 7$ is vertical.

Parallel to $x = 7$ is vertical;

$x = c$, point $(-5, -1)$

$x = -5$

17. $m = \dfrac{1}{8},\ b = 12$

$\qquad y = mx + b$

$\qquad y = \dfrac{1}{8}x + 12$

$\qquad 8y = x + 96$

$\ x - 8y = -96$

18. Yes; it passes the vertical line test.

19. No; it does not pass the vertical line test.

20. $h(x) = x^3 - x$

    a. $h(-1) = (-1)^3 - (-1) = -1 + 1 = 0$

    b. $h(0) = (0)^3 - (0) = 0$

    c. $h(4) = (4)^3 - (4) = 64 - 4 = 60$

21. $x + 1 \neq 0 \Rightarrow x \neq -1$, therefore $(-\infty, -1) \cup (-1, \infty)$ or all real numbers except -1.

22. D: $(-\infty, \infty)$, R: $x \le 4$, $(-\infty, 4]$

23. D: $(-\infty, \infty)$, R: $(-\infty, \infty)$

24. $f(7) = 20$ corresponds to the ordered pair $(7, 20)$.

25. The bar for Denmark extends to about 210 on the horizontal axis. The average water use per person per day in Denmark is approximately 210 liters.

26. The bar for Australia extends to about 490 on the horizontal axis. The average water use per person per day in Australia is approximately 490 liters.

27. The highest point on the graph corresponds to 7 on the horizontal axis, denoting July. The average high temperature is the greatest in July.

28. April corresponds to 4 on the horizontal axis. Moving horizontally to the left from the point on the graph above 4, we reach approximately 63 on the vertical axis. The average high temperature for April is approximately 63°F.

29. The points for months 1, 2, 3, 11, and 12 lie below 60 on the vertical axis. Thus, the average high temperature is below 60°F in January, February, March, November, and December.

Chapter 3 Cumulative Review

1. a. $2 < 3$

   b. $7 > 4$

   c. $72 > 27$

2. $\dfrac{56}{64} = \dfrac{7 \cdot 8}{8 \cdot 8} = \dfrac{7}{8}$

3. $\dfrac{2}{15} \cdot \dfrac{5}{13} = \dfrac{2 \cdot 5}{3 \cdot 5 \cdot 13} = \dfrac{2}{39}$

4. $\dfrac{10}{3} + \dfrac{5}{21} = \dfrac{10 \cdot 7}{3 \cdot 7} + \dfrac{5}{21}$

$= \dfrac{70 + 5}{21}$

$= \dfrac{75}{21}$

$= \dfrac{3 \cdot 25}{3 \cdot 7}$

$= \dfrac{25}{7}$

$= 3\dfrac{4}{7}$

5. $\dfrac{3 + |4 - 3| + 2^2}{6 - 3} = \dfrac{3 + |1| + 2^2}{6 - 3} = \dfrac{3 + 1 + 4}{6 - 3} = \dfrac{8}{3}$

6. $16 - 3 \cdot 3 + 2^4 = 16 - 3 \cdot 3 + 16$
$= 16 - 9 + 16$
$= 23$

7. a. $-8 + (-11) = -19$

   b. $-5 + 35 = 30$

   c. $0.6 + (-1.1) = -0.5$

   d. $-\dfrac{7}{10} + \left(-\dfrac{1}{10}\right) = -\dfrac{8}{10} = -\dfrac{4}{5}$

   e. $11.4 + (-4.7) = 6.7$

   f. $-\dfrac{3}{8} + \dfrac{2}{5} = -\dfrac{3 \cdot 5}{8 \cdot 5} + \dfrac{2 \cdot 8}{5 \cdot 8} = \dfrac{-15 + 16}{40} = \dfrac{1}{40}$

8. $|9 + (-20)| + |-10| = |-11| + |-10| = 11 + 10 = 21$

9. a. $-14 - 8 + 10 - (-6) = -14 + (-8) + 10 + 6$
$= -6$

   b. $1.6 - (-10.3) + (-5.6) = 1.6 + 10.3 + (-5.6)$
$= 6.3$

10. $-9 - (3 - 8) = -9 - (-5) = -9 + 5 = -4$

11. Let $x = -2$ and $y = -4$.

   a. $5x - y = 5(-2) - (-4) = -10 + 4 = -6$

   b. $x^4 - y^2 = (-2)^4 - (-4)^2 = 16 - 16 = 0$

c. $\dfrac{3x}{2y} = \dfrac{3(-2)}{2(-4)} = \dfrac{-6}{-8} = \dfrac{3}{4}$

12. $\dfrac{x}{-10} = 2$

Let $x = -20$.

$\dfrac{-20}{-10} \overset{?}{=} 2$

$2 = 2$ True

-20 is a solution to the equation.

13. a. $10 + (x + 12) = 10 + x + 12 = x + 22$

    b. $-3(7x) = -21x$

14. $(12 + x) - (4x - 7) = 12 + x - 4x + 7 = 19 - 3x$

15. a. $-3y: -3$

    b. $22z^4: 22$

    c. $y = 1y: 1$

    d. $-x = -1x: -1$

    e. $\dfrac{x}{7} = \dfrac{1}{7}x: \dfrac{1}{7}$

16. $-5(x - 7) = -5x - (-5)(7) = -5x + 35$

17. $\begin{aligned} x - 7 &= 10 \\ x - 7 + 7 &= 10 + 7 \\ x &= 17 \end{aligned}$

18. $\begin{aligned} 5(3 + z) - (8z + 9) &= -4 \\ 15 + 5z - 8z - 9 &= -4 \\ -3z + 6 &= -4 \\ -3z &= -10 \\ z &= \dfrac{10}{3} \end{aligned}$

19. $\begin{aligned} 12a - 8a &= 10 + 2a - 13 - 7 \\ 4a &= 2a - 10 \\ 4a - 2a &= 2a - 2a - 10 \\ 2a &= -10 \\ \dfrac{2a}{2} &= \dfrac{-10}{2} \\ a &= -5 \end{aligned}$

20. $\begin{aligned} \dfrac{x}{4} - 1 &= -7 \\ 4\left(\dfrac{x}{4}\right) - 4(1) &= 4(-7) \\ x - 4 &= -28 \\ x &= -24 \end{aligned}$

21. Sum
= first integer + second integer + third integer
$\begin{aligned} \text{Sum} &= x + (x + 1) + (x + 2) \\ &= x + x + 1 + x + 2 \\ &= 3x + 3 \end{aligned}$

22. $\begin{aligned} \dfrac{x}{3} - 2 &= \dfrac{x}{3} \\ 3\left(\dfrac{x}{3}\right) - 3(2) &= 3\left(\dfrac{x}{3}\right) \\ x - 6 &= x \\ -6 &= 0 \end{aligned}$

This is false. There is no solution.

23. $\begin{aligned} \dfrac{2(a + 3)}{3} &= 6a + 2 \\ 2(a + 3) &= 3(6a + 2) \\ 2a + 6 &= 18a + 6 \\ -16a + 6 &= 6 \\ -16a &= 0 \\ a &= 0 \end{aligned}$

24. $\begin{aligned} x + 2y &= 6 \\ x - x + 2y &= 6 - x \\ 2y &= 6 - x \\ \dfrac{2y}{2} &= \dfrac{6 - x}{2} \\ y &= \dfrac{6 - x}{2} \end{aligned}$

25. Let x = the number of Republican representatives and $x + 31$ = the number of Democratic representatives.
$\begin{aligned} x + x + 31 &= 435 \\ 2x + 31 &= 435 \\ 2x &= 404 \\ x &= 202 \end{aligned}$
$x + 31 = 233$
There were 202 Republican representatives and 233 Democratic.

26.
$$5(x+4) \geq 4(2x+3)$$
$$5x+20 \geq 8x+12$$
$$-3x+20 \geq 12$$
$$-3x \geq -8$$
$$\frac{-3x}{-3} \leq \frac{-8}{-3}$$
$$x \leq \frac{8}{3}, \left(-\infty, \frac{8}{3}\right]$$

27. The perimeter of a rectangle is given by the formula $P = 2l + 2w$. Let l = the length of the garden.
$$P = 2l + 2w$$
$$140 = 2l + 2w$$
$$140 = 2l + 2(30)$$
$$140 = 2l + 60$$
$$80 = 2l$$
$$40 = l$$
The length of the garden is 40 feet.

28.
$$-3 < 4x - 1 \leq 2$$
$$-2 < 4x \leq 3$$
$$-\frac{1}{2} < x \leq \frac{3}{4}, \left(-\frac{1}{2}, \frac{3}{4}\right]$$

29.
$$y = mx + b$$
$$y - b = mx + b - b$$
$$y - b = mx$$
$$\frac{y-b}{m} = \frac{mx}{m}$$
$$\frac{y-b}{m} = x$$

30. $y = -5x$

x	y
0	0
−1	5
2	−10

31. Let x = the amount of 70% acid.
No. of liters · Strength = Amt of Acid

70%	x	0.7	$0.7x$
40%	$12 - x$	0.4	$0.4(12 - x)$
50%	12	0.5	$0.5(12)$

$$0.7x + 0.4(12 - x) = 0.5(12)$$
$$0.7x + 4.8 - 0.4x = 6$$
$$0.3x + 4.8 = 6$$
$$0.3x = 1.2$$
$$x = 4$$
$$12 - x = 12 - 4 = 8$$
Mix 4 liters of 70% acid with 8 liters of 40% acid.

32. $y = -3x + 5$

x	y
−1	8
0	5
1	2

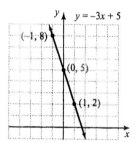

33. $x \geq -1, [-1, \infty)$

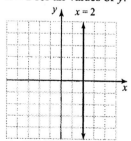

34. $2x + 4y = -8$
x-intercept, $y = 0$
$2x + 4(0) = -8 \Rightarrow x = -4: (-4, 0)$
y-intercept, $x = 0$
$2(0) + 4y = -8 \Rightarrow y = -2: (0, -2)$

35.
$$-1 \leq 2x - 3 < 5$$
$$2 \leq 2x < 8$$
$$1 \leq x < 4, [1, 4)$$

36. $x = 2$
$x = 2$ for all values of y.

37. a. $x - 2y = 6$
$(6, 0)$
$(6) - 2(0) \stackrel{?}{=} 6$
$6 = 6$ Yes

b. $x - 2y = 6$
$(0, 3)$
$(0) - 2(3) \stackrel{?}{=} 6$
$-6 \neq 6$ No

c. $x - 2y = 6$
$\left(1, -\dfrac{5}{2}\right)$
$(1) - 2\left(-\dfrac{5}{2}\right) \stackrel{?}{=} 6$
$1 + 5 \stackrel{?}{=} 6$
$6 = 6$ Yes

38. $(0, 5)$ and $(-5, 4)$
$m = \dfrac{y_2 - y_1}{x_2 - x_1} = \dfrac{4 - 5}{-5 - 0} = \dfrac{-1}{-5} = \dfrac{1}{5}$

39. a. linear; because it can be written in the form $Ax + By = C$.

b. linear; because it can be written in the form $Ax + By = C$.

c. not linear; because y is squared.

d. linear; because it can be written in the form $Ax + By = C$.

40. $x = -10$ is a vertical line. The slope is undefined.

41. $y = -1$ is horizontal, slope is 0.

42. $2x - 5y = 10$
$-5y = -2x + 10$
$y = \dfrac{2}{5}x - 2$
$y = mx + b$
$m = \dfrac{2}{5},\ b = -2$
The slope is $\dfrac{2}{5}$.
The y-intercept is $(0, -2)$.

43. $m = \dfrac{1}{4};\ b = -3$
$y = mx + b$
$y = \dfrac{1}{4}x + (-3)$
$y = \dfrac{1}{4}x - 3$

44. $(2, 3)$ and $(0, 0)$
$m = \dfrac{y_2 - y_1}{x_2 - x_1} = \dfrac{0 - 3}{0 - 2} = \dfrac{-3}{-2} = \dfrac{3}{2}$
Point: $(0, 0)$
$y - y_1 = m(x - x_1)$
$y - 0 = \dfrac{3}{2}(x - 0)$
$2y = 3x$
$3x - 2y = 0$

Chapter 4

Section 4.1

Practice Exercises

1. $\begin{cases} 4x - y = 2 \\ y = 3x \end{cases}$

$(4, 12)$

$4(4) - 12 \overset{?}{=} 2$

$16 - 12 \overset{?}{=} 2$

$\qquad 4 = 2$ False

$(4, 12)$ is not a solution of the system.

2. $\begin{cases} x - 3y = -7 \\ 2x + 9y = 1 \end{cases}$

$(-4, 1)$

$-4 - 3(1) \overset{?}{=} -7 \qquad\qquad 2(-4) + 9(1) \overset{?}{=} 1$

$\quad -4 - 3 \overset{?}{=} -7 \qquad\qquad\quad -8 + 9 \overset{?}{=} 1$

$\qquad\quad -7 = -7$ True $\qquad\qquad\quad 1 = 1$ True

$(-4, 1)$ is a solution of the system.

3. $\begin{cases} x - y = 3 \\ x + 2y = 18 \end{cases}$

$x - y = 3$			$x + 2y = 18$	
x	y		x	y
-4	-7		-4	11
0	-3		0	9
4	1		4	7

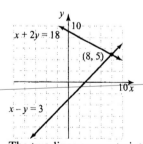

The two lines appear to intersect at $(8, 5)$.

$x - y = 3 \qquad\qquad\qquad x + 2y = 18$

$8 - 5 \overset{?}{=} 3 \qquad\qquad\quad 8 + 2(5) \overset{?}{=} 18$

$\qquad 3 = 3$ True $\qquad\qquad 8 + 10 \overset{?}{=} 18$

$\qquad\qquad\qquad\qquad\qquad\qquad 18 = 18$ True

$(8, 5)$ is the solution of the system.

4. $\begin{cases} -4x + 3y = -3 \\ \qquad\quad y = -5 \end{cases}$

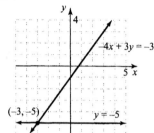

The two lines appear to intersect at $(-3, -5)$.
Check.

$-4x + 3y = -3 \qquad\qquad\quad y = -5$

$-4(-3) + 3(-5) \overset{?}{=} -3 \qquad -5 = -5$ True

$\qquad 12 - 15 \overset{?}{=} -3$

$\qquad\qquad -3 = -3$ True

$(-3, -5)$ is the solution of the system.

5. $\begin{cases} 3y = 9x \\ 6x - 2y = 12 \end{cases}$

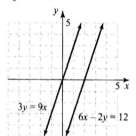

The lines appear to be parallel. To confirm this, write both equations in slope-intercept form.

$3y = 9x \qquad\qquad\qquad 6x - 2y = 12$

$\;y = 3x \qquad\qquad\qquad\quad -2y = -6x + 12$

$\qquad\qquad\qquad\qquad\qquad\quad y = 3x - 6$

The slopes are the same, so the lines are parallel. Thus, there is no solution of the system and the system is inconsistent.

6. $\begin{cases} \qquad x - y = 4 \\ -2x + 2y = -8 \end{cases}$

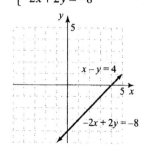

The graphs appear to be identical. To confirm this, write both equations in slope-intercept form.

$$x - y = 4 \qquad\qquad -2x + 2y = -8$$
$$-y = -x + 4 \qquad\qquad -x + y = -4$$
$$y = x - 4 \qquad\qquad y = x - 4$$

The equations are identical. Thus, there is an infinite number of solutions of the system; the system is consistent; the equations are dependent.

7. $\begin{cases} 5x + 4y = 6 \\ x - y = 3 \end{cases}$

Write each equation in slope-intercept form.

$$5x + 4y = 6 \qquad\qquad x - y = 3$$
$$4y = -5x + 6 \qquad\qquad -y = -x + 3$$
$$y = -\frac{5}{4}x + \frac{3}{2} \qquad\qquad y = x - 3$$

The slopes are not equal, so the two lines are neither parallel nor identical and must intersect. Therefore, this system has one solution and is consistent.

8. $\begin{cases} -\dfrac{2}{3}x + y = 6 \\ 3y = 2x + 5 \end{cases}$

Write each equation in slope-intercept form.

$$-\frac{2}{3}x + y = 6 \qquad\qquad 3y = 2x + 5$$
$$y = \frac{2}{3}x + 6 \qquad\qquad y = \frac{2}{3}x + \frac{5}{3}$$

The slope of each line is $\dfrac{2}{3}$, but they have different *y*-intercepts. Therefore, the lines are parallel. The system has no solution and is inconsistent.

Calculator Explorations

1. $\begin{cases} y = -2.68x + 1.21 \\ y = 5.22x - 1.68 \end{cases}$

The approximate point of intersection is $(0.37, 0.23)$.

2. $\begin{cases} y = 4.25x + 3.89 \\ y = -1.88x + 3.21 \end{cases}$

The approximate point of intersection is $(-0.11, 3.42)$.

3. $\begin{cases} 4.3x - 2.9y = 5.6 \\ 8.1x + 7.6y = -14.1 \end{cases}$

The approximate point of intersection is $(0.03, -1.89)$.

4. $\begin{cases} -3.6x - 8.6y = 10 \\ -4.5x + 9.6y = -7.7 \end{cases}$

The approximate point of intersection is $(-0.41, -0.99)$.

Vocabulary and Readiness Check

1. In a system of linear equations in two variables, if the graphs of the equations are the same, the equations are <u>dependent</u> equations.

2. Two or more linear equations are called a <u>system of linear equations</u>.

3. A system of equations that has at least one solution is called a <u>consistent</u> system.

4. A <u>solution</u> of a system of two equations in two variables is an ordered pair of numbers that is a solution of both equations in the system.

5. A system of equations that has no solution is called an <u>inconsistent</u> system.

6. In a system of linear equations in two variables, if the graphs of the equations are different, the equations are <u>independent</u> equations.

7. One solution, $(-1, 3)$

8. No solution

9. Infinite number of solutions

10. One solution, $(3, 4)$

Exercise Set 4.1

2. a. Let $x = 5$ and $y = 0$.

$$\begin{array}{ll} 2x + y = 5 & x + 3y = 5 \\ 2(5) + 0 \stackrel{?}{=} 5 & 5 + 3(0) \stackrel{?}{=} 5 \\ 10 = 5 \quad \text{False} & 5 + 0 \stackrel{?}{=} 5 \\ & 5 = 5 \quad \text{True} \end{array}$$

$(5, 0)$ is not a solution of the system.

b. Let $x = 2$ and $y = 1$.

$$\begin{array}{ll} 2x + y = 5 & x + 3y = 5 \\ 2(2) + 1 \stackrel{?}{=} 5 & 2 + 3(1) \stackrel{?}{=} 5 \\ 4 + 1 \stackrel{?}{=} 5 & 2 + 3 \stackrel{?}{=} 5 \\ 5 = 5 \quad \text{True} & 5 = 5 \quad \text{True} \end{array}$$

$(2, 1)$ is a solution of the system.

4. a. Let $x = -2$ and $y = -4$

$$\begin{array}{l} 2x - 3y = 8 \\ 2(-2) - 3(-4) \stackrel{?}{=} 8 \\ -4 + 12 \stackrel{?}{=} 8 \\ 8 = 8 \quad \text{True} \end{array}$$

$$\begin{array}{l} x - 2y = 6 \\ -2 - 2(-4) \stackrel{?}{=} 6 \\ -2 + 8 \stackrel{?}{=} 6 \\ 6 = 6 \quad \text{True} \end{array}$$

$(-2, -4)$ is a solution of the system.

b. Let $x = 7$ and $y = 2$.

$$\begin{array}{ll} 2x - 3y = 8 & x - 2y = 6 \\ 2(7) - 3(2) \stackrel{?}{=} 8 & 7 - 2(2) \stackrel{?}{=} 6 \\ 14 - 6 \stackrel{?}{=} 8 & 7 - 4 \stackrel{?}{=} 6 \\ 8 = 8 \quad \text{True} & 3 = 6 \quad \text{False} \end{array}$$

$(7, 2)$ is not a solution of the system.

6. a. Let $x = -4$ and $y = 0$.

$$\begin{array}{ll} x + 5y = -4 & -2x = 10y + 8 \\ -4 + 5(0) \stackrel{?}{=} -4 & -2(-4) \stackrel{?}{=} 10(0) + 8 \\ -4 = -4 \quad \text{True} & 8 = 8 \quad \text{True} \end{array}$$

$(-4, 0)$ is a solution of the system.

b. Let $x = 6$ and $y = -2$.

$$\begin{array}{ll} x + 5y = -4 & -2x = 10y + 8 \\ 6 + 5(-2) \stackrel{?}{=} -4 & -2(6) \stackrel{?}{=} 10(-2) + 8 \\ 6 - 10 \stackrel{?}{=} -4 & -12 \stackrel{?}{=} -20 + 8 \\ -4 = -4 \quad \text{True} & -12 = -12 \quad \text{True} \end{array}$$

$(6, -2)$ is a solution of the system.

8. a. Let $x = 0$ and $y = 1$.

$$\begin{array}{ll} 4x = 1 - y & x - 3y = -8 \\ 4(0) \stackrel{?}{=} 1 - 1 & 0 - 3(1) \stackrel{?}{=} -8 \\ 0 = 0 \quad \text{True} & 0 - 3 \stackrel{?}{=} -8 \\ & -3 = -8 \quad \text{False} \end{array}$$

$(0, 1)$ is not a solution of the system.

b. Let $x = \dfrac{1}{6}$ and $y = \dfrac{1}{3}$.

$$\begin{array}{ll} 4x = 1 - y & x - 3y = -8 \\ 4\left(\dfrac{1}{6}\right) \stackrel{?}{=} 1 - \left(\dfrac{1}{3}\right) & \dfrac{1}{6} - 3\left(\dfrac{1}{3}\right) \stackrel{?}{=} -8 \\ \dfrac{2}{3} \stackrel{?}{=} 1 - \dfrac{1}{3} & \dfrac{1}{6} - 1 \stackrel{?}{=} -8 \\ \dfrac{2}{3} = \dfrac{2}{3} \quad \text{True} & -\dfrac{5}{6} = -8 \quad \text{False} \end{array}$$

$\left(\dfrac{1}{6}, \dfrac{1}{3}\right)$ is not a solution of the system.

10. $\begin{cases} x + y = 3 \\ x - y = 5 \end{cases}$

The solution of the system is $(4, -1)$, consistent and independent.

12. $\begin{cases} x + y = 1 \\ -x + y = -3 \end{cases}$

The solution of the system is $(2, -1)$, consistent and independent.

14. $\begin{cases} y = -3x \\ 2x - y = -5 \end{cases}$

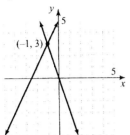

The solution of the system is $(-1, 3)$, consistent and independent.

16. $\begin{cases} y = 3x - 4 \\ y = x + 2 \end{cases}$

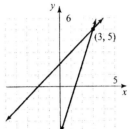

The solution of the system is $(3, 5)$, consistent and independent.

18. $\begin{cases} 2x + y = 1 \\ 3x + y = 0 \end{cases}$

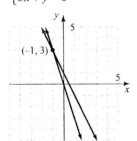

The solution of the system is $(-1, 3)$, consistent and independent.

20. $\begin{cases} y = x - 1 \\ y = -3x - 5 \end{cases}$

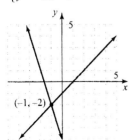

The solution of the system is $(-1, -2)$, consistent and independent.

22. $\begin{cases} x - y = 4 \\ x - y = 1 \end{cases}$

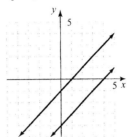

There is no solution, inconsistent and independent.

24. $\begin{cases} x + y = 5 \\ x = 4 \end{cases}$

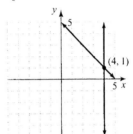

The solution of the system is $(4, 1)$, consistent and independent.

26. $\begin{cases} x + 3y = 7 \\ 2x - 3y = -4 \end{cases}$

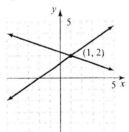

The solution of the system is $(1, 2)$, consistent and independent.

28. $\begin{cases} y + 2x = 3 \\ 4x = 2 - 2y \end{cases}$

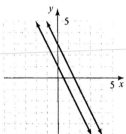

There is no solution, inconsistent and independent.

30. $\begin{cases} x - 2y = -6 \\ -2x + 4y = 12 \end{cases}$

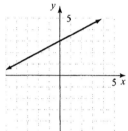

There is an infinite number of solutions, consistent and dependent.

32. $\begin{cases} x = -5 \\ y = 3 \end{cases}$

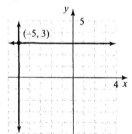

The solution of the system is (−5, 3), consistent and independent.

34. $\begin{cases} y = x + 5 \\ y = -2x - 4 \end{cases}$

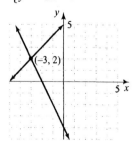

The solution of the system is (−3, 2), consistent and independent.

36. $\begin{cases} 4x - y = 7 \\ 2x - 3y = -9 \end{cases}$

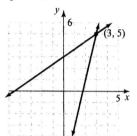

The solution of the system is (3, 5), consistent and independent.

38. $\begin{cases} 3x - y = 6 \\ \dfrac{1}{3}y = -2 + x \end{cases}$

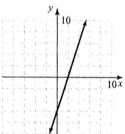

There is an infinite number of solutions, consistent and dependent.

40. $\begin{cases} 3x + y = 1 \\ 3x + 2y = 6 \end{cases} \rightarrow \begin{cases} y = -3x + 1 \\ y = -\dfrac{3}{2}x + 3 \end{cases}$

The lines are intersecting; there is one solution.

42. $\begin{cases} 3x + y = 0 \\ 2y = -6 \end{cases} \rightarrow \begin{cases} y = -3x \\ y = -3x \end{cases}$

The lines are identical; there is an infinite number of solutions.

44. $\begin{cases} 3x - y = 2 \\ \dfrac{1}{3}y = -2 + 3x \end{cases} \rightarrow \begin{cases} y = 3x - 2 \\ y = 9x - 6 \end{cases}$

The lines are intersecting; there is one solution.

46. $\begin{cases} y = 3 \\ x = -4 \end{cases}$

The lines are intersecting; there is one solution.

48. $\begin{cases} 2y = x+2 \\ y+2x = 3 \end{cases} \rightarrow \begin{cases} y = \dfrac{1}{2}x+1 \\ y = -2x+3 \end{cases}$

The lines are intersecting; there is one solution.

50. $\begin{cases} 8y+6x = 4 \\ 4y-2 = 3x \end{cases} \rightarrow \begin{cases} y = -\dfrac{3}{4}x+\dfrac{1}{2} \\ y = \dfrac{3}{4}x+\dfrac{1}{2} \end{cases}$

The lines are intersecting; there is one solution.

52. $\begin{cases} 2x+y = 0 \\ y = -2x+1 \end{cases} \rightarrow \begin{cases} y = -2x \\ y = -2x+1 \end{cases}$

The lines are parallel; there is no solution.

54. $-2x+3(x+6) = 17$
$-2x+3x+18 = 17$
$x+18 = 17$
$x = -1$
The solution is -1.

56. $-y+12\left(\dfrac{y-1}{4}\right) = 3$
$-y+3(y-1) = 3$
$-y+3y-3 = 3$
$2y-3 = 3$
$2y = 6$
$y = 3$
The solution is 3.

58. $3z-(4z-2) = 9$
$3z-4z+2 = 9$
$-z+2 = 9$
$-z = 7$
$z = -7$
The solution is -7.

60. Answers may vary

62. Answers may vary

64. Answers may vary

66. The graph for shellfish is above or intersects the graph for fish for the years 2003, 2004, and 2005.

68. The graph for GM is lower than the graph for Toyota for the years 2004, 2005, and 2006.

70. In 2005, Toyota sold approximately 2.3 million cars and GM sold approximately 1.6 million cars. Toyota sold approximately $2.3 - 1.6 = 0.7$ million, or 700,000 more cars than GM in 2005.

72. Answers may vary

74. Answers may vary

Section 4.2

Practice Exercises

1. $\begin{cases} 2x-y = 9 \\ x = y+1 \end{cases}$

Substitute $y + 1$ for x in the first equation.
$2x-y = 9$
$2(y+1)-y = 9$
$2y+2-y = 9$
$y+2 = 9$
$y = 7$
Let $y = 7$ in the second equation.
$x = y + 1 = 7 + 1 = 8$
The solution of the system is $(8, 7)$.
Check.

$2x-y = 9$	$x = y+1$
$2(8)-7 \overset{?}{=} 9$	$8 \overset{?}{=} 7+1$
$16-7 \overset{?}{=} 9$	$8 = 8$ True
$9 = 9$ True	

The solution of the system is $(8, 7)$.

2. $\begin{cases} 7x-y = -15 \\ y = 2x \end{cases}$

Substitute $2x$ for y in the first equation.
$7x-y = -15$
$7x-2x = -15$
$5x = -15$
$x = -3$
Let $x = -3$ in the second equation.
$y = 2x = 2(-3) = -6$
The solution of the system is $(-3, -6)$.

3. $\begin{cases} x+3y = 6 \\ 2x+3y = 10 \end{cases}$

Solve the first equation for x.
$x+3y = 6$
$x = -3y+6$

Substitute $-3y + 6$ for x in the second equation.

$$2x + 3y = 10$$
$$2(-3y + 6) + 3y = 10$$
$$-6y + 12 + 3y = 10$$
$$-3y + 12 = 10$$
$$-3y = -2$$
$$y = \frac{2}{3}$$

Let $y = \frac{2}{3}$ in the equation for x.

$$x = 3y + 6 = -3\left(\frac{2}{3}\right) + 6 = -2 + 6 = 4$$

The solution of the system is $\left(4, \frac{2}{3}\right)$.

4. $\begin{cases} 5x + 3y = -9 \\ -2x + y = 8 \end{cases}$

Solve the second equation for y.
$$-2x + y = 8$$
$$y = 2x + 8$$

Substitute $2x + 8$ for y in the first equation.
$$5x + 3y = -9$$
$$5x + 3(2x + 8) = -9$$
$$5x + 6x + 24 = -9$$
$$11x + 24 = -9$$
$$11x = -33$$
$$x = -3$$

Let $x = -3$ in the equation for y.
$$y = 2x + 8 = 2(-3) + 8 = -6 + 8 = 2$$
The solution of the system is $(-3, 2)$.

5. $\begin{cases} \frac{1}{4}x - y = 2 \\ x = 4y + 8 \end{cases}$

Substitute $4y + 8$ for x in the first equation.

$$\frac{1}{4}x - y = 2$$

$$\frac{1}{4}(4y + 8) - y = 2$$

$$y + 2 - y = 2$$
$$2 = 2$$

The two linear equations are equivalent. Thus, the system has an infinite number of solutions.

6. $\begin{cases} 4x - 3y = 12 \\ -8x + 6y = -30 \end{cases}$

Solve the first equation for x.

$$4x - 3y = 12$$
$$4x = 3y + 12$$
$$x = \frac{3}{4}y + 3$$

Substitute $\frac{3}{4}y + 3$ for x in the second equation.

$$-8x + 6y = -30$$

$$-8\left(\frac{3}{4}y + 3\right) + 6y = -30$$

$$-6y - 24 + 6y = -30$$
$$-24 = -30$$

The false statement $-24 = -30$ indicates that the system has no solution and is inconsistent.

Vocabulary and Readiness Check

1. Since $x = 1$, $y = 4x = 4(1) = 4$ and the solution is $(1, 4)$.

2. There is no solution, since $0 = 34$ is a false statement.

3. There is an infinite number of solutions, since the statement $0 = 0$ is true for all values of the variables.

4. Since $y = 0$, $x = y + 5 = 0 + 5 = 5$ and the solution is $(5, 0)$.

5. Since $x = 0$ and $x + y = 0$, $y = -x = -0 = 0$ and the solution is $(0, 0)$.

6. There is an infinite number of solutions, since the statement $0 = 0$ is true for all values of the variables.

Exercise Set 4.2

2. $\begin{cases} x + y = 20 \\ x = 3y \end{cases}$

Substitute $3y$ for x in the first equation.
$$3y + y = 20$$
$$4y = 20$$
$$y = 5$$
Let $y = 5$ in the second equation.
$$x = 3(5) = 15$$
The solution is $(15, 5)$.

4. $\begin{cases} x + y = 6 \\ y = -4x \end{cases}$

Substitute $-4x$ for y in the first equation.

$$x + (-4x) = 6$$
$$-3x = 6$$
$$x = -2$$

Let $x = -2$ in the second equation.
$$y = -4(-2) = 8$$
The solution is $(-2, 8)$.

6. $\begin{cases} y = 2x + 3 \\ 5y - 7x = 18 \end{cases}$

Substitute $2x + 3$ for y in the second equation.
$$5(2x + 3) - 7x = 18$$
$$10x + 15 - 7x = 18$$
$$3x + 15 = 18$$
$$3x = 3$$
$$x = 1$$

Let $x = 1$ in the first equation.
$$y = 2(1) + 3 = 5$$
The solution is $(1, 5)$.

8. $\begin{cases} y = 5x - 3 \\ y = 8x + 4 \end{cases}$

Substitute $5x - 3$ for y in the second equation.
$$5x - 3 = 8x + 4$$
$$-3x - 3 = 4$$
$$-3x = 7$$
$$x = -\frac{7}{3}$$

Let $x = -\frac{7}{3}$ in the first equation.
$$y = 5\left(-\frac{7}{3}\right) - 3 = -\frac{35}{3} - \frac{9}{3} = -\frac{44}{3}$$

The solution is $\left(-\frac{7}{3}, -\frac{44}{3}\right)$.

10. $\begin{cases} 4x - 3y = 10 \\ y = x - 5 \end{cases}$

Substitute $x - 5$ for y in the first equation.
$$4x - 3(x - 5) = 10$$
$$4x - 3x + 15 = 10$$
$$x = -5$$

Let $x = -5$ in the second equation.
$$y = (-5) - 5 = -10$$
The solution is $(-5, -10)$.

12. $\begin{cases} x + 3y = -5 \\ 2x + 2y = 6 \end{cases}$

Solve the first equation for x.
$$x = -5 - 3y$$
Substitute $-5 - 3y$ for x in the second equation.

$$2(-5 - 3y) + 2y = 6$$
$$-10 - 6y + 2y = 6$$
$$-4y = 16$$
$$y = -4$$

Let $y = -4$ in $x = -5 - 3y$.
$$x = -5 - 3(-4) = 7$$
The solution is $(7, -4)$.

14. $\begin{cases} 2x + 3y = 18 \\ x = 2y - 5 \end{cases}$

Substitute $2y - 5$ for x in the first equation.
$$2(2y - 5) + 3y = 18$$
$$4y - 10 + 3y = 18$$
$$7y = 28$$
$$y = 4$$

Let $y = 4$ in the second equation.
$$x = 2(4) - 5 = 3$$
The solution is $(3, 4)$.

16. $\begin{cases} 3y - x = 6 \\ 4x + 12y = 0 \end{cases}$

Solve the first equation for x.
$$x = 3y - 6$$

Substitute $3y - 6$ for x in the second equation.
$$4(3y - 6) + 12y = 0$$
$$12y - 24 + 12y = 0$$
$$24y = 24$$
$$y = 1$$

Substitute 1 for y in $x = 3y - 6$.
$$x = 3(1) - 6 = -3$$
The solution of the system is $(-3, 1)$.

18. $\begin{cases} 2y = x + 2 \\ 6x - 12y = 0 \end{cases}$

Solve the first equation for x.
$$x = 2y - 2$$
Substitute $2y - 2$ for x in the second equation.
$$6(2y - 2) - 12y = 0$$
$$12y - 12 - 12y = 0$$
$$-12 = 0 \quad \text{False}$$
The system has no solution.

20. $\begin{cases} 3x + y = -14 \\ 4x + 3y = -22 \end{cases}$

Solve the first equation for y.
$$y = -14 - 3x$$

Substitute $-14 - 3x$ for y in the second equation.

$$4x + 3(-14 - 3x) = -22$$
$$4x - 42 - 9x = -22$$
$$-5x = 20$$
$$x = -4$$
Let $x = -4$ in $y = -14 - 3x$.
$$y = -14 - 3(-4) = -2$$
The solution is $(-4, -2)$.

22. $\begin{cases} 5x + 4y - 2 = -6 + 7y - 3x \\ \quad 8x - 3y = -4 \\ \\ \quad 3x + 4x = y + 3 \\ \quad 7x - 3 = y \end{cases}$

Substitute $7x - 3$ for y in the first equation.
$$8x - 3(7x - 3) = -4$$
$$8x - 21x + 9 = -4$$
$$-13x = -13$$
$$x = 1$$
Let $x = 1$ in $y = 7x - 3$.
$$y = 7(1) - 3 = 4$$
The solution is $(1, 4)$.

24. $\begin{cases} 10x - 5y = -21 \\ \quad x + 3y = 0 \end{cases}$

Solve the second equation for x.
$$x = -3y$$
Substitute $-3y$ for x in the first equation.
$$10(-3y) - 5y = -21$$
$$-30y - 5y = -21$$
$$-35y = -21$$
$$y = \frac{3}{5}$$
Let $y = \frac{3}{5}$ in $x = -3y$.
$$x = -3\left(\frac{3}{5}\right) = -\frac{9}{5}$$
The solution is $\left(-\frac{9}{5}, \frac{3}{5}\right)$.

26. $\begin{cases} 2x - y = -7 \\ 4x - 3y = -11 \end{cases}$

Solve the first equation for y.
$$y = 2x + 7$$
Substitute $2x + 7$ for y in the second equation.
$$4x - 3(2x + 7) = -11$$
$$4x - 6x - 21 = -11$$
$$-2x = 10$$
$$x = -5$$
Let $x = -5$ in $y = 2x + 7$.

$$y = 2(-5) + 7 = -3$$
The solution is $(-5, -3)$.

28. $\begin{cases} -x + 3y = 18 \\ -3x + 2y = 19 \end{cases}$

Solve the first equation for x.
$$x = 3y - 18$$
Substitute $3y - 18$ for x in the second equation.
$$-3(3y - 18) + 2y = 19$$
$$-9y + 54 + 2y = 19$$
$$-7y = -35$$
$$y = 5$$
Let $y = 5$ in $x = 3y - 18$.
$$x = 3(5) - 18 = -3$$
The solution is $(-3, 5)$.

30. $\begin{cases} 6x + 3y = 12 \\ 9x + 6y = 15 \end{cases}$

Solve the first equation for y.
$$2x + y = 4$$
$$y = 4 - 2x$$
Substitute $4 - 2x$ for y in the second equation.
$$9x + 6(4 - 2x) = 15$$
$$9x + 24 - 12x = 15$$
$$-3x = -9$$
$$x = 3$$
Let $x = 3$ in $y = 4 - 2x$.
$$y = 4 - 2(3) = -2$$
The solution is $(3, -2)$.

32. $\begin{cases} 2x + 4y = 6 \\ 5x + 10y = 16 \end{cases}$

Solve the first equation for x.
$$x + 2y = 3$$
$$x = 3 - 2y$$
Substitute $3 - 2y$ for x in the second equation.
$$5(3 - 2y) + 10y = 16$$
$$15 - 10y + 10y = 16$$
$$15 = 16 \quad \text{False}$$
The system has no solution.

34. $\begin{cases} \dfrac{1}{4}x - 2y = 1 \\ \quad x - 8y = 4 \end{cases}$

Solve the second equation for x.
$$y = 8y + 4$$
Substitute $8y + 4$ for x in the first equation.

$$\frac{1}{4}(8y+4)-2y=1$$
$$2y+1-2y=1$$
$$1=1$$

The system has an infinite number of solutions.

36. $\begin{cases} x=\dfrac{5}{6}y-2 \\ 12x-5y=-9 \end{cases}$

Substitute $\dfrac{5}{6}y-2$ for x in the second equation.

$$12\left(\frac{5}{6}y-2\right)-5y=-9$$
$$10y-24-5y=-9$$
$$5y=15$$
$$y=3$$

Let $y=3$ in the first equation.

$$x=\frac{5}{6}(3)-2=\frac{1}{2}$$

The solution is $\left(\dfrac{1}{2},\,3\right)$.

38. $\begin{cases} 5x+2y-4x-2y=2(2y+6)-7 \\ \qquad\qquad\qquad x=4y+12-7 \\ \qquad\qquad\qquad x=4y+5 \\ \\ \quad 3(2x-y)-4x=1+9 \\ \quad 6x-3y-4x=10 \\ \quad 2x-3y=10 \end{cases}$

Substitute $4y+5$ for x in the second equation.
$$2(4y+5)-3y=10$$
$$8y+10-3y=10$$
$$5y=0$$
$$y=0$$
Let $y=0$ in $x=4y+5$.
$$x=4(0)+5=5$$
The solution is $(5,\,0)$.

40. $\quad -x+y=10$
$$5(-x+y)=5(10)$$
$$-5x+5y=50$$

42. $\quad 5a-7b=-4$
$$-4(5a-7b)=-4(-4)$$
$$-20a+28b=16$$

44. $\quad -2x\ +5y$
$$\underline{\quad 2x+11y\quad}$$
$$\qquad\quad 16y$$

46. $\quad 9q+p$
$$\underline{-9q-p}$$
$$\qquad\quad 0$$

48. Answers may vary

50. The solution is $(0,\,0)$.

52. a. 1

    b. 0

    c. infinite number

54. a. $\begin{cases} y=-6.17x+719 \\ y=33.9x+534 \end{cases}$

Substitute $33.9x+534$ for y in the first equation.
$$33.9x+534=-6.17x+719$$
$$40.07x=185$$
$$x\approx 4.617$$
Let $x\approx 4.617$ in the first equation.
$$y\approx -6.17(4.617)+719\approx 690.5$$
To the nearest tenth, the solution is $(4.6,\,690.5)$.

    b. Answers may vary

    c.

Adult Contemporary and Spanish Radio Stations

Answers may vary

56. $\begin{cases} y=3.1x-16.35 \\ y=-9.7x+28.45 \end{cases}$

Substitute $-9.7x+28.45$ for y in the first equation.
$$-9.7x+28.45=3.1x-16.35$$
$$-12.8x=-44.8$$
$$x=3.5$$
Let $x=3.5$ in $y=3.1x-16.35$.
$$y=3.1(3.5)-16.35=-5.5$$
The solution is $(3.5,\,-5.5)$.

58. $\begin{cases} x+y=-15.2 \\ -2x+5y=-19.3 \end{cases}$

Solve the first equation for y.

$y=-x-15.2$

Substitute $-x-15.2$ for y in the second equation.

$-2x+5(-x-15.2)=-19.3$

$-2x-5x-76=-19.3$

$-7x=56.7$

$x=-8.1$

Let $x=-8.1$ in $y=-x-15.2$.

$y=-(-8.1)-15.2=-7.1$

The solution is $(-8.1,-7.1)$.

Section 4.3

Practice Exercises

1. $\begin{cases} x-y=2 \\ x+y=8 \end{cases}$

Add the left sides of the equations together and the right sides of the equations together.

$x-y=2$

$\underline{x+y=8}$

$2x\quad=10$

$x=5$

Let $x=5$ in the first equation.

$x-y=2$

$5-y=2$

$3=y$

The solution is $(5,3)$.

Check.

$x-y=2 \qquad x+y=8$

$5-3\overset{?}{=}2 \qquad 5+3\overset{?}{=}8$

$2=2$ True $\qquad 8=8$ True

The solution of the system is $(5,3)$.

2. $\begin{cases} x-2y=11 \\ 3x-y=13 \end{cases}$

Multiply both sides of the first equation by -3 and add to the second equation.

$-3x+6y=-33$

$\underline{3x-y=13}$

$5y=-20$

$y=-4$

Let $y=-4$ in the first equation.

$x-2y=11$

$x-2(-4)=11$

$x+8=11$

$x=3$

The solution of the system is $(3,-4)$.

3. $\begin{cases} x-3y=5 \\ 2x-6y=-3 \end{cases}$

Multiply both sides of the first equation by -2 and add to the second equation.

$-2x+6y=-10$

$\underline{2x-6y=-3}$

$0=-13$ False

The system has no solution.

4. $\begin{cases} 4x-3y=5 \\ -8x+6y=-10 \end{cases}$

Multiply the first equation by 2 and add to the second equation.

$8x-6y=10$

$\underline{-8x+6y=-10}$

$0=0$ True

The equations are equivalent, so the system has an infinite number of solutions.

5. $\begin{cases} 4x+3y=14 \\ 3x-2y=2 \end{cases}$

Multiply the first equation by 2 and the second equation by 3 and add.

$8x+6y=28$

$\underline{9x-6y=6}$

$17x\quad=34$

$x=2$

Let $x=2$ in the second equation.

$3x-2y=2$

$3(2)-2y=2$

$6-2y=2$

$-2y=-4$

$y=2$

The solution of the system is $(2,2)$.

6. $\begin{cases} -2x+\dfrac{3y}{2}=5 \\ -\dfrac{x}{2}-\dfrac{y}{4}=\dfrac{1}{2} \end{cases}$

Clear fractions by multiplying the first equation by 2 and the second by 4.

$\begin{cases} -4x+3y=10 \\ -2x-y=2 \end{cases}$

Multiply the second simplified equation by 3 and add.

$$-4x + 3y = 10$$
$$\underline{-6x - 3y = 6}$$
$$-10x \qquad = 16$$

$$x = -\frac{16}{10} = -\frac{8}{5}$$

Now multiply the second simplified equation by –2 and add.

$$-4x + 3y = 10$$
$$\underline{4x + 2y = -4}$$
$$5y = 6$$

$$y = \frac{6}{5}$$

The solution of the system is $\left(-\dfrac{8}{5}, \dfrac{6}{5}\right)$.

Exercise Set 4.3

2. $\begin{cases} 4x + y = 13 \\ 2x - y = 5 \end{cases}$

$$4x + y = 13$$
$$\underline{2x - y = 5}$$
$$6x \qquad = 18$$
$$x = 3$$

Let $x = 3$ in the first equation.
$$4(3) + y = 13$$
$$12 + y = 13$$
$$y = 1$$
The solution of the system is $(3, 1)$.

4. $\begin{cases} x - 2y = -11 \\ -x + 5y = 23 \end{cases}$

$$x - 2y = -11$$
$$\underline{-x + 5y = 23}$$
$$3y = 12$$
$$y = 4$$

Let $y = 4$ in the first equation.
$$x - 2(4) = -11$$
$$x - 8 = -11$$
$$x = -3$$
The solution of the system is $(-3, 4)$.

6. $\begin{cases} 4x + y = -13 \\ 6x - 3y = -15 \end{cases}$

Multiply the first equation by 3.
$$12x + 3y = -39$$
$$\underline{6x - 3y = -15}$$
$$18x \qquad = -54$$
$$x = -3$$

Let $x = -3$ in the first equation.

$$4(-3) + y = -13$$
$$-12 + y = -13$$
$$y = -1$$
The solution of the system is $(-3, -1)$.

8. $\begin{cases} 4x + 2y = 2 \\ 3x - 2y = 12 \end{cases}$

$$4x + 2y = 2$$
$$\underline{3x - 2y = 12}$$
$$7x \qquad = 14$$
$$x = 2$$

Let $x = 2$ in the first equation.
$$4(2) + 2y = 2$$
$$8 + 2y = 2$$
$$2y = -6$$
$$y = -3$$
The solution of the system is $(2, -3)$.

10. $\begin{cases} x + 4y = 14 \\ 5x + 3y = 2 \end{cases}$

Multiply the first equation by –5.
$$-5x - 20y = -70$$
$$\underline{5x + 3y = 2}$$
$$-17y = -68$$
$$y = 4$$

Let $y = 4$ in the first equation.
$$x + 4(4) = 14$$
$$x + 16 = 14$$
$$x = -2$$
The solution of the system is $(-2, 4)$.

12. $\begin{cases} x - y = 1 \\ -x + 2y = 0 \end{cases}$

$$x \; - y = 1$$
$$\underline{-x + 2y = 0}$$
$$y = 1$$

Let $y = 1$ in the first equation.
$$x - 1 = 1$$
$$x = 2$$
The solution of the system is $(2, 1)$.

14. $\begin{cases} 3x + y = 4 \\ 9x + 3y = 6 \end{cases}$

Multiply the first equation by –3.
$$-9x - 3y = -12$$
$$\underline{9x + 3y = 6}$$
$$0 = -6 \quad \text{False}$$

The system has no solution.

16. $\begin{cases} 2x + y = 6 \\ 4x + 2y = 12 \end{cases}$

Multiply the first equation by -2.

$-4x - 2y = -12$

$\underline{4x + 2y = 12}$

$0 = 0$

There are an infinite number of solutions.

18. $\begin{cases} 6x - 5y = 25 \\ 4x + 15y = 13 \end{cases}$

Multiply the first equation by 3.

$18x - 15y = 75$

$\underline{4x + 15y = 13}$

$22x = 88$

$x = 4$

Let $x = 4$ in the first equation.

$6(4) - 5y = 25$

$24 - 5y = 25$

$-5y = 1$

$y = -\dfrac{1}{5}$

The solution of the system is $\left(4, -\dfrac{1}{5} \right)$.

20. $\begin{cases} 10x + 3y = -12 \\ 5x = -4y - 16 \end{cases}$

Add $4y$ to both sides of the second equation. Then multiply the second equation by -2 and add.

$10x + 3y = -12$

$\underline{-10x - 8y = 32}$

$-5y = 20$

$y = -4$

Let $y = -4$ in the second equation.

$5x = -4(-4) - 16$

$5x = 0$

$x = 0$

The solution of the system is $(0, -4)$.

22. $\begin{cases} -2x + 3y = 10 \\ 3x + 4y = 2 \end{cases}$

Multiply the first equation by 3 and the second by 2.

$-6x + 9y = 30$

$\underline{6x + 8y = 4}$

$17y = 34$

$y = 2$

Let $y = 2$ in the second equation.

$3x + 4(2) = 2$

$3x + 8 = 2$

$3x = -6$

$x = -2$

The solution of the system is $(-2, 2)$.

24. $\begin{cases} 9x - 3y = 12 \\ 12x - 4y = 18 \end{cases}$

Multiply the first equation by 4 and the second equation by -3.

$36x - 12y = 48$

$\underline{-36x + 12y = -54}$

$0 = -6$ False

The system has no solution.

26. $\begin{cases} 6x - 5y = 7 \\ 4x - 6y = 7 \end{cases}$

Multiply the first equation by -2 and the second equation by 3.

$-12x + 10y = -14$

$\underline{12x - 18y = 21}$

$-8y = 7$

$y = -\dfrac{7}{8}$

Multiply the first equation by -6 and the second equation by 5.

$-36x + 30y = -42$

$\underline{20x - 30y = 35}$

$-16x = -7$

$x = \dfrac{7}{16}$

The solution of the system is $\left(\dfrac{7}{16}, -\dfrac{7}{8} \right)$.

28. $\begin{cases} \dfrac{x}{2} + \dfrac{y}{8} = 3 \\ x - \dfrac{y}{4} = 0 \end{cases}$

Multiply the first equation by 8 and the second equation by 4.

$4x + y = 24$

$\underline{4x - y = 0}$

$8x = 24$

$x = 3$

Multiply the second equation of the simplified system by -1.

$$4x + y = 24$$
$$\underline{-4x + y = 0}$$
$$2y = 24$$
$$y = 12$$

The solution of the system is (3, 12).

30. $\begin{cases} \dfrac{3}{2}x + 4y = 1 \\ 9x + 24y = 5 \end{cases}$

Multiply the first equation by –6.

$$-9x - 24y = -6$$
$$\underline{9x + 24y = 5}$$
$$0 = -1 \quad \text{False}$$

The system has no solution.

32. $\begin{cases} 2x - \dfrac{3y}{4} = -3 \\ x + \dfrac{y}{9} = \dfrac{13}{3} \end{cases}$

Multiply the first equation by 4 and the second equation by 9.

$$\begin{cases} 8x - 3y = -12 \\ 9x + y = 39 \end{cases}$$

Multiply the second equation of the simplified system by 3.

$$8x - 3y = -12$$
$$\underline{27x + 3y = 117}$$
$$35x = 105$$
$$x = 3$$

Let $x = 3$ in $9x + y = 39$.
$$9(3) + y = 39$$
$$27 + y = 39$$
$$y = 12$$

The solution of the system is (3, 12).

34. $\begin{cases} -9(x + 3) = 8y \\ 3x - 3y = 8 \end{cases} \rightarrow \begin{cases} -9x - 27 = 8y \\ 3x - 3y = 8 \end{cases}$

$\rightarrow \begin{cases} -9x - 8y = 27 \\ 3x - 3y = 8 \end{cases}$

Multiply the second equation by 3.

$$-9x - 8y = 27$$
$$\underline{9x - 9y = 24}$$
$$-17y = 51$$
$$y = -3$$

Let $y = -3$ in the second equation.

$$3x - 3(-3) = 8$$
$$3x + 9 = 8$$
$$3x = -1$$
$$x = -\frac{1}{3}$$

The solution of the system is $\left(-\dfrac{1}{3}, -3 \right)$.

36. $\begin{cases} \dfrac{x}{2} + \dfrac{y}{4} = 1 \\ -\dfrac{x}{4} - \dfrac{y}{8} = 1 \end{cases}$

Multiply the first equation by 4 and the second equation by 8.

$$2x + y = 4$$
$$\underline{-2x - y = 8}$$
$$0 = 12 \quad \text{False}$$

The system has no solution.

38. $\begin{cases} 3x + \dfrac{7}{2}y = \dfrac{3}{4} \\ -\dfrac{x}{2} + \dfrac{5}{3}y = -\dfrac{5}{4} \end{cases}$

Multiply the first equation by 4 and the second by 24.

$$12x + 14y = 3$$
$$\underline{-12x + 40y = -30}$$
$$54y = -27$$
$$y = -\frac{1}{2}$$

Let $y = -\dfrac{1}{2}$ in the first equation.

$$3x + \frac{7}{2}\left(-\frac{1}{2} \right) = \frac{3}{4}$$
$$3x - \frac{7}{4} = \frac{3}{4}$$
$$3x = \frac{10}{4}$$
$$x = \frac{10}{12} = \frac{5}{6}$$

The solution of the system is $\left(\dfrac{5}{6}, -\dfrac{1}{2} \right)$.

40. $\begin{cases} -2.5x - 6.5y = 47 \\ 0.5x - 4.5y = 37 \end{cases}$

Multiply the second equation by 5.

$$-2.5x - 6.5y = 47$$
$$\underline{2.5x - 22.5y = 185}$$
$$-29y = 232$$
$$y = -8$$

Let $y = -8$ in the second equation.
$$0.5x - 4.5(-8) = 37$$
$$0.5x + 36 = 37$$
$$0.5x = 1$$
$$x = 2$$
The solution of the system is $(2, -8)$.

42. $\begin{cases} 0.04x - 0.05y = 0.105 \\ 0.2x - 0.6y = 1.05 \end{cases}$

Multiply the first equation by 1000 and the second by -200.
$$40x - 50y = 105$$
$$\underline{-40x + 120y = -210}$$
$$70y = -105$$
$$y = -1.5$$

Let $y = -1.5$ in the second equation.
$$0.2x - 0.6(-1.5) = 1.05$$
$$0.2x + 0.9 = 1.05$$
$$0.2x = 0.15$$
$$x = 0.75$$
The solution of the system is $(0.75, -1.5)$.

44. $\begin{cases} 4x - 5y = 6 \\ y = 3x - 10 \end{cases}$

Substitute $3x - 10$ for y in the first equation.
$$4x - 5(3x - 10) = 6$$
$$4x - 15x + 50 = 6$$
$$-11x = -44$$
$$x = 4$$
Let $x = 4$ in the second equation.
$$y = 3(4) - 10 = 2$$
The solution is $(4, 2)$.

46. $\begin{cases} x + 3y = 5 \\ 5x + 6y = -2 \end{cases}$

Multiply the first equation by -2.
$$-2x - 6y = -10$$
$$\underline{5x + 6y = -2}$$
$$3x = -12$$
$$x = -4$$
Let $x = -4$ in the first equation.
$$-4 + 3y = 5$$
$$3y = 9$$
$$y = 3$$
The solution is $(-4, 3)$.

48. $\begin{cases} 3y = x + 14 \\ 2x - 3y = -16 \end{cases}$

Subtract x from both sides of the first equation.
$$-x + 3y = 14$$
$$\underline{2x - 3y = -16}$$
$$x = -2$$
Let $x = -2$ in the first equation.
$$3y = -2 + 14$$
$$3y = 12$$
$$y = 4$$
The solution of the system is $(-2, 4)$.

50. $\begin{cases} y = 6x - 5 \\ y = 4x - 11 \end{cases}$

Substitute $4x - 11$ for y in the first equation.
$$4x - 11 = 6x - 5$$
$$-2x = 6$$
$$x = -3$$
Let $x = -3$ in the second equation.
$$y = 4(-3) - 11 = -23$$
The solution is $(-3, -23)$.

52. $\begin{cases} x + \dfrac{1}{3}y = \dfrac{5}{12} \\ 8x + 3y = 4 \end{cases}$

Multiply the first equation by -9.
$$-9x - 3y = -\frac{15}{4}$$
$$\underline{8x + 3y = 4}$$
$$-x = \frac{1}{4}$$
$$x = -\frac{1}{4}$$

Substitute $-\dfrac{1}{4}$ for x in the second equation.

$$8\left(-\frac{1}{4}\right) + 3y = 4$$
$$-2 + 3y = 4$$
$$3y = 6$$
$$y = 2$$

The solution of the system is $\left(-\dfrac{1}{4}, 2\right)$.

54. $\begin{cases} \dfrac{x+5}{2} = \dfrac{y+14}{4} \\ \dfrac{x}{3} = \dfrac{2y+2}{6} \end{cases}$

Multiply the first equation by 4 and the second

equation by –6.

$$\begin{cases} 2(x+5) = y+14 \\ 2x+10 = y+14 \\ 2x - y = 4 \\ \\ -2x = -2y - 2 \\ -2x + 2y = -2 \end{cases}$$

$$\begin{array}{r} 2x - y = 4 \\ -2x + 2y = -2 \\ \hline y = 2 \end{array}$$

Let $y = 2$ in $2x - y = 4$.

$$\begin{array}{r} 2x - 2 = 4 \\ 2x = 6 \\ x = 3 \end{array}$$

The solution of the system is (3, 2).

56. $\begin{cases} 5x - 2y = -19.8 \\ -3x + 5y = -3.7 \end{cases}$

Multiply the first equation by 5 and the second equation by 2.

$$\begin{array}{r} 25x - 10y = -99 \\ -6x + 10y = -7.4 \\ \hline 19x = -106.4 \\ x = -5.6 \end{array}$$

Let $x = -5.6$ in the first equation.

$$\begin{array}{r} 5(-5.6) - 2y = -19.8 \\ -28 - 2y = -19.8 \\ -2y = 8.2 \\ y = -4.1 \end{array}$$

The solution of the system is (–5.6, –4.1).

58. Let n = an integer.
$n + (n + 1) + (n + 2) = 66$

60. Let x = a number.
$2(8 + x) = x - 20$

62. Let x = a number.
$\dfrac{1}{x} - \dfrac{2x}{7}$

64. $\begin{cases} 3x - y = -8 \\ 5x + 3y = 2 \end{cases}$

    a. Multiply the first equation by –5 and the second by 3.

$$\begin{array}{r} -15x + 5y = 40 \\ 15x + 9y = 6 \\ \hline 14y = 46 \\ y = \dfrac{46}{14} = \dfrac{23}{7} \end{array}$$

Let $y = \dfrac{23}{7}$ in the first equation.

$$\begin{array}{r} 3x - \dfrac{23}{7} = -8 \\ 3x = -\dfrac{56}{7} + \dfrac{23}{7} \\ 3x = -\dfrac{33}{7} \\ x = -\dfrac{11}{7} \end{array}$$

The solution of the system is $\left(-\dfrac{11}{7}, \dfrac{23}{7} \right)$.

    b. Multiply the first equation by 3.

$$\begin{array}{r} 9x - 3y = -24 \\ 5x + 3y = 2 \\ \hline 14x = -22 \\ x = -\dfrac{11}{7} \end{array}$$

Let $x = -\dfrac{11}{7}$ in the first equation.

$$\begin{array}{r} 3\left(-\dfrac{11}{7} \right) - y = -8 \\ -\dfrac{33}{7} - y = -8 \\ -y = -\dfrac{56}{7} + \dfrac{33}{7} \\ -y = -\dfrac{23}{7} \\ y = \dfrac{23}{7} \end{array}$$

The solution of the system is $\left(-\dfrac{11}{7}, \dfrac{23}{7} \right)$.

66. $\begin{cases} -2x - y = 0 \\ -2x + 3y = 6 \end{cases}$

$$\begin{array}{r} -6x - 3y = 0 \\ -2x + 3y = 6 \\ \hline -8x = 6 \end{array}$$

The correct sum is **a**; answers may vary.

68. Answers may vary

70. $\begin{cases} x + y = 4 \\ 2x + by = 8 \end{cases}$

Multiply the first equation by –2.

$-2x - 2y = -8$
$\underline{2x + by = 8}$
$(b - 2)y = 0$

a. The system has an infinite number of solutions if this statement is true.
$b = 2$

b. The system has a single solution if $(b - 2) \neq 2$. $b =$ any real number except 2.

72. $\begin{cases} 5.1x - 2.4y = 3.15 \\ -15.3x + 1.2y = 27.75 \end{cases}$

Multiply the first equation by 3.

$15.3x - 7.2y = 9.45$
$\underline{-15.3x + 1.2y = 27.75}$
$-6y = 37.2$
$y = -6.2$

Let $y = -6.2$ in the first equation.
$5.1x - 2.4(-6.2) = 3.15$
$5.1x + 14.88 = 3.15$
$5.1x = -11.73$
$x = -2.3$

The solution of the system is (–2.3, –6.2).

74. a. $\begin{cases} -0.7x + y = 4.6 \\ 1.3x + y = 26.9 \end{cases}$

Multiply the first equation by –1.

$0.7x - y = -4.6$
$\underline{1.3x + y = 26.9}$
$2x = 22.3$
$x \approx 11$

Let $x = 11$ in the first equation.
$-0.7(11) + y = 4.6$
$\underline{-7.7 + y = 4.6}$
$y \approx 12$

The solution of the system is (11, 12) [or (11, 13); answers may vary].

b. In 2007 (1996 + 11), the number of skateboarders equaled the number of in-line skaters.

c. $y = 12$ or 13, so 12 or 13 million.

Integrated Review

1. $\begin{cases} 2x - 3y = -11 \\ y = 4x - 3 \end{cases}$

Substitute $4x - 3$ for y in the first equation.
$2x - 3(4x - 3) = -11$
$2x - 12x + 9 = -11$
$-10x = -20$
$x = 2$

Let $x = 2$ in the second equation.
$y = 4(2) - 3 = 5$
The solution of the system is (2, 5).

2. $\begin{cases} 4x - 5y = 6 \\ y = 3x - 10 \end{cases}$

Substitute $3x - 10$ for y in the first equation.
$4x - 5(3x - 10) = 6$
$4x - 15x + 50 = 6$
$-11x = -44$
$x = 4$

Let $x = 4$ in the second equation.
$y = 3(4) - 10 = 2$
The solution of the system is (4, 2).

3. $\begin{cases} x + y = 3 \\ x - y = 7 \end{cases}$

$x + y = 3$
$\underline{x - y = 7}$
$2x \quad\ = 10$
$x = 5$

Let $x = 5$ in the first equation.
$5 + y = 3$
$y = -2$
The solution of the system is (5, –2).

4. $\begin{cases} x - y = 20 \\ x + y = -8 \end{cases}$

$x - y = 20$
$\underline{x + y = -8}$
$2x \quad\ = 12$
$x = 6$

Let $x = 6$ in the second equation.
$6 + y = -8$
$y = -14$
The solution of the system is (6, –14).

5. $\begin{cases} x + 2y = 1 \\ 3x + 4y = -1 \end{cases}$

Solve the first equation for x.
$x = 1 - 2y$

Substitute $1 - 2y$ for x in the second equation.
$$3(1 - 2y) + 4y = -1$$
$$3 - 6y + 4y = -1$$
$$-2y = -4$$
$$y = 2$$
Let $y = 2$ in $x = 1 - 2y$.
$$x = 1 - 2(2) = -3$$
The solution is $(-3, 2)$.

6. $\begin{cases} x + 3y = 5 \\ 5x + 6y = -2 \end{cases}$

Solve the first equation for x.
$$x = 5 - 3y$$
Substitute $5 - 3y$ for x in the second equation.
$$5(5 - 3y) + 6y = -2$$
$$25 - 15y + 6y = -2$$
$$-9y = -27$$
$$y = 3$$
Let $y = 3$ in $x = 5 - 3y$.
$$x = 5 - 3(3) = -4$$
The solution is $(-4, 3)$.

7. $\begin{cases} y = x + 3 \\ 3x - 2y = -6 \end{cases}$

Substitute $x + 3$ for y in the second equation.
$$3x - 2(x + 3) = -6$$
$$3x - 2x - 6 = -6$$
$$x = 0$$
Let $x = 0$ in the first equation.
$$y = 0 + 3 = 3$$
The solution is $(0, 3)$.

8. $\begin{cases} y = -2x \\ 2x - 3y = -16 \end{cases}$

Substitute $-2x$ for y in the second equation.
$$2x - 3(-2x) = -16$$
$$2x + 6x = -16$$
$$8x = -16$$
$$x = -2$$
Let $x = -2$ in the first equation.
$$y = -2(-2) = 4$$
The solution is $(-2, 4)$.

9. $\begin{cases} y = 2x - 3 \\ y = 5x - 18 \end{cases}$

Substitute $5x - 18$ for y in the first equation.
$$5x - 18 = 2x - 3$$
$$3x = 15$$
$$x = 5$$
Let $x = 5$ in the second equation.

$$y = 5(5) - 18 = 7$$
The solution is $(5, 7)$.

10. $\begin{cases} y = 6x - 5 \\ y = 4x - 11 \end{cases}$

Substitute $6x - 5$ for y in the second equation.
$$6x - 5 = 4x - 11$$
$$2x = -6$$
$$x = -3$$
Let $x = -3$ in the first equation.
$$y = 6(-3) - 5 = -23$$
The solution is $(-3, -23)$.

11. $\begin{cases} x + \dfrac{1}{6}y = \dfrac{1}{2} \\ 3x + 2y = 3 \end{cases}$

Multiply the first equation by 6.
$$\begin{cases} 6x + y = 3 \\ 3x + 2y = 3 \end{cases}$$
Multiply the first equation of the simplified system by -2.
$$\begin{array}{r} -12x - 2y = -6 \\ 3x + 2y = 3 \\ \hline -9x \quad\quad = -3 \end{array}$$
$$x = \frac{1}{3}$$
Multiply the second equation of the simplified system by -2.
$$\begin{array}{r} 6x + y = 3 \\ -6x - 4y = -6 \\ \hline -3y = -3 \\ y = 1 \end{array}$$

The solution of the system is $\left(\dfrac{1}{3}, 1 \right)$.

12. $\begin{cases} x + \dfrac{1}{3}y = \dfrac{5}{12} \\ 8x + 3y = 4 \end{cases}$

Multiply the first equation by 12.
$$\begin{cases} 12x + 4y = 5 \\ 8x + 3y = 4 \end{cases}$$
Multiply the first equation of the simplified system by 2 and the second equation by -3.
$$\begin{array}{r} 24x + 8y = 10 \\ -24x - 9y = -12 \\ \hline -y = -2 \\ y = 2 \end{array}$$
Multiply the first equation of the simplified

system by 3 and the second equation by –4.
$$36x + 12y = 15$$
$$\underline{-32x - 12y = -16}$$
$$4x \qquad = -1$$
$$x = -\frac{1}{4}$$

The solution of the system is $\left(-\frac{1}{4}, 2\right)$.

13. $\begin{cases} x - 5y = 1 \\ -2x + 10y = 3 \end{cases}$

Multiply the first equation by 2.
$$2x - 10y = 2$$
$$\underline{-2x + 10y = 3}$$
$$0 = 5 \quad \text{False}$$

The system has no solution.

14. $\begin{cases} -x + 2y = 3 \\ 3x - 6y = -9 \end{cases}$

Multiply the first equation by 3.
$$-3x + 6y = 9$$
$$\underline{3x - 6y = -9}$$
$$0 = 0$$

The equations in the original system are equivalent and there is an infinite number of solutions.

15. $\begin{cases} 0.2x - 0.3y = -0.95 \\ 0.4x + 0.1y = 0.55 \end{cases}$

Multiply both equations by 10.
$$\begin{cases} 2x - 3y = -9.5 \\ 4x + y = 5.5 \end{cases}$$

Multiply the first equation of the simplified system by –2.
$$-4x + 6y = 19$$
$$\underline{4x + y = 5.5}$$
$$7y = 24.5$$
$$y = 3.5$$

Multiply the second equation of the simplified system by 3.
$$2x - 3y = -9.5$$
$$\underline{12x + 3y = 16.5}$$
$$14x = 7$$
$$x = 0.5$$

The solution of the system is (0.5, 3.5).

16. $\begin{cases} 0.08x - 0.04y = -0.11 \\ 0.02x - 0.06y = -0.09 \end{cases}$

Multiply both equations by 100.

$\begin{cases} 8x - 4y = -11 \\ 2x - 6y = -9 \end{cases}$

Multiply the second equation of the simplified system by –4.
$$8x - 4y = -11$$
$$\underline{-8x + 24y = 36}$$
$$20y = 25$$
$$y = 1.25$$

Multiply the first equation of the simplified system by –3 and the second equation by 2.
$$-24x + 12y = 33$$
$$\underline{4x - 12y = -18}$$
$$-20x = 15$$
$$x = -0.75$$

The solution of the system is (–0.75, 1.25).

17. $\begin{cases} x = 3y - 7 \\ 2x - 6y = -14 \end{cases}$

Substitute $3y - 7$ for x in the second equation.
$$2(3y - 7) - 6y = -14$$
$$6y - 14 - 6y = -14$$
$$-14 = -14$$

The equations in the original system are equivalent and there is an infinite number of solutions.

18. $\begin{cases} y = \dfrac{x}{2} - 3 \\ 2x - 4y = 0 \end{cases}$

Substitute $\dfrac{x}{2} - 3$ for y in the second equation.
$$2x - 4\left(\frac{x}{2} - 3\right) = 0$$
$$2x - 2x + 12 = 0$$
$$12 = 0 \quad \text{False}$$

There is no solution.

19. $\begin{cases} 2x + 5y = -1 \\ 3x - 4y = 33 \end{cases}$

Multiply the first equation by 4 and the second equation by 5.
$$8x + 20y = -4$$
$$\underline{15x - 20y = 165}$$
$$23x = 161$$
$$x = 7$$

Let $x = 7$ in the first equation.

$$2(7) + 5y = -1$$
$$14 + 5y = -1$$
$$5y = -15$$
$$y = -3$$

The solution of the system is $(7, -3)$.

20. $\begin{cases} 7x - 3y = 2 \\ 6x + 5y = -21 \end{cases}$

Multiply the first equation by 5 and the second equation by 3.

$$35x - 15y = 10$$
$$\underline{18x + 15y = -63}$$
$$53x \qquad = -53$$
$$x = -1$$

Let $x = -1$ in the first equation.

$$7(-1) - 3y = 2$$
$$-7 - 3y = 2$$
$$-3y = 9$$
$$y = -3$$

The solution of the system is $(-1, -3)$.

21. Answers may vary

22. Answers may vary

Section 4.4

Practice Exercises

1. $\begin{cases} 3x + 2y - z = 0 & (1) \\ x - y + 5z = 2 & (2) \\ 2x + 3y + 3z = 7 & (3) \end{cases}$

Multiply equation (2) by 2 and add to equation (1) to eliminate y.

$$\begin{cases} 3x + 2y - z = 0 \\ 2(x - y + 5z) = 2(2) \end{cases}$$

$$\begin{cases} 3x - 2y \quad - z = 0 \\ 2x - 2y + 10z = 4 \end{cases}$$
$$\overline{5x \qquad + 9z = 4 \quad (4)}$$

Multiply equation (2) by 3 and add to equation (3) to eliminate y again.

$$\begin{cases} 3(x - y + 5z) = 3(2) \\ 2x + 3y + 3z = 7 \end{cases}$$

$$\begin{cases} 3x - 3y + 15z = 6 \\ 2x + 3y \quad + 3z = 7 \end{cases}$$
$$\overline{5x + \qquad 18z = 13 \quad (5)}$$

Multiply equation (4) by -1 and add to equation (5) to eliminate x.

$$\begin{cases} -1(5x + 9z) = -1(4) \\ 5x + 18z = 13 \end{cases}$$

$$\begin{cases} -5x \quad - 9z = -4 \\ 5x + 18z = 13 \end{cases}$$
$$\overline{\qquad 9z = 9}$$
$$z = 1$$

Replace z with 1 in equation (4) or (5).

$$5x + 9z = 4$$
$$5x + 9(1) = 4$$
$$5x = -5$$
$$x = -1$$

Replace x with -1 and z with 1 in equation (1), (2), or (3).

$$x - y + 5z = 2$$
$$-1 - y + 5(1) = 2$$
$$-y + 4 = 2$$
$$-y = -2$$
$$y = 2$$

The solution is $(-1, 2, 1)$. To check, let $x = -1$, $y = 2$, and $z = 1$ in all three original equations of the system.

2. $\begin{cases} 6x - 3y + 12z = 4 & (1) \\ -6x + 4y - 2z = 7 & (2) \\ -2x + y - 4z = 3 & (3) \end{cases}$

Multiply equation (3) by 3 and add to equation (1) to eliminate x.

$$\begin{cases} 6x - 3y + 12z = 4 \\ 3(-2x + y - 4z) = 3(3) \end{cases}$$

$$\begin{cases} 6x - 3y + 12z = 4 \\ -6x + 3y - 12z = 9 \end{cases}$$
$$\overline{\qquad 0 = 13 \quad \text{False}}$$

Since the statement is false, this system is inconsistent and has no solution. The solution set is $\{\ \}$ or $\varnothing$.

3. $\begin{cases} 3x + 4y \quad = 0 & (1) \\ 9x \quad - 4z = 6 & (2) \\ -2y + 7z = 1 & (3) \end{cases}$

Equation (2) has no term containing the variable y. Eliminate y using equations (1) and (3). Multiply equation (3) by 2 and add to equation (1).

$$\begin{cases} 3x + 4y = 0 \\ 2(-2y + 7z) = 2(1) \end{cases}$$

$$\begin{cases} 3x + 4y \quad = 0 \\ -4y + 14z = 2 \end{cases}$$
$$\overline{3x \qquad + 14z = 2 \quad (4)}$$

Multiply equation (4) by -3 and add to equation (2) to eliminate x.

$$\begin{cases} 9x - 4z = 6 \\ -3(3x + 14z) = -3(2) \end{cases}$$

$$\begin{cases} 9x \phantom{{}-{}} - 4z = 6 \\ -9x - 52z = -6 \end{cases}$$
$$\begin{aligned} -56z &= 0 \\ z &= 0 \end{aligned}$$

Replace z with 0 in equation (2) and solve for x.

$$9x - 4z = 6$$
$$9x - 4(0) = 6$$
$$9x = 6$$
$$x = \frac{6}{9} = \frac{2}{3}$$

Replace z with 0 in equation (3) and solve for y.

$$-2y + 7z = 1$$
$$-2y + 7(0) = 1$$
$$-2y = 1$$
$$y = -\frac{1}{2}$$

The solution is $\left(\frac{2}{3}, -\frac{1}{2}, 0\right)$.

4. $\begin{cases} 2x + y - 3z = 6 & (1) \\ x + \dfrac{1}{2}y - \dfrac{3}{2}z = 3 & (2) \\ -4x - 2y + 6z = -12 & (3) \end{cases}$

Multiply both sides of equation (2) by 2 to eliminate fractions, and multiply both sides of equation (3) by $-\dfrac{1}{2}$ since all coefficients in equation (3) are divisible by 2 and the coefficient of x is negative. The resulting system is

$$\begin{cases} 2x + y - 3z = 6 \\ 2x + y - 3z = 6 \\ 2x + y - 3z = 6 \end{cases}$$

Since the three equations are identical, there are infinitely many solutions of the system. The equations are dependent. The solution set can be written as $\{(x, y, z) | 2x + y - 3z = 6\}$.

5. $\begin{cases} x + 2y + 4z = 16 & (1) \\ x \phantom{{}+2y} + 2z = -4 & (2) \\ y - 3z = 30 & (3) \end{cases}$

Solve equation (2) for x and equation (3) for y.

$$\begin{aligned} x + 2z &= -4 & y - 3z &= 30 \\ x &= -2z - 4 & y &= 3z + 30 \end{aligned}$$

Substitute $-2z - 4$ for x and $3z + 30$ for y in equation (1) and solve for z.

$$x + 2y + 4z = 16$$
$$(-2z - 4) + 2(3z + 30) + 4z = 16$$
$$-2z - 4 + 6z + 60 + 4z = 16$$
$$8z + 56 = 16$$
$$8z = -40$$
$$z = -5$$

Use $x = -2z - 4$ to find x:
$x = -2(-5) - 4 = 10 - 4 = 6$.
Use $y = 3z + 30$ to find y:
$y = 3(-5) + 30 = -15 + 30 = 15$.
The solution is $(6, 15, -5)$.

Exercise Set 4.4

2. a. $x + y + z = -1$
$$2 + 1 + (-4) \stackrel{?}{=} -1$$
$$-1 = -1$$
a is true.

b. $x - y - z = -3$
$$2 - 1 - (-4) \stackrel{?}{=} -3$$
$$5 = -3$$
b is false.

c. $2x - y + z = -1$
$$2(2) - 1 + (-4) \stackrel{?}{=} -1$$
$$-1 = -1$$
c is true.

d. $-x - 3y - z = -1$
$$-2 - 3(1) - (-4) \stackrel{?}{=} -1$$
$$-1 = -1$$
d is true.

Equations a, c, and d.

4. No; answers may vary

6. $\begin{cases} x + y - z = -1 & (1) \\ -4x - y + 2z = -7 & (2) \\ 2x - 2y - 5z = 7 & (3) \end{cases}$

Add E1 and E2.
$$-3x + z = -8$$
Multiply E1 by 2 and add to E3 to get
$$4x - 7z = 5$$
Solve the new system:
$$\begin{cases} -3x + z = -8 \\ 4x - 7z = 5 \end{cases}$$
Multiply the first equation by 7.
$$\begin{cases} -21x + 7z = -56 \\ 4x - 7z = 5 \end{cases}$$

Add the equations to get $-17x = -51$

$$x = 3.$$

Replace x with 3 in the equation $-3x + z = -8$.

$$-3(3) + z = -8$$
$$z = 1$$

Replace x with 3 and z with 1 in E1.

$$3 + y - 1 = -1$$
$$y = -3$$

The solution is $(3, -3, 1)$.

8. $\begin{cases} 5x = 5 & (1) \\ 2x + y = 4 & (2) \\ 3x + y - 4z = -15 & (3) \end{cases}$

Solve E1 for x: $x = 1$

Replace x with 1 in E2.

$$2(1) + y = 4$$
$$y = 2$$

Replace x with 1 and y with 2 in E3.

$$3(1) + 2 - 4z = -15$$
$$5 - 4z = -15$$
$$-4z = -20$$
$$z = 5$$

The solution is $(1, 2, 5)$.

10. $\begin{cases} 2x - 3y + z = 5 & (1) \\ x + y + z = 0 & (2) \\ 4x + 2y + 4z = 4 & (3) \end{cases}$

Multiply E2 by -1 and add to E1.

$$\begin{array}{r} -x - y - z = 0 \\ 2x - 3y + z = 5 \\ \hline x - 4y = 5 \quad (4) \end{array}$$

Multiply E2 by -4 and add to E3.

$$\begin{array}{r} -4x - 4y - 4z = 0 \\ 4x + 2y + 4z = 4 \\ \hline -2y = 4 \\ y = -2 \end{array}$$

Replace y with -2 in E4.

$$x - 4(-2) = 5$$
$$x + 8 = 5$$
$$x = -3$$

Replace x with -3 and y with -2 in E2.

$$-3 + (-2) + z = 0$$
$$-5 + z = 0$$
$$z = 5$$

The solution is $(-3, -2, 5)$.

12. $\begin{cases} 3x + y - 2z = 2 & (1) \\ -6x - 2y + 4z = -2 & (2) \\ 9x + 3y - 6z = 6 & (3) \end{cases}$

Multiply E1 by 2 and add to E2.

$$\begin{array}{r} 6x + 2y - 4z = 4 \\ -6x - 2y + 4z = -2 \\ \hline 0 = 2 \quad \text{False} \end{array}$$

Inconsistent system; the solution set is $\varnothing$.

14. $\begin{cases} 5y - 7z = 14 & (1) \\ 2x + y + 4z = 10 & (2) \\ 2x + 6y - 3z = 30 & (3) \end{cases}$

Multiply E2 by -1 and add to E3.

$$\begin{array}{r} -2x - y - 4z = -10 \\ 2x + 6y - 3z = 30 \\ \hline 5y - 7z = 20 \quad (4) \end{array}$$

Multiply E4 by -1 and add to E1.

$$\begin{array}{r} -5y + 7z = -20 \\ 5y - 7z = 14 \\ \hline 0 = -6 \quad \text{False} \end{array}$$

Inconsistent system; the solution set is $\varnothing$.

16. $\begin{cases} x - 5y = 0 & (1) \\ x - z = 0 & (2) \\ -x + 5z = 0 & (3) \end{cases}$

Add E2 and E3.

$$4z = 0$$
$$z = 0$$

Replace z with 0 in E2.

$$x - 0 = 0$$
$$x = 0$$

Replace x with 0 in E1.

$$0 - 5y = 0$$
$$y = 0$$

The solution is $(0, 0, 0)$.

18. $\begin{cases} x + 2y = 6 & (1) \\ 7x + 3y + z = -33 & (2) \\ x - z = 16 & (3) \end{cases}$

Add E2 and E3.

$$8x + 3y = -17 \quad (4)$$

Multiply E1 by -8 and to E4.

$$\begin{array}{r} -8x - 16y = -48 \\ 8x + 3y = -17 \\ \hline -13y = -65 \\ y = 5 \end{array}$$

Replace y with 5 in E1.

$$x + 2(5) = 6$$
$$x + 10 = 6$$
$$x = -4$$

Replace x with -4 in E3.

$-4 - z = 16$

$z = -20$

The solution is $(-4, 5, -20)$.

20. $\begin{cases} 5x + y + 3z = 1 & (1) \\ x - y + 3z = -7 & (2) \\ -x + y = 1 & (3) \end{cases}$

Add E2 and E3.

$3z = -6$ or $z = -2$

Add E1 to E2.

$6x + 6z = -6$

$x + z = -1$

Replace z with -2 in this equation.

$x + (-2) = -1$ so $x = 1$

Replace x with 1 and z with -2 in E1.

$5(1) + y + 3(-2) = 1$

$y - 1 = 1$

$y = 2$

The solution is $(1, 2, -2)$.

22. $\begin{cases} 4x - y + 3z = 10 & (1) \\ x + y - z = 5 & (2) \\ 8x - 2y + 6z = 10 & (3) \end{cases}$

Multiply E1 by -2 and add to E3.

$-8x + 2y - 6z = -20$

$\underline{8x - 2y + 6z = 10}$

$ 0 = -10$ False

Inconsistent system; the solution set is $\varnothing$.

24. $\begin{cases} 4x + y - z = 8 & (1) \\ x - y + 2z = 3 & (2) \\ 3x - y + z = 6 & (3) \end{cases}$

Add E1 and E2.

$5x + z = 11$ (4)

Add E1 and E3.

$7x = 14$ or $x = 2$

Replace x with 2 in E4.

$5(2) + z = 11$

$z = 1$

Replace x with 2 and z with 1 in E1.

$4(2) + y - 1 = 8$

$y + 7 = 8$

$y = 1$

The solution is $(2, 1, 1)$.

26. $\begin{cases} -6x + 12y + 3z = -6 & (1) \\ 2x - 4y - z = 2 & (2) \\ -x + 2y + \dfrac{z}{2} = -1 & (3) \end{cases}$

Multiply E3 by 2 and add to E2.

$-2x + 4y + z = -2$

$\underline{2x - 4y - z = 2}$

$ 0 = 0$

The system is dependent. The solution set is $\{(x, y, z) | 2x - 4y - z = 2\}$.

28. $\begin{cases} 7x + 4y = 10 & (1) \\ x - 4y + 2z = 6 & (2) \\ y - 2z = -1 & (3) \end{cases}$

Add E1 to E2.

$8x + 2z = 16$ (4)

Add 4 times E3 to E2.

$4y - 8z = -4$

$\underline{x - 4y + 2z = 6}$

$x - 6z = 2$ (5)

Add 3 times E4 to E5.

$24x + 6z = 48$

$\underline{x - 6z = 2}$

$25x = 50$

$x = 2$

Replace x with 2 in E5.

$2 - 6z = 2$

$-6z = 0$

$z = 0$

Replace z with 0 in E3 to get $y = -1$. The solution is $(2, -1, 0)$.

30. $\begin{cases} 3x - 3y + z = -1 & (1) \\ 3x - y - z = 3 & (2) \\ -6x + y + 2z = -6 & (3) \end{cases}$

Add E1 and E2.

$6x - 4y = 2$ or $3x - 2y = 1$ (4)

Add twice E2 to E3.

$6x - 2y - 2z = 6$

$\underline{-6x + y + 2z = -6}$

$-y = 0$

$y = 0$

Replace y with 0 in E4.

$3x - 2(0) = 1$

$3x = 1$

$x = \dfrac{1}{3}$

Replace x with $\frac{1}{3}$ and y with 0 in E1.

$$3\left(\frac{1}{3}\right) - 3(0) + z = -1$$
$$1 + z = -1$$
$$z = -2$$

The solution is $\left(\frac{1}{3}, 0, -2\right)$.

32. $\begin{cases} \frac{1}{3}x - \frac{1}{4}y + z = -9 & (1) \\ \frac{1}{2}x - \frac{1}{3}y - \frac{1}{4}z = -6 & (2) \\ x - \frac{1}{2}y - z = -8 & (3) \end{cases}$

Multiply E1 and E2 by 12, and multiply E3 by 2.

$\begin{cases} 4x - 3y + 12z = -108 & (4) \\ 6x - 4y - 3z = -72 & (5) \\ 2x - y - 2z = -16 & (6) \end{cases}$

Add -3 times E6 to E4.

$-6x + 3y + 6z = 48$

$\underline{4x - 3y + 12z = -108}$

$-2x \quad\quad + 18z = -60 \quad (7)$

Add -4 times E6 to E5.

$-8x + 4y + 8z = 64$

$\underline{6x - 4y - 3z = -72}$

$-2x \quad\quad + 5z = -8 \quad (8)$

Add -1 times E7 to E8.

$2x - 18z = 60$

$\underline{-2x + 5z = -8}$

$-13z = 52$

$z = -4$

Replace z with -4 in E8.

$-2x + 5(-4) = -8$

$-2x = 12$

$x = -6$

Replace x with -6 and z with -4 in E6.

$2(-6) - y - 2(-4) = -16$

$-4 - y = -16$

$y = 12$

The solution is $(-6, 12, -4)$.

34. Let $x =$ the first number, then
$x + 5 =$ the second number.

$2x + 5(x + 5) = 53$
$2x + 5x + 25 = 53$
$7x = 28$
$x = 4$

$x + 5 = 4 + 5 = 9$
The numbers are 4 and 9.

36. $7(2x - 1) + 4 = 11(3x - 2)$
$14x - 7 + 4 = 33x - 22$
$-19x = -19$
$x = 1$

38. $z - 3(z + 7) = 6(2z + 1)$
$z - 3z - 21 = 12z + 6$
$-2z - 21 = 12z + 6$
$-14z = 27$
$z = -\dfrac{27}{14}$

40. Answers may vary

42. Answers may vary

44. $\begin{cases} x + 3y + z = -3 & (1) \\ -x + y + 2z = -14 & (2) \\ 3x + 2y - z = 12 & (3) \end{cases}$

Add E1 and E3.

$4x + 5y = 9 \quad (4)$

Add -2 times E1 to E2.

$-2x - 6y - 2z = 6$

$\underline{-x + y + 2z = -14}$

$-3x - 5y \quad\quad = -8 \quad (5)$

Add E4 and E5 to get $x = 1$.
Replace x with 1 in E4.

$4(1) + 5y = 9$
$5y = 5$
$y = 1$

Replace x and y with 1 in E1.

$1 + 3(1) + z = -3$
$z + 4 = -3$
$z = -7$

The solution is $(1, 1, -7)$, and

$\dfrac{x}{2} + \dfrac{y}{3} + \dfrac{z}{9} = \dfrac{1}{2} + \dfrac{1}{3} - \dfrac{7}{9}$

$= \dfrac{9}{18} + \dfrac{6}{18} - \dfrac{14}{18}$

$= \dfrac{1}{18}.$

46. $\begin{cases} 5x + 4y = 29 & (1) \\ y + z - w = -2 & (2) \\ 5x + z = 23 & (3) \\ y - z + w = 4 & (4) \end{cases}$

Add E2 and E4.

$2y = 2$ or $y = 1$

Replace y with 1 in E1.
$$5x + 4(1) = 29$$
$$5x = 25$$
$$x = 5$$
Replace x with 5 in E3.
$$5(5) + z = 23$$
$$z = -2$$
Replace y with 1 and z with -2 in E4.
$$1 - (-2) + w = 4$$
$$w = 1$$
The solution is $(5, 1, -2, 1)$.

48. $\begin{cases} 2x & -z & = -1 & (1) \\ & y + z + w = 9 & (2) \\ & y & -2w = -6 & (3) \\ x + y & = 3 & (4) \end{cases}$

Solve E2 for w.
$$w = 9 - y - z \quad (5)$$
Substitute into E3.
$$y - 2(9 - y - z) = -6$$
$$3y + 2z = 12 \quad (6)$$
A new system is
$$\begin{cases} 2x & -z = -1 & (7) \\ 3y + 2z = 12 & (8) \\ x + y & = 3 & (9) \end{cases}$$
Add 2 times E7 and E8.
$$4x \quad -2z = -2$$
$$\underline{\quad\quad 3y + 2z = 12}$$
$$4x + 3y \quad = 10 \quad (10)$$
Add -4 times E9 to E10.
$$-4x - 4y = -12$$
$$\underline{\quad 4x + 3y = 10}$$
$$-y = -2$$
$$y = 2$$
Replace y with 2 in E9.
$$x + 2 = 3$$
$$x = 1$$
Replace x with 1 in E7.
$$2(1) - z = -1$$
$$3 = z$$
Replace y with 2 and z with 3 in E5.
$$w = 9 - 2 - 3 = 4$$
The solution is $(1, 2, 3, 4)$.

50. Infinite number of solutions

Section 4.5

Practice Exercises

1. a. We are given a system of equations.
$$\begin{cases} y = -0.16x + 113.9 \\ y = 1.06x + 62.3 \end{cases}$$
We want to know the year x in which the pounds y are the same. Since both equations are solved for y, we use the substitution method. Substitute $-0.16x + 113.9$ for y in the second equation.
$$-0.16x + 113.9 = 1.06x + 62.3$$
$$-1.22x = -51.6$$
$$x = \frac{-51.6}{-1.22} \approx 42.30$$
Since we are only asked to give the year, we need only solve for x. The consumption of red meat and poultry will be the same about 42.30 years after 1995, or in about 2037.

b. Yes; answers may vary.

2. Let $x =$ first number
$y =$ second number
"A first number is five more than a second number" is translated as $x = y + 5$. "Twice the first number is 2 less than 3 times the second number" is translated as $2x = 3y - 2$.
We solve the following system.
$$\begin{cases} x = y + 5 \\ 2x = 3y - 2 \end{cases}$$
Since the first equation is solved for x, we use substitution. Substitute $y + 5$ for x in the second equation.
$$2(y + 5) = 3y - 2$$
$$2y + 10 = 3y - 2$$
$$12 = y$$
Replace y with 12 in the equation $x = y + 5$ and solve for x.
$$x = 12 + 5 = 17$$
The numbers are 12 and 17.

3. Let $x =$ price for adult admission
and $y =$ price per child admission.
$$\begin{cases} 3x + 3y = 75 \\ 2x + 4y = 62 \end{cases}$$
Multiply the first equation by 2 and the second equation by -3.

$$6x + 6y = 150$$
$$\underline{-6x - 12y = -186}$$
$$-6y = -36$$
$$y = 6$$

Let $y = 6$ in the second equation.
$$2x + 4y = 62$$
$$2x + 4(6) = 62$$
$$2x + 24 = 62$$
$$2x = 38$$
$$x = 19$$

a. $x = 19$, so the adult price is $19.

b. $y = 6$, so the child price is $6.

c. $5(19) + 15(6) = 95 + 90 = 185 < 200$
No, the regular rates are less than the group rate.

4. Let x = speed of the V150
y = speed of the Atlantique
We summarize the information in a chart. Both trains have traveled two hours.

	Rate	•	Time	=	Distance
V150	x		2		$2x$
Atlantique	y		2		$2y$

The trains are 2150 kilometers apart, so the sum of the distances is 2150: $2x + 2y = 2150$.

The V150 is 75 kph faster than the Atlantique: $x = y + 75$.

We solve the following system.
$$\begin{cases} 2x + 2y = 2150 \\ x = y + 75 \end{cases}$$

Since the second equation is solved for x, we use substitution. Substitute $y + 75$ for x in the first equation.
$$2(y + 75) + 2y = 2150$$
$$2y + 150 + 2y = 2150$$
$$4y + 150 = 2150$$
$$4y = 2000$$
$$y = 500$$

To find x, we replace y with 500 in the second equation.
$$x = 500 + 75 = 575$$
The speed of the V150 is 575 kph, and the speed of the Atlantique is 500 kph.

5. Let x = amount of 99% acid
y = amount of water (0%)

Both x and y are measured in liters. We use a table to organize the given data.

	Amount	Acid Strength	Amount of Pure Acid
99% acid	x	99%	$0.99x$
Water	y	0%	$0y$

The amount of 99% acid and water combined must equal 1 liter, so $x + y = 1$.
The amount of pure acid in the mixture must equal the sum of the amounts of pure acid in the 99% acid and in the water, so
$0.99x + 0y = 0.05(1)$, which simplifies to
$0.99x = 0.05$.
We solve the following system.
$$\begin{cases} x + y = 1 \\ 0.99x = 0.05 \end{cases}$$
Since the second equation does not contain y, we solve it for x.
$$0.99x = 0.05$$
$$x = \frac{0.05}{0.99} \approx 0.05$$
To find y, we replace x with 0.05 in the first equation.
$$x + y = 1$$
$$0.05 + y = 1$$
$$y = 0.95$$
The teacher should use 0.05 liter of the 99% HCL solution and 0.95 liter of water.

6. Let x = the number of packages.
The firm charges the customer $4.50 for each package, so the revenue equation is $R(x) = 4.5x$.
Each package costs $2.50 to produce and the equipment costs $3000, so the cost equation is
$C(x) = 2.5x + 3000$.
Since the break-even point is when $R(x) = C(x)$, we solve the equation $4.5x = 2.5x + 3000$.
$$4.5x = 2.5x + 3000$$
$$2x = 3000$$
$$x = 1500$$
The company must sell 1500 packages to break even.

7. Let x = measure of smallest angle
y = measure of largest angle
z = measure of third angle
The sum of the measures is 180°:
$$x + y + z = 180.$$

The measure of the largest angle is 40° more than the measure of the smallest angle:
$y = x + 40$.

The measure of the remaining angle is 20° more than the measure of the smallest angle:
$y = x + 20$.

We solve the following system.

$$\begin{cases} x + y + z = 1180 \\ y = x + 40 \\ z = x + 20 \end{cases}$$

We substitute $x + 40$ for y and $x + 20$ for z in the first equation.

$$x + (x + 40) + (x + 20) = 180$$
$$3x + 60 = 180$$
$$3x = 120$$
$$x = 40$$

Then $y = x + 40 = 40 + 40 = 80$ and $z = x + 20 = 40 + 20 = 60$.
The angle measures are 40°, 60°, and 80°.

Exercise Set 4.5

2. a. The equal sides are shorter than the third side, not longer.

b. The equal sides are 1 inch longer than the third side.
$P = a + b + c = 7 + 7 + 6 = 20$

c. There are no equal sides.

Choice **b** is correct.

4. a. $2c + 4t = 2(12) + 4(4) = 24 + 16 = 40$
$3c + 5t = 3(12) + 5(4)$
$= 36 + 20$
$= 56 \neq 55$

b. $2c + 4t = 2(15) + 4(2) = 30 + 8 = 38 \neq 40$

c. $2c + 4t = 2(10) + 4(5) = 20 + 20 = 40$
$3c + 5t = 3(10) + 5(5) = 30 + 25 = 55$

Choice **c** is correct.

6. a. $15 = 3(5)$
$15 + 5 = 20 \neq 28$

b. $20 \neq 3(8)$

c. $21 = 3(7)$
$21 + 7 = 28$

Choice **c** is correct.

8. Let x = the first number and y = the second number.

$$\begin{cases} x + y = 16 \\ x + 3y + 2 = 18 \end{cases}$$

10. Let x = the amount in the checking account and y = the amount in the savings account.

$$\begin{cases} x + y = 2300 \\ y = 4x \end{cases}$$

12. Let x = the first number and y = the second number.

$$\begin{cases} x + y = 76 \\ x - y = 52 \end{cases}$$

$$\begin{aligned} x + y &= 76 \\ \underline{x - y} &= \underline{52} \\ 2x &= 128 \\ x &= 64 \end{aligned}$$

Let $x = 64$ in the first equation.
$64 + y = 76$
$y = 12$
The numbers are 64 and 12.

14. Let x = the first number and y = the second number.

$$\begin{cases} x + y = 25 \\ x = 2y + 4 \end{cases}$$

Substitute $2y + 4$ for x in the first equation.
$2y + 4 + y = 25$
$3y = 21$
$y = 7$
Let $y = 7$ in the second equation.
$x = 2(7) + 4 = 18$
The numbers are 18 and 7.

16. Let x = home runs hit by Howard and y = home runs hit by Ortiz.

$$\begin{cases} x = y + 4 \\ x + y = 112 \end{cases}$$

Substitute $y + 4$ for x in the second equation.
$y + 4 + y = 112$
$2y = 108$
$y = 54$
Let $y = 54$ in the first equation.
$x = 54 + 4 = 58$
Howard hit 58 home runs and Ortiz hit 54.

18. Let x = the price of a DVD and y = the price of a CD.

$$\begin{cases} 5x + 2y = 65 \\ 3x + 4y = 81 \end{cases}$$

Multiply the first equation by -2.

$-10x - 4y = -130$
$\underline{\quad 3x + 4y = 81 \quad}$
$-7x \qquad = -49$
$\qquad x = 7$

Let $x = 7$ in the first equation.
$5(7) + 2y = 65$
$35 + 2y = 65$
$\quad 2y = 30$
$\quad y = 15$

The price of a DVD is $7 and the price of a CD is $15.

20. Let x = the number of 39¢ stamps and y = the number of 24¢ stamps.
$$\begin{cases} x + y = 40 \\ 0.3x + 0.24y = 14.85 \end{cases}$$

Solve the first equation for y.
$y = 40 - x$.
Substitute $40 - x$ for y in the second equation.
$0.39x + 0.24(40 - x) = 14.85$
$0.39x + 9.6 - 0.24x = 14.85$
$\qquad 0.15x = 5.25$
$\qquad x = 35$

Let $x = 35$ in $y = 40 - x$.
$y = 40 - 35$
$y = 5$
35 of the 39¢ stamps and 5 of the 24¢.

22. Let x = shares of EBay stock and y = shares of Amazon stock.
$$\begin{cases} 30.82x + 38.84y = 2866.60 \\ y = x + 20 \end{cases}$$

Substitute $x + 20$ for y in the first equation.
$30.82x + 38.84(x + 20) = 2866.60$
$30.82x + 38.84x + 776.80 = 2866.60$
$\qquad 69.66x = 2089.80$
$\qquad x = 30$

Let $x = 30$ in the second equation.
$y = 30 + 20 = 50$
Pho Lin owns 30 shares of EBay and 50 shares of Amazon.

24. Let x = the daily fee and y = the charge per mile.
$$\begin{cases} 5x + 300y = 178 \\ 4x + 500y = 197 \end{cases}$$

Multiply the first equation by 4 and the second equation by -5.
$20x + 1200y = 712$
$\underline{-20x - 2500y = -985}$
$\qquad -1300y = -273$
$\qquad y = 0.21$

Let $y = 0.21$ in the first equation.
$5x + 300(0.21) = 178$
$\quad 5x + 63 = 178$
$\quad 5x = 115$
$\quad x = 23$

The daily fee is $23 and the mileage charge is $0.21 per mile.

26.

d	=	r	·	t
Downstream	10		$x + y$	$1\frac{1}{4}$
Upstream	10		$x - y$	4

$$\begin{cases} \dfrac{5}{4}(x + y) = 10 \\ 4(x - y) = 10 \end{cases}$$

Multiply the first equation by $\dfrac{4}{5}$ and the second equation $\dfrac{1}{4}$.
$x + y = 8$
$\underline{x - y = 2.5}$
$2x \quad = 10.5$
$\quad x = 5.25$

Let $x = 5.25$ in $x + y = 8$.
$5.25 + y = 8$
$\quad y = 2.75$

The rate of the current is 2.75 miles per hour.

28.

d	=	r	·	t
With the wind	2400		$x + y$	$4\frac{3}{4}$
Into the wind	2400		$x - y$	6

$$\begin{cases} \dfrac{19}{4}(x + y) = 2400 \\ 6(x - y) = 2400 \end{cases}$$

Multiply the first equation by $\dfrac{4}{19}$ and the second equation by $\dfrac{1}{6}$.
$x + y = 505.26$
$\underline{x - y = 400}$
$2x \quad = 905.26$
$\quad x \approx 452.63$

Let $x = 452.63$ in $x + y = 505.26$.

$452.63 + y = 505.26$

$y \approx 52.63$

The plane can fly 452.6 miles per hour in still air. The speed of the wind is 52.6 miles per hour.

30. Let x = the speed of the westbound train and y = the speed of the eastbound train. Recall that $d = r \cdot t$.

$$\begin{cases} \dfrac{5}{4}x + \dfrac{5}{4}y = 150 \\ x = 2y \end{cases}$$

Substitute $2y$ for x in the first equation.

$\dfrac{5}{4}(2y) + \dfrac{5}{4}y = 150$

$\dfrac{10}{4}y + \dfrac{5}{4}y = 150$

$\dfrac{15}{4}y = 150$

$y = 40$

Let $y = 40$ in the second equation.

$x = 2(40) = 80$

The speed of the westbound train is 80 miles per hour and the speed of the eastbound train is 40 miles per hour.

32. Let x = liters of 40% solution and y = liters of 10% solution.

Concentration Rate	Ounces of Solution	Ounces of Pure Acid
0.40	x	$0.4x$
0.10	y	$0.1y$
0.25	15	$0.25(15)$

$$\begin{cases} x + y = 15 \\ 0.4x + 0.1y = 0.25(15) \end{cases}$$

Multiply the second equation by -10.

$\quad x + y = 15$

$\underline{-4x - y = -37.5}$

$\quad -3x = -22.5$

$\quad\quad x = 7.5$

Let $y = 7.5$ in the first equation.

$x + 7.5 = 15$

$\quad\quad x = 7.5$

$7\dfrac{1}{2}$ ounces of 40% solution and $7\dfrac{1}{2}$ ounces of 10% solution should be mixed.

34. Let x = pounds of macadamia nuts and y = pounds of standard mix.

	Cost Rate	Pounds of nuts	Dollars Cost
macadamia	16.50	x	$16.50x$
standard mix	9.25	y	$9.25y$
Mixture	10	40	$10(40)$

$$\begin{cases} x + y = 40 \\ 16.50x + 9.25y = 10(40) \end{cases}$$

Solve the first equation for y.

$y = 40 - x$

Substitute $40 - x$ for y in the second equation.

$16.50x + 9.25(40 - x) = 10(40)$

$16.50x + 370 - 9.25x = 400$

$7.25x = 30$

$x \approx 4.14$

Let $x = 4.14$ in the first equation.

$4.14 + y = 40$

$y \approx 35.86$

The mixture needs 4.1 pounds of macadamia nuts and 35.9 pounds of the standard mix.

36. Let x = the first angle and y = the second angle.

$$\begin{cases} x + y = 180 \\ x = 4y + 20 \end{cases}$$

Substitute $4y + 20$ for x in the first equation.

$4y + 20 + y = 180$

$5y = 160$

$y = 32$

Let $y = 32$ in the second equation.

$x = 4(32) + 20 = 148$

The angles are 148° and 32°.

38. Let x = the first angle and y = the second angle.

$$\begin{cases} x + y = 180 \\ x = 2y + 18 \end{cases}$$

Substitute $2y + 18$ for x in the first equation.

$2y + 18 + y = 180$

$3y = 162$

$y = 54$

Let $y = 54$ in the second equation.

$x = 2(54) + 18 = 126$

The angles are 126° and 54°.

40. Let x = the number of adults and y = the number of children.

$$\begin{cases} x + y = 387 \\ 6.80x + 3.40y = 2444.60 \end{cases}$$

Solve the first equation for y.

$y = 387 - x$

Substitute $387 - x$ for y in the second equation.

$6.80x + 3.40(387 - x) = 2444.60$

$6.80x + 1315.80 - 3.40x = 2444.60$

$3.40x = 1128.80$

$x = 332$

Let $x = 332$ in $y = 387 - x$.

$y = 387 - 332 = 55$

332 adults and 55 children attended.

42. Let x = the rate of the slower car and y = the rate of the faster car.

	r	$\cdot$ t	$=$ d
Slower car	x	3	$3x$
Faster car	y	3	$3y$

$$\begin{cases} y = x + 1 \\ 3x + 3y = 123 \end{cases}$$

Substitute $x + 1$ for y in the second equation.

$3x + 3(x + 1) = 123$

$3x + 3x + 3 = 123$

$6x = 120$

$x = 20$

Let $x = 20$ in the first equation.

$y = 20 + 1 = 21$

The rate of the faster car is 21 miles per hour. The rate of the slower car is 20 miles per hour.

44. Let x = ounces of 10% solution and y = ounces of 50% solution.

Concentration Rate	Ounces of Solution	Ounces of Pure Acid
0.10	x	$0.10x$
0.50	y	$0.50y$
0.20	120	$0.20(120)$

$$\begin{cases} x + y = 120 \\ 0.10x + 0.50y = 0.20(120) \end{cases}$$

Multiply the second equation by -10.

$\begin{array}{r} x + y = 120 \\ -x - 5y = -240 \\ \hline -4y = -120 \\ y = 30 \end{array}$

Let $y = 30$ in the first equation.

$x + 30 = 120$

$x = 90$

90 ounces of 10% solution and 30 ounces of 50% solution.

46. Let x = the width and y = the length.

$$\begin{cases} 2x + 2y = 60 \\ y = x + 6 \end{cases}$$

Substitute $x + 6$ for y in the first equation.

$2x + 2(x + 6) = 60$

$2x + 2x + 12 = 60$

$4x = 48$

$x = 12$

Let $x = 12$ in the second equation.

$y = 12 + 6 = 18$

The width is 12 inches and the length is 18 inches.

48. a. $\begin{cases} y = -x + 54.2 & (1) \\ y = x + 45.8 & (2) \end{cases}$

Substitute $x + 45.8$ for y in E1.

$x + 45.8 = -x + 54.2$

$2x = 8.4$

$x = 4.2$

$2000 + 4 = 2004$

The year would be 2004.

b. No

50. $\begin{cases} y = -0.40x + 15.9 \\ y = 0.14x + 11.9 \end{cases}$

Substitute $0.14x + 11.9$ for y in E1.

$0.14x + 11.9 = -0.40x + 15.9$

$0.54x = 4$

$x = \dfrac{4}{0.54} \approx 7.4$

The year would be 1987.

52. $\begin{cases} x + 2y = 180 \\ y + (3x - 10) = 180, \text{ or} \end{cases}$

$\begin{cases} x + 2y = 180 & (1) \\ 3x + y = 190 & (2) \end{cases}$

Multiply E1 by -3 and add to E2.

$-3x - 6y = -540$

$\underline{3x + y = 190}$

$-5y = -350$

$y = 70$

Replace y with 70 in E1.

$x + 2(70) = 180$

$x + 140 = 180$

$x = 40$

The value of x is 40° and the value of y is 70°.

54. $C(x) = 12x + 15,000$

$R(x) = 32x$

$32x = 12x + 15,000$

$20x = 15,000$

$x = 750$

750 units

56. $C(x) = 0.8x + 900$

$R(x) = 2x$

$2x = 0.8x + 900$

$1.2x = 900$

$x = 750$

750 units

58. $C(x) = 105x + 70,000$

$R(x) = 245x$

$245x = 105x + 70,000$

$140x = 70,000$

$x = 500$

500 units

60. a. $R(x) = 31x$

b. $C(x) = 15x + 500$

c. $R(x) = C(x)$

$31x = 15x + 500$

$16x = 500$

$x = 31.25,$ or 32 baskets

62. Let x = liters of 25% solution,

y = liters of 40% solution, and

z = liters of 50% solution.

$$\begin{cases} x + y + z = 200 \\ 0.25x + 0.40y + 0.50z = 0.32(200) \\ x = 2y \end{cases}$$

Multiply E2 by 100.

$$\begin{cases} x + y + z = 200 & (1) \\ 25x + 40y + 50z = 6400 & (2) \\ x = 2y & (3) \end{cases}$$

Replace x with $2y$ in E1 and E2 and simplify.

$$\begin{cases} 3y + z = 200 & (4) \\ 90y + 50z = 6400 & (5) \end{cases}$$

Multiply E4 by –50 and add to E5.

$-150y - 50z = -10,000$

$\underline{90y + 50z = 6400}$

$-60y = -3600$ (5)

$y = 60$

Replace y with 60 in E4 and E3.

$3(60) + z = 200$ and $x = 2y$

$180 + z = 200$ $x = 2(60)$

$z = 20$ $x = 120$

25% solution: 120 L

40% solution: 60 L

50% solution: 20 L

64. Let x = measure of smallest angle,

y = measure of largest, and

z = measure of remaining side.

$$\begin{cases} x + y + z = 180 & (1) \\ y = x + 90 & (2) \\ z = x + 30 & (3) \end{cases}$$

Substitute $y = x + 90$ and $z = x + 30$ in E1.

$x + (x + 90) + (x + 30) = 180$

$3x + 120 = 180$

$3x = 60$

$x = 20$

Replace x with 20 in E2 and E3.

$y = 20 + 90 = 110$ and $z = 20 + 30 = 50$

The measures are 20°, 50°, and 110°.

66. Let o = the ones digit, t = the tens digit and h = the hundreds digit.

$$\begin{cases} h + t + o = 15 & (1) \\ t = 2h & (2) \\ o = h - 1 & (3) \end{cases}$$

Substitute $t = 2h$ and $o = h - 1$ into E1.

$h + (2h) + (h - 1) = 15$

$4h - 1 = 15$

$4h = 16$

$h = 4$

Use this value in E2 and E3.

$t = 2(4) = 8$

$o = 4 - 1 = 3$

The number is 483.

68. Let x = number of free throws,

y = number of two-point field goals, and

z = number of three-point field goals

$$\begin{cases} x+2y+3z=654 \\ x=y-3 \\ z=\dfrac{1}{5}y-27 \end{cases}$$

Rewrite the system in a more convenient form.

$$\begin{cases} x+2y+\ 3z=654 & (1) \\ x-\ y\ \ \ \ \ \ =-3 & (2) \\ -y+5z=-135 & (3) \end{cases}$$

Multiply E2 by -1 and add to E1.

$$\begin{array}{r} x+2y+3z=654 \\ -x\ +y\ \ \ \ \ \ =3 \\ \hline 3y+3z=657 \ \ (4) \end{array}$$

Multiply E3 by 3 and add to E4.

$$\begin{array}{r} -3y+15z=-405 \\ 3y+3z=657 \\ \hline 18z=252 \\ z=14 \end{array}$$

Replace z with 14 in E3.

$-y+5(14)=-135$

$\ \ -y+70=-135$

$\ \ \ \ \ \ 205=y$

Replace y with 205 in E2.

$x-205=-3$

$\ \ \ \ \ \ x=202$

He made 202 free throws, 205 two-point field goals, and 14 three-point field goals.

70. $\begin{cases} x+y+z+72=360 \\ y+(z-13)=180 \\ x+(z+15)=180 \end{cases}$

$\begin{cases} x+y+z=288 & (1) \\ y+z=193 & (2) \\ x\ \ \ \ +z=165 & (3) \end{cases}$

Multiply E2 by -1 and add to E1.

$$\begin{array}{r} x+y+z=288 \\ -y-z=-193 \\ \hline x\ \ \ \ \ \ \ \ \ \ =95 \end{array}$$

Use this value in E3.

$95+z=165$

$\ \ \ \ \ \ \ z=70$

Replace z with 70 in E2.

$y+70=193$

$\ \ \ \ \ \ y=123$

$x=95$, $y=123$, and $z=70$.

72. $2x-7\le 5x+11$

$\ \ -3x-7\le 11$

$\ \ \ \ \ \ -3x\le 18$

$\ \ \ \ \ \ \dfrac{-3x}{-3}\ge\dfrac{18}{-3}$

$\ \ \ \ \ \ \ \ x\ge -6, [-6,\infty)$

74. $\dfrac{2}{3}x<\dfrac{1}{3}$

$\ \ 2x<1$

$\ \ x<\dfrac{1}{2}, \left(-\infty,\dfrac{1}{2}\right)$

76. Since the resulting solution cannot be less than 50% acid, **a** (25%) is impossible.
Since the resulting solution cannot be more than 100% acid, **b** (150%) is impossible.
Since $50\%<62\%<100\%$ and $50\%<90\%<100\%$, the possible acid strengths are **c** and **d**.

78. Let $x=$ the width and $y=$ the length.

$$\begin{cases} 2x+y=152 \\ x=0.5y+4 \end{cases}$$

Substitute $0.5y+4$ for x in the first equation.

$2(0.5y+4)+y=152$

$\ \ \ \ \ \ y+8+y=152$

$\ \ \ \ \ \ \ \ 2y+8=152$

$\ \ \ \ \ \ \ \ \ \ \ 2y=144$

$\ \ \ \ \ \ \ \ \ \ \ \ \ y=72$

Let $y=72$ in the second equation.

$x=0.5(72)+4=40$

The width is 40 feet and the length is 72 feet.

80. Let $x=$ the first angle and $y=$ the second angle.

$$\begin{cases} x+y=90 \\ x=6y \end{cases}$$

Substitute $6y$ for x in the first equation.

$6y+y=90$

$\ \ \ \ 7y=90$

$\ \ \ \ \ \ y=12\dfrac{6}{7}$

Let $y=12\dfrac{6}{7}$ in the first equation.

$x+12\dfrac{6}{7}=90$

$\ \ \ \ \ \ \ x=77\dfrac{1}{7}$

The angles are $12\dfrac{6}{7}°$ and $77\dfrac{1}{7}°$.

82. $y = ax^2 + bx + c$

(1, 6): $6 = a + b + c$ (1)

$(-1, -2)$: $-2 = a - b + c$ (2)

$(0, -1)$: $-1 = c$ (3)

Substitute $c = -1$ in E1 and E2 to obtain

$\begin{cases} a + b = 7 & \text{(from E1)} \\ a - b = -1 & \text{(from E2)} \end{cases}$

Add these equations.

$2a = 6$

$a = 3$

Replace a with 3 in $a + b = 7$.

$3 + b = 7$ so $b = 4$

Therefore, $a = 3$, $b = 4$, and $c = -1$.

Chapter 4 Vocabulary Check

1. In a system of linear equations in two variables, if the graphs of the equations are the same, the equations are <u>dependent</u> equations.

2. Two or more linear equations are called a <u>system of linear equations</u>.

3. A system of equations that has at least one solution is called a <u>consistent</u> system.

4. A <u>solution</u> of a system of two equations in two variables is an ordered pair of numbers that is a solution of both equations in the system.

5. Two algebraic methods for solving systems of equations are <u>addition</u> and <u>substitution</u>.

6. A system of equations that has no solution is called an <u>inconsistent</u> system.

7. In a system of linear equations in two variables, if the graphs of the equations are different, the equations are <u>independent</u> equations.

Chapter 4 Review

1. a. Let $x = 12$ and $y = 4$.

$2x - 3y = 12$

$2(12) - 3(4) \overset{?}{=} 12$

$24 - 12 \overset{?}{=} 12$

$12 = 12$ True

$3x + 4y = 1$

$3(12) + 4(4) \overset{?}{=} 1$

$36 + 16 \overset{?}{=} 1$

$52 = 1$ False

(12, 4) is not a solution of the system.

b. Let $x = 3$ and $y = -2$.

$2x - 3y = 12$

$2(3) - 3(-2) \overset{?}{=} 12$

$6 + 6 \overset{?}{=} 12$

$2 = 12$ True

$3x + 4y = 1$

$3(3) + 4(-2) \overset{?}{=} 1$

$9 - 8 \overset{?}{=} 1$

$1 = 1$ True

$(3, -2)$ is a solution of the system.

c. Let $x = -3$ and $y = 6$.

$2x - 3y = 12$

$2(-3) - 3(6) \overset{?}{=} 12$

$-6 - 18 \overset{?}{=} 12$

$-24 = 12$ False

$3x + 4y = 1$

$3(-3) + 4(6) \overset{?}{=} 1$

$-9 + 24 \overset{?}{=} 1$

$15 = 1$ False

$(-3, 6)$ is not a solution of the system.

2. a. Let $x = \dfrac{3}{4}$ and $y = -3$.

$4x + y = 0$

$4\left(\dfrac{3}{4}\right) - 3 \overset{?}{=} 0$

$3 - 3 \overset{?}{=} 0$

$0 = 0$ True

$-8x - 5y = 9$

$-8\left(\dfrac{3}{4}\right) - 5(-3) \overset{?}{=} 9$

$-6 + 15 \overset{?}{=} 9$

$9 = 9$ True

$\left(\dfrac{3}{4}, -3\right)$ is a solution of the system.

b. Let $x = -2$ and $y = 8$.

$4x + y = 0$

$4(-2) + 8 \overset{?}{=} 0$

$-8 + 8 \overset{?}{=} 0$

$0 = 0$ True

$$-8x - 5y = 9$$
$$-8(-2) - 5(8) \stackrel{?}{=} 9$$
$$16 - 40 \stackrel{?}{=} 9$$
$$-24 = 9 \quad \text{False}$$

$(-2, 8)$ is not a solution of the system.

c. Let $x = \dfrac{1}{2}$ and $y = -2$.

$$4x + y = 0$$
$$4\left(\dfrac{1}{2}\right) - 2 \stackrel{?}{=} 0$$
$$2 - 2 \stackrel{?}{=} 0$$
$$0 = 0 \quad \text{True}$$

$$-8x - 5y = 9$$
$$-8\left(\dfrac{1}{2}\right) - 5(-2) \stackrel{?}{=} 9$$
$$-4 + 10 \stackrel{?}{=} 9$$
$$6 = 9 \quad \text{False}$$

$\left(\dfrac{1}{2}, -2\right)$ is not a solution of the system.

3. a. Let $x = -6$ and $y = -8$.

$$5x - 6y = 18$$
$$5(-6) - 6(-8) \stackrel{?}{=} 18$$
$$-30 + 48 \stackrel{?}{=} 18$$
$$18 = 18 \quad \text{True}$$

$$2y - x = -4$$
$$2(-8) - (-6) \stackrel{?}{=} -4$$
$$-16 + 6 \stackrel{?}{=} -4$$
$$-10 = -4 \quad \text{False}$$

$(-6, -8)$ is not a solution of the system.

b. Let $x = 3$ and $y = \dfrac{5}{2}$.

$$5x - 6y = 18$$
$$5(3) - 6\left(\dfrac{5}{2}\right) \stackrel{?}{=} 18$$
$$15 - 15 \stackrel{?}{=} 18$$
$$0 = 18 \quad \text{False}$$

$$2y - x = -4$$
$$2\left(\dfrac{5}{2}\right) - 3 \stackrel{?}{=} -4$$
$$5 - 3 \stackrel{?}{=} -4$$
$$2 = -4 \quad \text{False}$$

$\left(3, \dfrac{5}{2}\right)$ is not a solution of the system.

c. Let $x = 3$ and $y = -\dfrac{1}{2}$.

$$5x - 6y = 18$$
$$5(3) - 6\left(-\dfrac{1}{2}\right) \stackrel{?}{=} 18$$
$$15 + 3 \stackrel{?}{=} 18$$
$$18 = 18 \quad \text{True}$$

$$2y - x = -4$$
$$2\left(-\dfrac{1}{2}\right) - 3 \stackrel{?}{=} -4$$
$$-1 - 3 \stackrel{?}{=} -4$$
$$-4 = -4 \quad \text{True}$$

$\left(3, -\dfrac{1}{2}\right)$ is a solution of the system.

4. a. Let $x = 2$ and $y = 2$.

$2x + 3y = 1$	$3y - x = 4$
$2(2) + 3(2) \stackrel{?}{=} 1$	$3(2) - 2 \stackrel{?}{=} 4$
$4 + 6 \stackrel{?}{=} 1$	$6 - 2 \stackrel{?}{=} 4$
$10 = 1 \quad \text{False}$	$4 = 4 \quad \text{True}$

$(2, 2)$ is not a solution of the system.

b. Let $x = -1$ and $y = 1$.

$2x + 3y = 1$	$3y - x = 4$
$2(-1) + 3(1) \stackrel{?}{=} 1$	$3(1) - (-1) \stackrel{?}{=} 4$
$-2 + 3 \stackrel{?}{=} 1$	$3 + 1 \stackrel{?}{=} 4$
$1 = 1 \quad \text{True}$	$4 = 4 \quad \text{True}$

$(-1, 1)$ is a solution of the system.

c. Let $x = 2$ and $y = -1$.

$$2x + 3y = 1$$
$$2(2) + 3(-1) \stackrel{?}{=} 1$$
$$4 - 3 \stackrel{?}{=} 1$$
$$1 = 1 \quad \text{True}$$

$$3y - x = 4$$
$$3(-1) - 2 \stackrel{?}{=} 4$$
$$-3 - 2 \stackrel{?}{=} 4$$
$$-5 = 4 \quad \text{False}$$

$(2, -1)$ is not a solution of the system.

5. $\begin{cases} x + y = 5 \\ x - 1 = y \end{cases}$

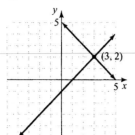

The solution of the system is (3, 2).

6. $\begin{cases} x + y = 3 \\ x - y = -1 \end{cases}$

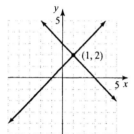

The solution of the system is (1, 2).

7. $\begin{cases} x = 5 \\ y = -1 \end{cases}$

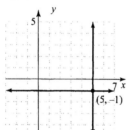

The solution of the system is (5, −1).

8. $\begin{cases} x = -3 \\ y = 2 \end{cases}$

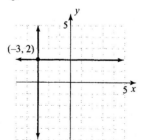

The solution of the system is (−3, 2).

9. $\begin{cases} 2x + y = 5 \\ x = -3y \end{cases}$

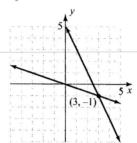

The solution of the system is (3, −1).

10. $\begin{cases} 3x + y = -2 \\ y = -5x \end{cases}$

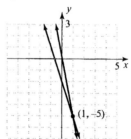

The solution of the system is (1, −5).

11. $\begin{cases} y = 3x \\ -6x + 2y = 6 \end{cases}$

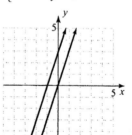

There is no solution.

12. $\begin{cases} x - 2y = 2 \\ -2x + 4y = -4 \end{cases}$

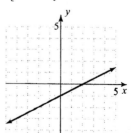

There is an infinite number of solutions.

13. $\begin{cases} y = 2x + 6 \\ 3x - 2y = -11 \end{cases}$

Substitute $2x + 6$ for y in the second equation.
$3x - 2(2x + 6) = -11$
$3x - 4x - 12 = -11$
$-x = 1$
$x = -1$
Let $x = -1$ in the first equation.
$y = 2(-1) + 6 = 4$
The solution is $(-1, 4)$.

14. $\begin{cases} y = 3x - 7 \\ 2x - 3y = 7 \end{cases}$

Substitute $3x - 7$ for y in the second equation.
$2x - 3(3x - 7) = 7$
$2x - 9x + 21 = 7$
$-7x = -14$
$x = 2$
Let $x = 2$ in the first equation.
$y = 3(2) - 7 = -1$
The solution is $(2, -1)$.

15. $\begin{cases} x + 3y = -3 \\ 2x + y = 4 \end{cases}$

Solve the first equation for x.
$x = -3y - 3$
Substitute $-3y - 3$ for x in the second equation.
$2(-3y - 3) + y = 4$
$-6y - 6 + y = 4$
$-5y = 10$
$y = -2$
Let $y = -2$ in $x = -3y - 3$.
$x = -3(-2) - 3 = 3$
The solution is $(3, -2)$.

16. $\begin{cases} 3x + y = 11 \\ x + 2y = 12 \end{cases}$

Solve the first equation for y.
$y = 11 - 3x$
Substitute $11 - 3x$ for y in the second equation.
$x + 2(11 - 3x) = 12$
$x + 22 - 6x = 12$
$-5x = -10$
$x = 2$
Let $x = 2$ in $y = 11 - 3x$.
$y = 11 - 3(2) = 5$
The solution is $(2, 5)$.

17. $\begin{cases} 4y = 2x + 6 \\ x - 2y = -3 \end{cases}$

Solve the second equation for x.
$x = 2y - 3$
Substitute $2y - 3$ for x in the first equation.
$4y = 2(2y - 3) + 6$
$4y = 4y - 6 + 6$
$0 = 0$
The system has an infinite number of solutions.

18. $\begin{cases} 9x = 6y + 3 \\ 6x - 4y = 2 \end{cases}$

Solve the first equation for y.
$9x = 6y + 3$
$9x - 3 = 6y$
$\dfrac{3}{2}x - \dfrac{1}{2} = y$
Substitute $\dfrac{3}{2}x - \dfrac{1}{2}$ for y in the second equation.
$6x - 4\left(\dfrac{3}{2}x - \dfrac{1}{2}\right) = 2$
$6x - 6x + 2 = 2$
$2 = 2$
The system has an infinite number of solutions.

19. $\begin{cases} x + y = 6 \\ y = -x - 4 \end{cases}$

Substitute $-x - 4$ for y in the first equation.
$x + (-x - 4) = 6$
$x - x - 4 = 6$
$-4 = 6$ False
There is no solution.

20. $\begin{cases} -3x + y = 6 \\ y = 3x + 2 \end{cases}$

Substitute $3x + 2$ for y in the first equation.
$-3x + (3x + 2) = 6$
$-3x + 3x + 2 = 6$
$2 = 6$ False
There is no solution.

21. $\begin{cases} 2x + 3y = -6 \\ x - 3y = -12 \end{cases}$

$\begin{array}{r} 2x + 3y = -6 \\ \underline{x - 3y = -12} \\ 3x = -18 \\ x = -6 \end{array}$

Let $x = -6$ in the first equation.

$$2(-6) + 3y = -6$$
$$-12 + 3y = -6$$
$$3y = 6$$
$$y = 2$$

The solution of the system is (–6, 2).

22. $\begin{cases} 4x + y = 15 \\ -4x + 3y = -19 \end{cases}$

$$4x + y = 15$$
$$\underline{-4x + 3y = -19}$$
$$4y = -4$$
$$y = -1$$

Let $y = -1$ in the first equation.
$$4x + (-1) = 15$$
$$4x - 1 = 15$$
$$4x = 16$$
$$x = 4$$

The solution of the system is (4, –1).

23. $\begin{cases} 2x - 3y = -15 \\ x + 4y = 31 \end{cases}$

Multiply the second equation by –2.
$$2x - 3y = -15$$
$$\underline{-2x - 8y = -62}$$
$$-11y = -77$$
$$y = 7$$

Let $y = 7$ in the second equation.
$$x + 4(7) = 31$$
$$x + 28 = 31$$
$$x = 3$$

The solution of the system is (3, 7).

24. $\begin{cases} x - 5y = -22 \\ 4x + 3y = 4 \end{cases}$

Multiply the first equation by –4.
$$-4x + 20y = 88$$
$$\underline{4x + 3y = 4}$$
$$23y = 92$$
$$y = 4$$

Let $y = 4$ in the first equation.
$$x - 5(4) = -22$$
$$x - 20 = -22$$
$$x = -2$$

The solution of the system is (–2, 4).

25. $\begin{cases} 2x - 6y = -1 \\ -x + 3y = \dfrac{1}{2} \end{cases}$

Multiply the second equation by 2.
$$2x - 6y = -1$$
$$\underline{-2x + 6y = 1}$$
$$0 = 0$$

There is an infinite number of solutions.

26. $\begin{cases} 0.6x - 0.3y = -1.5 \\ 0.04x - 0.02y = -0.1 \end{cases}$

Multiply the first equation by 20 and the second equation by –300.
$$12x - 6y = -30$$
$$\underline{-12x + 6y = 30}$$
$$0 = 0$$

There are an infinite number of solutions.

27. $\begin{cases} \dfrac{3}{4}x + \dfrac{2}{3}y = 2 \\ x + \dfrac{y}{3} = 6 \end{cases}$

Multiply the first equation by 12 and the second equation by 3.
$$\begin{cases} 9x + 8y = 24 \\ 3x + y = 18 \end{cases}$$

Multiply the second equation in the simplified system by –3.
$$9x + 8y = 24$$
$$\underline{-9x - 3y = -54}$$
$$5y = -30$$
$$y = -6$$

Let $y = -6$ in $3x + y = 18$.
$$3x + (-6) = 18$$
$$3x = 24$$
$$x = 8$$

The solution of the system is (8, –6).

28. $\begin{cases} 10x + 2y = 0 \\ 3x + 5y = 33 \end{cases}$

Multiply the first equation by –5 and the second equation by 2.
$$-50x - 10y = 0$$
$$\underline{6x + 10y = 66}$$
$$-44x = 66$$
$$x = -\dfrac{3}{2}$$

Let $x = -\dfrac{3}{2}$ in the first equation.

$$10\left(-\frac{3}{2}\right)+2y=0$$
$$-15+2y=0$$
$$2y=15$$
$$y=\frac{15}{2}$$

The solution is $\left(-\frac{3}{2},\frac{15}{2}\right)$.

29. $\begin{cases} x+z=4 \ \ (1) \\ 2x-y=4 \ \ (2) \\ x+y-z=0 \ \ (3) \end{cases}$

Adding E2 and E3 gives $3x-z=4$ (4)
Adding E1 and E4 gives $4x=8$ or $x=2$
Replace x with 2 in E1.
$$2+z=4$$
$$z=2$$
Replace x with 2 and z with 2 in E3.
$$2+y-2=0$$
$$y=0$$
The solution is (2, 0, 2).

30. $\begin{cases} 2x+5y=4 \ \ (1) \\ x-5y+z=-1 \ \ (2) \\ 4x-z=11 \ \ (3) \end{cases}$

Add E2 and E3.
$$5x-5y=10 \ \ (4)$$
Add E1 and E4.
$$7x=14$$
$$x=2$$
Replace x with 2 in E1.
$$2(2)+5y=4$$
$$4+5y=4$$
$$5y=0$$
$$y=0$$
Replace x with 2 in E3.
$$4(2)-z=11$$
$$8-z=11$$
$$z=-3$$
The solution is (2, 0, –3).

31. $\begin{cases} 4y+2z=5 \ \ (1) \\ 2x+8y=5 \ \ (2) \\ 6x+4z=1 \ \ (3) \end{cases}$

Multiply E1 by –2 and add to E2.
$$-8y-4z=-10$$
$$\underline{2x+8y=5}$$
$$2x-4z=-5 \ \ (4)$$
Add E3 and E4.

$$8x=-4$$
$$x=-\frac{1}{2}$$

Replace x with $-\frac{1}{2}$ in E2.
$$2\left(-\frac{1}{2}\right)+8y=5$$
$$-1+8y=5$$
$$8y=6$$
$$y=\frac{3}{4}$$

Replace x with $-\frac{1}{2}$ in E3.
$$6\left(-\frac{1}{2}\right)+4z=1$$
$$-3+4z=1$$
$$4z=4$$
$$z=1$$

The solution is $\left(-\frac{1}{2},\frac{3}{4},1\right)$.

32. $\begin{cases} 5x+7y=9 \ \ (1) \\ 14y-z=28 \ \ (2) \\ 4x+2z=-4 \ \ (3) \end{cases}$

Dividing E3 by 2 gives $2x+z=-2$.
Add this equation to E2.
$$2x+z=-2$$
$$\underline{14y-z=28}$$
$$2x+14y=26 \text{ or } x+7y=13 \ \ (4)$$
Multiply E4 by –1 and add to E1.
$$-x-7y=-13$$
$$\underline{5x+7y=9}$$
$$4x=-4$$
$$x=-1$$
Replace x with –1 in E4.
$$-1+7y=13$$
$$7y=14$$
$$y=2$$
Replace x with –1 in E3.
$$4(-1)+2z=-4$$
$$-4+2z=-4$$
$$2z=0$$
$$z=0$$
The solution is (–1, 2, 0).

33. $\begin{cases} 3x-2y+2z=5 \ \ (1) \\ -x+6y+z=4 \ \ (2) \\ 3x+14y+7z=20 \ \ (3) \end{cases}$

Multiply E2 by 3 and add to E1.

$$3x - 2y + 2z = 5$$
$$\underline{-3x + 18y + 3z = 12}$$
$$16y + 5z = 17 \quad (4)$$

Multiply E3 by –1 and add to E1.
$$3x - 2y + 2z = 5$$
$$\underline{-3x - 14y - 7z = -20}$$
$$-16y - 5z = -15 \quad (5)$$

Add E4 and E5.
$$16y + 5z = 17$$
$$\underline{-16y - 5z = -15}$$
$$0 = 2 \quad \text{False}$$

The system is inconsistent. The solution is $\varnothing$.

34. $\begin{cases} x + 2y + 3z = 11 & (1) \\ \quad\quad y + 2z = 3 & (2) \\ 2x \quad\quad + 2z = 10 & (3) \end{cases}$

Multiply E2 by –2 and add to E1.
$$x + 2y + 3z = 11$$
$$\underline{-2y - 4z = -6}$$
$$x \quad\quad - z = 5 \quad (4)$$

Multiply E4 by 2 and add to E3.
$$2x + 2z = 10$$
$$\underline{2x - 2z = 10}$$
$$4x \quad\quad = 20$$
$$x = 5$$

Replace x with 5 in E3.
$$2(5) + 2z = 10$$
$$10 + 2z = 10$$
$$2z = 0$$
$$z = 0$$

Replace z with 0 in E2.
$$y + 2(0) = 3$$
$$y + 0 = 3$$
$$y = 3$$

The solution is (5, 3, 0).

35. $\begin{cases} 7x - 3y + 2z = 0 & (1) \\ 4x - 4y - z = 2 & (2) \\ 5x + 2y + 3z = 1 & (3) \end{cases}$

Multiply E2 by 2 and add to E1.
$$7x - 3y + 2z = 0$$
$$\underline{8x - 8y - 2z = 4}$$
$$15x - 11y \quad = 4 \quad (4)$$

Multiply E2 by 3 and add to E3.
$$12x - 12y - 3z = 6$$
$$\underline{5x + 2y + 3z = 1}$$
$$17x - 10y \quad = 7 \quad (5)$$

Solve the new system.

$\begin{cases} 15x - 11y = 4 & (4) \\ 17x - 10y = 7 & (5) \end{cases}$

Multiply E4 by –10, multiply E5 by 11, and add.
$$-150x + 110y = -40$$
$$\underline{187x - 110y = 77}$$
$$37x \quad\quad = 37$$
$$x = 1$$

Replace x with 1 in E4.
$$15(1) - 11y = 4$$
$$15 - 11y = 4$$
$$-11y = -11$$
$$y = 1$$

Replace x with 1 and y with 1 in E1.
$$7(1) - 3(1) + 2z = 0$$
$$4 + 2z = 0$$
$$2z = -4$$
$$z = -2$$

The solution is (1, 1, –2).

36. $\begin{cases} x - 3y - 5z = -5 & (1) \\ 4x - 2y + 3z = 13 & (2) \\ 5x + 3y + 4z = 22 & (3) \end{cases}$

Multiply E1 by –4 and add to E2.
$$-4x + 12y + 20z = 20$$
$$\underline{4x - 2y + 3z = 13}$$
$$10y + 23z = 33 \quad (4)$$

Multiply E1 by –5 and add to E3.
$$-5x + 15y + 25z = 25$$
$$\underline{5x + 3y + 4z = 22}$$
$$18y + 29z = 47 \quad (5)$$

Solve the new system.

$\begin{cases} 10y + 23z = 33 & (4) \\ 18y + 29z = 47 & (5) \end{cases}$

Multiply E4 by 9, multiply E5 by –5 and add.
$$90y + 207z = 297$$
$$\underline{-90y - 145z = -235}$$
$$62z = 62$$
$$z = 1$$

Replace z with 1 in E4.
$$10y + 23(1) = 33$$
$$10y = 10$$
$$y = 1$$

Replace y with 1 and z with 1 in E1.
$$x - 3(1) - 5(1) = -5$$
$$x - 8 = -5$$
$$x = 3$$

The solution is (3, 1, 1).

37. Let x = the larger number and
y = the smaller number.
$$\begin{cases} x+y=16 \\ 3x-y=72 \end{cases}$$

$$\begin{array}{r} x+y=16 \\ \underline{3x-y=72} \\ 4x\quad\ =88 \\ x=22 \end{array}$$

Let $x = 22$ in the first equation.
$$\begin{array}{r} 22+y=16 \\ y=-6 \end{array}$$

The numbers are -6 and 22.

38. Let x = the number of orchestra seats and
y = the number of balcony seats.
$$\begin{cases} x+y=360 \\ 45x+35y=15,150 \end{cases}$$

Solve the first equation for x.
$x = 360 - y$
Substitute $360 - y$ for x in the second equation.
$$\begin{array}{r} 45(360-y)+35y=15,150 \\ 16,200-45y+35y=15,150 \\ -10y=-1050 \\ y=105 \end{array}$$

Let $y = 105$ in $x = 360 - y$.
$x = 360 - 105 = 255$
There are 255 orchestra seats and 105 balcony seats.

39. Let x = the riverboat's speed in still water and
y = the rate of the current.

	d	$=$	r	$\cdot$	t
Downriver	340		$x+y$		14
Upriver	340		$x-y$		19

$$\begin{cases} 14(x+y)=340 \\ 19(x-y)=340 \end{cases}$$

Multiply the first equation by $\dfrac{1}{14}$ and the second

equation by $\dfrac{1}{19}$.

$$\begin{array}{r} x+y=\dfrac{340}{14}\approx 24.29 \\ \underline{x-y=\dfrac{340}{19}\approx 17.89} \\ 2x\qquad\quad \approx 42.18 \\ x\approx 21.09 \end{array}$$

Multiply the second equation of the simplified system by -1.
$$\begin{array}{r} x+y\approx 24.29 \\ \underline{-x+y\approx -17.89} \\ 2y\approx 6.4 \\ y\approx 3.2 \end{array}$$

The riverboat's speed in still water is 21.1 miles per hour. The rate of the current is 3.2 miles per hour.

40. Let x = amount of 6% solution and
y = amount of 14% solution.

Concentration Rate	Amount of Solution	Amount of Pure Acid
0.06	x	$0.06x$
0.14	y	$0.14y$
0.12	50	$0.12(50)$

$$\begin{cases} x+y=50 \\ 0.06x+0.14y=0.12(50) \end{cases}$$

Multiply the first equation by -6 and the second equation by 100.
$$\begin{array}{r} -6x-6y=-300 \\ \underline{6x+14y=600} \\ 8y=300 \\ y=37.5 \end{array}$$

Let $y = 37.5$ in the first equation.
$$\begin{array}{r} x+37.5=50 \\ x=12.5 \end{array}$$

$12\dfrac{1}{2}$ cc of 6% solution and $37\dfrac{1}{2}$ cc of 14% solution.

41. Let x = the cost of an egg and
y = the cost of a strip of bacon.
$$\begin{cases} 3x+4y=3.80 \\ 2x+3y=2.75 \end{cases}$$

Multiply the first equation by -2 and the second equation by 3.
$$\begin{array}{r} -6x-8y=-7.60 \\ \underline{6x+9y=8.25} \\ y=0.65 \end{array}$$

Let $y = 0.65$ in the first equation.

$3x + 4(0.65) = 3.80$

$3x + 2.60 = 3.80$

$3x = 1.20$

$x = 0.40$

An egg costs 40¢ and a strip of bacon costs 65¢.

42. Let x = the time spent walking and y = the time spent jogging.

	r	$\cdot$ t	$= d$
Walking	4	x	$4x$
Jogging	7.5	y	$7.5y$

$$\begin{cases} x + y = 3 \\ 4x + 7.5y = 15 \end{cases}$$

Multiply the first equation by -4.

$-4x \quad -4y = -12$

$\underline{4x + 7.5y = 15}$

$3.5y = 3$

$y \approx 0.857$

Let $y = 0.857$ in the first equation.

$x + 0.857 = 3$

$x \approx 2.143$

He spent 2.14 hours walking and 0.86 hours jogging.

43. Let x = the number of pennies, y = the number of nickels, and z = the number dimes.

$$\begin{cases} x + y + z = 53 & (1) \\ 0.01x + 0.05y + 0.10z = 2.77 & (2) \\ y = z + 4 & (3) \end{cases}$$

Clear the decimals from E2 by multiplying by 100.

$x + 5y + 10z = 277$ (4)

Replace y with $z + 4$ in E1.

$x + z + 4 + z = 53$

$x + 2z = 49$ (5)

Replace y with $z + 4$ in E4.

$x + 5(z + 4) + 10z = 277$

$x + 15z = 257$ (6)

Solve the new system.

$$\begin{cases} x + 2z = 49 & (5) \\ x + 15z = 257 & (6) \end{cases}$$

Multiply E5 by -1 and add to E6.

$-x - 2z = -49$

$\underline{x + 15z = 257}$

$13z = 208$

$z = 16$

Replace z with 16 in E3.

$x + 2(16) = 49$

$x + 32 = 49$

$x = 17$

Replace z with 16 in E3.

$y = 16 + 4 = 20$

He has 17 pennies, 20 nickels, and 16 dimes in his jar.

44. Let c = pounds of chocolate used, n = pounds of nuts used, and r = pounds of raisins used.

$$\begin{cases} r = 2n & (1) \\ c + n + r = 45 & (2) \\ 3.00c + 2.70n + 2.25r = 2.80(45) & (3) \end{cases}$$

Replace r with $2n$ in E2.

$c + n + 2n = 45$

$c + 3n = 45$

$c = -3n + 45$

Replace r with $2n$ and c with $-3n + 45$ in E3.

$3.00(-3n + 45) + 2.70n + 2.25(2n) = 126$

$-9n + 135 + 2.7n + 4.5n = 126$

$-1.8n + 135 = 126$

$-1.8n = -9$

$n = 5$

Replace n with 5 in E1.

$r = 2(5) = 10$

Replace n with 5 and r with 10 in E2.

$c + 5 + 10 = 45$

$c + 15 = 45$

$c = 30$

She should use 30 pounds of creme-filled chocolates, 5 pounds of chocolate-covered nuts, and 10 pounds of chocolate-covered raisins.

45. Let x = length of the equal side and y = length of the third side.

$$\begin{cases} 2x + y = 73 & (1) \\ y = x + 7 & (2) \end{cases}$$

Replace y with $x + 7$ in E1.

$2x + x + 7 = 73$

$3x = 66$

$x = 22$

Replace x with 22 in E2.

$y = 22 + 7 = 29$

Two sides of the triangle have length 22 cm and the third side has length 29 cm.

46. Let f = the first number, s = the second number, and t = the third number.

$$\begin{cases} f+s+t=295 & (1) \\ f=s+5 & (2) \\ f=2t & (3) \end{cases}$$

Solve E2 for s and E3 for t.

$$s = f - 5$$

$$t = \frac{f}{2}$$

Replace s with $f - 5$ and t with $\frac{f}{2}$ in E1.

$$f + f - 5 + \frac{f}{2} = 295$$

$$\frac{5}{2}f = 300$$

$$f = 120$$

Replace f with 300 in the equation $s = f - 5$.

$$s = 120 - 5 = 115$$

Replace f with 120 the equation $\frac{f}{2}$.

$$t = \frac{120}{2} = 60$$

The first number is 120, the second number is 115, and the third number is 60.

47. $\begin{cases} x - 2y = 1 \\ 2x + 3y = -12 \end{cases}$

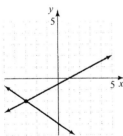

The solution is $(-3, -2)$.

48. $\begin{cases} 3x - y = -4 \\ 6x - 2y = -8 \end{cases}$

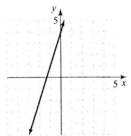

There is an infinite number of solutions.

49. $\begin{cases} x + 4y = 11 \\ 5x - 9y = -3 \end{cases}$

Solve the first equation for x.

$$x = 11 - 4y$$

Substitute $11 - 4y$ for x in the second equation.

$$5(11 - 4y) - 9y = -3$$

$$55 - 20y - 9y = -3$$

$$-29y = -58$$

$$y = 2$$

Let $y = 2$ in the first equation.

$$x + 4(2) = 11$$

$$x + 8 = 11$$

$$x = 3$$

The solution is $(3, 2)$.

50. $\begin{cases} x + 9y = 16 \\ 3x - 8y = 13 \end{cases}$

Solve the first equation for x.

$$x = 16 - 9y$$

Substitute $16 - 9y$ for x in the second equation.

$$3(16 - 9y) - 8y = 13$$

$$48 - 27y - 8y = 13$$

$$-35y = -35$$

$$y = 1$$

Let $y = 1$ in the first equation.

$$x + 9(1) = 16$$

$$x + 9 = 16$$

$$x = 7$$

The solution is $(7, 1)$.

51. $\begin{cases} y = -2x \\ 4x + 7y = -15 \end{cases}$

Substitute $-2x$ for y in the second equation.

$$4x + 7(-2x) = -15$$

$$4x - 14x = -15$$

$$-10x = -15$$

$$x = \frac{3}{2} = 1\frac{1}{2}$$

Let $x = \frac{3}{2}$ in the first equation.

$$y = -2\left(\frac{3}{2}\right) = -3$$

The solution is $\left(1\frac{1}{2}, -3\right)$.

52. $\begin{cases} 3y = 2x + 15 \\ -2x + 3y = 21 \end{cases}$

Solve the first equation for x.

$$3y = 2x + 15$$
$$3y - 15 = 2x$$
$$\frac{3}{2}y - \frac{15}{2} = x$$

Substitute $\frac{3}{2}y - \frac{15}{2}$ for x in the second equation.

$$-2\left(\frac{3}{2}y - \frac{15}{2}\right) + 3y = 21$$
$$-3y + 15 + 3y = 21$$
$$15 = 21 \quad \text{False}$$

The system has no solution.

53. $\begin{cases} 3x - y = 4 \\ 4y = 12x - 16 \end{cases}$

Solve the first equation for y.
$$3x - 4 = y$$
Substitute $3x - 4$ for y in the second equation.
$$4(3x - 4) = 12x - 16$$
$$12x - 16 = 12x - 16$$
$$0 = 0$$
There is an infinite number of solutions.

54. $\begin{cases} x + y = 19 \\ x - y = -3 \end{cases}$

$$\begin{array}{r} x + y = 19 \\ x - y = -3 \\ \hline 2x = 16 \\ x = 8 \end{array}$$

Let $x = 8$ in the first equation.
$$8 + y = 19$$
$$y = 11$$
The solution is (8, 11).

55. $\begin{cases} x - 3y = -11 \\ 4x + 5y = -10 \end{cases}$

Solve the first equation for x.
$$x = 3y - 11$$
Substitute $3y - 11$ for x in the second equation.
$$4(3y - 11) + 5y = -10$$
$$12y - 44 + 5y = -10$$
$$17y = 34$$
$$y = 2$$
Let $y = 2$ in the first equation.
$$x - 3(2) = -11$$
$$x - 6 = -11$$
$$x = -5$$
The solution is (−5, 2).

56. $\begin{cases} -x - 15y = 44 \\ 2x + 3y = 20 \end{cases}$

Solve the first equation for x.
$$-x - 15y = 44$$
$$-x = 15y + 44$$
$$x = -15y - 44$$

Substitute $-15y - 44$ for x in the second equation.
$$2(-15y - 44) + 3y = 20$$
$$-30y - 88 + 3y = 20$$
$$-27y = 108$$
$$y = -4$$

Let $y = -4$ in $x = -15y - 44$.
$$x = -15(-4) - 44 = 60 - 44 = 16$$
The solution is (16, −4).

57. $\begin{cases} x - 3y + 2z = 0 & (1) \\ 9y - z = 22 & (2) \\ 5x + 3z = 10 & (3) \end{cases}$

Multiply E1 by 3 and add to E2.
$$3x - 9y + 6z = 0$$
$$\underline{9y - z = 22}$$
$$3x + 5z = 22 \quad (4)$$

Multiply E3 by −5 and E4 by 3 and add the results.
$$-25x - 15z = -50$$
$$\underline{9x + 15z = 66}$$
$$-16x = 16$$
$$x = -1$$

Replace x with −1 in E3.
$$5(-1) + 3z = 10$$
$$-5 + 3z = 10$$
$$3z = 15$$
$$z = 5$$
Replace z with 5 in E2.
$$9y - 5 = 22$$
$$9y = 27$$
$$y = 3$$
The solution is (−1, 3, 5).

58. $\begin{cases} x - 4y = 4 \\ \dfrac{1}{8}x - \dfrac{1}{2}y = 3 \end{cases}$

Multiply the second by −8 and add to the first equation to eliminate x.
$$\begin{cases} x - 4y = 4 \\ -x + 4y = -24 \end{cases}$$

The equation $0 = -20$ is false. The system has no solution. The solution set is { } or $\varnothing$.

59. Let x = the larger number and
y = the smaller number.
$$\begin{cases} x+y=12 \\ x+3y=20 \end{cases}$$
Multiply the first equation by -1.
$$\begin{array}{r} -x-y=-12 \\ x+3y=20 \\ \hline 2y=8 \\ y=4 \end{array}$$
Let $y=4$ in the first equation.
$$x+4=12$$
$$x=8$$
The numbers are 4 and 8.

60. Let x = the smaller number and
y = the larger number.
$$\begin{cases} x-y=-18 \\ 2x-y=-23 \end{cases}$$
Multiply the first equation by -1.
$$\begin{array}{r} -x+y=18 \\ 2x-y=-23 \\ \hline x=-5 \end{array}$$
Let $x=-5$ in the first equation.
$$-5-y=-18$$
$$-y=-13$$
$$y=13$$
The numbers are -5 and 13.

61. Let x = the number of nickels and
y = the number of dimes.
$$\begin{cases} x+y=65 \\ 0.05x+0.10y=5.30 \end{cases}$$
Multiply the first equation by -5 and the second equation by 100.
$$\begin{array}{r} -5x-5y=-325 \\ 5x+10y=530 \\ \hline 5y=205 \\ y=41 \end{array}$$
Let $y=41$ in the first equation.
$$x+41=65$$
$$x=24$$
There are 24 nickels and 41 dimes.

62. Let x = the number of 13¢ stamps and
y = the number of 22¢ stamps.
$$\begin{cases} x+y=26 \\ 0.13x+0.22y=4.19 \end{cases}$$
Multiply the first equation by -13 and the second equation by 100.

$$\begin{array}{r} -13x-13y=-338 \\ 13x+22y=419 \\ \hline 9y=81 \\ y=9 \end{array}$$
Let $y=9$ in the first equation.
$$x+9=26$$
$$x=17$$
They purchased 17 13¢ stamps and
9 22¢ stamps.

63. Let x = length of the shortest side
y = length of the second side
z = length of the third side
We solve the system
$$\begin{cases} x+y+z=126 \\ y=2x \\ z=x+14 \end{cases}$$
We substitute $2x$ for y and $x+14$ for z in the first equation.
$$x+2x+(x+14)=126$$
$$4x+14=126$$
$$4x=112$$
$$x=28$$
Now we find y and z.
$$y=2x=2(28)=56$$
$$z=x+14=28+14=42$$
The lengths are 28 units, 42 units, and 56 units.

Chapter 4 Test

1. False; one solution, infinitely many solutions, or no solutions are the only possibilities.

2. False; a solution of a system of equations must be a solution of each equation in the system.

3. True

4. False; $x=0$ is part of the solution.

5. Let $x=1$ and $y=-1$.
$$\begin{array}{ll} 2x-3y=5 & 6x+y=1 \\ 2(1)-3(-1)\overset{?}{=}5 & 6(1)+(-1)\overset{?}{=}1 \\ 2+3\overset{?}{=}5 & 6-1\overset{?}{=}1 \\ 5=5 \ \text{True} & 5=1 \ \text{False} \end{array}$$
$(1,-1)$ is not a solution of the system.

6. Let $x=3$ and $y=-4$.
$$4x-3y=24$$
$$4(3)-3(-4)\overset{?}{=}24$$
$$12+12\overset{?}{=}24$$
$$24=24 \ \text{True}$$

$$4x + 5y = -8$$
$$4(3) + 5(-4) \stackrel{?}{=} -8$$
$$12 - 20 \stackrel{?}{=} -8$$
$$-8 = -8 \quad \text{True}$$
$(3, -4)$ is a solution of the system.

7. $\begin{cases} y - x = 6 \\ y + 2x = -6 \end{cases}$

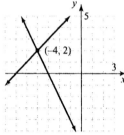

The solution is $(-4, 2)$.

8. $\begin{cases} 3x - 2y = -14 \\ x + 3y = -1 \end{cases}$

Solve the second equation for x.

$x = -3y - 1$

Substitute $-3y - 1$ for x in the first equation.

$$3(-3y - 1) - 2y = -14$$
$$-9y - 3 - 2y = -14$$
$$-11y = -11$$
$$y = 1$$

Let $y = 1$ in $x = -3y - 1$.

$x = -3(1) - 1 = -4$

The solution is $(-4, 1)$.

9. $\begin{cases} \dfrac{1}{2}x + 2y = -\dfrac{15}{4} \\ 4x = -y \end{cases}$

Solve the second equation for y.

$y = -4x$

Substitute $-4x$ for y in the first equation.

$$\frac{1}{2}x + 2(-4x) = -\frac{15}{4}$$
$$\frac{1}{2}x - 8x = -\frac{15}{4}$$
$$-\frac{15}{2}x = -\frac{15}{4}$$
$$x = \frac{1}{2}$$

Let $x = \dfrac{1}{2}$ in the equation $y = -4x$.

$$y = -4\left(\frac{1}{2}\right) = -2$$

The solution is $\left(\dfrac{1}{2}, -2\right)$.

10. $\begin{cases} 3x + 5y = 2 \\ 2x - 3y = 14 \end{cases}$

Multiply the first equation by 2 and the second equation by -3.

$$6x + 10y = 4$$
$$\underline{-6x + 9y = -42}$$
$$19y = -38$$
$$y = -2$$

Let $y = -2$ in the first equation.

$$3x + 5(-2) = 2$$
$$3x - 10 = 2$$
$$3x = 12$$
$$x = 4$$

The solution is $(4, -2)$.

11. $\begin{cases} 4x - 6y = 7 \\ -2x + 3y = 0 \end{cases}$

Multiply the second equation by 2.

$$4x - 6y = 7$$
$$\underline{-4x + 6y = 0}$$
$$0 = 7$$

The system is inconsistent. There is no solution.

12. $\begin{cases} 3x + y = 7 \\ 4x + 3y = 1 \end{cases}$

Solve the first equation for y.

$y = 7 - 3x$

Substitute $7 - 3x$ for y in the second equation.

$$4x + 3(7 - 3x) = 1$$
$$4x + 21 - 9x = 1$$
$$-5x = -20$$
$$x = 4$$

Let $x = 4$ in $y = 7 - 3x$.

$y = 7 - 3(4) = -5$

The solution is $(4, -5)$.

13. $\begin{cases} 3(2x+y)=4x+20 \\ \quad 6x+3y=4x+20 \\ \quad 2x+3y=20 \\ \\ \quad x-2y=3 \end{cases}$

Multiply the second equation by -2.

$2x+3y=20$
$\underline{-2x+4y=-6}$
$\quad\quad 7y=14$
$\quad\quad\; y=2$

Let $y=2$ in the second equation.

$x-2(2)=3$
$\quad x-4=3$
$\quad\quad\; x=7$

The solution of the system is $(7,2)$.

14. $\begin{cases} \dfrac{x-3}{2}=\dfrac{2-y}{4} \\ \dfrac{7-2x}{3}=\dfrac{y}{2} \end{cases}$

Multiply the first equation by 4 and the second equation by 6.

$\begin{cases} 2(x-3)=2-y \\ \quad 2x-6=2-y \\ \quad 2x+y=8 \\ \\ 2(7-2x)=3y \\ \quad 14-4x=3y \\ \quad 4x+3y=14 \end{cases}$

Multiply the first equation by -3.

$-6x-3y=-24$
$\underline{\;\;4x+3y=14}$
$-2x\quad\quad=-10$
$\quad\quad x=5$

Let $x=5$ in the first equation.

$2(5)+y=8$
$\quad 10+y=8$
$\quad\quad\; y=-2$

The solution of the system is $(5,-2)$.

15. Let $x=$ the larger number and $y=$ the smaller number.

$\begin{cases} x+y=124 \\ x-y=32 \end{cases}$

$x+y=124$
$\underline{x-y=32}$
$2x\quad=156$
$\quad x=78$

Let $x=78$ in the first equation.

$78+y=124$
$\quad\; y=46$

The numbers are 78 and 46.

16. Let $x=$ cc's of 12% solution and $y=$ cc's of 16% solution.

Concentration Rate	cc's of Solution	cc's of salt
12%	x	$0.12x$
22%	80	$0.22(80)$
16%	y	$0.16y$

$\begin{cases} \quad\quad\quad\; x+80=y \\ 0.12x+0.22(80)=0.16y \end{cases}$

Multiply the first equation by -16 and the second equation by 100.

$-16x-1280=-16y$
$\underline{\;\;12x+1760=16y}$
$\;-4x+480=0$
$\quad\; -4x=-480$
$\quad\quad\; x=120$

Should add 120 cc's of 12% solution

17. Let $x=$ the number of thousands of farms in Texas and $y=$ the number of thousands of farms in Missouri.

$\begin{cases} x+y=336 \\ x-y=116 \end{cases}$

$x+y=336$
$\underline{x-y=116}$
$2x\quad=452$
$\quad x=226$

Let $x=226$ in the first equation.

$226+y=336$
$\quad\quad\; y=110$

There are 226,000 farms in Texas and 110,000 farms in Missouri.

18. $\begin{cases} 2x-3y\quad\quad=4 \quad (1) \\ \quad\quad 3y+2z=2 \quad (2) \\ \;x\quad\quad -z=-5 \;\; (3) \end{cases}$

Add E1 and E2.

$2x+2z=6$ or $x+z=3$ (4)

Add E3 and E4.

$x+z=3$
$\underline{x-z=-5}$
$2x\quad=-2$
$\quad x=-1$

Replace x with -1 in E3.
$$-1-z=-5$$
$$-z=-4 \text{ so } z=4$$
Replace x with -1 in E1.
$$2(-1)-3y=4$$
$$-2-3y=4$$
$$-3y=6$$
$$y=-2$$
The solution is $(-1, -2, 4)$.

19. $\begin{cases} 3x-2y-z=-1 & (1) \\ 2x-2y=4 & (2) \\ 2x-2z=-12 & (3) \end{cases}$

Multiply E2 by -1 and add to E1.
$$\begin{array}{r} 3x-2y-z=-1 \\ -2x+2y=-4 \\ \hline x \qquad -z=-5 \quad (4) \end{array}$$
Multiply E4 by -2 and add to E3.
$$\begin{array}{r} 2x-2z=-12 \\ -2x+2z=10 \\ \hline 0=-2 \text{ False} \end{array}$$

The system is inconsistent. The solution set is $\varnothing$.

20. Let x = measure of the smallest angle. Then the largest angle has a measure of $5x - 3$, and the remaining angle has a measure of $2x - 1$. The sum of the three angles must add to $180°$:
$$a+b+c=180$$
$$x+(5x-3)+(2x-1)=180$$
$$x+5x-3+2x-1=180$$
$$8x-4=180$$
$$8x=184$$
$$x=23$$
$$5x-3=5(23)-3=115-3=112$$
$$2x-1=2(23)-1=46-1=45$$
The angle measures are $23°$, $45°$, and $112°$.

Chapter 4 Cumulative Review

1. a. $-1 < 0$

   b. $7 = \dfrac{14}{2}$

   c. $-5 > -6$

2. a. $5^2 = 5 \cdot 5 = 25$

   b. $2^5 = 2 \cdot 2 \cdot 2 \cdot 2 \cdot 2 = 32$

3. a. commutative property of multiplication

   b. associative property of addition

   c. identity element for addition

   d. commutative property of multiplication

   e. multiplicative inverse property

   f. additive inverse property

   g. commutative and associative properties of multiplication

4. Let $x = 8$, $y = 5$.
$$y^2 - 3x = 5^2 - 3(8) = 25 - 24 = 1$$

5. $(2x-3)-(4x-2) = 2x-3-4x+2 = -2x-1$

6. $7-12+(-5)-2+(-2)$
$$= 7+(-12)+(-5)+(-2)+(-2)$$
$$= 7+(-21)$$
$$= -14$$

7.
$$7 = -5(2a-1)-(-11a+6)$$
$$7 = -10a+5+11a-6$$
$$7 = a-1$$
$$7+1 = a-1+1$$
$$8 = a$$

8. Let $x = -7$, $y = -3$.
$$2y^2 - x^2 = 2(-3)^2 - (-7)^2$$
$$= 2(9)-49$$
$$= 18-49$$
$$= -31$$

9.
$$\frac{5}{2}x = 15$$
$$\frac{2}{5} \cdot \frac{5}{2}x = \frac{2}{5} \cdot 15$$
$$x = 6$$

10. $0.4y-6.7+y-0.3-2.6y$
$$= 0.4y+y+(-2.6y)+(-6.7)+(-0.3)$$
$$= -1.2y-7$$

11.
$$\frac{x}{2} - 1 = \frac{2}{3}x - 3$$
$$6\left(\frac{x}{2} - 1\right) = 6\left(\frac{2}{3}x - 3\right)$$
$$3x - 6 = 4x - 18$$
$$-x - 6 = -18$$
$$-x = -12$$
$$x = 12$$

12.
$$7(x - 2) - 6(x + 1) = 20$$
$$7x - 14 - 6x - 6 = 20$$
$$x - 20 = 20$$
$$x = 40$$

13. Let x = the number.
$$2(x + 4) = 4x - 12$$
$$2x + 8 = 4x - 12$$
$$-2x + 8 = -12$$
$$-2x = -20$$
$$x = 10$$
The number is 10.

14.
$$5(y - 5) = 5y + 10$$
$$5y - 25 = 5y + 10$$
$$-25 = 10$$
False statement; there is no solution.

15.
$$y = mx + b$$
$$y - b = mx + b - b$$
$$y - b = mx$$
$$\frac{y - b}{m} = \frac{mx}{m}$$
$$\frac{y - b}{m} = x$$

16. Let x = the number.
$$5(x - 1) = 6x$$
$$5x - 5 = 6x$$
$$-x - 5 = 0$$
$$-x = 5$$
$$x = -5$$
The number is -5.

17.
$$-2x \le -4$$
$$\frac{-2x}{-2} \ge \frac{-4}{-2}$$
$$x \ge 2, [2, \infty)$$

18.
$$P = a + b + c$$
$$P - a - c = a + b + c - a - c$$
$$P - a - c = b$$

19. $x = -2y$

x	y
0	0
-4	2

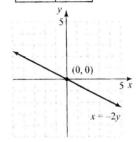

20.
$$3x + 7 \ge x - 9$$
$$2x + 7 \ge -9$$
$$2x \ge -16$$
$$x \ge -8, [-8, \infty)$$

21. $(-1, 5)$ and $(2, -3)$
$$m = \frac{y_2 - y_1}{x_2 - x_1} = \frac{-3 - 5}{2 - (-1)} = \frac{-8}{3} = -\frac{8}{3}$$

22. $x - 3y = 3$

x	y
0	-1
3	0
9	2

23. $y = \dfrac{3}{4}x + 6$
$$y = mx + b$$
$$m = \frac{3}{4}$$

24. $(-1, 3)$ and $(2, -8)$
$$m = \frac{y_2 - y_1}{x_2 - x_1} = \frac{-8 - 3}{2 - (-1)} = -\frac{11}{3}$$
A parallel line has the same slope.
Slope is $-\dfrac{11}{3}$.

25. $3x - 4y = 4$

$-4y = -3x + 4$

$y = \dfrac{-3x}{-4} + \dfrac{4}{-4}$

$y = \dfrac{3}{4}x - 1$

$y = mx + b$

$m = \dfrac{3}{4}, \; b = -1$

Slope is $\dfrac{3}{4}$, y-intercept is $(0, -1)$.

26. $y = 7x + 0$

$y = mx + b$

$m = 7, b = 0$

Slope is 7, y-intercept is $(0, 0)$.

27. $m = -2$, with point $(-1, 5)$

$y - y_1 = m(x - x_1)$

$y - 5 = -2[x - (-1)]$

$y - 5 = -2x - 2$

$2x + y = 3$

28. Line: $y = 4x - 5 \quad m_1 = 4$

Line 2: $-4x + y = 7 \quad y = 4x + 7 \quad m_2 = 4$

$m_2 = m_1$

The lines are parallel.

29. A vertical line has an equation $x = c$.

Point, $(-1, 5)$

$x = -1$

30. $m = -5$, with point $(-2, 3)$

$y - y_1 = m(x - x_1)$

$y - 3 = -5[x - (-2)]$

$y - 3 = -5x - 10$

$y = -5x - 7$

31. Domain is $\{-1, 0, 3\}$

Range is $\{-2, 0, 2, 3\}$

32. $f(x) = 5x^2 - 6$

$f(0) = 5(0)^2 - 6 = -6$

$f(-2) = 5(-2)^2 - 6 = 5(4) - 6 = 14$

33. a. function

b. not a function

34. a. not a function

b. function

c. not a function

35. $\begin{cases} 3x - y = 4 \\ y = 3x - 4, \; m = 3 \\ x + 2y = 8 \\ y = -\dfrac{1}{2}x + 4, \; m = -\dfrac{1}{2} \end{cases}$

Because they have different slopes, there is only one solution.

36. a. Let $x = 1$ and $y = -4$.

$2x - y = 6$

$2(1) - (-4) \stackrel{?}{=} 6$

$2 + 4 \stackrel{?}{=} 6$

$6 = 6 \quad$ True

$3x + 2y = -5$

$3(1) + 2(-4) \stackrel{?}{=} -5$

$3 - 8 \stackrel{?}{=} -5$

$-5 = -5 \quad$ True

$(1, -4)$ is a solution of the system.

b. Let $x = 0$ and $y = 6$.

$2x - y = 6 \qquad\qquad 3x + 2y = -5$

$2(0) - (6) \stackrel{?}{=} 6 \qquad$ Test not needed

$0 - 6 \stackrel{?}{=} 6$

$-6 = 6 \quad$ False

$(0, 6)$ is not a solution of the system.

c. Let $x = 3$ and $y = 0$.

$2x - y = 6$

$2(3) - (0) \stackrel{?}{=} 6$

$6 - 0 \stackrel{?}{=} 6$

$6 = 6 \quad$ True

$3x + 2y = -5$

$3(3) + 2(0) \stackrel{?}{=} -5$

$9 + 0 \stackrel{?}{=} -5$

$9 = -5 \quad$ False

$(3, 0)$ is not a solution of the system.

37. $\begin{cases} x + 2y = 7 \\ 2x + 2y = 13 \end{cases}$

Solve the first equation for x.

$x = 7 - 2y$

Substitute $7 - 2y$ for x in the second equation.

$2(7-2y)+2y=13$
$14-4y+2y=13$
$-2y=-1$
$y=\dfrac{1}{2}$

Let $y=\dfrac{1}{2}$ in $x=7-2y$.

$x=7-2\left(\dfrac{1}{2}\right)=6$

The solution is $\left(6,\dfrac{1}{2}\right)$.

38. $\begin{cases}3x-4y=10\\ y=2x\end{cases}$

Substitute $2x$ for y in the first equation.
$3x-4(2x)=10$
$3x-8x=10$
$-5x=10$
$x=-2$
Let $x=-2$ in the second equation.
$y=2(-2)=-4$
The solution is $(-2,-4)$.

39. $\begin{cases}x+y=7\\ x-y=5\end{cases}$

$\begin{array}{r}x+y=7\\ x-y=5\\ \hline 2x=12\\ x=6\end{array}$

Let $x=6$ in the first equation.
$6+y=7$
$y=1$
The solution to the system is $(6,1)$.

40. $\begin{cases}x=5y-3\\ x=8y+4\end{cases}$

Substitute $8y+4$ for x in the first equation.
$8y+4=5y-3$
$3y+4=-3$
$3y=-7$
$y=-\dfrac{7}{3}$

Let $y=-\dfrac{7}{3}$ in the second equation.

$x=8\left(-\dfrac{7}{3}\right)+4$

$x=-\dfrac{56}{3}+\dfrac{12}{3}$

$x=-\dfrac{44}{3}$

The solution is $\left(-\dfrac{44}{3},-\dfrac{7}{3}\right)$.

41. $\begin{cases}3x-y+z=-15 & (1)\\ x+2y-z=1 & (2)\\ 2x+3y-2z=0 & (3)\end{cases}$

Add E1 and E2.
$4x+y=-14$ (4)
Multiply E1 by 2 and add to E3.
$\begin{array}{r}6x-2y+2z=-30\\ 2x+3y-2z=0\\ \hline 8x+y=-30\ (5)\end{array}$

Solve the new system:
$\begin{cases}4x+y=-14 & (4)\\ 8x+y=-30 & (5)\end{cases}$
Multiply E4 by -1 and add to E5.
$\begin{array}{r}-4x-y=14\\ 8x+y=-30\\ \hline 4x=-16\\ x=-4\end{array}$

Replace x with -4 in E4.
$4(-4)+y=-14$
$-16+y=-14$
$y=2$
Replace x with -4 and y with 2 in E1.
$3(-4)-(2)+z=-15$
$-12-2+z=-15$
$-14+z=-15$
$z=-1$
The solution is $(-4,2,-1)$.

42. $\begin{cases}x-2y+z=0 & (1)\\ 3x-y-2z=-15 & (2)\\ 2x-3y+3z=7 & (3)\end{cases}$

Multiply E1 by 2 and add to E2.
$\begin{array}{r}2x-4y+2z=0\\ 3x-y-2z=-15\\ \hline 5x-5y=-15\ \text{or}\ x-y=-3\ (4)\end{array}$

Multiply E1 by -3 and add to E3.
$\begin{array}{r}-3x+6y-3z=0\\ 2x-3y+3z=7\\ \hline -x+3y=7\ (5)\end{array}$

Add E4 and E5.
$$2y = 4$$
$$y = 2$$
Replace y with 2 in E4.
$$x - 2 = -3$$
$$x = -1$$
Replace x with -1 and y with 2 in E1.
$$-1 - 2(2) + z = 0$$
$$-5 + z = 0$$
$$z = 5$$
The solution is $(-1, 2, 5)$.

43. Let $x =$ the first number and
$y =$ the second number.
$$\begin{cases} x = y - 4 \\ 4x = 2y + 6 \end{cases}$$

Substitute $y - 4$ for x in the second equation.
$$4(y - 4) = 2y + 6$$
$$4y - 16 = 2y + 6$$
$$2y = 22$$
$$y = 11$$
Let $y = 11$ in $x = y - 4$.
$$x = 11 - 4 = 7$$
The numbers are 7 and 11.

44. Let $x =$ the first number and
$y =$ the second number.
$$\begin{cases} x + y = 37 \\ x - y = 21 \end{cases}$$

$$\begin{array}{r} x + y = 37 \\ \underline{x - y = 21} \\ 2x \quad\;\; = 58 \\ x = 29 \end{array}$$

Let $x = 29$ in the first equation.
$$29 + y = 37$$
$$y = 8$$
The numbers are 29 and 8.

Chapter 5

Practice Exercises

1. a. $3^3 = 3 \cdot 3 \cdot 3 = 27$

    b. Use 4 as a factor once, $4^1 = 4$

    c. $(-8)^2 = (-8)(-8) = 64$

    d. $-8^2 = -(8 \cdot 8) = -64$

    e. $\left(\dfrac{3}{4}\right)^3 = \dfrac{3}{4} \cdot \dfrac{3}{4} \cdot \dfrac{3}{4} = \dfrac{27}{64}$

    f. $(0.3)^4 = (0.3)(0.3)(0.3)(0.3) = 0.0081$

    g. $3 \cdot 5^2 = 3 \cdot 25 = 75$

2. a. If x is 3, $3x^4 = 3 \cdot (3)^4$
        $= 3 \cdot (3 \cdot 3 \cdot 3 \cdot 3)$
        $= 3 \cdot 81$
        $= 243$

    b. If x is -4, $\dfrac{6}{x^2} = \dfrac{6}{(-4)^2} = \dfrac{6}{(-4)(-4)} = \dfrac{6}{16} = \dfrac{3}{8}$

3. a. $3^4 \cdot 3^6 = 3^{4+6} = 3^{10}$

    b. $y^3 \cdot y^2 = y^{3+2} = y^5$

    c. $z \cdot z^4 = z^1 \cdot z^4 = z^{1+4} = z^5$

    d. $x^3 \cdot x^2 \cdot x^6 = x^{3+2+6} = x^{11}$

    e. $(-2)^5 \cdot (-2)^3 = (-2)^{5+3} = (-2)^8$

    f. $b^3 \cdot t^5$, cannot be simplified because b and t are different bases.

4. $(-5y^3)(-3y^4) = -5 \cdot y^3 \cdot -3 \cdot y^4$
    $= -5 \cdot -3 \cdot y^3 \cdot y^4$
    $= 15y^7$

5. a. $(y^7 z^3)(y^5 z) = (y^7 \cdot y^5) \cdot (z^3 \cdot z^1)$
        $= y^{12} \cdot z^4 \text{ or } y^{12} z^4$

    b. $(-m^4 n^4)(7mn^{10})$
        $= (-1 \cdot 7) \cdot (m^4 \cdot m^1) \cdot (n^4 \cdot n^{10})$
        $= (-7) \cdot (m^5) \cdot (n^{14}) \text{ or } -7m^5 n^{14}$

6. a. $(x^4)^3 = x^{4 \cdot 3} = x^{12}$

    b. $(z^3)^7 = z^{3 \cdot 7} = z^{21}$

    c. $[(-2)^3]^5 = (-2)^{3 \cdot 5} = (-2)^{15}$

7. a. $(pr)^5 = p^5 \cdot r^5 = p^5 r^5$

    b. $(6b)^2 = 6^2 \cdot b^2 = 36b^2$

    c. $\left(\dfrac{1}{4}x^2 y\right)^3 = \left(\dfrac{1}{4}\right)^3 \cdot (x^2)^3 \cdot y^3$
        $= \dfrac{1}{64} \cdot x^6 \cdot y^3$
        $= \dfrac{1}{64}x^6 y^3$

    d. $(-3a^3 b^4 c)^4 = (-3)^4 \cdot (a^3)^4 \cdot (b^4)^4 \cdot c^4$
        $= 81a^{12} b^{16} c^4$

8. a. $\left(\dfrac{x}{y^2}\right)^5 = \dfrac{x^5}{(y^2)^5} = \dfrac{x^5}{y^{10}}, \; y \neq 0$

    b. $\left(\dfrac{2a^4}{b^3}\right)^5 = \dfrac{2^5 \cdot (a^4)^5}{(b^3)^5} = \dfrac{32a^{20}}{b^{15}}, \; b \neq 0$

9. a. $\dfrac{z^8}{z^4} = z^{8-4} = z^4$

    b. $\dfrac{(-5)^5}{(-5)^3} = (-5)^{5-3} = (-5)^2 = 25$

    c. $\dfrac{8^8}{8^6} = 8^{8-6} = 8^2 = 64$

d. $\dfrac{q^5}{t^2}$ cannot be simplified because q and t are different bases.

e. Begin by grouping common bases.

$$\dfrac{6x^3y^7}{xy^5} = 6 \cdot \dfrac{x^3}{x} \cdot \dfrac{y^7}{y^5} = 6 \cdot x^{3-1} \cdot y^{7-5} = 6x^2y^2$$

10. a. $-3^0 = -1 \cdot 3^0 = -1 \cdot 1 = -1$

b. $(-3)^0 = 1$

c. $8^0 = 1$

d. $(0.2)^0 = 1$

e. $(xz)^0 = x^0 \cdot z^0 = 1 \cdot 1 = 1$

11. a. This is a quotient raised to a power, so we use the power of a quotient rule.

$$\left(\dfrac{5}{xz}\right)^3 = \dfrac{5^3}{x^3z^3} = \dfrac{125}{x^3z^3}$$

b. This is a product raised to a power, so we use the power of a product rule.
$$(2z^8x^5)^4 = 2^4(z^8)^4(x^5)^4 = 16z^{32}x^{20}$$

c. Use the power of a product or quotient rule; then use the power rule for exponents.

$$\left(\dfrac{-3x^3}{y^4}\right)^3 = \dfrac{(-3)^3(x^3)^3}{(y^4)^3} = -\dfrac{27x^9}{y^{12}}$$

Vocabulary and Readiness Check

1. Repeated multiplication of the same factor can be written using an <u>exponent</u>.

2. In 5^2, the 2 is called the <u>exponent</u> and the 5 is called the <u>base</u>.

3. To simplify $x^2 \cdot x^7$, keep the base and <u>add</u> the exponents.

4. To simplify $(x^3)^6$, keep the base and <u>multiply</u> the exponents.

5. The understood exponent on the term y is <u>1</u>.

6. If $x^{\square} = 1$, the exponent is <u>0</u>.

7. In $\underline{3}^2$, the base is <u>3</u> and the exponent is <u>2</u>.

8. In $(\underline{-3})^6$, the base is <u>-3</u> and the exponent is <u>6</u>.

9. In $-\underline{4}^2$, the base is <u>4</u> and the exponent is <u>2</u>.

10. In $5 \cdot 3^4$, the base 5 has exponent 1 and the base 3 has exponent 4.

11. In $5x^2$, the base 5 has exponent 1 and the base x has exponent 2.

12. In $(\underline{5x})^2$, the base is <u>$5x$</u> and the exponent is <u>2</u>.

Exercise Set 5.1

2. $-3^2 = -3 \cdot 3 = -9$

4. $(-3)^2 = (-3)(-3) = 9$

6. $-4^3 = -4 \cdot 4 \cdot 4 = -64$

8. $(-4)^3 = (-4)(-4)(-4) = -64$

10. $(0.2)^5 = (0.2)(0.2)(0.2)(0.2)(0.2) = 0.00032$

12. $\left(-\dfrac{1}{9}\right)^2 = \left(-\dfrac{1}{9}\right)\left(-\dfrac{1}{9}\right) = \dfrac{1}{81}$

14. $9 \cdot 1^7 = 9 \cdot 1 \cdot 1 \cdot 1 \cdot 1 \cdot 1 \cdot 1 \cdot 1 = 9$

16. $-4 \cdot 3^3 = -4 \cdot 3 \cdot 3 \cdot 3 = -108$

18. Answers may vary

20. $x^3 = (-2)^3 = (-2)(-2)(-2) = -8$

22. $4x^2 = 4(-1)^2 = 4(-1)(-1) = 4$

24. $-4x^2y^3 = -4(2)^2(-1)^3$
$= -4(2)(2)(-1)(-1)(-1)$
$= 16$

26. $\dfrac{10}{3y^3} = \dfrac{10}{3(5)^3} = \dfrac{10}{3(5)(5)(5)} = \dfrac{10}{375} = \dfrac{2}{75}$

28. $y^2 \cdot y = y^{2+1} = y^3$

30. $(-5)^7 \cdot (-5)^6 = (-5)^{7+6} = (-5)^{13}$

32. $(-2z^3)(-2z^2) = -2(-2)z^{3+2} = 4z^5$

34. $(a^2 b)(a^{13} b^{17}) = a^{2+13} b^{1+17} = a^{15} b^{18}$

36. $(-7a^3 b^3)(7a^{19} b) = -7(7)a^{3+19} b^{3+1} = -49a^{22} b^4$

38. $(12x^5)(-x^6)(x^4) = 12(-1)x^{5+6+4} = -12x^{15}$

40. $A = (9y^7)(2y^{10}) = 9(2)y^{7+10} = 18y^{17}$

     The area is $18y^{17}$ square meters.

42. $(y^7)^5 = y^{7 \cdot 5} = y^{35}$

44. $(ab)^6 = a^6 b^6$

46. $(4x^6)^2 = 4^2 x^{6 \cdot 2} = 16x^{12}$

48. $(a^4 b)^7 = a^{4 \cdot 7} b^{1 \cdot 7} = a^{28} b^7$

50. $(-3x^7 yz^2)^3 = (-3)^3 x^{7 \cdot 3} y^{1 \cdot 3} z^{2 \cdot 3} = -27x^{21} y^3 z^6$

52. $\left(\dfrac{q}{t}\right)^{11} = \dfrac{q^{11}}{t^{11}}$

54. $\left(\dfrac{xy}{7}\right)^2 = \dfrac{x^2 y^2}{7^2} = \dfrac{x^2 y^2}{49}$

56. $\left(\dfrac{xy^4}{-3z^3}\right)^3 = \dfrac{x^3 y^{4 \cdot 3}}{(-3)^3 z^{3 \cdot 3}} = \dfrac{x^3 y^{12}}{-27z^9}$

58. $A = \pi(5y)^2 = \pi(5)^2 y^2 = 25y^2 \pi$

     The area is $25y^2 \pi$ square centimeters.

60. $V = \pi(4x)^2(5x^3)$

     $= \pi \cdot 4^2 x^2 \cdot 5x^3$

     $= \pi \cdot 16 \cdot 5 \cdot x^{2+3}$

     $= 80x^5 \pi$

     The volume is $80x^5 \pi$ cubic meters.

62. $\dfrac{y^{10}}{y^9} = y^{10-9} = y^1 = y$

64. $\dfrac{(-6)^{13}}{(-6)^{11}} = (-6)^{13-11} = (-6)^2 = 36$

66. $\dfrac{x^8 y^6}{xy^5} = x^{8-1} y^{6-5} = x^7 y^1 = x^7 y$

68. $\dfrac{9a^4 b^7}{27ab^2} = \dfrac{9}{27} a^{4-1} b^{7-2} = \dfrac{1}{3} a^3 b^5 = \dfrac{a^3 b^5}{3}$

70. $23^0 = 1$

72. $(4y)^0 = 1$

74. $-2x^0 = -2(1) = -2$

76. $-3^0 + 4^0 = -1 + 1 = 0$

78. $(-9)^2 = (-9)(-9) = 81$

80. $\left(\dfrac{2}{3}\right)^3 = \dfrac{2}{3} \cdot \dfrac{2}{3} \cdot \dfrac{2}{3} = \dfrac{8}{27}$

82. $\left(\dfrac{pt}{3}\right)^3 = \dfrac{p^3 t^3}{3^3} = \dfrac{p^3 t^3}{27}$

84. $x^2 x^{15} x = x^{2+15+1} = x^{18}$

86. $(3y^4)(-5y) = 3(-5)y^{4+1} = -15y^5$

88. $(y^2 z^2)(y^{15} z^{13}) = y^{2+15} z^{2+13} = y^{17} z^{15}$

90. $(-3s^5 t)(-7st^{10}) = (-3)(-7)s^{5+1} t^{1+10} = 21s^6 t^{11}$

92. $(t^5)^{11} = t^{5 \cdot 11} = t^{55}$

94. $(-3xy^2 a^3)^3 = (-3)^3 x^3 y^{2 \cdot 3} a^{3 \cdot 3} = -27x^3 y^6 a^9$

96. $\dfrac{5x^9}{x^3} = 5x^{9-3} = 5x^6$

98. $(2ab)^5 = 2^5 a^5 b^5 = 32a^5 b^5$

100. $7^2 - 7^0 = 49 - 1 = 48$

102. $\left(\dfrac{2ab}{6yz}\right)^4 = \dfrac{2^4 a^4 b^4}{6^4 y^4 z^4} = \dfrac{16a^4 b^4}{1296 y^4 z^4} = \dfrac{a^4 b^4}{81 y^4 z^4}$

104. $\dfrac{x^{12} y^{13}}{x^5 y^7} = x^{12-5} y^{13-7} = x^7 y^6$

106. $-6z + 20 - 3z = -6z - 3z + 20 = -9z + 20$

108. $10y - 14 - y - 14 = 10y - y - 14 - 14 = 9y - 28$

110. $-3(w+7) + 5(w+1) = -3w - 21 + 5w + 5$
$ = 2w - 16$

112. $x^{14} \cdot x^{23} = x^{14+23} = x^{37}$
Add the exponents; choice a.

114. $\dfrac{x^{35}}{x^{17}} = x^{35-17} = x^{18}$
Subtract the exponents; choice b.

116. Answers may vary

118. Answers may vary

120. $S = 6x^2 = 6(5)^2 = 6(25) = 150$
The surface area is 150 square meters.

122. We use the surface area formula.

124. Answers may vary

126. $b^{9a} b^{4a} = b^{9a+4a} = b^{13a}$

128. $(2a^{4b})^4 = 2^4 a^{4b \cdot 4} = 16a^{16b}$

130. $\dfrac{y^{15b}}{y^{6b}} = y^{15b-6b} = y^{9b}$

132. $A = P\left(1 + \dfrac{r}{12}\right)^3$

$A = 500{,}000\left(1 + \dfrac{0.0525}{12}\right)^3$

$ = 500{,}000(1.004375)^3$

$ \approx 506{,}591$

Section 5.2

Practice Exercises

1. a. The exponent on y is 3, so the degree of $5y^3$ is 3.

b. $10xy$ can be written as $10x^1 y^1$. The degree of the term is the sum of the exponents, so the degree is $1 + 1 = 2$.

c. The degree of $z = z^1$ is 1.

d. $-3a^2 b^5 c$ can be written as $-3a^2 b^5 c^1$. The degree of the term is the sum of the exponents, so the degree is $2 + 5 + 1$ or 8.

e. The constant, 8, can be written as $8x^0$ (since $x^0 = 1$). The degree of 8 or $8x^0$ is 0.

2. a. The degree of the trinomial $5b^2 - 3b + 7$ is 2, the greatest degree of any of its terms.

b. Rewrite the binomial as $7t^1 + 3$, the degree is 1.

c. The degree of the polynomial $5x^2 + 3x - 6x^3 + 4$ is 3.

3.

Term	numerical coefficient	degree of term
$-3x^3 y^2$	-3	5
$4xy^2$	4	3
$-y^2$	-1	2
$3x$	3	1
-2	-2	0

4. a. $P(x) = -2x^2 - x + 7$
$P(1) = -2(1)^2 - 1 + 7 = 4$

b. $P(x) = -2x^2 - x + 7$
$P(-4) = -2(-4)^2 - (-4) + 7 = -21$

5. To find each height, we evaluate $P(t)$ when $t = 1$ and when $t = 2$.

$$P(t) = -16t^2 + 130$$

$$P(1) = -16(1)^2 + 130$$
$$= -16 + 130$$
$$= 114$$

The height of the camera at 1 second is 114 feet.

$$P(t) = -16t^2 + 130$$

$$P(2) = -16(2)^2 + 130$$
$$= -16(4) + 130$$
$$= -64 + 130$$
$$= 66$$

The height of the camera at 2 seconds is 66 feet.

6. a. $-4y + 2y = (-4 + 2)y = -2y$

   b. These terms cannot be combined because z and $5z^3$ are not like terms.

   c. $7a^2 - 5 - 3a^2 - 7 = 7a^2 - 3a^2 - 5 - 7$
$$= 4a^2 - 12$$

   d. $\dfrac{3}{8}x^3 - x^2 + \dfrac{5}{6}x^4 + \dfrac{1}{12}x^3 - \dfrac{1}{2}x^4$

$$= \left(\dfrac{5}{6} - \dfrac{1}{2}\right)x^4 + \left(\dfrac{3}{8} + \dfrac{1}{12}\right)x^3 - x^2$$

$$= \left(\dfrac{5}{6} - \dfrac{3}{6}\right)x^4 + \left(\dfrac{9}{24} + \dfrac{2}{24}\right)x^3 - x^2$$

$$= \dfrac{2}{6}x^4 + \dfrac{11}{24}x^3 - x^2$$

$$= \dfrac{1}{3}x^4 + \dfrac{11}{24}x^3 - x^2$$

7. $9xy - 3x^2 - 4yx + 5y^2 = -3x^2 + (9 - 4)xy + 5y^2$
$$= -3x^2 + 5xy + 5y^2$$

8. $x \cdot x + 2 \cdot x + 2 \cdot 2 + 5 \cdot x + x \cdot 3x$
$$= x^2 + 2x + 4 + 5x + 3x^2$$
$$= 4x^2 + 7x + 4$$

9. a. $(4y^2 + x - 3y - 7) + (x + y^2 - 2)$
$$= 4y^2 + x - 3y - 7 + x + y^2 - 2$$
$$= 4y^2 + y^2 - 3y + x + x - 7 - 2$$
$$= 5^2 - 3y + 2x - 9$$

   b. $(-8a^2 b - ab^2 + 10) + (-2ab^2 - 10)$
$$= -8a^2 b - ab^2 + 10 - 2ab^2 - 10$$
$$= -8a^2 b - ab^2 - 2ab^2 + 10 - 10$$
$$= -8a^2 b - 3ab^2$$

10. $(3x^2 - 9x + 11) + (-3x^2 + 7x^3 + 3x - 4)$
$$= 7x^3 + 3x^2 - 3x^2 - 9x + 3x + 11 - 4$$
$$= 7x^3 - 6x + 7$$

11. First, change the sign of each term of the second polynomial and then add.

$$(3x^3 - 5x^2 + 4x) - (x^3 - x^2 + 6)$$
$$= (3x^3 - 5x^2 + 4x) + (-x^3 + x^2 - 6)$$
$$= 3x^3 - x^3 - 5x^2 + x^2 + 4x - 6$$
$$= 2x^3 - 4x^2 + 4x - 6$$

12. $[(8x - 11) + (2x + 5)] - (3x + 5)$
$$= 8x - 11 + 2x + 5 - 3x - 5$$
$$= 8x + 2x - 3x - 11 + 5 - 5$$
$$= 7x - 11$$

13. a. $(3a^2 - 4ab + 7b^2) + (-8a^2 + 3ab - b^2)$
$$= 3a^2 - 4ab + 7b^2 - 8a^2 + 3ab - b^2$$
$$= -5a^2 - ab + 6b^2$$

   b. $(5x^2 y^2 - 6xy - 4xy^2)$
$$\qquad\qquad - (2x^2 y^2 + 4xy - 5 + 6y^2)$$
$$= 5x^2 y^2 - 6xy - 4xy^2 - 2x^2 y^2$$
$$\qquad\qquad - 4xy + 5 - 6y^2$$
$$= 3x^2 y^2 - 10xy - 4xy^2 - 6y^2 + 5$$

Graphing Calculator Explorations

1. $(2x^2 + 7x + 6) + (x^3 - 6x^2 - 14)$
$$= x^3 - 4x^2 + 7x - 8$$

2. $(-14x^3 - x + 2) + (-x^3 + 3x^2 + 4x)$
$= -15x^3 + 3x^2 + 3x + 2$

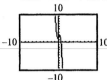

3. $(1.8x^2 - 6.8x - 1.7) - (3.9x^2 - 3.6x)$
$= -2.1x^2 - 3.2x - 1.7$

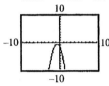

4. $(-4.8x^2 + 12.5x - 7.8) - (3.1x^2 - 7.8x)$
$= -7.9x^2 + 20.3x - 7.8$

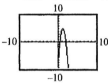

5. $(1.29x - 5.68) + (7.69x^2 - 2.55x + 10.98)$
$= 7.69x^2 - 1.26x + 5.3$

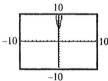

6. $(-0.98x^2 - 1.56x + 5.57) + (4.36x - 3.71)$
$= -0.98x^2 + 2.8x + 1.86$

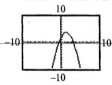

Vocabulary and Readiness Check

1. A <u>binomial</u> is a polynomial with exactly 2 terms.

2. A <u>monomial</u> is a polynomial with exactly one term.

3. A <u>trinomial</u> is a polynomial with exactly three terms.

4. The numerical factor of a term is called the <u>coefficient</u>.

5. A number term is also called a <u>constant</u>.

6. The degree of a polynomial is the <u>greatest</u> degree of any term of the polynomial.

7. $-9y - 5y = (-9 - 5)y = -14y$

8. $6m^5 + 7m^5 = (6 + 7)m^5 = 13m^5$

9. $x + 6x = (1 + 6)x = 7x$

10. $7z - z = (7 - 1)z = 6z$

11. $5m^2 + 2m$ Not like terms.

12. $8p^3 + 3p^2$ Not like terms.

Exercise Set 5.2

2. $-6y + y^2 + 4$ is a trinomial because it has three terms. The degree is 2, the greatest degree of any of its terms.

4. $5a^2 + 3a^3 - 4a^4$ is a trinomial because it has three terms. The degree is 4, the greatest degree of any of its terms.

6. $7r^2s^2 + 2r - 3s^5$ is a trinomial because it has three terms. The degree is 5, the greatest degree of any of its terms.

8. $5y + 2$ is a binomial because it has two terms. The degree is 1 because $5y$ is $5y^1$.

	Polynomial	Degree
10.	$8x^2y^2 - 7x^3 + 6xy - 1$	4
12.	$4z^6 + 3z^2$	6

14. $Q(x) = 5x^2 - 1$
$Q(4) = 5(4)^2 - 1 = 5(16) - 1 = 80 - 1 = 79$

16. $P(x) = x^2 + x + 1$
$P(-4) = (-4)^2 + (-4) + 1 = 16 - 4 + 1 = 13$

18. $Q(x) = 5x^2 - 1$

$Q(0) = 5(0)^2 - 1 = 0 - 1 = -1$

20. $P(x) = x^2 + x + 1$

$P\left(\dfrac{1}{2}\right) = \left(\dfrac{1}{2}\right)^2 + \dfrac{1}{2} + 1$

$= \dfrac{1}{4} + \dfrac{1}{2} + 1$

$= \dfrac{1}{4} + \dfrac{2}{4} + \dfrac{4}{4}$

$= \dfrac{7}{4}$

22. $P(t) = -16t^2 + 1150$

$P(7) = -16(7^2) + 1150 = -784 + 1150 = 366$

After 7 seconds, the height is 366 feet.

24. $P(t) = -16t^2 + 1150$

$P(6) = -16(6)^2 + 1150 = -576 + 1150 = 574$

After 6 seconds, the height is 574 feet.

26. $18x^3 - 4x^3 = (18 - 4)x^3 = 14x^3$

28. $12k^3 - 9k^3 + 11 = (12 - 9)k^3 + 11 = 3k^3 + 11$

30. $5y + 7y - 6y = (5 + 7 - 6)y = 6y$

32. $7.6y + 3.2y^2 - 8y - 2.5y^2$

$= (3.2 - 2.5)y^2 + (7.6 - 8)y$

$= 0.7y^2 - 0.4y$

34. $\dfrac{1}{6}x^4 - \dfrac{1}{7}x^2 + 5 - \dfrac{1}{2}x^4 - \dfrac{3}{7}x^2 + \dfrac{1}{3}$

$= \left(\dfrac{1}{6} - \dfrac{1}{2}\right)x^4 + \left(\dfrac{1}{-7} - \dfrac{3}{7}\right)x^2 + \left(5 + \dfrac{1}{3}\right)$

$= \left(\dfrac{1}{6} - \dfrac{3}{6}\right)x^4 - \dfrac{4}{7}x^2 + \left(\dfrac{15}{3} + \dfrac{1}{3}\right)$

$= -\dfrac{2}{6}x^4 - \dfrac{4}{7}x^2 + \dfrac{16}{3}$

$= -\dfrac{1}{3}x^4 - \dfrac{4}{7}x^2 + \dfrac{16}{3}$

36. $x^2y + xy - y + 10x^2y - 2y + xy$

$= (1 + 10)x^2y + (1 + 1)xy + (-1 - 2)y$

$= 11x^2y + 2xy - 3y$

38. $(3x - 8) + (4x^2 - 3x + 3)$

$= 3x - 8 + 4x^2 - 3x + 3$

$= 4x^2 + (3x - 3x) + (-8 + 3)$

$= 4x^2 - 5$

40. $(5x^2 + 4) - (-2y^2 + 4) = 5x^2 + 4 + 2y^2 - 4$

$= 5x^2 + 2y^2 + (4 - 4)$

$= 5x^2 + 2y^2$

42. $4 - (-y - 4) = 4 + y + 4$

$= y + (4 + 4)$

$= y + 8$

44. $(-7x^2 + 4x + 7) - (-8x + 2)$

$= -7x^2 + 4x + 7 + 8x - 2$

$= -7x^2 + (4x + 8x) + (7 - 2)$

$= -7x^2 + 12x + 5$

46.

$\begin{array}{r} 7x^3 + 3 \\ +\, 2x^3 + 1 \\ \hline 9x^3 + 4 \end{array}$

48.

$\begin{array}{r} 5u^5 - 4u^2 + 3u - 7 \\ -\,(3u^5 + 6u^2 - 8u + 2) \\ \hline \end{array}$

$\begin{array}{r} 5u^5 - 4u^2 + 3u - 7 \\ +\,(-3u^5 - 6u^2 + 8u - 2) \\ \hline 2u^5 - 10u^2 + 11u - 9 \end{array}$

50.

$\begin{array}{r} 7a^2 - 9a + 6 \\ -\,(11a^2 - 4a + 2) \\ \end{array}$ $\begin{array}{r} 7a^2 - 9a + 6 \\ +\,(-11a^2 + 4a - 2) \\ \hline -4a^2 - 5a + 4 \end{array}$

52. $(3x - 9xy) - (2x + xy) = 3x - 9xy - 2x - xy$

$= x - 10xy$

54. $[(-5x - 7) + (12x + 3)] - (-12x - 3)$

$= -5x - 7 + 12x + 3 + 12x + 3$

$= -5x + 12x + 12x - 7 + 3 + 3$

$= 19x - 1$

56. $(7x^2 + 2x - 9) + (-3x^2 + 5)$

$= 7x^2 + 2x - 9 - 3x^2 + 5$

$= 4x^2 + 2x - 4$

58. $(-6y^2 + 3y - 4) - (9y^2 - 3y)$
$= -6y^2 + 3y - 4 - 9y^2 + 3y$
$= -15y^2 + 6y - 4$

60. $(6y^5 - 6y^3 + 4) + (-2y^5 - 8y^3 - 7)$
$= 6y^5 - 6y^3 + 4 - 2y^5 - 8y^3 - 7$
$= 4y^5 - 14y^3 - 3$

62. $(-a^2 + 1) - (a^2 - 3) + (5a^2 - 6a + 7)$
$= -a^2 + 1 - a^2 + 3 + 5a^2 - 6a + 7$
$= 3a^2 - 6a + 11$

64. $(y^2 - 4y + 1) - y = y^2 - 4y + 1 - y = y^2 - 5y + 1$

66. $(7y^2 + 9y - 8) - (5y^2 + 8y + 2)$
$= 7y^2 + 9y - 8 - 5y^2 - 8y - 2$
$= 2y^2 + y - 10$

68. $[(8y - x) + (3 + 8x^2)] - (5y + 7x^2)$
$= 8y - x + 3 + 8x^2 - 5y - 7x^2$
$= x^2 + 3y - x + 3$

70. $[(x^2 + 7x + 1) + (7x + 5)] - (4x^2 - 2x + 2)$
$= x^2 + 7x + 1 + 7x + 5 - 4x^2 + 2x - 2$
$= -3x^2 + 16x + 4$

72. $x \cdot 7 + 2x \cdot 2x + 2x \cdot 2x + 3 \cdot 6 + 4 \cdot 4$
$= 7x + 4x^2 + 4x^2 + 18 + 16$
$= 8x^2 + 7x + 34$

74. $5x + 3 + 4x + 3 + 2x + 6 + 3x + 7x$
$= (5x + 4x + 2x + 3x + 7x) + (3 + 3 + 6)$
$= 21x + 12$

76. $(x^2 - 6x - 2) + x^2 + (-x + 4) + 5x$
$= x^2 - 6x - 2 + x^2 - x + 4 + 5x$
$= 2x^2 - 2x + 2$
The perimeter is $(2x^2 - 2x + 2)$ centimeters.

78. $(13x - 7) - (2x + 2) = 13x - 7 - 2x - 2$
$= 11x - 9$
The length of the remaining piece is $(11x - 9)$ inches.

80. $(3x - 2 + 6y) + (7x - 2 - y)$
$= 3x - 2 + 6y + 7x - 2 - y$
$= 10x - 4 + 5y$

82. $(7a^2 - 3b^2 + 10) - (-2a^2 + b^2 - 12)$
$= 7a^2 - 3b^2 + 10 + 2a^2 - b^2 + 12$
$= 9a^2 - 4b^2 + 22$

84. $(a^2 - ab + 4b^2) + (6a^2 + 8ab - b^2)$
$= a^2 - ab + 4b^2 + 6a^2 + 8ab - b^2$
$= 7a^2 + 7ab + 3b^2$

86. $(3x^2y - 6xy + x^2y^2 - 5) - (11x^2y^2 - 1 + 5yx^2)$
$= 3x^2y - 6xy + x^2y^2 - 5 - 11x^2y^2 + 1 - 5yx^2$
$= -2x^2y - 6xy - 10x^2y^2 - 4$

88. $1.85x^2 - 3.76x + 9.25x^2 + 10.76 - 4.21x$
$= (1.85 + 9.25)x^2 + (-3.76 - 4.21)x + 10.76$
$= 11.1x^2 - 7.97x + 10.76$

90. $[(1.2x^2 - 3x + 9.1) - (7.8x^2 - 3.1 + 8)] + (1.2x - 6)$
$= 1.2x^2 - 3x + 9.1 - 7.8x^2 + 3.1 - 8 + 1.2x - 6$
$= -6.6x^2 - 1.8x - 1.8$

92. $-7x(x) = -7 \cdot x \cdot x = -7x^2$

94. $6r^3(7r^{10}) = 6 \cdot 7 \cdot r^3 \cdot r^{10} = 42r^{13}$

96. $-z^2y(11zy) = -1z^2y(11zy)$
$= -1 \cdot 11 \cdot y \cdot y \cdot z^2 \cdot z$
$= -11y^2z^3$

98. Answers may vary

100. Answers may vary

102. $5x + 5x = (5 + 5)x = 10x$
choice c

104. $(15x - 3) - (5x - 3) = 15x - 3 - 5x + 3$
$= 15x - 5x - 3 + 3$
$= (15 - 5)x$
$= 10x$
choice c

106. a. $x + x = (1 + 1)x = 2x$

   b. $x \cdot x = x^{1+1} = x^2$

   c. $-x - x = (-1 - 1)x = -2x$

   d. $(-x)(-x) = (-x)^{1+1} = (-x)^2 = x^2$

108. $(9y^{5a} - 4y^{3a} + 1.5y) - (6y^{5a} - y^{3a} + 4.7y)$
$= 9y^{5a} - 4y^{3a} + 1.5y - 6y^{5a} + y^{3a} - 4.7y$
$= 9y^{5a} - 6y^{5a} - 4y^{3a} + y^{3a} + 1.5y - 4.7y$
$= 3y^{5a} - 3y^{3a} - 3.2y$

110. $(14z^{5x} + 3z^{2x} + z) - (2z^{5x} - 10z^{2x} + 3z)$
$= 14z^{5x} + 3z^{2x} + z - 2z^{5x} + 10z^{2x} - 3z$
$= 14z^{5x} - 2z^{5x} + 3z^{2x} + 10z^{2x} + z - 3z$
$= 12z^{5x} + 13z^{2x} - 2z$

112. $R(x) + P(x) = (5x^2 - 7) + (3x + 3)$
$= 5x^2 + 3x - 7 + 3$
$= 5x^2 + 3x - 4$

114. $P(x) - Q(x) = (3x + 3) - (4x^2 - 6x + 3)$
$= 3x + 3 - 4x^2 + 6x - 3$
$= -4x^2 + 3x + 6x + 3 - 3$
$= -4x^2 + 9x$

116. $-5[P(x)] - Q(x)$
$= -5(3x + 3) - (4x^2 - 6x + 3)$
$= -5(3x) + (-5)(3) - 4x^2 + 6x - 3$
$= -15x - 15 - 4x^2 + 6x - 3$
$= -4x^2 - 15x + 6x - 15 - 3$
$= -4x^2 - 9x - 18$

118. $P(x) = 8x + 3$

   a. $P(a) = 8a + 3$

   b. $P(-x) = 8(-x) + 3 = -8x + 3$

   c. $P(x + h) = 8(x + h) + 3 = 8x + 8h + 3$

120. $P(x) = -4x$

   a. $P(a) = -4a$

   b. $P(-x) = -4(-x) = 4x$

   c. $P(x + h) = -4(x + h) = -4x - 4h$

122. $0.74x^2 + 2.6x + 3.2 = 0.74(20)^2 + 2.6(20) + 3.2$
$= 296 + 52 + 3.2$
$= 351.2$
Expect 351.2 million or 351,200,000 wireless subscribers in 2010.

124. $(-3.5x^2 + 33.3x + 392) + (19x + 141)$
$= -3.5x^2 + (33.3 + 19)x + 392 + 141$
$= -3.5x^2 + 52.3x + 533$

Section 5.3

Practice Exercises

   1. $5y \cdot 2y = (5 \cdot 2)(y \cdot y) = 10y^2$

   2. $(5z^3) \cdot (-0.4z^5) = (5 \cdot -0.4)(z^3 \cdot z^5) = -2z^8$

   3. $\left(-\dfrac{1}{9}b^6\right)\left(-\dfrac{7}{8}b^3\right) = \left(-\dfrac{1}{9} \cdot -\dfrac{7}{8}\right)(b^6 \cdot b^3) = \dfrac{7}{72}b^9$

   4. a. $3x(5x^5 + 5) = 3x(5x^5) + 3x(5) = 15x^6 + 15x$

      b. $-5x^3(2x^2 - 9x + 2)$
$= -5x^3(2x^2) + (-5x^3)(-9x) + (-5x^3)(2)$
$= -10x^5 + 45x^4 - 10x^3$

   5. Multiply each term of the first binomial by each term of the second.
$(5x - 2)(2x + 3)$
$= 5x(2x) + 5x(3) + (-2)(2x) + (-2)(3)$
$= 10x^2 + 15x - 4x - 6$
$= 10x^2 + 11x - 6$

   6. Recall that $a^2 = a \cdot a$, so
$(5x - 3y)^2 = (5x - 3y)(5x - 3y)$. Multiply each term of the first binomial by each term of the second.
$(5x - 3y)(5x - 3y)$
$= 5x(5x) + 5x(-3y) + (-3y)(5x) + (-3y)(-3y)$
$= 25x^2 - 15xy - 15xy + 9y^2$
$= 25x^2 - 30xy + 9y^2$

7. Multiply each term of the first polynomial by each term of the second.

$(y+4)(2y^2-3y+5)$
$= y(2y^2)+y(-3y)+y(5)+4(2y^2)$
$\qquad +4(-3y)+4(5)$
$= 2y^3-3y^2+5y+8y^2-12y+20$
$= 2y^3+5y^2-7y+20$

8. Write $(s+2t)^3$ as $(s+2t)(s+2t)(s+2t)$.
$(s+2t)(s+2t)(s+2t)$
$= (s^2+2st+2st+4t^2)(s+2t)$
$= (s^2+4st+4t^2)(s+2t)$
$= (s^2+4st+4t^2)s+(s^2+4st+4t^2)(2t)$
$= s^3+4s^2t+4st^2+2s^2t+8st^2+8t^3$
$= s^3+6s^2t+12st^2+8t^3$

9.
$$
\begin{array}{r}
5x^2-3x+5 \\
\times \qquad x-4 \\
\hline
-20x^2+12x-20 \\
5x^3-3x^2+5x \qquad\ \\
\hline
5x^3-23x^2+17x-20
\end{array}
$$

10.
$$
\begin{array}{r}
x^3-2x^2+1 \\
\times \qquad x^2+2 \\
\hline
2x^3-4x^2+2 \\
x^5-2x^4 \qquad +x^2 \qquad\ \\
\hline
x^5-2x^4+2x^3-3x^2+2
\end{array}
$$

11.
$$
\begin{array}{r}
5x^2+2x-2 \\
x^2-x+3 \\
\hline
15x^2+6x-6 \\
-5x^3-2x^2+2x \qquad\ \\
5x^4+2x^3-2x^2 \qquad\qquad\ \\
\hline
5x^4-3x^3+11x^2+8x-6
\end{array}
$$

Vocabulary and Readiness Check

1. The expression $5x(3x+2)$ equals $5x\cdot 3x+5x\cdot 2$ by the <u>distributive</u> property.

2. The expression $(x+4)(7x-1)$ equals $x(7x-1)+4(7x-1)$ by the <u>distributive</u> property.

3. The expression $(5y-1)^2$ equals <u>$(5y-1)(5y-1)$</u>.

4. The expression $9x\cdot 3x$ equals <u>$27x^2$</u>.

5. $x^3\cdot x^5=x^{3+5}=x^8$

6. $x^2\cdot x^6=x^{2+6}=x^8$

7. x^3+x^5 cannot be simplified.

8. x^2+x^6 cannot be simplified.

9. $x^7\cdot x^7=x^{7+7}=x^{14}$

10. $x^{11}\cdot x^{11}=x^{11+11}=x^{22}$

11. $x^7+x^7=(1+1)x^7=2x^7$

12. $x^{11}+x^{11}=(1+1)x^{11}=2x^{11}$

Exercise Set 5.3

2. $9t^6(-3t^5)=9(-3)(t^6\cdot t^5)=-27t^{11}$

4. $(-5.2x^4)(3x^4)=(-5.2\cdot 3)(x^4\cdot x^4)=-15.6x^8$

6. $\left(-\dfrac{3}{4}y^7\right)\left(\dfrac{1}{7}y^4\right)=\left(-\dfrac{3}{4}\cdot\dfrac{1}{7}\right)\left(y^7\cdot y^4\right)=-\dfrac{3}{28}y^{11}$

8. $(x)(5x^4)(-6x^7)=5(-6)(x\cdot x^4\cdot x^7)=-30x^{12}$

10. $2x(6x+3)=(2x)(6x)+(2x)(3)=12x^2+6x$

12. $-3a(2a+7)=-3a(2a)+(-3a)(7)=-6a^2-21a$

14. $4x(5x^2-6x-10)$
$= 4x(5x^2)+4x(-6x)+4x(-10)$
$= 20x^3-24x^2-40x$

16. $-4b^2(3b^3-12b^2-6)$
$= -4b^2(3b^3)+(-4b^2)(-12b^2)+(-4b^2)(-6)$
$= -12b^5+48b^4+24b^2$

18. $-x(6y^3-5xy^2+x^2y-5x^3)$
$= -x(6y^3)+(-x)(-5xy^2)+(-x)(x^2y)$
$\qquad\qquad +(-x)(-5x^3)$
$= -6xy^3+5x^2y^2-x^3y+5x^4$

20. $\dfrac{1}{3}y^2(9y^2 - 6y + 1)$

$= \dfrac{1}{3}y^2(9y^2) + \dfrac{1}{3}y^2(-6y) + \dfrac{1}{3}y^2(1)$

$= 3y^4 - 2y^3 + \dfrac{1}{3}y^2$

22. $(x+2)(x+9) = x(x) + x(9) + 2(x) + 2(9)$
$= x^2 + 9x + 2x + 18$
$= x^2 + 11x + 18$

24. $(y-10)(y+11)$
$= y(y) + y(11) + (-10)(y) + (-10)(11)$
$= y^2 + 11y - 10y - 110$
$= y^2 + y - 110$

26. $\left(x + \dfrac{3}{5}\right)\left(x - \dfrac{2}{5}\right)$

$= x(x) + x\left(-\dfrac{2}{5}\right) + \dfrac{3}{5}(x) + \dfrac{3}{5}\left(-\dfrac{2}{5}\right)$

$= x^2 - \dfrac{2}{5}x + \dfrac{3}{5}x - \dfrac{6}{25}$

$= x^2 + \dfrac{1}{5}x - \dfrac{6}{25}$

28. $(5x^2 + 2)(6x^2 + 2)$
$= (5x^2)(6x^2) + 5x^2(2) + 2(6x^2) + 2(2)$
$= 30x^4 + 10x^2 + 12x^2 + 4$
$= 30x^4 + 22x^2 + 4$

30. $(6x - 7)^2$
$= (6x - 7)(6x - 7)$
$= 6x(6x) + 6x(-7) + (-7)(6x) + (-7)(-7)$
$= 36x^2 - 42x - 42x + 49$
$= 36x^2 - 84x + 49$

32. $(8x - 3)(2x - 4)$
$= 8x(2x) + 8x(-4) + (-3)(2x) + (-3)(-4)$
$= 16x^2 - 32x - 6x + 12$
$= 16x^2 - 38x + 12$

34. $(x^2 + 4)^2 = (x^2 + 4)(x^2 + 4)$
$= x^2(x^2) + x^2(4) + 4(x^2) + 4(4)$
$= x^4 + 4x^2 + 4x^2 + 16$
$= x^4 + 8x^2 + 16$

36. a. $9x^2(-10x^2) = 9(-10)(x^2 \cdot x^2) = -90x^4$

b. $9x^2 - 10x^2 = (9 - 10)x^2 = (-1)x^2 = -x^2$

c. Answers may vary

38. $(x + 3)(x^2 + 5x - 8)$
$= x(x^2) + x(5x) + x(-8) + 3(x^2) + 3(5x) + 3(-8)$
$= x^3 + 5x^2 - 8x + 3x^2 + 15x - 24$
$= x^3 + 8x^2 + 7x - 24$

40. $(a + 2)(a^3 - 3a^2 + 7)$
$= a(a^3) + a(-3a^2) + a(7) + 2(a^3) + 2(-3a^2) + 2(7)$
$= a^4 - 3a^3 + 7a + 2a^3 - 6a^2 + 14$
$= a^4 - a^3 - 6a^2 + 7a + 14$

42. $(3 + b)(2 - 5b - 3b^2)$
$= 3(2) + 3(-5b) + 3(-3b^2) + b(2) + b(-5b) + b(-3b^2)$
$= 6 - 15b - 9b^2 + 2b - 5b^2 - 3b^3$
$= -3b^3 - 14b^2 - 13b + 6$

44. $(y - 1)^3 = (y - 1)(y - 1)(y - 1)$
$= (y^2 - y - y + 1)(y - 1)$
$= (y^2 - 2y + 1)(y - 1)$
$= (y^2 - 2y + 1)y + (y^2 - 2y + 1)(-1)$
$= y^3 - 2y^2 + y - y^2 + 2y - 1$
$= y^3 - 3y^2 + 3y - 1$

46. $(3x + 4)^3$
$= (3x + 4)(3x + 4)(3x + 4)$
$= (9x^2 + 12x + 12x + 16)(3x + 4)$
$= (9x^2 + 24x + 16)(3x + 4)$
$= (9x^2 + 24x + 16)3x + (9x^2 + 24x + 16)4$
$= 27x^3 + 72x^2 + 48x + 36x^2 + 96x + 64$
$= 27x^3 + 108x^2 + 144x + 64$

48.

$$
\begin{array}{r}
4x - 7 \\
\times \quad 5x + 1 \\
\hline
4x - 7 \\
20x^2 - 35x \\
\hline
20x^2 - 31x - 7
\end{array}
$$

50.

$$
\begin{array}{r}
8x^2 + 2x - 4 \\
\times \quad 4x - 5 \\
\hline
-40x^2 - 10x + 20 \\
32x^3 + 8x^2 - 16x \\
\hline
32x^3 - 32x^2 - 26x + 20
\end{array}
$$

52.

$$
\begin{array}{r}
3x^2 - x + 2 \\
\times \quad x^2 + 2x + 1 \\
\hline
3x^2 - x + 2 \\
6x^3 - 2x^2 + 4x \\
3x^4 - x^3 + 2x^2 \\
\hline
3x^4 + 5x^3 + 3x^2 + 3x + 2
\end{array}
$$

54. $-4.2x(-2x^5) = -4.2(-2)(x \cdot x^5) = 8.4x^6$

56. $-5x(x^2 - 3x + 10)$
$= -5x(x^2) + (-5x)(-3x) + (-5x)(10)$
$= -5x^3 + 15x^2 - 50x$

58. $(3y + 4)(y + 11) = 3y(y) + 3y(11) + 4(y) + 4(11)$
$\qquad = 3y^2 + 33y + 4y + 44$
$\qquad = 3y^2 + 37y + 44$

60. $\left(m + \dfrac{2}{9}\right)\left(m - \dfrac{1}{9}\right)$

$= m(m) + m\left(-\dfrac{1}{9}\right) + \dfrac{2}{9}(m) + \dfrac{2}{9}\left(-\dfrac{1}{9}\right)$

$= m^2 - \dfrac{1}{9}m + \dfrac{2}{9}m - \dfrac{2}{81}$

$= m^2 + \dfrac{1}{9}m - \dfrac{2}{81}$

62. $(7y + 2)^2 = (7y + 2)(7y + 2)$
$\qquad = 7y(7y) + 7y(2) + 2(7y) + 2(2)$
$\qquad = 49y^2 + 14y + 14y + 4$
$\qquad = 49y^2 + 28y + 4$

64. $(t + 3)(t^2 - 5t + 5)$
$= t(t^2) + t(-5t) + t(5) + 3(t^2) + 3(-5t) + 3(5)$
$= t^3 - 5t^2 + 5t + 3t^2 - 15t + 15$
$= t^3 - 2t^2 - 10t + 15$

66. $(3y - 1)^3 = (3y - 1)(3y - 1)(3y - 1)$
$\qquad = (9y^2 - 3y - 3y + 1)(3y - 1)$
$\qquad = (9y^2 - 6y + 1)(3y - 1)$
$\qquad = (9y^2 - 6y + 1)3y + (9y^2 - 6y + 1)(-1)$
$\qquad = 27y^3 - 18y^2 + 3y - 9y^2 + 6y - 1$
$\qquad = 27y^3 - 27y^2 + 9y - 1$

68. $(5x + 4)(x^2 - x + 4)$
$\qquad = 5x(x^2) + 5x(-x) + 5x(4) + 4(x^2) + 4(-x) + 4(4)$
$\qquad = 5x^3 - 5x^2 + 20x + 4x^2 - 4x + 16$
$\qquad = 5x^3 - x^2 + 16x + 16$

70.

$$
\begin{array}{r}
a^2 + 3a - 2 \\
\times \quad 2a^2 - 5a - 1 \\
\hline
-a^2 - 3a + 2 \\
-5a^3 - 15a^2 + 10a \\
2a^4 + 6a^3 - 4a^2 \\
\hline
2a^4 + a^3 - 20a^2 + 7a + 2
\end{array}
$$

72. $(x + 4)^2 = (x + 4)(x + 4)$
$\qquad = x(x) + x(4) + 4(x) + 4(4)$
$\qquad = x^2 + 4x + 4x + 16$
$\qquad = x^2 + 8x + 16$
The area is $(x^2 + 8x + 16)$ square feet.

74. $(y - 1)^3 = (y - 1)(y - 1)(y - 1)$
$\qquad = (y^2 - y - y + 1)(y - 1)$
$\qquad = (y^2 - 2y + 1)(y - 1)$
$\qquad = (y^2 - 2y + 1)y + (y^2 - 2y + 1)(-1)$
$\qquad = y^3 - 2y^2 + y - y^2 + 2y - 1$
$\qquad = y^3 - 3y^2 + 3y - 1$
The volume is $(y^3 - 3y^2 + 3y - 1)$ cubic meters.

76. $(4p)^2 = (4p)(4p)$
$\qquad = (4 \cdot 4)(p \cdot p)$
$\qquad = 16p^2$

78. $(-7m^2)^2 = (-7m^2)(-7m^2)$
$\qquad = -7(-7)(m^2 \cdot m^2)$
$\qquad = 49m^4$

80. larger rectangle: $x(1 + 2x)$
left rectangle: $x \cdot 1 = x$
right rectangle: $x \cdot 2x = 2x^2$
left rectangle + right rectangle: $x + 2x^2$

82. entire figure: $(3x + 1)(3x + 1)$
top left rectangle: $3x \cdot 3x = 9x^2$
top right rectangle: $3x \cdot 1 = 3x$
bottom left rectangle: $1 \cdot 3x = 3x$
bottom right rectangle: $1 \cdot 1 = 1$
entire figure: $9x^2 + 3x + 3x + 1 = 9x^2 + 6x + 1$

84. $5a \cdot 6a = 5 \cdot 6(a \cdot a) = 30a^2$

86. $(5x + 2y)^2 = (5x + 2y)(5x + 2y)$
$ = 5x(5x) + 5x(2y) + 2y(5x) + 2y(2y)$
$ = 25x^2 + 10xy + 10xy + 4y^2$
$ = 25x^2 + 20xy + 4y^2$

88. $(2x - 1) + (10x - 7) = (2x + 10x) + (-1 - 7)$
$ = 12x - 8$

90. $(2x - 1)(10x - 7)$
$= 2x(10x) + 2x(-7) + (-1)(10x) + (-1)(-7)$
$= 20x^2 - 14x - 10x + 7$
$= 20x^2 - 24x + 7$

92. $(2x - 1) - (10x - 7) = 2x - 1 - 10x + 7$
$ = (2x - 10x) + (-1 + 7)$
$ = -8x + 6$

94. a. $(2 + 3)^2 = (5)^2 = 5 \cdot 5 = 25$
$ 2^2 + 3^2 = (2 \cdot 2) + (3 \cdot 3) = 4 + 9 = 13$

b. $(8 + 10)^2 = (18)^2 = 18 \cdot 18 = 324$
$ 8^2 + 10^2 = (8 \cdot 8) + (10 \cdot 10) = 64 + 100 = 164$

96. larger rectangle:
$(x + 1)(x + 4) = x(x) + x(4) + 1(x) + 1(4)$
$ = x^2 + 4x + x + 4$
$ = x^2 + 5x + 4$
small square: $x \cdot x = x^2$
shaded region: $x^2 + 5x + 4 - x^2 = 5x + 4$
The area of the shaded region is $(5x + 4)$ square units.

Section 5.4

Practice Exercises

1. $(x + 2)(x - 5)$
$= (x)(x) + (x)(-5) + (2)(x) + (2)(-5)$
$= x^2 - 5x + 2x - 10$
$= x^2 - 3x - 10$

2. $(4x - 9)(x - 1)$
$= 4x(x) + 4x(-1) + (-9)(x) + (-9)(-1)$
$= 4x^2 - 4x - 9x + 9$
$= 4x^2 - 13x + 9$

3. $3(x + 5)(3x - 1) = 3(3x^2 - x + 15x - 5)$
$ = 3(3x^2 + 14x - 5)$
$ = 9x^2 + 42x - 15$

4. $(4x - 1)^2$
$= (4x - 1)(4x - 1)$
$= (4x)(4x) + (4x)(-1) + (-1)(4x) + (-1)(-1)$
$= 16x^2 - 4x - 4x + 1$
$= 16x^2 - 8x + 1$

5. a. $(b + 3)^2 = b^2 + 2(b)(3) + 3^2 = b^2 + 6b + 9$

b. $(x - y)^2 = x^2 - 2(x)(y) + y^2 = x^2 - 2xy + y^2$

c. $(3y + 2)^2 = (3y)^2 + 2(3y)(2) + 2^2$
$ = 9y^2 + 12y + 4$

d. $(a^2 - 5b)^2 = (a^2)^2 - 2(a^2)(5b) + (5b)^2$
$ = a^4 - 10a^2b + 25b^2$

6. a. $3(x + 5)(x - 5) = 3(x^2 - 5^2)$
$ = 3x(x^2 - 25)$
$ = 3x^2 - 75$

b. $(4b - 3)(4b + 3) = (4b)^2 - 3^2 = 16b^2 - 9$

c. $\left(x + \dfrac{2}{3}\right)\left(x - \dfrac{2}{3}\right) = x^2 - \left(\dfrac{2}{3}\right)^2 = x^2 - \dfrac{4}{9}$

d. $(5s + t)(5s - t) = (5s)^2 - t^2 = 25s^2 - t^2$

e. $(2y - 3z^2)(2y + 3z^2) = (2y)^2 - (3z^2)^2$
$$= 4y^2 - 9z^4$$

6. $(3y - 5)(2y - 7) = 6y^2 - 21y - 10y + 35$
$$= 6y^2 - 31y + 35$$

7. a. $(4x + 3)(x - 6) = 4x^2 - 24x + 3x - 18$
$$= 4x^2 - 21x - 18$$

8. $(2x - 9)(x - 11) = 2x^2 - 22x - 9x + 99$
$$= 2x^2 - 31x + 99$$

b. $(7b - 2)^2 = (7b)^2 - 2(7b)(2) + 2^2$
$$= 49b^2 - 28b + 4$$

10. $(6x + 2)(x - 2) = 6x^2 - 12x + 2x - 4$
$$= 6x^2 - 10x - 4$$

c. $(x + 0.4)(x - 0.4) = x^2 - (0.4)^2 = x^2 - 0.16$

12. $(x + 7)^2 = x^2 + 2(x)(7) + 7^2 = x^2 + 14x + 49$

d. $(x^2 - 3)(3x^4 + 2) = 3x^6 + 2x^2 - 9x^4 - 6$

14. $(7x - 3)^2 = (7x)^2 - 2(7x)(3) + (3)^2$
$$= 49x^2 - 42x + 9$$

e. $(x + 1)(x^2 + 5x - 2)$
$$= x(x^2 + 5x - 2) + 1(x^2 + 5x - 2)$$
$$= x^3 + 5x^2 - 2x + x^2 + 5x - 2$$
$$= x^3 + 6x^2 + 3x - 2$$

16. $(5a + 2)^2 = (5a)^2 + 2(5a)(2) + 2^2$
$$= 25a^2 + 20a + 4$$

18. $(6s - 2)^2 = (6s)^2 - 2(6s)(2) + 2^2$
$$= 36s^2 - 24s + 4$$

Vocabulary and Readiness Check

1. $(x + 4)^2 = x^2 + 2(x)(4) + 4^2$
$$= x^2 + 8x + 16 \neq x^2 + 16$$
The statement is false.

20. Answers may vary

22. $(b + 3)(b - 3) = b^2 - 3^2 = b^2 - 9$

2. $(x + 6)(2x - 1) = 2x^2 - x + 12x - 6$
$$= 2x^2 + 11x - 6$$
The statement is true.

24. $(4x - 5)(4x + 5) = (4x)^2 - 5^2 = 16x^2 - 25$

26. $\left(10x + \dfrac{2}{7}\right)\left(10x - \dfrac{2}{7}\right) = (10x)^2 - \left(\dfrac{2}{7}\right)^2$
$$= 100x^2 - \dfrac{4}{49}$$

3. $(x + 4)(x - 4) = x^2 - 4^2 = x^2 - 16 \neq x^2 + 16$
The statement is false.

4. $(x - 1)(x^3 + 3x - 1)$
$$= x(x^3 + 3x - 1) - 1(x^3 + 3x - 1)$$
$$= x^4 + 3x^2 - x - x^3 - 3x + 1$$
$$= x^4 - x^3 + 3x^2 - 4x + 1$$
This is a polynomial of degree 4; the statement is false.

28. $(2x - y)(2x + y) = (2x)^2 - y^2 = 4x^2 - y^2$

30. $(5x - 1.3)(5x + 1.3) = (5x)^2 - (1.3)^2$
$$= 25x^2 - 1.69$$

32. $(a - 5)(a - 7) = a^2 - 7a - 5a + 35$
$$= a^2 - 12a + 35$$

Exercise Set 5.4

2. $(x + 5)(x - 1) = x^2 - 1x + 5x - 5 = x^2 + 4x - 5$

34. $(b - 2)^2 = b^2 - 2(b)(2) + 2^2 = b^2 - 4b + 4$

4. $(y - 12)(y + 4) = y^2 + 4y - 12y - 48$
$$= y^2 - 8y - 48$$

36. $(6a + 7)(6a + 5) = 36a^2 + 30a + 42a + 35$
$$= 36a^2 + 72a + 35$$

38. $(x - 10)(x + 10) = x^2 - 10^2 = x^2 - 100$

40. $(4a-2)^2 = (4a)^2 - 2(4a)(2) + 2^2$
$\qquad = 16a^2 - 16a + 4$

42. $(x^3 - 2)(5x + y) = 5x^4 + x^3 y - 10x - 2y$

44. $(x-2)(x^2 - 4x + 2)$
$\qquad = x(x^2 - 4x + 2) - 2(x^2 - 4x + 2)$
$\qquad = x^3 - 4x^2 + 2x - 2x^2 + 8x - 4$
$\qquad = x^3 - 6x^2 + 10x - 4$

46. $(5b - 4x)^2 = (5b)^2 - 2(5b)(4x) + (4x)^2$
$\qquad\qquad = 25b^2 - 40bx + 16x^2$

48. $(11x - 7y)(11x + 7y)$
$\qquad = (11x)^2 - (7y)^2$
$\qquad = 121x^2 - 49y^2$

50. $(a^4 + 5)(a^4 + 6) = a^8 + 6a^4 + 5a^4 + 30$
$\qquad\qquad = a^8 + 11a^4 + 30$

52. $\left(3x + \dfrac{1}{5}\right)\left(3x - \dfrac{1}{5}\right) = (3x)^2 - \left(\dfrac{1}{5}\right)^2$
$\qquad\qquad\qquad\qquad = 9x^2 - \dfrac{1}{25}$

54. $(x^5 + 5)(x^2 - 8) = x^7 - 8x^5 + 5x^2 - 40$

56. $2(3b + 7)^2 = 2[(3b)^2 + 2(3b)(7) + 7^2]$
$\qquad\qquad = 2(9b^2 + 42b + 49)$
$\qquad\qquad = 18b^2 + 84b + 98$

58. $(3y - 13)(y - 3) = 3y^2 - 9y - 13y + 39$
$\qquad\qquad\qquad = 3y^2 - 22y + 39$

60. $(3s - 4)(3s + 4) = (3s)^2 - 4^2 = 9s^2 - 16$

62. $\left(\dfrac{2}{3}a - b^2\right)\left(\dfrac{2}{3}a - b^2\right)$
$\qquad = \left(\dfrac{2}{3}a - b^2\right)^2$
$\qquad = \left(\dfrac{2}{3}a\right)^2 - 2\left(\dfrac{2}{3}a\right)(b^2) + (b^2)^2$
$\qquad = \dfrac{4}{9}a^2 - \dfrac{4}{3}ab^2 + b^4$

64. $4x^3(2x^2 + 5x - 1)$
$\qquad = 4x^3(2x^2) + 4x^3(5x) + 4x^3(-1)$
$\qquad = 8x^5 + 20x^4 - 4x^3$

66. $(6r - 2x)(6r + 2x) = (6r)^2 - (2x)^2 = 36r^2 - 4x^2$

68. $(4s - 2y)^2 = (4s)^2 - 2(4s)(2y) + (2y)^2$
$\qquad\qquad = 16s^2 - 16sy + 4y^2$

70. $(3x + 5)(3x - 5) = (3x)^2 - 5^2 = 9x^2 - 25$

72. $(3x + 2)^2 = (3x)^2 + 2(3x)(2) + (2)^2$
$\qquad\qquad = 9x^2 + 12x + 4$

74. $\left(\dfrac{a}{2} + 4y\right)\left(\dfrac{a}{2} - 4y\right) = \left(\dfrac{a}{2}\right)^2 - (4y)^2 = \dfrac{a^2}{4} - 16y^2$

76. $\left(\dfrac{y}{6} - 8\right)\left(\dfrac{y}{6} + 8\right) = \left(\dfrac{y}{6}\right)^2 - 8^2 = \dfrac{y^2}{36} - 64$

78. $(b + 3)(2b^2 + b - 3)$
$\qquad = b(2b^2 + b - 3) + 3(2b^2 + b - 3)$
$\qquad = 2b^3 + b^2 - 3b + 6b^2 + 3b - 9$
$\qquad = 2b^3 + 7b^2 - 9$

80. $(3x - 2)(x - 4) = 3x^2 - 12x - 2x + 8$
$\qquad\qquad\qquad = 3x^2 - 14x + 8$
The area is $(3x^2 - 14x + 8)$ square inches.

82. $\dfrac{x^3 y^6}{xy^2} = x^{3-1}y^{6-2} = x^2 y^4$

84. $\dfrac{-6a^8 y}{3a^4 y} = \dfrac{-6}{3}a^{8-4}y^{1-1} = -2a^4$

86. $\dfrac{-48ab^6}{32ab^3} = \dfrac{-48}{32}a^{1-1}b^{6-3} = -\dfrac{3b^3}{2}$

88. $(-1, 2)$ and $(1, 1)$
$\qquad m = \dfrac{y_2 - y_1}{x_2 - x_1} = \dfrac{1 - 2}{1 - (-1)} = -\dfrac{1}{2}$

90. $(0, 3)$ and $(2, 0)$

$$m = \frac{y_2 - y_1}{x_2 - x_1} = \frac{0 - 3}{2 - 0} = -\frac{3}{2}$$

92. $(a - b)(a + b) = a^2 - b^2$

Choice a

94. $(a + b)^2 (a - b)^2 = (a^2 + 2ab + b^2)(a^2 - 2ab + b^2)$

Choice e

96. When squaring the binomial, the first term in the result is $(5x^{\square})^2 = 25x^{2\square}$. Thus, $2\square = 6$ so $\square = 3$.

98. $(2x + 3)(2x - 3) - x \cdot x = 4x^2 - 9 - x^2$

$$= 3x^2 - 9$$

The shaded area is $(3x^2 - 9)$ square units.

100. $(3x - 4)(3x + 4) - 4 \cdot x \cdot x = 9x^2 - 16 - 4x^2$

$$= 5x^2 - 16$$

The shaded area is $(5x^2 - 16)$ square centimeters.

102. $(2y + 11)(2y + 11) = (2y + 11)^2$

$$= (2y)^2 + 2(2y)(11) + 11^2$$

$$= 4y^2 + 44y + 121$$

The area is $(4y^2 + 44y + 121)$ square units.

104. Answers may vary

106. $[(a + c) - 5][(a + c) + 5] = (a + c)^2 - 5^2$

$$= a^2 + 2ac + c^2 - 25$$

108. $[(x - 2) + y][(x - 2) - y] = (x - 2)^2 - y^2$

$$= x^2 - 4x + 4 - y^2$$

Integrated Review

1. $(5x^2)(7x^3) = (5 \cdot 7)(x^2 \cdot x^3) = 35x^5$

2. $(4y^2)(8y^7) = (4 \cdot 8)(y^2 \cdot y^7) = 32y^9$

3. $-4^2 = -(4 \cdot 4) = -16$

4. $(-4)^2 = (-4)(-4) = 16$

5. $(x - 5)(2x + 1) = 2x^2 + x - 10x - 5$

$$= 2x^2 - 9x - 5$$

6. $(3x - 2)(x + 5) = 3x^2 + 15x - 2x - 10$

$$= 3x^2 + 13x - 10$$

7. $(x - 5) + (2x + 1) = x - 5 + 2x + 1 = 3x - 4$

8. $(3x - 2) + (x + 5) = 3x - 2 + x + 5 = 4x + 3$

9. $\dfrac{7x^9 y^{12}}{x^3 y^{10}} = 7x^{9-3} y^{12-10} = 7x^6 y^2$

10. $\dfrac{20a^2 b^8}{14a^2 b^2} = \dfrac{20}{14} a^{2-2} b^{8-2} = \dfrac{10b^6}{7}$

11. $(12m^7 n^6)^2 = 12^2 m^{7 \cdot 2} n^{6 \cdot 2} = 144 m^{14} n^{12}$

12. $(4y^9 z^{10})^3 = 4^3 y^{9 \cdot 3} z^{10 \cdot 3} = 64 y^{27} z^{30}$

13. $3(4y - 3)(4y + 3) = 3[(4y)^2 - 3^2]$

$$= 3(16y^2 - 9)$$

$$= 48y^2 - 27$$

14. $2(7x - 1)(7x + 1) = 2[(7x)^2 - 1^2]$

$$= 2(49x^2 - 1)$$

$$= 98x^2 - 2$$

15. $(x^7 y^5)^9 = x^{7 \cdot 9} y^{5 \cdot 9} = x^{63} y^{45}$

16. $(3^1 x^9)^3 = 3^{1 \cdot 3} x^{9 \cdot 3} = 3^3 x^{27} = 27 x^{27}$

17. $(7x^2 - 2x + 3) - (5x^2 + 9)$

$$= 7x^2 - 2x + 3 - 5x^2 - 9$$

$$= 2x^2 - 2x - 6$$

18. $(10x^2 + 7x - 9) - (4x^2 - 6x + 2)$

$$= 10x^2 + 7x - 9 - 4x^2 + 6x - 2$$

$$= 6x^2 + 13x - 11$$

19. $0.7y^2 - 1.2 + 1.8y^2 - 6y + 1 = 2.5y^2 - 6y - 0.2$

20. $7.8x^2 - 6.8x + 3.3 + 0.6x^2 - 9$

$$= 8.4x^2 - 6.8x - 5.7$$

21. $(x+4y)^2 = x^2 + 2(x)(4y) + (4y)^2$
$\qquad = x^2 + 8xy + 16y^2$

22. $(y-9z)^2 = y^2 - 2(y)(9z) + (9z)^2$
$\qquad = y^2 - 18yz + 81z^2$

23. $(x+4y) + (x+4y) = x + 4y + x + 4y = 2x + 8y$

24. $(y-9z) + (y-9z) = y - 9z + y - 9z = 2y - 18z$

25. $7x^2 - 6xy + 4(y^2 - xy) = 7x^2 - 6xy + 4y^2 - 4xy$
$\qquad = 7x^2 - 10xy + 4y^2$

26. $5a^2 - 3ab + 6(b^2 - a^2) = 5a^2 - 3ab + 6b^2 - 6a^2$
$\qquad = -a^2 - 3ab + 6b^2$

27. $(x-3)(x^2 + 5x - 1)$
$\qquad = x(x^2 + 5x - 1) - 3(x^2 + 5x - 1)$
$\qquad = x^3 + 5x^2 - x - 3x^2 - 15x + 3$
$\qquad = x^3 + 2x^2 - 16x + 3$

28. $(x+1)(x^2 - 3x - 2)$
$\qquad = x(x^2 - 3x - 2) + 1(x^2 - 3x - 2)$
$\qquad = x^3 - 3x^2 - 2x + x^2 - 3x - 2$
$\qquad = x^3 - 2x^2 - 5x - 2$

29. $(2x^3 - 7)(3x^2 + 10)$
$\qquad = 2x^3(3x^2) + 2x^3(10) - 7(3x^2) - 7(10)$
$\qquad = 6x^5 + 20x^3 - 21x^2 - 70$

30. $(5x^3 - 1)(4x^4 + 5)$
$\qquad = 5x^3(4x^4) + 5x^3(5) - 1(4x^4) - 1(5)$
$\qquad = 20x^7 + 25x^3 - 4x^4 - 5$

31. $(2x-7)(x^2 - 6x + 1)$
$\qquad = 2x(x^2 - 6x + 1) - 7(x^2 - 6x + 1)$
$\qquad = 2x^3 - 12x^2 + 2x - 7x^2 + 42x - 7$
$\qquad = 2x^3 - 19x^2 + 44x - 7$

32. $(5x-1)(x^2 + 2x - 3)$
$\qquad = 5x(x^2 + 2x - 3) - 1(x^2 + 2x - 3)$
$\qquad = 5x^3 + 10x^2 - 15x - x^2 - 2x + 3$
$\qquad = 5x^3 + 9^2 - 17x + 3$

33. $5x^3 + 5y^3$ cannot be simplified.

34. $(5x^3)(5y^3) = 5 \cdot 5x^3 y^3 = 25x^3 y^3$

35. $(5x^3)^3 = 5^3 x^{3\cdot3} = 125x^9$

36. $\dfrac{5x^3}{5y^3} = \dfrac{x^3}{y^3}$

37. $x + x = 2x$

38. $x \cdot x = x^2$

Section 5.5

Practice Exercises

1. a. $5^{-3} = \dfrac{1}{5^3} = \dfrac{1}{125}$

$\quad$ **b.** $3y^{-4} = 3 \cdot \dfrac{1}{y^4} = \dfrac{3}{y^4}$

$\quad$ **c.** $3^{-1} + 2^{-1} = \dfrac{1}{3} + \dfrac{1}{2} = \dfrac{2}{6} + \dfrac{3}{6} = \dfrac{5}{6}$

$\quad$ **d.** $(-5)^{-2} = \dfrac{1}{(-5)^2} = \dfrac{1}{(-5)(-5)} = \dfrac{1}{25}$

$\quad$ **e.** $\dfrac{1}{x^{-5}} = \dfrac{1}{\frac{1}{x^5}} = x^5$

$\quad$ **f.** $\dfrac{1}{4^{-3}} = \dfrac{1}{\frac{1}{4^3}} = \dfrac{4^3}{1} = 64$

2. a. $\dfrac{1}{s^{-5}} = \dfrac{s^5}{1} = s^5$

$\quad$ **b.** $\dfrac{1}{2^{-3}} = \dfrac{2^3}{1} = 8$

$\quad$ **c.** $\dfrac{x^{-7}}{y^{-5}} = \dfrac{y^5}{x^7}$

$\quad$ **d.** $\dfrac{4^{-3}}{3^{-2}} = \dfrac{3^2}{4^3} = \dfrac{9}{64}$

3. a. $\dfrac{x^{-3}}{x^2} = x^{-3-2} = x^{-5} = \dfrac{1}{x^5}$

b. $\dfrac{5}{y^{-7}} = 5 \cdot \dfrac{1}{y^{-7}} = 5 \cdot y^7 = 5y^7$

c. $\dfrac{z}{z^{-4}} = \dfrac{z^1}{z^{-4}} = z^{1-(-4)} = z^5$

4. a. $\left(\dfrac{3}{4}\right)^{-2} = \dfrac{3^{-2}}{4^{-2}} = \dfrac{4^2}{3^2} = \dfrac{16}{9}$

b. $\dfrac{x^2(x^5)^3}{x^7} = \dfrac{x^2 \cdot x^{15}}{x^7}$

$= \dfrac{x^{2+15}}{x^7}$

$= \dfrac{x^{17}}{x^7}$

$= x^{17-7}$

$= x^{10}$

c. $\left(\dfrac{5p^8}{q}\right)^{-2} = \dfrac{5^{-2}(p^8)^{-2}}{q^{-2}}$

$= \dfrac{5^{-2} p^{-16}}{q^{-2}}$

$= \dfrac{q^2}{5^2 p^{16}}$

$= \dfrac{q^2}{25 p^{16}}$

d. $\dfrac{6^{-2} x^{-4} y^{-7}}{6^{-3} x^3 y^{-9}} = 6^{-2-(-3)} x^{-4-3} y^{-7-(-9)}$

$= 6^1 x^{-7} y^2$

$= \dfrac{6y^2}{x^7}$

e. $(a^4 b^{-3})^{-5} = a^{-20} b^{15} = \dfrac{b^{15}}{a^{20}}$

f. $\left(\dfrac{-3x^4 y}{x^2 y^{-2}}\right)^3 = \dfrac{(-3)^3 x^{12} y^3}{x^2 y^{-2}}$

$= \dfrac{-27 x^{12} y^3}{x^6 y^{-6}}$

$= -27 x^{12-6} y^{3-(-6)}$

$= -27 x^6 y^9$

5. a. $0.000007 = 7 \times 10^{-6}$
The decimal point is moved 6 places, and the original number is less than 1, so the count is -6.

b. $20,700,000 = 2.07 \times 10^7$
The decimal point is moved 7 places, and the original number is 10 or greater, so the count is 7.

c. $0.0043 = 4.3 \times 10^{-3}$
The decimal point is moved 3 places, and the original number is less than 1, so the count is -3.

d. $812,000,000 = 8.12 \times 10^8$
The decimal point is moved 8 places, and the original number is 10 or greater, so the count is 8.

6. a. Move the decimal point 4 places to the left.
$3.67 \times 10^{-4} = 0.000367$

b. Move the decimal point 6 places to the right.
$8.954 \times 10^6 = 8,954,000$

c. Move the decimal point 5 places to the left.
$2.009 \times 10^{-5} = 0.00002009$

d. Move the decimal point 3 places to the right.
$4.054 \times 10^3 = 4054$

7. a. $(5 \times 10^{-4})(8 \times 10^6) = (5 \cdot 8) \times (10^{-4} \cdot 10^6)$
$= 40 \times 10^2$
$= 4000$

b. $\dfrac{64 \times 10^3}{32 \times 10^{-7}} = \dfrac{64}{32} \times 10^{3-(-7)}$
$= 2 \times 10^{10}$
$= 20,000,000,000$

Calculator Explorations

1. $5.31 \times 10^3 = 5.31$ EE 3

2. $-4.8 \times 10^{14} = -4.8$ EE 14

3. $6.6 \times 10^{-9} = 6.6$ EE -9

4. $-9.9811 \times 10^{-2} = -9.9811$ EE -2

5. $3,000,000 \times 5,000,000 = 1.5 \times 10^{13}$

6. $230,000 \times 1000 = 2.3 \times 10^8$

7. $(3.26 \times 10^6)(2.5 \times 10^{13}) = 8.15 \times 10^{19}$

8. $(8.76 \times 10^{-4})(1.237 \times 10^9) = 1.083612 \times 10^6$

Vocabulary and Readiness Check

1. The expression x^{-3} equals $\dfrac{1}{x^3}$.

2. The expression 5^{-4} equals $\dfrac{1}{625}$.

3. The number 3.021×10^{-3} is written in <u>scientific notation</u>.

4. The number 0.0261 is written in <u>standard form</u>.

5. $5x^{-2} = 5 \cdot \dfrac{1}{x^2} = \dfrac{5}{x^2}$

6. $3x^{-3} = 3 \cdot \dfrac{1}{x^3} = \dfrac{3}{x^3}$

7. $\dfrac{1}{y^{-6}} = \dfrac{1}{\frac{1}{y^6}} = \dfrac{y^6}{1} = y^6$

8. $\dfrac{1}{x^{-3}} = \dfrac{1}{\frac{1}{x^3}} = \dfrac{x^3}{1} = x^3$

9. $\dfrac{4}{y^{-3}} = \dfrac{4}{\frac{1}{y^3}} = 4 \cdot \dfrac{y^3}{1} = 4y^3$

10. $\dfrac{16}{y^{-7}} = \dfrac{16}{\frac{1}{y^7}} = 16 \cdot \dfrac{y^7}{1} = 16y^7$

Exercise Set 5.5

2. $6^{-2} = \dfrac{1}{6^2} = \dfrac{1}{36}$

4. $(-3)^{-5} = \dfrac{1}{(-3)^5} = -\dfrac{1}{243}$

6. $(7x)^{-3} = \dfrac{1}{(7x)^3} = \dfrac{1}{7^3 x^3} = \dfrac{1}{343x^3}$

8. $\left(\dfrac{1}{8}\right)^{-2} = \dfrac{1^{-2}}{8^{-2}} = \dfrac{8^2}{1^2} = 64$

10. $\left(-\dfrac{1}{8}\right)^{-2} = \dfrac{(-1)^{-2}}{(8)^{-2}} = \dfrac{8^2}{(-1)^2} = \dfrac{64}{1} = 64$

12. $4^{-1} + 4^{-2} = \dfrac{1}{4^1} + \dfrac{1}{4^2} = \dfrac{1}{4} + \dfrac{1}{16} = \dfrac{4}{16} + \dfrac{1}{16} = \dfrac{5}{16}$

14. $\dfrac{1}{q^{-5}} = q^5$

16. $\dfrac{r^{-5}}{s^{-2}} = \dfrac{s^2}{r^5}$

18. $\dfrac{y}{y^{-3}} = y^{1-(-3)} = y^4$

20. $\dfrac{x^{-4}}{x^{-1}} = x^{-4-(-1)} = x^{-3} = \dfrac{1}{x^3}$

22. $4^{-2} - 4^{-3} = \dfrac{1}{4^2} - \dfrac{1}{4^3} = \dfrac{1}{16} - \dfrac{1}{64} = \dfrac{4}{64} - \dfrac{1}{64} = \dfrac{3}{64}$

24. $\dfrac{-1}{y^{-6}} = -1(y^6) = -y^6$

26. $5^0 + (-5)^0 = 1 + 1 = 2$

28. $\dfrac{y^4 y^5}{y^6} = y^{4+5-6} = y^3$

30. $\dfrac{y^3 y}{y^{-2}} = y^{3+1-(-2)} = y^6$

32. $\dfrac{(x^2)^8 x}{x^9} = \dfrac{x^{16} x}{x^9} = x^{16+1-9} = x^8$

34. $\dfrac{p}{p^{-3} q^{-5}} = p^{1-(-3)} q^5 = p^4 q^5$

36. $(z^5 x^5)^{-3} = z^{5(-3)} x^{5(-3)} = z^{-15} x^{-15} = \dfrac{1}{z^{15} x^{15}}$

38. $\dfrac{(y^4)^2}{y^{12}} = \dfrac{y^8}{y^{12}} = y^{8-12} = y^{-4} = \dfrac{1}{y^4}$

40. $\dfrac{(x^2)^5}{(x^4)^3} = \dfrac{x^{10}}{x^{12}} = x^{10-12} = x^{-2} = \dfrac{1}{x^2}$

42. $\dfrac{27r^4}{3r^6} = \dfrac{27}{3} \cdot r^{4-6} = 9r^{-2} = \dfrac{9}{r^2}$

44. $\dfrac{15a^4}{-15a^5} = \dfrac{15}{-15} \cdot a^{4-5} = -1(a^{-1}) = -\dfrac{1}{a}$

46. $\dfrac{-5x^4 y^5}{15x^4 y^2} = \dfrac{-5}{15} \cdot x^{4-4} y^{5-2} = -\dfrac{1}{3} \cdot y^3 = -\dfrac{y^3}{3}$

48. $(-5a^4 b^{-7})(-a^{-4} b^3) = -5(-1)a^{4+(-4)} a^{-7+3}$
$= 5a^0 b^{-4}$
$= \dfrac{5}{b^4}$

50. $(4^{-1} x^5)^{-2} = 4^{-1(-2)} x^{5(-2)} = 4^2 x^{-10} = \dfrac{16}{x^{10}}$

52. $\left(\dfrac{a^5 b}{a^7 b^{-2}}\right)^{-3} = \dfrac{a^{5(-3)} b^{-3}}{a^{7(-3)} b^{-2(-3)}}$
$= \dfrac{a^{-15} b^{-3}}{a^{-21} b^6}$
$= a^{-15-(-21)} b^{-3-6}$
$= a^6 b^{-9}$
$= \dfrac{a^6}{b^9}$

54. $\dfrac{3^{-1} x^4}{3^3 x^{-7}} = 3^{-1-3} x^{4-(-7)} = 3^{-4} x^{11} = \dfrac{x^{11}}{3^4} = \dfrac{x^{11}}{81}$

56. $\dfrac{5^{-1} z^7}{5^{-2} z^9} = 5^{-1-(-2)} z^{7-9} = 5^1 z^{-2} = \dfrac{5}{z^2}$

58. $\dfrac{6^{-5} x^{-1} y^2}{6^{-2} x^{-4} y^4} = 6^{-5-(-2)} x^{-1-(-4)} y^{2-4}$
$= 6^{-3} x^3 y^{-2}$
$= \dfrac{x^3}{6^3 y^2}$
$= \dfrac{x^3}{216 y^2}$

60. $\left(\dfrac{r^{-2} s^{-3}}{r^{-4} s^{-3}}\right)^{-3} = \dfrac{r^{-2(-3)} s^{-3(-3)}}{r^{-4(-3)} s^{-3(-3)}}$
$= \dfrac{r^6 s^9}{r^{12} s^9}$
$= r^{6-12} s^{9-9}$
$= r^{-6} s^0$
$= \dfrac{1}{r^6}$

62. $\dfrac{(rs)^{-3}}{(r^2 s^3)^2} = \dfrac{r^{-3} s^{-3}}{r^{2(2)} s^{3(2)}}$
$= \dfrac{r^{-3} s^{-3}}{r^4 s^6}$
$= r^{-3-4} s^{-3-6}$
$= r^{-7} s^{-9}$
$= \dfrac{1}{r^7 s^9}$

64. $\dfrac{(-3x^2 y^2)^{-2}}{(xyz)^{-2}} = \dfrac{(-3)^{-2} x^{-4} y^{-4}}{x^{-2} y^{-2} z^{-2}}$
$= (-3)^{-2} x^{-4-(-2)} y^{-4-(-2)} z^2$
$= (-3)^{-2} x^{-2} y^{-2} z^2$
$= \dfrac{z^2}{(-3)^2 x^2 y^2}$
$= \dfrac{z^2}{9x^2 y^2}$

66. $\dfrac{-8xa^2b}{-5xa^5b} = \dfrac{-8}{-5} \cdot x^{1-1}a^{2-5}b^{1-1} = \dfrac{8}{5}x^0 a^{-3}b^0 = \dfrac{8}{5a^3}$

68. $\dfrac{(a^6 b^{-2})^4}{(4a^{-3}b^{-3})^3} = \dfrac{a^{6(4)}b^{-2(4)}}{4^3 a^{-3(3)}b^{-3(3)}}$

$\qquad = \dfrac{a^{24}b^{-8}}{4^3 a^{-9}b^{-9}}$

$\qquad = \dfrac{1}{64}a^{24-(-9)}b^{-8-(-9)}$

$\qquad = \dfrac{1}{64}a^{33}b$

$\qquad = \dfrac{a^{33}b}{64}$

70. $9,300,000,000 = 9.3 \times 10^9$

72. $0.00000017 = 1.7 \times 10^{-7}$

74. $0.00194 = 1.94 \times 10^{-3}$

76. $700,000 = 7.0 \times 10^5$

78. $20,000,000 = 2 \times 10^7$

80. $13,600 = 1.36 \times 10^4$

82. $9.056 \times 10^{-4} = 0.0009056$

84. $4.8 \times 10^{-6} = 0.0000048$

86. $9.07 \times 10^{10} = 90,700,000,000$

88. $6.02214199 \times 10^{23}$
$= 602,214,199,000,000,000,000,000$

90. $6.067 \times 10^9 = 6,067,000,000$

92. The shortest bar corresponds to The Weather Channel, with 35,000,000 or 3.5×10^7 visits.

94. $1.08 \times 10^{11} = 108,000,000,000$

96. $23,000,000,000 = 2.3 \times 10^{10}$

98. $(2.5 \times 10^6)(2 \times 10^{-6}) = (2.5 \cdot 2) \times (10^6 \cdot 10^{-6})$
$\qquad = 5.0 \times 10^0$
$\qquad = 5$

100. $(5 \times 10^6)(4 \times 10^{-8}) = (5 \cdot 4) \times (10^6 \cdot 10^{-8})$
$\qquad = 20 \times 10^{-2}$
$\qquad = 2.0 \times 10^{-1}$
$\qquad = 0.2$

102. $\dfrac{25 \times 10^{-4}}{5 \times 10^{-9}} = \dfrac{25}{5} \times 10^{-4-(-9)} = 5 \times 10^5 = 500,000$

104. $\dfrac{0.4 \times 10^5}{0.2 \times 10^{11}} = \dfrac{0.4}{0.2} \times 10^{5-11} = 2 \times 10^{-6} = 0.000002$

106. $\dfrac{27y^{14}}{3y^7} = \dfrac{27}{3} \cdot y^{14-7} = 9y^7$

108. $\dfrac{18a^7 b^{17}}{30a^7 b} = \dfrac{18}{30} \cdot a^{7-7}b^{17-1} = \dfrac{3b^{16}}{5}$

110. $\dfrac{2}{x}(3x^5 + x^4 - 2) = \dfrac{2}{x}(3x^5) + \dfrac{2}{x}(x^4) + \dfrac{2}{x}(-2)$
$\qquad = 6x^4 + 2x^3 - \dfrac{4}{x}$

112. $\dfrac{1}{2}\left(\dfrac{5x^{-3}}{7}\right)\left(\dfrac{4}{x}\right) = \dfrac{20}{14} \cdot \dfrac{x^{-3}}{x}$
$\qquad = \dfrac{10}{7} \cdot (x^{-3-1})$
$\qquad = \dfrac{10}{7}x^{-4}$
$\qquad = \dfrac{10}{7x^4}$

114. $(2a^3)^3 a^{-3} + a^{11}a^{-5} = 2^3 a^{3\cdot3}a^{-3} + a^{11+(-5)}$
$\qquad = 8a^{9+(-3)} + a^6$
$\qquad = 8a^6 + a^6$
$\qquad = 9a^6$

116. $7^{-2} = \dfrac{1}{7^2} = \dfrac{1}{49}$

118. Answers may vary

120. Answers may vary

122. $a^{-4m} \cdot a^{5m} = a^{-4m+5m} = a^m$

124. $(3y^{2z})^3 = 3^3 y^{2z \cdot 3} = 27 y^{6z}$

126. $(2.63 \times 10^{12})(-1.5 \times 10^{-10}) = -394.5$

128. $t = \dfrac{d}{r}$

$t = \dfrac{238,857}{1.86 \times 10^5} = \dfrac{238,857}{186,000} \approx 1.3$

It takes 1.3 seconds for the reflected light of the moon to reach Earth.

Section 5.6

Practice Exercises

1. $\dfrac{8t^3 + 4t^2}{4t^2} = \dfrac{8t^3}{4t^2} + \dfrac{4t^2}{4t^2} = 2t + 1$

   Check: $4t^2(2t+1) = 4t^2(2t) + 4t^2(1)$

$= 8t^3 + 4t^2$

2. $\dfrac{16x^6 + 20x^3 - 12x}{4x^2} = \dfrac{16x^6}{4x^2} + \dfrac{20x^3}{4x^2} - \dfrac{12x}{4x^2}$

$= 4x^4 + 5x - \dfrac{3}{x}$

   Check: $4x^2\left(4x^4 + 5x - \dfrac{3}{x}\right)$

$= 4x^2(4x^4) + 4x^2(5x) - 4x^2\left(\dfrac{3}{x}\right)$

$= 16x^6 + 20x^3 - 12x$

3. $\dfrac{15x^4 y^4 - 10xy + y}{5xy} = \dfrac{15x^4 y^4}{5xy} - \dfrac{10xy}{5xy} + \dfrac{y}{5xy}$

$= 3x^3 y^3 - 2 + \dfrac{1}{5x}$

   Check: $5xy\left(3x^3 y^3 - 2 + \dfrac{1}{5x}\right)$

$= 5xy(3x^3 y^3) - 5xy(2) + 5xy\left(\dfrac{1}{5x}\right)$

$= 15x^4 y^4 - 10xy + y$

4.

$$
\begin{array}{r}
x+3 \\
x+2 \overline{\smash)\ x^2 + 5x + 6} \\
\underline{x^2 + 2x} \\
3x + 6 \\
\underline{3x + 6} \\
0
\end{array}
$$

Check: $(x+2) \cdot (x+3) + 0 = x^2 + 5x + 6$

The quotient checks.

5.

$$
\begin{array}{r}
2x+3 \\
2x+1 \overline{\smash)\ 4x^2 + 8x - 7} \\
\underline{4x^2 + 2x} \\
6x - 7 \\
\underline{6x + 3} \\
-10
\end{array}
$$

$\dfrac{4x^2 + 8x - 7}{2x + 1} = 2x + 3 + \dfrac{-10}{2x + 1}$

Check:

$(2x+1)(2x+3) + (-10) = (4x^2 + 8x + 3) - 10$

$= 4x^2 + 8x - 7$

The quotient checks.

6. Rewrite $11x - 3 + 9x^3$ as $9x^3 + 0x^2 + 11x - 3$.

$$
\begin{array}{r}
3x^2 - 2x + 5 \\
3x+2 \overline{\smash)\ 9x^3 + 0x^2 + 11x\ -3} \\
\underline{9x^3 + 6x^2} \\
-6x^2 + 11x \\
\underline{-6x^2\ -4x} \\
15x\ -3 \\
\underline{15x + 10} \\
-13
\end{array}
$$

$\dfrac{11x - 3 + 9x^3}{3x + 2} = 3x^2 - 2x + 5 + \dfrac{-13}{3x + 2}$

7. Rewrite $x^2 + 2$ as $x^2 + 0x + 2$.

$$
\begin{array}{r}
3x^2 - 2x - 9 \\
x^2 + 0x + 2 \overline{\smash{\big)}\ 3x^4 - 2x^3 - 3x^2 \quad + x + 4} \\
\underline{3x^4 + 0x^3 + 6x^2} \\
-2x^3 - 9x^2 \quad + x \\
\underline{-2x^3 + 0x^2 - 4x} \\
-9x^2 + 5x \ + 4 \\
\underline{-9x^2 + 0x - 18} \\
5x + 22
\end{array}
$$

$$\frac{3x^4 - 2x^3 - 3x^2 + x + 4}{x^2 + 2} = 3x^2 - 2x - 9 + \frac{5x + 22}{x^2 + 2}$$

Vocabulary and Readiness Check

1. In $6\overline{\smash{\big)}18}^{\,3}$, the 18 is the <u>dividend</u>, the 3 is the <u>quotient</u> and the 6 is the <u>divisor</u>.

2. In $x+1\overline{\smash{\big)}x^2+3x+2}^{\,x+2}$, the $x+1$ is the <u>divisor</u>, the $x^2 + 3x + 2$ is the <u>dividend</u> and the $x + 2$ is the <u>quotient</u>.

3. $\dfrac{a^6}{a^4} = a^{6-4} = 2$

4. $\dfrac{p^8}{p^3} = p^{8-3} = p^5$

5. $\dfrac{y^2}{y} = \dfrac{y^2}{y^1} = y^{2-1} = y$

6. $\dfrac{a^3}{a} = \dfrac{a^3}{a^1} = a^{3-1} = a^2$

Exercise Set 5.6

2. $\dfrac{15x^2 - 9x^5}{x} = \dfrac{15x^2}{x} - \dfrac{9x^5}{x} = 15x - 9x^4$

4. $\dfrac{8x^3 - 4x^2 + 6x + 2}{2} = \dfrac{8x^3}{2} - \dfrac{4x^2}{2} + \dfrac{6x}{2} + \dfrac{2}{2}$
$= 4x^3 - 2x^2 + 3x + 1$

6. $\dfrac{14m^2 - 27m^3}{7m} = \dfrac{14m^2}{7m} - \dfrac{27m^3}{7m} = 2m - \dfrac{27m^2}{7}$

8. $\dfrac{6x^5 + 3x^4}{3x^4} = \dfrac{6x^5}{3x^4} + \dfrac{3x^4}{3x^4} = 2x + 1$

10. $\dfrac{6a^2 - 4a + 12}{-2a^2} = \dfrac{6a^2}{-2a^2} - \dfrac{4a}{-2a^2} + \dfrac{12}{-2a^2}$
$= -3 + \dfrac{2}{a} - \dfrac{6}{a^2}$

12. $\dfrac{-12a^3 + 36a - 15}{3a} = \dfrac{-12a^3}{3a} + \dfrac{36a}{3a} - \dfrac{15}{3a}$
$= -4a^2 + 12 - \dfrac{5}{a}$

14.
$$
\begin{array}{r}
x + 2 \\
x + 5 \overline{\smash{\big)}\ x^2 + 7x + 10} \\
\underline{x^2 + 5x} \\
2x + 10 \\
\underline{2x + 10} \\
0
\end{array}
$$

$$\frac{x^2 + 7x + 10}{x + 5} = x + 2$$

16.
$$
\begin{array}{r}
3x + 2 \\
x + 2 \overline{\smash{\big)}\ 3x^2 + 8x + 4} \\
\underline{3x^2 + 6x} \\
2x + 4 \\
\underline{2x + 4} \\
0
\end{array}
$$

$$\frac{3x^2 + 8x + 4}{x + 2} = 3x + 2$$

18.
$$
\begin{array}{r}
3x + 2 \\
x - 1 \overline{\smash{\big)}\ 3x^2 - x - 4} \\
\underline{3x^2 - 3x} \\
2x - 4 \\
\underline{2x - 2} \\
-2
\end{array}
$$

$$\frac{3x^2 - x - 4}{x - 1} = 3x + 2 - \frac{2}{x - 1}$$

20.

$$\begin{array}{r} 2x^2+3x-4 \\ 2x+3\overline{\smash{\big)}\,4x^3+12x^2+\ x-14} \\ \underline{4x^3\ +6x^2} \\ 6x^2\ +x \\ \underline{6x^2+9x} \\ -8x-14 \\ \underline{-8x-12} \\ -2 \end{array}$$

$$\frac{4x^3+12x^2+x-14}{2x+3}=2x^2+3x-4-\frac{2}{2x+3}$$

22.

$$\begin{array}{r} x+5 \\ 3x+2\overline{\smash{\big)}\,3x^2+17x\ +7} \\ \underline{3x^2\ +2x} \\ 15x\ +7 \\ \underline{15x+10} \\ -3 \end{array}$$

$$\frac{3x^2+17x+7}{3x+2}=x+5-\frac{3}{3x+2}$$

24.

$$\begin{array}{r} 4x^2-x-5 \\ x+3\overline{\smash{\big)}\,4x^3+11x^2-8x-10} \\ \underline{4x^3+12x^2} \\ -x^2-8x \\ \underline{-x^2-3x} \\ -5x-10 \\ \underline{-5x-15} \\ 5 \end{array}$$

$$\frac{4x^3+11x^2-8x-10}{x+3}=4x^2-x-5+\frac{5}{x+3}$$

26. Rewrite a^2-49 as $a^2+0a-49$.

$$\begin{array}{r} a+7 \\ a-7\overline{\smash{\big)}\,a^2+0a-49} \\ \underline{a^2-7a} \\ 7a-49 \\ \underline{7a-49} \\ 0 \end{array}$$

$$\frac{a^2-49}{a-7}=a+7$$

28. Rewrite x^3+64 as $x^3+0x^2+0x+64$.

$$\begin{array}{r} x^2-4x+16 \\ x+4\overline{\smash{\big)}\,x^3+0x^2\ +0x+64} \\ \underline{x^3+4x^2} \\ -4x^2\ +0x \\ \underline{-4x^2-16x} \\ 16x+64 \\ \underline{16x+64} \\ 0 \end{array}$$

$$\frac{x^3+64}{x+4}=x^2-4x+16$$

30. Rewrite $7-5x^2$ as $-5x^2+0x+7$.

$$\begin{array}{r} -5x+15 \\ x+3\overline{\smash{\big)}\,-5x^2\ +0x\ +7} \\ \underline{-5x^2-15x} \\ 15x+\ 7 \\ \underline{15x+45} \\ -38 \end{array}$$

$$\frac{7-5x^2}{x+3}=-5x+15-\frac{38}{x+3}$$

32. Rewrite $-3y+2y^2-15$ as $2y^2-3y-15$.

$$\begin{array}{r} y-4 \\ 2y+5\overline{\smash{\big)}\,2y^2-3y-15} \\ \underline{2y^2+5y} \\ -8y-15 \\ \underline{-8y-20} \\ 5 \end{array}$$

$$\frac{-3y+2y^2-15}{2y+5}=y-4+\frac{5}{2y+5}$$

34. $\dfrac{m^3n^2-mn^4}{mn}=\dfrac{m^3n^2}{mn}-\dfrac{mn^4}{mn}=m^2n-n^3$

36.

$$\begin{array}{r} 6w-2 \\ 3w+4\overline{\smash{\big)}\,18w^2+18w-8} \\ \underline{18w^2+24w} \\ -6w-8 \\ \underline{-6w-8} \\ 0 \end{array}$$

$$\frac{18w^2+18w-8}{3w+4}=6w-2$$

38.

$$\frac{11x^3y^3 - 33xy + x^2y^2}{11xy} = \frac{11x^3y^3}{11xy} - \frac{33xy}{11xy} + \frac{x^2y^2}{11xy}$$

$$= x^2y^2 - 3 + \frac{xy}{11}$$

40.

$$\begin{array}{r}
2x^2 - x - 1 \\
x+2 \overline{\smash{\big)}\ 2x^3 + 3x^2 - 3x + 4} \\
\underline{2x^3 + 4x^2} \\
-x^2 - 3x \\
\underline{-x^2 - 2x} \\
-x + 4 \\
\underline{-x - 2} \\
6
\end{array}$$

$$\frac{2x^3 + 3x^2 - 3x + 4}{x+2} = 2x^2 - x - 1 + \frac{6}{x+2}$$

42.

$$\begin{array}{r}
2x - 5 \\
x+3 \overline{\smash{\big)}\ 2x^2 + x - 15} \\
\underline{2x^2 + 6x} \\
-5x - 15 \\
\underline{-5x - 15} \\
0
\end{array}$$

$$\frac{2x^2 + x - 15}{x+3} = 2x - 5$$

44.

$$\frac{2x^3 + 12x^2 + 16}{4x^2} = \frac{2x^3}{4x^2} + \frac{12x^2}{4x^2} + \frac{16}{4x^2}$$

$$= \frac{x}{2} + 3 + \frac{4}{x^2}$$

46.

$$\begin{array}{r}
2x + 3 \\
x-6 \overline{\smash{\big)}\ 2x^2 - 9x + 15} \\
\underline{2x^2 - 12x} \\
3x + 15 \\
\underline{3x - 18} \\
33
\end{array}$$

$$\frac{2x^2 - 9x + 15}{x-6} = 2x + 3 + \frac{33}{x-6}$$

48.

$$\begin{array}{r}
x - 4 \\
4x+3 \overline{\smash{\big)}\ 4x^2 - 13x - 12} \\
\underline{4x^2 + 3x} \\
-16x - 12 \\
\underline{-16x - 12} \\
0
\end{array}$$

$$\frac{4x^2 - 13x - 12}{4x + 3} = x - 4$$

50.

$$\frac{8y^6 - 3y^2 - 4y}{4y} = \frac{8y^6}{4y} - \frac{3y^2}{4y} - \frac{4y}{4y} = 2y^5 - \frac{3y}{4} - 1$$

52.

$$\begin{array}{r}
x^2 - 4x + 16 \\
x-4 \overline{\smash{\big)}\ x^3 - 8x^2 + 32x - 64} \\
\underline{x^3 - 4x^2} \\
-4x^2 + 32x \\
\underline{-4x^2 + 16x} \\
16x - 64 \\
\underline{16x - 64} \\
0
\end{array}$$

$$\frac{x^3 - 8x^2 + 32x - 64}{x-4} = x^2 - 4x + 16$$

54. Rewrite $3x^3 + 11x + 12$ as $3x^3 + 0x^2 + 11x + 12$.

$$\begin{array}{r}
3x^2 - 12x + 59 \\
x+4 \overline{\smash{\big)}\ 3x^3 + 0x^2 + 11x + 12} \\
\underline{3x^3 + 12x^2} \\
-12x^2 + 11x \\
\underline{-12x^2 - 48x} \\
59x + 12 \\
\underline{59x + 236} \\
-224
\end{array}$$

$$\frac{3x^3 + 11x + 12}{x+4} = 3x^2 - 12x + 59 - \frac{224}{x+4}$$

56. Rewrite $3 - 7x^2$ as $-7x^2 + 0x + 3$.

$$
\begin{array}{r}
-7x - 21 \\
x - 3 \overline{\smash{\big)}\,-7x^2 + 0x + 3} \\
\underline{-7x^2 + 21x} \\
-21x + 3 \\
\underline{-21x + 63} \\
-60
\end{array}
$$

$$\frac{3 - 7x^2}{x - 3} = -7x - 21 - \frac{60}{x - 3}$$

58. Rewrite $x^6 - x^4$ as
$x^6 + 0x^5 - x^4 + 0x^3 + 0x^2 + 0x + 0.$

$$
\begin{array}{r}
x^3 \qquad\quad - x - 1 \\
x^3 + 1 \overline{\smash{\big)}\,x^6 + 0x^5 - x^4 + 0x^3 + 0x^2 + 0x + 0} \\
\underline{x^6 \qquad\qquad\quad + x^3} \\
-x^4 - x^3 + 0x^2 + 0x \\
\underline{-x^4 \qquad\qquad - x} \\
-x^3 + 0x^2 + x + 0 \\
\underline{-x^3 \qquad\qquad - 1} \\
x + 1
\end{array}
$$

$$\frac{x^6 - x^4}{x^3 + 1} = x^3 - x - 1 + \frac{x + 1}{x^3 + 1}$$

60. $-4a(3a^2 - 4) = -4a(3a^2) - 4a(-4)$
$$= -12a^3 + 16a$$

62. $4y(y^2 - 8y - 4) = 4y(y^2) + 4y(-8y) + 4y(-4)$
$$= 4y^3 - 32y^2 - 16y$$

64. $-9xy(4xyz + 7xy^2z + 2)$
$$= -9xy(4xyz) - 9xy(7xy^2z) - 9xy(2)$$
$$= -36x^2y^2z - 63x^2y^3z - 18xy$$

66. $-7sr(6s^2r + 9sr^2 + 9rs + 8)$
$$= -7sr(6s^2r) - 7sr(9sr^2) - 7sr(9rs) - 7sr(8)$$
$$= -42s^3r^2 - 63s^2r^3 - 63s^2r^2 - 56sr$$

68. The 2005 concert tour of The Rolling Stones grossed approximately \$162 million.

70. The shortest guitar corresponds to Pink Floyd, (1994).

72. $V = l \cdot w \cdot h, \ \dfrac{V}{wh} = l$

$$\frac{36x^5 - 12x^3 + 6x^2}{2x(3x)} = \frac{36x^5 - 12x^3 + 6x^2}{6x^2}$$
$$= \frac{36x^5}{6x^2} - \frac{12x^3}{6x^2} + \frac{6x^2}{6x^2}$$
$$= 6x^3 - 2x + 1$$

The length is $(6x^3 - 2x + 1)$ feet.

74. Answers may vary

76. $A = bh, \ h = \dfrac{A}{b}$

$$h = \frac{10x^2 + 31x + 15}{5x + 3}$$

$$
\begin{array}{r}
2x + 5 \\
5x + 3 \overline{\smash{\big)}\,10x^2 + 31x + 15} \\
\underline{10x^2 + 6x} \\
25x + 15 \\
\underline{25x + 15} \\
0
\end{array}
$$

The height is $(2x + 5)$ meters.

78. $$\frac{18x^{10a} - 12x^{8a} + 14x^{5a} - 2x^{3a}}{2x^{3a}}$$
$$= \frac{18x^{10a}}{2x^{3a}} - \frac{12x^{8a}}{2x^{3a}} + \frac{14x^{5a}}{2x^{3a}} - \frac{2x^{3a}}{2x^{3a}}$$
$$= 9x^{7a} - 6x^{5a} + 7x^{2a} - 1$$

The Bigger Picture

1. $-5.7 + (-0.23) = -5.93$

2. $\dfrac{1}{2} - \dfrac{9}{10} = \dfrac{5}{10} - \dfrac{9}{10} = \dfrac{-4}{10} = -\dfrac{2}{5}$

3. $(-5x^2y^3)(-x^7y) = (-5 \cdot -1)(x^2 \cdot x^7)(y^3 \cdot y)$
$$= 5x^9y^4$$

4. $2^{-3}a^{-7}a^3 = \dfrac{1}{2^3} \cdot \dfrac{1}{a^7} \cdot a^3 = \dfrac{1}{8} \cdot \dfrac{a^3}{a^7} = \dfrac{1}{8} \cdot a^{-4} = \dfrac{1}{8a^4}$

5. $(7y^3 - 6y + 2) - (y^3 + 2y^2 + 2)$
$$= 7y^3 - 6y + 2 - y^3 - 2y^2 - 2$$
$$= 6y^3 - 2y^2 - 6y$$

6. $(9y^2 - 3y) - (y^2 + 7) = 9y^2 - 3y - y^2 - 7$
$$= 8y^2 - 3y - 7$$

7. $(x - 3)(4x^2 - x + 7)$
$$= x(4x^2) + x(-x) + x(7) - 3(4x^2) - 3(-x) - 3(7)$$
$$= 4x^3 - x^2 + 7x - 12x^2 + 3x - 21$$
$$= 4x^3 - 13x^2 + 10x - 21$$

8. $(6m - 5)^2 = (6m)^2 - 2(6m)(5) + 5^2$
$$= 36m^2 - 60m + 25$$

9. $\dfrac{20n^2 - 5n + 10}{5n} = \dfrac{20n^2}{5n} - \dfrac{5n}{5n} + \dfrac{10}{5n} = 4n - 1 + \dfrac{2}{n}$

10.
$$\begin{array}{r}
2x - 6 \\
3x - 1 \overline{)6x^2 - 20x + 20} \\
\underline{6x^2 - 2x} \\
-18x + 20 \\
\underline{-18x + 6} \\
14
\end{array}$$

$$\dfrac{6x^2 - 20x + 20}{3x - 1} = 2x - 6 + \dfrac{14}{3x - 1}$$

11. $-6x = 3.6$
$$x = \dfrac{3.6}{-6}$$
$$x = -0.6$$

12. $-6x < 3.6$
$$x > \dfrac{3.6}{-6}$$
$$x > -0.6$$
$$(-0.6, \infty)$$

13. $6x + 6 \geq 8x + 2$
$$6x \geq 8x - 4$$
$$-2x \geq -4$$
$$x \leq \dfrac{-4}{-2}$$
$$x \leq 2$$
$$(-\infty, 2]$$

14. $7y + 3(y - 1) = 4(y + 1) - 3$
$$7y + 3y - 3 = 4y + 4 - 3$$
$$10y - 3 = 4y + 1$$
$$6y - 3 = 1$$
$$6y = 4$$
$$\dfrac{6y}{6} = \dfrac{4}{6}$$
$$y = \dfrac{2}{3}$$

Section 5.7

Practice Exercises

1. Since $x - c = x - 1$, c is 1.

$$\begin{array}{r|rrrr}
1 & 4 & -3 & 6 & 5 \\
& & 4 & 1 & 7 \\
\hline
& 4 & 1 & 7 & 12
\end{array}$$

$$4x^2 + x + 7 + \dfrac{12}{x - 1}$$

2. Since $x - c = x + 3 = x - (-3)$, c is -3.

$$\begin{array}{r|rrrrr}
-3 & 1 & 3 & -5 & 6 & 12 \\
& & -3 & 0 & 15 & -63 \\
\hline
& 1 & 0 & -5 & 21 & -51
\end{array}$$

$$x^3 - 5x + 21 - \dfrac{51}{x + 3}$$

3. a. $P(x) = x^3 - 5x - 2$
$$P(2) = 2^3 - 5(2) - 2$$
$$= 8 - 10 - 2$$
$$= -4$$

b. Since $x - c = x - 2$, c is 2.

$$\begin{array}{r|rrrr}
2 & 1 & 0 & -5 & -2 \\
& & 2 & 4 & -2 \\
\hline
& 1 & 2 & -1 & -4
\end{array}$$

The remainder is -4.

4.
$$\begin{array}{r|rrrrrr}
3 & 2 & -18 & 0 & 90 & 59 & 0 \\
& & 6 & -36 & -108 & -54 & 15 \\
\hline
& 2 & -12 & -36 & -18 & 5 & 15
\end{array}$$

$$P(3) = 15$$

Exercise Set 5.7

2. $x - 2 = x - c$ where $c = 2$.

$$
\begin{array}{r|rrr}
2 & 1 & -14 & 24 \\
  &   & 2   & -24 \\
\hline
  & 1 & -12 & 0
\end{array}
$$

$$\frac{x^2 - 14x + 24}{x - 2} = x - 12$$

4. $x + 4 = x - c$ where $c = -4$.

$$
\begin{array}{r|rrr}
-4 & 1 & 12 & 32 \\
   &   & -4 & -32 \\
\hline
   & 1 & 8 & 0
\end{array}
$$

$$\frac{x^2 + 12x + 32}{x + 4} = x + 8$$

6. $x + 5 = x - c$ where $c = -5$.

$$
\begin{array}{r|rrrr}
-5 & 1 & 6 & 4 & -7 \\
   &   & -5 & -5 & 5 \\
\hline
   & 1 & 1 & -1 & -2
\end{array}
$$

$$\frac{x^3 + 6x^2 + 4x - 7}{x + 5} = x^2 + x - 1 - \frac{2}{x + 5}$$

8. $x - 1 = x - c$ where $c = 1$.

$$
\begin{array}{r|rrr}
1 & 3 & 0 & -4 \\
  &   & 3 & 3 \\
\hline
  & 3 & 3 & -1
\end{array}
$$

$$\frac{3x^2 - 4}{x - 1} = 3x + 3 - \frac{1}{x - 1}$$

10. $P(x) = x^2 - x + 3$

   a. $P(5) = 5^2 - 5 + 3 = 25 - 5 + 3 = 23$

   b.

$$
\begin{array}{r|rrr}
5 & 1 & -1 & 3 \\
  &   & 5 & 20 \\
\hline
  & 1 & 4 & 23
\end{array}
$$

   Thus, $P(5) = 23$.

12. $P(x) = 8x^5 + 7x + 4$
$$= 8x^5 + 0x^4 + 0x^3 + 0x^2 + 7x + 4$$

    a. $P(-3) = 8(-3)^5 + 7(-3) + 4$
$$= 8(-243) - 21 + 4$$
$$= -1944 - 21 + 4$$
$$= -1961$$

    b.

-3	8	0	0	0	7	4
		-24	72	-216	648	-1965
	8	-24	72	-216	655	-1961

    Thus, $P(-3) = -1961$.

14. $P(x) = 5x^4 - 4x^3 + 2x - 1$
$$= 5x^4 - 4x^3 + 0x^2 + 2x - 1$$

    a. $P(-1) = 5(-1)^4 - 4(-1)^3 + 2(-1) - 1$
$$= 5 \cdot 1 - 4(-1) - 2 - 1$$
$$= 5 + 4 - 2 - 1$$
$$= 6$$

    b.

-1	5	-4	0	2	-1
		-5	9	-9	7
	5	-9	9	-7	6

    Thus, $P(-1) = 6$.

16. $x^2 + 12 = x^2 + 0x + 12; \; x + 2 = x - (-2)$

-2	1	0	12
		-2	4
	1	-2	16

$$\frac{x^2 + 12}{x + 2} = x - 2 + \frac{16}{x + 2}$$

18.

3	1	-5	7	-4
		3	-6	3
	1	-2	1	-1

$$\frac{x^3 - 5x^2 + 7x - 4}{x - 3} = x^2 - 2x + 1 - \frac{1}{x - 3}$$

20. $x + 2 = x - (-2)$

-2	3	5	-1	1	-2
		-6	2	-2	2
	3	-1	1	-1	0

$$\frac{3x^4 + 5x^3 - x^2 + x - 2}{x + 2} = 3x^3 - x^2 + x - 1$$

22. $x + 4 = x - (-4)$

-4	3	7	-6
		-12	20
	3	-5	14

$$\frac{3x^2 + 7x - 6}{x + 4} = 3x - 5 + \frac{14}{x + 4}$$

24. $x + \dfrac{3}{4} = x - \left(-\dfrac{3}{4}\right)$

$-\frac{3}{4}$	8	-6	-5	3
		-6	9	-3
	8	-12	4	0

$$\frac{8x^3 - 6x^2 - 5x + 3}{x + \frac{3}{4}} = 8x^2 - 12x + 4$$

26. $y + \dfrac{2}{3} = y - \left(-\dfrac{2}{3}\right)$

$-\frac{2}{3}$	9	9	-1	2
		-6	-2	2
	9	3	-3	4

$$\frac{9y^3 + 9y^2 - y + 2}{y + \frac{2}{3}} = 9y^2 + 3y - 3 + \frac{4}{y + \frac{2}{3}}$$

28.

2	1	4	-1	-16	-4
		2	12	22	12
	1	6	11	6	8

$$\frac{x^4 + 4x^3 - x^2 - 16x - 4}{x - 2}$$
$$= x^3 + 6x^2 + 11x + 6 + \frac{8}{x - 2}$$

30.

2	1	0	0	-8
		2	4	8
	1	2	4	0

$$\frac{y^3 - 8}{y - 2} = y^2 + 2y + 4$$

32. $x + 3 = x - (-3)$

-3	4	12	1	-12
		-12	0	-3
	4	0	1	-15

$$\frac{4x^3 + 12x^2 + x - 12}{x + 3} = 4x^2 + 1 - \frac{15}{x + 3}$$

34.

2	1	5	-4	-6
		2	14	20
	1	7	10	14

Thus, $P(2) = 14$.

36.

-2	4	5	-6	-4
		-8	6	0
	4	-3	0	-4

Thus, $P(-2) = -4$.

38.

-2	1	0	-3	-2	5
		-2	4	-2	8
	1	-2	1	-4	13

Thus, $P(-2) = 13$.

40.

$\frac{1}{2}$	4	-2	1	-1	-4
		2	0	$\frac{1}{2}$	$-\frac{1}{4}$
	4	0	1	$-\frac{1}{2}$	$-\frac{17}{4}$

Thus, $P\left(\dfrac{1}{2}\right) = -\dfrac{17}{4}$.

42.

$$\begin{array}{c|ccccc}
\frac{2}{3} & 1 & 0 & -2 & 4 & -5 & 6 \\
& & \frac{2}{3} & \frac{4}{9} & -\frac{28}{27} & \frac{160}{81} & -\frac{490}{243} \\
\hline
& 1 & \frac{2}{3} & -\frac{14}{9} & \frac{80}{27} & -\frac{245}{81} & \frac{968}{243}
\end{array}$$

Thus, $P\left(\dfrac{2}{3}\right) = \dfrac{968}{243}$.

44. Answers may vary

46. $4 - 2x = 17 - 5x$
$$3x = 13$$
$$x = \frac{13}{3}$$

The solution is $\dfrac{13}{3}$.

48.
$$\frac{2x}{9} + 1 = \frac{7}{9}$$
$$9\left(\frac{2x}{9} + 1\right) = 9\left(\frac{7}{9}\right)$$
$$2x + 9 = 7$$
$$2x = -2$$
$$x = -1$$

The solution is -1.

50. $3^4 = 3 \cdot 3 \cdot 3 \cdot 3 = 81$

52. $-2^5 = -(2 \cdot 2 \cdot 2 \cdot 2 \cdot 2) = -32$

54. $4 \cdot 3^3 = 4 \cdot (3 \cdot 3 \cdot 3) = 4 \cdot 27 = 108$

56. Let $x = -5$.
$$x^3 = (-5)^3 = (-5)(-5)(-5) = -125$$

58. Let $x = -1$.
$$3x^2 = 3(-1)^2 = 3(1) = 3$$

60. $(x^4 - 6) \div (x^3 + 3x - 1)$ is not a candidate for synthetic division since $x^3 + 3x - 1$ does not have the form $x - c$.

62. $(3x^2 + 7x - 1) \div \left(x - \dfrac{1}{3}\right)$ is a candidate for synthetic division since $x - \dfrac{1}{3}$ is in the form $x - c$, where $c = \dfrac{1}{3}$.

64. $V = lwh$ so $w = \dfrac{V}{lh}$

$$= \frac{x^4 + 6x^3 - 7x^2}{x^2(x + 7)}$$

$$= \frac{x^4 + 6x^3 - 7x^2}{x^3 + 7x^2}$$

$$\begin{array}{r}
x - 1 \\
x^3 + 7x^2 \overline{)\,x^4 + 6x^3 - 7x^2} \\
\underline{x^4 + 7x^3} \\
-x^3 - 7x^2 \\
\underline{-x^3 - 7x^2} \\
0
\end{array}$$

The width is $(x - 1)$ meters.

66.

$$\begin{array}{r}
2x^2 + \frac{1}{2}x - 5 \\
x + 2 \overline{)\,2x^3 + \frac{9}{2}x^2 - 4x - 10} \\
\underline{2x^3 + 4x^2} \\
\frac{1}{2}x^2 - 4x \\
\underline{\frac{1}{2}x^2 + x} \\
-5x - 10 \\
\underline{-5x - 10} \\
0
\end{array}$$

Answer: $2x^2 + \dfrac{1}{2}x - 5$

68.

$$\begin{array}{c|cccc}
2 & 1 & -2 & -3 & 6 \\
& & 2 & 0 & -6 \\
\hline
& 1 & 0 & -3 & 0
\end{array}$$

Remainder $= 0$. Therefore,
$$x^3 - 2x^2 - 3x + 6 = (x - 2)(x^2 - 3).$$

70. $(2x^2 + 5x - 6)(x - 5) + 3$
$$= 2x^3 - 10x^2 + 5x^2 - 25x - 6x + 30 + 3$$
$$= 2x^3 - 5x^2 - 31x + 33$$

72. Answers may vary

Chapter 5 Vocabulary Check

1. A <u>term</u> is a number or the product of numbers and variables raised to powers.

2. The <u>FOIL</u> method may be used when multiplying two binomials.

3. A polynomial with exactly 3 terms is called a <u>trinomial</u>.

4. The <u>degree of a polynomial</u> is the greatest degree of any term of the polynomial.

5. A polynomial with exactly 2 terms is called a <u>binomial</u>.

6. The <u>coefficient</u> of a term is its numerical factor.

7. The <u>degree of a term</u> is the sum of the exponents on the variables in the term.

8. A polynomial with exactly 1 term is called a <u>monomial</u>.

9. Monomials, binomials, and trinomials are all examples of <u>polynomials</u>.

Chapter 5 Review

1. In 7^9, the base is 7 and the exponent is 9.

2. In $(-5)^4$, the base is -5 and the exponent is 4.

3. In -5^4, the base is 5 and the exponent is 4.

4. In x^6, the base is x and the exponent is 6.

5. $8^3 = 8 \cdot 8 \cdot 8 = 512$

6. $(-6)^2 = (-6)(-6) = 36$

7. $-6^2 = -6 \cdot 6 = -36$

8. $-4^3 - 4^0 = -64 - 1 = -65$

9. $(3b)^0 = 1$

10. $\dfrac{8b}{8b} = 1$

11. $y^2 \cdot y^7 = y^{2+7} = y^9$

12. $x^9 \cdot x^5 = x^{9+5} = x^{14}$

13. $(2x^5)(-3x^6) = (2 \cdot -3)(x^5 \cdot x^6) = -6x^{11}$

14. $(-5y^3)(4y^4) = (-5 \cdot 4)(y^3 \cdot y^4) = -20y^7$

15. $(x^4)^2 = x^{4 \cdot 2} = x^8$

16. $(y^3)^5 = y^{3 \cdot 5} = y^{15}$

17. $(3y^6)^4 = 3^4(y^6)^4 = 81y^{24}$

18. $2^3(x^3)^3 = 8x^9$

19. $\dfrac{x^9}{x^4} = x^{9-4} = x^5$

20. $\dfrac{z^{12}}{z^5} = z^{12-5} = z^7$

21. $\dfrac{a^5 b^4}{ab} = a^{5-1}b^{4-1} = a^4 b^3$

22. $\dfrac{x^4 y^6}{xy} = x^{4-1}y^{6-1} = x^3 y^5$

23. $\dfrac{12xy^6}{3x^4 y^{10}} = \dfrac{12}{3}x^{1-3}y^{6-10} = 4x^{-2}y^{-4} = \dfrac{4}{x^2 y^4}$

24. $\dfrac{2x^7 y^8}{8xy^2} = \dfrac{2}{8}x^{7-1}y^{8-2} = \dfrac{x^6 y^6}{4}$

25. $5a^7(2a^4)^3 = 5a^7(2^3)(a^4)^3$
$= (5 \cdot 8)(a^7 \cdot a^{12})$
$= 40a^{19}$

26. $(2x)^2(9x) = (2^2 \cdot x^2)(9x)$
$= (4 \cdot 9)(x^2 \cdot x)$
$= 36x^3$

27. $(-5a)^0 + 7^0 + 8^0 = 1 + 1 + 1 = 3$

28. $8x^0 + 9^0 = 8(1) + 1 = 9$

29. $\left(\dfrac{3x^4}{4y}\right)^3 = \dfrac{3^3 x^{4 \cdot 3}}{4^3 y^3} = \dfrac{27x^{12}}{64y^3}$, choice b.

30. $\left(\dfrac{5a^6}{b^3}\right)^2 = \dfrac{5^2 a^{6\cdot2}}{b^{3\cdot2}} = \dfrac{25a^{12}}{b^6}$, choice c.

31. The degree of $-5x^4y^3$ is $4 + 3 = 7$.

32. The degree of $10x^3y^2z$ is $3 + 2 + 1 = 6$.

33. The degree of $35a^5bc^2$ is $5 + 1 + 2 = 8$.

34. The degree of $95xyz$ is $1 + 1 + 1 = 3$.

35. The degree is 5 because y^5 is the term with the highest degree.

36. The degree is 2 because $9y^2$ is the term with the highest degree.

37. The degree is 5 because $-28x^2y^3$ is the term with the highest degree.

38. The degree is 6 because $6x^2y^2z^2$ is the term with the highest degree.

39. a.

Term	Numerical Coefficient	Degree of Term
x^2y^2	1	4
$5x^2$	5	2
$-7y^2$	-7	2
$11xy$	11	2
-1	-1	0

    b. The degree is 4.

40. $2x^2 + 20x$:

$x = 1$: $2(1)^2 + 20(1) = 22$

$x = 3$: $2(3)^2 + 20(3) = 78$

$x = 5.1$: $2(5.1)^2 + 20(5.1) = 154.02$

$x = 10$: $2(10)^2 + 20(10) = 400$

41. $6a^2 + 4a + 9a^2 = (6 + 9)a^2 + 4a$
$$= 15a^2 + 4a$$

42. $21x^2 + 3x + x^2 + 6 = (21 + 1)x^2 + 3x + 6$
$$= 22x^2 + 3x + 6$$

43. $4a^2b - 3b^2 - 8q^2 - 10a^2b + 7q^2$
$$= (4a^2b - 10a^2b) - 3b^2 + (-8q^2 + 7q^2)$$
$$= -6a^2b - 3b^2 - q^2$$

44. $2s^{14} + 3s^{13} + 12s^{12} - s^{10}$ cannot be combined.

45. $(3x^2 + 2x + 6) + (5x^2 + x)$
$$= 3x^2 + 2x + 6 + 5x^2 + x$$
$$= 8x^2 + 3x + 6$$

46. $(2x^5 + 3x^4 + 4x^3 + 5x^2) + (4x^2 + 7x + 6)$
$$= 2x^5 + 3x^4 + 4x^3 + 5x^2 + 4x^2 + 7x + 6$$
$$= 2x^5 + 3x^4 + 4x^3 + 9x^2 + 7x + 6$$

47. $(-5y^2 + 3) - (2y^2 + 4) = -5y^2 + 3 - 2y^2 - 4$
$$= -7y^2 - 1$$

48. $(3x^2 - 7xy + 7y^2) - (4x^2 - xy + 9y^2)$
$$= 3x^2 - 7xy + 7y^2 - 4x^2 + xy - 9y^2$$
$$= -x^2 - 6xy - 2y^2$$

49. $(7x - 14y) - (3x - y) = 7x - 14y - 3x + y$
$$= 4x - 13y$$

50. $[(x^2 + 7x + 9) + (x^2 + 4)] - (4x^2 + 8x - 7)$
$$= x^2 + 7x + 9 + x^2 + 4 - 4x^2 - 8x + 7$$
$$= -2x^2 - x + 20$$

51. $P(x) = 9x^2 - 7x + 8$
$P(6) = 9(6)^2 - 7(6) + 8$
$$= 9(36) - 42 + 8$$
$$= 324 - 42 + 8$$
$$= 290$$

52. $P(x) = 9x^2 - 7x + 8$
$P(-2) = 9(-2)^2 - 7(-2) + 8$
$$= 9(4) + 14 + 8$$
$$= 36 + 14 + 8$$
$$= 58$$

53. $(x^2y+5)+(2x^2y-6x+1)+(x^2y+5)$
$\quad\quad +(2x^2y-6x+1)$
$\quad = x^2y+2x^2y+x^2y+2x^2y-6x-6x$
$\quad\quad +5+1+5+1$
$\quad = 6x^2y-12x+12$

The perimeter is $(6x^2y-12x+12)$ cm.

54. Let $x=8$.
$$f(8)=754(8)^2-228(8)+80,134$$
$$=126,566$$
Revenues from software sales in 2009 are predicted to be $126,566 million.

55. $4(2a+7)=4(2a)+4(7)=8a+28$

56. $9(6a-3)=9(6a)-9(3)=54a-27$

57. $-7x(x^2+5)=-7x(x^2)-7x(5)=-7x^3-35x$

58. $-8y(4y^2-6)=-8y(4y^2)-8y(-6)$
$\quad\quad =-32y^3+48y$

59. $(3a^3-4a+1)(-2a)$
$\quad = 3a^3(-2a)-4a(-2a)+1(-2a)$
$\quad = -6a^4+8a^2-2a$

60. $(6b^3-4b+2)(7b)=6b^3(7b)-4b(7b)+2(7b)$
$\quad\quad\quad\quad = 42b^4-28b^2+14b$

61. $(2x+2)(x-7)=2x^2-14x+2x-14$
$\quad\quad\quad\quad = 2x^2-12x-14$

62. $(2x-5)(3x+2)=6x^2+4x-15x-10$
$\quad\quad\quad\quad = 6x^2-11x-10$

63. $(x-9)^2=(x-9)(x-9)$
$\quad\quad = x^2-9x-9x+81$
$\quad\quad = x^2-18x+81$

64. $(x-12)^2=(x-12)(x-12)$
$\quad\quad = x^2-12x-12x+144$
$\quad\quad = x^2-24x+144$

65. $(4a-1)(a+7)=4a^2+28a-a-7$
$\quad\quad\quad\quad = 4a^2+27a-7$

66. $(6a-1)(7a+3)=42a^2+18a-7a-3$
$\quad\quad\quad\quad = 42a^2+11a-3$

67. $(5x+2)^2=(5x+2)(5x+2)$
$\quad\quad = 25x^2+10x+10x+4$
$\quad\quad = 25x^2+20x+4$

68. $(3x+5)^2=(3x+5)(3x+5)$
$\quad\quad = 9x^2+15x+15x+25$
$\quad\quad = 9x^2+30x+25$

69. $(x+7)(x^3+4x-5)$
$\quad = x(x^3+4x-5)+7(x^3+4x-5)$
$\quad = x^4+4x^2-5x+7x^3+28x-35$
$\quad = x^4+7x^3+4x^2+23x-35$

70. $(x+2)(x^5+x+1)=x(x^5+x+1)+2(x^5+x+1)$
$\quad\quad\quad\quad = x^6+x^2+x+2x^5+2x+2$
$\quad\quad\quad\quad = x^6+2x^5+x^2+3x+2$

71. $(x^2+2x+4)(x^2+2x-4)$
$\quad = x^2(x^2+2x-4)+2x(x^2+2x-4)$
$\quad\quad\quad +4(x^2+2x-4)$
$\quad = x^4+2x^3-4x^2+2x^3+4x^2-8x$
$\quad\quad\quad +4x^2+8x-16$
$\quad = x^4+4x^3+4x^2-16$

72. $(x^3+4x+4)(x^3+4x-4)$
$\quad = x^3(x^3+4x-4)+4x(x^3+4x-4)$
$\quad\quad\quad +4(x^3+4x-4)$
$\quad = x^6+4x^4-4x^3+4x^4+16x^2-16x+4x^3$
$\quad\quad\quad +16x-16$
$\quad = x^6+8x^4+16x^2-16$

73. $(x+7)^3=(x+7)(x+7)(x+7)$
$\quad\quad = (x^2+7x+7x+49)(x+7)$
$\quad\quad = (x^2+14x+49)(x+7)$
$\quad\quad = (x^2+14x+49)x+(x^2+14x+49)7$
$\quad\quad = x^3+14x^2+49x+7x^2+98x+343$
$\quad\quad = x^3+21x^2+147x+343$

74. $(2x-5)^3$
$= (2x-5)(2x-5)(2x-5)$
$= (4x^2 -10x -10x +25)(2x-5)$
$= (4x^2 -20x +25)(2x-5)$
$= (4x^2 -20x +25)(2x) + (4x^2 -20x +25)(-5)$
$= 8x^3 -40x^2 +50x -20x^2 +100x -125$
$= 8x^3 -60x^2 +150x -125$

75. $(x+7)^2 = x^2 + 2(x)(7) + 7^2 = x^2 +14x +49$

76. $(x-5)^2 = x^2 - 2(x)(5) + 5^2 = x^2 -10x +25$

77. $(3x-7)^2 = (3x)^2 - 2(3x)(7) + 7^2$
$\qquad = 9x^2 -42x +49$

78. $(4x+2)^2 = (4x)^2 + 2(4x)(2) + 2^2$
$\qquad = 16x^2 +16x +4$

79. $(5x-9)^2 = (5x)^2 - 2(5x)(9) + 9^2$
$\qquad = 25x^2 -90x +81$

80. $(5x+1)(5x-1) = (5x)^2 - 1^2 = 25x^2 -1$

81. $(7x+4)(7x-4) = (7x)^2 - 4^2 = 49x^2 -16$

82. $(a+2b)(a-2b) = a^2 - (2b)^2 = a^2 -4b^2$

83. $(2x-6)(2x+6) = (2x)^2 - 6^2 = 4x^2 -36$

84. $(4a^2 -2b)(4a^2 +2b) = (4a^2)^2 - (2b)^2$
$\qquad\qquad = 16a^4 -4b^2$

85. $(3x-1)^2 = (3x)^2 - 2(3x)(1) + 1^2$
$\qquad = 9x^2 -6x +1$
The area is $(9x^2 -6x +1)$ square meters.

86. $(5x+2)(x-1) = 5x^2 -5x +2x -2$
$\qquad = 5x^2 -3x -2$
The area is $(5x^2 -3x -2)$ square miles.

87. $7^{-2} = \dfrac{1}{7^2} = \dfrac{1}{49}$

88. $-7^{-2} = -\dfrac{1}{7^2} = -\dfrac{1}{49}$

89. $2x^{-4} = \dfrac{2}{x^4}$

90. $(2x)^{-4} = \dfrac{1}{(2x)^4} = \dfrac{1}{16x^4}$

91. $\left(\dfrac{1}{5}\right)^{-3} = \dfrac{1^{-3}}{5^{-3}} = \dfrac{5^3}{1^3} = 125$

92. $\left(\dfrac{-2}{3}\right)^{-2} = \dfrac{(-2)^{-2}}{3^{-2}} = \dfrac{3^2}{(-2)^2} = \dfrac{9}{4}$

93. $2^0 + 2^{-4} = 1 + \dfrac{1}{2^4} = \dfrac{16}{16} + \dfrac{1}{16} = \dfrac{17}{16}$

94. $6^{-1} - 7^{-1} = \dfrac{1}{6} - \dfrac{1}{7} = \dfrac{7}{42} - \dfrac{6}{42} = \dfrac{1}{42}$

95. $\dfrac{x^5}{x^{-3}} = x^{5-(-3)} = x^8$

96. $\dfrac{z^4}{z^{-4}} = z^{4-(-4)} = z^8$

97. $\dfrac{r^{-3}}{r^{-4}} = r^{-3-(-4)} = r$

98. $\dfrac{y^{-2}}{y^{-5}} = y^{-2-(-5)} = y^3$

99. $\left(\dfrac{bc^{-2}}{bc^{-3}}\right)^4 = \dfrac{b^4 c^{-8}}{b^4 c^{-12}} = b^{4-4} c^{-8-(-12)} = c^4$

100. $\left(\dfrac{x^{-3}y^{-4}}{x^{-2}y^{-5}}\right)^{-3} = \dfrac{x^9 y^{12}}{x^6 y^{15}}$
$\qquad\qquad = x^{9-6} y^{12-15}$
$\qquad\qquad = x^3 y^{-3}$
$\qquad\qquad = \dfrac{x^3}{y^3}$

101. $\dfrac{x^{-4}y^{-6}}{x^2y^7} = x^{-4-2}y^{-6-7}$

$\qquad = x^{-6}y^{-13}$

$\qquad = \dfrac{1}{x^6y^{13}}$

102. $\dfrac{a^5b^{-5}}{a^{-5}b^5} = a^{5-(-5)}b^{-5-5} = a^{10}b^{-10} = \dfrac{a^{10}}{b^{10}}$

103. $a^{6m}a^{5m} = a^{6m+5m} = a^{11m}$

104. $\dfrac{(x^{5+h})^3}{x^5} = \dfrac{x^{3(5+h)}}{x^5}$

$\qquad = \dfrac{x^{15+3h}}{x^5}$

$\qquad = x^{15+3h-5}$

$\qquad = x^{10+3h}$

105. $(3xy^{2z})^3 = 3^3x^3y^{2z(3)} = 27x^3y^{6z}$

106. $a^{m+2}a^{m+3} = a^{(m+2)+(m+3)} = a^{2m+5}$

107. $0.00027 = 2.7 \times 10^{-4}$

108. $0.8868 = 8.868 \times 10^{-1}$

109. $80{,}800{,}000 = 8.08 \times 10^7$

110. $868{,}000 = 8.68 \times 10^5$

111. $91{,}000{,}000 = 9.1 \times 10^7$

112. $150{,}000 = 1.5 \times 10^5$

113. $8.67 \times 10^5 = 867{,}000$

114. $3.86 \times 10^{-3} = 0.00386$

115. $8.6 \times 10^{-4} = 0.00086$

116. $8.936 \times 10^5 = 893{,}600$

117. $1.43128 \times 10^{15} = 1{,}431{,}280{,}000{,}000{,}000$

118. $1 \times 10^{-10} = 0.0000000001$

119. $(8 \times 10^4)(2 \times 10^{-7}) = (8 \cdot 2) \times (10^4 \cdot 10^{-7})$

$\qquad = 16 \times 10^{-3}$

$\qquad = 0.016$

120. $\dfrac{8 \times 10^4}{2 \times 10^{-7}} = \dfrac{8}{2} \times 10^{4-(-7)}$

$\qquad = 4 \times 10^{11}$

$\qquad = 400{,}000{,}000{,}000$

121. $\dfrac{x^2 + 21x + 49}{7x^2} = \dfrac{x^2}{7x^2} + \dfrac{21x}{7x^2} + \dfrac{49}{7x^2}$

$\qquad = \dfrac{1}{7} + \dfrac{3}{x} + \dfrac{7}{x^2}$

122. $\dfrac{5a^3b - 15ab^2 + 20ab}{-5ab} = \dfrac{5a^3b}{-5ab} - \dfrac{15ab^2}{-5ab} + \dfrac{20ab}{-5ab}$

$\qquad = -a^2 + 3b - 4$

123.
$$
\begin{array}{r}
a+1 \\
a-2 \overline{\smash{)}\, a^2 - a + 4} \\
\underline{a^2 - 2a} \\
a + 4 \\
\underline{a - 2} \\
6
\end{array}
$$

$(a^2 - a + 4) \div (a - 2) = a + 1 + \dfrac{6}{a-2}$

124.
$$
\begin{array}{r}
4x \\
x+5 \overline{\smash{)}\, 4x^2 + 20x + 7} \\
\underline{4x^2 + 20x} \\
7
\end{array}
$$

$(4x^2 + 20x + 7) \div (x + 5) = 4x + \dfrac{7}{x+5}$

125.
$$
\begin{array}{r}
a^2 + 3a + 8 \\
a-2 \overline{\smash{)}\, a^3 + a^2 + 2a + 6} \\
\underline{a^3 - 2a^2} \\
3a^2 + 2a \\
\underline{3a^2 - 6a} \\
8a + 6 \\
\underline{8a - 16} \\
22
\end{array}
$$

$\dfrac{a^3 + a^2 + 2a + 6}{a-2} = a^2 + 3a + 8 + \dfrac{22}{a-2}$

126.

$$3b-2 \overline{)\begin{array}{l} 3b^2 - 4b \\ 9b^3 - 18b^2 + 8b - 1 \end{array}}$$

$$\underline{9b^3 - 6b^2}$$
$$-12b^2 + 8b$$
$$\underline{-12b^2 + 8b}$$
$$-1$$

$$\frac{9b^3 - 18b^2 + 8b - 1}{3b - 2} = 3b^2 - 4b - \frac{1}{3b - 2}$$

127.

$$2x-1 \overline{)\begin{array}{l} 2x^3 - x^2 + 2 \\ 4x^4 - 4x^3 + x^2 + 4x - 3 \end{array}}$$

$$\underline{4x^4 - 2x^3}$$
$$-2x^3 + x^2$$
$$\underline{-2x^3 + x^2}$$
$$4x - 3$$
$$\underline{4x - 2}$$
$$-1$$

$$\frac{4x^4 - 4x^3 + x^2 + 4x - 3}{2x - 1} = 2x^3 - x^2 + 2 - \frac{1}{2x - 1}$$

128. Rewrite $-10x^2 - x^3 - 21x + 18$ as

$-x^3 - 10x^2 - 21x + 18$.

$$x-6 \overline{)\begin{array}{l} -x^2 - 16x - 117 \\ -x^3 - 10x^2 - 21x + 18 \end{array}}$$

$$\underline{-x^3 + 6x^2}$$
$$-16x^2 - 21x$$
$$\underline{-16x^2 + 96x}$$
$$-117x + 18$$
$$\underline{-117x + 702}$$
$$-684$$

$$\frac{-10x^2 - x^3 - 21x + 18}{x - 6} = -x^2 - 16x - 117 - \frac{684}{x - 6}$$

129.

$$\frac{15x^3 - 3x^2 + 60}{3x^2} = \frac{15x^3}{3x^2} - \frac{3x^2}{3x^2} + \frac{60}{3x^2}$$
$$= 5x - 1 + \frac{20}{x^2}$$

The width is $\left(5x - 1 + \dfrac{20}{x^2} \right)$ feet.

130.

$$\frac{21a^3b^6 + 3a - 3}{3} = \frac{21a^3b^6}{3} + \frac{3a}{3} - \frac{3}{3}$$
$$= 7a^3b^6 + a - 1$$

The length of a side is $(7a^3b^6 + a - 1)$ units.

131. $3x^3 + 12x - 4 = 3x^3 + 0x^2 + 12x - 4$

2	3	0	12	-4
		6	12	48
	3	6	24	44

$$\frac{3x^3 + 12x - 4}{x - 2} = 3x^2 + 6x + 24 + \frac{44}{x - 2}$$

132. $x + \dfrac{3}{2} = x - \left(-\dfrac{3}{2} \right)$

$-\frac{3}{2}$	3	2	-4	-1
		$-\frac{9}{2}$	$\frac{15}{4}$	$\frac{3}{8}$
	3	$-\frac{5}{2}$	$-\frac{1}{4}$	$-\frac{5}{8}$

$$\frac{3x^3 + 2x^2 - 4x - 1}{x + \frac{3}{2}} = 3x^2 - \frac{5}{2}x - \frac{1}{4} - \frac{5}{8\left(x + \frac{3}{2} \right)}$$

133. $x^5 - 1 = x^5 + 0x^4 + 0x^3 + 0x^2 + 0x - 1$;

$x + 1 = x - (-1)$

-1	1	0	0	0	0	-1
		-1	1	-1	1	-1
	1	-1	1	-1	1	-2

$$\frac{x^5 - 1}{x + 1} = x^4 - x^3 + x^2 - x + 1 - \frac{2}{x + 1}$$

134. $x^3 - 81 = x^3 + 0x^2 + 0x - 81$

3	1	0	0	-81
		3	9	27
	1	3	9	-54

$$\frac{x^3 - 81}{x - 3} = x^2 + 3x + 9 - \frac{54}{x - 3}$$

135. $x^3 - x^2 + 3x^4 - 2 = 3x^4 + x^3 - x^2 + 0x - 2$

$$
\begin{array}{r|rrrrr}
4 & 3 & 1 & -1 & 0 & -2 \\
  &   & 12 & 52 & 204 & 816 \\
\hline
  & 3 & 13 & 51 & 204 & 814
\end{array}
$$

$$\frac{x^3 - x^2 + 3x^4 - 2}{x - 4}$$
$$= 3x^3 + 13x^2 + 51x + 204 + \frac{814}{x-4}$$

136. $3x^4 - 2x^2 + 10 = 3x^4 + 0x^3 - 2x^2 + 0x + 10$
$x + 2 = x - (-2)$

$$
\begin{array}{r|rrrrr}
-2 & 3 & 0 & -2 & 0 & 10 \\
   &   & -6 & 12 & -20 & 40 \\
\hline
   & 3 & -6 & 10 & -20 & 50
\end{array}
$$

$$\frac{3x^4 - 2x^2 + 10}{x + 2} = 3x^3 - 6x^2 + 10x - 20 + \frac{50}{x+2}$$

137. $P(x) = 3x^5 + 0x^4 + 0x^3 + 0x^2 - 9x + 7$

$$
\begin{array}{r|rrrrrr}
4 & 3 & 0 & 0 & 0 & -9 & 7 \\
  &   & 12 & 48 & 192 & 768 & 3036 \\
\hline
  & 3 & 12 & 48 & 192 & 759 & 3043
\end{array}
$$

Thus, $P(4) = 3043$.

138. $P(x) = 3x^5 + 0x^4 + 0x^3 + 0x^2 - 9x + 7$

$$
\begin{array}{r|rrrrrr}
-5 & 3 & 0 & 0 & 0 & -9 & 7 \\
   &   & -15 & 75 & -375 & 1875 & -9330 \\
\hline
   & 3 & -15 & 75 & -375 & 1866 & -9323
\end{array}
$$

Thus, $P(-5) = -9323$.

139. $\left(-\dfrac{1}{2}\right)^3 = \left(-\dfrac{1}{2}\right)\left(-\dfrac{1}{2}\right)\left(-\dfrac{1}{2}\right) = -\dfrac{1}{8}$

140. $(4xy^2)(x^3y^5) = 4(x \cdot x^3)(y^2 \cdot y^5)$
$$= 4x^{1+3}y^{2+5}$$
$$= 4x^4y^7$$

141. $\dfrac{18x^9}{27x^3} = \dfrac{18}{27}x^{9-3} = \dfrac{2x^6}{3}$

142. $\left(\dfrac{3a^4}{b^2}\right)^3 = \dfrac{3^3(a^4)^3}{(b^2)^3} = \dfrac{27a^{12}}{b^6}$

143. $(2x^{-4}y^3)^{-4} = 2^{-4}(x^{-4})^{-4}(y^3)^{-4}$
$$= \dfrac{1}{2^4}x^{16}y^{-12}$$
$$= \dfrac{x^{16}}{16y^{12}}$$

144. $\dfrac{a^{-3}b^6}{9^{-1}a^{-5}b^{-2}} = 9a^{-3-(-5)}b^{6-(-2)} = 9a^2b^8$

145. $(6x + 2) + (5x - 7) = 6x + 2 + 5x - 7 = 11x - 5$

146. $(-y^2 - 4) + (3y^2 - 6) = -y^2 - 4 + 3y^2 - 6$
$$= 2y^2 - 10$$

147. $(8y^2 - 3y + 1) - (3y^2 + 2) = 8y^2 - 3y^2 - 3y + 1 - 2$
$$= 5y^2 - 3y - 1$$

148. $(5x^2 + 2x - 6) - (-x - 4) = 5x^2 + 2x - 6 + x + 4$
$$= 5x^2 + 3x - 2$$

149. $4x(7x^2 + 3) = 4x(7x^2) + 4x(3)$
$$= 28x^3 + 12x$$

150. $(2x + 5)(3x - 2) = 6x^2 - 4x + 15x - 10$
$$= 6x^2 + 11x - 10$$

151. $(x - 3)(x^2 + 4x - 6)$
$$= x(x^2 + 4x - 6) - 3(x^2 + 4x - 6)$$
$$= x^3 + 4x^2 - 6x - 3x^2 - 12x + 18$$
$$= x^3 + x^2 - 18x + 18$$

152. $(7x - 2)(4x - 9) = 28x^2 - 63x - 8x + 18$
$$= 28x^2 - 71x + 18$$

153. $(5x + 4)^2 = (5x)^2 + 2(5x)(4) + 4^2$
$$= 25x^2 + 40x + 16$$

154. $(6x + 3)(6x - 3) = (6x)^2 - (3)^2 = 36x^2 - 9$

155. $\dfrac{8a^4 - 2a^3 + 4a - 5}{2a^3} = \dfrac{8a^4}{2a^3} - \dfrac{2a^3}{2a^3} + \dfrac{4a}{2a^3} - \dfrac{5}{2a^3}$

$$= 4a - 1 + \dfrac{2}{a^2} - \dfrac{5}{2a^3}$$

156.

$$\begin{array}{r} x - 3 \\ x+5\overline{)x^2 + 2x + 10} \\ \underline{x^2 + 5x} \\ -3x + 10 \\ \underline{-3x - 15} \\ 25 \end{array}$$

$$\dfrac{x^2 + 2x + 10}{x + 5} = x - 3 + \dfrac{25}{x + 5}$$

157.

$$\begin{array}{r} 2x^2 + 7x + 5 \\ 2x-3\overline{)4x^3 + 8x^2 \ -11x + 4} \\ \underline{4x^3 - 6x^2} \\ 14x^2 - 11x \\ \underline{14x^2 - 21x} \\ 10x + 4 \\ \underline{10x - 15} \\ 19 \end{array}$$

$$\dfrac{4x^3 + 8x^2 - 11x + 4}{2x - 3} = 2x^2 + 7x + 5 + \dfrac{19}{2x - 3}$$

Chapter 5 Test

1. $2^5 = 2 \cdot 2 \cdot 2 \cdot 2 \cdot 2 = 32$

2. $(-3)^4 = (-3)(-3)(-3)(-3) = 81$

3. $-3^4 = -3 \cdot 3 \cdot 3 \cdot 3 = -81$

4. $4^{-3} = \dfrac{1}{4^3} = \dfrac{1}{64}$

5. $(3x^2)(-5x^9) = (3)(-5)(x^2 \cdot x^9) = -15x^{11}$

6. $\dfrac{y^7}{y^2} = y^{7-2} = y^5$

7. $\dfrac{r^{-8}}{r^{-3}} = r^{-8-(-3)} = r^{-5} = \dfrac{1}{r^5}$

8. $\left(\dfrac{x^2 y^3}{x^3 y^{-4}}\right)^2 = \dfrac{x^4 y^6}{x^6 y^{-8}}$

$$= x^{4-6} y^{6-(-8)}$$

$$= x^{-2} y^{14}$$

$$= \dfrac{y^{14}}{x^2}$$

9. $\left(\dfrac{6^2 x^{-4} y^{-1}}{6^3 x^{-3} y^7}\right) = 6^{2-3} x^{-4-(-3)} y^{-1-7}$

$$= 6^{-1} x^{-1} y^{-8}$$

$$= \dfrac{1}{6xy^8}$$

10. $563,000 = 5.63 \times 10^5$

11. $0.0000863 = 8.63 \times 10^{-5}$

12. $1.5 \times 10^{-3} = 0.0015$

13. $6.23 \times 10^4 = 62,300$

14. $(1.2 \times 10^5)(3 \times 10^{-7}) = (1.2)(3) \times 10^{5-7}$

$$= 3.6 \times 10^{-2}$$

$$= 0.036$$

15. a.

Term	Numerical Coefficient	Degree of Term
$4xy^2$	4	3
$7xyz$	7	3
$x^3 y$	1	4
-2	-2	0

   b. The degree is 4.

16. $5x^2 + 4xy - 7x^2 + 11 + 8xy$

$$= (5x^2 - 7x^2) + (4xy + 8xy) + 11$$

$$= -2x^2 + 12xy + 11$$

17. $(8x^3 + 7x^2 + 4x - 7) + (8x^3 - 7x - 6)$

$$= 8x^3 + 7x^2 + 4x - 7 + 8x^3 - 7x - 6$$

$$= 16x^3 + 7x^2 - 3x - 13$$

18.
$$5x^3 + x^2 + 5x - 2$$
$$-(8x^3 - 4x^2 + x - 7)$$

$$5x^3 + x^2 + 5x - 2$$
$$-8x^3 + 4x^2 - x + 7$$
$$\overline{-3x^3 + 5x^2 + 4x + 5}$$

19. $[(8x^2 + 7x + 5) + (x^3 - 8)] - (4x + 2)$
$= 8x^2 + 7x + 5 + x^3 - 8 - 4x - 2$
$= x^3 + 8x^2 + 3x - 5$

20. $(3x + 7)(x^2 + 5x + 2)$
$= 3x(x^2 + 5x + 2) + 7(x^2 + 5x + 2)$
$= 3x^3 + 15x^2 + 6x + 7x^2 + 35x + 14$
$= 3x^3 + 22x^2 + 41x + 14$

21. $3x^2(2x^2 - 3x + 7)$
$= 3x^2(2x^2) + 3x^2(-3x) + 3x^2(7)$
$= 6x^4 - 9x^3 + 21x^2$

22. $(x + 7)(3x - 5) = 3x^2 - 5x + 21x - 35$
$= 3x^2 + 16x - 35$

23. $\left(3x - \dfrac{1}{5}\right)\left(3x + \dfrac{1}{5}\right) = (3x)^2 - \left(\dfrac{1}{5}\right)^2 = 9x^2 - \dfrac{1}{25}$

24. $(4x - 2)^2 = (4x)^2 - 2(4x)(2) + 2^2$
$= 16x^2 - 16x + 4$

25. $(x^2 - 9b)(x^2 + 9b) = (x^2)^2 - (9b)^2 = x^4 - 81b^2$

26. $-16t^2 + 1001$
$t = 0$: $-16(0)^2 + 1001 = 1001$ ft
$t = 1$: $-16(1)^2 + 1001 = 985$ ft
$t = 3$: $-16(3)^2 + 1001 = 857$ ft
$t = 5$: $-16(5)^2 + 1001 = 601$ ft

27. $(2x + 3)(2x - 3) = (2x)^2 - (3)^2 = 4x^2 - 9$

The area is $(4x^2 - 9)$ square inches.

28. $\dfrac{4x^2 + 24xy - 7x}{8xy} = \dfrac{4x^2}{8xy} + \dfrac{24xy}{8xy} - \dfrac{7x}{8xy}$
$= \dfrac{x}{2y} + 3 - \dfrac{7}{8y}$

29.
$$\require{enclose}
\begin{array}{r}
x + 2 \\
x + 5 \enclose{longdiv}{x^2 + 7x + 10} \\
\underline{x^2 + 5x } \\
2x + 10 \\
\underline{2x + 10} \\
0
\end{array}$$

$\dfrac{x^2 + 7x + 10}{x + 5} = x + 2$

30. Rewrite $27x^3 - 8$ as $27x^3 + 0x^2 + 0x - 8$.

$$\begin{array}{r}
9x^2 - 6x + 4 \\
3x + 2 \enclose{longdiv}{27x^3 + 0x^2 + 0x - 8} \\
\underline{27x^3 + 18x^2 } \\
-18x^2 + 0x \\
\underline{-18x^2 - 12x } \\
12x - 8 \\
\underline{12x + 8} \\
-16
\end{array}$$

$\dfrac{27x^3 - 8}{3x + 2} = 9x^2 - 6x + 4 - \dfrac{16}{3x + 2}$

31. $h(t) = -16t^2 + 96t + 880$

a. $h(1) = -16(1)^2 + 96(1) + 880$
$= -16 + 96 + 880$
$= 960$
The height of the pebble is 960 feet when $t = 1$.

b. $h(5.1) = -16(5.1)^2 + 96(5.1) + 880$
$= -16(26.01) + 489.6 + 880$
$= -416.16 + 489.6 + 880$
$= 953.44$
The height of the pebble is 953.44 feet when $t = 5.1$.

c. The pebble hits the ground when $h(t) = 0$.
$0 = -16t^2 + 96t + 880$
$0 = -16(t^2 - 6t - 55)$
$0 = -16(t + 5)(t - 11)$

$t + 5 = 0$ or $t - 11 = 0$
$t = -5$ $t = 11$

Since the time cannot be negative, the pebble hits the ground when $t = 11$ seconds.

32. $4x^4 - 3x^3 - x - 1 = 4x^4 - 3x^3 + 0x^2 - x - 1$
$x + 3 = x - (-3)$

$$
\begin{array}{r|rrrrr}
-3 & 4 & -3 & 0 & -1 & -1 \\
   &   & -12 & 45 & -135 & 408 \\
\hline
   & 4 & -15 & 45 & -136 & 407
\end{array}
$$

$\dfrac{4x^4 - 3x^3 - x - 1}{x + 3}$
$= 4x^3 - 15x^2 + 45x - 136 + \dfrac{407}{x + 3}$

33. $P(x) = 4x^4 + 0x^3 + 7x^2 - 2x - 5$

$$
\begin{array}{r|rrrrr}
-2 & 4 & 0 & 7 & -2 & -5 \\
   &   & -8 & 16 & -46 & 96 \\
\hline
   & 4 & -8 & 23 & -48 & 91
\end{array}
$$

Thus, $P(-2) = 91$.

Chapter 5 Cumulative Review

1. a. $8 \geq 8$ is true since $8 = 8$.

   b. $8 \leq 8$ is true since $8 = 8$.

   c. $23 \leq 0$ is false.

   d. $23 \geq 0$ is true

2. a. $|-7.2| = 7.2$

   b. $|0| = 0$

   c. $\left|-\dfrac{1}{2}\right| = \dfrac{1}{2}$

3. a. $\dfrac{4}{5} \div \dfrac{5}{16} = \dfrac{4}{5} \cdot \dfrac{16}{5} = \dfrac{64}{25}$

   b. $\dfrac{7}{10} \div 14 = \dfrac{7}{10} \div \dfrac{14}{1} = \dfrac{7}{10} \cdot \dfrac{1}{14} = \dfrac{7}{10 \cdot 7 \cdot 2} = \dfrac{1}{20}$

c. $\dfrac{3}{8} \div \dfrac{3}{10} = \dfrac{3}{8} \cdot \dfrac{10}{3} = \dfrac{3 \cdot 2 \cdot 5}{2 \cdot 4 \cdot 3} = \dfrac{5}{4}$

4. a. $\dfrac{3}{4} \cdot \dfrac{7}{21} = \dfrac{3 \cdot 7}{4 \cdot 3 \cdot 7} = \dfrac{1}{4}$

   b. $\dfrac{1}{2} \cdot 4\dfrac{5}{6} = \dfrac{1}{2} \cdot \dfrac{29}{6} = \dfrac{29}{12} = 2\dfrac{5}{12}$

5. a. $3^2 = 3 \cdot 3 = 9$

   b. $5^3 = 5 \cdot 5 \cdot 5 = 125$

   c. $2^4 = 2 \cdot 2 \cdot 2 \cdot 2 = 16$

   d. $7^1 = 7$

   e. $\left(\dfrac{3}{7}\right)^2 = \left(\dfrac{3}{7}\right)\left(\dfrac{3}{7}\right) = \dfrac{9}{49}$

6. Let $x = 5$ and $y = 1$.
$$
\begin{aligned}
\dfrac{2x - 7y}{x^2} &= \dfrac{2(5) - 7(1)}{5^2} \\
&= \dfrac{10 - 7}{25} \\
&= \dfrac{3}{25}
\end{aligned}
$$

7. a. $-3 + (-7) = -10$

   b. $-1 + (-20) = -21$

   c. $-2 + (-10) = -12$

8. $8 + 3(2 \cdot 6 - 1) = 8 + 3(12 - 1)$
$= 8 + 3(11)$
$= 8 + 33$
$= 41$

9. $-4 - 8 = -4 + (-8) = -12$

10. $x = 1$
$5x^2 + 2 = x - 8$
$5(1)^2 + 2 \overset{?}{=} 1 - 8$
$5 + 2 \overset{?}{=} -7$
$7 \overset{?}{=} -7$ False
$x = 1$ is not a solution.

11. a. The reciprocal of 22 is $\dfrac{1}{22}$.

   b. The reciprocal of $\dfrac{3}{16}$ is $\dfrac{16}{3}$.

   c. The reciprocal of -10 is $-\dfrac{1}{10}$.

   d. The reciprocal of $-\dfrac{9}{13}$ is $-\dfrac{13}{9}$.

12. a. $7 - 40 = 7 + (-40) = -33$

   b. $-5 - (-10) = -5 + 10 = 5$

13. a. $5 + (4 + 6) = (5 + 4) + 6$

   b. $(-1 \cdot 2) \cdot 5 = -1 \cdot (2 \cdot 5)$

14. $\dfrac{4(-3) + (-8)}{5 + (-5)} = \dfrac{-12 + (-8)}{0}$ is undefined.

15. a. $10 + (x + 12) = 10 + (12 + x)$
$$= (10 + 12) + x$$
$$= 22 + x$$

   b. $-3(7x) = (-3 \cdot 7)x = -21x$

16. $-2(x + 3y - z) = -2(x) + (-2)(3y) - (-2)(z)$
$$= -2x - 6y + 2z$$

17. a. $5(x + 2) = 5x + 5(2) = 5x + 10$

   b. $-2(y + 0.3z - 1)$
$$= -2(y) + (-2)(0.3z) - (-2)(1)$$
$$= -2y - 0.6z + 2y$$

   c. $-(x + y - 2z + 6)$
$$= -1(x + y - 2z + 6)$$
$$= -1(x) + (-1)(y) - (-1)(2z) + (-1)(6)$$
$$= -x - y + 2z - 6$$

18. $2(6x - 1) - (x - 7) = 12x - 2 - x + 7$
$$= 11x + 5$$

19. $x - 7 = 10$
$$x - 7 + 7 = 10 + 7$$
$$x = 17$$

20. Let x = a number.
$$(x + 7) - 2x$$

21. $\dfrac{5}{2}x = 15$
$$\dfrac{2}{5} \cdot \dfrac{5}{2}x = \dfrac{2}{5} \cdot 15$$
$$x = 6$$

22. $2x + \dfrac{1}{8} = x - \dfrac{3}{8}$
$$x + \dfrac{1}{8} = -\dfrac{3}{8}$$
$$x = -\dfrac{4}{8}$$
$$x = -\dfrac{1}{2}$$

23. Let x = a number.
$$7 + 2x = x - 3$$
$$7 + x = -3$$
$$x = -10$$
The number is -10.

24. $10 = 5j - 2$
$$12 = 5j$$
$$\dfrac{12}{5} = j$$

25. Let x = a number.
$$2(x + 4) = 4x - 12$$
$$2x + 8 = 4x - 12$$
$$-2x + 8 = -12$$
$$-2x = -20$$
$$x = 10$$
The number is 10.

26. $\dfrac{7x + 5}{3} = x + 3$
$$3\left(\dfrac{7x + 5}{3}\right) = 3(x + 3)$$
$$7x + 5 = 3x + 9$$
$$4x + 5 = 9$$
$$4x = 4$$
$$x = 1$$

27. Let x = the width and $3x - 2$ = the length.
$$2L + 2W = P$$
$$2(3x - 2) + 2x = 28$$
$$6x - 4 + 2x = 28$$
$$8x - 4 = 28$$
$$8x = 32$$
$$x = 4$$
$$3x - 2 = 3(4) - 2 = 10$$
The width is 4 feet and the length is 10 feet.

28. $x < 5, (-\infty, 5)$

29.
$$F = \frac{9}{5}C + 32$$
$$F - 32 = \frac{9}{5}C$$
$$\frac{5}{9}(F - 32) = C$$
$$\frac{5F - 160}{9} = C$$

30. a. $x = -1$ is a vertical line and the slope is undefined.

     b. $y = 7$ is a horizontal line and the slope is zero.

31. $2 < x \le 4$

32. $m = \dfrac{y_2 - y_1}{x_2 - x_1} = \dfrac{2}{20} = \dfrac{1}{10} \cdot 100\% = 10\%$

33. $3x + y = 12$

     a. $(0, \ ): 3(0) + y = 12$
$$y = 12, \ (0, 12)$$

     b. $(\ , 6): 3x + 6 = 12$
$$3x = 6$$
$$x = 2, \ (2, 6)$$

     c. $(-1, \ ): 3(-1) + y = 12$
$$-3 + y = 12$$
$$y = 15, \ (-1, 15)$$

34. $\begin{cases} 3x + 2y = -8 \\ 2x - 6y = -9 \end{cases}$

Multiply the first equation by 3 and add.
$$\begin{aligned} 9x + 6y &= -24 \\ \underline{2x - 6y} &= \underline{-9} \\ 11x \quad\ &= -33 \\ x &= -3 \end{aligned}$$

Replace x with -3 in the first equation.

$$3(-3) + 2y = -8$$
$$-9 + 2y = -8$$
$$2y = 1$$
$$y = \frac{1}{2}$$

The solution to the system is $\left(-3, \dfrac{1}{2}\right)$.

35. $2x + y = 5$

x	y
0	5
$\dfrac{5}{2}$	0

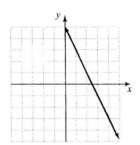

36. $\begin{cases} x = -3y + 3 \\ 2x + 9y = 5 \end{cases}$

Replace x with $-3y + 3$ in the second equation.
$$2(-3y + 3) + 9y = 5$$
$$-6y + 6 + 9y = 5$$
$$3y + 6 = 5$$
$$3y = -1$$
$$y = -\frac{1}{3}$$

Replace y with $-\dfrac{1}{3}$ in the first equation.

$$x = -3\left(-\frac{1}{3}\right) + 3 = 1 + 3 = 4$$

The solution to the system is $\left(4, -\dfrac{1}{3}\right)$.

37.

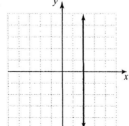

38. a. $(-5)^2 = (-5)(-5) = 25$

   b. $-5^2 = -(5)(5) = -25$

   c. $2 \cdot 5^2 = 2 \cdot 5 \cdot 5 = 50$

39. $x = 5$ is a vertical line and the slope is undefined.

40. $\dfrac{(z^2)^3 \cdot z^7}{z^9} = \dfrac{z^6 \cdot z^7}{z^9} = z^{6+7-9} = z^4$

41. $(2x^3 + 8x^2 - 6x) - (2x^3 - x^2 + 1)$
$= 2x^3 + 8x^2 - 6x - 2x^3 + x^2 - 1$
$= 2x^3 - 2x^3 + 8x^2 + x^2 - 6x - 1$
$= 9x^2 - 6x - 1$

42. $(5y^2 - 6) - (y^2 + 2) = 5y^2 - 6 - y^2 - 2 = 4y^2 - 8$

43. $(2x^2)(-3x^5) = (2 \cdot -3)(x^2 \cdot x^5) = -6x^{2+5} = -6x^7$

44. $-x^2$

   a. $-(2)^2 = -4$

   b. $-(-2)^2 = -4$

45. $(11x^3 - 12x^2 + x - 3) + (x^3 - 10x + 5)$
$= 11x^3 - 12x^2 + x - 3 + x^3 - 10x + 5$
$= 11x^3 + x^3 - 12x^2 + x - 10x - 3 + 5$
$= 12x^3 - 12x^2 - 9x + 2$

46. $(10x^2 - 3)(10x^2 + 3) = (10x^2)^2 - 3^2$
$= 100x^4 - 9$

47. $(2x - y)^2 = (2x)^2 - 2(2x)(y) + (y)^2$
$= 4x^2 - 4xy + y^2$

48. $(10x^2 + 3)^2 = (10x^2)^2 + 2(10x^2)(3) + 3^2$
$= 100x^4 + 60x^2 + 9$

49. $\dfrac{6m^2 + 2m}{2m} = \dfrac{6m^2}{2m} + \dfrac{2m}{2m} = 3m + 1$

50. a. $5^{-1} = \dfrac{1}{5}$

   b. $7^{-2} = \dfrac{1}{7^2} = \dfrac{1}{49}$

Chapter 6

Section 6.1

Practice Exercises

1. a. $36 = 2 \cdot 2 \cdot 3 \cdot 3 = 2^2 \cdot 3^2$
$42 = 2 \cdot 3 \cdot 7$
$\text{GCF} = 2 \cdot 3 = 6$

b. $35 = 5 \cdot 7$
$44 = 2 \cdot 2 \cdot 11$
$\text{GCF} = 1$

c. $12 = 2 \cdot 2 \cdot 3 = 2^2 \cdot 3$
$16 = 2 \cdot 2 \cdot 2 \cdot 2 = 2^4$
$40 = 2 \cdot 2 \cdot 2 \cdot 5 = 2^3 \cdot 5$
$\text{GCF} = 2^2 = 4$

2. a. The GCF is y^4 since 4 is the smallest exponent to which y is raised.

b. The GCF is x^1 or x, since 1 is the smallest exponent on x.

3. a. $5y^4 = 5 \cdot y^4$
$15y^2 = 3 \cdot 5 \cdot y^2$
$-20y^3 = -1 \cdot 2 \cdot 2 \cdot 5 \cdot y^3$
$\text{GCF} = 5 \cdot y^2 = 5y^2$

b. $4x^2 = 2 \cdot 2 \cdot x^2$
$x^3 = x^3$
$3x^8 = 3 \cdot x^8$
$\text{GCF} = x^2$

c. The GCF of a^4, a^3, and a^2 is a^2.
The GCF of b^2, b^5, and b^3 is b^2.
Thus, the GCF of a^4b^2, a^3b^5, and a^2b^3 is a^2b^2.

4. a. $4t + 12; \text{GCF} = 4$
$4t + 12 = 4 \cdot t + 4 \cdot 3 = 4(t + 3)$

b. $y^8 + y^4; \text{GCF} = y^4$
$y^8 + y^4 = y^4 \cdot y^4 + y^4 \cdot 1 = y^4(y^4 + 1)$

5. $-8b^6 + 16b^4 - 8b^2$
$= -8b^2(b^4) - 8b^2(-2b^2) - 8b^2(1)$
$= -8b^2(b^4 - 2b^2 + 1) \text{ or } 8b^2(-b^4 + 2b^2 - 1)$

6. $5x^4 - 20x = 5x(x^3 - 4)$

7. $\frac{5}{9}z^5 + \frac{1}{9}z^4 - \frac{2}{9}z^3 = \frac{1}{9}z^3(5z^2 + z - 2)$

8. $8a^2b^4 - 20a^3b^3 + 12ab^3 = 4ab^3(2ab - 5a^2 + 3)$

9. $8(y - 2) + x(y - 2) = (y - 2)(8 + x)$

10. $7xy^3(p + q) - (p + q) = 7xy^3(p + q) - 1(p + q)$
$= (p + q)(7xy^3 - 1)$

11. $xy + 3y + 4x + 12 = (xy + 3y) + (4x + 12)$
$= y(x + 3) + 4(x + 3)$
$= (x + 3)(y + 4)$
Check: $(x + 3)(y + 4) = xy + 3y + 4x + 12$

12. $2xy + 3y^2 - 2x - 3y = (2xy + 3y^2) + (-2x - 3y)$
$= y(2x + 3y) - 1(2x + 3y)$
$= (2x + 3y)(y - 1)$

13. $7a^3 + 5a^2 + 7a + 5 = (7a^3 + 5a^2) + (7a + 5)$
$= a^2(7a + 5) + 1(7a + 5)$
$= (7a + 5)(a^2 + 1)$

14. $4xy + 15 - 12x - 5y = 4xy - 12x - 5y + 15$
$= (4xy - 12x) + (-5y + 15)$
$= 4x(y - 3) - 5(y - 3)$
$= (y - 3)(4x - 5)$

15. $9y - 18 + y^3 - 4y^2 = 9(y - 2) + y^2(y - 4)$
There is no common binomial factor, so it cannot be factored by grouping.

16. $3xy - 3ay - 6ax + 6a^2 = 3(xy - ay - 2ax + 2a^2)$
$= 3[y(x - a) - 2a(x - a)]$
$= 3(x - a)(y - 2a)$

Vocabulary and Readiness Check

1. Since $5 \cdot 4 = 20$, the numbers 5 and 4 are called <u>factors</u> of 20.

2. The <u>greatest common factor</u> of a list of integers is the largest integer that is a factor of all the integers in the list.

3. The greatest common factor of a list of common variables raised to powers is the variable raised to the <u>least</u> exponent in the list.

4. The process of writing a polynomial as a product is called <u>factoring</u>.

5. $7(x + 3) + y(x + 3)$ is a sum, not a product. The statement is false.

6. $3x^3 + 6x + x^2 + 2 = 3x(x^2 + 2) + (x^2 + 2)$
$$= (x^2 + 2)(3x + 1)$$
The statement is false.

7. $14 = 2 \cdot 7$

8. $15 = 3 \cdot 5$

9. The GCF of 18 and 3 is 3.

10. The GCF of 7 and 35 is 7.

11. The GCF of 20 and 15 is 5.

12. The GCF of 6 and 15 is 3.

Exercise Set 6.1

2. $36 = 2 \cdot 2 \cdot 3 \cdot 3 = 2^2 \cdot 3^2$
$90 = 2 \cdot 3 \cdot 3 \cdot 5 = 2 \cdot 3^2 \cdot 5$
$GCF = 2 \cdot 3 \cdot 3 = 18$

4. $30 = 2 \cdot 3 \cdot 5$
$75 = 3 \cdot 5 \cdot 5 = 3 \cdot 5^2$
$135 = 3 \cdot 3 \cdot 3 \cdot 5 = 3^3 \cdot 5$
$GCF = 3 \cdot 5 = 15$

6. $15 = 3 \cdot 5$
$25 = 5 \cdot 5$
$27 = 3 \cdot 3 \cdot 3 = 3^3$
$GCF = 1$

8. The GCF of x^3, x^2, and x^5 is x^2.

10. The GCF of y^8, y^{10}, and y^{12} is y^8.

12. The GCF of p^7, p^8, and p^9 is p^7.

The GCF of q, q^2, and q^3 is q.

Thus, the GCF of p^7q, p^8q^2, and p^9q^3 is p^7q.

14. $20y = 2 \cdot 2 \cdot 5 \cdot y$
$15 = 3 \cdot 5$
$GCF = 5$

16. $32x^5 = 2 \cdot 2 \cdot 2 \cdot 2 \cdot 2 \cdot x^5$
$18x^2 = 2 \cdot 3 \cdot 3 \cdot x^2$
$GCF = 2 \cdot x^2 = 2x^2$

18. $-21x^3 = -1 \cdot 3 \cdot 7 \cdot x^3$
$14x = 2 \cdot 7 \cdot x$
$GCF = 7 \cdot x = 7x$

20. $15y^2 = 3 \cdot 5 \cdot y^2$
$5y^7 = 5 \cdot y^7$
$-20y^3 = -1 \cdot 2 \cdot 2 \cdot 5 \cdot y^3$
$GCF = 5 \cdot y^2 = 5y^2$

22. $7x^3y^3 = 7 \cdot x^3 \cdot y^3$
$-21x^2y^2 = -1 \cdot 3 \cdot 7 \cdot x^2 \cdot y^2$
$14xy^4 = 2 \cdot 7 \cdot x \cdot y^4$
$GCF = 7 \cdot x \cdot y^2 = 7xy^2$

24. $40x^7y^2z = 2 \cdot 2 \cdot 2 \cdot 5 \cdot x^7 \cdot y^2 \cdot z$
$64x^9y = 2 \cdot 2 \cdot 2 \cdot 2 \cdot 2 \cdot 2 \cdot x^9 \cdot y$
$GCF = 2 \cdot 2 \cdot 2 \cdot x^7 \cdot y = 8x^7y$

26. $18a + 12 = 6(3a + 2)$

28. $42x - 7 = 7(6x - 1)$

30. $y^5 + 6y^4 = y^4(y + 6)$

32. $5x^2 + 10x^6 = 5x^2(1 + 2x^4)$

34. $7x + 21y - 7 = 7(x + 3y - 1)$

36. $12x^3 + 16x^2 - 8x = 4x(3x^2 + 4x - 2)$

38. $x^9 y^6 + x^3 y^5 - x^4 y^3 + x^3 y^3$
$= x^3 y^3 (x^6 y^3 + y^2 - x + 1)$

40. $9y^6 - 27y^4 + 18y^2 + 6 = 3(3y^6 - 9y^4 + 6y^2 + 2)$

42. $\dfrac{2}{5} y^7 - \dfrac{4}{5} y^5 + \dfrac{3}{5} y^2 - \dfrac{2}{5} y$
$= \dfrac{1}{5} y(2y^6 - 4y^4 + 3y - 2)$

44. $x(y^2 + 1) - 3(y^2 + 1) = (y^2 + 1)(x - 3)$

46. $8(x + 2) - y(x + 2) = (x + 2)(8 - y)$

48. $q(b^3 - 5) + (b^3 - 5) = q(b^3 - 5) + 1(b^3 - 5)$
$= (b^3 - 5)(q + 1)$

50. $-7y - 21 = -7(y + 3)$

52. $-5y^3 + y^6 = -y^3(5 - y^3)$

54. $-5m^6 + 10m^5 - 5m^3 = -5m^3(m^3 - 2m^2 + 1)$

56. $x^3 + 4x^2 + 3x + 12 = x^2(x + 4) + 3(x + 4)$
$= (x + 4)(x^2 + 3)$

58. $xy + y + 2x + 2 = y(x + 1) + 2(x + 1)$
$= (x + 1)(y + 2)$

60. $16x^3 - 28x^2 + 12x - 21 = 4x^2(4x - 7) + 3(4x - 7)$
$= (4x - 7)(4x^2 + 3)$

62. $8w^2 + 7wv + 8w + 7v = w(8w + 7v) + 1(8w + 7v)$
$= (8w + 7v)(w + 1)$

64. $6x - 42 + xy - 7y = 6(x - 7) + y(x - 7)$
$= (x - 7)(6 + y)$

66. $2x^3 - x^2 - 10x + 5 = x^2(2x - 1) - 5(2x - 1)$
$= (2x - 1)(x^2 - 5)$

68. $5xy - 15x - 6y + 18 = 5x(y - 3) - 6(y - 3)$
$= (y - 3)(5x - 6)$

70. $6m^2 - 5mn - 6m + 5n = m(6m - 5n) - 1(6m - 5n)$
$= (6m - 5n)(m - 1)$

72. $4y^4 + y^2 + 20y^3 + 5y$
$= y(4y^3 + y + 20y^2 + 5)$
$= y[y(4y^2 + 1) + 5(4y^2 + 1)]$
$= y(4y^2 + 1)(y + 5)$

74. $90 + 15y^2 - 18x - 3xy^2 = 3(30 + 5y^2 - 6x - xy^2)$
$= 3[5(6 + y^2) - x(6 + y^2)]$
$= 3(6 + y^2)(5 - x)$

76. $10xy - 15x^2 = 5x(2y - 3x)$

78. $z(y - 4) + 3(y - 4) = (y - 4)(z + 3)$

80. $5x^3 y - 15x^2 y + 10xy = 5xy(x^2 - 3x + 2)$

82. $15x^3 + 5x^2 - 6x - 2 = 5x^2(3x + 1) - 2(3x + 1)$
$= (3x + 1)(5x^2 - 2)$

84. $-21x^3 y - 49x^2 y^2 = -7x^2 y(3x + 7y)$

86. $16x^2 + 4xy^2 + 8xy + 2y^3$
$= 2(8x^2 + 2xy^2 + 4xy + y^3)$
$= 2[2x(4x + y^2) + y(4x + y^2)]$
$= 2(4x + y^2)(2x + y)$

88. $(y + 3)(y + 6) = y^2 + 6y + 3y + 18 = y^2 + 9y + 18$

90. $(x - 5)(x + 10) = x^2 + 10x - 5x - 50$
$= x^2 + 5x - 50$

	Two Numbers	Their Product	Their Sum
92.	4, 5	20	9
94.	−2, −8	16	−10
96.	−8, 3	−24	−5

98. $(a + 6)(a + 2)$ is factored.

100. $5(2y + z) - b(2y + z)$ is not factored.

102. Answers may vary

104. Answers may vary

106. a. $45x^2 + 95x = 45(2)^2 + 95(2)$
$= 180 + 190$
$= 370$
There were 370 million, or 370,000,000, single digital downloads in 2005.

b. Let $x = 2009 - 2003 = 6$
$45x^2 + 95x = 45(6)^2 + 95(6) = 2190$
We predict 2190 million, or 2,190,000,000, single digital downloads in 2009.

c. $45x^2 + 95x = 5x(9x + 19)$

108. Subtract the area of the inner rectangle from the area of the outer rectangle.
Outer rectangle: $A = l \cdot w$
$A = 12x \cdot x^2 = 12x^3$
Inner rectangle: $A = l \cdot w$
$A = 2 \cdot x = 2x$
The area of the shaded region is given by the expression $12x^3 - 2x = 2x(6x^2 - 1)$.

110. Area $= 4n^4 - 24n = 4n(n^3 - 6)$
Since the width is $4n$ units, the length is $(n^3 - 6)$ units.

112. $x^{2n} + 2x^n + 3x^n + 6 = x^n(x^n + 2) + 3(x^n + 2)$
$= (x^n + 2)(x^n + 3)$

114. $3x^{2n} + 21x^n - 5x^n - 35$
$= 3x^n(x^n + 7) - 5(x^n + 7)$
$= (x^n + 7)(3x^n - 5)$

Section 6.2

Practice Problems

1.

Positive Factors of 6	Sum of Factors
1, 6	7
2, 3	5

$x^2 + 5x + 6 = (x + 2)(x + 3)$

2.

Negative Factors of 70	Sum of Factors
-1, -70	-71
-2, -35	-37
-5, -14	-19
-7, -10	-17

$x^2 - 17x + 70 = (x - 7)(x - 10)$

3.

Factors of -14	Sum of Factors
-1, 14	13
1, -14	-13
-2, 7	5
2, -7	-5

$x^2 + 5x - 14 = (x - 2)(x + 7)$

4. The first term of each binomial is p. Then look for two numbers whose product is -63 and whose sum is -2.
$p^2 - 2p - 63 = (p - 9)(p + 7)$

5. The first term of each binomial is b. Then look for two numbers whose product is 1 and whose sum is 5. There are no such numbers.
$b^2 + 5b + 1$ is a prime polynomial.

6. The first term of each polynomial is x. Then look for two terms whose product is $12y^2$ and whose sum is $7y$.
$x^2 + 7xy + 12y^2 = (x + 3y)(x + 4y)$

7. The first term of each polynomial is x^2. Then look for two numbers whose product is 12 and whose sum is 13.
$x^4 + 13x^2 + 12 = (x^2 + 1)(x^2 + 12)$

8. $48 - 14x + x^2 = x^2 - 14x + 48$
The first term of each binomial is x. Then look for two factors whose product is 48 and whose sum is -14.
$x^2 - 14x + 48 = (x - 6)(x - 8)$

9. $4x^2 - 24x + 36 = 4(x^2 - 6x + 9)$
The first term of each binomial is x. Then look for two factors whose product is 9 and whose sum is -6.
$4(x^2 - 6x + 9) = 4(x - 3)(x - 3)$ or $4(x - 3)^2$

10. $3y^4 - 18y^3 - 21y^2 = 3y^2(y^2 - 6y - 7)$
The first term of each binomial is y. Then look for two factors whose product is -7 and whose sum is -6.
$3y^2(y^2 - 6y - 7) = 3y^2(y - 7)(y + 1)$

Vocabulary and Readiness Check

1. The statement is true.

2. The statement is true.

3. Since $4x - 12 = 4(x - 3)$, the statement is false.

4. $(x + 2y)^2 = (x + 2y)(x + 2y) \neq (x + 2y)(x + y)$
The statement is false.

5. $x^2 + 9x + 20 = (x + 4)(x + 5)$

6. $x^2 + 12x + 35 = (x + 5)(x + 7)$

7. $x^2 - 7x + 12 = (x - 4)(x - 3)$

8. $x^2 - 13x + 22 = (x - 2)(x - 11)$

9. $x^2 + 4x + 4 = (x + 2)(x + 2)$

10. $x^2 + 10x + 24 = (x + 6)(x + 4)$

Exercise Set 6.2

2. $x^2 + 6x + 8 = (x + 4)(x + 2)$

4. $y^2 - 12y + 11 = (y - 11)(y - 1)$

6. $x^2 - 10x + 25 = (x - 5)(x - 5)$ or $(x - 5)^2$

8. $x^2 - x - 30 = (x - 6)(x + 5)$

10. $x^2 + 4x - 32 = (x + 8)(x - 4)$

12. $x^2 - 7x + 5$ is a prime polynomial.

14. $x^2 + 6xy + 8y^2 = (x + 4y)(x + 2y)$

16. $y^4 - 3y^2 - 70 = (y^2 - 10)(y^2 + 7)$

18. $17 + 18n + n^2 = n^2 + 18n + 17 = (n + 17)(n + 1)$

20. $6q - 27 + q^2 = q^2 + 6q - 27 = (q - 3)(q + 9)$

22. $a^2 - 9ab + 18b^2 = (a - 3b)(a - 6b)$

24. $3x^2 + 30x + 63 = 3(x^2 + 10x + 21)$
$= 3(x + 7)(x + 3)$

26. $3x^3 - 12x^2 - 36x = 3x(x^2 - 4x - 12)$
$= 3x(x - 6)(x + 2)$

28. $x^2 - 4xy - 77y^2 = (x - 11y)(x + 7y)$

30. $x^2 + 19x + 60 = (x + 4)(x + 15)$

32. $x^2 - 5x - 14 = (x - 7)(x + 2)$

34. $r^2 - 10r + 21 = (r - 7)(r - 3)$

36. $x^2 - xy - 6y^2 = (x - 3y)(x + 2y)$

38. $4x^2 - 4x - 48 = 4(x^2 - x - 12) = 4(x - 4)(x + 3)$

40. $2x^2 - 24x + 70 = 2(x^2 - 12x + 35)$
$= 2(x - 7)(x - 5)$

42. $x^2 + x - 42 = (x + 7)(x - 6)$

44. $x^2 + 4x - 10$ is a prime polynomial.

46. $x^2 - 9x + 14 = (x - 7)(x - 2)$

48. $3x^3 + 3x^2 - 126x = 3x(x^2 + x - 42)$
$= 3x(x + 7)(x - 6)$

50. $3x^2 y - 9xy + 45y = 3y(x^2 - 3x + 15)$

52. $x^2 - 4x - 32 = (x - 8)(x + 4)$

54. $x^2 - 3xy - 4y^2 = (x - 4y)(x + y)$

56. $50 + 20t + 2t^2 = 2t^2 + 20t + 50$
$= 2(t^2 + 10t + 25)$
$= 2(t + 5)(t + 5)$ or $2(t + 5)^2$

58. $x^3 - 3x^2 - 28x = x(x^2 - 3x - 28)$
$= x(x - 7)(x + 4)$

60. $3x^6 + 30x^5 + 72x^4 = 3x^4(x^2 + 10x + 24)$
$= 3x^4(x + 6)(x + 4)$

62. $7a^3b - 35a^2b^2 + 42ab^3 = 7ab(a^2 - 5ab + 6b^2)$
$= 7ab(a - 3b)(a - 2b)$

64. $48 - 20n + 2n^2 = 2n^2 - 20n + 48$
$= 2(n^2 - 10n + 24)$
$= 2(n - 6)(n - 4)$

66. $-x^2 + 8x - 7 = -1(x^2 - 8x + 7) = -1(x - 7)(x - 1)$

68. $\frac{1}{3}y^2 - \frac{5}{3}y - 8 = \frac{1}{3}(y^2 - 5y - 24) = \frac{1}{3}(y - 8)(y + 3)$

70. $a^2b^3 + ab^2 - 30b = b(a^2b^2 + ab - 30)$
$= b(ab - 5)(ab + 6)$

72. $(3x + 2)(x + 4) = 3x^2 + 12x + 2x + 8$
$= 3x^2 + 14x + 8$

74. $(4z - 7)(7z - 1) = 28z^2 - 4z - 49z + 7$
$= 28z^2 - 53z + 7$

76. $(y - 5x)(6y + 5x) = 6y^2 + 5xy - 30xy - 25x^2$
$= 6y^2 - 25xy - 25x^2$

78. To factor $x^2 + 13x + 42$, think of two numbers whose <u>product</u> is 42 and whose <u>sum</u> is 13.

80. Answers may vary

82. $P = 2l + 2w$
$l = 12x^2$ and $w = 2x^3 + 16x$, so
$P = 2(12x^2) + 2(2x^3 + 16x)$
$= 24x^2 + 4x^3 + 32x$
$= 4x^3 + 24x^2 + 32x$
$= 4x(x^2 + 6x + 8)$
$= 4x(x + 4)(x + 2)$
The perimeter of the rectangle is given by the polynomial $4x^3 + 24x^2 + 32x$ which factors as $4x(x + 4)(x + 2)$.

84. $x^2 + x + \frac{1}{4} = \left(x + \frac{1}{2}\right)\left(x + \frac{1}{2}\right)$ or $\left(x + \frac{1}{2}\right)^2$

86. $y^2(x + 1) - 2y(x + 1) - 15(x + 1)$
$= (x + 1)(y^2 - 2y - 15)$
$= (x + 1)(y - 5)(y + 3)$

88. $x^{2n} + 5x^n + 6 = (x^n + 2)(x^n + 3)$

90. c must be the product of positive numbers that sum to 6.
$6 = 1 + 5; \ 1 \cdot 5 = 5$
$6 = 2 + 4; \ 2 \cdot 4 = 8$
$6 = 3 + 3; \ 3 \cdot 3 = 9$
$x^2 + 6x + c$ if factorable when c is 5, 8, or 9.

92. c must be the product of negative numbers that sum to -4.
$-4 = -1 + (-3); \ -1 \cdot -3 = 3$
$-4 = -2 + (-2); \ -2 \cdot -2 = 4$
$y^2 - 4y + c$ if factorable when c is 3 or 4.

94. b must be the sum of positive numbers whose product is 15.
$15 = 1 \cdot 15; \ 1 + 15 = 16$
$15 = 3 \cdot 5; \ 3 + 5 = 8$
$x^2 + bx + 15$ is factorable when b is 8 or 16.

96. b must be the positive sum of a positive number and a negative number whose product is -27.
$-27 = 27 \cdot -1; \ 27 + (-1) = 26$
$-27 = 9 \cdot -3; \ 9 + (-3) = 6$
$m^2 + bm - 27$ is factorable when b is 6 or 26.

Section 6.3

Practice Exercises

1. Factors of $2x^2$: $2x^2 = 2x \cdot x$
   Factors of 15: $15 = 1 \cdot 15$, $15 = 3 \cdot 5$
   Try possible combinations.
   Factored form: $2x^2 + 11x + 15 = (2x + 5)(x + 3)$

2. Factors of $15x^2$: $15x^2 = 15x \cdot x$, $15x^2 = 5x \cdot 3x$
   Factors of 8: $8 = -1 \cdot -8$, $8 = -2 \cdot -4$
   Try possible combinations.
   Factored form: $15x^2 - 22x + 8 = (5x - 4)(3x - 2)$

3. Factors of $4x^2$: $4x^2 = 4x \cdot x$, $4x^2 = 2x \cdot 2x$
   Factors of -3: $-3 = -1 \cdot 3$, $-3 = 1 \cdot -3$
   Try possible combinations.
   Factored form: $4x^2 + 11x - 3 = (4x - 1)(x + 3)$

4. Factors of $21x^2$: $21x^2 = 21x \cdot x$, $21x^2 = 3x \cdot 7x$
   Factors of
   $-2y^2$: $-2y^2 = -2y \cdot y$, $-2y^2 = 2y \cdot -y$
   Try possible combinations.
   Factored form:
   $21x^2 + 11xy - 2y^2 = (7x - y)(3x + 2y)$

5. Factors of $2x^4$: $2x^4 = 2x^2 \cdot x^2$
   Factors of -7: $-7 = -7 \cdot 1$, $-7 = 7 \cdot -1$
   Try possible combinations.
   $2x^4 - 5x^2 - 7 = (2x^2 - 7)(x^2 + 1)$

6. $3x^3 + 17x^2 + 10x = x(3x^2 + 17x + 10)$
   Factors of $3x^2$: $3x^2 = 3x \cdot x$
   Factors of 10: $10 = 1 \cdot 10$, $10 = 2 \cdot 5$
   Try possible combinations:
   $3x^3 + 17x^2 + 10x = x(3x^2 + 17x + 10)$
   $\qquad\qquad\qquad = x(3x + 2)(x + 5)$

7. $-8x^2 + 2x + 3 = -1(8x^2 - 2x - 3)$
   $\qquad\qquad\qquad = -1(4x - 3)(2x + 1)$

8. $x^2 = (x)^2$ and $49 = 7^2$
   Is $2 \cdot x \cdot 7 = 14x$ the middle term? Yes.
   $x^2 + 14x + 49 = (x + 7)^2$

9. $4x^2 = (2x)^2$ and $9y^2 = (3y)^2$
   Is $2 \cdot 2x \cdot 3y = 12xy$ the middle term? No.
   Try other possibilities.
   $4x^2 + 20xy + 9y^2 = (2x + 9y)(2x + y)$

10. $36n^4 = (6n^2)^2$ and $1 = 1^2$
    Is $2 \cdot 6n^2 \cdot 1 = 12n^2$ the middle term? Yes, the opposite of the middle term.
    $36n^4 - 12n^2 + 1 = (6n^2 - 1)^2$

11. $12x^3 - 84x^2 + 147x = 3x(4x^2 - 28x + 49)$
    $\qquad\qquad\qquad = 3x[(2x)^2 - 2 \cdot 2x \cdot 7 + 7^2]$
    $\qquad\qquad\qquad = 3x(2x - 7)^2$

Vocabulary and Readiness Check

1. A perfect square trinomial is a trinomial that is the square of a binomial.

2. The term $25y^2$ written as a square is $(5y)^2$.

3. The expression $x^2 + 10xy + 25y^2$ is called a perfect square trinomial.

4. The factorization $(x + 5y)(x + 5y)$ may also be written as $(x + 5y)^2$.

5. no

6. yes

7. $64 = 8^2$

8. $9 = 3^2$

9. $121a^2 = (11a)^2$

10. $81b^2 = (9b)^2$

11. $36p^4 = (6p^2)^2$

12. $4q^4 = (2q^2)^2$

Exercise Set 6.3

2. $2y^2 + 27y + 25 = (2y + 25)(y + 1)$

4. $6y^2 + 11y - 10 = (2y + 5)(3y - 2)$

6. $4y^2 - 20y + 25 = (2y - 5)(2y - 5)$

8. $3x^2 + 8x + 4 = (3x + 2)(x + 2)$

10. $21x^2 - 31x + 10 = (21x - 10)(x - 1)$

12. $36r^2 - 5r - 24 = (9r - 8)(4r + 3)$

14. $3x^2 + 20x - 63 = (3x - 7)(x + 9)$

16. $12x^2 + 17x + 5 = (12x + 5)(x + 1)$

18. $3n^2 + 20n + 5$ is prime.

20. $8x^2 - 14xy + 3y^2 = (4x - y)(2x - 3y)$

22. $25n^2 - 5n - 6 = (5n + 2)(5n - 3)$

24. $8a^3 + 14a^2 + 3a = a(8a^2 + 14a + 3)$
$$= a(4a + 1)(2a + 3)$$

26. $12x^2 - 14x - 10 = 2(6x^2 - 7x - 5)$
$$= 2(3x - 5)(2x + 1)$$

28. $16t + 15t^2 - 15 = 15t^2 + 16t - 15 = (5t - 3)(3t + 5)$

30. $8x^2y + 34xy - 84y = 2y(4x^2 + 17x - 42)$
$$= 2y(4x - 7)(x + 6)$$

32. $6x^2 - 11x - 10 = (3x + 2)(2x - 5)$

34. $-x^2 + 4x + 21 = -1(x^2 - 4x - 21)$
$$= -1(x + 3)(x - 7)$$

36. $6x^3 - 31x^2 + 5x = x(6x^2 - 31x + 5)$
$$= x(x - 5)(6x - 1)$$

38. $36x^2 + 55x - 14 = (4x + 7)(9x - 2)$

40. $x^2 + 18x + 81 = x^2 + 2 \cdot x \cdot 9 + 9^2 = (x + 9)^2$

42. $x^2 - 12x + 36 = x^2 - 2 \cdot x \cdot 6 + 6^2 = (x - 6)^2$

44. $25x^2 - 20x + 4 = (5x)^2 - 2 \cdot 5x \cdot 2 + 2^2$
$$= (5x - 2)^2$$

46. $m^4 + 10m^2 + 25 = (m^2)^2 + 2 \cdot m^2 \cdot 5 + 5^2$
$$= (m^2 + 5)^2$$

48. $3y^2 - 6y + 3 = 3(y^2 - 2y + 1)$
$$= 3(y^2 - 2 \cdot y \cdot 1 + 1^2)$$
$$= 3(y - 1)^2$$

50. $9y^2 + 48y + 64 = (3y)^2 + 2 \cdot 3y \cdot 8 + 8^2$
$$= (3y + 8)^2$$

52. $2x^2 + 7x - 72 = (2x - 9)(x + 8)$

54. $24x^2 - 49x + 15 = (8x - 3)(3x - 5)$

56. $2a^2 + 11ab + 5b^2 = (2a + b)(a + 5b)$

58. $-7x + 12 + x^2 = x^2 - 7x + 12 = (x - 3)(x - 4)$

60. $m^2 + 20mn + 100n^2 = m^2 + 2 \cdot m \cdot 10n + (10n)^2$
$$= (m + 10n)^2$$

62. $x^2y^2 - 14xy + 49 = (xy)^2 - 2 \cdot xy \cdot 7 + 7^2$
$$= (xy - 7)^2$$

64. $24y^2x + 7yx - 5x = x(24y^2 + 7y - 5)$
$$= x(8y + 5)(3y - 1)$$

66. $6x^3 - 28x^2 + 16x = 2x(3x^2 - 14x + 8)$
$$= 2x(3x - 2)(x - 4)$$

68. $12x^3 - 34x^2 + 24x = 2x(6x^2 - 17x + 12)$
$$= 2x\big(3x - 4)(2x - 3)\big)$$

70. $42x^4 - 99x^3y - 15x^2y^2$
$$= 3x^2(14x^2 - 33xy - 5y^2)$$
$$= 3x^2(2x - 5y)(7x + y)$$

72. $-15x^2 + 26x - 8 = -1(15x^2 - 26x + 8)$
$$= -1(3x - 4)(5x - 2)$$

74. $9q^4 - 42q^3 + 49q^2 = q^2(9q^2 - 42q + 49)$
$$= q^2[(3q)^2 - 2 \cdot 3q \cdot 7 + 7^2]$$
$$= q^2(3q - 7)^2$$

76. $y + 8y^2 - 9 = 8y^2 + y - 9 = (y-1)(8y+9)$

78. $54a^2 + 39ab - 8b^2 = (9a + 8b)(6a - b)$

80. $1 + 16x^2 + x^4 = x^4 + 16x^2 + 1$ is prime.

82. $25x^2 - 60xy + 36y^2 = (5x)^2 - 2 \cdot 5x \cdot 6y + (6y)^2$
$$= (5x - 6y)^2$$

84. $42a^2 - 43a + 6 = (7a - 6)(6a - 1)$

86. $-3t + 4t^2 - 7 = 4t^2 - 3t - 7 = (4t - 7)(t + 1)$

88. $3r^2 + 10r - 8 = (3r - 2)(r + 4)$

90. $y^3 + 12y^2 + 36y = y(y^2 + 12y + 36)$
$$= y(y^2 + 2 \cdot y \cdot 6 + 6^2)$$
$$= y(y + 6)^2$$

92. $3a^2b^2 + 12ab + 1$ is prime.

94. $5m^5 + 26m^3h^2 + 5mh^4$
$$= m(5m^4 + 26m^2h^2 + 5h^4)$$
$$= m(5m^2 + h^2)(m^2 + 5h^2)$$

96. $(y^2 + 3)(y^2 - 3) = y^4 - 3y^2 + 3y^2 - 9 = y^4 - 9$

98. $(z - 2)(z^2 + 2z + 4) = z^3 + 2z^2 + 4z - 2z^2 - 4z - 8$
$$= z^3 - 8$$

100. Look for the graph with the greatest height difference from the previous graph. The income range with the greatest income increase is $35,000–$49,999.

102. Answers may vary

104. In a, b, and d one term can be factored further.

106. $(x + 3y)^2 = x^2 + 2 \cdot x \cdot 3y + (3y)^2$
$$= x^2 + 6xy + 9y^2$$

108. $P = 2l + 2w$
$$= 2(-22y + 7) + 2(3y^2)$$
$$= -44y + 14 + 6y^2$$
$$= 6y^2 - 44y + 14$$
$$= 2(3y^2 - 22y + 7)$$
$$= 2(3y - 1)(y - 7)$$

110. $27x^2 + 2x - \dfrac{1}{9} = \left(3x + \dfrac{1}{3}\right)\left(9x - \dfrac{1}{3}\right)$

112. $3x^2(a + 3)^3 - 10x(a + 3)^3 + 25(a + 3)^3$
$$= (a + 3)^3(3x^2 - 10x + 25)$$

114. $9x^2 = (3x)^2;\ 25 = 5^2;\ 2 \cdot 3x \cdot 5 = 30x;\ 30$

116. The square represents a perfect square trinomial.

118. $b = 5;\ 2y^2 + 5y + 3 = (2y + 3)(y + 1)$
$$b = 7;\ 2y^2 + 7y + 3 = (2y + 1)(y + 3)$$

120. $c = 21;\ 11y^2 - 40y + 21 = (11y - 7)(y - 3)$
$$c = 29;\ 11y^2 - 40y + 29 = (11y - 29)(y - 1)$$
$$c = 36;\ 11y^2 - 40y + 36 = (11y - 18)(y - 2)$$

122. $-12r^3x^2 + 38r^2x^2 + 14rx^2$
$$= -2rx^2(6r^2 - 19r - 7)$$
$$= -2rx^2(2r - 7)(3r + 1)$$

124. $3x^2(a + 3)^3 - 28x(a + 3)^3 + 25(a + 3)^3$
$$= (a + 3)^3(3x^2 - 28x + 25)$$
$$= (a + 3)^3(x - 1)(3x - 25)$$

126. $2x^{2n} + 5x^n - 12 = (2x^n - 3)(x^n + 4)$

Section 6.4

Practice Exercises

1.

Factors of $ac = 60$	Sum of Factors
1, 60	61
2, 30	32
3, 20	23
4, 15	19
5, 12	17
6, 10	16

← correct sum
$b = 61$.

$$5x^2 + 61x + 12 = 5x^2 + 1x + 60x + 12$$
$$= x(5x+1) + 12(5x+1)$$
$$= (5x+1)(x+12)$$

2.

Factors of $ac = 60$	Sum of Factors
−1, −60	−61
−2, −30	−32
−3, −20	−23
−4, −15	−19
−5, −12	−17
−6, −10	−60

← Correct sum
$b = -19$

$$12x^2 - 19x + 5 = 12x^2 - 15x - 4x + 5$$
$$= 3x(4x-5) - 1(4x-5)$$
$$= (4x-5)(3x-1)$$

3. $30x^2 - 14x - 4 = 2(15x^2 - 7x - 2)$

Find two numbers whose product is
$ac = 15(-2) = -30$ and whose sum is b, −7. The numbers are −10 and 3.
$$2(15x^2 - 7x - 2) = 2(15x^2 - 10x + 3x - 2)$$
$$= 2[5x(3x-2) + 1(3x-2)]$$
$$= 2(3x-2)(5x+1)$$

4. $40m^4 + 5m^3 - 35m^2 = 5m^2(8m^2 + m - 7)$

Find two numbers whose product is
$ac = 8(-7) = -56$ and whose sum is b, 1. The numbers are 8 and −7.
$$5m^2(8m^2 + m - 7) = 5m^2(8m^2 + 8m - 7m - 7)$$
$$= 5m^2[8m(m+1) - 7(m+1)]$$
$$= 5m^2(m+1)(8m-7)$$

5. Find two numbers whose product is
$ac = 16 \cdot 9 = 144$ and whose sum is b, 24. The numbers are 12 and 12.
$$16x^2 + 24x + 9 = 16x^2 + 12x + 12x + 9$$
$$= 4x(4x+3) + 3(4x+3)$$
$$= (4x+3)(4x+3)$$
$$= (4x+3)^2$$

Exercise Set 6.4

2. $x^2 + 5x + 3x + 15 = x(x+5) + 3(x+5)$
   $$= (x+5)(x+3)$$

4. $z^2 + 10z - 7z - 70 = z(z+10) - 7(z+10)$
   $$= (z+10)(z-7)$$

6. $4x^2 - 9x - 32x + 72 = x(4x-9) - 8(4x-9)$
   $$= (4x-9)(x-8)$$

8. $2y^4 - 10y^2 + 7y^2 - 35 = 2y^2(y^2-5) + 7(y^2-5)$
   $$= (y^2-5)(2y^2+7)$$

10. **a.** $2 \cdot 12 = 24; 2 + 12 = 14; 2, 12$

   b. $14x = 2x + 12x$

   c. $8x^2 + 14x + 3 = 8x^2 + 2x + 12x + 3$
   $$= 2x(4x+1) + 3(4x+1)$$
   $$= (4x+1)(2x+3)$$

12. **a.** $-10 \cdot (-3) = 30; -10 + (-3) = -13; -10, -3$

   b. $-13x = -10x - 3x$

   c. $6x^2 - 13x + 5 = 6x^2 - 10x - 3x + 5$
   $$= 2x(3x-5) - 1(3x-5)$$
   $$= (3x-5)(2x-1)$$

14. $ac = 15 \cdot 2 = 30; b = 11;$ two numbers: 5, 6

$$15x^2 + 11x + 2 = 15x^2 + 5x + 6x + 2$$
$$= 5x(3x + 1) + 2(3x + 1)$$
$$= (3x + 1)(5x + 2)$$

16. $ac = 8 \cdot (-9) = -72; b = -1;$ two numbers: $-9, 8$

$$8x^2 - x - 9 = 8x^2 - 9x + 8x - 9$$
$$= x(8x - 9) + 1(8x - 9)$$
$$= (8x - 9)(x + 1)$$

18. $ac = 30 \cdot 3 = 90; b = -23;$ two numbers: $-18, -5$

$$30x^2 - 23x + 3 = 30x^2 - 18x - 5x + 3$$
$$= 6x(5x - 3) - 1(5x - 3)$$
$$= (5x - 3)(6x - 1)$$

20. $ac = 2 \cdot 3 = 6; b = -7;$ two numbers: $-1, -6$

$$2x^2 - 7x + 3 = 2x^2 - x - 6x + 3$$
$$= x(2x - 1) - 3(2x - 1)$$
$$= (2x - 1)(x - 3)$$

22. $20x + 25x^2 + 4 = 25x^2 + 20x + 4$

$ac = 25 \cdot 4 = 100; b = 20;$ two numbers: 10, 10

$$25x^2 + 20x + 4 = 25x^2 + 10x + 10x + 4$$
$$= 5x(5x + 2) + 2(5x + 2)$$
$$= (5x + 2)(5x + 2)$$
$$= (5x + 2)^2$$

24. $ac = 6(-10) = -60; b = -11;$

two numbers: 4, -15

$$6x^2 - 11x - 10 = 6x^2 + 4x - 15x - 10$$
$$= 2x(3x + 2) - 5(3x + 2)$$
$$= (3x + 2)(2x - 5)$$

26. $ac = 21 \cdot 2 = 42; b = -13;$ two numbers: $-6, -7$

$$21x^2 - 13x + 2 = 21x^2 - 6x - 7x + 2$$
$$= 3x(7x - 2) - 1(7x - 2)$$
$$= (7x - 2)(3x - 1)$$

28. $3x^3 + 8x^2 + 4x = x(3x^2 + 8x + 4)$

$ac = 3 \cdot 4 = 12; b = 8;$ two numbers: 2, 6

$$x(3x^2 + 8x + 4) = x(3x^2 + 2x + 6x + 4)$$
$$= x[x(3x + 2) + 2(3x + 2)]$$
$$= x(3x + 2)(x + 2)$$

30. $4y^2 - 2y - 12 = 2(2y^2 - y - 6)$

$ac = 2(-6) = -12; b = -1;$ two numbers: 3, -4

$$2(2y^2 - y - 6) = 2(2y^2 + 3y - 4y - 6)$$
$$= 2[y(2y + 3) - 2(2y + 3)]$$
$$= 2(2y + 3)(y - 2)$$

32. $-25x + 12 + 12x^2 = 12x^2 - 25x + 12$

$ac = 12 \cdot 12 = 144; b = -25;$

two numbers: $-16, -9$

$$12x^2 - 25x + 12 = 12x^2 - 16x - 9x + 12$$
$$= 4x(3x - 4) - 3(3x - 4)$$
$$= (3x - 4)(4x - 3)$$

34. $30a^2 + 38a - 20 = 2(15a^2 + 19a - 10)$

$ac = 15(-10) = -150; b = 19;$

two numbers: 25, -6

$$2(15a^2 + 19a - 10) = 2(15a^2 + 25a - 6a - 10)$$
$$= 2[5a(3a + 5) - 2(3a + 5)]$$
$$= 2(3a + 5)(5a - 2)$$

36. $10a^3 + 17a^2 + 3a = a(10a^2 + 17a + 3)$

$ac = 10(3) = 30; b = 17;$ two numbers: 15, 2

$$a(10a^2 + 17a + 3) = a(10a^2 + 15a + 2a + 3)$$
$$= a[5a(2a + 3) + 1(2a + 3)]$$
$$= a(2a + 3)(5a + 1)$$

38. $30x^3 - 155x^2 + 25x = 5x(6x^2 - 31x + 5)$

$ac = 6 \cdot 5 = 30; b = -31;$ two numbers: $-1, -30$

$$5x(6x^2 - 31x + 5) = 5x(6x^2 - x - 30x + 5)$$
$$= 5x[x(6x - 1) - 5(6x - 1)]$$
$$= 5x(6x - 1)(x - 5)$$

40. $6r^2t + 7rt^2 + t^3 = t(6r^2 + 7rt + t^2)$

$ac = 6 \cdot 1 = 6; b = 7;$ two numbers: 1, 6

$$t(6r^2 + 7rt + t^2) = t(6r^2 + rt + 6rt + t^2)$$
$$= t[r(6r + t) + t(6r + t)]$$
$$= t(6r + t)(r + t)$$

42. $ac = 36 \cdot 1 = 36; b = 6;$ there are no two numbers.

$36z^2 + 6z + 1$ is prime.

44. $3x^2 + 42xy + 147y^2 = 3(x^2 + 14xy + 49y^2)$

$ac = 1 \cdot 49 = 49;\ b = 14;$ two numbers: 7, 7

$3(x^2 + 14xy + 49y^2) = 3(x^2 + 7xy + 7xy + 49y^2)$
$= 3[x(x + 7y) + 7y(x + 7y)]$
$= 3(x + 7y)(x + 7y)$
$= 3(x + 7y)^2$

46. $30a^2 + 5ab - 25b^2 = 5(6a^2 + ab - 5b^2)$

$ac = 6 \cdot (-5) = -30;\ b = 1;$ two numbers: 6, -5

$5(6a^2 + ab - 5b^2) = 5(6a^2 + 6ab - 5ab - 5b^2)$
$= 5[6a(a + b) - 5b(a + b)]$
$= 5(a + b)(6a - 5b)$

48. $20s^4 + 61s^3 t + 3s^2 t^2 = s^2(20s^2 + 61st + 3t^2)$

$ac = 20 \cdot 3 = 60;\ b = 61;$ two numbers: 1, 60

$s^2(20s^2 + 61st + 3t^2)$
$= s^2(20s^2 + st + 60st + 3t^2)$
$= s^2[s(20s + t) + 3t(20s + t)]$
$= s^2(20s + t)(s + 3t)$

50. $32n^4 - 112n^2 + 98 = 2(16n^4 - 56n^2 + 49)$

$ac = 16 \cdot 49 = 784;\ b = -56;$
two numbers: $-28, -28$

$2(16n^4 - 56n^2 + 49)$
$= 2(16n^4 - 28n^2 - 28n^2 + 49)$
$= 2[4n^2(4n^2 - 7) - 7(4n^2 - 7)]$
$= 2(4n^2 - 7)(4n^2 - 7)$
$= 2(4n^2 - 7)^2$

52. $33 + 14x + x^2 = x^2 + 14x + 33$

$ac = 1 \cdot 33 = 33;\ b = 14;$ two numbers: 3, 11

$x^2 + 14x + 33 = x^2 + 3x + 11x + 33$
$= x(x + 3) + 11(x + 3)$
$= (x + 3)(x + 11)$

54. $5 - 12x + 7x^2 = 7x^2 - 12x + 5$

$ac = 7 \cdot 5 = 35;\ b = -12;$ two numbers: $-5, -7$

$7x^2 - 12x + 5 = 7x^2 - 5x - 7x + 5$
$= x(7x - 5) - 1(7x - 5)$
$= (7x - 5)(x - 1)$

56. $(y - 5)(y + 5) = y^2 - 5^2 = y^2 - 25$

58. $(x + 7)(x + 7) = x^2 + 2 \cdot x \cdot 7 + 7^2 = x^2 + 14x + 49$

60. $(8y + 9)(8y - 9) = (8y)^2 - 9^2 = 64y^2 - 81$

62. $(2z - 1)(4z^2 + 2z + 1) = (2z)^3 - 1^3 = 8z^3 - 1$

64. $3(7x^2 + 11xy + 4y^2) = 21x^2 + 33xy + 12y^2$

$ac = 7 \cdot 4 = 28;\ b = 11;$ two numbers = 4, 7

$3(7x^2 + 11xy + 4y^2) = 3(7x^2 + 4xy + 7xy + 4y^2)$
$= 3[x(7x + 4y) + y(7x + 4y)]$
$= 3(7x + 4y)(x + y)$

66. $x^{2n} + 6x^n + 10x^n + 60 = x^n(x^n + 6) + 10(x^n + 6)$
$= (x^n + 6)(x^n + 10)$

68. $ac = 12 \cdot 25 = 300;\ b = -40;$
two numbers: $-30, -10$

$12x^{2n} - 40x^n + 25 = 12x^{2n} - 30x^n - 10x^n + 25$
$= 6x^n(2x^n - 5) - 5(2x^n - 5)$
$= (2x^n - 5)(6x^n - 5)$

Section 6.5

Practice Exercises

1. $x^2 - 81 = x^2 - 9^2 = (x + 9)(x - 9)$

2. a. $9x^2 - 1 = (3x)^2 - 1^2 = (3x + 1)(3x - 1)$

   b. $36a^2 - 49b^2 = (6a)^2 - (7b)^2$
$= (6a + 7b)(6a - 7b)$

   c. $p^2 - \dfrac{25}{36} = p^2 - \left(\dfrac{5}{6}\right)^2 = \left(p + \dfrac{5}{6}\right)\left(p - \dfrac{5}{6}\right)$

3. $p^4 - q^{10} = (p^2)^2 - (q^5)^2 = (p^2 + q^5)(p^2 - q^5)$

4. a. $z^4 - 81 = (z^2)^2 - 9^2$
$= (z^2 + 9)(z^2 - 9)$
$= (z^2 + 9)(z + 3)(z - 3)$

   b. $m^2 + 49$ is a prime polynomial.

5. $36y^3 - 25y = y(36y^2 - 25)$
$= y[(6y)^2 - 5^2]$
$= y(6y + 5)(6y - 5)$

6. $80y^4 - 5 = 5(16y^2 - 1)$
$$= 5[(4y)^2 - 1^2]$$
$$= 5(4y + 1)(4y - 1)$$

7. $-9x^2 + 100 = -1(9x^2 - 100)$
$$= -1[(3x)^2 - 10^2]$$
$$= -1(3x + 10)(3x - 10)$$

8. $x^3 + 64 = x^3 + 4^3$
$$= (x + 4)(x^2 - x \cdot 4 + 4^2)$$
$$= (x + 4)(x^2 - 4x + 16)$$

9. $x^3 - 125 = x^3 - 5^3$
$$= (x - 5)(x^2 + x \cdot 5 + 5^2)$$
$$= (x - 5)(x^2 + 5x + 25)$$

10. $27y^3 + 1 = (3y)^3 + 1^3$
$$= (3y + 1)[(3y)^2 - 3y \cdot 1 + 1^2]$$
$$= (3y + 1)(9y^2 - 3y + 1)$$

11. $32x^3 - 500y^3$
$$= 4(8x^3 - 125y^3)$$
$$= 4[(2x)^3 - (5y)^3]$$
$$= 4(2x - 5y)[(2x)^2 + 2x \cdot 5y + (5y)^2]$$
$$= 4(2x - 5y)(4x^2 + 10xy + 25y^2)$$

Calculator Explorations

x	$x^2 - 2x + 1$	$x^2 - 2x - 1$	$(x-1)^2$
5	16	14	16
-3	16	14	16
2.7	2.89	0.89	2.89
-12.1	171.61	169.61	171.61
0	1	-1	1

Vocabulary and Readiness Check

1. The expression $x^3 - 27$ is called a <u>difference of two cubes</u>.

2. The expression $x^2 - 49$ is called a <u>difference of two squares</u>.

3. The expression $z^3 + 1$ is called a <u>sum of two cubes</u>.

4. The binomial $y^2 + 9$ is prime. The statement is false.

5. $64 = 8^2$

6. $100 = 10^2$

7. $49x^2 = (7x)^2$

8. $25y^4 = (5y^2)^2$

9. $64 = 4^3$

10. $1 = 1^3$

11. $8y^3 = (2y)^3$

12. $x^6 = (x^2)^3$

Exercise Set 6.5

2. $x^2 - 36 = x^2 - 6^2 = (x + 6)(x - 6)$

4. $49m^2 - 1 = (7m)^2 - 1^2 = (7m + 1)(7m - 1)$

6. $49a^2 - 16 = (7a)^2 - 4^2 = (7a + 4)(7a - 4)$

8. $196a^2 - 49b^2 = (13a)^2 - (7b)^2$
$$= (13a + 7b)(13a - 7b)$$

10. $a^2b^2 - 16 = (ab)^2 - 4^2 = (ab - 4)(ab + 4)$

12. $y^2 - \dfrac{1}{16} = y^2 - \left(\dfrac{1}{4}\right)^2 = \left(y + \dfrac{1}{4}\right)\left(y - \dfrac{1}{4}\right)$

14. $-9t^2 + 1 = -1(9t^2 - 1)$
$$= -1[(3t)^2 - 1^2]$$
$$= -1(3t + 1)(3t - 1)$$

16. $49y^2 + 1$ is the sum of two squares, $(7y)^2 + 1^2$, not the difference of two squares. $49y^2 + 1$ is a prime polynomial.

18. $-1 + y^2 = -1(1 - y^2)$
$\qquad = -1(1^2 - y^2)$
$\qquad = -1(1 + y)(1 - y)$ or $(-1 + y)(1 + y)$

20. $n^4 - 16 = (n^2)^2 - 4^2$
$\qquad = (n^2 + 4)(n^2 - 4)$
$\qquad = (n^2 + 4)(n + 2)(n - 2)$

22. $n^4 - r^6 = (n^2)^2 - (r^3)^2 = (n^2 + r^3)(n^2 - r^3)$

24. $p^3 + 1 = p^3 + 1^3$
$\qquad = (p + 1)(p^2 - p \cdot 1 + 1^2)$
$\qquad = (p + 1)(p^2 - p + 1)$

26. $27y^3 - 1 = (3y)^3 - 1^3$
$\qquad = (3y - 1)[(3y)^2 + 3y \cdot 1 + 1^2]$
$\qquad = (3y - 1)(9y^2 + 3y + 1)$

28. $y^3 + 64z^3 = y^3 + (4z)^3$
$\qquad = (y + 4z)[y^2 - y \cdot 4z + (4z)^2]$
$\qquad = (y + 4z)(y^2 - 4yz + 16z^2)$

30. $6r^3 + 162 = 6(r^3 + 27)$
$\qquad = 6(r^3 + 3^3)$
$\qquad = 6(r + 3)(r^2 - r \cdot 3 + 3^2)$
$\qquad = 6(r + 3)(r^2 - 3r + 9)$

32. $a^3 b^3 - 8 = (ab)^3 - 2^3$
$\qquad = (ab - 2)[(ab)^2 + ab \cdot 2 + 2^2]$
$\qquad = (ab - 2)(a^2 b^2 + 2ab + 4)$

34. $24x^3 - 81y^3$
$\qquad = 3(8x^3 - 27y^3)$
$\qquad = 3[(2x)^3 - (3y)^3]$
$\qquad = 3(2x - 3y)[(2x)^2 + 2x \cdot 3y + (3y)^2]$
$\qquad = 3(2x - 3y)(4x^2 + 6xy + 9y^2)$

36. $q^2 - 121 = q^2 - 11^2 = (q + 11)(q - 11)$

38. $x^2 - 225y^2 = x^2 - (15y)^2 = (x + 15y)(x - 15y)$

40. $125 - r^3 = 5^3 - r^3$
$\qquad = (5 - r)(5^2 + 5 \cdot r + r^2)$
$\qquad = (5 - r)(25 + 5r + r^2)$

42. $32t^2 - 50 = 2(16t^2 - 25)$
$\qquad = 2[(4t)^2 - 5^2]$
$\qquad = 2(4t + 5)(4t - 5)$

44. $36x^2 y - 25y = y(36x^2 - 25)$
$\qquad = y[(6x)^2 - 5^2]$
$\qquad = y(6x - 5)(6x + 5)$

46. $2x^3 + 54 = 2(x^3 + 27)$
$\qquad = 2(x^3 + 3^3)$
$\qquad = 2(x + 3)(x^2 - x \cdot 3 + 3^2)$
$\qquad = 2(x + 3)(x^2 - 3x + 9)$

48. $x^3 y - 4xy^3 = xy(x^2 - 4y^2)$
$\qquad = xy[x^2 - (2y)^2]$
$\qquad = xy(x + 2y)(x - 2y)$

50. $225a^2 - 81b^2 = 9(25a^2 - 9b^2)$
$\qquad = 9[(5a)^2 - (3b)^2]$
$\qquad = 9(5a + 3b)(5a - 3b)$

52. $12x^2 - 27 = 3(4x^2 - 9)$
$\qquad = 3[(2x)^2 - 3^2]$
$\qquad = 3(2x + 3)(2x - 3)$

54. $a^3 b^3 - c^9 = (ab)^3 - (c^3)^3$
$\qquad = (ab - c^3)[(ab)^2 + ab \cdot c^3 + (c^3)^2]$
$\qquad = (ab - c^3)(a^2 b^2 + abc^3 + c^6)$

56. $100 - \dfrac{4}{81} n^2 = 10^2 - \left(\dfrac{2}{9} n\right)^2$
$\qquad = \left(10 - \dfrac{2}{9} n\right)\left(10 + \dfrac{2}{9} n\right)$

58. $s^3 + 216 = s^3 + 6^3$
$\qquad = (s + 6)(s^2 - s \cdot 6 + 6^2)$
$\qquad = (s + 6)(s^2 - 6s + 36)$

60. $y^3 + 64y = y(y^2 + 64)$

62. $n^9 - n^5 = n^5(n^4 - 1)$
$$= n^5[(n^2)^2 - 1^2]$$
$$= n^5(n^2 + 1)(n^2 - 1)$$
$$= n^5(n^2 + 1)(n + 1)(n - 1)$$

64. $100x^3y - 49xy^3 = xy(100x^2 - 49y^2)$
$$= xy[(10x)^2 - (7y)^2]$$
$$= xy(10x + 7y)(10x - 7y)$$

66. $8x^3y^3 + x^3y = x^3y(8y^2 + 1)$

68. $64m^4 - 27mn^3$
$$= m(64m^3 - 27n^3)$$
$$= m[(4m)^3 - (3n)^3]$$
$$= m(4m - 3n)[(4m)^2 + 4m \cdot 3n + (3n)^2]$$
$$= m(4m - 3n)(16m^2 + 12mn + 9n^2)$$

70. $25y^4 - 100y^2 = 25y^2(y^2 - 4)$
$$= 25y^2(y^2 - 2^2)$$
$$= 25y^2(y + 2)(y - 2)$$

72. $y + 5 = 0$
$$y + 5 - 5 = 0 - 5$$
$$y = -5$$

74. $3x - 9 = 0$
$$3x - 9 + 9 = 0 + 9$$
$$3x = 9$$
$$\frac{3x}{3} = \frac{9}{3}$$
$$x = 3$$

76. $4a + 2 = 0$
$$4a + 2 - 2 = 0 - 2$$
$$4a = -2$$
$$\frac{4a}{4} = \frac{-2}{4}$$
$$a = -\frac{1}{2}$$

78. Let $x = 2006 - 2000 = 6$.
$$-1.2x^2 + 4x + 80 = -1.2(6)^2 + 4(6) + 80$$
$$= -43.2 + 24 + 80$$
$$= 60.8$$
60.8% of college students had credit cards in 2006.

80. Answers may vary

82. $(y - 6)^2 - z^2 = (y - 6 + z)(y - 6 - z)$

84. $m^2(n + 8) - 9(n + 8) = (n + 8)(m^2 - 9)$
$$= (n + 8)(m^2 - 3^2)$$
$$= (n + 8)(m + 3)(m - 3)$$

86. $(x^2 + 2x + 1) - 36y^2 = (x + 1)^2 - 36y^2$
$$= (x + 1)^2 - (6y)^2$$
$$= (x + 1 + 6y)(x + 1 - 6y)$$

88. $x^{2n} - 81 = (x^n)^2 - 9^2 = (x^n + 9)(x^n - 9)$

90. $5 - y$, since
$$(5 - y)(5 + y) = 25 + 5y - 5y - y^2$$
$$= 25 - y^2$$
$$= 5^2 - y^2$$

92. Answers may vary

94. a. Let $t = 1$.
$$529 - 16t^2 = 529 - 16(1)^2$$
$$= 529 - 16(1)$$
$$= 529 - 16$$
$$= 513$$
After 1 second the height of the bolt is 513 feet.

b. Let $t = 4$.
$$529 - 16t^2 = 529 - 16(4)^2$$
$$= 529 - 16(16)$$
$$= 529 - 256$$
$$= 273$$
After 4 seconds the height of the bolt is 273 feet.

c. When the object hits the ground, its height is zero feet. Thus, to find the time, t, when the object's height is zero feet above the ground, we set the expression $529 - 16t^2$ equal to 0 and solve for t.

$$529 - 16t^2 = 0$$
$$529 - 16t^2 + 16t^2 = 0 + 16t^2$$
$$529 = 16t^2$$
$$\frac{529}{16} = \frac{16t^2}{16}$$
$$33.0625 = t^2$$
$$\sqrt{33.0625} = \sqrt{t^2}$$
$$5.75 = t$$

Thus, the object will hit the ground after approximately 6 seconds.

d. $529 - 16t^2 = 23^2 - (4t)^2 = (23 + 4t)(23 - 4t)$

96. a. Let $t = 2$.

$$784 - 16t^2 = 784 - 16(2)^2 = 720$$

After 2 seconds the height is 720 feet.

b. Let $t = 5$.

$$784 - 16t^2 = 784 - 16(5)^2 = 384$$

After 5 seconds the height is 384 feet.

c. When he reaches ground level, the height is 0.

$$0 = 784 - 16t^2$$
$$16t^2 = 784$$
$$t^2 = 49$$
$$t = \sqrt{49}$$
$$t = 7$$

He reaches ground level after 7 seconds.

d. $784 - 16t^2 = 16(49 - t^2)$
$$= 16(7^2 - t^2)$$
$$= 16(7 + t)(7 - t)$$

Integrated Review

Practice Exercises

1. $6x^2 - 11x + 3$
$ac = 6 \cdot 3 = 18; \; b = -11;$ two numbers: $-2, -9$
$6x^2 - 11x + 3 = 6x^2 - 2x - 9x + 3$
$$= 2x(3x - 1) - 3(3x - 1)$$
$$= (3x - 1)(2x - 3)$$

2. $3x^3 + x^2 - 12x - 4 = (3x^3 + x^2) + (-12x - 4)$
$$= x^2(3x + 1) - 4(3x + 1)$$
$$= (3x + 1)(x^2 - 4)$$
$$= (3x + 1)(x + 2)(x - 2)$$

3. $27x^2 - 3y^2 = 3(9x^2 - y^2)$
$$= 3[(3x)^2 - y^2]$$
$$= 3(3x + y)(3x - y)$$

4. $8a^3 + b^3 = (2a)^3 + b^3$
$$= (2a + b)[(2a)^2 - 2a \cdot b + b^2]$$
$$= (2a + b)(4a^2 - 2ab + b^2)$$

5. $60x^3y^2 - 66x^2y^2 - 36xy^2$
$$= 6xy^2(10x^2 - 11x - 6)$$
$$= 6xy^2(5x + 2)(2x - 3)$$

Integrated Review

1. $x^2 + 2xy + y^2 = (x + y)(x + y) = (x + y)^2$

2. $x^2 - 2xy + y^2 = (x - y)(x - y) = (x - y)^2$

3. $a^2 + 11a - 12 = (a + 12)(a - 1)$

4. $a^2 - 11a + 10 = (a - 10)(a - 1)$

5. $a^2 - a - 6 = (a - 3)(a + 2)$

6. $a^2 - 2a + 1 = (a - 1)(a - 1) = (a - 1)^2$

7. $x^2 + 2x + 1 = (x + 1)(x + 1) = (x + 1)^2$

8. $x^2 + x - 2 = (x + 2)(x - 1)$

9. $x^2 + 4x + 3 = (x + 3)(x + 1)$

10. $x^2 + x - 6 = (x + 3)(x - 2)$

11. $x^2 + 7x + 12 = (x + 4)(x + 3)$

12. $x^2 + x - 12 = (x + 4)(x - 3)$

13. $x^2 + 3x - 4 = (x + 4)(x - 1)$

14. $x^2 - 7x + 10 = (x - 5)(x - 2)$

15. $x^2 + 2x - 15 = (x + 5)(x - 3)$

16. $x^2 + 11x + 30 = (x + 6)(x + 5)$

17. $x^2 - x - 30 = (x - 6)(x + 5)$

18. $x^2 + 11x + 24 = (x + 8)(x + 3)$

19. $2x^2 - 98 = 2(x^2 - 49)$
$$= 2(x^2 - 7^2)$$
$$= 2(x + 7)(x - 7)$$

20. $3x^2 - 75 = 3(x^2 - 25)$
$$= 3(x^2 - 5^2)$$
$$= 3(x + 5)(x - 5)$$

21. $x^2 + 3x + xy + 3y = x(x + 3) + y(x + 3)$
$$= (x + 3)(x + y)$$

22. $3y - 21 + xy - 7x = 3(y - 7) + x(y - 7)$
$$= (y - 7)(3 + x)$$

23. $x^2 + 6x - 16 = (x + 8)(x - 2)$

24. $x^2 - 3x - 28 = (x - 7)(x + 4)$

25. $4x^3 + 20x^2 - 56x = 4x(x^2 + 5x - 14)$
$$= 4x(x + 7)(x - 2)$$

26. $6x^3 - 6x^2 - 120x = 6x(x^2 - x - 20)$
$$= 6x(x - 5)(x + 4)$$

27. $12x^2 + 34x + 24 = 2(6x^2 + 17x + 12)$
$$= 2(6x^2 + 9x + 8x + 12)$$
$$= 2[3x(2x + 3) + 4(2x + 3)]$$
$$= 2(2x + 3)(3x + 4)$$

28. $8a^2 + 6ab - 5b^2 = 8a^2 + 10ab - 4ab - 5b^2$
$$= 2a(4a + 5b) - b(4a + 5b)$$
$$= (4a + 5b)(2a - b)$$

29. $4a^2 - b^2 = (2a)^2 - b^2 = (2a + b)(2a - b)$

30. $28 - 13x - 6x^2 = 28 - 21x + 8x - 6x^2$
$$= 7(4 - 3x) + 2x(4 - 3x)$$
$$= (4 - 3x)(7 + 2x)$$

31. $20 - 3x - 2x^2 = 20 - 8x + 5x - 2x^2$
$$= 4(5 - 2x) + x(5 - 2x)$$
$$= (5 - 2x)(4 + x)$$

32. $x^2 - 2x + 4$ is a prime polynomial.

33. $a^2 + a - 3$ is a prime polynomial.

34. $6y^2 + y - 15 = 6y^2 + 10y - 9y - 15$
$$= 2y(3y + 5) - 3(3y + 5)$$
$$= (3y + 5)(2y - 3)$$

35. $4x^2 - x - 5 = 4x^2 - 5x + 4x - 5$
$$= x(4x - 5) + 1(4x - 5)$$
$$= (4x - 5)(x + 1)$$

36. $x^2y - y^3 = y(x^2 - y^2) = y(x - y)(x + y)$

37. $4t^2 + 36 = 4(t^2 + 9)$

38. $x^2 + x + xy + y = x(x + 1) + y(x + 1)$
$$= (x + 1)(x + y)$$

39. $ax + 2x + a + 2 = x(a + 2) + 1(a + 2)$
$$= (a + 2)(x + 1)$$

40. $18x^3 - 63x^2 + 9x = 9x(2x^2 - 7x + 1)$

41. $12a^3 - 24a^2 + 4a = 4a(3a^2 - 6a + 1)$

42. $x^2 + 14x - 32 = (x + 16)(x - 2)$

43. $x^2 - 14x - 48$ is prime.

44. $16a^2 - 56ab + 49b^2 = (4a)^2 - 2(4a)(7b) + (7b)^2$
$$= (4a - 7b)^2$$

45. $25p^2 - 70pq + 49q^2 = (5p)^2 - 2(5p)(7q) + (7q)^2$
$$= (5p - 7q)^2$$

46. $7x^2 + 24xy + 9y^2 = 7x^2 + 3xy + 21xy + 9y^2$
$$= x(7x + 3y) + 3y(7x + 3y)$$
$$= (7x + 3y)(x + 3y)$$

47. $125 - 8y^3 = 5^3 - (2y)^3$
$\qquad = (5 - 2y)[5^2 + 5 \cdot 2y + (2y)^2]$
$\qquad = (5 - 2y)(25 + 10y + 4y^2)$

48. $64x^3 + 27 = (4x)^3 + 3^3$
$\qquad = (4x + 3)[(4x)^2 - 4x \cdot 3 + 3^2]$
$\qquad = (4x + 3)(16x^2 - 12x + 9)$

49. $-x^2 - x + 30 = -1(x^2 + x - 30) = -(x + 6)(x - 5)$

50. $-x^2 + 6x - 8 = -1(x^2 - 6x + 8) = -(x - 2)(x - 4)$

51. $14 + 5x - x^2 = (7 - x)(2 + x)$

52. $3 - 2x - x^2 = (3 + x)(1 - x)$

53. $3x^4y + 6x^3y - 72x^2y = 3x^2y(x^2 + 2x - 24)$
$\qquad = 3x^2y(x + 6)(x - 4)$

54. $2x^3y + 8x^2y^2 - 10xy^3 = 2xy(x^2 + 4xy - 5y^2)$
$\qquad = 2xy(x + 5y)(x - y)$

55. $5x^3y^2 - 40x^2y^3 + 35xy^4 = 5xy^2 - 8xy + 7y^2)$
$\qquad = 5xy^2(x - 7y)(x - y)$

56. $4x^4y - 8x^3y - 60x^2y = 4x^2y(x^2 - 2x - 15)$
$\qquad = 4x^2y(x - 5)(x + 3)$

57. $12x^3y + 243xy = 3xy(4x^2 + 81)$

58. $6x^3y^2 + 8xy^2 = 2xy^2(3x^2 + 4)$

59. $4 - x^2 = 2^2 - x^2 = (2 + x)(2 - x)$

60. $9 - y^2 = 3^2 - y^2 = (3 + y)(3 - y)$

61. $3rs - s + 12r - 4 = s(3r - 1) + 4(3r - 1)$
$\qquad = (3r - 1)(s + 4)$

62. $x^3 - 2x^2 + 3x - 6 = x^2(x - 2) + 3(x - 2)$
$\qquad = (x - 2)(x^2 + 3)$

63. $4x^2 - 8xy - 3x + 6y = 4x(x - 2y) - 3(x - 2y)$
$\qquad = (x - 2y)(4x - 3)$

64. $4x^2 - 2xy - 7yz + 14xz$
$\qquad = 2x(2x - y) + 7z(-y + 2x)$
$\qquad = (2x - y)(2x + 7z)$

65. $6x^2 + 18xy + 12y^2 = 6(x^2 + 3xy + 2y^2)$
$\qquad = 6(x + 2)(x + y)$

66. $12x^2 + 46xy - 8y^2 = 2(6x^2 + 23xy - 4y^2)$
$\qquad = 2(6x^2 + 24xy - xy - 4y^2)$
$\qquad = 2[6x(x + 4y) - y(x + 4y)]$
$\qquad = 2(x + 4y)(6x - y)$

67. $xy^2 - 4x + 3y^2 - 12 = x(y^2 - 4) + 3(y^2 - 4)$
$\qquad = (y^2 - 4)(x + 3)$
$\qquad = (y^2 - 2^2)(x + 3)$
$\qquad = (y + 2)(y - 2)(x + 3)$

68. $x^2y^2 - 9x^2 + 3y^2 - 27 = x^2(y^2 - 9) + 3(y^2 - 9)$
$\qquad = (y^2 - 9)(x^2 + 3)$
$\qquad = (y^2 - 3^2)(x^2 + 3)$
$\qquad = (y - 3)(y + 3)(x^2 + 3)$

69. $5(x + y) + x(x + y) = (x + y)(5 + x)$

70. $7(x - y) + y(x - y) = (x - y)(7 + y)$

71. $14t^2 - 9t + 1 = 14t^2 - 7t - 2t + 1$
$\qquad = 7t(2t - 1) - 1(2t - 1)$
$\qquad = (2t - 1)(7t - 1)$

72. $3t^2 - 5t + 1$ is a prime polynomial.

73. $3x^2 + 2x - 5 = 3x^2 + 5x - 3x - 5$
$\qquad = x(3x + 5) - 1(3x + 5)$
$\qquad = (3x + 5)(x - 1)$

74. $7x^2 + 19x - 6 = 7x^2 + 21x - 2x - 6$
$\qquad = 7x(x + 3) - 2(x + 3)$
$\qquad = (x + 3)(7x - 2)$

75. $x^2 + 9xy - 36y^2 = (x + 12y)(x - 3y)$

76. $3x^2 + 10xy - 8y^2 = 3x^2 - 2xy + 12xy - 8y^2$
$\qquad = x(3x - 2y) + 4y(3x - 2y)$
$\qquad = (3x - 2y)(x + 4y)$

77. $1 - 8ab - 20a^2b^2 = 1 - 10ab + 2ab - 20a^2b^2$
$$= 1(1 - 10ab) + 2ab(1 - 10ab)$$
$$= (1 - 10ab)(1 + 2ab)$$

78. $1 - 7ab - 60a^2b^2 = 1 - 12ab + 5ab - 60a^2b^2$
$$= 1(1 - 12ab) + 5ab(1 - 12ab)$$
$$= (1 - 12ab)(1 + 5ab)$$

79. $9 - 10x^2 + x^4 = (9 - x^2)(1 - x^2)$
$$= (3^2 - x^2)(1^2 - x^2)$$
$$= (3 + x)(3 - x)(1 + x)(1 - x)$$

80. $36 - 13x^2 + x^4 = (9 - x^2)(4 - x^2)$
$$= (3^2 - x^2)(2^2 - x^2)$$
$$= (3 + x)(3 - x)(2 + x)(2 - x)$$

81. $x^4 - 14x^2 - 32 = (x^2 + 2)(x^2 - 16)$
$$= (x^2 + 2)(x^2 - 4^2)$$
$$= (x^2 + 2)(x + 4)(x - 4)$$

82. $x^4 - 22x^2 - 75 = (x^2 + 3)(x^2 - 25)$
$$= (x^2 + 3)(x^2 - 5^2)$$
$$= (x^2 + 3)(x + 5)(x - 5)$$

83. $x^2 - 23x + 120 = (x - 15)(x - 8)$

84. $y^2 + 22y + 96 = (y + 16)(y + 6)$

85. $6x^3 - 28x^2 + 16x = 2x(3x^2 - 14x + 8)$
$$= 2x(3x - 2)(x - 4)$$

86. $6y^3 - 8y^2 - 30y = 2y(3y^2 - 4y - 15)$
$$= 2y(3y + 5)(y - 3)$$

87. $27x^3 - 125y^3 = (3x)^3 - (5y)^3$
$$= (3x - 5y)[(3x)^2 + 3x \cdot 5y + (5y)^2]$$
$$= (3x - 5y)(9x^2 + 15xy + 25y^2)$$

88. $216y^3 - z^3 = (6y)^3 - z^3$
$$= (6y - z)[(6y)^2 + 6y \cdot z + z^2]$$
$$= (6y - z)(36y^2 + 6yz + z^2)$$

89. $x^3y^3 + 8z^3 = (xy)^3 + (2z)^3$
$$= (xy + 2z)[(xy)^2 - xy \cdot 2z + (2z)^2]$$
$$= (xy + 2z)(x^2y^2 - 2xyz + 4z^2)$$

90. $27a^3b^3 + 8 = (3ab)^3 + 2^3$
$$= (3ab + 2)[(3ab)^2 - 3ab \cdot 2 + 2^2]$$
$$= (3ab + 2)(9a^2b^2 - 6ab + 4)$$

91. $2xy - 72x^3y = 2xy(1 - 36x^2)$
$$= 2xy[1^2 - (6x)^2]$$
$$= 2xy(1 + 6x)(1 - 6x)$$

92. $2x^3 - 18x = 2x(x^2 - 9)$
$$= 2x(x^2 - 3^2)$$
$$= 2x(x + 3)(x - 3)$$

93. $x^3 + 6x^2 - 4x - 24 = x^2(x + 6) - 4(x + 6)$
$$= (x + 6)(x^2 - 4)$$
$$= (x + 6)(x^2 - 2^2)$$
$$= (x + 6)(x + 2)(x - 2)$$

94. $x^3 - 2x^2 - 36x + 72 = x^2(x - 2) - 36(x - 2)$
$$= (x - 2)(x^2 - 36)$$
$$= (x - 2)(x^2 - 6^2)$$
$$= (x - 2)(x + 6)(x - 6)$$

95. $6a^3 + 10a^2 = 2a^2(3a + 5)$

96. $4n^2 - 6n = 2n(2n - 3)$

97. $a^2(a + 2) + 2(a + 2) = (a + 2)(a^2 + 2)$

98. $a - b + x(a - b) = (a - b)(1 + x)$

99. $x^3 - 28 + 7x^2 - 4x = x^3 + 7x^2 - 28 - 4x$
$$= x^2(x + 7) - 4(7 + x)$$
$$= (x + 7)(x^2 - 4)$$
$$= (x + 7)(x^2 - 2^2)$$
$$= (x + 7)(x + 2)(x - 2)$$

100. $a^3 - 45 - 9a + 5a^2 = a^3 + 5a^2 - 9a - 45$
$$= a^2(a + 5) - 9(a + 5)$$
$$= (a + 5)(a^2 - 9)$$
$$= (a + 5)(a^2 - 3^2)$$
$$= (a + 5)(a + 3)(a - 3)$$

101. $(x - y)^2 - z^2 = (x - y + z)(x - y - z)$

102. $(x+2y)^2 - 9 = (x+2y)^2 - 3^2$
$$= (x+2y+3)(x+2y-3)$$

103. $81 - (5x+1)^2 = 9^2 - (5x+1)^2$
$$= [9+(5x+1)][9-(5x+1)]$$
$$= (9+5x+1)(9-5x-1)$$

104. $b^2 - (4a+c)^2$
$$= [b+(4a+c)][b-(4a+c)]$$
$$= (b+4a+c)(b-4a-c)$$

105. Answers may vary

106. Yes; $9x^2 + 81y^2 = 9(x^2 + 9y^2)$

107. a, c

Section 6.6

Practice Exercises

1. $(x+4)(x-5) = 0$
$x+4 = 0$ or $x-5 = 0$
    $x = -4$ $x = 5$
Check:
Let $x = -4$.
  $(x+4)(x-5) = 0$
  $(-4+4)(-4-5) \stackrel{?}{=} 0$
         $0(-9) = 0$ True
Let $x = 5$.
  $(x+4)(x-5) = 0$
  $(5+4)(5-5) \stackrel{?}{=} 0$
        $9(0) = 0$ True

The solutions are -4 and 5.

2. $x(7x-6) = 0$
$x = 0$ or $7x-6 = 0$
           $7x = 6$
           $x = \dfrac{6}{7}$
Check:
Let $x = 0$.
  $x(7x-6) = 0$
  $0(7 \cdot 0 - 6) \stackrel{?}{=} 0$
     $0(-6) = 0$ True

Let $x = \dfrac{6}{7}$.
  $x(7x-6) = 0$
  $\dfrac{6}{7}\left(7 \cdot \dfrac{6}{7} - 6\right) \stackrel{?}{=} 0$
    $\dfrac{6}{7}(6-6) \stackrel{?}{=} 0$
     $\dfrac{6}{7}(0) = 0$ True

The solutions are 0 and $\dfrac{6}{7}$.

3. $x^2 - 8x - 48 = 0$
$(x+4)(x-12) = 0$
$x+4 = 0$ or $x-12 = 0$
  $x = -4$ $x = 12$
Check:
Let $x = -4$.
    $x^2 - 8x - 48 = 0$
  $(-4)^2 - 8(-4) - 48 \stackrel{?}{=} 0$
    $16 + 32 - 48 \stackrel{?}{=} 0$
       $48 - 48 \stackrel{?}{=} 0$
           $0 = 0$ True
Let $x = 12$.
    $x^2 - 8x - 48 = 0$
  $12^2 - 8 \cdot 12 - 48 \stackrel{?}{=} 0$
    $144 - 96 - 48 \stackrel{?}{=} 0$
      $48 - 48 \stackrel{?}{=} 0$
          $0 = 0$ True
The solutions are -4 and 12.

4. $9x^2 - 24x = -16$
$9x^2 - 24x + 16 = 0$
$(3x-4)(3x-4) = 0$
    $3x - 4 = 0$
       $3x = 4$
        $x = \dfrac{4}{3}$
The solution is $\dfrac{4}{3}$.

5.
$$x(3x+7)=6$$
$$3x^2+7x=6$$
$$3x^2+7x-6=0$$
$$(3x-2)(x+3)=0$$
$$3x-2=0 \quad \text{or} \quad x+3=0$$
$$3x=2 \qquad\qquad x=-3$$
$$x=\frac{2}{3}$$

The solutions are $\frac{2}{3}$ and -3.

6.
$$-3x^2-6x+72=0$$
$$-3(x^2+2x-24)=0$$
$$-3(x+6)(x-4)=0$$
$$x+6=0 \quad \text{or} \quad x-4=0$$
$$x=-6 \qquad\qquad x=4$$

The solutions are -6 and 4.

7.
$$7x^3-63x=0$$
$$7x(x^2-9)=0$$
$$7x(x+3)(x-3)=0$$
$$7x=0 \quad \text{or} \quad x+3=0 \quad \text{or} \quad x-3=0$$
$$x=0 \qquad\quad x=-3 \qquad\qquad x=3$$

The solutions are 0, -3, and 3.

8.
$$(3x-2)(2x^2-13x+15)=0$$
$$(3x-2)(2x-3)(x-5)=0$$
$$3x-2=0 \quad \text{or} \quad 2x-3=0 \quad \text{or} \quad x-5=0$$
$$3x=2 \qquad\qquad 2x=3 \qquad\qquad x=5$$
$$x=\frac{2}{3} \qquad\qquad x=\frac{3}{2}$$

The solutions are $\frac{2}{3}$, $\frac{3}{2}$, and 5.

9. $5x^3+5x^2-30x=0$
$$5x(x^2+x-6)=0$$
$$5x(x+3)(x-2)=0$$
$$5x=0 \quad \text{or} \quad x+3=0 \quad \text{or} \quad x-2=0$$
$$x=0 \qquad\qquad x=-3 \qquad\qquad x=2$$

The solutions are 0, -3, and 2.

10. $y=x^2-6x+8$
$$0=x^2-6x+8$$
$$0=(x-4)(x-2)$$
$$x-4=0 \quad \text{or} \quad x-2=0$$
$$x=4 \qquad\qquad x=2$$

The *x*-intercepts of the graph of $y=x^2-6x+8$ are $(2, 0)$ and $(4, 0)$.

Calculator Explorations

1. $-0.9, 2.2$

2. $-2.5, 3.5$

3. no real solution

4. no real solution

5. $-1.8, 2.8$

6. $-0.9, 0.3$

Vocabulary and Readiness Check

1. An equation that can be written in the form $ax^2+bx+c=0$, (with $a \neq 0$), is called a <u>quadratic</u> equation.

2. If the product of two numbers is 0, then at least one of the numbers must be <u>0</u>.

3. The solutions to $(x-3)(x+5)=0$ are <u>3, −5</u>.

4. If $a \cdot b = 0$, then <u>$a=0$ or $b=0$</u>.

5. $3, 7$

6. $5, 2$

7. $-8, -6$

8. $-2, -3$

9. $-1, 3$

10. $1, -2$

Exercise Set 6.6

2. $(x+4)(x-10)=0$
$$x+4=0 \quad \text{or} \quad x-10=0$$
$$x=-4 \qquad\qquad x=10$$
The solutions are -4 and 10.

4. $(x+11)(x+1)=0$
$$x+11=0 \quad \text{or} \quad x+1=0$$
$$x=-11 \qquad\qquad x=-1$$
The solutions are -11 and -1.

6. $x(x-7)=0$
$$x=0 \quad \text{or} \quad x-7=0$$
$$x=7$$
The solutions are 0 and 7.

8. $2x(x + 12) = 0$
$2x = 0$ or $x + 12 = 0$
$x = 0$ $x = -12$
The solutions are 0 and -12.

10. $(3x - 2)(5x + 1) = 0$
$3x - 2 = 0$ or $5x + 1 = 0$
$3x = 2$ $5x = -1$
$x = \dfrac{2}{3}$ $x = -\dfrac{1}{5}$
The solutions are $\dfrac{2}{3}$ and $-\dfrac{1}{5}$.

12. $(9x + 1)(4x - 3) = 0$
$9x + 1 = 0$ or $4x - 3 = 0$
$9x = -1$ $4x = 3$
$x = -\dfrac{1}{9}$ $x = \dfrac{3}{4}$
The solutions are $-\dfrac{1}{9}$ and $\dfrac{3}{4}$.

14. $\left(x + \dfrac{2}{9}\right)\left(x - \dfrac{1}{4}\right) = 0$

$x + \dfrac{2}{9} = 0$ or $x - \dfrac{1}{4} = 0$

$x = -\dfrac{2}{9}$ $x = \dfrac{1}{4}$

The solutions are $-\dfrac{2}{9}$ and $\dfrac{1}{4}$.

16. $(x + 1.7)(x + 2.3) = 0$
$x + 1.7 = 0$ or $x + 2.3 = 0$
$x = -1.7$ $x = -2.3$
The solutions are -1.7 and -2.3.

18. Answers may vary. Possible answer:
If $x = 0$ and $x = -2$ are the solutions, then
$x = 0$ or $x = -2$
            $x + 2 = 0$
$x(x + 2) = 0$

20. $x^2 + 2x - 63 = 0$
$(x + 9)(x - 7) = 0$
$x + 9 = 0$ or $x - 7 = 0$
$x = -9$ $x = 7$
The solutions are -9 and 7.

22. $x^2 - 5x + 6 = 0$
$(x - 3)(x - 2) = 0$
$x - 3 = 0$ or $x - 2 = 0$
$x = 3$ $x = 2$
The solutions are 3 and 2.

24. $x^2 - 3x = 0$
$x(x - 3) = 0$
$x = 0$ or $x - 3 = 0$
                $x = 3$
The solutions are 0 and 3.

26. $x^2 - 5x = 24$
$x^2 - 5x - 24 = 0$
$(x - 8)(x + 3) = 0$
$x - 8 = 0$ or $x + 3 = 0$
$x = 8$ $x = -3$
The solutions are 8 and -3.

28. $x^2 = 9$
$x^2 - 9 = 0$
$(x + 3)(x - 3) = 0$
$x + 3 = 0$ or $x - 3 = 0$
$x = -3$ $x = 3$
The solutions are -3 and 3.

30. $(x + 3)(x + 8) = x$
$x^2 + 11x + 24 = x$
$x^2 + 10x + 24 = 0$
$(x + 6)(x + 4) = 0$
$x + 6 = 0$ or $x + 4 = 0$
$x = -6$ $x = -4$
The solutions are -6 and -4.

32. $x(4x - 11) = 3$
$4x^2 - 11x = 3$
$4x^2 - 11x - 3 = 0$
$(4x + 1)(x - 3) = 0$
$4x + 1 = 0$ or $x - 3 = 0$
$4x = -1$ $x = 3$
$x = -\dfrac{1}{4}$
The solutions are $-\dfrac{1}{4}$ and 3.

34.
$$-2y^2 + 72 = 0$$
$$-2(y^2 - 36) = 0$$
$$-2(y + 6)(y - 6) = 0$$
$$y + 6 = 0 \quad \text{or} \quad y - 6 = 0$$
$$y = -6 \qquad\qquad y = 6$$
The solutions are -6 and 6.

36.
$$6x^2 + 57x = 30$$
$$6x^2 + 57x - 30 = 0$$
$$3(2x^2 + 19x - 10) = 0$$
$$3(2x - 1)(x + 10) = 0$$
$$2x - 1 = 0 \quad \text{or} \quad x + 10 = 0$$
$$2x = 1 \qquad\qquad x = -10$$
$$x = \frac{1}{2}$$
The solutions are $\frac{1}{2}$ and -10.

38. $x^3 - 14x^2 + 49x = 0$
$$x(x^2 - 14x + 49) = 0$$
$$x(x - 7)(x - 7) = 0$$
$$x = 0 \quad \text{or} \quad x - 7 = 0$$
$$x = 7$$
The solutions are 0 and 7.

40. $(2x + 5)(4x^2 + 20x + 25) = 0$
$$(2x + 5)(2x + 5)^2 = 0$$
$$(2x + 5)^3 = 0$$
$$2x + 5 = 0$$
$$2x = -5$$
$$x = -\frac{5}{2}$$
The solution is $-\frac{5}{2}$.

42.
$$4y^3 - 36y = 0$$
$$4y(y^2 - 9) = 0$$
$$4y(y - 3)(y + 3) = 0$$
$$4y = 0 \quad \text{or} \quad y - 3 = 0 \quad \text{or} \quad y + 3 = 0$$
$$y = 0 \qquad\qquad y = 3 \qquad\qquad y = -3$$
The solutions are 0, 3, and -3.

44. $15x^3 + 24x^2 - 63x = 0$
$$3x(5x^2 + 8x - 21) = 0$$
$$3x(5x - 7)(x + 3) = 0$$
$$3x = 0 \quad \text{or} \quad 5x - 7 = 0 \quad \text{or} \quad x + 3 = 0$$
$$x = 0 \qquad\qquad 5x = 7 \qquad\qquad x = -3$$
$$x = \frac{7}{5}$$
The solutions are 0, $\frac{7}{5}$, and -3.

46. $(x - 6)(x + 7) = 0$
$$x - 6 = 0 \quad \text{or} \quad x + 7 = 0$$
$$x = 6 \qquad\qquad x = -7$$
The solutions are 6 and -7.

48. $x^2 + 15x = 0$
$$x(x + 15) = 0$$
$$x = 0 \quad \text{or} \quad x + 15 = 0$$
$$x = -15$$
The solutions are 0 and -15.

50. $5(3 - 4x) = 9$
$$15 - 20x = 9$$
$$-20x = -6$$
$$x = \frac{-6}{-20}$$
$$x = \frac{3}{10}$$
The solution is $\frac{3}{10}$.

52.
$$4y^2 - 81 = 0$$
$$(2y + 9)(2y - 9) = 0$$
$$2y + 9 = 0 \quad \text{or} \quad 2y - 9 = 0$$
$$2y = -9 \qquad\qquad 2y = 9$$
$$y = -\frac{9}{2} \qquad\qquad y = \frac{9}{2}$$
The solutions are $-\frac{9}{2}$ and $\frac{9}{2}$.

54. $(2x - 9)(x^2 + 5x - 36) = 0$
$$(2x - 9)(x + 9)(x - 4) = 0$$
$$2x - 9 = 0 \quad \text{or} \quad x + 9 = 0 \quad \text{or} \quad x - 4 = 0$$
$$2x = 9 \qquad\qquad x = -9 \qquad\qquad x = 4$$
$$x = \frac{9}{2}$$
The solutions are $\frac{9}{2}$, -9, and 4.

56. $x^2 - 26 = -11x$
$x^2 + 11x - 26 = 0$
$(x+13)(x-2) = 0$
$x+13 = 0$ or $x-2 = 0$
$x = -13$ $x = 2$
The solutions are -13 and 2.

58. $12x^2 + 7x - 12 = 0$
$(4x-3)(3x+4) = 0$
$4x-3 = 0$ or $3x+4 = 0$
$4x = 3$ $3x = -4$
$x = \dfrac{3}{4}$ $x = -\dfrac{4}{3}$
The solutions are $\dfrac{3}{4}$ and $-\dfrac{4}{3}$.

60. $9x^2 + 7x = 2$
$9x^2 + 7x - 2 = 0$
$(9x-2)(x+1) = 0$
$9x-2 = 0$ or $x+1 = 0$
$9x = 2$ $x = -1$
$x = \dfrac{2}{9}$
The solutions are $\dfrac{2}{9}$ and -1.

62. $3x^2 - 6x - 9 = 0$
$3(x^2 - 2x - 3) = 0$
$3(x-3)(x+1) = 0$
$x-3 = 0$ or $x+1 = 0$
$x = 3$ $x = -1$
The solutions are 3 and -1.

64. $(y-5)(y-2) = 28$
$y^2 - 7y + 10 = 28$
$y^2 - 7y - 18 = 0$
$(y-9)(y+2) = 0$
$y-9 = 0$ or $y+2 = 0$
$y = 9$ $y = -2$
The solutions are 9 and -2.

66. $3x^3 + x^2 - 21x = 0$
$x(36x^2 + x - 21) = 0$
$x(9x+7)(4x-3) = 0$
$x = 0$ or $9x+7 = 0$ or $4x-3 = 0$
$9x = -7$ $4x = 3$
$x = -\dfrac{7}{9}$ $x = \dfrac{3}{4}$
The solutions are 0, $-\dfrac{7}{9}$, and $\dfrac{3}{4}$.

68. $x^2 + 22x + 121 = 0$
$(x+11)^2 = 0$
$x+11 = 0$
$x = -11$
The solution is -11.

70. $9y = 6y^2$
$0 = 6y^2 - 9y$
$0 = 3y(2y-3)$
$3y = 0$ or $2y-3 = 0$
$y = 0$ $2y = 3$
$y = \dfrac{3}{2}$
The solutions are 0 and $\dfrac{3}{2}$.

72. $3x^3 - 27x = 0$
$3x(x^2 - 9) = 0$
$3x(x+3)(x-3) = 0$
$3x = 0$ or $x+3 = 0$ or $x-3 = 0$
$x = 0$ $x = -3$ $x = 3$
The solutions are 0, -3, and 3.

74. $2x^2 + 12x - 1 = 4 + 3x$
$2x^2 + 9x - 5 = 0$
$(2x-1)(x+5) = 0$
$2x-1 = 0$ or $x+5 = 0$
$2x = 1$ $x = -5$
$x = \dfrac{1}{2}$
The solutions are $\dfrac{1}{2}$ and -5.

76. $4x^2 - 20x = -5x^2 - 6x - 5$

$9x^2 - 14x + 5 = 0$

$(9x - 5)(x - 1) = 0$

$9x - 5 = 0$ or $x - 1 = 0$

     $9x = 5$ $x = 1$

       $x = \dfrac{5}{9}$

The solutions are $\dfrac{5}{9}$ and 1.

78. Let $y = 0$ and solve for x.

$y = (5x - 3)(x - 4)$

$0 = (5x - 3)(x - 4)$

$5x - 3 = 0$ or $x - 4 = 0$

     $5x = 3$ $x = 4$

       $x = \dfrac{3}{5}$

The x-intercepts are $\left(\dfrac{3}{5}, 0\right)$ and $(4, 0)$.

80. Let $y = 0$ and solve for x.

$y = x^2 + 7x + 6$

$0 = x^2 + 7x + 6$

$0 = (x + 6)(x + 1)$

$x + 6 = 0$ or $x + 1 = 0$

     $x = -6$ $x = -1$

The x-intercepts are $(-6, 0)$ and $(-1, 0)$.

82. Let $y = 0$ and solve for x.

$y = 4x^2 + 11x + 6$

$0 = 4x^2 + 11x + 6$

$0 = (4x + 3)(x + 2)$

$4x + 3 = 0$ or $x + 2 = 0$

     $4x = -3$ $x = -2$

       $x = -\dfrac{3}{4}$

The x-intercepts are $\left(-\dfrac{3}{4}, 0\right)$ and $(-2, 0)$.

84. d; x-intercepts are $(5, 0), (-2, 0)$

86. f; x-intercepts are $(0, 0), (4, 0)$

88. a; $y = 2x^2 - 2 = 2(x - 1)(x + 1)$

x-intercepts are $(-1, 0), (1, 0)$

90. $\dfrac{2}{3} + \dfrac{3}{7} = \dfrac{2 \cdot 7}{3 \cdot 7} + \dfrac{3 \cdot 3}{7 \cdot 3} = \dfrac{14}{21} + \dfrac{9}{21} = \dfrac{14 + 9}{21} = \dfrac{23}{21}$

92. $\dfrac{5}{9} - \dfrac{5}{12} = \dfrac{5 \cdot 4}{9 \cdot 4} - \dfrac{5 \cdot 3}{12 \cdot 3} = \dfrac{20}{36} - \dfrac{15}{36} = \dfrac{20 - 15}{36} = \dfrac{5}{36}$

94. $\dfrac{5}{12} - \dfrac{3}{10} = \dfrac{5 \cdot 5}{12 \cdot 5} - \dfrac{3 \cdot 6}{10 \cdot 6}$

$= \dfrac{25}{60} - \dfrac{18}{60}$

$= \dfrac{25 - 18}{60}$

$= \dfrac{7}{60}$

96. $\dfrac{3}{7} \cdot \dfrac{12}{17} = \dfrac{3 \cdot 12}{7 \cdot 17} = \dfrac{36}{119}$

98. Didn't solve the linear equations correctly.

$(x - 4)(x + 2) = 0$

$x - 4 = 0$ or $x + 2 = 0$

     $x = 4$ $x = -2$

100. Answers may vary. Possible answer: If the solutions are $x = 0$, $x = 1$, and $x = 2$, then, by the zero factor property,

$x = 0$ or $x = 1$ or $x = 2$

                  $x - 1 = 0$ $x - 2 = 0$

     $x(x - 1)(x - 2) = 0$

       $(x^2 - x)(x - 2) = 0$

$x^3 - x^2 - 2x^2 + 2x = 0$

        $x^3 - 3x^2 + 2x = 0$

102. $y = -16x^2 + 100x$

a.

time x	0	1	2	3	4	5	6	7
height y	0	84	136	156	144	100	24	−84

b. The rocket strikes the ground when the height, y, is zero feet. This occurs after approximately 6 seconds.

c. The maximum height of the rocket is approximately 156 ft.

d.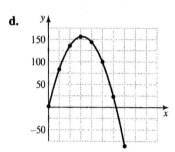

104. $(2x - 3)(x + 6) = (x - 9)(x + 2)$
$$2x^2 + 9x - 18 = x^2 - 7x - 18$$
$$x^2 + 16x = 0$$
$$x(x + 16) = 0$$
$$x = 0 \quad \text{or} \quad x + 16 = 0$$
$$x = -16$$
The solutions are 0 and −16.

106. $(x + 6)(x - 6) = (2x - 9)(x + 4)$
$$x^2 - 36 = 2x^2 - x - 36$$
$$0 = x^2 - x$$
$$0 = x(x - 1)$$
$$0 = x \quad \text{or} \quad 0 = x - 1$$
$$1 = x$$
The solutions are 0 and 1.

The Bigger Picture

1. $-7 + (-27) = -34$

2. $\dfrac{(x^3)^4}{(x^{-2})^5} = \dfrac{x^{12}}{x^{-10}} = x^{12-(-10)} = x^{22}$

3. $(x^3 - 6x^2 + 2) - (5x^3 - 6)$
$$= x^3 - 6x^2 + 2 - 5x^3 + 6$$
$$= x^3 - 5x^3 - 6x^2 + 2 + 6$$
$$= -4x^3 - 6x^2 + 8$$

4. $\dfrac{3y^3 - 3y^2 + 9}{3y^2} = \dfrac{3y^3}{3y^2} - \dfrac{3y^2}{3y^2} + \dfrac{9}{3y^2} = y - 1 + \dfrac{3}{y^2}$

5. $10x^3 - 250x = 10x(x^2 - 25)$
$$= 10x(x^2 - 5^2)$$
$$= 10x(x + 5)(x - 5)$$

6. $x^2 - 36x + 35 = (x - 1)(x - 35)$

7. $6xy + 15x - 6y - 15 = 3(2xy + 5x - 2y - 5)$
$$= 3[x(2y + 5) - 1(2y + 5)]$$
$$= 3(2y + 5)(x - 1)$$

8. $5xy^2 - 2xy - 7x = x(5y^2 - 2y - 7)$
$$= x(5y - 7)(y + 1)$$

9. $(x - 5)(2x + 1) = 0$
$x - 5 = 0$ or $2x + 1 = 0$
$x = 5$ $\qquad x = -\dfrac{1}{2}$

The solutions are 5 and $-\dfrac{1}{2}$.

10. $5x - 5 = 0$
$5x = 5$
$x = 1$
The solution is 1.

11. $x(x - 12) = 28$
$x^2 - 12x = 28$
$x^2 - 12x - 28 = 0$
$(x + 2)(x - 14) = 0$
$x + 2 = 0$ or $x - 14 = 0$
$x = -2$ $\qquad x = 14$
The solutions are -2 and 14.

12. $7(x - 3) + 2(5x + 1) = 14$
$7x - 21 + 10x + 2 = 14$
$17x - 19 = 14$
$17x = 33$
$x = \dfrac{33}{17}$

The solution is $\dfrac{33}{17}$.

Exercise Set 6.7

2. Let x = the width, then $2x$ = the length.

4. Let x = the first even integer, then
$x + 2$ = the next consecutive even integer.

6. Let x = the height, then $5x - 3$ = the base.

8. Let $x + 3$ = length and $x - 2$ = width.
$A = lw$
$84 = (x + 3)(x - 2)$
$84 = x^2 + x - 6$
$0 = x^2 + x - 90$
$x^2 + x - 90 = 0$
$(x + 10)(x - 9) = 0$
$x + 10 = 0$ or $x - 9 = 0$
$x = -10$ $\qquad x = 9$
Since the dimensions cannot be negative, we discard $x = -10$. The length is $9 + 3 = 12$ inches and the width is $9 - 2 = 7$ inches.

10. The perimeter is the sum of the lengths of the sides.
$85 = 2x + (2x + 5) + (x^2 + 3)$
$85 = 2x + 2x + 5 + x^2 + 3$
$85 = x^2 + 4x + 8$
$0 = x^2 + 4x - 77$
$x^2 + 4x - 77 = 0$
$(x + 11)(x - 7) = 0$
$x + 11 = 0$ or $x - 7 = 0$
$x = -11$ $\qquad x = 7$
Since the dimensions cannot be negative, we discard $x = -11$. The lengths of the sides are $2(7) = 14$ feet, $2(7) + 5 = 19$ feet, and
$7^2 + 3 = 52$ feet.

12. Let x = the radius.
$A = \pi r^2$
$25\pi = \pi(x)^2$
$25\pi = \pi x^2$
$0 = \pi x^2 - 25\pi$
$0 = \pi(x^2 - 25)$
$0 = \pi(x + 5)(x - 5)$
$x + 5 = 0$ or $x - 5 = 0$
$x = -5$ $\qquad x = 5$
Since the radius cannot be negative, we discard $x = -5$. The radius is 5 kilometers.

14. Find t when $h = 0$.
$$h = -16t^2 + 400$$
$$0 = -16t^2 + 400$$
$$0 = -16(t^2 - 25)$$
$$0 = -16(t+5)(t-5)$$
$$t+5 = 0 \quad \text{or} \quad t-5 = 0$$
$$t = -5 \qquad\qquad t = 5$$
Since the time t cannot be negative, the compass hits the ground after 5 seconds.

16. Let $x =$ the width then $x + 9 =$ the length.
$$A = lw$$
$$112 = (x+9)(x)$$
$$112 = x^2 + 9x$$
$$0 = x^2 + 9x - 112$$
$$0 = (x+16)(x-7)$$
$$x+16 = 0 \quad \text{or} \quad x-7 = 0$$
$$x = -16 \qquad\qquad x = 7$$
Since the dimensions cannot be negative, discard $x = -16$. The width is 7 inches and the length is $7 + 9 = 16$ inches.

18. Let $n = 15$.
$$D = \frac{1}{2}n(n-3)$$
$$D = \frac{1}{2} \cdot 15(15-3) = \frac{15}{2}(12) = 90$$
A polygon with 15 sides has 90 diagonals.

20. Let $D = 14$ and solve for n.
$$D = \frac{1}{2}n(n-3)$$
$$14 = \frac{1}{2}n(n-3)$$
$$28 = n^2 - 3n$$
$$0 = n^2 - 3n - 28$$
$$0 = (n-7)(n+4)$$
$$n-7 = 0 \quad \text{or} \quad n+4 = 0$$
$$n = 7 \qquad\qquad n = -4$$
The polygon has 7 sides.

22. Let $x =$ the unknown number.
$$x + x^2 = 182$$
$$x^2 + x - 182 = 0$$
$$(x+14)(x-13) = 0$$
$$x+14 = 0 \quad \text{or} \quad x-13 = 0$$
$$x = -14 \qquad\qquad x = 13$$
The two numbers are -14 and 13.

24. Let $x =$ the first page number, then $x + 1 =$ next page number.
$$x(x+1) = 420$$
$$x^2 + x = 420$$
$$x^2 + x - 420 = 0$$
$$(x-20)(x+21) = 0$$
$$x-20 = 0 \quad \text{or} \quad x+21 = 0$$
$$x = 20 \qquad\qquad x = -21$$
Since the page number is not negative, the page numbers are 20 and 21.

26.
$$a^2 + b^2 = c^2$$
$$30^2 + x^2 = (x+10)^2$$
$$900 + x^2 = x^2 + 20x + 100$$
$$800 = 20x$$
$$40 = x$$
The length of the guy wire is $40 + 10 = 50$ feet.

28. Let $x =$ the length of a side of the original square. Then $x + 5 =$ the length of a side of the larger square.
$$100 = (x+5)^2$$
$$100 = x^2 + 10x + 25$$
$$0 = x^2 + 10x - 75$$
$$0 = (x+15)(x-5)$$
$$x+15 = 0 \quad \text{or} \quad x-5 = 0$$
$$x = -15 \qquad\qquad x = 5$$
Since the length cannot be negative, the sides of the original square are 5 meters each.

30. Let $x =$ the length of the shorter leg. Then $x + 9 =$ the length of the longer leg. By the Pythagorean theorem,
$$x^2 + (x+9)^2 = 45^2$$
$$x^2 + x^2 + 18x + 81 = 2025$$
$$2x^2 + 18x + 81 = 2025$$
$$2x^2 + 18x - 1944 = 0$$
$$2(x^2 + 9x - 972) = 0$$
$$2(x+36)(x-27) = 0$$
$$x+36 = 0 \quad \text{or} \quad x-27 = 0$$
$$x = -36 \qquad\qquad x = 27$$
Since the length cannot be negative, the legs of the triangle are 27 cm and $27 + 9 = 36$ cm.

32. Let x = the base of the triangle, then
$x - 2$ = the height.

$$A = \frac{1}{2}bh$$
$$60 = \frac{1}{2}(x)(x - 2)$$
$$120 = x^2 - 2x$$
$$0 = x^2 - 2x - 120$$
$$0 = (x - 12)(x + 10)$$
$$x - 12 = 0 \quad \text{or} \quad x + 10 = 0$$
$$x = 12 \qquad\qquad x = -10$$

Since the length of the base cannot be negative, the base is 12 millimeters.

34. Let x = the length of the shorter leg, then
$x + 10$ = the length of the longer leg and
$2x - 10$ = the length of the hypotenuse. By the Pythagorean theorem,

$$x^2 + (x + 10)^2 = (2x - 10)^2$$
$$x^2 + x^2 + 20x + 100 = 4x^2 - 40x + 100$$
$$0 = 2x^2 - 60x$$
$$0 = 2x(x - 30)$$
$$2x = 0 \quad \text{or} \quad x - 30 = 0$$
$$x = 0 \qquad\qquad x = 30$$

Since the length cannot be zero miles, the leg is 30 miles.

36. Find t when $h = 0$.

$$h = -16t^2 + 961$$
$$0 = -16t^2 + 961$$
$$0 = -(16t^2 - 961)$$
$$0 = -(4t - 31)(4t + 31)$$
$$4t - 31 = 0 \quad \text{or} \quad 4t + 31 = 0$$
$$t = \frac{31}{4} \qquad\qquad t = -\frac{31}{4}$$

Since time cannot be negative, the object reaches the ground in $\frac{31}{4} = 7.75$ seconds.

38. Let $P = 2000$ and $A = 2420$.

$$A = P(1 + r)^2$$
$$2420 = 2000(1 + r)^2$$
$$2420 = 2000 + 4000r + 2000r^2$$
$$0 = 2000r^2 + 4000r - 420$$
$$0 = 20(100r^2 + 200r - 21)$$
$$0 = 20(10r - 1)(10r + 21)$$

$$10r - 1 = 0 \quad \text{or} \quad 10r + 21 = 0$$
$$10r = 1 \qquad\qquad 10r = -21$$
$$r = \frac{1}{10} \qquad\qquad r = -\frac{21}{10}$$
$$r = 0.1 \qquad\qquad r = -2.1$$

Since the interest rate cannot be negative $r = 0.1$ and the rate is 10%.

40. Let x = the length and $\frac{1}{2}x - 2$ = the width.

$$A = lw$$
$$160 = x\left(\frac{1}{2}x - 2\right)$$
$$160 = \frac{1}{2}x^2 - 2x$$
$$320 = x^2 - 4x$$
$$0 = x^2 - 4x - 320$$
$$0 = (x + 16)(x - 20)$$
$$x + 16 = 0 \quad \text{or} \quad x - 20 = 0$$
$$x = -16 \qquad\qquad x = 20$$

Since the length cannot be negative, the length is 20 inches. The width is $\frac{1}{2}(20) - 2 = 8$ inches.

42. Let $C = 120$.

$$C = \frac{n(n - 1)}{2}$$
$$120 = \frac{n(n - 1)}{2}$$
$$240 = n^2 - n$$
$$0 = n^2 - n - 240$$
$$0 = (n + 15)(n - 16)$$
$$n + 15 = 0 \quad \text{or} \quad n - 16 = 0$$
$$n = -15 \qquad\qquad n = 16$$

Since the number of telephones cannot be negative, the solution is 16 telephones.

44. In 2005, the size of the average farm was about 450 acres.

46. In 2005, there were approximately 2.1 million farms.

48. Answers may vary

50. $\dfrac{20}{35} = \dfrac{2 \cdot 2 \cdot 5}{5 \cdot 7} = \dfrac{4}{7}$

52. $\dfrac{27}{18} = \dfrac{3 \cdot 3 \cdot 3}{2 \cdot 3 \cdot 3} = \dfrac{3}{2}$

54. $\dfrac{14}{42} = \dfrac{2 \cdot 7}{2 \cdot 3 \cdot 7} = \dfrac{1}{3}$

56. Let x = the rate (in mph) of the slower boat, then $x + 7$ = the rate (in mph) of the faster boat. After one hour, the slower boat has traveled x miles and the faster boat has traveled $x + 7$ miles. By the Pythagorean theorem,

$$x^2 + (x+7)^2 = 17^2$$
$$x^2 + x^2 + 14x + 49 = 289$$
$$2x^2 + 14x + 49 = 289$$
$$2x^2 + 14x - 240 = 0$$
$$2(x^2 + 7x - 120) = 0$$
$$2(x + 15)(x - 8) = 0$$
$$x + 15 = 0 \quad \text{or} \quad x - 8 = 0$$
$$x = -15 \qquad \qquad x = 8$$

Since the rate cannot be negative, the slower boat travels at 8 mph. The faster boat travels at 8 + 7 = 15 mph.

58. Let x = the first number, then $20 - x$ = the other number.

$$x^2 + (20 - x)^2 = 218$$
$$x^2 + 400 - 40x + x^2 = 218$$
$$2x^2 - 40x + 400 = 218$$
$$2x^2 - 40x + 182 = 0$$
$$2(x^2 - 20x + 91) = 0$$
$$2(x - 13)(x - 7) = 0$$
$$x - 13 = 0 \quad \text{or} \quad x - 7 = 0$$
$$x = 13 \qquad \qquad x = 7$$

The numbers are 13 and 7.

60. Let x = the length of the boom. Then $2x + 28$ = the height of the mainsail. The area of the mainsail is $0.60(3000) = 1800$ square feet.

$$A = \frac{1}{2}bh$$
$$1800 = \frac{1}{2}(x)(2x + 28)$$
$$1800 = x^2 + 14x$$
$$0 = x^2 + 14x - 1800$$
$$0 = (x - 36)(x + 50)$$
$$x - 36 = 0 \quad \text{or} \quad x + 50 = 0$$
$$x = 36 \qquad \qquad x = -50$$

Since the length cannot be negative, the length of the boom is 36 feet and the height of the mainsail is $2(36) + 28 = 100$ feet.

62. Let x = the width of the walk, then
$24 - 2x$ = the length of the garden, and
$16 - 2x$ = the width of the garden.

$$A = lw$$
$$180 = (24 - 2x)(16 - 2x)$$
$$180 = 384 - 80x + 4x^2$$
$$0 = 204 - 80x + 4x^2$$
$$0 = 4(51 - 20x + x^2)$$
$$0 = 4(17 - x)(3 - x)$$
$$17 - x = 0 \quad \text{or} \quad 3 - x = 0$$
$$17 = x \qquad \qquad x = 3$$

Since the walk cannot be wider than 8 yards, the width of the walk is 3 yards.

Chapter 6 Review

1. $6x^2 - 15x = 3x(2x - 5)$

2. $2x^3y - 6x^2y^2 - 8xy^3 = 2xy(x^2 - 3xy - 4y^2)$
$\qquad\qquad\qquad\qquad\qquad = 2xy(x - 4y)(x + y)$

3. $20x^2 + 12x = 4x(5x + 3)$

4. $6x^2y^2 - 3xy^3 = 3xy^2(2x - y)$

5. $-8x^3y + 6x^2y^2 = -2x^2y(4x - 3y)$

6. $3x(2x + 3) - 5(2x + 3) = (2x + 3)(3x - 5)$

7. $5x(x + 1) - (x + 1) = (x + 1)(5x - 1)$

8. $3x^2 - 3x + 2x - 2 = 3x(x - 1) + 2(x - 1)$
$\qquad\qquad\qquad\qquad = (x - 1)(3x + 2)$

9. $6x^2 + 10x - 3x - 5 = 2x(3x + 5) - 1(3x + 5)$
$\qquad\qquad\qquad\qquad\quad = (3x + 5)(2x - 1)$

10. $3a^2 + 9ab + 3b^2 + ab = 3a(a + 3b) + b(3b + a)$
$\qquad\qquad\qquad\qquad\qquad = (a + 3b)(3a + b)$

11. $x^2 + 6x + 8 = (x + 4)(x + 2)$

12. $x^2 - 11x + 24 = (x - 8)(x - 3)$

13. $x^2 + x + 2$ is a prime polynomial.

14. $x^2 - 5x - 6 = (x - 6)(x + 1)$

15. $x^2 + 2x - 8 = (x+4)(x-2)$

16. $x^2 + 4xy - 12y^2 = (x+6y)(x-2y)$

17. $x^2 + 8xy + 15y^2 = (x+5y)(x+3y)$

18. $3x^2y + 6xy^2 + 3y^3 = 3y(x^2 + 2xy + y^2)$
$$= 3y(x+y)(x+y)$$
$$= 3y(x+y)^2$$

19. $72 - 18x - 2x^2 = 2(36 - 9x - x^2)$
$$= 2(3-x)(12+x)$$

20. $32 + 12x - 4x^2 = 4(8 + 3x - x^2)$

21. $2x^2 + 11x - 6 = (2x-1)(x+6)$

22. $4x^2 - 7x + 4$ is a prime polynomial.

23. $4x^2 + 4x - 3 = 4x^2 + 6x - 2x - 3$
$$= 2x(2x+3) - 1(2x+3)$$
$$= (2x+3)(2x-1)$$

24. $6x^2 + 5xy - 4y^2 = 6x^2 + 8xy - 3xy - 4y^2$
$$= 2x(3x+4y) - y(3x+4y)$$
$$= (3x+4y)(2x-y)$$

25. $6x^2 - 25xy + 4y^2 = (6x-y)(x-4y)$

26. $18x^2 - 60x + 50 = 2(9x^2 - 30x + 25)$
$$= 2[(3x)^2 - 2 \cdot 3x \cdot 5 + 5^2]$$
$$= 2(3x-5)^2$$

27. $2x^2 - 23xy - 39y^2 = 2x^2 - 26xy + 3xy - 39y^2$
$$= 2x(x-13y) + 3y(x-13y)$$
$$= (x-13y)(2x+3y)$$

28. $4x^2 - 28xy + 49y^2 = [(2x)^2 - 2 \cdot 2x \cdot 7y + (7y)^2]$
$$= (2x-7y)^2$$

29. $18x^2 - 9xy - 20y^2 = 18x^2 - 24xy + 15xy - 20y^2$
$$= 6x(3x-4y) + 5y(3x-4y)$$
$$= (3x-4y)(6x+5y)$$

30. $36x^3y + 24x^2y^2 - 45xy^3$
$$= 3xy(12x^2 + 8xy - 15y^2)$$
$$= 3xy(12x^2 + 18xy - 10xy - 15y^2)$$
$$= 3xy[6x(2x+3y) - 5y(2x+3y)]$$
$$= 3xy(2x+3y)(6x-5y)$$

31. $4x^2 - 9 = (2x)^2 - 3^2 = (2x+3)(2x-3)$

32. $9t^2 - 25s^2 = (3t)^2 - (5s)^2 = (3t+5s)(3t-5s)$

33. $16x^2 + y^2$ is a prime polynomial.

34. $x^3 - 8y^3 = x^3 - (2y)^3$
$$= (x-2y)[x^2 + x \cdot 2y + (2y)^2]$$
$$= (x-2y)(x^2 + 2xy + 4y^2)$$

35. $8x^3 + 27 = (2x)^3 + 3^3$
$$= (2x+3)[(2x)^2 - 2x \cdot 3 + 3^2]$$
$$= (2x+3)(4x^2 - 6x + 9)$$

36. $2x^3 + 8x = 2x(x^2 + 4)$

37. $54 - 2x^3y^3 = 2(27 - x^3y^3)$
$$= 2[3^3 - (xy)^3]$$
$$= 2(3-xy)[3^2 + 3 \cdot xy + (xy)^2]$$
$$= 2(3-xy)(9 + 3xy + x^2y^2)$$

38. $9x^2 - 4y^2 = (3x)^2 - (2y)^2 = (3x-2y)(3x+2y)$

39. $16x^4 - 1 = (4x^2)^2 - 1^2$
$$= (4x^2 + 1)(4x^2 - 1)$$
$$= (4x^2 + 1)[(2x)^2 - 1^2]$$
$$= (4x^2 + 1)(2x+1)(2x-1)$$

40. $x^4 + 16$ is a prime polynomial.

41. $(x+6)(x-2) = 0$
$$x+6 = 0 \quad \text{or} \quad x-2 = 0$$
$$x = -6 \qquad\qquad x = 2$$
The solutions are –6 and 2.

42. $3x(x + 1)(7x - 2) = 0$

$3x = 0$ or $x + 1 = 0$ or $7x - 2 = 0$

$x = 0$ $x = -1$ $7x = 2$

$x = \dfrac{2}{7}$

The solutions are 0, –1, and $\dfrac{2}{7}$.

43. $4(5x + 1)(x + 3) = 0$

$5x + 1 = 0$ or $x + 3 = 0$

$5x = -1$ $x = -3$

$x = -\dfrac{1}{5}$

The solutions are $-\dfrac{1}{5}$ and –3.

44. $x^2 + 8x + 7 = 0$

$(x + 7)(x + 1) = 0$

$x + 7 = 0$ or $x + 1 = 0$

$x = -7$ $x = -1$

The solutions are –7 and –1.

45. $x^2 - 2x - 24 = 0$

$(x - 6)(x + 4) = 0$

$x - 6 = 0$ or $x + 4 = 0$

$x = 6$ $x = -4$

The solutions are 6 and –4.

46. $x^2 + 10x = -25$

$x^2 + 10x + 25 = 0$

$(x + 5)(x + 5) = 0$

$x + 5 = 0$ or $x + 5 = 0$

$x = -5$ $x = -5$

The solution is –5.

47. $x(x - 10) = -16$

$x^2 - 10x = -16$

$x^2 - 10x + 16 = 0$

$(x - 8)(x - 2) = 0$

$x - 8 = 0$ or $x - 2 = 0$

$x = 8$ $x = 2$

The solutions are 8 and 2.

48. $(3x - 1)(9x^2 + 3x + 1) = 0$

$3x - 1 = 0$ or $9x^2 + 3x + 1 = 0$

$9x^2 + 3x + 1$ is a prime polynomial.

$3x - 1 = 0$

$3x = 1$

$x = \dfrac{1}{3}$

The solution is $\dfrac{1}{3}$.

49. $56x^2 - 5x - 6 = 0$

$56x^2 + 16x - 21x - 6 = 0$

$8x(7x + 2) - 3(7x + 2) = 0$

$(7x + 2)(8x - 3) = 0$

$7x + 2 = 0$ or $8x - 3 = 0$

$7x = -2$ $8x = 3$

$x = -\dfrac{2}{7}$ $x = \dfrac{3}{8}$

The solutions are $-\dfrac{2}{7}$ and $\dfrac{3}{8}$.

50. $20x^2 - 7x - 6 = 0$

$(4x - 3)(5x + 2) = 0$

$4x - 3 = 0$ or $5x + 2 = 0$

$4x = 3$ $5x = -2$

$x = \dfrac{3}{4}$ $x = -\dfrac{2}{5}$

The solutions are $\dfrac{3}{4}$ and $-\dfrac{2}{5}$.

51. $5(3x + 2) = 4$

$15x + 10 = 4$

$15x = -6$

$x = -\dfrac{6}{15} = -\dfrac{2}{5}$

The solution is $-\dfrac{2}{5}$.

52. $6x^2 - 3x + 8 = 0$

The equation has no real solution.

53. $12 - 5t = -3$

$-5t = -15$

$t = 3$

The solution is 3.

54. $5x^3 + 20x^2 + 20x = 0$
$5x(x^2 + 4x + 4) = 0$
$5x(x + 2)(x + 2) = 0$
$x + 2 = 0$ or $5x = 0$
$x = -2$ $x = 0$
The solutions are -2 and 0.

55. $4t^3 - 5t^2 - 21t = 0$
$t(4t^2 - 5t - 21) = 0$
$t(4t + 7)(t - 3) = 0$
$t = 0$ or $4t + 7 = 0$ or $t - 3 = 0$
$\phantom{t = 0 \text{ or } } 4t = -7 \phantom{ \text{ or } } t = 3$
$$t = -\frac{7}{4}$$
The solutions are 0, $-\dfrac{7}{4}$, and 3.

56. Answers may vary. Possible answer:
$(x - 4)(x - 5) = 0$
$x^2 - 9x + 20 = 0$

57. a. $7 \neq 2 \cdot 5$

    b. $10 = 2 \cdot 5$
$P = 2l + 2w$
$ = 2(10) + 2(5)$
$ = 20 + 10$
$ = 30 \neq 24$

    c. $8 = 2 \cdot 4$
$P = 2l + 2w = 2(8) + 2(4) = 16 + 8 = 24$

    d. $10 \neq 2 \cdot 2$

Choice **c** gives the correct dimensions.

58. a. $3 \cdot 8 + 1 = 25 \neq 10$

    b. $3 \cdot 4 + 1 = 13$
$A = lw = 13(4) = 52 \neq 80$

    c. $3 \cdot 4 + 1 = 13 \neq 20$

    d. $3 \cdot 5 + 1 = 16$
$A = lw = 5(16) = 80$

Choice **d** gives the correct dimensions.

59. $ x^2 = 81$
$ x^2 - 81 = 0$
$(x - 9)(x + 9) = 0$
$x - 9 = 0$ or $x + 9 = 0$
$x = 9 x = -9$
Since length is not negative, the length of the side is 9 units.

60. $(2x + 3) + (3x + 1) + (x^2 - 3x) + (x + 3) = 47$
$ x^2 + 3x + 7 = 47$
$ x^2 + 3x - 40 = 0$
$ (x - 5)(x + 8) = 0$
$x - 5 = 0$ or $x + 8 = 0$
$x = 5 x = -8$
Length is not negative, so $x = 5$. The lengths are:
$x + 3 = 5 + 3 = 8$ units
$2x + 3 = 2(5) + 3 = 13$ units
$3x + 1 = 3(5) + 1 = 16$ units
$x^2 - 3x = 5^2 - 3(5) = 10$ units

61. Let $x =$ the width of the flag. Then
$2x - 15 =$ the length of the flag.
$ A = lw$
$ 500 = (2x - 15)(x)$
$ 500 = 2x^2 - 15x$
$ 0 = 2x^2 - 15x - 500$
$ 0 = (2x + 25)(x - 20)$
$2x + 25 = 0$
$2x = -25$ or $x - 20 = 0$
$$x = -\frac{25}{2} x = 20$$
Since the dimensions cannot be negative, the width is 20 inches and the length is
$2(20) - 15 = 25$ inches.

62. Let $x =$ the height of the sail, then
$4x =$ the base of the sail.
$$A = \frac{1}{2}bh$$
$$162 = \frac{1}{2}(4x)(x)$$
$$162 = 2x^2$$
$$0 = 2x^2 - 162$$
$$0 = 2(x^2 - 81)$$
$$0 = 2(x + 9)(x - 9)$$
$x + 9 = 0$ or $x - 9 = 0$
$x = -9 x = 9$
Since the dimensions cannot be negative, the height is 9 yards and the base is $4 \cdot 9 = 36$ yards.

63. Let x = the first integer. Then
$x + 1$ = the next consecutive integer.
$$x(x+1) = 380$$
$$x^2 + x = 380$$
$$x^2 + x - 380 = 0$$
$$(x+20)(x-19) = 0$$
$$x + 20 = 0 \quad \text{or} \quad x - 19 = 0$$
$$x = -20 \qquad\qquad x = 19$$
The integers are 19 and 20.

64. a. Let $h = 2800$ and solve for t.
$$h = -16t^2 + 440t$$
$$2800 = -16t^2 + 440t$$
$$0 = -16t^2 + 440t - 2800$$
$$0 = -8(2t^2 - 55t + 350)$$
$$0 = -8(2t - 35)(t - 10)$$
$$2t - 35 = 0 \quad \text{or} \quad t - 10 = 0$$
$$2t = 35 \qquad\qquad t = 10$$
$$t = \frac{35}{2}$$
$$t = 17.5$$
The solutions are 17.5 sec and 10 sec. There are two answers because the rocket reaches a height of 2800 feet on its way up and on its way back down.

b. Let $h = 0$ and solve for t.
$$h = -16t^2 + 440t$$
$$0 = -16t^2 + 440t$$
$$0 = -8t(2t - 55)$$
$$-8t = 0 \quad \text{or} \quad 2t - 55 = 0$$
$$t = 0 \qquad\qquad 2t = 55$$
$$t = \frac{55}{2}$$
$$t = 27.5$$
$t = 0$ is when the rocket is launched, so it reaches the ground again after 27.5 seconds.

65. Find t when $h = 0$.
$$h = -16t^2 + 625$$
$$0 = -16t^2 + 625$$
$$0 = -1(16t^2 - 625)$$
$$0 = -1[(4t)^2 - (25)^2]$$
$$0 = -1(4t + 25)(4t - 25)$$

$$4t + 25 = 0 \qquad \text{or} \quad 4t - 25 = 0$$
$$t = -\frac{25}{4} \qquad\qquad t = \frac{25}{4}$$
Since time cannot be negative, the object reaches the ground after $\frac{25}{4} = 6.25$ seconds.

66. Let x = the length of the longer leg, then
$x - 8$ = the length of the shorter leg and
$x + 8$ = the length of the hypotenuse.
By the Pythagorean theorem,
$$x^2 + (x-8)^2 = (x+8)^2$$
$$x^2 + x^2 - 16x + 64 = x^2 + 16x + 64$$
$$x^2 - 32x = 0$$
$$x(x-32) = 0$$
$$x = 0 \quad \text{or} \quad x - 32 = 0$$
$$x = 32$$
Since the length cannot be 0 cm, the length of the longer leg is 32 cm.

67. $7x - 63 = 7(x - 9)$

68. $11x(4x - 3) - 6(4x - 3) = (4x - 3)(11x - 6)$

69. $m^2 - \dfrac{4}{25} = m^2 - \left(\dfrac{2}{5}\right)^2 = \left(m + \dfrac{2}{5}\right)\left(m - \dfrac{2}{5}\right)$

70. $3x^3 - 4x^2 + 6x - 8 = x^2(3x - 4) + 2(3x - 4)$
$$= (3x - 4)(x^2 + 2)$$

71. $xy + 2x - y - 2 = x(y + 2) - 1(y + 2)$
$$= (y + 2)(x - 1)$$

72. $2x^2 + 2x - 24 = 2(x^2 + x - 12) = 2(x + 4)(x - 3)$

73. $3x^3 - 30x^2 + 27x = 3x(x^2 - 10x + 9)$
$$= 3x(x - 9)(x - 1)$$

74. $4x^2 - 81 = (2x)^2 - 9^2 = (2x + 9)(2x - 9)$

75. $2x^2 - 18 = 2(x^2 - 9)$
$$= 2(x^2 - 3^2)$$
$$= 2(x + 3)(x - 3)$$

76. $16x^2 - 24x + 9 = (4x)^2 - 2 \cdot 4x \cdot 3 + 3^2$
$$= (4x - 3)^2$$

77. $5x^2 + 20x + 20 = 5(x^2 + 4x + 4)$
$$= 5(x^2 + 2 \cdot x \cdot 2 + 2^2)$$
$$= 5(x + 2)^2$$

78. $2x^2 + 5x - 12 = (2x - 3)(x + 4)$

79. $4x^2 y - 6xy^2 = 2xy(2x - 3y)$

80. $8x^2 - 15x - x^3 = -x(-8x + 15 + x^2)$
$$= -x(x^2 - 8x + 15)$$
$$= -x(x - 5)(x - 3)$$

81. $125x^3 + 27 = (5x)^3 + 3^3$
$$= (5x + 3)[(5x)^2 - 5x \cdot 3 + 3^2]$$
$$= (5x + 3)(25x^2 - 15x + 9)$$

82. $24x^2 - 3x - 18 = 3(8x^2 - x - 6)$

83. $(x + 7)^2 - y^2 = [(x + 7) + y][(x + 7) - y]$
$$= (x + 7 + y)(x + 7 - y)$$

84. $x^2(x + 3) - 4(x + 3) = (x + 3)(x^2 - 4)$
$$= (x + 3)(x^2 - 2^2)$$
$$= (x + 3)(x - 2)(x + 2)$$

85. $54a^3 b - 2b = 2b(27a^3 - 1)$
$$= 2b[(3a)^3 - 1^3]$$
$$= 2b(3a - 1)[(3a)^2 + 3a \cdot 1 + 1^2]$$
$$= 2b(3a - 1)(9a^2 + 3a + 1)$$

86. To factor $x^2 + 2x - 48$, think of two numbers whose product is $\underline{-48}$ and whose sum if $\underline{2}$.

87. The first step is to factor out the GCF, 3.

88. $(x^2 - 2) + (x^2 - 4x) + (3x^2 - 5x)$
$$= x^2 + x^2 + 3x^2 - 4x - 5x - 2$$
$$= 5x^2 - 9x - 2$$
$$= (5x + 1)(x - 2)$$

89. $2(2x^2 + 3) + 2(6x^2 - 14x)$
$$= 4x^2 + 6 + 12x^2 - 28x$$
$$= 16x^2 - 28x + 6$$
$$= 2(8x^2 - 14x + 3)$$
$$= 2(4x - 1)(2x - 3)$$

90. $2x^2 - x - 28 = 0$
$(2x + 7)(x - 4) = 0$
$2x + 7 = 0 \quad$ or $\quad x - 4 = 0$
$\qquad x = -\dfrac{7}{2} \qquad\qquad x = 4$

The solutions are $-\dfrac{7}{2}$ and 4.

91. $\qquad x^2 - 2x = 15$
$\qquad x^2 - 2x - 15 = 0$
$\qquad (x + 3)(x - 5) = 0$
$x + 3 = 0 \quad$ or $\quad x - 5 = 0$
$\quad x = -3 \qquad\qquad x = 5$
The solutions are -3 and 5.

92. $2x(x + 7)(x + 4) = 0$
$2x = 0 \quad$ or $\quad x + 7 = 0 \quad$ or $\quad x + 4 = 0$
$\quad x = 0 \qquad\qquad x = -7 \qquad\qquad x = -4$
The solutions are 0, -7, and -4.

93. $\qquad x(x - 5) = -6$
$\qquad x^2 - 5x = -6$
$\qquad x^2 - 5x + 6 = 0$
$\qquad (x - 3)(x - 2) = 0$
$x - 3 = 0 \quad$ or $\quad x - 2 = 0$
$\quad x = 3 \qquad\qquad x = 2$
The solutions are 3 and 2.

94. $\qquad x^2 = 16x$
$\quad x^2 - 16x = 0$
$\quad x(x - 16) = 0$
$x = 0 \quad$ or $\quad x - 16 = 0$
$\qquad\qquad\qquad x = 16$
The solutions are 0 and 16.

95. $(x^2 + 3) + (4x + 5) + 2x = 48$
$\qquad\qquad x^2 + 6x + 8 = 48$
$\qquad\qquad x^2 + 6x - 40 = 0$
$\qquad\qquad (x - 4)(x + 10) = 0$
$x - 4 = 0 \quad$ or $\quad x + 10 = 0$
$\quad x = 4 \qquad\qquad x = -10$
Since the length cannot be negative, $x = 4$.
The lengths are:
$x^2 + 3 = 4^2 + 3 = 19$ inches
$4x + 5 = 4 \cdot 4 + 5 = 21$ inches
$2x = 2 \cdot 4 = 8$ inches

96. Let x = length, then $x - 4$ = width.
$A = lw$
$12 = x(x-4)$
$12 = x^2 - 4x$
$0 = x^2 - 4x - 12$
$0 = (x-6)(x+2)$
$x - 6 = 0$ or $x + 2 = 0$
$x = 6$ $x = -2$
Since length cannot be negative, the length is 6 inches and the width is $6 - 4 = 2$ inches.

97. Find t when $h = 0$.
$h = -16t^2 + 729$
$0 = -16t^2 + 729$
$0 = -(16t^2 - 729)$
$0 = -[(4t)^2 - (27)^2]$
$0 = -(4t + 27)(4t - 27)$
$4t + 27 = 0$ or $4t - 27 = 0$
$t = -\dfrac{27}{4}$ $t = \dfrac{27}{4}$
Since time cannot be negative, the object reaches the ground in $\dfrac{27}{4} = 6.75$ seconds.

98. Area of large figure – Area of circle
$= [(6x)(5x) - 2x^2] - \pi x^2$
$= 30x^2 - 2x^2 - \pi x^2$
$= 28x^2 - \pi x^2$
$= x^2(28 - \pi)$

Chapter 6 Test

1. $x^2 + 11x + 28 = (x+7)(x+4)$

2. $49 - m^2 = (7^2 - m^2) = (7-m)(7+m)$

3. $y^2 + 22y + 121 = y^2 + 2 \cdot y \cdot 11 + 11^2 = (y+11)^2$

4. $4(a+3) - y(a+3) = (a+3)(4-y)$

5. $x^2 + 4$ is the sum of two perfect squares (not the difference). The polynomial is prime.

6. $y^2 - 8y - 48 = (y-12)(y+4)$

7. $x^2 + x - 10$ is a prime polynomial.

8. $9x^3 + 39x^2 + 12x = 3x(3x^2 + 13x + 4)$
$= 3x(3x+1)(x+4)$

9. $3a^2 + 3ab - 7a - 7b = 3a(a+b) - 7(a+b)$
$= (a+b)(3a-7)$

10. $3x^2 - 5x + 2 = (3x-2)(x-1)$

11. $x^2 + 14xy + 24y^2 = (x+12y)(x+2y)$

12. $180 - 5x^2 = 5(36 - x^2)$
$= 5(6^2 - x^2)$
$= 5(6+x)(6-x)$

13. $6t^2 - t - 5 = (6t+5)(t-1)$

14. $xy^2 - 7y^2 - 4x + 28 = y^2(x-7) - 4(x-7)$
$= (x-7)(y^2 - 4)$
$= (x-7)(y^2 - 2^2)$
$= (x-7)(y+2)(y-2)$

15. $x - x^5 = x(1 - x^4)$
$= x[1 - (x^2)^2]$
$= x(1+x^2)(1-x^2)$
$= x(1+x^2)(1^2 - x^2)$
$= x(1+x^2)(1+x)(1-x)$

16. $-xy^3 - x^3y = xy(y^2 + x^2)$

17. $64x^3 - 1 = (4x)^3 - 1^3$
$= (4x-1)[(4x)^2 + 4x \cdot 1 + 1^2]$
$= (4x-1)(16x^2 + 4x + 1)$

18. $8y^3 - 64 = 8(y^3 - 8)$
$= 8(y^3 - 2^3)$
$= 8(y-2)(y^2 + y \cdot 2 + 2^2)$
$= 8(y-2)(y^2 + 2y + 4)$

19. $(x-3)(x+9) = 0$
$x - 3 = 0$ or $x + 9 = 0$
$x = 3$ $x = -9$
The solutions are 3 and –9.

20.
$$x^2 + 5x = 14$$
$$x^2 + 5x - 14 = 0$$
$$(x+7)(x-2) = 0$$
$$x + 7 = 0 \quad \text{or} \quad x - 2 = 0$$
$$x = -7 \qquad\qquad x = 2$$
The solutions are -7 and 2.

21.
$$x(x+6) = 7$$
$$x^2 + 6x = 7$$
$$x^2 + 6x - 7 = 0$$
$$(x+7)(x-1) = 0$$
$$x + 7 = 0 \quad \text{or} \quad x - 1 = 0$$
$$x = -7 \qquad\qquad x = 1$$
The solutions are -7 and 1.

22. $3x(2x - 3)(3x + 4) = 0$
$$3x = 0 \quad \text{or} \quad 2x - 3 = 0 \quad \text{or} \quad 3x + 4 = 0$$
$$x = 0 \qquad\qquad 2x = 3 \qquad\qquad 3x = -4$$
$$x = \frac{3}{2} \qquad\qquad x = -\frac{4}{3}$$

The solutions are 0, $\dfrac{3}{2}$, and $-\dfrac{4}{3}$.

23.
$$5t^3 - 45t = 0$$
$$5t(t^2 - 9) = 0$$
$$5t(t+3)(t-3) = 0$$
$$5t = 0 \quad \text{or} \quad t + 3 = 0 \quad \text{or} \quad t - 3 = 0$$
$$t = 0 \qquad\qquad t = -3 \qquad\qquad t = 3$$
The solutions are 0, -3, and 3.

24. $t^2 - 2t - 15 = 0$
$$(t-5)(t+3) = 0$$
$$t - 5 = 0 \quad \text{or} \quad t + 3 = 0$$
$$t = 5 \qquad\qquad t = -3$$
The solutions are 5 and -3.

25.
$$6x^2 = 15x$$
$$6x^2 - 15x = 0$$
$$3x(2x - 5) = 0$$
$$3x = 0 \quad \text{or} \quad 2x - 5 = 0$$
$$x = 0 \qquad\qquad 2x = 5$$
$$x = \frac{5}{2}$$

The solutions are 0 and $\dfrac{5}{2}$.

26. Let $x =$ the altitude of the triangle, then $x + 9 =$ the base.
$$A = \frac{1}{2}bh$$
$$68 = \frac{1}{2}(x+9)(x)$$
$$136 = x^2 + 9x$$
$$0 = x^2 + 9x - 136$$
$$0 = (x+17)(x-8)$$
$$x + 17 = 0 \quad \text{or} \quad x - 8 = 0$$
$$x = -17 \qquad\qquad x = 8$$
Since the length of the base cannot be negative, the base is $8 + 9 = 17$ feet.

27. Let $x =$ the first number, then $17 - x =$ the other number.
$$x^2 + (17 - x)^2 = 145$$
$$x^2 + 289 - 34x + x^2 = 145$$
$$2x^2 - 34x + 144 = 0$$
$$2(x^2 - 17x + 72) = 0$$
$$2(x - 9)(x - 8) = 0$$
$$x - 9 = 0 \quad \text{or} \quad x - 8 = 0$$
$$x = 9 \qquad\qquad x = 8$$
The numbers are 8 and 9.

28. Find t when $h = 0$.
$$h = -16t^2 + 784$$
$$0 = -16t^2 + 784$$
$$0 = -16(t^2 - 49)$$
$$0 = -16(t + 7)(t - 7)$$
$$t + 7 = 0 \quad \text{or} \quad t - 7 = 0$$
$$t = -7 \qquad\qquad t = 7$$
Since the time cannot be negative, the object reaches the ground after 7 seconds.

29. Let $x =$ length of the shorter leg, then $x + 10 =$ length of hypotenuse, and $x + 5 =$ length of longer leg.
$$x^2 + (x+5)^2 = (x+10)^2$$
$$x^2 + x^2 + 10x + 25 = x^2 + 20x + 100$$
$$x^2 - 10x - 75 = 0$$
$$(x+5)(x-15) = 0$$
$$x + 5 = 0 \quad \text{or} \quad x - 15 = 0$$
$$x = -5 \qquad\qquad x = 15$$
Since length cannot be negative, the lengths of the triangle sides are:
shorter leg $= 15$ cm, longer leg $= 20$ cm, hypotenuse $= 25$ cm.

Chapter 6 Cumulative Review

1. a. $9 \leq 11$

b. $8 > 1$

c. $3 \neq 4$

2. a. $|-5| > |-3|$

b. $|0| < |-2|$

3. a. $\dfrac{42}{49} = \dfrac{6 \cdot 7}{7 \cdot 7} = \dfrac{6}{7}$

b. $\dfrac{11}{27} = \dfrac{11}{3 \cdot 3 \cdot 3} = \dfrac{11}{27}$

c. $\dfrac{88}{20} = \dfrac{4 \cdot 22}{4 \cdot 5} = \dfrac{22}{5}$

4. Let $x = 20$ and $y = 10$.
$$\frac{x}{y} + 5x = \frac{20}{10} + 5(20) = 2 + 100 = 102$$

5. $\dfrac{8 + 2 \cdot 3}{2^2 - 1} = \dfrac{8 + 6}{4 - 1} = \dfrac{14}{3}$

6. Let $x = -20$ and $y = 10$.
$$\frac{x}{y} + 5x = \frac{-20}{10} + 5(-20) = -2 - 100 = -102$$

7. a. $3 + (-7) + (-8) = 3 + (-15) = -12$

b. $[7 + (-10)] + \left[-2 + |-4|\right] = -3 + (-2 + 4)$
$$= -3 + 2$$
$$= -1$$

8. Let $x = -20$ and $y = -10$.
$$\frac{x}{y} + 5x = \frac{-20}{-10} + 5(-20) = 2 - 100 = -98$$

9. a. $(-6)(4) = -24$

b. $2(-1) = -2$

c. $(-5)(-10) = 50$

10. $5 - 2(3x - 7) = 5 - 6x + 14 = -6x + 19$

11. a. $7x - 3x = (7 - 3)x = 4x$

b. $10y^2 + y^2 = (10 + 1)y^2 = 11y^2$

c. $8x^2 + 2x - 3x = 8x^2 + (2 - 3)x = 8x^2 - x$

12. $0.8y + 0.2(y - 1) = 1.8$
$$0.8y + 0.2y - 0.2 = 1.8$$
$$1.0y - 0.2 = 1.8$$
$$y = 2.0$$

13. $\dfrac{y}{7} = 20$
$$7\left(\frac{y}{7}\right) = 7(20)$$
$$y = 140$$

14. $\dfrac{x}{-7} = -4$
$$-7\left(\frac{x}{-7}\right) = -7(-4)$$
$$x = 28$$

15. $-3x = 33$
$$\frac{-3x}{-3} = \frac{33}{-3}$$
$$x = -11$$

16. $-\dfrac{2}{3}x = -22$
$$\left(-\frac{3}{2}\right)\left(-\frac{2}{3}\right)x = \left(-\frac{3}{2}\right)(-22)$$
$$x = 33$$

17. $8(2 - t) = -5t$
$$16 - 8t = -5t$$
$$16 - 8t + 5t = -5t + 5t$$
$$16 - 3t = 0$$
$$16 - 16 - 3t = -16$$
$$-3t = -16$$
$$\frac{-3t}{-3} = \frac{-16}{-3}$$
$$t = \frac{16}{3}$$

18.
$$-z = \frac{7z+3}{5}$$
$$5(-z) = 5\left(\frac{7z+3}{5}\right)$$
$$-5z = 7z+3$$
$$-5z - 7z = 7z - 7z + 3$$
$$-12z = 3$$
$$\frac{-12z}{-12} = \frac{3}{-12}$$
$$z = -\frac{1}{4}$$

19. Let x = the length of the shorter piece and
$3x$ = the length of the longer piece.
$$x + 3x = 48$$
$$4x = 48$$
$$x = 12$$
$$3x = 3(12) = 36$$
The pieces are 12 inches and 36 inches in length.

20.
$$3x + 9 \leq 5(x-1)$$
$$3x + 9 \leq 5x - 5$$
$$-2x + 9 \leq -5$$
$$2x \leq -14$$
$$\frac{-2x}{-2} \geq \frac{-14}{-2}$$
$$x \geq 7, [7, \infty)$$

21. $y = -\frac{1}{3}x + 2$

x	y
0	2
−3	3
3	1

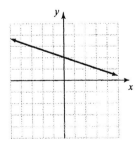

22. $-7x - 8y = -9$
$$(-1, 2): \quad -7(-1) - 8(2) \stackrel{?}{=} -9$$
$$7 - 16 \stackrel{?}{=} -9$$
$$-9 = -9 \quad \text{True}$$
$(-1, 2)$ is a solution of the equation.

23. $3x - 4y = 4$
$$-4y = -3x + 4$$
$$y = \frac{3}{4}x - 1$$
$$y = mx + b$$
$$\text{slope} = \frac{3}{4}; \; y\text{-intercept} = (0, -1)$$

24. $(5, -6)$ and $(5, 2)$
$$m = \frac{y_2 - y_1}{x_2 - x_1} = \frac{2 - (-6)}{5 - 5} = \frac{8}{0}$$
The slope is undefined.

25. a. If $x = 5$, $2x^3 = 2(5)^3 = 2(125) = 250$.

   b. If $x = -3$, $\dfrac{9}{x^2} = \dfrac{9}{(-3)^2} = \dfrac{9}{9} = 1$.

26. $7x - 3y = 2$
$$-3y = -7x + 2$$
$$y = \frac{-7x}{-3} + \frac{2}{-3}$$
$$y = \frac{7}{3}x - \frac{2}{3}$$
$$y = mx + b$$
$$\text{slope} = \frac{7}{3}; \; y\text{-intercept} = \left(0, -\frac{2}{3}\right)$$

27. a. $3x^2$ has degree 2.

   b. $-2^3 x^5$ has degree 5.

   c. y has degree 1.

   d. $12x^2 yz^3$ has degree $2 + 1 + 3 = 6$.

   e. 5 has degree 0.

28. Vertical line has equation $x = c$.
Point $(0, 7)$
$x = 0$

29. $(2x^3 + 8x^2 - 6x) - (2x^3 - x^2 + 1)$
$= 2x^3 + 8x^2 - 6x - 2x^3 + x^2 - 1$
$= 9x^2 - 6x - 1$

30. $m = 4,\ b = \dfrac{1}{2}$
$y = mx + b$
$y = 4x + \dfrac{1}{2}$
$2y = 8x + 1$
$8x - 2y = -1$

31. $(3x + 2)(2x - 5)$
$= 3x(2x) + 3x(-5) + 2(2x) + 2(-5)$
$= 6x^2 - 15x + 4x - 10$
$= 6x^2 - 11x - 10$

32. $(-4, 0)$ and $(6, -1)$
$m = \dfrac{y_2 - y_1}{x_2 - x_1} = \dfrac{-1 - 0}{6 - (-4)} = -\dfrac{1}{10}$
$m = -\dfrac{1}{10},\ \text{point } (-4, 0)$
$y - y_1 = m(x - x_1)$
$y - 0 = -\dfrac{1}{10}[x - (-4)]$
$y = -\dfrac{1}{10}x - \dfrac{4}{10}$
$10y = -x - 4$
$x + 10y = -4$

33. $(3y + 1)^2 = (3y)^2 + 2(3y)(1) + 1^2 = 9y^2 + 6y + 1$

34. $\begin{cases} -x + 3y = 18 \\ -3x + 2y = 19 \end{cases}$
Multiply the first equation by -3.
$\begin{aligned} 3x - 9y &= -54 \\ \underline{-3x + 2y} &= \underline{19} \\ -7y &= -35 \\ y &= 5 \end{aligned}$
Substitute 5 for y in the first equation.
$-x + 3(5) = 18$
$-x + 15 = 18$
$-x = 3$
$x = -3$
The solution to the system is $(-3, 5)$.

35. a. $3^{-2} = \dfrac{1}{3^2} = \dfrac{1}{9}$

b. $2x^{-3} = \dfrac{2}{x^3}$

c. $2^{-1} + 4^{-1} = \dfrac{1}{2} + \dfrac{1}{4}$
$= \dfrac{1 \cdot 2}{2 \cdot 2} + \dfrac{1}{4}$
$= \dfrac{2}{4} + \dfrac{1}{4}$
$= \dfrac{2 + 1}{4}$
$= \dfrac{3}{4}$

d. $(-2)^{-4} = \dfrac{1}{(-2)^4} = \dfrac{1}{16}$

e. $\dfrac{1}{y^{-4}} = y^4$

f. $\dfrac{1}{7^{-2}} = 7^2 = 49$

36. $\dfrac{(5a^7)^2}{a^5} = \dfrac{5^2 a^{14}}{a^5} = 25a^{14-5} = 25a^9$

37. a. $367{,}000{,}000 = 3.67 \times 10^8$

b. $0.000003 = 3.0 \times 10^{-6}$

c. $20{,}520{,}000{,}000 = 2.052 \times 10^{10}$

d. $0.00085 = 8.5 \times 10^{-4}$

38. $(3x - 7y)^2 = (3x)^2 - 2(3x)(7y) + (7y)^2$
$= 9x^2 - 42xy + 49y^2$

39.

$$\begin{array}{r} x+4 \\ x+3\overline{\smash{\big)}\,x^2+7x+12} \\ \underline{x^2+3x} \\ 4x+12 \\ \underline{4x+12} \\ 0 \end{array}$$

$$\frac{x^2+7x+12}{x+3}=x+4$$

40.
$$\frac{(xy)^{-3}}{(x^5y^6)^3}=\frac{x^{-3}y^{-3}}{x^{15}y^{18}}$$
$$=x^{-3-15}y^{-3-18}$$
$$=x^{-18}y^{-21}$$
$$=\frac{1}{x^{18}y^{21}}$$

41. a. $x^3,\ x^7,\ x^5:\text{GCF}=x^3$

b. $y,\ y^4,\ y^7:\text{GCF}=y$

42. $z^3+7z+z^2+7=z(z^2+7)+1(z^2+7)$
$$=(z^2+7)(z+1)$$

43. $x^2+7x+12=(x+4)(x+3)$

44. $2x^3+2x^2-84x=2x(x^2+x-42)$
$$=2x(x+7)(x-6)$$

45. $8x^2-22x+5=8x^2-20x-2x+5$
$$=4x(2x-5)-1(2x-5)$$
$$=(2x-5)(4x-1)$$

46. $-4x^2-23x+6=-1(4x^2+23x-6)$
$$=-(4x^2-x+24x-6)$$
$$=-[x(4x-1)+6(4x-1)]$$
$$=-(4x-1)(x+6)$$

47. $25a^2-9b^2=(5a)^2-(3b)^2=(5a+3b)(5a-3b)$

48. $9xy^2-16x=x(9y^2-16)$
$$=x[(3y)^2-4^2]$$
$$=x(3y+4)(3y-4)$$

49. $(x-3)(x+1)=0$
$$x-3=0 \quad \text{or} \quad x+1=0$$
$$x=3 \qquad\qquad x=-1$$
The solutions are 3 and -1.

50.
$$x^2-13x=-36$$
$$x^2-13x+36=0$$
$$(x-9)(x-4)=0$$
$$x-9=0 \quad \text{or} \quad x-4=0$$
$$x=9 \qquad\qquad x=4$$
The solutions are 9 and 4.

Chapter 7

Practice Exercises

1. a. The denominator of $f(x)$ is never 0.
Domain: $\{x | x$ is a real number$\}$

   b. Undefined values when
$x + 3 = 0$, or $x = -3$
Domain: $\{x | x$ is a real number and $x \neq -3\}$

   c. Undefined values when
$$x^2 - 5x + 6 = 0$$
$$(x - 3)(x - 2) = 0$$
$$x - 3 = 0 \quad \text{or} \quad x - 2 = 0$$
$$x = 3 \quad \text{or} \quad x = 2$$
Domain:
$\{x | x$ is a real number and $x \neq 2, x \neq 3\}$

2. a. $\dfrac{5z^4}{10z^5 - 5z^4} = \dfrac{5z^4 \cdot 1}{5z^4(2z - 1)}$
$$= 1 \cdot \dfrac{1}{2z - 1} = \dfrac{1}{2z - 1}$$

   b. $\dfrac{5x^2 + 13x + 6}{6x^2 + 7x - 10} = \dfrac{(5x + 3)(x + 2)}{(6x - 5)(x + 2)}$
$$= \dfrac{5x + 3}{6x - 5} \cdot 1$$
$$= \dfrac{5x + 3}{6x - 5}$$

3. a. $\dfrac{x + 3}{3 + x} = \dfrac{x + 3}{x + 3} = 1$

   b. $\dfrac{3 - x}{x - 3} = \dfrac{-1(-3 + x)}{x - 3} = \dfrac{-1(x - 3)}{x - 3} = \dfrac{-1}{1} = -1$

4. $\dfrac{20 - 5x^2}{x^2 + x - 6} = \dfrac{5(4 - x^2)}{(x + 3)(x - 2)}$
$$= \dfrac{5(2 + x)(2 - x)}{(x + 3)(x - 2)}$$
$$= \dfrac{5(2 + x) \cdot (-1)(x - 2)}{(x + 3)(x - 2)}$$
$$= -\dfrac{5(2 + x)}{x + 3}$$

5. a. $\dfrac{x^3 + 64}{4 + x} = \dfrac{(x + 4)(x^2 - 4x + 16)}{x + 4}$
$$= x^2 - 4x + 16$$

   b. $\dfrac{5z^2 + 10}{z^3 - 3z^2 + 2z - 6} = \dfrac{5(z^2 + 2)}{(z^3 - 3z^2) + (2z - 6)}$
$$= \dfrac{5(z^2 + 2)}{z^2(z - 3) + 2(z - 3)}$$
$$= \dfrac{5(z^2 + 2)}{(z - 3)(z^2 + 2)}$$
$$= \dfrac{5}{z - 3}$$

6. $-\dfrac{x + 3}{6x - 11} = \dfrac{-(x + 3)}{6x - 11} = \dfrac{-x - 3}{6x - 11}$
Also,
$$-\dfrac{x + 3}{6x - 11} = \dfrac{x + 3}{-(6x - 11)} = \dfrac{x + 3}{-6x + 11} \quad \text{or} \quad \dfrac{x + 3}{11 - 6x}$$

Thus, some equivalent forms of $-\dfrac{x + 3}{6x - 11}$ are

$\dfrac{-(x + 3)}{6x - 11}, \dfrac{-x - 3}{6x - 11}, \dfrac{x + 3}{-(6x - 11)}, \dfrac{x + 3}{-6x + 11}$, and

$\dfrac{x + 3}{11 - 6x}$.

7. a. $C(100) = \dfrac{3.2(100) + 400}{100} = \dfrac{720}{100} = 7.2$
$7.20 per tee shirt

   b. $C(1000) = \dfrac{3.2(1000) + 400}{1000} = \dfrac{3600}{1000} = 3.6$
$3.60 per tee shirt

Graphing Calculator Explorations

1.
$$x^2 - 4 = 0$$
$$(x + 2)(x - 2) = 0$$
$$x + 2 = 0 \quad \text{or} \quad x - 2 = 0$$
$$x = -2 \quad \text{or} \quad x = 2$$
Domain: $\{x | x$ is a real number and $x \neq -2, x \neq 2\}$

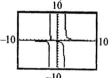

2.
$$x^2 - 9 = 0$$
$$(x+3)(x-3) = 0$$
$$x + 3 = 0 \quad \text{or} \quad x - 3 = 0$$
$$x = -3 \quad \text{or} \quad x = 3$$
Domain: $\{x | x \text{ is a real number and } x \neq -3, x \neq 3\}$

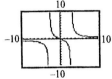

3.
$$2x^2 + 7x - 4 = 0$$
$$(2x - 1)(x + 4) = 0$$
$$2x - 1 = 0 \quad \text{or} \quad x + 4 = 0$$
$$2x = 1 \quad \text{or} \quad x = -4$$
$$x = \frac{1}{2}$$
Domain:
$$\left\{ x \middle| x \text{ is a real number and } x \neq -4, x \neq \frac{1}{2} \right\}$$

4.
$$4x^2 - 19x - 5 = 0$$
$$(4x + 1)(x - 5) = 0$$
$$4x + 1 = 0 \quad \text{or} \quad x - 5 = 0$$
$$4x = -1 \quad \text{or} \quad x = 5$$
$$x = -\frac{1}{4}$$
Domain:
$$\left\{ x \middle| x \text{ is a real number and } x \neq -\frac{1}{4}, x \neq 5 \right\}$$

Vocabulary and Readiness Check

1. A <u>rational</u> expression is an expression that can be written as the quotient $\dfrac{P}{Q}$ of two polynomials P and Q as long as $Q \neq 0$.

2. A rational expression is undefined if the denominator is <u>0</u>.

3. The <u>domain</u> of the rational function $f(x) = \dfrac{2}{x}$ is $\{x | x \text{ is a real number and } x \neq 0\}$.

4. A rational expression is <u>simplified</u> if the numerator and denominator have no common factors other than 1 or −1.

5. The expression $\dfrac{x^2 + 2}{2 + x^2}$ simplifies to <u>1</u>.

6. The expression $\dfrac{y - z}{z - y}$ simplifies to <u>−1</u>.

7. For a rational expression, $-\dfrac{a}{b} = \dfrac{-a}{\underline{b}} = \dfrac{a}{\underline{-b}}$.

8. The statement $\dfrac{a - 6}{a + 2} = \dfrac{-(a - 6)}{-(a + 2)} = \dfrac{-a + 6}{-a - 2}$ is true.

9. No, $\dfrac{x}{x + 7}$ cannot be simplified.

10. Yes, $\dfrac{3 + x}{x + 3}$ can be simplified because $3 + x = x + 3$.

11. Yes, $\dfrac{5 - x}{x - 5}$ can be simplified because $5 - x = -1(x - 5)$.

12. No, $\dfrac{x + 2}{x + 8}$ cannot be simplified.

Exercise Set 7.1

2. 2 is never 0, so the domain of $g(x) = \dfrac{4 - 3x}{2}$ is $\{x | x \text{ is a real number}\}$.

4.
$$3t = 0$$
$$t = 0$$
The domain of $v(t) = -\dfrac{5t + t^2}{3t}$ is $\{t | t \text{ is a real number and } t \neq 0\}$.

6. $-2 + x = 0$

   $x = 2$

   The domain of $f(x) = \dfrac{-4x}{-2+x}$ is

   $\{x | x$ is a real number and $x \neq 2\}$.

8. $2x + 5 = 0$

   $2x = -5$

   $x = -\dfrac{5}{2}$

   The domain of $g(x) = \dfrac{-2}{2x+5}$ is

   $\left\{ x \middle| x \text{ is a real number and } x \neq -\dfrac{5}{2} \right\}$.

10. $2x^2 - 14x + 20 = 0$

    $2(x^2 - 7x + 10) = 0$

    $2(x - 2)(x - 5) = 0$

    $x - 2 = 0$ or $x - 5 = 0$

    $x = 2$ or $x = 5$

    The domain of $h(x) = \dfrac{5 - 3x}{2x^2 - 14x + 20}$ is

    $\{x | x$ is a real number and $x \neq 2, x \neq 5\}$.

12. $x^2 - 7x = 0$

    $x(x - 7) = 0$

    $x = 0$ or $x - 7 = 0$

    $x = 0$ or $x = 7$

    The domain of $R(x) = \dfrac{5}{x^2 - 7x}$ is

    $\{x | x$ is a real number and $x \neq 0, x \neq 7\}$.

14. $-\dfrac{x+11}{x-4} = \dfrac{-(x+11)}{x-4} = \dfrac{-x-11}{x-4}$

    $-\dfrac{x+11}{x-4} = \dfrac{x+11}{-(x-4)} = \dfrac{x+11}{-x+4}$ or $\dfrac{x+11}{4-x}$

16. $-\dfrac{8y-1}{y-15} = \dfrac{-(8y-1)}{y-15} = \dfrac{-8y+1}{y-15}$ or $\dfrac{1-8y}{y-15}$

    $-\dfrac{8y-1}{y-15} = \dfrac{8y-1}{-(y-15)} = \dfrac{8y-1}{-y+15}$ or $\dfrac{8y-1}{15-y}$

18. $\dfrac{y+9}{9+y} = \dfrac{y+9}{y+9} = 1$

20. $\dfrac{y-9}{9-y} = \dfrac{y-9}{-1(y-9)} = \dfrac{1}{-1} = -1$

22. $\dfrac{3}{9x+6} = \dfrac{3}{3(3x+2)} = \dfrac{1}{3x+2}$

24. $\dfrac{-4x-4y}{x+y} = \dfrac{-4(x+y)}{x+y} = -4$

26. $\dfrac{9x+99}{x^2+11x} = \dfrac{9(x+11)}{x(x+11)} = \dfrac{9}{x}$

28. $\dfrac{x-3}{x^2-6x+9} = \dfrac{x-3}{(x-3)(x-3)} = \dfrac{1}{x-3}$

30. $\dfrac{12x^2+4x-1}{2x+1} = \dfrac{(6x-1)(2x+1)}{2x+1} = 6x-1$

32. $\dfrac{x^4-10x^3}{x^2-17x+70} = \dfrac{x^3(x-10)}{(x-7)(x-10)} = \dfrac{x^3}{x-7}$

34. $\dfrac{5x^2-500}{35x+350} = \dfrac{5(x^2-100)}{35(x+10)}$

    $= \dfrac{5(x+10)(x-10)}{5 \cdot 7(x+10)}$

    $= \dfrac{x-10}{7}$

36. $\dfrac{49-y^2}{y-7} = \dfrac{(7+y)(7-y)}{y-7}$

    $= \dfrac{(7+y)(-1)(y-7)}{y-7}$

    $= -(y+7)$ or $-y-7$

38. $\dfrac{24y^2-8y^3}{15y-5y^2} = \dfrac{8y^2(3-y)}{5y(3-y)} = \dfrac{8y}{5}$

40. $\dfrac{ab+ac+b^2+bc}{b+c} = \dfrac{a(b+c)+b(b+c)}{b+c}$

    $= \dfrac{(b+c)(a+b)}{b+c}$

    $= a+b$

42. $\dfrac{x^3+64}{x+4} = \dfrac{(x+4)(x^2-4x+16)}{x+4} = x^2-4x+16$

44. $\dfrac{3-x}{x^3-27}=\dfrac{-(x-3)}{(x-3)(x^2+3x+9)}=\dfrac{-1}{x^2+3x+9}$

46. $\dfrac{2xy+2x-3y-3}{2xy+4x-3y-6}=\dfrac{2x(y+1)-3(y+1)}{2x(y+2)-3(y+2)}$

$=\dfrac{(y+1)(2x-3)}{(y+2)(2x-3)}$

$=\dfrac{y+1}{y+2}$

48. $\dfrac{2x^2-x-3}{2x^3-3x^2+2x-3}=\dfrac{(2x-3)(x+1)}{x^2(2x-3)+1(2x-3)}$

$=\dfrac{(2x-3)(x+1)}{(x^2+1)(2x-3)}$

$=\dfrac{x+1}{x^2+1}$

50. $\dfrac{8x^3-27}{4x^2+6x+9}=\dfrac{(2x-3)(4x^2+6x+9)}{4x^2+6x+9}=2x-3$

52. $f(x)=\dfrac{x-2}{-5+x}$

$f(-5)=\dfrac{-5-2}{-5+(-5)}=\dfrac{-7}{-10}=\dfrac{7}{10}$

$f(0)=\dfrac{0-2}{-5+0}=\dfrac{-2}{-5}=\dfrac{2}{5}$

$f(10)=\dfrac{10-2}{-5+10}=\dfrac{8}{5}$

54. $s(t)=\dfrac{t^3+1}{t^2+1}$

$s(-1)=\dfrac{(-1)^3+1}{(-1)^2+1}=\dfrac{-1+1}{1+1}=\dfrac{0}{2}=0$

$s(1)=\dfrac{1^3+1}{1^2+1}=\dfrac{1+1}{1+1}=\dfrac{2}{2}=1$

$s(2)=\dfrac{2^3+1}{2^2+1}=\dfrac{8+1}{4+1}=\dfrac{9}{5}$

56. $f(x)=\dfrac{100,000x}{100-x}$

a. $f(20)=\dfrac{100,000(20)}{100-20}$

$=\dfrac{2,000,000}{80}$

$=25,000$

It costs \$25,000 to remove 20% of the pollutants from the bayou.

b. $f(60)=\dfrac{100,000(60)}{100-60}$

$=\dfrac{6,000,000}{40}$

$=150,000$

$f(80)=\dfrac{100,000(80)}{100-80}$

$=\dfrac{8,000,000}{20}$

$=400,000$

The cost of removing 60% of the pollutants from the bayou is \$150,000, and the cost of removing 80% of the pollutants from the bayou is \$400,000.

c. $f(90)=\dfrac{100,000(90)}{100-90}$

$=\dfrac{9,000,000}{10}$

$=\$900,000$

$f(95)=\dfrac{100,000(95)}{100-95}$

$=\dfrac{9,500,000}{5}$

$=\$1,900,000$

$f(99)=\dfrac{100,000(99)}{100-99}$

$=\dfrac{9,900,000}{1}$

$=\$9,900,000$

answers may vary

d. $100-x=0$

$-x=-100$

$x=100$

The domain of f is
$\{x|x$ is a real number and $x\neq 100\}$.

58. Let $w = 148$ and $h = 66$.

$$B = \frac{703w}{h^2}$$

$$B = \frac{703(148)}{66^2} = \frac{104,044}{4356} \approx 24$$

No, the person should not lose weight.

60. Let $t = 80$.

$$i = \frac{5840}{t + 29}$$

$$i = \frac{5840}{80 + 29} = \frac{5840}{109} \approx 53.6$$

The engineers should expect a rainfall intensity of 53.6 millimeters per hour.

62. a. $R = \dfrac{150x^2}{x^2 + 3}$

$$= \frac{150(1)^2}{1^2 + 3}$$

$$= \frac{150}{4}$$

$$= \$37.5 \text{ million}$$

b. $R = \dfrac{150x^2}{x^2 + 3}$

$$= \frac{150(2)^2}{2^2 + 3}$$

$$= \frac{600}{7}$$

$$\approx \$85.7 \text{ million}$$

c. $85.7 - 37.5 = \$48.2$ million

64. $\dfrac{5}{27} \cdot \dfrac{2}{5} = \dfrac{5 \cdot 2}{27 \cdot 5} = \dfrac{2}{27}$

66. $\dfrac{7}{8} \div \dfrac{1}{2} = \dfrac{7}{8} \cdot \dfrac{2}{1} = \dfrac{7 \cdot 2}{2 \cdot 4 \cdot 1} = \dfrac{7}{4}$

68. $\dfrac{8}{15} \div \dfrac{5}{8} = \dfrac{8}{15} \cdot \dfrac{8}{5} = \dfrac{8 \cdot 8}{15 \cdot 5} = \dfrac{64}{75}$

70. $\dfrac{7m - 9}{7} = \dfrac{7m}{7} - \dfrac{9}{7} = m - \dfrac{9}{7}$

The given simplification is incorrect.

72. $\dfrac{46}{54} = \dfrac{2 \cdot 23}{2 \cdot 27} = \dfrac{23}{27}$

The given simplification is incorrect.

74. No; answers may vary

76. Answers may vary

78. $f(x) = \dfrac{1}{x}$

x	$\frac{1}{4}$	$\frac{1}{2}$	1	2	4
y	4	2	1	$\frac{1}{2}$	$\frac{1}{4}$

x	-4	-2	-1	$-\frac{1}{2}$	$-\frac{1}{4}$
y	$-\frac{1}{4}$	$-\frac{1}{2}$	-1	-2	-4

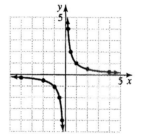

80. $y = \dfrac{x^2 - 25}{x + 5} = \dfrac{(x + 5)(x - 5)}{(x + 5)} = x - 5,\ x \neq -5$

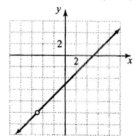

82. $y = \dfrac{x^2 + x - 12}{x + 4} = \dfrac{(x + 4)(x - 3)}{(x + 4)} = x - 3,\ x \neq -4$

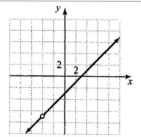

Section 7.2

Practice Exercises

1. a. $\dfrac{4a}{5} \cdot \dfrac{3}{b^2} = \dfrac{4a \cdot 3}{5 \cdot b^2} = \dfrac{12a}{5b^2}$

b. $\dfrac{-3p^4}{q^2} \cdot \dfrac{2q^3}{9p^4} = \dfrac{-3p^4 \cdot 2q^3}{q^2 \cdot 9p^4}$

$\phantom{\dfrac{-3p^4}{q^2} \cdot \dfrac{2q^3}{9p^4}} = \dfrac{-1 \cdot 3 \cdot p^4 \cdot 2 \cdot q \cdot q^2}{q^2 \cdot 3 \cdot 3 \cdot p^4}$

$\phantom{\dfrac{-3p^4}{q^2} \cdot \dfrac{2q^3}{9p^4}} = -\dfrac{2q}{3}$

2. $\dfrac{x^2 - x}{5x} \cdot \dfrac{15}{x^2 - 1} = \dfrac{x(x-1)}{5x} \cdot \dfrac{3 \cdot 5}{(x+1)(x-1)}$

$\phantom{\dfrac{x^2 - x}{5x}} = \dfrac{x(x-1) \cdot 3 \cdot 5}{5x \cdot (x+1)(x-1)}$

$\phantom{\dfrac{x^2 - x}{5x}} = \dfrac{3}{x+1}$

3. $\dfrac{6 - 3x}{6x + 6x^2} \cdot \dfrac{3x^2 - 2x - 5}{x^2 - 4}$

$ = \dfrac{3(2-x)}{2 \cdot 3 \cdot x(1+x)} \cdot \dfrac{(x+1)(3x-5)}{(x+2)(x-2)}$

$ = \dfrac{3(2-x)(x+1)(3x-5)}{2 \cdot 3x(1+x)(x+2)(x-2)}$

$ = \dfrac{-1(x-2)(x+1)(3x-5)}{2x(x+1)(x+2)(x-2)}$

$ = -\dfrac{3x-5}{2x(x+2)}$

4. $\dfrac{5a^3 b^2}{24} \div \dfrac{10a^5}{6} = \dfrac{5a^3 b^2}{24} \cdot \dfrac{6}{10a^5}$

$\phantom{\dfrac{5a^3 b^2}{24}} = \dfrac{5a^3 b^2 \cdot 6}{4 \cdot 6 \cdot 2 \cdot 5 \cdot a^2 \cdot a^3}$

$\phantom{\dfrac{5a^3 b^2}{24}} = \dfrac{b^2}{8a^2}$

5. $\dfrac{(3x+1)(x-5)}{3} \div \dfrac{4x - 20}{9}$

$ = \dfrac{(3x+1)(x-5)}{3} \cdot \dfrac{9}{4x - 20}$

$ = \dfrac{(3x+1)(x-5) \cdot 3 \cdot 3}{3 \cdot 4(x-5)}$

$ = \dfrac{3(3x+1)}{4}$

6. $\dfrac{10x - 2}{x^2 - 9} \div \dfrac{5x^2 - x}{x + 3} = \dfrac{10x - 2}{x^2 - 9} \cdot \dfrac{x + 3}{5x^2 - x}$

$ = \dfrac{2(5x - 1)(x + 3)}{(x + 3)(x - 3) \cdot x(5x - 1)}$

$ = \dfrac{2}{x(x - 3)}$

7. $\dfrac{3x^2 - 11x - 4}{2x - 8} \div \dfrac{9x + 3}{6} = \dfrac{3x^2 - 11x - 4}{2x - 8} \cdot \dfrac{6}{9x + 3}$

$ = \dfrac{(3x + 1)(x - 4) \cdot 2 \cdot 3}{2(x - 4) \cdot 3(3x + 1)}$

$ = \dfrac{1}{1} \text{ or } 1$

8. a. $\dfrac{y + 9}{8x} \cdot \dfrac{y + 9}{2x} = \dfrac{(y + 9) \cdot (y + 9)}{8x \cdot 2x} = \dfrac{(y + 9)^2}{16x^2}$

b. $\dfrac{y + 9}{8x} \div \dfrac{y + 9}{2} = \dfrac{y + 9}{8x} \cdot \dfrac{2}{y + 9}$

$ = \dfrac{(y + 9) \cdot 2}{2 \cdot 4 \cdot x \cdot (y + 9)}$

$ = \dfrac{1}{4x}$

c. $\dfrac{35x - 7x^2}{x^2 - 25} \cdot \dfrac{x^2 + 3x - 10}{x^2 + 4x}$

$ = \dfrac{7x(5 - x)}{(x + 5)(x - 5)} \cdot \dfrac{(x - 2)(x + 5)}{x(x + 4)}$

$ = \dfrac{7x \cdot (-1)(x - 5) \cdot (x - 2)(x + 5)}{(x + 5)(x - 5) \cdot x(x + 4)}$

$ = -\dfrac{7(x - 2)}{x + 4}$

Vocabulary and Readiness Check

1. The expressions $\dfrac{x}{2y}$ and $\dfrac{2y}{x}$ are called reciprocals.

2. $\dfrac{a}{b} \cdot \dfrac{c}{d} = \dfrac{a \cdot c}{b \cdot d}$ or $\dfrac{ac}{bd}$

3. $\dfrac{a}{b} \div \dfrac{c}{d} = \dfrac{a \cdot d}{b \cdot c}$ or $\dfrac{ad}{bc}$

4. $\dfrac{x}{7} \cdot \dfrac{x}{6} = \dfrac{x^2}{42}$

5. $\dfrac{x}{7} \div \dfrac{x}{6} = \dfrac{6}{7}$

Exercise Set 7.2

2. $\dfrac{9x^2}{y} \cdot \dfrac{4y}{3x^3} = \dfrac{9x^2 \cdot 4y}{y \cdot 3x^3} = \dfrac{3 \cdot 3 \cdot x^2 \cdot 4 \cdot y}{y \cdot 3 \cdot x \cdot x^2} = \dfrac{12}{x}$

4. $\dfrac{6x^2}{10x^3} \cdot \dfrac{5x}{12} = \dfrac{6x^2 \cdot 5x}{10x^3 \cdot 12} = \dfrac{6 \cdot x^2 \cdot 5 \cdot x}{2 \cdot 5 \cdot x \cdot x^2 \cdot 2 \cdot 6} = \dfrac{1}{4}$

6. $-\dfrac{9x^3 y^2}{18xy^5} \cdot y^3 = -\dfrac{9x^3 y^2 y^3}{18xy^5} = -\dfrac{9x \cdot x^2 \cdot y^5}{2 \cdot 9 \cdot x \cdot y^5} = -\dfrac{x^2}{2}$

8. $\dfrac{4x-24}{20x} \cdot \dfrac{5}{x-6} = \dfrac{(4x-24) \cdot 5}{20x(x-6)} = \dfrac{4(x-6) \cdot 5}{4 \cdot 5x(x-6)} = \dfrac{1}{x}$

10. $\dfrac{x^2+x}{8} \cdot \dfrac{16}{x+1} = \dfrac{(x^2+x) \cdot 16}{8(x+1)} = \dfrac{x(x+1) \cdot 2 \cdot 8}{8(x+1)} = 2x$

12. $\dfrac{(m-n)^2}{m+n} \cdot \dfrac{m}{m^2-mn} = \dfrac{(m-n)^2 \cdot m}{(m+n) \cdot (m^2-mn)}$
$= \dfrac{(m-n)(m-n) \cdot m}{(m+n) \cdot m \cdot (m-n)}$
$= \dfrac{m-n}{m+n}$

14. $\dfrac{a^2-4a+4}{a^2-4} \cdot \dfrac{a+3}{a-2} = \dfrac{(a-2)^2 \cdot (a+3)}{(a+2)(a-2) \cdot (a-2)}$
$= \dfrac{a+3}{a+2}$

16. $\dfrac{x^2+9x+20}{x^2-15x+44} \cdot \dfrac{x^2-11x+28}{x^2+12x+35}$
$= \dfrac{(x+4)(x+5) \cdot (x-7)(x-4)}{(x-11)(x-4) \cdot (x+5)(x+7)}$
$= \dfrac{(x+4)(x-7)}{(x-11)(x+7)}$

18. $\dfrac{9y^4}{6y} \div \dfrac{y^2}{3} = \dfrac{9y^4}{6y} \cdot \dfrac{3}{y^2}$
$= \dfrac{9y^4 \cdot 3}{6yy^2}$
$= \dfrac{9y \cdot y^3 \cdot 3}{2 \cdot 3 \cdot y^3}$
$= \dfrac{9y}{2}$

20. $\dfrac{7a^2b}{3ab^2} \div \dfrac{21a^2b^2}{14ab} = \dfrac{7a^2b}{3ab^2} \cdot \dfrac{14ab}{21a^2b^2}$
$= \dfrac{7a^2b \cdot 14ab}{3ab^2 \cdot 21a^2b^2}$
$= \dfrac{7a^2b \cdot 2 \cdot 7ab}{3ab^2 \cdot 3 \cdot 7a^2b^2}$
$= \dfrac{7 \cdot 2}{3b \cdot 3b}$
$= \dfrac{14}{9b^2}$

22. $\dfrac{(x+3)^2}{5} \div \dfrac{5x+15}{25} = \dfrac{(x+3)^2}{5} \cdot \dfrac{25}{5x+15}$
$= \dfrac{(x+3)(x+3) \cdot 5 \cdot 5}{5 \cdot 5(x+3)}$
$= x+3$

24. $\dfrac{9x^5}{a^2-b^2} \div \dfrac{27x^2}{3b-3a} = \dfrac{9x^5}{a^2-b^2} \cdot \dfrac{3b-3a}{27x^2}$
$= \dfrac{9x^2 \cdot x^3 \cdot (-1)(3)(a-b)}{(a+b)(a-b) \cdot 3 \cdot 9x^2}$
$= -\dfrac{x^2}{a+b}$

26. $\dfrac{(m-n)^2}{m+n} \div \dfrac{m^2-mn}{m} = \dfrac{(m-n)^2}{m+n} \cdot \dfrac{m}{m^2-mn}$
$= \dfrac{(m-n)(m-n)m}{(m+n) \cdot m \cdot (m-n)}$
$= \dfrac{m-n}{m+n}$

28.
$$\frac{x-3}{2-x} \div \frac{x^2+3x-18}{x^2+2x-8} = \frac{x-3}{2-x} \cdot \frac{x^2+2x-8}{x^2+3x-18}$$
$$= \frac{(x-3)\cdot(x+4)(x-2)}{-(x-2)\cdot(x+6)(x-3)}$$
$$= -\frac{x+4}{x+6}$$

30.
$$\frac{\dfrac{x+1}{(x+1)(2x+3)} \div \dfrac{20x+100}{2x+3}}{}$$
$$= \frac{x+1}{(x+1)(2x+3)} \cdot \frac{2x+3}{20x+100}$$
$$= \frac{(x+1)\cdot(2x+3)}{(x+1)(2x+3)\cdot 20(x+5)}$$
$$= \frac{1}{20(x+5)}$$

32.
$$\frac{6x+6}{5} \div \frac{9x+9}{10} = \frac{6x+6}{5} \cdot \frac{10}{9x+9}$$
$$= \frac{2\cdot 3(x+1)\cdot 2\cdot 5}{5\cdot 3\cdot 3(x+1)}$$
$$= \frac{4}{3}$$

34.
$$\frac{3x^2+12x}{6} \cdot \frac{9}{2x+8} = \frac{3x(x+4)\cdot 3\cdot 3}{2\cdot 3\cdot 2(x+4)} = \frac{9x}{4}$$

36.
$$\frac{3x+6}{20} \div \frac{4x+8}{8} = \frac{3x+6}{20} \cdot \frac{8}{4x+8}$$
$$= \frac{3(x+2)\cdot 4\cdot 2}{2\cdot 10\cdot 4\cdot(x+2)}$$
$$= \frac{3}{10}$$

38.
$$\frac{x^2-y^2}{3x^2+3xy} \cdot \frac{3x^2+6x}{3x^2-2xy-y^2}$$
$$= \frac{(x+y)(x-y)\cdot 3x(x+2)}{3x(x+y)(3x+y)(x-y)}$$
$$= \frac{x+2}{3x+y}$$

40.
$$\frac{x+3}{x^2-9} \div \frac{5x+15}{(x-3)^2} = \frac{x+3}{x^2-9} \cdot \frac{(x-3)^2}{5x+15}$$
$$= \frac{(x+3)\cdot(x-3)^2}{(x+3)(x-3)\cdot 5(x+3)}$$
$$= \frac{x-3}{5(x+3)}$$

42.
$$\frac{3y}{3-x} \div \frac{12xy}{x^2-9} = \frac{3y}{3-x} \cdot \frac{x^2-9}{12xy}$$
$$= \frac{3\cdot y\cdot(x+3)(x-3)}{-1\cdot(x-3)\cdot 3\cdot 4x\cdot y}$$
$$= -\frac{x+3}{4x}$$

44.
$$\frac{b^2+2b-3}{b^2+b-2} \cdot \frac{b^2-4}{b^2+6b+8}$$
$$= \frac{(b+3)(b-1)(b+2)(b-2)}{(b+2)(b-1)(b+2)(b+4)}$$
$$= \frac{(b+3)(b-2)}{(b+2)(b+4)}$$

46.
$$\frac{9x+18}{4x^2-3x} \cdot \frac{4x^2-11x+6}{x^2-4}$$
$$= \frac{9(x+2)\cdot(4x-3)(x-2)}{x(4x-3)\cdot(x+2)(x-2)}$$
$$= \frac{9}{x}$$

48.
$$\frac{36n^2-64}{3n^2+10n+8} \div \frac{3n^2-13n+12}{n^2-5n-14}$$
$$= \frac{36n^2-64}{3n^2+10n+8} \cdot \frac{n^2-5n-14}{3n^2-13n+12}$$
$$= \frac{4(3n+4)(3n-4)\cdot(n+2)(n-7)}{(3n+4)(n+2)\cdot(3n-4)(n-3)}$$
$$= \frac{4(n-7)}{n-3}$$

50.
$$\frac{4x^2+4x+1}{4x+2} \div \frac{4x+2}{16}$$
$$= \frac{4x^2+4x+1}{4x+2} \cdot \frac{16}{4x+2}$$
$$= \frac{(2x+1)(2x+1)\cdot 2\cdot 2\cdot 4}{2(2x+1)\cdot 2(2x+1)}$$
$$= \frac{4}{1}$$
$$= 4$$

52. $\dfrac{x^2+2x-xy-2y}{x^2-y^2} \div \dfrac{2x+4}{x+y}$

$= \dfrac{x^2+2x-xy-2y}{x^2-y^2} \cdot \dfrac{x+y}{2x+4}$

$= \dfrac{x(x+2)-y(x+2)}{(x-y)(x+y)} \cdot \dfrac{x+y}{2(x+2)}$

$= \dfrac{(x-y)(x+2)\cdot x+y}{(x-y)(x+y)\cdot 2(x+2)}$

$= \dfrac{1}{2}$

54. $\dfrac{16x^2+2x}{16x^2+10x+1} \cdot \dfrac{1}{4x^2+2x}$

$= \dfrac{2x(8x+1)\cdot 1}{(8x+1)(2x+1)\cdot 2x(2x+1)}$

$= \dfrac{1}{(2x+1)(2x+1)}$

$= \dfrac{1}{(2x+1)^2}$

56. $\dfrac{9y}{3y-3} \cdot \dfrac{y^3-1}{y^3+y^2+y} = \dfrac{9y\cdot(y-1)(y^2+y+1)}{3(y-1)\cdot y(y^2+y+1)}$
$\qquad\qquad\qquad\qquad\qquad = 3$

58. $\dfrac{x^3+27y^3}{6x} \div \dfrac{x^2-9y^2}{x^2-3xy}$

$= \dfrac{x^3+27y^3}{6x} \cdot \dfrac{x^2-3xy}{x^2-9y^2}$

$= \dfrac{(x+3y)(x^2-3xy+9y^2)\cdot x(x-3y)}{6x\cdot(x-3y)(x+3y)}$

$= \dfrac{x^2-3xy+9y^2}{6}$

60. $\dfrac{3}{15}+\dfrac{6}{15}=\dfrac{9}{15}=\dfrac{3}{5}$

62. $\dfrac{4}{3}-\dfrac{8}{3}=-\dfrac{4}{3}$

64. $-\dfrac{3}{2}+\left(\dfrac{1}{2}-\dfrac{3}{2}\right)=-\dfrac{3}{2}+\left(-\dfrac{2}{2}\right)=-\dfrac{5}{2}$

66. $5x-y=10$

x	y
0	–10
2	0

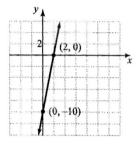

68. $\dfrac{2}{3}\cdot\dfrac{2}{4}=\dfrac{2\cdot 2}{3\cdot 4}=\dfrac{2\cdot 2}{3\cdot 2\cdot 2}=\dfrac{1}{3}\neq\dfrac{2}{7}$

The statement is false.

70. $\dfrac{7}{a}\cdot\dfrac{3}{a}=\dfrac{7\cdot 3}{a\cdot a}=\dfrac{21}{a^2}\neq\dfrac{21}{a}$

The statement is false.

72. $A=s^2$

$A=\left(\dfrac{2x}{5x+3}\right)^2$

$= \dfrac{2x}{5x+3}\cdot\dfrac{2x}{5x+3}$

$= \dfrac{2x\cdot 2x}{(5x+3)\cdot(5x+3)}$

$= \dfrac{4x^2}{(5x+3)^2}$

The area of the square is

$\dfrac{4x^2}{(5x+3)^2}$ square meters.

74. $\left(\dfrac{x^2-9}{x^2-1}\cdot\dfrac{x^2+2x+1}{2x^2+9x+9}\right)\div\dfrac{2x+3}{1-x}$

$= \dfrac{x^2-9}{x^2-1}\cdot\dfrac{x^2+2x+1}{2x^2+9x+9}\cdot\dfrac{1-x}{2x+3}$

$= \dfrac{(x+3)(x-3)(x+1)(x+1)(-1)(x-1)}{(x+1)(x-1)(2x+3)(x+3)(2x+3)}$

$= -\dfrac{(x-3)(x+1)}{(2x+3)^2}$

76. $\left(\dfrac{x^2y^2 - xy}{4x - 4y} \div \dfrac{3y - 3x}{8x - 8y}\right) \cdot \dfrac{y - x}{8}$

$= \left(\dfrac{x^2y^2 - xy}{4x - 4y} \cdot \dfrac{8x - 8y}{3y - 3x}\right) \cdot \dfrac{y - x}{8}$

$= \dfrac{xy(xy - 1) \cdot 8(x - y)(y - x)}{4(x - y) \cdot 3(y - x) \cdot 8}$

$= \dfrac{xy(xy - 1)}{12}$

78. Answers may vary

Section 7.3

Practice Exercises

1. $\dfrac{7a}{4b} + \dfrac{a}{4b} = \dfrac{7a + a}{4b} = \dfrac{8a}{4b} = \dfrac{2a}{b}$

2. $\dfrac{3x}{3x - 2} - \dfrac{2}{3x - 2} = \dfrac{3x - 2}{3x - 2} = \dfrac{1}{1}$ or 1

3. $\dfrac{4x^2 + 15x}{x + 3} - \dfrac{8x + 15}{x + 3} = \dfrac{(4x^2 + 15x) - (8x + 15)}{x + 3}$

$= \dfrac{4x^2 + 15x - 8x - 15}{x + 3}$

$= \dfrac{4x^2 + 7x - 15}{x + 3}$

$= \dfrac{(x + 3)(4x - 5)}{x + 3}$

$= 4x - 5$

4. a. Find the prime factorization of each denominator.
$14 = 2 \cdot 7$
$21 = 3 \cdot 7$
The greatest number of times that the factor 2 appears is 1. The greatest number of times that the factor 3 appears is 1. The greatest number of times that the factor 7 appears is 1.
$\text{LCD} = 2^1 \cdot 3^1 \cdot 7^1 = 42$

b. Factor each denominator.
$9y = 3 \cdot 3 \cdot y = 3^2 \cdot y$
$15y^3 = 3 \cdot 5 \cdot y^3$
The greatest number of times that the factor 3 appears is 2. The greatest number of times that the factor 5 appears is 1. The greatest number of times that the factor y appears is 3.
$\text{LCD} = 3^2 \cdot 5^1 \cdot y^3 = 9 \cdot 5 \cdot y^3 = 45y^3$

5. a. The denominators $y - 5$ and $y - 4$ are completely factored already. The factor $y - 5$ appears once and the factor $y - 4$ appears once.
$\text{LCD} = (y - 5)(y - 4)$

b. The denominators a and $a + 2$ cannot be factored further. The factor a appears once and the factor $a + 2$ appears once.
$\text{LCD} = a(a + 2)$

6. Factor each denominator.
$(2x - 1)^2 = (2x - 1)^2$
$6x - 3 = 3(2x - 1)$
The greatest number that the factor $2x - 1$ appears in any one denominator is 2.
The greatest number of times that the factor 3 appears is 1.
$\text{LCD} = 3(2x - 1)^2$

7. Factor each denominator.
$x^2 + 5x + 4 = (x + 1)(x + 4)$
$x^2 - 16 = (x - 4)(x + 4)$
$\text{LCD} = (x + 1)(x + 4)(x - 4)$

8. The denominators $3 - x$ and $x - 3$ are opposites. That is, $3 - x = -1(x - 3)$. Use $x - 3$ or $3 - x$ as the LCD.
$\text{LCD} = x - 3$ or $\text{LCD} = 3 - x$

9. a. Since $5y(7xy) = 35xy^2$, multiply by 1 in the form of $\dfrac{7xy}{7xy}$.

$\dfrac{3x}{5y} = \dfrac{3x}{5y} \cdot 1 = \dfrac{3x}{5y} \cdot \dfrac{7xy}{7xy} = \dfrac{3x(7xy)}{5y(7xy)} = \dfrac{21x^2y}{35xy^2}$

b. First, factor the denominator on the right.
$\dfrac{9x}{4x + 7} = \dfrac{}{2(4x + 7)}$
To obtain the denominator on the right from the denominator on the left, multiply by 1 in the form of $\dfrac{2}{2}$.

$\dfrac{9x}{4x + 7} = \dfrac{9x}{4x + 7} \cdot \dfrac{2}{2}$

$= \dfrac{9x \cdot 2}{(4x + 7) \cdot 2}$

$= \dfrac{18x}{2(4x + 7)}$ or $\dfrac{18x}{8x + 14}$

10. First, factor the denominator $x^2 - 2x - 15$ as $(x + 3)(x - 5)$. If we multiply the original denominator $(x + 3)(x - 5)$ by $x - 2$, the result is the new denominator $(x - 2)(x + 3)(x - 5)$. Thus, we multiply by 1 in the form $\dfrac{x-2}{x-2}$.

$$\frac{3}{x^2 - 2x - 15} = \frac{3}{(x+3)(x-5)}$$
$$= \frac{3}{(x+3)(x-5)} \cdot \frac{x-2}{x-2}$$
$$= \frac{3(x-2)}{(x+3)(x-5)(x-2)}$$
$$= \frac{3x-6}{(x-2)(x+30(x-5)}$$

Vocabulary and Readiness Check

1. $\dfrac{7}{11} + \dfrac{2}{11} = \dfrac{9}{\underline{11}}$

2. $\dfrac{7}{11} - \dfrac{2}{11} = \dfrac{5}{\underline{11}}$

3. $\dfrac{a}{b} + \dfrac{c}{b} = \dfrac{a+c}{\underline{b}}$

4. $\dfrac{a}{b} - \dfrac{c}{b} = \dfrac{a-c}{\underline{b}}$

5. $\dfrac{5}{x} - \dfrac{6+x}{x} = \dfrac{5-(6+x)}{\underline{x}}$

Exercise Set 7.3

2. $\dfrac{x+1}{7} + \dfrac{6}{7} = \dfrac{x+1+6}{7} = \dfrac{x+7}{7}$

4. $\dfrac{3p}{2q} + \dfrac{11p}{2q} = \dfrac{3p+11p}{2q} = \dfrac{14p}{2q} = \dfrac{7p}{q}$

6. $\dfrac{8y}{y-2} - \dfrac{16}{y-2} = \dfrac{8y-16}{y-2} = \dfrac{8(y-2)}{y-2} = 8$

8. $\dfrac{9}{y+9} + \dfrac{y-5}{y+9} = \dfrac{9+y-5}{y+9} = \dfrac{y+4}{y+9}$

10. $\dfrac{x^2+9x}{x+7} - \dfrac{4x+14}{x+7} = \dfrac{x^2+9x-4x-14}{x+7}$
$$= \frac{x^2+5x-14}{x+7}$$
$$= \frac{(x+7)(x-2)}{x+7}$$
$$= x-2$$

12. $\dfrac{3y}{y^2+3y-10} - \dfrac{6}{y^2+3y-10} = \dfrac{3y-6}{y^2+3y-10}$
$$= \frac{3(y-2)}{(y+5)(y-2)}$$
$$= \frac{3}{y+5}$$

14. $\dfrac{3x-1}{x^2+5x-6} - \dfrac{2x-7}{x^2+5x-6} = \dfrac{3x-1-(2x-7)}{x^2+5x-6}$
$$= \frac{3x-1-2x+7}{x^2+5x-6}$$
$$= \frac{x+6}{x^2+5x-6}$$
$$= \frac{x+6}{(x+6)(x-1)}$$
$$= \frac{1}{x-1}$$

16. $\dfrac{4p-3}{2p+7} + \dfrac{3p+8}{2p+7} = \dfrac{4p-3+3p+8}{2p+7} = \dfrac{7p+5}{2p+7}$

18. $\dfrac{6x^2}{2x-5} - \dfrac{25+2x^2}{2x-5} = \dfrac{6x^2-25-2x^2}{2x-5}$
$$= \frac{4x^2-25}{2x-5}$$
$$= \frac{(2x-5)(2x+5)}{(2x-5)}$$
$$= 2x+5$$

20. $\dfrac{7x+1}{x-4} - \dfrac{2x+21}{x-4} = \dfrac{7x+1-(2x+21)}{x-4}$
$$= \frac{7x+1-2x-21}{x-4}$$
$$= \frac{5x-20}{x-4}$$
$$= \frac{5(x-4)}{x-4}$$
$$= 5$$

22. $8y = 2^3 \cdot y$

$4y^5 = 2^2 \cdot y^5$

$\text{LCD} = 2^3 \cdot y^5 = 8y^5$

24. $6y = 2 \cdot 3y$

$4y + 12 = 2^2(y+3)$

$\text{LCD} = 2^2 \cdot 3y \cdot (y+3) = 12y(y+3)$

26. $\text{LCD} = (x-1)(x+5)$

28. $4x + 20 = 4(x+5)$

$\text{LCD} = 4(x+5)$

30. $7x - 14 = 7(x-2)$

$\text{LCD} = 7(x-2)^2$

32. $4x - 12 = 2^2 \cdot (x-3)$

$2x^2 - 12x + 18 = 2(x^2 - 6x + 9) = 2(x-3)^2$

$\text{LCD} = 2^2(x-3)^2 = 4(x-3)^2$

34. $3x - 7 = 3x - 7$

$7 - 3x = -(3x-7)$

$\text{LCD} = 3x - 7 \text{ or } 7 - 3x$

36. $x^2 + 4x + 3 = (x+3)(x+1)$

$x^2 + 10x + 21 = (x+3)(x+7)$

$\text{LCD} = (x+7)(x+3)(x+1)$

38. $4x^2 + 5x + 1 = (4x+1)(x+1)$

$3x^2 - 2x - 1 = (3x+1)(x-1)$

$\text{LCD} = (4x+1)(x+1)(3x+1)(x-1)$

40. $x^2 - 25 = (x+5)(x-5)$

$3x^3 - 15x^2 = 3x^2(x-5)$

$\text{LCD} = 3x^2(x+5)(x-5)$

42. $\dfrac{3}{9y^5} = \dfrac{3(8y^4)}{9y^5(8y^4)} = \dfrac{24y^4}{72y^9}$

44. $\dfrac{5}{4y^2x} = \dfrac{5(8yx)}{4y^2x(8yx)} = \dfrac{40yx}{32y^3x^2}$

46. $\dfrac{4x+1}{3x+6} = \dfrac{(4x+1)(y)}{3(x+2)(y)} = \dfrac{4xy+y}{3y(x+2)}$

48. $\dfrac{5+y}{2x^2+10} = \dfrac{5+y}{2(x^2+5)} = \dfrac{(5+y)(2)}{2(x^2+5)(2)} = \dfrac{10+2y}{4(x^2+5)}$

50. $\dfrac{5x}{x^3 + 2x^2 - 3x} = \dfrac{5x}{x(x-1)(x+3)}$

$= \dfrac{5x \cdot (x-5)}{x(x-1)(x+3) \cdot (x-5)}$

$= \dfrac{5x^2 - 25x}{x(x-1)(x-5)(x+3)}$

52. $\dfrac{6m-5}{3x^2-9} = \dfrac{(6m-5)(4)}{(3x^2-9)(4)} = \dfrac{24m-20}{12x^2-36}$

54. $\dfrac{5x}{7} \cdot \dfrac{9x}{7} = \dfrac{5x \cdot 9x}{7 \cdot 7} = \dfrac{45x^2}{49}$

56. $\dfrac{x+3}{4} - \dfrac{2x-1}{4} = \dfrac{x+3-(2x-1)}{4}$

$= \dfrac{x+3-2x+1}{4}$

$= \dfrac{-x+4}{4}$

58. $\dfrac{x^2+5x}{x^2-25} \cdot \dfrac{3x-15}{x^2} = \dfrac{x(x+5) \cdot 3(x-5)}{(x+5)(x-5) \cdot x^2} = \dfrac{3}{x}$

60. $\dfrac{-2x}{x^3-8x} \div \dfrac{3x}{x^3-8x} = \dfrac{-2x}{x^3-8x} \cdot \dfrac{x^3-8x}{3x}$

$= \dfrac{-2x(x^3-8x)}{(x^3-8x)(3x)}$

$= -\dfrac{2}{3}$

62. $\dfrac{x^3+7x^2}{3x^3-x^2} \div \dfrac{5x^2+36x+7}{9x^2-1}$

$= \dfrac{x^3+7x^2}{3x^3-x^2} \cdot \dfrac{9x^2-1}{5x^2+36x+7}$

$= \dfrac{x^2(x+7) \cdot (3x+1)(3x-1)}{x^2(3x-1) \cdot (5x+1)(x+7)}$

$= \dfrac{3x+1}{5x+1}$

64. $\text{LCD} = 10$

$\dfrac{9}{10} - \dfrac{3}{5} = \dfrac{9}{10} - \dfrac{3(2)}{5(2)} = \dfrac{9}{10} - \dfrac{6}{10} = \dfrac{3}{10}$

66. $15 = 3 \cdot 5$

$9 = 3^2$

$LCD = 3^2 \cdot 5 = 45$

$\dfrac{11}{15} + \dfrac{5}{9} = \dfrac{11(3)}{15(3)} + \dfrac{5(5)}{9(5)} = \dfrac{33}{45} + \dfrac{25}{45} = \dfrac{33+25}{45} = \dfrac{58}{45}$

68. $30 = 2 \cdot 3 \cdot 5$

$18 = 2 \cdot 3^2$

$LCD = 2 \cdot 3^2 \cdot 5 = 90$

$\dfrac{7}{30} + \dfrac{3}{18} = \dfrac{7(3)}{30(3)} + \dfrac{3(5)}{18(5)} = \dfrac{21+15}{90} = \dfrac{36}{90} = \dfrac{2}{5}$

70. Answers may vary

72. $\dfrac{3}{x} - \dfrac{y}{x} = \dfrac{3-y}{x}$

The correct choice is c.

74. $\dfrac{3}{x} \div \dfrac{y}{x} = \dfrac{3}{x} \cdot \dfrac{x}{y} = \dfrac{3 \cdot x}{x \cdot y} = \dfrac{3}{y}$

The correct choice is a.

76. $\dfrac{8y}{2-x} = \dfrac{(8y)(-1)}{(2-x)(-1)} = \dfrac{-8y}{x-2} = -\dfrac{8y}{x-2}$

78. $\dfrac{x-3}{-(x-2)} = \dfrac{(x-3)(-1)}{-(x-2)(-1)} = \dfrac{3-x}{x-2}$

80. $P = \dfrac{x+1}{x+3} + \dfrac{5}{x+3} + \dfrac{x+4}{x+3} + \dfrac{5}{x+3}$

$= \dfrac{x+1+5+x+4+5}{x+3}$

$= \dfrac{2x+15}{x+3}$

The perimeter is $\dfrac{2x+15}{x+3}$ inches.

82. Answers may vary

84. Since $8 = 2^3$ and $12 = 2^2 \cdot 3$, the least common multiple of 8 and 12 is $2^3 \cdot 3 = 24$. Since $8 \cdot 3 = 24$ and $12 \cdot 2 = 24$, buy three packages of hot dogs and two packages of buns.

86. Answers may vary

88. Answers may vary

Section 7.4

Practice Exercises

1. a. Since $5 = 5$ and $15 = 3 \cdot 5$, the LCD $= 3 \cdot 5 = 15$.

$\dfrac{2x}{5} - \dfrac{6x}{15} = \dfrac{2x(3)}{5(3)} - \dfrac{6x}{15}$

$= \dfrac{6x}{15} - \dfrac{6x}{15}$

$= \dfrac{6x-6x}{15}$

$= \dfrac{0}{15}$

$= 0$

b. Since $8a = 2^3 \cdot a$ and $12a^2 = 2^2 \cdot 3 \cdot a^2$, the LCD $= 2^3 \cdot 3 \cdot a^2 = 24a^2$.

$\dfrac{7}{8a} + \dfrac{5}{12a^2} = \dfrac{7(3a)}{8a(3a)} + \dfrac{5(2)}{12a^2(2)}$

$= \dfrac{21a}{24a^2} + \dfrac{10}{24a^2}$

$= \dfrac{21a+10}{24a^2}$

2. Since $x^2 - 25 = (x+5)(x-5)$, the LCD $= (x+5)(x-5)$.

$\dfrac{12x}{x^2-25} - \dfrac{6}{x+5} = \dfrac{12x}{(x+5)(x-5)} - \dfrac{6(x-5)}{(x+5)(x-5)}$

$= \dfrac{12x - 6(x-5)}{(x+5)(x-5)}$

$= \dfrac{12x - 6x + 30}{(x+5)(x-5)}$

$= \dfrac{6x+30}{(x+5)(x-5)}$

$= \dfrac{6(x+5)}{(x+5)(x-5)}$

$= \dfrac{6}{x-5}$

3. The LCD is $5y(y + 1)$.

$$\frac{3}{5y} + \frac{2}{y+1} = \frac{3(y+1)}{5y(y+1)} + \frac{2(5y)}{(y+1)(5y)}$$

$$= \frac{3(y+1) + 2(5y)}{5y(y+1)}$$

$$= \frac{3y + 3 + 10y}{5y(y+1)}$$

$$= \frac{13y + 3}{5y(y+1)}$$

4. $x - 5$ and $5 - x$ are opposites. Write the denominator $5 - x$ as $-(x - 5)$ and simplify.

$$\frac{6}{x-5} - \frac{7}{5-x} = \frac{6}{x-5} - \frac{7}{-(x-5)}$$

$$= \frac{6}{x-5} - \frac{-7}{x-5}$$

$$= \frac{6 - (-7)}{x-5}$$

$$= \frac{13}{x-5}$$

5. Note that 2 is the same as $\frac{2}{1}$. The LCD of $\frac{2}{1}$

and $\frac{b}{b+3}$ is $b + 3$.

$$2 + \frac{b}{b+3} = \frac{2}{1} + \frac{b}{b+3}$$

$$= \frac{2(b+3)}{1(b+3)} + \frac{b}{b+3}$$

$$= \frac{2(b+3) + b}{b+3}$$

$$= \frac{2b + 6 + b}{b+3}$$

$$= \frac{3b + 6}{b+3} \text{ or } \frac{3(b+2)}{b+3}$$

6. First, factor the denominators.

$$\frac{5}{2x^2 + 3x} - \frac{3x}{4x+6} = \frac{5}{x(2x+3)} - \frac{3x}{2(2x+3)}$$

The LCD is $2x(2x + 3)$.

$$\frac{5}{2x^2 + 3x} - \frac{3x}{4x+6} = \frac{5(2)}{x(2x+3)(2)} - \frac{3x(x)}{2(2x+3)(x)}$$

$$= \frac{10 - 3x^2}{2x(2x+3)}$$

7. First, factor the denominators.

$$x^2 + 7x + 12 = (x+4)(x+3)$$

$$x^2 - 9 = (x+3)(x-3)$$

$$\text{LCD} = (x+4)(x+3)(x-3)$$

$$\frac{2x}{x^2 + 7x + 12} + \frac{3x}{x^2 - 9}$$

$$= \frac{2x}{(x+4)(x+3)} + \frac{3x}{(x+3)(x-3)}$$

$$= \frac{2x(x-3)}{(x+4)(x+3)(x-3)} + \frac{3x(x+4)}{(x+3)(x-3)(x+4)}$$

$$= \frac{2x(x-3) + 3x(x+4)}{(x+4)(x+3)(x-3)}$$

$$= \frac{2x^2 - 6x + 3x^2 + 12x}{(x+4)(x+3)(x-3)}$$

$$= \frac{5x^2 + 6x}{(x+4)(x+3)(x-3)} \text{ or } \frac{x(5x+6)}{(x+4)(x+3)(x-3)}$$

Vocabulary and Readiness Check

1. The first step to perform on $\frac{3}{4} - \frac{y}{4}$ is to subtract the numerators and place the difference over the common denominator; choice d.

2. The first step to perform on $\frac{2}{a} \cdot \frac{3}{a+6}$ is to multiply the numerators and multiply the denominators; choice c.

3. The first step to perform on $\frac{x+1}{x} \div \frac{x-1}{x}$ is to multiply the first rational expression by the reciprocal of the second rational expression; choice a.

4. The first step to perform on $\frac{9}{x-2} - \frac{x}{x+2}$ is to find the LCD and write each expression as an equivalent expression with the LCD as denominator; choice b.

Exercise Set 7.4

2. $\text{LCD} = 6 \cdot 7 \cdot a = 42a$

$$\frac{15}{7a} + \frac{8}{6a} = \frac{15(6)}{7a(6)} + \frac{8(7)}{6a(7)}$$

$$= \frac{90}{42a} + \frac{56}{42a}$$

$$= \frac{146}{42a}$$

$$= \frac{73(2)}{21a(2)}$$

$$= \frac{73}{21a}$$

4. $\text{LCD} = 5d$

$$\frac{4c}{d} - \frac{8d}{5} = \frac{4c(5)}{d(5)} - \frac{8d \cdot d}{5d}$$

$$= \frac{20c}{5d} - \frac{8d^2}{5d}$$

$$= \frac{20c - 8d^2}{5d}$$

6. $\text{LCD} = 3x^2$

$$\frac{14}{3x^2} + \frac{6}{x} = \frac{14}{3x^2} + \frac{6(3x)}{x(3x)} = \frac{14}{3x^2} + \frac{18x}{3x^2} = \frac{14 + 18x}{3x^2}$$

8. $3x + 12 = 3(x + 4)$
$\text{LCD} = 3(x + 4)$

$$\frac{8}{x+4} - \frac{3}{3x+12} = \frac{8(3)}{(x+4)(3)} - \frac{3}{3(x+4)}$$

$$= \frac{24}{3(x+4)} - \frac{3}{3(x+4)}$$

$$= \frac{24 - 3}{3(x+4)}$$

$$= \frac{21}{3(x+4)}$$

$$= \frac{7}{x+4}$$

10. $x^2 - 16 = (x-4)(x+4)$
$\text{LCD} = (x-4)(x+4)$

$$\frac{5}{x-4} + \frac{4x}{x^2-16} = \frac{5(x+4)}{(x-4)(x+4)} + \frac{4x}{(x-4)(x+4)}$$

$$= \frac{5(x+4) + 4x}{(x-4)(x+4)}$$

$$= \frac{5x + 20 + 4x}{(x-4)(x+4)}$$

$$= \frac{9x + 20}{(x-4)(x+4)}$$

12. $\text{LCD} = y^2(2y+1)$

$$\frac{5}{y^2} - \frac{y}{2y+1} = \frac{5(2y+1)}{y^2(2y+1)} - \frac{y(y^2)}{(2y+1)(y^2)}$$

$$= \frac{5(2y+1) - y(y^2)}{y^2(2y+1)}$$

$$= \frac{10y + 5 - y^3}{y^2(2y+1)}$$

14. $4 - y = -(y - 4)$
$\text{LCD} = y - 4$

$$\frac{15}{y-4} + \frac{20}{4-y} = \frac{15}{y-4} + \frac{20}{-(y-4)}$$

$$= \frac{15}{y-4} + \frac{-20}{y-4}$$

$$= \frac{15 - 20}{y-4}$$

$$= -\frac{5}{y-4}$$

16. $7 - a = -(a - 7)$
$\text{LCD} = a - 7$

$$\frac{5}{a-7} + \frac{5}{7-a} = \frac{5}{a-7} + \frac{5}{-(a-7)}$$

$$= \frac{5}{a-7} + \frac{-5}{a-7}$$

$$= \frac{5 + (-5)}{a-7}$$

$$= 0$$

18. $1 - 25x^2 = -(25x^2 - 1)$

LCD $= 25x^2 - 1$

$$\frac{-9}{25x^2 - 1} + \frac{7}{1 - 25x^2} = \frac{-9}{(25x^2 - 1)} + \frac{7}{-(25x^2 - 1)}$$
$$= \frac{-9}{25x^2 - 1} + \frac{-7}{25x^2 - 1}$$
$$= \frac{-9 - 7}{25x^2 - 1}$$
$$= \frac{-16}{25x^2 - 1}$$

20. LCD $= x^2$

$$\frac{7}{x^2} - 5x = \frac{7}{x^2} - \frac{5x \cdot x^2}{x^2} = \frac{7}{x^2} - \frac{5x^3}{x^2} = \frac{7 - 5x^3}{x^2}$$

22. LCD $= y + 5$

$$\frac{6y}{y+5} + 1 = \frac{6y}{y+5} + \frac{1}{1}$$
$$= \frac{6y}{y+5} + \frac{1(y+5)}{1(y+5)}$$
$$= \frac{6y}{y+5} + \frac{y+5}{y+5}$$
$$= \frac{6y + y + 5}{y+5}$$
$$= \frac{7y + 5}{y+5}$$

24. LCD $= 2x - 3$

$$\frac{7}{2x-3} - 3 = \frac{7}{2x-3} - \frac{3}{1}$$
$$= \frac{7}{2x-3} - \frac{3(2x-3)}{1(2x-3)}$$
$$= \frac{7}{2x-3} - \frac{6x-9}{2x-3}$$
$$= \frac{7 - (6x-9)}{2x-3}$$
$$= \frac{7 - 6x + 9}{2x-3}$$
$$= \frac{16 - 6x}{2x-3}$$

26. LCD $= 3y$

$$\frac{-y+1}{y} - \frac{2y-5}{3y} = \frac{(-y+1)(3)}{y(3)} - \frac{2y-5}{3y}$$
$$= \frac{(-y+1)(3) - (2y-5)}{3y}$$
$$= \frac{-3y+3-2y+5}{3y}$$
$$= \frac{-5y+8}{3y} \text{ or } -\frac{5y-8}{3y}$$

28. $\dfrac{7x}{x-3} - \dfrac{4x+9}{x-3} = \dfrac{7x - (4x+9)}{x-3}$
$$= \frac{7x - 4x - 9}{x-3}$$
$$= \frac{3x - 9}{x-3}$$
$$= \frac{3(x-3)}{x-3}$$
$$= 3$$

30. $\dfrac{5x}{6} + \dfrac{11x^2}{2} = \dfrac{5x}{6} + \dfrac{11x^2(3)}{2(3)}$
$$= \frac{5x}{6} + \frac{33x^2}{6}$$
$$= \frac{5x + 33x^2}{6}$$

32. LCD $= (x-2)^2$

$$\frac{5x}{(x-2)^2} - \frac{3}{x-2} = \frac{5x}{(x-2)^2} - \frac{3(x-2)}{(x-2)(x-2)}$$
$$= \frac{5x - 3(x-2)}{(x-2)^2}$$
$$= \frac{5x - 3x + 6}{(x-2)^2}$$
$$= \frac{2x + 6}{(x-2)^2}$$
$$= \frac{2(x+3)}{(x-2)^2}$$

34. $LCD = 3y(y + 5)$

$$\frac{1}{y+5} + \frac{2}{3y} = \frac{1(3y)}{(y+5)(3y)} + \frac{2(y+5)}{3y(y+5)}$$

$$= \frac{3y}{3y(y+5)} + \frac{2y+10}{3y(y+5)}$$

$$= \frac{3y+2y+10}{3y(y+5)}$$

$$= \frac{5y+10}{3y(y+5)}$$

$$= \frac{5(y+2)}{3y(y+5)}$$

36. $LCD = x$

$$\frac{6}{x} - 1 = \frac{6}{x} - \frac{1}{1} = \frac{6}{x} - \frac{1(x)}{1(x)} = \frac{6-x}{x}$$

38. $LCD = (x-10)(x-3)$

$$\frac{9x}{x-10} - \frac{x}{x-3}$$

$$= \frac{9x(x-3)}{(x-10)(x-3)} - \frac{x(x-10)}{(x-3)(x-10)}$$

$$= \frac{9x(x-3) - x(x-10)}{(x-10)(x-3)}$$

$$= \frac{9x^2 - 27x - x^2 + 10x}{(x-10)(x-3)}$$

$$= \frac{8x^2 - 17x}{(x-10)(x-3)} \text{ or } \frac{x(8x-17)}{(x-10)(x-3)}$$

40. $4 - 3n = -(3n - 4)$

$LCD = 3n - 4$

$$\frac{10}{3n-4} - \frac{5}{4-3n} = \frac{10}{3n-4} - \frac{5}{-(3n-4)}$$

$$= \frac{10}{3n-4} + \frac{5}{3n-4}$$

$$= \frac{10+5}{3n-4}$$

$$= \frac{15}{3n-4}$$

42. $LCD = (x+1)(x+5)^2$

$$\frac{5}{(x+1)(x+5)} - \frac{2}{(x+5)^2}$$

$$= \frac{5(x+5)}{(x+1)(x+5)(x+5)} - \frac{2(x+1)}{(x+5)^2(x+1)}$$

$$= \frac{5(x+5) - 2(x+1)}{(x+1)(x+5)^2}$$

$$= \frac{5x+25 - 2x - 2}{(x+1)(x+5)^2}$$

$$= \frac{3x+23}{(x+1)(x+5)^2}$$

44. $x^2 - 4 = (x-2)(x+2)$

$x^2 - 4x + 4 = (x-2)^2$

$LCD = (x-2)^2(x+2)$

$$\frac{x}{x^2-4} - \frac{5}{x^2-4x+4}$$

$$= \frac{x(x-2)}{(x-2)(x+2)(x-2)} - \frac{5(x+2)}{(x-2)^2(x+2)}$$

$$= \frac{x^2-2x}{(x-2)^2(x+2)} - \frac{5x+10}{(x-2)^2(x+2)}$$

$$= \frac{x^2-2x-(5x+10)}{(x-2)^2(x+2)}$$

$$= \frac{x^2-2x-5x-10}{(x-2)^2(x+2)}$$

$$= \frac{x^2-7x-10}{(x-2)^2(x+2)}$$

46. $x^2 - y^2 = (x+y)(x-y)$

$LCD = (x+y)(x-y)$

$$\frac{1}{x+y} - \frac{y}{x^2-y^2} = \frac{1(x-y)}{(x+y)(x-y)} - \frac{y}{(x+y)(x-y)}$$

$$= \frac{x-y}{(x+y)(x-y)} - \frac{y}{(x+y)(x-y)}$$

$$= \frac{x-y-y}{(x+y)(x-y)}$$

$$= \frac{x-2y}{(x+y)(x-y)}$$

48. $\text{LCD} = (5x+1)^2$

$$\frac{x-6}{5x+1} + \frac{6}{(5x+1)^2} = \frac{(x-6)(5x+1)}{(5x+1)(5x+1)} + \frac{6}{(5x+1)^2}$$
$$= \frac{(x-6)(5x+1)+6}{(5x+1)^2}$$
$$= \frac{5x^2-29x-6+6}{(5x+1)^2}$$
$$= \frac{5x^2-29x}{(5x+1)^2} \text{ or } \frac{x(5x-29)}{(5x+1)^2}$$

50. $4-2a = -(2a-4) = -2(a-2)$

$\text{LCD} = 2(a-2)$

$$\frac{-1}{a-2} + \frac{4}{4-2a} = \frac{-1}{a-2} + \frac{4}{-2(a-2)}$$
$$= \frac{-1}{a-2} + \frac{-4}{2(a-2)}$$
$$= \frac{-1(2)}{(a-2)(2)} + \frac{-4}{2(a-2)}$$
$$= \frac{-2-4}{2(a-2)}$$
$$= \frac{-6}{2(x-2)}$$
$$= -\frac{3}{a-2}$$

52. $x^2+4x+4 = (x+2)^2$

$\text{LCD} = (x+2)^2$

$$\frac{2}{x^2+4x+4} + \frac{1}{x+2} = \frac{2}{(x+2)^2} + \frac{1(x+2)}{(x+2)(x+2)}$$
$$= \frac{2}{(x+2)^2} + \frac{x+2}{(x+2)(x+2)}$$
$$= \frac{2+x+2}{(x+2)^2}$$
$$= \frac{x+4}{(x+2)^2}$$

54. $y^2-3y+2 = (y-2)(y-1)$

$\text{LCD} = (y-2)(y-1)$

$$\frac{-7}{y^2-3y+2} - \frac{2}{y-1}$$
$$= \frac{-7}{(y-2)(y-1)} - \frac{2(y-2)}{(y-1)(y-2)}$$
$$= \frac{-7-2(y-2)}{(y-2)(y-1)}$$
$$= \frac{-7-2y+4}{(y-2)(y-1)}$$
$$= \frac{-2y-3}{(y-2)(y-1)} \text{ or } -\frac{2y+3}{(y-2)(y-1)}$$

56. $y^2-81 = (y+9)(y-9)$

$\text{LCD} = 2(y+9)(y-9)$

$$\frac{27}{y^2-81} + \frac{3}{2(y+9)}$$
$$= \frac{27}{(y+9)(y-9)} + \frac{3}{2(y+9)}$$
$$= \frac{27(2)}{(y+9)(y-9)(2)} + \frac{3(y-9)}{2(y+9)(y-9)}$$
$$= \frac{54+3y-27}{2(y+9)(y-9)}$$
$$= \frac{3y+27}{2(y+9)(y-9)}$$
$$= \frac{3(y+9)}{2(y+9)(y-9)}$$
$$= \frac{3}{2(y-9)}$$

58. $x^2+12x+20 = (x+10)(x+2)$

$x^2+8x-20 = (x+10)(x-2)$

$\text{LCD} = (x+10)(x+2)(x-2)$

$$\frac{x+4}{x^2+12x+20} + \frac{x+1}{x^2+8x-20}$$
$$= \frac{(x+4)(x-2)}{(x+10)(x+2)(x-2)} + \frac{(x+1)(x+2)}{(x+10)(x-2)(x+2)}$$
$$= \frac{(x+4)(x-2)+(x+1)(x+2)}{(x+10)(x+2)(x-2)}$$
$$= \frac{x^2+2x-8+x^2+3x+2}{(x+10)(x+2)(x-2)}$$
$$= \frac{2x^2+5x-6}{(x+10)(x+2)(x-2)}$$

60. $5y^2 - 25y + 30 = 5(y-2)(y-3)$

$\quad 4y^2 - 8y = 4y(y-2)$

$\quad$ LCD $= 20y(y-2)(y-3)$

$$\frac{6}{5y^2 - 25y + 30} - \frac{2}{4y^2 - 8y}$$

$$= \frac{6(4y)}{5(y-2)(y-3)(4y)} - \frac{2(5)(y-3)}{4y(y-2)(5)(y-3)}$$

$$= \frac{6(4y) - 2(5)(y-3)}{20y(y-2)(y-3)}$$

$$= \frac{24y - 10y + 30}{20y(y-2)(y-3)}$$

$$= \frac{14y + 30}{20y(y-2)(y-3)}$$

$$= \frac{2(7y + 15)}{2 \cdot 10y(y-2)(y-3)}$$

$$= \frac{7y + 15}{10y(y-2)(y-3)}$$

62. $\dfrac{9z+5}{15} \cdot \dfrac{5z}{81z^2 - 25} = \dfrac{9z + 5 \cdot 5z}{3 \cdot 5 \cdot (9z - 5)(9z + 5)}$

$$= \frac{z}{3(9z - 5)}$$

64. $\dfrac{2z^2}{4z-1} - \dfrac{z - 2z^2}{4z - 1} = \dfrac{2z^2 - z + 2z^2}{4z - 1}$

$$= \frac{4z^2 - z}{4z - 1}$$

$$= \frac{z(4z - 1)}{(4z - 1)}$$

$$= z$$

66. $\dfrac{9}{x^2 - 1} \div \dfrac{12}{3x + 3} = \dfrac{9}{x^2 - 1} \cdot \dfrac{3x + 3}{12}$

$$= \frac{3 \cdot 3 \cdot 3(x + 1)}{(x - 1)(x + 1) \cdot 3 \cdot 2 \cdot 2}$$

$$= \frac{9}{4(x - 1)}$$

68. $2x^2 + 5x - 3 = (2x - 1)(x + 3)$

$\quad$ LCD $= (2x - 1)(x + 3)$

$$\frac{4}{2x^2 + 5x - 3} + \frac{2}{x + 3}$$

$$= \frac{4}{(2x - 1)(x + 3)} + \frac{2(2x - 1)}{(x + 3)(2x - 1)}$$

$$= \frac{4 + 2(2x - 1)}{(2x - 1)(x + 3)}$$

$$= \frac{4 + 4x - 2}{(2x - 1)(x + 3)}$$

$$= \frac{4x + 2}{(2x - 1)(x + 3)}$$

70. $\quad 5x - 1 = 8$

$\quad 5x - 1 + 1 = 8 + 1$

$\quad\quad\quad 5x = 9$

$\quad\quad\quad \dfrac{5x}{5} = \dfrac{9}{5}$

$\quad\quad\quad\quad x = \dfrac{9}{5}$

72. $\quad\quad 4x^2 - 9 = 0$

$\quad (2x + 3)(2x - 3) = 0$

$\quad 2x + 3 = 0 \quad$ or $\quad 2x - 3 = 0$

$\quad\quad 2x = -3 \quad\quad\quad 2x = 3$

$\quad\quad\quad x = -\dfrac{3}{2} \quad\quad\quad x = \dfrac{3}{2}$

The solutions are $x = -\dfrac{3}{2}$ and $x = \dfrac{3}{2}$.

74. $2(3x + 1) + 15 = -7$

$\quad 6x + 2 + 15 = -7$

$\quad\quad 6x + 17 = -7$

$\quad\quad\quad\quad 6x = -24$

$\quad\quad\quad\quad x = -4$

76. $x^2 - 4 = (x-2)(x+2)$

LCD $= x(x-2)(x+2)$

$\dfrac{5}{x-2} + \dfrac{7x}{x^2-4} - \dfrac{11}{x}$

$= \dfrac{5(x)(x+2)}{(x-2)(x)(x+2)} + \dfrac{7x(x)}{(x-2)(x+2)(x)}$
$\quad - \dfrac{11(x-2)(x+2)}{x(x-2)(x+2)}$

$= \dfrac{5x(x+2) + 7x^2 - 11(x-2)(x+2)}{x(x-2)(x+2)}$

$= \dfrac{5x^2 + 10x + 7x^2 - 11x^2 + 44}{x(x-2)(x+2)}$

$= \dfrac{x^2 + 10x + 44}{x(x-2)(x+2)}$

78. $x^2 + 6x + 5 = (x+5)(x+1)$

$x^2 + 4x - 5 = (x+5)(x-1)$

$x^2 - 1 = (x+1)(x-1)$

LCD $= (x+5)(x+1)(x-1)$

$\dfrac{8}{x^2+6x+5} - \dfrac{3x}{x^2+4x-5} + \dfrac{2}{x^2-1}$

$= \dfrac{8(x-1)}{(x+5)(x+1)(x-1)} - \dfrac{3x(x+1)}{(x+5)(x-1)(x+1)}$
$\quad + \dfrac{2(x+5)}{(x+1)(x-1)(x+5)}$

$= \dfrac{8x-8}{(x+5)(x+1)(x-1)} - \dfrac{3x^2+3x}{(x+5)(x+1)(x-1)}$
$\quad + \dfrac{2x+10}{(x+5)(x+1)(x-1)}$

$= \dfrac{8x - 8 - 3x^2 - 3x + 2x + 10}{(x+5)(x+1)(x-1)}$

$= \dfrac{-3x^2 + 7x + 2}{(x+5)(x+1)(x-1)}$

80. $x^2 - 3x - 4 = (x-4)(x+1)$

$x^2 + 6x + 5 = (x+1)(x+5)$

$x^2 + x - 20 = (x-4)(x+5)$

LCD $= (x-4)(x+1)(x+5)$

$\dfrac{x+10}{x^2-3x-4} - \dfrac{8}{x^2+6x+5} - \dfrac{9}{x^2+x-20}$

$= \dfrac{(x+10)(x+5)}{(x-4)(x+1)(x+5)} - \dfrac{8(x-4)}{(x+1)(x+5)(x-4)}$
$\quad - \dfrac{9(x+1)}{(x-4)(x+5)(x+1)}$

$= \dfrac{(x+10)(x+5) - 8(x-4) - 9(x+1)}{(x-4)(x+1)(x+5)}$

$= \dfrac{x^2 + 15x + 50 - 8x + 32 - 9x - 9}{(x-4)(x+1)(x+5)}$

$= \dfrac{x^2 - 2x + 73}{(x-4)(x+1)(x+5)}$

82. $P = 2L + 2W$

$P = 2\left(\dfrac{3}{y-5}\right) + 2\left(\dfrac{2}{y}\right)$

$\quad = \dfrac{6}{y-5} + \dfrac{4}{y}$

$\quad = \dfrac{6(y)}{(y-5)(y)} + \dfrac{4(y-5)}{y(y-5)}$

$\quad = \dfrac{6y + 4y - 20}{y(y-5)}$

$\quad = \dfrac{10y - 20}{y(y-5)}$

The perimeter is $\dfrac{10y-20}{y(y-5)}$ feet.

$A = LW$

$A = \dfrac{3}{y-5} \cdot \dfrac{2}{y} = \dfrac{3 \cdot 2}{(y-5)(y)} = \dfrac{6}{y(y-5)}$

The area is $\dfrac{6}{y(y-5)}$ square feet.

84. $\dfrac{DA}{A+12} - \dfrac{D(A+1)}{24}$

$= \dfrac{DA(24)}{(A+12)(24)} - \dfrac{D(A+1)(A+12)}{24(A+12)}$

$= \dfrac{24DA - D(A^2 + 13A + 12)}{24(A+12)}$

$= \dfrac{24DA - DA^2 - 13DA - 12D}{24(A+12)}$

$= \dfrac{11DA - DA^2 - 12D}{24(A+12)}$

86. Answers may vary

88. $180° - \left(\dfrac{x+2}{x}\right)° = \left(180 - \dfrac{x+2}{x}\right)°$

$= \left(\dfrac{180x}{x} - \dfrac{x+2}{x}\right)°$

$= \left(\dfrac{180x - x - 2}{x}\right)°$

$= \left(\dfrac{179x - 2}{x}\right)°$

90. Answers may vary

The Bigger Picture

1. $-8.6 + (-9.1) = -17.7$

2. $(-8.6)(-9.1) = 78.26$

3. $14 - (-14) = 14 + 14 = 28$

4. $3x^4 - 7 + x^4 - x^2 - 10 = 3x^4 + x^4 - x^2 - 7 - 10$
$= 4x^4 - x - 17$

5. $\dfrac{5x^2 - 5}{25x + 25} = \dfrac{5(x+1)(x-1)}{5 \cdot 5(x+1)} = \dfrac{x-1}{5}$

6. $\dfrac{7x}{x^2 + 4x + 3} \div \dfrac{x}{2x+6} = \dfrac{7x}{x^2 + 4x + 3} \cdot \dfrac{2x+6}{x}$

$= \dfrac{7 \cdot x \cdot 2 \cdot (x+3)}{(x+3)(x+1) \cdot x}$

$= \dfrac{14}{x+1}$

7. $9 = 3 \cdot 3 = 3^2$
$6 = 2 \cdot 3$
$\text{LCD} = 2 \cdot 3^2$
$\dfrac{2}{9} - \dfrac{5}{6} = \dfrac{2(2)}{9(2)} - \dfrac{5(3)}{6(3)} = \dfrac{4}{18} - \dfrac{15}{18} = -\dfrac{11}{18}$

8. $9 = 3 \cdot 3 = 3^2$
$\text{LCD} = 3^2 \cdot 5$
$\dfrac{x}{9} - \dfrac{x+3}{5} = \dfrac{x(5)}{9(5)} - \dfrac{(x+3)(9)}{5(9)}$

$= \dfrac{5x - 9(x+3)}{45}$

$= \dfrac{5x - 9x - 27}{45}$

$= \dfrac{-4x - 27}{45} \text{ or } -\dfrac{4x + 27}{45}$

9. $9x^3 - 2x^2 - 11x = x(9x^2 - 2x - 11)$
$= x(9x - 11)(x + 1)$

10. $12xy - 21x + 4y - 7 = 3x(4y - 7) + 1(4y - 7)$
$= (4y - 7)(3x + 1)$

11. $7x - 14 = 5x + 10$
$2x - 14 = 10$
$2x = 24$
$x = 12$

12. $\dfrac{-x+2}{5} < \dfrac{3}{10}$

$10\left(\dfrac{-x+2}{5}\right) < 10\left(\dfrac{3}{10}\right)$

$2(-x+2) < 3$

$-2x + 4 < 3$

$-2x < -1$

$\dfrac{-2x}{-2} > \dfrac{-1}{-2}$

$x > \dfrac{1}{2}$

$\left(\dfrac{1}{2}, \infty\right)$

13.
$$1+4(x+4) = 3^2 + x$$
$$1+4x+16 = 9 + x$$
$$4x+17 = 9 + x$$
$$3x+17 = 9$$
$$3x = -8$$
$$x = -\frac{8}{3}$$

14.
$$x(x-2) = 24$$
$$x^2 - 2x = 24$$
$$x^2 - 2x - 24 = 0$$
$$(x+4)(x-6) = 0$$
$$x+4 = 0 \quad \text{or} \quad x-6 = 0$$
$$x = -4 \qquad\qquad x = 6$$
The solutions are $x = -4, 6$.

Section 7.5

Practice Exercises

1. The LCD of 3, 5, and 15 is 15.
$$\frac{x}{3} + \frac{4}{5} = \frac{12}{5}$$
$$15\left(\frac{x}{3} + \frac{4}{5}\right) = 15\left(\frac{2}{15}\right)$$
$$15\left(\frac{x}{3}\right) + 15\left(\frac{4}{5}\right) = 15\left(\frac{2}{15}\right)$$
$$5 \cdot x + 12 = 2$$
$$5x = -10$$
$$x = -2$$

Check: $\frac{x}{3} + \frac{4}{5} = \frac{2}{15}$
$$\frac{-2}{3} + \frac{4}{5} \overset{?}{=} \frac{2}{15}$$
$$\frac{2}{15} = \frac{2}{15} \quad \text{True}$$

This number checks, so the solution is –2.

2. The LCD of 4, 3, and 12 is 12.
$$\frac{x+4}{4} - \frac{x-3}{3} = \frac{11}{12}$$
$$12\left(\frac{x+4}{4} - \frac{x-3}{3}\right) = 12\left(\frac{11}{12}\right)$$
$$12\left(\frac{x+4}{4}\right) - 12\left(\frac{x-3}{3}\right) = 12\left(\frac{11}{12}\right)$$
$$3(x+4) - 4(x-3) = 11$$
$$3x+12 - 4x+12 = 11$$
$$-x+24 = 11$$
$$-x = -13$$
$$x = 13$$

Check: $\frac{x+4}{4} - \frac{x-3}{3} = \frac{11}{12}$
$$\frac{13+4}{4} - \frac{13-3}{3} \overset{?}{=} \frac{11}{12}$$
$$\frac{17}{4} - \frac{10}{3} \overset{?}{=} \frac{11}{12}$$
$$\frac{11}{12} = \frac{11}{12} \quad \text{True}$$

The solution is 13.

3. In this equation, 0 cannot be a solution. The LCD is x.
$$8 + \frac{7}{x} = x+2$$
$$x\left(8 + \frac{7}{x}\right) = x(x+2)$$
$$x(8) + x\left(\frac{7}{x}\right) = x \cdot x + x \cdot 2$$
$$8x+7 = x^2 + 2x$$
$$0 = x^2 - 6x - 7$$
$$0 = (x+1)(x-7)$$
$$x+1 = 0 \quad \text{or} \quad x-7 = 0$$
$$x = -1 \qquad\qquad x = 7$$
Neither –1 nor 7 makes the denominator in the original equation equal to 0.
Check:
$x = -1$
$$8 + \frac{7}{x} = x+2$$
$$8 + \frac{7}{-1} \overset{?}{=} -1+2$$
$$8 + (-7) \overset{?}{=} 1$$
$$1 = 1 \quad \text{True}$$

$x = 7$

$8 + \dfrac{7}{7} \overset{?}{=} 7 + 2$

$8 + 1 \overset{?}{=} 9$

$9 = 9$　True

Both -1 and 7 are solutions.

4. $x^2 - 5x - 14 = (x + 2)(x - 7)$

The LCD is $(x + 2)(x - 7)$.

$$\frac{6x}{x^2 - 5x - 14} - \frac{3}{x + 2} = \frac{1}{x - 7}$$

$$(x+2)(x-7)\left(\frac{6x}{x^2-5x-14} - \frac{3}{x+2}\right) = (x+2)(x-7)\left(\frac{1}{x-7}\right)$$

$$(x+2)(x-7)\cdot\frac{6x}{x^2-5x-14} - (x+2)(x-7)\cdot\frac{3}{x+2} = (x+2)(x-7)\cdot\frac{1}{x-7}$$

$$6x - 3(x - 7) = x + 2$$
$$6x - 3x + 21 = x + 2$$
$$3x + 21 = x + 2$$
$$2x = -19$$
$$x = -\frac{19}{2}$$

Check by replacing x with $-\dfrac{19}{2}$ in the original equation. The solution is $-\dfrac{19}{2}$.

5. The LCD is $x - 2$.

$$\frac{7}{x-2} = \frac{3}{x-2} + 4$$

$$(x-2)\left(\frac{7}{x-2}\right) = (x-2)\left(\frac{3}{x-2} + 4\right)$$

$$(x-2)\cdot\frac{7}{x-2} = (x-2)\cdot\frac{3}{x-2} + (x-2)\cdot 4$$

$$7 = 3 + 4x - 8$$
$$7 = 4x - 5$$
$$12 = 4x$$
$$3 = x$$

Check by replacing x with 3 in the original equation. The solution is 3.

6. From the denominators in the equation, 5 can't be a solution. The LCD is $x - 5$.

$$x + \frac{x}{x-5} = \frac{5}{x-5} - 7$$

$$(x-5)\left(x + \frac{x}{x-5}\right) = (x-5)\left(\frac{5}{x-5} - 7\right)$$

$$(x-5)(x) + (x-5)\left(\frac{x}{x-5}\right) = (x-5)\left(\frac{5}{x-5}\right) - (x-5)(7)$$

$$x^2 - 5x + x = 5 - 7x + 35$$
$$x^2 - 4x = 40 - 7x$$
$$x^2 + 3x - 40 = 0$$
$$(x+8)(x-5) = 0$$

$x + 8 = 0$ or $x - 5 = 0$
$x = -8$ $x = 5$
Since 5 can't be a solution, check by replacing x with -8 in the original equation. The only solution is -8.

7. The LCD is abx.

$$\frac{1}{a} + \frac{1}{b} = \frac{1}{x}$$

$$abx\left(\frac{1}{a} + \frac{1}{b}\right) = abx\left(\frac{1}{x}\right)$$

$$abx\left(\frac{1}{a}\right) + abx\left(\frac{1}{b}\right) = abx \cdot \frac{1}{x}$$

$$bx + ax = ab$$

$$ax = ab - bx$$

$$ax = b(a - x)$$

$$\frac{ax}{a - x} = b$$

Calculator Explorations

1. $y_1 = \frac{x-4}{2} - \frac{x-3}{9}$, $y_2 = \frac{5}{18}$
   Use INTERSECT

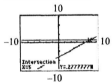

   The solution of the equation is 5.

2. $y_1 = 3 - \frac{6}{x}$, $y_2 = x + 8$
   Use INTERSECT

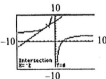

   One solution is -3.

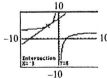

   The other solution is -2.

3. $y_1 = \frac{2x}{x-4}$, $y_2 = \frac{8}{x-4} + 1$

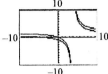

   Using TRACE and ZOOM, it is clear that the curves never intersect. The equation has no solution.

4. $y_1 = x + \frac{14}{x-2}$, $y_2 = \frac{7x}{x-2} + 1$
   Use INTERSECT

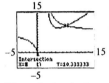

   The solution is 8.

Exercise Set 7.5

2. The LCD is 5.

$$\frac{x}{5} - 2 = 9$$

$$5\left(\frac{x}{5} - 2\right) = 5(9)$$

$$5\left(\frac{x}{5}\right) - 5(2) = 5(9)$$

$$x - 10 = 45$$

$$x = 55$$

   Check: $\frac{x}{5} - 2 = 9$

$$\frac{55}{5} - 2 \stackrel{?}{=} 9$$

$$11 - 2 \stackrel{?}{=} 9$$

$$9 = 9 \quad \text{True}$$

   The solution is 55.

4. The LCD is 18.

$$\frac{x}{6} + \frac{4x}{3} = \frac{x}{18}$$

$$18\left(\frac{x}{6} + \frac{4x}{3}\right) = 18\left(\frac{x}{18}\right)$$

$$18\left(\frac{x}{6}\right) + 18\left(\frac{4x}{3}\right) = 18\left(\frac{x}{18}\right)$$

$$3x + 24x = x$$

$$26x = 0$$

$$x = 0$$

Check: $\dfrac{x}{6}+\dfrac{4x}{3}=\dfrac{x}{18}$

$\dfrac{0}{6}+\dfrac{4(0)}{3} \stackrel{?}{=} \dfrac{0}{18}$

$0 = 0$ True

The solution is 0.

6. The LCD is x.

$5+\dfrac{4}{x}=1$

$x\left(5+\dfrac{4}{x}\right)=x(1)$

$x\cdot 5 + x\cdot\dfrac{4}{x}=x\cdot 1$

$5x+4=x$

$4=-4x$

$-1=x$

Check: $5+\dfrac{4}{x}=1$

$5+\dfrac{4}{-1} \stackrel{?}{=} 1$

$5-4 \stackrel{?}{=} 1$

$1=1$ True

The solution is -1.

8. The LCD is y.

$6+\dfrac{5}{y}=y-\dfrac{2}{y}$

$y\left(6+\dfrac{5}{y}\right)=y\left(y-\dfrac{2}{y}\right)$

$y(6)+y\left(\dfrac{5}{y}\right)=y(y)-y\left(\dfrac{2}{y}\right)$

$6y+5=y^2-2$

$0=y^2-6y-7$

$0=(y+1)(y-7)$

$y+1=0$ or $y-7=0$

$y=-1$ $y=7$

Check $y=-1$: $6+\dfrac{5}{y}=y-\dfrac{2}{y}$

$6+\dfrac{5}{-1} \stackrel{?}{=} -1-\dfrac{2}{-1}$

$6+(-5) \stackrel{?}{=} -1+2$

$1=1$ True

Check $y=7$: $6+\dfrac{5}{y}=y-\dfrac{2}{y}$

$6+\dfrac{5}{7} \stackrel{?}{=} 7-\dfrac{2}{7}$

$\dfrac{47}{4}=\dfrac{47}{7}$ True

Both -1 and 7 are solutions.

10. The LCD is 30.

$\dfrac{b}{5}=\dfrac{b+2}{6}$

$30\left(\dfrac{b}{5}\right)=30\left(\dfrac{b+2}{6}\right)$

$6b=5(b+2)$

$6b=5b+10$

$b=10$

Check: $\dfrac{b}{5}=\dfrac{b+2}{6}$

$\dfrac{10}{5} \stackrel{?}{=} \dfrac{10+2}{6}$

$2=2$ True

The solution is 10.

12. The LCD is 8.

$\dfrac{a+5}{4}+\dfrac{a+5}{2}=\dfrac{a}{8}$

$8\left(\dfrac{a+5}{4}+\dfrac{a+5}{2}\right)=8\left(\dfrac{a}{8}\right)$

$8\left(\dfrac{a+5}{4}\right)+8\left(\dfrac{a+5}{2}\right)=a$

$2(a+5)+4(a+5)=a$

$2a+10+4a+20=a$

$6a+30=a$

$5a=-30$

$a=-6$

Check: $\dfrac{a+5}{4}+\dfrac{a+5}{2}=\dfrac{a}{8}$

$\dfrac{-6+5}{4}+\dfrac{-6+5}{2} \stackrel{?}{=} \dfrac{-6}{8}$

$-\dfrac{1}{4}-\dfrac{1}{2} \stackrel{?}{=} -\dfrac{3}{4}$

$-\dfrac{1}{4}-\dfrac{2}{4} \stackrel{?}{=} -\dfrac{3}{4}$

$-\dfrac{3}{4}=-\dfrac{3}{4}$ True

The solution is -6.

14. The LCD is $4 - 3x$.

$$\frac{6}{4-3x} = -3$$

$$(4-3x)\left(\frac{6}{4-3x}\right) = (4-3x)(-3)$$

$$6 = -12 + 9x$$

$$18 = 9x$$

$$2 = x$$

Check: $\quad \dfrac{6}{4-3x} = -3$

$$\frac{6}{4-3(2)} \stackrel{?}{=} -3$$

$$\frac{6}{4-6} \stackrel{?}{=} -3$$

$$\frac{6}{-2} = -3 \quad \text{True}$$

The solution is 2.

16. The LCD is $a + 2$.

$$\frac{2a}{a+2} - 5 = \frac{7a}{a+2}$$

$$(a+2)\left(\frac{2a}{a+2} - 5\right) = (a+2)\left(\frac{7a}{a+2}\right)$$

$$(a+2)\left(\frac{2a}{a+2}\right) - (a+2)(5) = (a+2)\left(\frac{7a}{a+2}\right)$$

$$2a - 5a - 10 = 7a$$

$$-3a - 10 = 7a$$

$$-10 = 10a$$

$$\frac{-10}{10} = \frac{10a}{10}$$

$$-1 = a$$

Check: $\quad \dfrac{2a}{a+2} - 5 = \dfrac{7a}{a+2}$

$$\frac{2(-1)}{-1+2} - 5 \stackrel{?}{=} \frac{7(-1)}{-1+2}$$

$$\frac{-2}{1} - 5 \stackrel{?}{=} \frac{-7}{1}$$

$$-7 = -7 \quad \text{True}$$

The solution is -1.

18. The LCD is $y - 2$.

$$\frac{2y}{y-2} - \frac{4}{y-2} = 4$$

$$(y-2)\left(\frac{2y}{y-2} - \frac{4}{y-2}\right) = (y-2)4$$

$$2y - 4 = 4y - 8$$
$$-4 + 8 = 4y - 2y$$
$$4 = 2y$$
$$\frac{4}{2} = \frac{2y}{2}$$
$$2 = y$$

In the original equation, 2 makes a denominator 0. This equation has no solution.

20. $x^2 - 4 = (x+2)(x-2)$

LCD $= (x+2)(x-2)$

$$\frac{1}{x+2} + \frac{4}{x^2-4} = 1$$

$$(x+2)(x-2)\left(\frac{1}{x+2} + \frac{4}{x^2-4}\right) = (x+2)(x-2)(1)$$

$$(x+2)(x-2)\cdot\frac{1}{x+2} + (x+2)(x-2)\cdot\frac{4}{(x+2)(x-2)} = (x+2)(x-2)(1)$$

$$x - 2 + 4 = x^2 - 4$$
$$x + 2 = x^2 - 4$$
$$0 = x^2 - x - 6$$
$$0 = (x-3)(x+2)$$

$$x - 3 = 0 \quad \text{or} \quad x + 2 = 0$$
$$x = 3 \qquad\qquad x = -2$$

In the original equation -2 makes a denominator 0, so -2 can't be a solution.

Check $x = 3$: $\dfrac{1}{x+2} + \dfrac{4}{x^2-4} = 1$

$$\frac{1}{3+2} + \frac{4}{3^2-4} \stackrel{?}{=} 1$$

$$\frac{1}{5} + \frac{4}{5} \stackrel{?}{=} 1$$

$$1 = 1 \quad \text{True}$$

The only solution is 3.

22. The LCD is $(y+1)$.

$$\frac{5y}{y+1} - \frac{3}{y+1} = 4$$

$$(y+1)\left(\frac{5y}{y+1} - \frac{3}{y+1}\right) = (y+1)(4)$$

$$(y+1)\left(\frac{5y}{y+1}\right) - (y+1)\left(\frac{3}{y+1}\right) = (y+1)(4)$$

$$5y - 3 = 4y + 4$$
$$y - 3 = 4$$
$$y = 7$$

Check: $\dfrac{5y}{y+1} - \dfrac{3}{y+1} = 4$

$\dfrac{5(7)}{7+1} - \dfrac{3}{7+1} \stackrel{?}{=} 4$

$\dfrac{35}{8} - \dfrac{3}{8} \stackrel{?}{=} 4$

$\dfrac{32}{8} \stackrel{?}{=} 4$

$4 = 4$ True

The solution is 7.

24. LCD $= (y-3)(y+3)$

$$\dfrac{4y}{y-3} - 3 = \dfrac{3y-1}{y+3}$$

$$(y-3)(y+3)\left(\dfrac{4y}{y-3} - 3\right) = (y-3)(y+3)\left(\dfrac{3y-1}{y+3}\right)$$

$$(y-3)(y+3)\cdot\dfrac{4y}{y-3} - (y-3)(y+3)\cdot 3 = (y-3)(y+3)\cdot\dfrac{3y-1}{y+3}$$

$$4y(y+3) - 3(y-3)(y+3) = (y-3)(3y-1)$$

$$4y^2 + 12y - 3y^2 + 27 = 3y^2 - 10y + 3$$

$$y^2 + 12y + 27 = 3y^2 - 10y + 3$$

$$0 = 2y^2 - 22y - 24$$

$$0 = y^2 - 11y - 12$$

$$0 = (y+1)(y-12)$$

$y + 1 = 0$ or $y - 12 = 0$

$y = -1$ $\qquad$ $y = 12$

Check $y = -1$: $\qquad \dfrac{4y}{y-3} - 3 = \dfrac{3y-1}{y+3}$

$$\dfrac{4(-1)}{-1-3} - 3 \stackrel{?}{=} \dfrac{3(-1)-1}{-1+3}$$

$$\dfrac{-4}{-4} - 3 \stackrel{?}{=} \dfrac{-3-1}{2}$$

$$1 - 3 \stackrel{?}{=} \dfrac{-4}{2}$$

$$-2 = -2 \quad \text{True}$$

Check $y = 12$: $\qquad \dfrac{4y}{y-3} - 3 = \dfrac{3y-1}{y+3}$

$$\dfrac{4(12)}{12-3} - 3 \stackrel{?}{=} \dfrac{3(12)-1}{12+3}$$

$$\dfrac{48}{9} - 3 \stackrel{?}{=} \dfrac{36-1}{15}$$

$$\dfrac{16}{3} - \dfrac{9}{3} \stackrel{?}{=} \dfrac{35}{15}$$

$$\dfrac{7}{3} = \dfrac{7}{3} \quad \text{True}$$

The solutions are -1 and 12.

26. The LCD is $3y$.

$$\frac{6}{3y}+\frac{3}{y}=1$$

$$3y\left(\frac{6}{3y}+\frac{3}{y}\right)=3y(1)$$

$$6+9=3y$$

$$15=3y$$

$$\frac{15}{3}=y$$

$$5=y$$

The solution is 5.

28. The LCD is $(x-6)(x-2)$.

$$\frac{5}{x-6}=\frac{x}{x-2}$$

$$(x-6)(x-2)\left(\frac{5}{x-6}\right)=(x-6)(x-2)\left(\frac{x}{x-2}\right)$$

$$5(x-2)=x(x-6)$$

$$5x-10=x^2-6x$$

$$0=x^2-11x+10$$

$$0=(x-1)(x-10)$$

$$x-1=0 \quad \text{or} \quad x-10=0$$

$$x=1 \qquad\qquad x=10$$

The solutions are 1 and 10.

30. The LCD is $6x$.

$$\frac{5}{3}-\frac{3}{2x}=\frac{3}{2}$$

$$6x\left(\frac{5}{3}-\frac{3}{2x}\right)=6x\left(\frac{3}{2}\right)$$

$$6x\cdot\frac{5}{3}-6x\cdot\frac{3}{2x}=6x\cdot\frac{3}{2}$$

$$10x-9=9x$$

$$-9=-x$$

$$9=x$$

The solution is 9.

32. The LCD is $(x + 1)(x - 1)$.

$$1 + \frac{3}{x+1} = \frac{x}{x-1}$$

$$(x+1)(x-1)\left(1 + \frac{3}{x+1}\right) = (x+1)(x-1)\left(\frac{x}{x-1}\right)$$

$$(x+1)(x-1)(1) + (x+1)(x-1)\left(\frac{3}{x+1}\right) = (x+1)(x-1)\left(\frac{x}{x-1}\right)$$

$$(x+1)(x-1) + 3(x-1) = x(x+1)$$

$$x^2 - 1 + 3x - 3 = x^2 + x$$

$$3x - 4 = x$$

$$-4 = -2x$$

$$\frac{-4}{-2} = x$$

$$2 = x$$

The solution is 2.

34. The LCD is 15.

$$\frac{3x}{5} - \frac{x-6}{3} = -\frac{2}{5}$$

$$15\left(\frac{3x}{5} - \frac{x-6}{3}\right) = 15\left(-\frac{2}{5}\right)$$

$$15 \cdot \frac{3x}{5} - 15 \cdot \frac{x-6}{3} = 15\left(-\frac{2}{5}\right)$$

$$9x - 5(x-6) = -6$$

$$9x - 5x + 30 = -6$$

$$4x + 30 = -6$$

$$4x = -36$$

$$x = -9$$

The solution is −9.

36. The LCD is $x(x + 4)$.

$$\frac{15}{x+4} = \frac{x-4}{x}$$

$$x(x+4)\left(\frac{15}{x+4}\right) = x(x+4)\left(\frac{x-4}{x}\right)$$

$$15x = x^2 - 16$$

$$0 = x^2 - 15x - 16$$

$$0 = (x-16)(x+1)$$

$$x - 16 = 0 \quad \text{or} \quad x + 1 = 0$$

$$x = 16 \qquad\qquad x = -1$$

The solutions are 16 and −1.

38. The LCD is $(x+2)(x-2)$.

$$\frac{1}{x+2} = \frac{4}{x^2-4} - \frac{1}{x-2}$$

$$(x+2)(x-2)\left(\frac{1}{x+2}\right) = (x+2)(x-2)\left(\frac{4}{x^2-4} - \frac{1}{x-2}\right)$$

$$(x+2)(x-2)\frac{1}{x+2} = (x+2)(x-2)\left(\frac{4}{x^2-4}\right) - (x+2)(x-2)\left(\frac{1}{x-2}\right)$$

$$x-2 = 4-(x+2)$$
$$x-2 = 4-x-2$$
$$x-2 = 2-x$$
$$2x = 4$$
$$x = 2$$

In the original equation, 2 makes a denominator 0. This equation has no solution.

40. The LCD is $(x+3)(x+4)$.

$$\frac{3}{x+3} = \frac{12x+19}{x^2+7x+12} - \frac{5}{x+4}$$

$$\frac{3}{x+3} = \frac{12x+19}{(x+3)(x+4)} - \frac{5}{x+4}$$

$$(x+3)(x+4)\left(\frac{3}{x+3}\right) = (x+3)(x+4)\left(\frac{12x+19}{(x+3)(x+4)} - \frac{5}{x+4}\right)$$

$$(x+3)(x+4)\left(\frac{3}{x+3}\right) = (x+3)(x+4)\left(\frac{12x+19}{(x+3)(x+4)}\right) - (x+3)(x+4)\left(\frac{5}{x+4}\right)$$

$$3(x+4) = 12x+19 - 5(x+3)$$
$$3x+12 = 12x+19 - 5x - 15$$
$$3x+12 = 7x+4$$
$$-4x = -8$$
$$x = 2$$

The solution is 2.

42. The LCD is $(t-1)(t+3)$.

$$\frac{2t+3}{t-1} - \frac{2}{t+3} = \frac{5-6t}{t^2+2t-3}$$

$$(t-1)(t+3)\left(\frac{2t+3}{t-1} - \frac{2}{t+3}\right) = (t-1)(t+3)\left(\frac{5-6t}{t^2+2t-3}\right)$$

$$(t-1)(t+3)\left(\frac{2t+3}{t-1}\right) - (t-1)(t+3)\left(\frac{2}{t+3}\right) = (t-1)(t+3)\left(\frac{5-6t}{(t-1)(t+3)}\right)$$

$$(t+3)(2t+3) - 2(t-1) = 5-6t$$
$$2t^2+9t+9 - 2t+2 = 5-6t$$
$$2t^2+7t+11 = 5-6t$$
$$2t^2+13t+6 = 0$$
$$(2t+1)(t+6) = 0$$

$$2t + 1 = 0 \quad \text{or} \quad t + 6 = 0$$
$$2t = -1 \qquad \qquad t = -6$$
$$t = -\frac{1}{2}$$

The solutions are $-\dfrac{1}{2}$ and -6.

44. $T = \dfrac{V}{Q}$

$$QT = Q\left(\frac{V}{Q}\right)$$
$$QT = V$$
$$Q = \frac{V}{T}$$

46. $i = \dfrac{A}{t + B}$

$$(t + B)i = (t + B)\left(\frac{A}{t + B}\right)$$
$$ti + Bi = A$$
$$ti = A - Bi$$
$$t = \frac{A - Bi}{i}$$

48. $\dfrac{A}{W} = L$

$$W\left(\frac{A}{W}\right) = W(L)$$
$$A = WL$$
$$\frac{A}{L} = \frac{WL}{L}$$
$$\frac{A}{L} = W$$

50. $C = \dfrac{D(A + 1)}{24}$

$$24(C) = 24\left(\frac{D(A+1)}{24}\right)$$
$$24C = D(A + 1)$$
$$24C = DA + D$$
$$24C - D = DA$$
$$\frac{24C - D}{D} = A$$

52. $W = \dfrac{CE^2}{2}$

$$2(W) = 2\left(\frac{CE^2}{2}\right)$$
$$2W = CE^2$$
$$\frac{2W}{E^2} = C$$

54.
$$\frac{1}{5} + \frac{2}{y} = \frac{1}{x}$$
$$5xy\left(\frac{1}{5} + \frac{2}{y}\right) = 5xy\left(\frac{1}{x}\right)$$
$$5xy \cdot \frac{1}{5} + 5xy \cdot \frac{2}{y} = 5xy \cdot \frac{1}{x}$$
$$xy + 10x = 5y$$
$$x(y + 10) = 5y$$
$$x = \frac{5y}{y + 10}$$

56. The reciprocal of $x + 1$ is $\dfrac{1}{x + 1}$.

58. The reciprocal of x, subtracted from the reciprocal of 5 is $\dfrac{1}{5} - \dfrac{1}{x}$.

60. If a strip of beach is cleaned in 4 hours, then $\dfrac{1}{4}$ of the beach is cleaned in 1 hour.

62. The graph crosses the x-axis at $x = -3$. It crosses the y-axis at $y = -1$. The x-intercept is $(-3, 0)$ and the y-intercept is $(0, -1)$.

64. The graph crosses the x-axis at $x = -3$ and $x = 3$. It crosses the y-axis at $y = 4$. The x-intercepts are $(-3, 0)$ and $(3, 0)$, and the y-intercept is $(0, 4)$.

66. Answers may vary

68. equation
$$\frac{1}{x} + \frac{5}{9} = \frac{2}{3}$$
$$9x\left(\frac{1}{x}\right) + 9x\left(\frac{5}{9}\right) = 9x\left(\frac{2}{3}\right)$$
$$9 + 5x = 6x$$
$$9 = x$$

70. expression

$$\frac{5}{x-1} - \frac{2}{x} = \frac{5}{x-1} \cdot \frac{x}{x} - \frac{2}{x} \cdot \frac{x-1}{x-1}$$

$$= \frac{5x - 2(x-1)}{x(x-1)}$$

$$= \frac{5x - 2x + 2}{x(x-1)}$$

$$= \frac{3x+2}{x(x-1)}$$

72. $\dfrac{5x}{2} + \dfrac{25x}{2} = 180$

$$\frac{30x}{2} = 180$$

$$15x = 180$$

$$x = 12$$

$$\frac{5x}{2} = \frac{5(12)}{2} = 30$$

$$\frac{25x}{2} = \frac{25(12)}{2} = 150$$

The supplementary angles are 30° and 150°.

74. $\dfrac{80}{x} + \dfrac{100}{x} = 90$

$$x\left(\frac{80}{x} + \frac{100}{x}\right) = x(90)$$

$$x\left(\frac{80}{x}\right) + x\left(\frac{100}{x}\right) = x(90)$$

$$80 + 100 = 90x$$

$$180 = 90x$$

$$\frac{180}{90} = \frac{90x}{90}$$

$$2 = x$$

$$\frac{80}{x} = \frac{80}{2} = 40$$

$$\frac{100}{x} = \frac{100}{2} = 50$$

The complementary angles are 40° and 50°.

76.

$$\frac{-2}{a^2+2a-8}+\frac{1}{a^2+9a+20}=\frac{-4}{a^2+3a-10}$$

$$\frac{-2}{(a+4)(a-2)}+\frac{1}{(a+4)(a+5)}=\frac{-4}{(a-2)(a+5)}$$

$$(a+4)(a+5)(a-2)\left(\frac{-2}{(a+4)(a-2)}+\frac{1}{(a+4)(a+5)}\right)=(a+4)(a+5)(a-2)\left(\frac{-4}{(a-2)(a+5)}\right)$$

$$(a+4)(a+5)(a-2)\left(\frac{-2}{(a+4)(a-2)}\right)+(a+4)(a+5)(a-2)\left(\frac{1}{(a+4)(a+5)}\right)=(a+4)(a+5)(a-2)\left(\frac{-4}{(a-2)(a+5)}\right)$$

$$-2(a+5)+1(a-2)=-4(a+4)$$
$$-2a-10+a-2=-4a-16$$
$$-a-12=-4a-16$$
$$3a-12=-16$$
$$3a=-4$$
$$a=-\frac{4}{3}$$

Integrated Review

1. expression

$$\frac{1}{x}+\frac{2}{3}=\frac{1(3)}{x(3)}+\frac{2(x)}{3(x)}=\frac{3}{3x}+\frac{2x}{3x}=\frac{3+2x}{3x}$$

2. expression

$$\frac{3}{a}+\frac{5}{6}=\frac{3(6)}{a(6)}+\frac{5(a)}{6(a)}=\frac{18}{6a}+\frac{5a}{6a}=\frac{18+5a}{6a}$$

3. equation

$$\frac{1}{x}+\frac{2}{3}=\frac{3}{x}$$
$$3x\left(\frac{1}{x}+\frac{2}{3}\right)=3x\left(\frac{3}{x}\right)$$
$$3x\left(\frac{1}{x}\right)+3x\left(\frac{2}{3}\right)=3x\left(\frac{3}{x}\right)$$
$$3+2x=9$$
$$2x=6$$
$$x=3$$

The solution is 3.

4. equation

$$\frac{3}{a}+\frac{5}{6}=1$$
$$6a\left(\frac{3}{a}+\frac{5}{6}\right)=6a(1)$$
$$6a\left(\frac{3}{a}\right)+6a\left(\frac{5}{6}\right)=6a$$
$$18+5a=6a$$
$$18=a$$

The solution is 18.

5. expression

$$\frac{2}{x-1} - \frac{1}{x} = \frac{2(x)}{(x-1)(x)} - \frac{1(x-1)}{x(x-1)}$$
$$= \frac{2x - (x-1)}{x(x-1)}$$
$$= \frac{x+1}{x(x-1)}$$

6. expression

$$\frac{4}{x-3} - \frac{1}{x} = \frac{4(x)}{(x-3)(x)} - \frac{1(x-3)}{x(x-3)}$$
$$= \frac{4x - (x-3)}{x(x-3)}$$
$$= \frac{4x - x + 3}{x(x-3)}$$
$$= \frac{3x + 3}{x(x-3)}$$
$$= \frac{3(x+1)}{x(x-3)}$$

7. equation

$$\frac{2}{x+1} - \frac{1}{x} = 1$$
$$x(x+1)\left(\frac{2}{x+1} - \frac{1}{x}\right) = x(x+1)(1)$$
$$x(x+1)\left(\frac{2}{x+1}\right) - x(x+1)\left(\frac{1}{x}\right) = x(x+1)$$
$$2x - (x+1) = x(x+1)$$
$$2x - x - 1 = x^2 + x$$
$$x - 1 = x^2 + x$$
$$-1 = x^2$$

There is no real number solution.

8. equation

$$\frac{4}{x-3} - \frac{1}{x} = \frac{6}{x(x-3)}$$
$$x(x-3)\left(\frac{4}{x-3} - \frac{1}{x}\right) = x(x-3)\left(\frac{6}{x(x-3)}\right)$$
$$x(x-3)\left(\frac{4}{x-3}\right) - x(x-3)\left(\frac{1}{x}\right) = 6$$
$$4x - (x-3) = 6$$
$$4x - x + 3 = 6$$
$$3x + 3 = 6$$
$$3x = 3$$
$$x = 1$$

The solution is 1.

9. expression

$$\frac{15x}{x+8} \cdot \frac{2x+16}{3x} = \frac{15x \cdot (2x+16)}{(x+8) \cdot 3x}$$
$$= \frac{3 \cdot 5 \cdot x \cdot 2 \cdot (x+8)}{(x+8) \cdot 3 \cdot x}$$
$$= 5 \cdot 2$$
$$= 10$$

10. expression

$$\frac{9z+5}{15} \cdot \frac{5z}{81z^2 - 25} = \frac{(9z+5) \cdot 5z}{15 \cdot (81z^2 - 25)}$$
$$= \frac{(9z+5) \cdot 5 \cdot z}{5 \cdot 3 \cdot (9z+5)(9z-5)}$$
$$= \frac{z}{3(9z-5)}$$

11. expression

$$\frac{2x+1}{x-3} + \frac{3x+6}{x-3} = \frac{2x+1+3x+6}{x-3} = \frac{5x+7}{x-3}$$

12. expression

$$\frac{4p-3}{2p+7} + \frac{3p+8}{2p+7} = \frac{4p-3+3p+8}{2p+7} = \frac{7p+5}{2p+7}$$

13. equation

$$\frac{x+5}{7} = \frac{8}{2}$$
$$14\left(\frac{x+5}{7}\right) = 14\left(\frac{8}{2}\right)$$
$$2(x+5) = 56$$
$$2x + 10 = 56$$
$$2x = 46$$
$$x = 23$$

The solution is 23.

14. equation

$$\frac{1}{2} = \frac{x-1}{8}$$
$$8\left(\frac{1}{2}\right) = 8\left(\frac{x-1}{8}\right)$$
$$4 = x - 1$$
$$5 = x$$

The solution is 5.

15. expression

$$\frac{5a+10}{18} \div \frac{a^2-4}{10a} = \frac{5a+10}{18} \cdot \frac{10a}{a^2-4}$$
$$= \frac{5(a+2)\cdot 2\cdot 5\cdot a}{2\cdot 9(a+2)(a-2)}$$
$$= \frac{5\cdot 5\cdot a}{9(a-2)}$$
$$= \frac{25a}{9(a-2)}$$

16. expression

$$\frac{9}{x^2-1} + \frac{12}{3x+3}$$
$$= \frac{9(3)}{(x+1)(x-1)(3)} + \frac{12(x-1)}{3(x+1)(x-1)}$$
$$= \frac{27+12x-12}{3(x-1)(x+1)}$$
$$= \frac{15+12x}{3(x+1)(x-1)}$$
$$= \frac{3(5+4x)}{3(x+1)(x-1)}$$
$$= \frac{4x+5}{(x+1)(x-1)}$$

17. expression

$$\frac{x+2}{3x-1} + \frac{5}{(3x-1)^2} = \frac{(x+2)(3x-1)}{(3x-1)(3x-1)} + \frac{5}{(3x-1)^2}$$
$$= \frac{3x^2+5x-2+5}{(3x-1)^2}$$
$$= \frac{3x^2+5x+3}{(3x-1)^2}$$

18. expression

$$\frac{4}{(2x-5)^2} + \frac{x+1}{2x-5} = \frac{4}{(2x-5)^2} + \frac{(x+1)(2x-5)}{(2x-5)(2x-5)}$$
$$= \frac{4+2x^2-3x-5}{(2x-5)^2}$$
$$= \frac{2x^2-3x-1}{(2x-5)^2}$$

19. expression

$$\frac{x-7}{x} - \frac{x+2}{5x} = \frac{(x-7)(5)}{x(5)} - \frac{x+2}{5x}$$
$$= \frac{5x-35-x-2}{5x}$$
$$= \frac{4x-37}{5x}$$

20. equation

$$\frac{9}{x^2-4} + \frac{2}{x+2} = \frac{-1}{x-2}$$
$$(x^2-4)\left(\frac{9}{x^2-4}\right) + (x^2-4)\left(\frac{2}{x+2}\right) = (x^2-4)\left(\frac{-1}{x-2}\right)$$
$$9 + (x-2)(2) = (x+2)(-1)$$
$$9 + 2x - 4 = -x - 2$$
$$2x + 5 = -x - 2$$
$$3x + 5 = -2$$
$$3x = -7$$
$$x = -\frac{7}{3}$$

The solution is $-\frac{7}{3}$.

21. equation

$$\frac{3}{x+3} = \frac{5}{x^2-9} - \frac{2}{x-3}$$
$$(x^2-9)\left(\frac{3}{x+3}\right) = (x^2-9)\left(\frac{5}{x^2-9}\right) - (x^2-9)\left(\frac{2}{x-3}\right)$$
$$(x-3)(3) = 5 - (x+3)(2)$$
$$3x - 9 = 5 - 2x - 6$$
$$3x - 9 = -2x - 1$$
$$5x - 9 = -1$$
$$5x = 8$$
$$x = \frac{8}{5}$$

The solution is $\frac{8}{5}$.

22. expression

$$\frac{10x-9}{x} - \frac{x-4}{3x} = \frac{(10x-9)(3)}{x(3)} - \frac{x-4}{3x}$$
$$= \frac{30x-27-x+4}{3x}$$
$$= \frac{29x-23}{3x}$$

Section 7.6

Practice Exercises

1. Solve the equation as a rational equation.

$$\frac{36}{x} = \frac{4}{11}$$

$$11x \cdot \frac{36}{x} = 11x \cdot \frac{4}{11}$$

$$11 \cdot 36 = x \cdot 4$$

$$396 = 4x$$

$$\frac{396}{4} = \frac{4x}{4}$$

$$99 = x$$

Solve the proportion using cross products.

$$\frac{36}{x} = \frac{4}{11}$$

$$36 \cdot 11 = x \cdot 4$$

$$396 = 4x$$

$$\frac{396}{4} = \frac{4x}{4}$$

$$99 = x$$

Check: Both methods give a solution of 99. To check, substitute 99 for x in the original proportion. The solution is 99.

2.
$$\frac{3x+2}{9} = \frac{x-1}{2}$$

$$2(3x+2) = 9(x-1)$$

$$6x+4 = 9x-9$$

$$6x = 9x-13$$

$$-3x = -13$$

$$\frac{-3x}{-3} = \frac{-13}{-3}$$

$$x = \frac{13}{3}$$

Check: Verify that $\frac{13}{3}$ is the solution.

3. Let x = price of seven 2-liter bottles of Diet Pepsi.

$$\frac{4 \text{ bottles}}{7 \text{ bottles}} = \frac{\text{price of 4 bottles}}{\text{price of 7 bottles}}$$

$$\frac{4}{7} = \frac{5.16}{x}$$

$$4x = 7(5.16)$$

$$4x = 36.12$$

$$x = 9.03$$

Check: Verify that 4 bottles is to 7 bottles as $5.16 is to $9.03.
Seven 2-liter bottles of Diet Pepsi cost $9.03.

4. Since the triangles are similar, their corresponding sides are in proportion.

$$\frac{20}{8} = \frac{15}{x}$$
$$20x = 8 \cdot 15$$
$$20x = 120$$
$$x = 6$$

Check: To check, replace x with 6 in the original proportion and see that a true statement results. The missing length is 6 meters.

5. Let x = the unknown number.

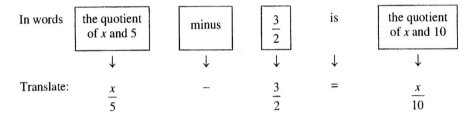

In words	the quotient of x and 5	minus	$\frac{3}{2}$	is	the quotient of x and 10
	↓	↓	↓	↓	↓
Translate:	$\dfrac{x}{5}$	$-$	$\dfrac{3}{2}$	$=$	$\dfrac{x}{10}$

The LCD is 10.

$$10\left(\frac{x}{5} - \frac{3}{2}\right) = 10\left(\frac{x}{10}\right)$$
$$10\left(\frac{x}{5}\right) - 10\left(\frac{3}{2}\right) = 10\left(\frac{x}{10}\right)$$
$$2x - 15 = x$$
$$x - 15 = 0$$
$$x = 15$$

Check: To check, verify that "the quotient of 15 and 5 minus $\dfrac{3}{2}$ is the quotient of 15 and 10," or $\dfrac{15}{5} - \dfrac{3}{2} = \dfrac{15}{10}$.

6. Let x = the time in hours it takes Cindy and Mary to complete the job together. Then

$\dfrac{1}{x}$ = the part of the job they complete in 1 hour.

	Hours to Complete Total Job	Part of Job Completed in 1 Hour
Cindy	3	$\dfrac{1}{3}$
Mary	4	$\dfrac{1}{4}$
Together	x	$\dfrac{1}{x}$

The part of the job Cindy completes in 1 hour, added to the part of the job Mary completes in 1 hour is equal to the part of the job they complete together in 1 hour.

$$\frac{1}{3}+\frac{1}{4}=\frac{1}{x}$$

$$12x\left(\frac{1}{3}\right)+12x\left(\frac{1}{4}\right)=12x\left(\frac{1}{x}\right)$$

$$4x+3x=12$$

$$7x=12$$

$$x=\frac{12}{7} \text{ or } 1\frac{5}{7}$$

Check: The proposed solution is reasonable since $1\frac{5}{7}$ hours is more than half of Cindy's time and less than half of Mary's time. Check $1\frac{5}{7}$ hours in the originally stated problem.

Cindy and Mary can complete the garden planting in $1\frac{5}{7}$ hours.

7. Let $x =$ the speed of the bus. Then since the car's speed is 15 mph faster than that of the bus, the speed of the car is $x + 15$.
Since distance = rate · time, or $d = r \cdot t$, then $t=\frac{d}{r}$.

The bus travels 180 miles in the same time that the car travels 240 miles.

	Distance =	Rate ·	Time
Bus	180	x	$\frac{180}{x}$
Car	240	$x+15$	$\frac{240}{x+15}$

Since the car and the bus traveled the same amount of time, $\frac{180}{x}=\frac{240}{x+15}$.

$$\frac{180}{x}=\frac{240}{x+15}$$

$$180(x+15)=240x$$

$$180x+2700=240x$$

$$2700=60x$$

$$45=x$$

The speed of the bus is 45 miles per hour. The speed of the car must then be $x + 15$ or 60 miles per hour.

Check: Find the time it takes the car to travel 240 miles and the time it takes the bus to travel 180 miles.

Car: $t=\frac{d}{r}=\frac{240}{60}=4$ hours

Bus: $t=\frac{d}{r}=\frac{180}{45}=4$ hours

Since the times are the same, the proposed solution is correct. The speed of the bus is 45 miles per hour and the speed of the car is 60 miles per hour.

Vocabulary and Readiness Check

1. If both people work together, they can complete the job in less time than either person working alone. That is, in less than 5 hours; choice c.

2. If both inlet pipes are on, they can fill the pond in less time than either pipe alone. That is, in less than 25 hours; choice a.

Exercise Set 7.6

2. $\frac{x}{2}=\frac{16}{6}$

$$6x=32$$

$$x=\frac{32}{6}=\frac{16}{3}$$

4. $\frac{9}{4x}=\frac{6}{2}$

$$24x=18$$

$$x=\frac{18}{24}$$

$$x=\frac{3}{4}$$

6. $\frac{x+1}{x+2}=\frac{5}{3}$

$$3(x+1)=5(x+2)$$

$$3x+3=5x+10$$

$$-2x=7$$

$$x=-\frac{7}{2}$$

8. $\frac{6}{11}=\frac{27}{3x-2}$

$$6(3x-2)=11(27)$$

$$18x-12=297$$

$$18x=309$$

$$x=\frac{309}{18}$$

$$x=\frac{103}{6}$$

10. Let x = the satellite's weight on Mars.
$$\frac{170}{65} = \frac{9000}{x}$$
$$170x = 65(9000)$$
$$170x = 585,000$$
$$x \approx 3441$$
The satellite's weight is 3441 pounds.

12. Let x = the length of the wall in feet.
$$\frac{1}{4} = \frac{3\frac{7}{8}}{x}$$
$$1x = 4\left(3\frac{7}{8}\right)$$
$$x = 4\left(\frac{31}{8}\right)$$
$$x = \frac{31}{2} = 15\frac{1}{2}$$

The length of the wall is $15\frac{1}{2}$ feet.

14. $\frac{12}{4} = \frac{18}{x}$
$$12x = 72$$
$$x = 6$$
The missing length is 6.

16. $\frac{12}{5} = \frac{10}{y}$
$$12y = 50$$
$$y = \frac{50}{12}$$
$$y = \frac{25}{6} = 4\frac{1}{6}$$

The missing length is $4\frac{1}{6}$ meters.

18. $\frac{12}{x+2} = \frac{4}{x-2}$
$$(x+2)(x-2)\left(\frac{12}{x+2}\right) = (x+2)(x-2)\left(\frac{4}{x-2}\right)$$
$$12(x-2) = 4(x+2)$$
$$12x - 24 = 4x + 8$$
$$8x = 32$$
$$x = 4$$
The unknown number is **4**.

20. $$x + 6\left(\frac{1}{x}\right) = -5$$
$$x\left(x + \frac{6}{x}\right) = x(-5)$$
$$x^2 + 6 = -5x$$
$$x^2 + 5x + 6 = 0$$
$$(x+3)(x+2) = 0$$
$$x + 3 = 0 \quad \text{or} \quad x + 2 = 0$$
$$x = -3 \qquad\qquad x = -2$$
The unknown number is -3 or -2.

22. Let x be the amount of time to complete the job working together.

	Hours to Complete Total Job	Part of Job Completed in 1 Hour
Experienced	3	$\frac{1}{3}$
Apprentice	6	$\frac{1}{6}$
Together	x	$\frac{1}{x}$

$$\frac{1}{3} + \frac{1}{6} = \frac{1}{x}$$
$$6x\left(\frac{1}{3}\right) + 6x\left(\frac{1}{6}\right) = 6x\left(\frac{1}{x}\right)$$
$$2x + x = 6$$
$$3x = 6$$
$$x = 2$$
Together, they can do it in 2 hours.

24. Let x be the amount of time to complete the job working together.

	Minutes to Complete Total Job	Part of Job Completed in 1 Minute
Larger belt	$4(2) = 8$	$\frac{1}{8}$
Smaller belt	$4(6) = 24$	$\frac{1}{24}$
Both belts	x	$\frac{1}{x}$

$$\frac{1}{8} + \frac{1}{24} = \frac{1}{x}$$

$$24x\left(\frac{1}{8}\right) + 24x\left(\frac{1}{24}\right) = 24x\left(\frac{1}{x}\right)$$

$$3x + x = 24$$

$$4x = 24$$

$$x = 6$$

Together, they can move them in 6 minutes.

26. Let r be the speed of the boat in still water.

	Distance = Rate · Time		
Upstream	9	$r - 3$	$\frac{9}{r-3}$
Downstream	11	$r + 3$	$\frac{11}{r+3}$

$$\frac{9}{r-3} = \frac{11}{r+3}$$

$$9(r+3) = 11(r-3)$$

$$9r + 27 = 11r - 33$$

$$60 = 2r$$

$$r = 30$$

The speed of the boat in still water is 30 miles per hour.

28. Let r be the rate of the truck on the flatland.

	Distance = Rate · Time		
Flatland	300	r	$\frac{300}{r}$
Mountain	180	$r - 20$	$\frac{180}{r-20}$

$$\frac{300}{r} = \frac{180}{r-20}$$

$$300(r-20) = 180r$$

$$300r - 6000 = 180r$$

$$120r = 6000$$

$$r = 50$$

and $r - 20 = 50 - 20 = 30$
Flatland rate: 50 miles per hour,
mountain rate: 30 miles per hour.

30. $\dfrac{x}{1} = \dfrac{20 \times 12}{9}$

$$x = \frac{240}{9}$$

$$x = 26\frac{2}{3}$$

The maximum number of students is 26.

32. $\dfrac{4x+5}{6} = \dfrac{7}{2}$

$$6\left(\frac{4x+5}{6}\right) = 6\left(\frac{7}{2}\right)$$

$$4x + 5 = 21$$

$$4x = 16$$

$$x = 4$$

The unknown number is 4.

34. Let x be the amount of time it takes them to paint the house together.

	Hours to Complete Total Job	Part of Job Completed in 1 Hour
Mr. Dodson	4	$\frac{1}{4}$
Son	5	$\frac{1}{5}$
Together	x	$\frac{1}{x}$

$$\frac{1}{4} + \frac{1}{5} = \frac{1}{x}$$

$$20x\left(\frac{1}{4}\right) + 20x\left(\frac{1}{5}\right) = 20x\left(\frac{1}{x}\right)$$

$$5x + 4x = 20$$

$$9x = 20$$

$$x = \frac{20}{9} = 2\frac{2}{9}$$

They can paint the house in $2\frac{2}{9}$ days.

36. Let r = the speed in still water.

	Distance = Rate · Time		
Downstream	9	$r + 6$	$\frac{9}{r+6}$
Upstream	3	$r - 6$	$\frac{3}{r-6}$

$$\frac{9}{r+6} = \frac{3}{r-6}$$
$$9(r-6) = 3(r+6)$$
$$9r - 54 = 3r + 18$$
$$6r = 72$$
$$r = 12$$
$$\frac{9}{r+6} = \frac{9}{12+6} = \frac{9}{18} = \frac{1}{2}$$

It takes $\frac{1}{2}$ hour each way for a total time of 1 hour for the 12 miles.

38. $\frac{30}{5} = \frac{y}{3}$
$$3(30) = 5y$$
$$90 = 5y$$
$$18 = y$$

The missing length is 18 feet.

40. $\frac{39}{250} = \frac{x}{50,000}$
$$39 \cdot 50,000 = 250 \cdot x$$
$$1,950,000 = 250x$$
$$\frac{1,950,000}{250} = x$$
$$7800 = x$$

We would expect 7800 people to have no health insurance.

42. $15\left(\frac{1}{x}\right) + \frac{9x-7}{x+2} = 9$
$$x(x+2)\left(\frac{15}{x} + \frac{9x-7}{x+2}\right) = x(x+2)(9)$$
$$x(x+2)\left(\frac{15}{x}\right) + x(x+2)\left(\frac{9x-7}{x+2}\right) = x(x+2)(9)$$
$$15(x+2) + x(9x-7) = 9x(x+2)$$
$$15x + 30 + 9x^2 - 7x = 9x^2 + 18x$$
$$30 = 10x$$
$$3 = x$$

The unknown number is 3.

44.

	Distance =	Rate	· Time
Jet	1080	$\frac{1080}{t}$	t
Car	240	$\frac{240}{(t+1)}$	$t+1$

$$\frac{1080}{t} = 6\left(\frac{240}{t+1}\right)$$
$$1080(t+1) = 1440t$$
$$1080t + 1080 = 1440t$$
$$1080 = 360t$$
$$3 = t$$
$$t + 1 = 3 + 1 = 4$$

The manager travels 3 hours by jet and 4 hours by car.

46. Let x be the number of ounces of concentrate for 5 gallons of water.
$$\frac{3}{2} = \frac{x}{5}$$
$$15 = 2x$$
$$7.5 = x$$

7.5 ounces of concentrate are needed for 5 gallons of water.

48.

	r ×	t =	d
upstream	$x-3$	$\frac{6}{x-3}$	6
downstream	$x+3$	$\frac{10}{x+3}$	10

Since the times are the same, $\frac{6}{x-3} = \frac{10}{x+3}$.

$$\frac{6}{x-3} = \frac{10}{x+3}$$
$$6(x+3) = 10(x-3)$$
$$6x + 18 = 10x - 30$$
$$18 = 4x - 30$$
$$48 = 4x$$
$$12 = x$$

The speed of the boat in still water is 12 miles per hour.

50. Let x be the speed of the second car. Then the speed of the one car is $x + 14$.

	Distance =	Rate	· Time
One Car	224	$x+14$	$\frac{224}{x+14}$
Second car	175	x	$\frac{175}{x}$

Since the times are the same $\dfrac{224}{x+14} = \dfrac{175}{x}$.

$$\dfrac{224}{x+14} = \dfrac{175}{x}$$
$$224x = 175(x+14)$$
$$224x = 175x + 2450$$
$$49x = 2450$$
$$x = 50$$
$$x + 14 = 50 + 14 = 64$$

The speed of the one car is 64 miles per hour and the speed of the second car is 50 miles per hour.

52. Let x be the time it takes the second proofreader to do the job alone.

	Hours to Complete Total Job	Part of Job Completed in 1 Hour
1st Proofreader	4	$\dfrac{1}{4}$
2nd Proofreader	x	$\dfrac{1}{x}$
Together	$2\dfrac{1}{2}$ or $\dfrac{5}{2}$	$\dfrac{2}{5}$

$$\dfrac{1}{4} + \dfrac{1}{x} = \dfrac{2}{5}$$
$$20x\left(\dfrac{1}{4}\right) + 20x\left(\dfrac{1}{x}\right) = 20x\left(\dfrac{2}{5}\right)$$
$$5x + 20 = 8x$$
$$20 = 3x$$
$$x = \dfrac{20}{3} = 6\dfrac{2}{3}$$

It takes the second proofreader $6\dfrac{2}{3}$ hours.

54. $\dfrac{x}{11} = \dfrac{2}{5}$ $\qquad$ $\dfrac{y}{14} = \dfrac{2}{5}$
$\quad\; 5x = 22$ $\qquad\quad\; 5y = 28$
$\quad\;\; x = \dfrac{22}{5}$ $\qquad\quad\;\; y = \dfrac{28}{5}$
$\quad\;\; x = 4.4$ ft $\qquad\quad y = 5.6$ ft

56. Let x be the number of calories in 2 ounces.
$$\dfrac{1280}{14} = \dfrac{x}{2}$$
$$1280 \cdot 2 = 14 \cdot x$$
$$2560 = 14x$$
$$\dfrac{2560}{14} = x$$
$$\dfrac{1280}{7} = x$$
$$182\dfrac{6}{7} = x$$

There are $182\dfrac{6}{7}$ calories in 2 ounces of Eagle Brand Milk.

58. Let r be the speed of the wind.

	Distance = Rate · Time		
With Wind	1575	$490 + r$	$\dfrac{1575}{490+r}$
Against Wind	1365	$490 - r$	$\dfrac{1365}{490-r}$

Since the times are the same, $\dfrac{1575}{490+r} = \dfrac{1365}{490-r}$.

$$\dfrac{1575}{490+r} = \dfrac{1365}{490-r}$$
$$1575(490 - r) = 1365(490 + r)$$
$$771,750 - 1575r = 668,850 + 1365r$$
$$102,900 = 2940r$$
$$35 = r$$

The speed of the wind is 35 miles per hour.

60.

	Minutes to Complete Total Job	Part of Job Completed in 1 Minute
1st Pump	$2x$	$\dfrac{1}{2x}$
2nd Pump	x	$\dfrac{1}{x}$
Together	18	$\dfrac{1}{18}$

$$\frac{1}{2x} + \frac{1}{x} = \frac{1}{18}$$

$$18x\left(\frac{1}{2x}\right) + 18x\left(\frac{1}{x}\right) = 18x\left(\frac{1}{18}\right)$$

$$9 + 18 = x$$

$$27 = x$$

$2x = 2(27) = 54$

The 1st pump takes 27 minutes and the 2nd takes 54 minutes.

62. Let x be the speed of the walker.
Then $x + 2$ is the speed of the jogger.

	Distance = Rate · Time		
Walker	3.6	x	$\frac{3.6}{x}$
Jogger	6	$x + 2$	$\frac{6}{x+2}$

Since the times are the same, $\frac{3.6}{x} = \frac{6}{x+2}$.

$$\frac{3.6}{x} = \frac{6}{x+2}$$

$$3.6(x + 2) = 6x$$

$$3.6x + 7.2 = 6x$$

$$7.2 = 2.4x$$

$$3 = x$$

$x + 2 = 3 + 2 = 5$

The speed of the walker is 3 miles per hour and the speed of the jogger is 5 miles per hour.

64. Let x be the time it takes pump C to fill the tank alone.

	Time	In one hour
Pump A	9	$\frac{1}{9}$
Pump B	15	$\frac{1}{15}$
Pump C	x	$\frac{1}{x}$
Together	5	$\frac{1}{5}$

$$\frac{1}{9} + \frac{1}{15} + \frac{1}{x} = \frac{1}{5}$$

$$45x\left(\frac{1}{9} + \frac{1}{15} + \frac{1}{x}\right) = 45x\left(\frac{1}{5}\right)$$

$$5x + 3x + 45 = 9x$$

$$8x + 45 = 9x$$

$$45 = x$$

It takes pump C 45 hours to fill the tank.

66.

	Time	In one hour
Mrs. Smith	8	$\frac{1}{8}$
Assistant	12	$\frac{1}{12}$
Together	x	$\frac{1}{x}$

$$\frac{1}{8} + \frac{1}{12} = \frac{1}{x}$$

$$24x\left(\frac{1}{8} + \frac{1}{12}\right) = 24x\left(\frac{1}{x}\right)$$

$$3x + 2x = 24$$

$$5x = 24$$

$$\frac{5x}{5} = \frac{24}{5}$$

$$x = 4\frac{4}{5}$$

It takes them $4\frac{4}{5}$ hours.

68. $\frac{7}{14} = \frac{4}{x}$

$7x = 56$

$x = 8$

The missing length is 8 units.

70. $\frac{14}{7} = \frac{7}{y}$

$14y = 49$

$y = \frac{49}{14} = 3.5$

The missing length is 3.5 units.

72. $(0, 4), (2, 10)$

$$m = \frac{10 - 4}{2 - 0} = \frac{6}{2} = 3$$

Since the slope is positive, the line moves upward.

74. $\dfrac{\frac{9}{5}+\frac{6}{5}}{\frac{17}{6}+\frac{7}{6}}=\dfrac{\frac{9+6}{5}}{\frac{17+7}{6}}$

$=\dfrac{\frac{15}{5}}{\frac{24}{6}}$

$=\dfrac{15}{5}\div\dfrac{24}{6}$

$=\dfrac{15}{5}\cdot\dfrac{6}{24}$

$=\dfrac{3\cdot5\cdot6}{5\cdot4\cdot6}$

$=\dfrac{3}{4}$

76. $\dfrac{\frac{1}{4}+\frac{5}{4}}{\frac{3}{8}+\frac{7}{8}}=\dfrac{\frac{1+5}{4}}{\frac{3+7}{8}}=\dfrac{\frac{6}{4}}{\frac{10}{8}}=\dfrac{6}{4}\div\dfrac{10}{8}=\dfrac{6}{4}\cdot\dfrac{8}{10}=\dfrac{6\cdot2\cdot4}{4\cdot2\cdot5}=\dfrac{6}{5}$

78. The capacity in 2004 was approximately 6500 megawatts, and the capacity in 2006 was approximately 11,500 megawatts.
$11,500-6500=5000$
The increase from 2004 to 2006 was approximately 5000 megawatts.

80. Answers may vary

82. Since a involves only quotients, while the left-hand side of b involves a difference of expressions, only a can be solved by using cross products immediately.

84. Yes; answers may vary.

86. From Exercise 75, we know that Diophantus died at age 84.
Age when son was born
$=\dfrac{1}{6}x+\dfrac{1}{12}x+\dfrac{1}{7}x+5$
$=\dfrac{1}{6}(84)+\dfrac{1}{12}(84)+\dfrac{1}{7}(84)+5$
$=14+7+12+5$
$=38$ years

Age of son when he died $=\dfrac{1}{2}x$
$=\dfrac{1}{2}(84)$
$=42$ years

88. Answers may vary

The Bigger Picture

1. $(3x-2)(4x^2-x-5)$
$=3x(4x^2-x-5)-2(4x^2-x-5)$
$=12x^3-3x^2-15x-8x^2+2x+10$
$=12x^3-11x^2-13x+10$

2. $(2x-y)^2=(2x)^2-2(2x)(y)+y^2$
$=4x^2-4xy+y^2$

3. $8y^3-20y^5=4y^3(2-5y^2)$

4. $9m^2-11mn+2n^2=9m^2-2mn-9mn+2n^2$
$=m(9m-2n)-n(9m-2n)$
$=(9m-2n)(m-n)$

5. $\dfrac{7}{x}=\dfrac{9}{x-10}$
$7(x-10)=9x$
$7x-70=9x$
$-70=2x$
$-35=x$

6. $\dfrac{7}{x}+\dfrac{9}{x-10}=\dfrac{7(x-10)}{x(x-10)}+\dfrac{9(x)}{(x-10)x}$
$=\dfrac{7(x-10)+9x}{x(x-10)}$
$=\dfrac{7x-70+9x}{x(x-10)}$
$=\dfrac{16x-70}{x(x-10)}$ or $\dfrac{2(8x-35)}{x(x-10)}$

7. $(-3x^5)\left(\dfrac{1}{2}x^7\right)(8x)=\left(-3\cdot\dfrac{1}{2}\cdot8\right)(x^5\cdot x^7\cdot x^1)$
$=-12x^{5+7+1}$
$=-12x^{13}$

8. $5x-1=|-4|+|-5|$
$5x-1=4+5$
$5x-1=9$
$5x=10$
$x=2$

9. $\dfrac{8-12}{12\div3\cdot2}=\dfrac{-4}{4\cdot2}=\dfrac{-4}{8}=-\dfrac{1}{2}$

10. $-2(3y-4) \le 5y-7-7y-1$

$\quad -6y+8 \le -2y-8$

$\quad\quad\quad 8 \le 4y-8$

$\quad\quad\quad 16 \le 4y$

$\quad\quad\quad 4 \le y$

$[4, \infty)$

11. $\quad\quad\quad\quad \dfrac{7}{x} + \dfrac{5}{2x+3} = \dfrac{-2}{x}$

$\quad x(2x+3)\left(\dfrac{7}{x} + \dfrac{5}{2x+3}\right) = x(2x+3)\left(\dfrac{-2}{x}\right)$

$x(2x+3)\cdot\dfrac{7}{x} + x(2x+3)\cdot\dfrac{5}{2x+3} = x(2x+3)\cdot\dfrac{-2}{x}$

$\quad\quad\quad 7(2x+3)+5x = -2(2x+3)$

$\quad\quad\quad 14x+21+5x = -4x-6$

$\quad\quad\quad 19x+21 = -4x-6$

$\quad\quad\quad 23x+21 = -6$

$\quad\quad\quad 23x = -27$

$\quad\quad\quad x = -\dfrac{27}{23}$

12. $\dfrac{(a^{-3}b^2)^{-5}}{ab^4} = \dfrac{a^{(-3)(-5)}b^{2(-5)}}{ab^4} = \dfrac{a^{15}b^{-10}}{ab^4} = \dfrac{a^{14}}{b^{14}}$

Section 7.7

Practice Exercises

1. a. $\dfrac{\frac{5k}{36m}}{\frac{15k}{9}} = \dfrac{5k}{36m} \div \dfrac{15k}{9}$

$\quad\quad = \dfrac{5k}{36m}\cdot\dfrac{9}{15k}$

$\quad\quad = \dfrac{5k\cdot 9}{36m\cdot 15k}$

$\quad\quad = \dfrac{1}{12m}$

b. $\dfrac{\frac{8x}{x-4}}{\frac{3}{x+4}} = \dfrac{8x}{x-4} \div \dfrac{3}{x+4}$

$\quad\quad = \dfrac{8x}{x-4}\cdot\dfrac{x+4}{3}$

$\quad\quad = \dfrac{8x(x+4)}{3(x-4)}$

c. $\dfrac{\frac{5}{a} + \frac{b}{a^2}}{\frac{5a}{b^2} + \frac{1}{b}} = \dfrac{\frac{5\cdot a}{a\cdot a} + \frac{b}{a^2}}{\frac{5a}{b^2} + \frac{1\cdot b}{b\cdot b}}$

$\quad\quad = \dfrac{\frac{5a+b}{a^2}}{\frac{5a+b}{b^2}}$

$\quad\quad = \dfrac{5a+b}{a^2}\cdot\dfrac{b^2}{5a+b}$

$\quad\quad = \dfrac{b^2(5a+b)}{a^2(5a+b)}$

$\quad\quad = \dfrac{b^2}{a^2}$

2. a. The LCD is $(x-4)(x+4)$.

$\dfrac{\frac{8x}{x-4}}{\frac{3}{x+4}} = \dfrac{\left(\frac{8x}{x-4}\right)\cdot(x-4)(x+4)}{\left(\frac{3}{x+4}\right)\cdot(x-4)(x+4)}$

$\quad\quad = \dfrac{8x(x+4)}{3(x-4)}$

b. The LCD is a^2b^2.

$\dfrac{\frac{b}{a^2} + \frac{1}{a}}{\frac{a}{b^2} + \frac{1}{b}} = \dfrac{\left(\frac{b}{a^2} + \frac{1}{a}\right)\cdot a^2b^2}{\left(\frac{a}{b^2} + \frac{1}{b}\right)\cdot a^2b^2}$

$\quad\quad = \dfrac{\frac{b}{a^2}\cdot a^2b^2 + \frac{1}{a}\cdot a^2b^2}{\frac{a}{b^2}\cdot a^2b^2 + \frac{1}{b}\cdot a^2b^2}$

$\quad\quad = \dfrac{b^3 + ab^2}{a^3 + a^2b}$

$\quad\quad = \dfrac{b^2(b+a)}{a^2(a+b)}$

$\quad\quad = \dfrac{b^2}{a^2}$

3. $\dfrac{3x^{-1}+x^{-2}y^{-1}}{y^{-2}+xy^{-1}}=\dfrac{\frac{3}{x}+\frac{1}{x^2y}}{\frac{1}{y^2}+\frac{x}{y}}$

The LCD is x^2y^2.

$$=\dfrac{\left(\frac{3}{x}+\frac{1}{x^2y}\right)\cdot x^2y^2}{\left(\frac{1}{y^2}+\frac{x}{y}\right)\cdot x^2y^2}$$

$$=\dfrac{\frac{3}{x}\cdot x^2y^2+\frac{1}{x^2y}\cdot x^2y^2}{\frac{1}{y^2}\cdot x^2y^2+\frac{x}{y}\cdot x^2y^2}$$

$$=\dfrac{3xy^2+y}{x^2+x^3y}\ \text{or}\ \dfrac{y(3xy+1)}{x^2(1+xy)}$$

4. $\dfrac{(3x)^{-1}-2}{5x^{-1}+2}=\dfrac{\frac{1}{3x}-2}{\frac{5}{x}+2}$

$$=\dfrac{\left(\frac{1}{3x}-2\right)\cdot 3x}{\left(\frac{5}{x}+2\right)\cdot 3x}$$

$$=\dfrac{\frac{1}{3x}\cdot 3x-2\cdot 3x}{\frac{5}{x}\cdot 3x+2\cdot 3x}$$

$$=\dfrac{1-6x}{15+6x}$$

Vocabulary and Readiness Check

1. $\dfrac{\frac{7}{x}}{\frac{1}{x}+\frac{z}{x}}=\dfrac{x\left(\frac{7}{x}\right)}{x\left(\frac{1}{x}\right)+x\left(\frac{z}{x}\right)}=\dfrac{7}{1+z}$

2. $\dfrac{\frac{x}{4}}{\frac{x^2}{2}+\frac{1}{4}}=\dfrac{4\left(\frac{x}{4}\right)}{4\left(\frac{x^2}{2}\right)+4\left(\frac{1}{4}\right)}=\dfrac{x}{2x^2+1}$

3. $x^{-2}=\dfrac{1}{x^2}$

4. $y^{-3}=\dfrac{1}{y^3}$

5. $2x^{-1}=\dfrac{2}{x}$

6. $(2x)^{-1}=\dfrac{1}{2x}$

7. $(9y)^{-1}=\dfrac{1}{9y}$

8. $9y^{-2}=\dfrac{9}{y^2}$

Exercise Set 7.7

2. $\dfrac{\frac{15}{2x}}{\frac{5}{6x}}=\dfrac{15}{2x}\cdot\dfrac{6x}{5}=\dfrac{90x}{10x}=9$

4. $\dfrac{2+\frac{1}{7}}{3-\frac{4}{7}}=\dfrac{7\left(2+\frac{1}{7}\right)}{7\left(3-\frac{4}{7}\right)}=\dfrac{14+1}{21-4}=\dfrac{15}{17}$

6. $\dfrac{\frac{x}{x+2}}{\frac{2}{x+2}}=\dfrac{x}{x+2}\cdot\dfrac{x+2}{2}=\dfrac{x}{2}$

8. $\dfrac{5-\frac{3}{x}}{x+\frac{2}{3x}}=\dfrac{3x\left(5-\frac{3}{x}\right)}{3x\left(x+\frac{2}{3x}\right)}=\dfrac{15x-9}{3x^2+2}=\dfrac{3(5x-3)}{3x^2+2}$

10. $\dfrac{\frac{x^2-9y^2}{xy}}{\frac{1}{y}-\frac{3}{x}}=\dfrac{xy\left(\frac{x^2-9y^2}{xy}\right)}{xy\left(\frac{1}{y}-\frac{3}{x}\right)}$

$$=\dfrac{x^2-9y^2}{x-3y}$$

$$=\dfrac{(x+3y)(x-3y)}{x-3y}$$

$$=x+3y$$

12. $\dfrac{\frac{x+3}{12}}{\frac{4x-5}{15}}=\dfrac{x+3}{12}\cdot\dfrac{15}{4x-5}=\dfrac{5(x+3)}{4(4x-5)}$

14. $\dfrac{\frac{2}{x^2}+\frac{1}{x}}{\frac{4}{x^2}-\frac{1}{x}}=\dfrac{x^2\left(\frac{2}{x^2}+\frac{1}{x}\right)}{x^2\left(\frac{4}{x^2}-\frac{1}{x}\right)}=\dfrac{2+x}{4-x}$

16.
$$\frac{\frac{1}{y}+\frac{3}{y^2}}{y+\frac{27}{y^2}} = \frac{y^2\left(\frac{1}{y}+\frac{3}{y^2}\right)}{y^2\left(y+\frac{27}{y^2}\right)}$$
$$= \frac{y+3}{y^3+27}$$
$$= \frac{y+3}{(y+3)(y^2-3y+9)}$$
$$= \frac{1}{y^2-3y+9}$$

18.
$$\frac{\frac{3}{x-4}-\frac{2}{4-x}}{\frac{2}{x-4}-\frac{2}{x}} = \frac{\frac{3}{x-4}-\frac{-2}{x-4}}{\frac{2x-2(x-4)}{x(x-4)}}$$
$$= \frac{\frac{5}{x-4}}{\frac{2x-2x+8}{x(x-4)}}$$
$$= \frac{5}{x-4}\cdot\frac{x(x-4)}{8}$$
$$= \frac{5x}{8}$$

20.
$$\frac{\frac{5}{a+2}-\frac{1}{a-2}}{\frac{3}{2+a}+\frac{6}{2-a}} = \frac{\frac{5}{a+2}-\frac{1}{a-2}}{\frac{3}{a+2}+\frac{-6}{a-2}}$$
$$= \frac{\frac{5(a-2)-1(a+2)}{(a+2)(a-2)}}{\frac{3(a-2)-6(a+2)}{(a+2)(a-2)}}$$
$$= \frac{\frac{5a-10-a-2}{(a+2)(a-2)}}{\frac{3a-6-6a-12}{(a+2)(a-2)}}$$
$$= \frac{4a-12}{(a+2)(a-2)}\cdot\frac{(a+2)(a-2)}{-3a-18}$$
$$= \frac{4(a-3)}{(a+2)(a-2)}\cdot\frac{(a+2)(a-2)}{-3(a+6)}$$
$$= -\frac{4(a-3)}{3(a+6)}$$

22.
$$\frac{2+\frac{1}{x}}{4x-\frac{1}{x}} = \frac{\left(2+\frac{1}{x}\right)\cdot x}{\left(4x-\frac{1}{x}\right)\cdot x}$$
$$= \frac{2x+1}{4x^2-1}$$
$$= \frac{2x+1}{(2x+1)(2x-1)}$$
$$= \frac{1}{2x-1}$$

24.
$$\frac{1-\frac{2}{x}}{x-\frac{4}{x}} = \frac{\left(1-\frac{2}{x}\right)\cdot x}{\left(x-\frac{4}{x}\right)\cdot x}$$
$$= \frac{x-2}{x^2-4}$$
$$= \frac{x-2}{(x-2)(x+2)}$$
$$= \frac{1}{x+2}$$

26.
$$\frac{\frac{7y}{x^2+xy}}{\frac{y^2}{x^2}} = \frac{7y}{x^2+xy}\div\frac{y^2}{x^2}$$
$$= \frac{7y}{x^2+xy}\cdot\frac{x^2}{y^2}$$
$$= \frac{7y}{x(x+y)}\cdot\frac{x^2}{y^2}$$
$$= \frac{7x}{y(x+y)}$$

28.
$$\frac{\frac{5}{x^2}-\frac{2}{x}}{\frac{1}{x}+2} = \frac{\left(\frac{5}{x^2}-\frac{2}{x}\right)x^2}{\left(\frac{1}{x}+2\right)x^2} = \frac{5-2x}{x+2x^2} = \frac{5-2x}{x(1+2x)}$$

30.
$$\frac{\frac{x}{4}-\frac{4}{x}}{1-\frac{4}{x}} = \frac{\left(\frac{x}{4}-\frac{4}{x}\right)4x}{\left(1-\frac{4}{x}\right)4x}$$
$$= \frac{x^2-16}{4x-16}$$
$$= \frac{(x+4)(x-4)}{4(x-4)}$$
$$= \frac{x+4}{4}$$

32.
$$\frac{\frac{x+3}{x^2-9}}{1+\frac{1}{x-3}} = \frac{\frac{x+3}{x^2-9}}{\frac{x-3}{x-3}+\frac{1}{x-3}}$$
$$= \frac{\frac{x+3}{x^2-9}}{\frac{x-3+1}{x-3}}$$
$$= \frac{x+3}{(x+3)(x-3)}\cdot\frac{x-3}{x-2}$$
$$= \frac{1}{x-2}$$

34. $\dfrac{\frac{2}{x+2}+\frac{6}{x+7}}{\frac{4x+13}{x^2+9x+14}}=\dfrac{\frac{2(x+7)+6(x+2)}{(x+2)(x+7)}}{\frac{4x+13}{x^2+9x+14}}$

$=\dfrac{\frac{2x+14+6x+12}{(x+2)(x+7)}}{\frac{4x+13}{x^2+9x+14}}$

$=\dfrac{8x+26}{(x+2)(x+7)}\cdot\dfrac{x^2+9x+14}{4x+13}$

$=\dfrac{2(4x+13)}{(x+2)(x+7)}\cdot\dfrac{(x+2)(x+7)}{4x+13}$

$=2$

36. $\dfrac{a^{-3}+b^{-1}}{a^{-2}}=\dfrac{\frac{1}{a^3}+\frac{1}{b}}{\frac{1}{a^2}}=\dfrac{a^3 b\left(\frac{1}{a^3}+\frac{1}{b}\right)}{a^3 b\left(\frac{1}{a^2}\right)}=\dfrac{b+a^3}{ab}$

38. $\dfrac{x^{-1}+y^{-1}}{3x^{-2}+5y^{-2}}=\dfrac{\frac{1}{x}+\frac{1}{y}}{\frac{3}{x^2}+\frac{5}{y^2}}$

$=\dfrac{x^2 y^2\left(\frac{1}{x}+\frac{1}{y}\right)}{x^2 y^2\left(\frac{3}{x^2}+\frac{5}{y^2}\right)}$

$=\dfrac{xy^2+x^2 y}{3y^2+5x^2}$

$=\dfrac{xy(y+x)}{3y^2+5x^2}$

40. $\dfrac{x^{-2}}{x+3x^{-1}}=\dfrac{\frac{1}{x^2}}{x+\frac{3}{x}}$

$=\dfrac{x^2\left(\frac{1}{x^2}\right)}{x^2\left(x+\frac{3}{x}\right)}$

$=\dfrac{1}{x^3+3x}$

$=\dfrac{1}{x(x^2+3)}$

42. $\dfrac{a^{-1}-4}{4+a^{-1}}=\dfrac{\frac{1}{a}-4}{4+\frac{1}{a}}=\dfrac{a\left(\frac{1}{a}-4\right)}{a\left(4+\frac{1}{a}\right)}=\dfrac{1-4a}{4a+1}$

44. $\dfrac{5x^{-2}-3y^{-1}}{x^{-1}+y^{-1}}=\dfrac{\frac{5}{x^2}-\frac{3}{y}}{\frac{1}{x}+\frac{1}{y}}$

$=\dfrac{x^2 y\left(\frac{5}{x^2}-\frac{3}{y}\right)}{x^2 y\left(\frac{1}{x}+\frac{1}{y}\right)}$

$=\dfrac{5y-3x^2}{xy+x^2}$

$=\dfrac{5y-3x^2}{x(y+x)}$

46. $\dfrac{a^{-1}+2a^{-2}}{2a^{-1}+(2a)^{-1}}=\dfrac{\frac{1}{a}+\frac{2}{a^2}}{\frac{2}{a}+\frac{1}{2a}}$

$=\dfrac{2a^2\left(\frac{1}{a}+\frac{2}{a^2}\right)}{2a^2\left(\frac{2}{a}+\frac{1}{2a}\right)}$

$=\dfrac{2a+4}{4a+a}$

$=\dfrac{2a+4}{5a}$ or $\dfrac{2(a+2)}{5a}$

48. $\dfrac{x^{-2}y^{-2}}{5x^{-1}+2y^{-1}}=\dfrac{\frac{1}{x^2 y^2}}{\frac{5}{x}+\frac{2}{y}}$

$=\dfrac{x^2 y^2\left(\frac{1}{x^2 y^2}\right)}{x^2 y^2\left(\frac{5}{x}+\frac{2}{y}\right)}$

$=\dfrac{1}{5xy^2+2x^2 y}$

$=\dfrac{1}{xy(5y+2x)}$

50. $\dfrac{3x^{-1}+3y^{-1}}{4x^{-2}-9y^{-2}}=\dfrac{\frac{3}{x}+\frac{3}{y}}{\frac{4}{x^2}-\frac{9}{y^2}}$

$=\dfrac{x^2 y^2\left(\frac{3}{x}+\frac{3}{y}\right)}{x^2 y^2\left(\frac{4}{x^2}-\frac{9}{y^2}\right)}$

$=\dfrac{3xy^2+3x^2 y}{4y^2-9x^2}$

$=\dfrac{3xy(y+x)}{(2y+3x)(2y-3x)}$

52. $\dfrac{-36xb^3}{9xb^2} = \dfrac{9xb^2 \cdot (-4b)}{9xb^2 \cdot 1} = -4b$

54. $\dfrac{48x^3y^2}{-4xy} = \dfrac{4xy \cdot 12x^2y}{4xy \cdot (-1)} = -12x^2y$

56. $f(x) = x^2 - 6$

$f(-1) = (-1)^2 - 6 = 1 - 6 = -5$

58. $\dfrac{\frac{a}{7}}{\frac{b}{13}} = \dfrac{a}{7} \div \dfrac{b}{13} = \dfrac{a}{7} \cdot \dfrac{13}{b}$

Both b and d are equivalent to the original expression.

60. $\dfrac{E}{\frac{I}{9}} = I \div \dfrac{I}{9} = E \cdot \dfrac{9}{I} = \dfrac{9E}{I}$

62. Answers may vary

64. $\dfrac{(x+2)^{-1} + (x-2)^{-1}}{(x^2-4)^{-1}} = \dfrac{\frac{1}{x+2} + \frac{1}{x-2}}{\frac{1}{x^2-4}}$

$= \dfrac{(x^2-4)\left(\frac{1}{x+2} + \frac{1}{x-2}\right)}{(x^2-4)\left(\frac{1}{x^2-4}\right)}$

$= \dfrac{(x-2) + (x+2)}{1}$

$= 2x$

66. $\dfrac{x}{1 - \frac{1}{1-\frac{1}{x}}} = \dfrac{x}{1 - \frac{1}{\frac{x-1}{x}}}$

$= \dfrac{x}{1 - \frac{x}{x-1}}$

$= \dfrac{(x-1)(x)}{(x-1)\left(1 - \frac{x}{x-1}\right)}$

$= \dfrac{x(x-1)}{x-1-x}$

$= \dfrac{x(x-1)}{-1}$

$= -x(x-1)$

68. $\dfrac{\frac{2}{x^2} - \frac{1}{xy} - \frac{1}{y^2}}{\frac{1}{x^2} - \frac{3}{xy} + \frac{2}{y^2}} = \dfrac{x^2y^2\left(\frac{2}{x^2} - \frac{1}{xy} - \frac{1}{y^2}\right)}{x^2y^2\left(\frac{1}{x^2} - \frac{3}{xy} + \frac{2}{y^2}\right)}$

$= \dfrac{2y^2 - xy - x^2}{y^2 - 3xy + 2x^2}$

$= \dfrac{(2y+x)(y-x)}{(y-2x)(y-x)}$

$= \dfrac{2y+x}{y-2x}$

70. $\dfrac{9x^{-1} - 5(x-y)^{-1}}{4(x-y)^{-1}} = \dfrac{\frac{9}{x} - \frac{5}{x-y}}{\frac{4}{x-y}}$

$= \dfrac{\frac{9(x-y)-5x}{x(x-y)}}{\frac{4}{x-y}}$

$= \dfrac{\frac{9x-9y-5x}{x(x-y)}}{\frac{4}{x-y}}$

$= \dfrac{4x-9y}{x(x-y)} \cdot \dfrac{x-y}{4}$

$= \dfrac{4x-9y}{4x}$

72. $f(x) = \dfrac{5}{x}$

a. $f(a+h) = \dfrac{5}{a+h}$

b. $f(a) = \dfrac{5}{a}$

c. $\dfrac{f(a+h) - f(a)}{h} = \dfrac{\frac{5}{a+h} - \frac{5}{a}}{h}$

d. $\dfrac{\frac{5}{a+h} - \frac{5}{a}}{h} = \dfrac{a(a+h)\left(\frac{5}{a+h} - \frac{5}{a}\right)}{ah(a+h)}$

$= \dfrac{5a - 5(a+h)}{ah(a+h)}$

$= \dfrac{5a - 5a - 5h}{ah(a+h)}$

$= \dfrac{-5h}{ah(a+h)}$

$= \dfrac{-5}{a(a+h)}$

74. $f(x) = \dfrac{2}{x^2}$

   a. $f(a+h) = \dfrac{2}{(a+h)^2}$

   b. $f(a) = \dfrac{2}{a^2}$

   c. $\dfrac{f(a+h) - f(a)}{h} = \dfrac{\frac{2}{(a+h)^2} - \frac{2}{a^2}}{h}$

   d. $\dfrac{\frac{2}{(a+h)^2} - \frac{2}{a^2}}{h} = \dfrac{a^2(a+h)^2\left(\frac{2}{(a+h)^2} - \frac{2}{a^2}\right)}{a^2(a+h)^2 \cdot h}$

$$= \frac{2a^2 - 2(a+h)^2}{a^2 h (a+h)^2}$$

$$= \frac{2a^2 - 2(a^2 + 2ah + h^2)}{a^2 h (a+h)^2}$$

$$= \frac{2a^2 - 2a^2 - 4ah - 2h^2}{a^2 h (a+h)^2}$$

$$= \frac{-4ah - 2h^2}{a^2 h (a+h)^2}$$

$$= \frac{-2h(2a + h)}{a^2 h (a+h)^2}$$

$$= \frac{-2(2a + h)}{a^2 (a+h)^2}$$

Chapter 7 Vocabulary Check

   1. A <u>ratio</u> is the quotient of two numbers.

   2. $\dfrac{x}{2} = \dfrac{7}{16}$ is an example of a <u>proportion</u>.

   3. If $\dfrac{a}{b} = \dfrac{c}{d}$, then ad and bc are called <u>cross products</u>.

   4. A <u>rational expression</u> is an expression that can be written in the form $\dfrac{P}{Q}$, where P and Q are polynomials and Q is not 0.

   5. In a <u>complex fraction</u>, the numerator or denominator or both may contain fractions.

   6. The <u>domain</u> of the rational function $f(x) = \dfrac{1}{x-3}$ is $\{x|x$ is a real number $x \neq 3\}$.

   7. The <u>reciprocal</u> of $\dfrac{9}{7}$ is $\dfrac{7}{9}$.

Chapter 7 Review

   1. 7 is never 0 so the domain of $f(x) = \dfrac{3-5x}{7}$ is $\{x|x$ is a real number$\}$.

   2. 11 is never 0 so the domain of $g(x) = \dfrac{2x+4}{11}$ is $\{x|x$ is a real number$\}$.

   3. $x - 5 = 0$

$$x = 5$$

The domain of $F(x) = \dfrac{-3x^2}{x-5}$ is $\{x|x$ is a real number and $x \neq 5\}$.

   4. $3x - 12 = 0$

$$3x = 12$$
$$x = 4$$

The domain of $h(x) = \dfrac{4x}{3x-12}$ is $\{x|x$ is a real number and $x \neq 4\}$.

   5. $x^2 + 8x = 0$

$$x(x+8) = 0$$
$$x = 0 \quad \text{or} \quad x + 8 = 0$$
$$x = 0 \quad \text{or} \quad x = -8$$

The domain of $f(x) = \dfrac{x^3 + 2}{x^2 + 8x}$ is $\{x|x$ is a real number and $x \neq 0,\ x \neq -8\}$.

   6. $3x^2 - 48 = 0$

$$3(x^2 - 16) = 0$$
$$3(x+4)(x-4) = 0$$
$$x + 4 = 0 \quad \text{or} \quad x - 4 = 0$$
$$x = -4 \quad \text{or} \quad x = 4$$

The domain of $G(x) = \dfrac{20}{3x^2 - 48}$ is $\{x|x$ is a real number and $x \neq -4,\ x \neq 4\}$.

7. $\dfrac{x-12}{12-x} = \dfrac{x-12}{-(x-12)} = -1$

8. $\dfrac{5x-15}{25x-75} = \dfrac{5(x-3)}{25(x-3)} = \dfrac{5}{25} = \dfrac{1}{5}$

9. $\dfrac{2x}{2x^2-2x} = \dfrac{2x}{2x(x-1)} = \dfrac{1}{x-1}$

10. $\dfrac{x+7}{x^2-49} = \dfrac{x+7}{(x-7)(x+7)} = \dfrac{1}{x-7}$

11. $\dfrac{2x^2+4x-30}{x^2+x-20} = \dfrac{2(x^2+2x-15)}{(x+5)(x-4)}$

$= \dfrac{2(x+5)(x-3)}{(x+5)(x-4)}$

$= \dfrac{2(x-3)}{x-4}$

12. $C(x) = \dfrac{35x+4200}{x}$

a. $C(50) = \dfrac{35(50)+4200}{50}$

$= \dfrac{1750+4200}{50}$

$= \dfrac{5950}{50}$

$= 119$

The average cost is \$119.

b. $C(100) = \dfrac{35(100)+4200}{100}$

$= \dfrac{3500+4200}{100}$

$= \dfrac{7700}{100}$

$= 77$

The average cost is \$77.

c. It will decrease.

13. $\dfrac{x^2+xa+xb+ab}{x^2-xc+bx-bc} = \dfrac{x(x+a)+b(x+a)}{x(x-c)+b(x-c)}$

$= \dfrac{(x+a)(x+b)}{(x-c)(x+b)}$

$= \dfrac{x+a}{x-c}$

14. $\dfrac{x^2+5x-2x-10}{x^2-3x-2x+6} = \dfrac{x(x+5)-2(x+5)}{x(x-3)-2(x-3)}$

$= \dfrac{(x+5)(x-2)}{(x-3)(x-2)}$

$= \dfrac{x+5}{x-3}$

15. $\dfrac{4-x}{x^3-64} = -\dfrac{x-4}{x^3-64}$

$= -\dfrac{x-4}{(x-4)(x^2+4x+16)}$

$= -\dfrac{1}{x^2+4x+16}$

16. $\dfrac{x^2-4}{x^3+8} = \dfrac{(x+2)(x-2)}{(x+2)(x^2-2x+4)} = \dfrac{x-2}{x^2-2x+4}$

17. $\dfrac{15x^3y^2}{z} \cdot \dfrac{z}{5xy^3} = \dfrac{15x^3y^2 \cdot z}{z \cdot 5xy^3}$

$= \dfrac{3 \cdot 5 \cdot x^2 \cdot x \cdot y^2 \cdot z}{z \cdot 5 \cdot x \cdot y^2 \cdot y}$

$= \dfrac{3x^2}{y}$

18. $\dfrac{-y^3}{8} \cdot \dfrac{9x^2}{y^3} = -\dfrac{y^3 \cdot 9x^2}{8 \cdot y^3} = -\dfrac{9x^2}{8}$

19. $\dfrac{x^2-9}{x^2-4} \cdot \dfrac{x-2}{x+3} = \dfrac{(x^2-9) \cdot (x-2)}{(x^2-4) \cdot (x+3)}$

$= \dfrac{(x-3)(x+3)(x-2)}{(x+2)(x-2)(x+3)}$

$= \dfrac{x-3}{x+2}$

20. $\dfrac{2x+5}{x-6} \cdot \dfrac{2x}{-x+6} = \dfrac{2x+5}{x-6} \cdot \dfrac{2x}{-(x-6)}$

$= \dfrac{2x+5}{x-6} \cdot \dfrac{-2x}{x-6}$

$= \dfrac{(2x+5) \cdot (-2x)}{(x-6) \cdot (x-6)}$

$= \dfrac{-2x(2x+5)}{(x-6)^2}$

21. $\dfrac{x^2-5x-24}{x^2-x-12} \div \dfrac{x^2-10x+16}{x^2+x-6}$

$= \dfrac{x^2-5x-24}{x^2-x-12} \cdot \dfrac{x^2+x-6}{x^2-10x+16}$

$= \dfrac{(x-8)(x+3)\cdot(x+3)(x-2)}{(x-4)(x+3)\cdot(x-8)(x-2)}$

$= \dfrac{x+3}{x-4}$

22. $\dfrac{4x+4y}{xy^2} \div \dfrac{3x+3y}{x^2y} = \dfrac{4x+4y}{xy^2} \cdot \dfrac{x^2y}{3x+3y}$

$= \dfrac{4(x+y)\cdot x\cdot x\cdot y}{x\cdot y\cdot y\cdot 3(x+y)}$

$= \dfrac{4x}{3y}$

23. $\dfrac{x^2+x-42}{x-3} \cdot \dfrac{(x-3)^2}{x+7}$

$= \dfrac{(x+7)(x-6)\cdot(x-3)(x-3)}{(x-3)\cdot(x+7)}$

$= (x-6)(x-3)$

24. $\dfrac{2a+2b}{3} \cdot \dfrac{a-b}{a^2-b^2} = \dfrac{2(a+b)\cdot(a-b)}{3\cdot(a+b)(a-b)} = \dfrac{2}{3}$

25. $\dfrac{2x^2-9x+9}{8x-12} \div \dfrac{x^2-3x}{2x} = \dfrac{2x^2-9x+9}{8x-12} \cdot \dfrac{2x}{x^2-3x}$

$= \dfrac{(2x-3)(x-3)\cdot 2x}{4(2x-3)\cdot x(x-3)}$

$= \dfrac{2}{4}$

$= \dfrac{1}{2}$

26. $\dfrac{x^2-y^2}{x^2+xy} \div \dfrac{3x^2-2xy-y^2}{3x^2+6x}$

$= \dfrac{x^2-y^2}{x^2+xy} \cdot \dfrac{3x^2+6x}{3x^2-2xy-y^2}$

$= \dfrac{(x-y)(x+y)\cdot 3x(x+2)}{x(x+y)\cdot(3x+y)(x-y)}$

$= \dfrac{3(x+2)}{3x+y}$

27. $\dfrac{x-y}{4} \div \dfrac{y^2-2y-xy+2x}{16x+24}$

$= \dfrac{x-y}{4} \cdot \dfrac{16x+24}{y^2-2y-xy+2x}$

$= \dfrac{x-y}{4} \cdot \dfrac{8(2x+3)}{y(y-2)-x(y-2)}$

$= \dfrac{x-y}{4} \cdot \dfrac{8(2x+3)}{(y-2)(y-x)}$

$= -\dfrac{y-x}{4} \cdot \dfrac{8(2x+3)}{(y-2)(y-x)}$

$= -\dfrac{2\cdot 4(y-x)(2x+3)}{4(y-2)(y-x)}$

$= -\dfrac{2(2x+3)}{y-2}$

28. $\dfrac{5+x}{7} \div \dfrac{xy+5y-3x-15}{7y-35}$

$= \dfrac{5+x}{7} \cdot \dfrac{7y-35}{xy+5y-3x-15}$

$= \dfrac{(5+x)\cdot 7(y-5)}{7\cdot(x+5)(y-3)}$

$= \dfrac{y-5}{y-3}$

29. $\dfrac{x}{x^2+9x+14} + \dfrac{7}{x^2+9x+14} = \dfrac{x+7}{x^2+9x+14}$

$= \dfrac{x+7}{(x+7)(x+2)}$

$= \dfrac{1}{x+2}$

30. $\dfrac{x}{x^2+2x-15} + \dfrac{5}{x^2+2x-15} = \dfrac{x+5}{x^2+2x-15}$

$= \dfrac{x+5}{(x+5)(x-3)}$

$= \dfrac{1}{x-3}$

31. $\dfrac{4x-5}{3x^2} - \dfrac{2x+5}{3x^2} = \dfrac{4x-5-(2x+5)}{3x^2}$

$= \dfrac{4x-5-2x-5}{3x^2}$

$= \dfrac{2x-10}{3x^2}$

32.
$$\frac{9x+7}{6x^2} - \frac{3x+4}{6x^2} = \frac{9x+7-(3x+4)}{6x^2}$$
$$= \frac{9x+7-3x-4}{6x^2}$$
$$= \frac{6x+3}{6x^2}$$
$$= \frac{3(2x+1)}{3\cdot 2x^2}$$
$$= \frac{2x+1}{2x^2}$$

33. $2x = 2 \cdot x$
$7x = 7 \cdot x$
$LCD = 2 \cdot 7 \cdot x = 14x$

34. $x^2 - 5x - 24 = (x-8)(x+3)$
$x^2 + 11x + 24 = (x+8)(x+3)$
$LCD = (x-8)(x+3)(x+8)$

35. $\dfrac{5}{7x} = \dfrac{5}{7x} \cdot \dfrac{2x^2y}{2x^2y} = \dfrac{5\cdot 2x^2y}{7x\cdot 2x^2y} = \dfrac{10x^2y}{14x^3y}$

36. $\dfrac{9}{4y} = \dfrac{9}{4y} \cdot \dfrac{4y^2x}{4y^2x} = \dfrac{9\cdot 4y^2x}{4y\cdot 4y^2x} = \dfrac{36y^2x}{16y^3x}$

37.
$$\frac{x+2}{x^2+11x+18} = \frac{x+2}{(x+9)(x+2)}$$
$$= \frac{(x+2)(x-5)}{(x+9)(x+2)(x-5)}$$
$$= \frac{x^2-3x-10}{(x+2)(x-5)(x+9)}$$

38.
$$\frac{3x-5}{x^2+4x+4} = \frac{3x-5}{(x+2)^2}$$
$$= \frac{(3x-5)(x+3)}{(x+2)^2(x+3)}$$
$$= \frac{3x^2+4x-15}{(x+2)^2(x+3)}$$

39. $\dfrac{4}{5x^2} - \dfrac{6}{y} = \dfrac{4(y)}{5x^2(y)} - \dfrac{6(5x^2)}{y(5x^2)} = \dfrac{4y-30x^2}{5x^2y}$

40.
$$\frac{2}{x-3} - \frac{4}{x-1} = \frac{2(x-1)}{(x-3)(x-1)} - \frac{4(x-3)}{(x-1)(x-3)}$$
$$= \frac{2(x-1)-4(x-3)}{(x-3)(x-1)}$$
$$= \frac{2x-2-4x+12}{(x-3)(x-1)}$$
$$= \frac{-2x+10}{(x-3)(x-1)}$$

41.
$$\frac{4}{x+3} - 2 = \frac{4}{x+3} - \frac{2(x+3)}{x+3}$$
$$= \frac{4-2(x+3)}{x+3}$$
$$= \frac{4-2x-6}{x+3}$$
$$= \frac{-2x-2}{x+3}$$

42.
$$\frac{3}{x^2+2x-8} + \frac{2}{x^2-3x+2}$$
$$= \frac{3}{(x+4)(x-2)} + \frac{2}{(x-1)(x-2)}$$
$$= \frac{3(x-1)}{(x+4)(x-2)(x-1)} + \frac{2(x+4)}{(x-1)(x-2)(x+4)}$$
$$= \frac{3(x-1)+2(x+4)}{(x+4)(x-2)(x-1)}$$
$$= \frac{3x-3+2x+8}{(x+4)(x-2)(x-1)}$$
$$= \frac{5x+5}{(x+4)(x-2)(x-1)}$$

43.
$$\frac{2x-5}{6x+9} - \frac{4}{2x^2+3x} = \frac{2x-5}{3(2x+3)} - \frac{4}{x(2x+3)}$$
$$= \frac{(2x-5)(x)}{3(2x+3)(x)} - \frac{4(3)}{x(2x+3)(3)}$$
$$= \frac{2x^2-5x-12}{3x(2x+3)}$$
$$= \frac{(2x+3)(x-4)}{3x(2x+3)}$$
$$= \frac{x-4}{3x}$$

44. $\dfrac{x-1}{x^2-2x+1}-\dfrac{x+1}{x-1}=\dfrac{x-1}{(x-1)^2}-\dfrac{x+1}{x-1}$

$\qquad =\dfrac{1}{x-1}-\dfrac{x+1}{x-1}$

$\qquad =\dfrac{1-(x+1)}{x-1}$

$\qquad =\dfrac{1-x-1}{x-1}$

$\qquad =\dfrac{-x}{x-1}$

$\qquad =-\dfrac{x}{x-1}$

45. $P=2l+2w$

$\qquad P=2\left(\dfrac{x}{8}\right)+2\left(\dfrac{x+2}{4x}\right)$

$\qquad =\dfrac{x}{4}+\dfrac{2(x+2)}{4x}$

$\qquad =\dfrac{x\cdot x}{4\cdot x}+\dfrac{2x+4}{4x}$

$\qquad =\dfrac{x^2+2x+4}{4x}$

$\quad A=l\cdot w$

$\quad A=\dfrac{x}{8}\cdot\dfrac{x+2}{4x}=\dfrac{x\cdot(x+2)}{8\cdot 4x}=\dfrac{x+2}{32}$

The perimeter is $\dfrac{x^2+2x+4}{4x}$ units and the area

is $\dfrac{x+2}{32}$ square units.

46. $P=\dfrac{3x}{4x-4}+\dfrac{2x}{3x-3}+\dfrac{x}{x-1}$

$\qquad =\dfrac{3x}{4(x-1)}+\dfrac{2x}{3(x-1)}+\dfrac{x}{x-1}$

$\qquad =\dfrac{3x(3)}{4(x-1)(3)}+\dfrac{2x(4)}{3(x-1)(4)}+\dfrac{x(12)}{(x-1)(12)}$

$\qquad =\dfrac{9x+8x+12x}{12(x-1)}$

$\qquad =\dfrac{29x}{12(x-1)}$

$\quad A=\dfrac{1}{2}\cdot b\cdot h$

$\quad A=\dfrac{1}{2}\cdot\dfrac{x}{x-1}\cdot\dfrac{6y}{5}=\dfrac{1\cdot x\cdot 2\cdot 3y}{2\cdot(x-1)\cdot 5}=\dfrac{3xy}{5(x-1)}$

The perimeter is $\dfrac{29x}{12(x-1)}$ units and the area is

$\dfrac{3xy}{5(x-1)}$ square units.

47. $\qquad\dfrac{n}{10}=9-\dfrac{n}{5}$

$\quad 10\left(\dfrac{n}{10}\right)=10\left(9-\dfrac{n}{5}\right)$

$\quad 10\left(\dfrac{n}{10}\right)=10(9)-10\left(\dfrac{n}{5}\right)$

$\qquad\quad n=90-2n$

$\qquad\quad 3n=90$

$\qquad\quad\ n=30$

48.

$$\frac{2}{x+1} - \frac{1}{x-2} = -\frac{1}{2}$$

$$2(x+1)(x-2)\left(\frac{2}{x+1} - \frac{1}{x-2}\right) = 2(x+1)(x-2)\left(-\frac{1}{2}\right)$$

$$2(x+1)(x-2)\left(\frac{2}{x+1}\right) - 2(x+1)(x-2)\left(\frac{1}{x-2}\right) = 2(x+1)(x-2)\left(-\frac{1}{2}\right)$$

$$4(x-2) - 2(x+1) = -(x+1)(x-2)$$

$$4x - 8 - 2x - 2 = -(x^2 - x - 2)$$

$$2x - 10 = -x^2 + x + 2$$

$$x^2 + x - 12 = 0$$

$$(x+4)(x-3) = 0$$

$$x + 4 = 0 \quad \text{or} \quad x - 3 = 0$$
$$x = -4 \qquad x = 3$$

49.

$$\frac{y}{2y+2} + \frac{2y-16}{4y+4} = \frac{y-3}{y+1}$$

$$\frac{y}{2(y+1)} + \frac{2y-16}{4(y+1)} = \frac{y-3}{y+1}$$

$$4(y+1)\left(\frac{y}{2(y+1)} + \frac{2y-16}{4(y+1)}\right) = 4(y+1)\left(\frac{y-3}{y+1}\right)$$

$$4(y+1)\left(\frac{y}{2(y+1)}\right) + 4(y+1)\left(\frac{2y-16}{4(y+1)}\right) = 4(y+1)\left(\frac{y-3}{y+1}\right)$$

$$2y + 2y - 16 = 4(y-3)$$

$$4y - 16 = 4y - 12$$

$$-16 = -12 \quad \text{False}$$

This equation has no solution.

50.

$$\frac{2}{x-3} - \frac{4}{x+3} = \frac{8}{x^2 - 9}$$

$$(x-3)(x+3)\left(\frac{2}{x-3} - \frac{4}{x+3}\right) = (x-3)(x+3)\left(\frac{8}{(x-3)(x+3)}\right)$$

$$(x-3)(x+3)\left(\frac{2}{x-3}\right) - (x-3)(x+3)\left(\frac{4}{x+3}\right) = 8$$

$$2(x+3) - 4(x-3) = 8$$

$$2x + 6 - 4x + 12 = 8$$

$$-2x + 18 = 8$$

$$-2x = -10$$

$$x = 5$$

51.

$$\frac{x-3}{x+1} - \frac{x-6}{x+5} = 0$$

$$(x+1)(x+5)\left(\frac{x-3}{x+1} - \frac{x-6}{x+5}\right) = (x+1)(x+5)(0)$$

$$(x+1)(x+5)\left(\frac{x-3}{x+1}\right) - (x+1)(x+5)\left(\frac{x-6}{x+5}\right) = 0$$

$$(x+5)(x-3) - (x+1)(x-6) = 0$$

$$x^2 + 2x - 15 - (x^2 - 5x - 6) = 0$$

$$x^2 + 2x - 15 - x^2 + 5x + 6 = 0$$

$$7x - 9 = 0$$

$$7x = 9$$

$$x = \frac{9}{7}$$

52.

$$x + 5 = \frac{6}{x}$$

$$x(x+5) = x\left(\frac{6}{x}\right)$$

$$x^2 + 5x = 6$$

$$x^2 + 5x - 6 = 0$$

$$(x+6)(x-1) = 0$$

$$x + 6 = 0 \quad \text{or} \quad x - 1 = 0$$

$$x = -6 \qquad\qquad x = 1$$

53.

$$\frac{4A}{5b} = x^2$$

$$4A = 5bx^2$$

$$\frac{4A}{5x^2} = \frac{5bx^2}{5x^2}$$

$$\frac{4A}{5x^2} = b$$

54.

$$\frac{x}{7} + \frac{y}{8} = 10$$

$$56\left(\frac{x}{7}\right) + 56\left(\frac{y}{8}\right) = 56(10)$$

$$8x + 7y = 560$$

$$7y = 560 - 8x$$

$$y = \frac{560 - 8x}{7}$$

55.

$$\frac{x}{2} = \frac{12}{4}$$

$$4x = 24$$

$$x = 6$$

56.
$$\frac{20}{1} = \frac{x}{25}$$
$$500 = x$$

57.
$$\frac{2}{x-1} = \frac{3}{x+3}$$
$$2(x+3) = 3(x-1)$$
$$2x+6 = 3x-3$$
$$6 = x-3$$
$$9 = x$$

58.
$$\frac{4}{y-3} = \frac{2}{y-3}$$
$$4(y-3) = 2(y-3)$$
$$4y-12 = 2y-6$$
$$2y-12 = -6$$
$$2y = 6$$
$$y = 3$$
$y = 3$ doesn't check, so this equation has no solution.

59. Let x = the number of parts processed in 45 minutes.
$$\frac{300}{20} = \frac{x}{45}$$
$$13,500 = 20x$$
$$675 = x$$
675 parts can be processed in 45 minutes.

60. Let x = the charge for 3 hours.
$$\frac{90.00}{8} = \frac{x}{3}$$
$$270.00 = 8x$$
$$33.75 = x$$
He charges $33.75 for 3 hours.

61.
$$5 \cdot \frac{1}{x} = \frac{3}{2} \cdot \frac{1}{x} + \frac{7}{6}$$
$$\frac{5}{x} = \frac{3}{2x} + \frac{7}{6}$$
$$6x\left(\frac{5}{x}\right) = 6x\left(\frac{3}{2x}\right) + 6x\left(\frac{7}{6}\right)$$
$$30 = 9 + 7x$$
$$21 = 7x$$
$$x = 3$$
The unknown number is 3.

62.
$$\frac{1}{x} = \frac{1}{4-x}$$
$$4-x = x$$
$$4 = 2x$$
$$2 = x$$
The unknown number is 2.

63. Let r be the rate of the faster car. Then the rate of the slower car is $r - 10$.

	Distance =	Rate ·	Time
Fast car	90	r	$\frac{90}{r}$
Slow car	60	$r-10$	$\frac{60}{r-10}$

$$\frac{90}{r} = \frac{60}{r-10}$$
$$90(r-10) = 60r$$
$$90r - 900 = 60r$$
$$-900 = -30r$$
$$30 = r$$
$$r - 10 = 30 - 10 = 20$$
The rate of the fast car is 30 miles per hour and the rate of the slower car is 20 miles per hour.

64. Let r be the speed of the boat in still water.

	Distance =	Rate ·	Time
Upstream	48	$r-4$	$\frac{48}{r-4}$
Downstream	72	$r+4$	$\frac{72}{r+4}$

$$\frac{48}{r-4} = \frac{72}{r+4}$$
$$48(r+4) = 72(r-4)$$
$$48r + 192 = 72r - 288$$
$$480 = 24r$$
$$r = 20$$
The speed of the boat in still water is 20 miles per hour.

65. Let x be the time it takes Maria working alone.

	Hours to Complete Total Job	Part of Job Completed in 1 Hour
Mark	7	$\frac{1}{7}$
Maria	x	$\frac{1}{x}$
Together	5	$\frac{1}{5}$

$$\frac{1}{7}+\frac{1}{x}=\frac{1}{5}$$
$$35x\left(\frac{1}{7}\right)+35x\left(\frac{1}{x}\right)=35x\left(\frac{1}{5}\right)$$
$$5x+35=7x$$
$$35=2x$$
$$x=\frac{35}{2}\text{ or }17\frac{1}{2}$$

It takes Maria $17\frac{1}{2}$ hours to complete the job alone.

66. Let x be the number of days it takes the pipes to fill the pond together.

	Days to Complete Total Job	Part of Job Completed in 1 Day
Pipe A	20	$\frac{1}{20}$
Pipe B	15	$\frac{1}{15}$
Together	x	$\frac{1}{x}$

$$\frac{1}{20}+\frac{1}{25}=\frac{1}{x}$$
$$60x\left(\frac{1}{20}\right)+60x\left(\frac{1}{15}\right)=60x\left(\frac{1}{x}\right)$$
$$3x+4x=60$$
$$7x=60$$
$$x=\frac{60}{7}=8\frac{4}{7}$$

Both pipes fill the pond in $8\frac{4}{7}$ days.

67. $\dfrac{2}{3}=\dfrac{10}{x}$
$2x=30$
$x=15$
The missing length is 15.

68. $\dfrac{12}{4}=\dfrac{18}{x}$
$12x=72$
$x=6$
The missing length is 6.

69. $\dfrac{\frac{5x}{27}}{-\frac{10xy}{21}}=\dfrac{5x}{27}\cdot-\dfrac{21}{10xy}=-\dfrac{5x\cdot3\cdot7}{3\cdot9\cdot5\cdot2\cdot x\cdot y}=-\dfrac{7}{18y}$

70. $\dfrac{\frac{3}{5}+\frac{2}{7}}{\frac{1}{5}+\frac{5}{6}}=\dfrac{\frac{21}{35}+\frac{10}{35}}{\frac{6}{30}+\frac{25}{30}}=\dfrac{\frac{31}{35}}{\frac{31}{30}}=\dfrac{31}{35}\cdot\dfrac{30}{31}=\dfrac{31\cdot5\cdot6}{5\cdot7\cdot31}=\dfrac{6}{7}$

71. $\dfrac{3-\frac{1}{y}}{2-\frac{1}{y}}=\dfrac{y\left(3-\frac{1}{y}\right)}{y\left(2-\frac{1}{y}\right)}=\dfrac{y(3)-y\left(\frac{1}{y}\right)}{y(2)-y\left(\frac{1}{y}\right)}=\dfrac{3y-1}{2y-1}$

72. $\dfrac{\frac{6}{x+2}+4}{\frac{8}{x+2}-4}=\dfrac{(x+2)\left(\frac{6}{x+2}+4\right)}{(x+2)\left(\frac{8}{x+2}-4\right)}$

$=\dfrac{(x+2)\left(\frac{6}{x+2}\right)+(x+2)(4)}{(x+2)\left(\frac{8}{x+2}\right)-(x+2)(4)}$

$=\dfrac{6+4x+8}{8-4x-8}$

$=\dfrac{4x+14}{-4x}$

$=-\dfrac{2(2x+7)}{2\cdot2x}$

$=-\dfrac{2x+7}{2x}$

73.
$$\frac{\frac{x-3}{x+3}+\frac{x+3}{x-3}}{\frac{x-3}{x+3}-\frac{x+3}{x-3}} = \frac{(x+3)(x-3)\left(\frac{x-3}{x+3}+\frac{x+3}{x-3}\right)}{(x+3)(x-3)\left(\frac{x-3}{x+3}-\frac{x+3}{x-3}\right)}$$
$$= \frac{(x-3)^2+(x+3)^2}{(x-3)^2-(x+3)^2}$$
$$= \frac{x^2-6x+9+x^2+6x+9}{x^2-6x+9-(x^2+6x+9)}$$
$$= \frac{2x^2+18}{x^2-6x+9-x^2-6x-9}$$
$$= \frac{2(x^2+9)}{-12x}$$
$$= -\frac{x^2+9}{6x}$$

74.
$$\frac{\frac{3}{x-1}-\frac{2}{1-x}}{\frac{2}{x-1}-\frac{2}{x}} = \frac{\frac{3}{x-1}+\frac{2}{x-1}}{\frac{2}{x-1}-\frac{2}{x}}$$
$$= \frac{\frac{5}{x-1}}{\frac{2}{x-1}-\frac{2}{x}}$$
$$= \frac{x(x-1)\frac{5}{x-1}}{x(x-1)\left(\frac{2}{x-1}-\frac{2}{x}\right)}$$
$$= \frac{5x}{2x-2(x-1)}$$
$$= \frac{5x}{2x-2x+2}$$
$$= \frac{5x}{2}$$

75. $\dfrac{x+y^{-1}}{\frac{x}{y}} = \dfrac{x+\frac{1}{y}}{\frac{x}{y}} = \dfrac{y\left(x+\frac{1}{y}\right)}{x\left(\frac{x}{y}\right)} = \dfrac{xy+1}{x}$

76. $\dfrac{x-xy^{-1}}{\frac{1+x}{y}} = \dfrac{x-\frac{x}{y}}{\frac{1+x}{y}} = \dfrac{y\left(x-\frac{x}{y}\right)}{y\left(\frac{1+x}{y}\right)} = \dfrac{xy-x}{1+x}$

77. $\dfrac{4x+12}{8x^2+24x} = \dfrac{4(x+3)}{2\cdot 4\cdot x(x+3)} = \dfrac{1}{2x}$

78. $\dfrac{x^3-6x^2+9x}{x^2+4x-21} = \dfrac{x(x-3)^2}{(x+7)(x-3)} = \dfrac{x(x-3)}{x+7}$

79.
$$\frac{x^2+9x+20}{x^2-25}\cdot\frac{x^2-9x+20}{x^2+8x+16}$$
$$= \frac{(x+4)(x+5)\cdot(x-4)(x-5)}{(x+5)(x-5)\cdot(x+4)(x+4)}$$
$$= \frac{x-4}{x+4}$$

80.
$$\frac{x^2-x-72}{x^2-x-30}\div\frac{x^2+6x-27}{x^2-9x+18}$$
$$= \frac{x^2-x-72}{x^2-x-30}\cdot\frac{x^2-9x+18}{x^2+6x-27}$$
$$= \frac{(x-9)(x+8)\cdot(x-3)(x-6)}{(x+5)(x-6)\cdot(x+9)(x-3)}$$
$$= \frac{(x-9)(x+8)}{(x+5)(x+9)}$$

81.
$$\frac{x}{x^2-36}+\frac{6}{x^2-36} = \frac{x+6}{x^2-36}$$
$$= \frac{x+6}{(x+6)(x-6)}$$
$$= \frac{1}{x-6}$$

82.
$$\frac{5x-1}{4x}-\frac{3x-2}{4x} = \frac{5x-1-(3x-2)}{4x}$$
$$= \frac{5x-1-3x+2}{4x}$$
$$= \frac{2x+1}{4x}$$

83.
$$\frac{4}{3x^2+8x-3}+\frac{2}{3x^2-7x+2}$$
$$= \frac{4}{(x+3)(3x-1)}+\frac{2}{(x-2)(3x-1)}$$
$$= \frac{4(x-2)}{(x+3)(3x-1)(x-2)}+\frac{2(x+3)}{(x-2)(3x-1)(x+3)}$$
$$= \frac{4(x-2)+2(x+3)}{(x+3)(3x-1)(x-2)}$$
$$= \frac{4x-8+2x+6}{(x+3)(3x-1)(x-2)}$$
$$= \frac{6x-2}{(x+3)(3x-1)(x-2)}$$
$$= \frac{2(3x-1)}{(x+3)(3x-1)(x-2)}$$
$$= \frac{2}{(x+3)(x-2)}$$

84.
$$\frac{3x}{x^2+9x+14}-\frac{6x}{x^2+4x-21}$$
$$=\frac{3x}{(x+7)(x+2)}-\frac{6x}{(x+7)(x-3)}$$
$$=\frac{3x(x-3)}{(x+7)(x+2)(x-3)}-\frac{6x(x+2)}{(x+7)(x-3)(x+2)}$$
$$=\frac{3x(x-3)-6x(x+2)}{(x+7)(x+2)(x-3)}$$
$$=\frac{3x^2-9x-6x^2-12x}{(x+7)(x+2)(x-3)}$$
$$=\frac{-3x^2-21x}{(x+7)(x+2)(x-3)}$$
$$=\frac{-3x(x+7)}{(x+7)(x+2)(x-3)}$$
$$=-\frac{3x}{(x+2)(x-3)}$$

85.
$$\frac{4}{a-1}+2=\frac{3}{a-1}$$
$$(a-1)\left(\frac{4}{a-1}\right)+(a-1)(2)=(a-1)\left(\frac{3}{a-1}\right)$$
$$4+2(a-1)=3$$
$$4+2a-2=3$$
$$2+2a=3$$
$$2a=1$$
$$a=\frac{1}{2}$$

86.
$$\frac{x}{x+3}+4=\frac{x}{x+3}$$
$$(x+3)\left(\frac{x}{x+3}\right)+(x+3)(4)=(x+3)\left(\frac{x}{x+3}\right)$$
$$x+4(x+3)=x$$
$$x+4x+12=x$$
$$5x+12=x$$
$$12=-4x$$
$$-3=x$$

Since $x=-3$ makes a denominator 0, the solution does not check. This equation has no solution.

87.
$$\frac{2x}{3}-\frac{1}{6}=\frac{x}{2}$$
$$6\left(\frac{2x}{3}\right)-6\left(\frac{1}{6}\right)=6\left(\frac{x}{2}\right)$$
$$4x-1=3x$$
$$-1=-x$$
$$1=x$$
The unknown number is 1.

88. Let x be the number of days it takes them to paint the house working together.

	Days to Complete Total Job	Part of Job Completed in 1 Day
Mr. Crocker	3	$\frac{1}{3}$
Son	4	$\frac{1}{4}$
Together	x	$\frac{1}{x}$

$$\frac{1}{3}+\frac{1}{4}=\frac{1}{x}$$
$$12x\left(\frac{1}{3}\right)+12x\left(\frac{1}{4}\right)=12x\left(\frac{1}{x}\right)$$
$$4x+3x=12$$
$$7x=12$$
$$x=\frac{12}{7}\text{ or }1\frac{5}{7}$$

Working together, Mr. Crocker and his son can paint the house in $1\frac{5}{7}$ days.

89.
$$\frac{5}{3}=\frac{10}{x}$$
$$5x=30$$
$$x=6$$
The missing length is 6.

90.
$$\frac{6}{18}=\frac{4}{x}$$
$$6x=72$$
$$x=12$$
The missing length is 12.

91.
$$\frac{\frac{1}{4}}{\frac{1}{3}+\frac{1}{2}}=\frac{12\left(\frac{1}{4}\right)}{12\left(\frac{1}{3}+\frac{1}{2}\right)}=\frac{12\left(\frac{1}{4}\right)}{12\left(\frac{1}{3}\right)+12\left(\frac{1}{2}\right)}=\frac{3}{4+6}=\frac{3}{10}$$

92. $\dfrac{4+\frac{2}{x}}{6+\frac{3}{x}} = \dfrac{x\left(4+\frac{2}{x}\right)}{x\left(6+\frac{3}{x}\right)}$

$= \dfrac{x(4)+x\left(\frac{2}{x}\right)}{x(6)+x\left(\frac{3}{x}\right)}$

$= \dfrac{4x+2}{6x+3}$

$= \dfrac{2(2x+1)}{3(2x+1)}$

$= \dfrac{2}{3}$

93. $\dfrac{y^{-2}}{1-y^{-2}} = \dfrac{\frac{1}{y^2}}{1-\frac{1}{y^2}} = \dfrac{y^2\left(\frac{1}{y^2}\right)}{y^2\left(1-\frac{1}{y^2}\right)} = \dfrac{1}{y^2-1}$

94. $\dfrac{4+x^{-1}}{3+x^{-1}} = \dfrac{4+\frac{1}{x}}{3+\frac{1}{x}} = \dfrac{x\left(4+\frac{1}{x}\right)}{x\left(3+\frac{1}{x}\right)} = \dfrac{4x+1}{3x+1}$

Chapter 7 Test

1. The rational expression is undefined when
$x^2+4x+3 = 0$
$(x+3)(x+1) = 0$
$x+3 = 0$ or $x+1 = 0$
$x = -3$ $x = -1$
The domain is
$\{x | x$ is a real number, $x = -1, x \neq -3\}$.

2. a. $C = \dfrac{100x+3000}{x}$

$= \dfrac{100(200)+3000}{200}$

$= \dfrac{20,000+3000}{200}$

$= \dfrac{23,000}{200}$

$= 115$

The average cost per desk is \$115.

b. $C = \dfrac{100x+3000}{x}$

$= \dfrac{100(1000)+3000}{1000}$

$= \dfrac{100,000+3000}{1000}$

$= \dfrac{103,000}{1000}$

$= 103$

The average cost per desk is \$103.

3. $\dfrac{3x-6}{5x-10} = \dfrac{3(x-2)}{5(x-2)} = \dfrac{3}{5}$

4. $\dfrac{x+6}{x^2+12x+36} = \dfrac{x+6}{(x+6)^2} = \dfrac{1}{x+6}$

5. $\dfrac{x+3}{x^3+27} = \dfrac{x+3}{(x+3)(x^2-3x+9)} = \dfrac{1}{x^2-3x+9}$

6. $\dfrac{2m^3-2m^2-12m}{m^2-5m+6} = \dfrac{2m(m^2-m-6)}{(m-3)(m-2)}$

$= \dfrac{2m(m-3)(m+2)}{(m-3)(m-2)}$

$= \dfrac{2m(m+2)}{m-2}$

7. $\dfrac{ay+3a+2y+6}{ay+3a+5y+15} = \dfrac{(y+3)(a+2)}{(y+3)(a+5)} = \dfrac{a+2}{a+5}$

8. $\dfrac{y-x}{x^2-y^2} = \dfrac{-(x-y)}{(x-y)(x+y)} = -\dfrac{1}{x+y}$

9. $\dfrac{3}{x-1} \cdot (5x-5) = \dfrac{3}{x-1} \cdot 5(x-1) = \dfrac{3 \cdot 5(x-1)}{x-1} = 15$

10. $\dfrac{y^2-5y+6}{2y+4} \cdot \dfrac{y+2}{2y-6} = \dfrac{(y-3)(y-2) \cdot (y+2)}{2(y+2) \cdot 2(y-3)}$

$= \dfrac{y-2}{4}$

11. $\dfrac{15x}{2x+5} - \dfrac{6-4x}{2x+5} = \dfrac{15x-(6-4x)}{2x+5}$

$= \dfrac{15x-6+4x}{2x+5}$

$= \dfrac{19x-6}{2x+5}$

12. $\dfrac{5a}{a^2-a-6}-\dfrac{2}{a-3}$

$=\dfrac{5a}{(a-3)(a+2)}-\dfrac{2(a+2)}{(a-3)(a+2)}$

$=\dfrac{5a-2(a+2)}{(a-3)(a+2)}$

$=\dfrac{5a-2a-4}{(a-3)(a+2)}$

$=\dfrac{3a-4}{(a-3)(a+2)}$

13. $\dfrac{6}{x^2-1}+\dfrac{3}{x+1}=\dfrac{6}{(x+1)(x-1)}+\dfrac{3(x-1)}{(x+1)(x-1)}$

$=\dfrac{6+3x-3}{(x+1)(x-1)}$

$=\dfrac{3x+3}{(x+1)(x-1)}$

$=\dfrac{3(x+1)}{(x+1)(x-1)}$

$=\dfrac{3}{x-1}$

14. $\dfrac{x^2-9}{x^2-3x}\div\dfrac{xy+5x+3y+15}{2x+10}$

$=\dfrac{x^2-9}{x^2-3x}\cdot\dfrac{2x+10}{xy+5x+3y+15}$

$=\dfrac{(x-3)(x+3)\cdot 2(x+5)}{x(x-3)\cdot(x+3)(y+5)}$

$=\dfrac{2(x+5)}{x(y+5)}$

15. $\dfrac{x+2}{x^2+11x+18}+\dfrac{5}{x^2-3x-10}=\dfrac{x+2}{(x+9)(x+2)}+\dfrac{5}{(x-5)(x+2)}$

$=\dfrac{(x+2)(x-5)}{(x+9)(x+2)(x-5)}+\dfrac{5(x+9)}{(x-5)(x+2)(x+9)}$

$=\dfrac{(x+2)(x-5)+5(x+9)}{(x+9)(x+2)(x-5)}$

$=\dfrac{x^2-3x-10+5x+45}{(x+9)(x+2)(x-5)}$

$=\dfrac{x^2+2x+35}{(x+9)(x+2)(x-5)}$

16.
$$\frac{4}{y} - \frac{5}{3} = -\frac{1}{5}$$
$$15y\left(\frac{4}{y} - \frac{5}{3}\right) = 15y\left(-\frac{1}{5}\right)$$
$$15y\left(\frac{4}{y}\right) - 15y\left(\frac{5}{3}\right) = 15y\left(-\frac{1}{5}\right)$$
$$60 - 25y = -3y$$
$$60 = 22y$$
$$\frac{60}{22} = y$$
$$y = \frac{30}{11}$$

17.
$$\frac{5}{y+1} = \frac{4}{y+2}$$
$$5(y+2) = 4(y+1)$$
$$5y + 10 = 4y + 4$$
$$y = -6$$

18.
$$\frac{a}{a-3} = \frac{3}{a-3} - \frac{3}{2}$$
$$2(a-3)\left(\frac{a}{a-3}\right) = 2(a-3)\left(\frac{3}{a-3} - \frac{3}{2}\right)$$
$$2a = 2(a-3)\left(\frac{3}{a-3}\right) - 2(a-3)\left(\frac{3}{2}\right)$$
$$2a = 6 - 3(a-3)$$
$$2a = 6 - 3a + 9$$
$$2a = 15 - 3a$$
$$5a = 15$$
$$a = 3$$
In the original equation, 3 makes a denominator 0. This equation has no solution.

19.
$$x - \frac{14}{x-1} = 4 - \frac{2x}{x-1}$$
$$(x-1)\left(x - \frac{14}{x-1}\right) = (x-1)\left(4 - \frac{2x}{x-1}\right)$$
$$x(x-1) - 14 = 4(x-1) - 2x$$
$$x^2 - x - 14 = 4x - 4 - 2x$$
$$x^2 - x - 14 = 2x - 4$$
$$x^2 - 3x - 10 = 0$$
$$(x-5)(x+2) = 0$$
$$x - 5 = 0 \quad \text{or} \quad x + 2 = 0$$
$$x = 5 \qquad\qquad x = -2$$

20.
$$\frac{10}{x^2-25}=\frac{3}{x+5}+\frac{1}{x-5}$$
$$\frac{10}{(x+5)(x-5)}=\frac{3}{x+5}+\frac{1}{x-5}$$
$$(x+5)(x-5)\left(\frac{10}{(x+5)(x-5)}\right)=(x+5)(x-5)\left(\frac{3}{x+5}\right)+(x+5)(x-5)\left(\frac{1}{x-5}\right)$$
$$10=3(x-5)+1(x+5)$$
$$10=3x-15+x+5$$
$$10=4x-10$$
$$20=4x$$
$$5=x$$

In the original equation 5 makes a denominator 0. This equation has no solution.

21. $\dfrac{\frac{5x^2}{yz^2}}{\frac{10x}{z^3}}=\dfrac{5x^2}{yz^2}\cdot\dfrac{z^3}{10x}=-\dfrac{5\cdot x\cdot x\cdot z\cdot z^2}{y\cdot z^2\cdot2\cdot5\cdot x}=\dfrac{xz}{2y}$

22. $\dfrac{5-\frac{1}{y^2}}{\frac{1}{y}+\frac{2}{y^2}}=\dfrac{y^2\left(5-\frac{1}{y^2}\right)}{y^2\left(\frac{1}{y}+\frac{2}{y^2}\right)}$

$$=\dfrac{y^2(5)-y^2\left(\frac{1}{y^2}\right)}{y^2\left(\frac{1}{y}\right)+y^2\left(\frac{2}{y^2}\right)}$$

$$=\dfrac{5y^2-1}{y+2}$$

23. Let $x=$ the number of defective bulbs.
$$\frac{85}{3}=\frac{510}{x}$$
$$85x=1530$$
$$x=18$$
Expect to find 18 defective bulbs.

24.
$$x + 5 \cdot \frac{1}{x} = 6$$
$$x + \frac{5}{x} = 6$$
$$x\left(x + \frac{5}{x}\right) = x(6)$$
$$x(x) + x\left(\frac{5}{x}\right) = x(6)$$
$$x^2 + 5 = 6x$$
$$x^2 - 6x + 5 = 0$$
$$(x - 5)(x - 1) = 0$$
$$x - 5 = 0 \quad \text{or} \quad x - 1 = 0$$
$$x = 5 \qquad\qquad x = 1$$
The unknown number is 5 or 1.

25. Let r be the speed of the boat in still water.

	Distance =	Rate ·	Time
Upstream	14	$r - 2$	$\frac{14}{r-2}$
Downstream	16	$r + 2$	$\frac{16}{r+2}$

$$\frac{14}{r-2} = \frac{16}{r+2}$$
$$14(r + 2) = 16(r - 2)$$
$$14r + 28 = 16r - 32$$
$$60 = 2r$$
$$r = 30$$

The speed of the boat in still water is 30 miles per hour.

26. Let x be the number of hours it takes to fill the tank using both pipes.

	Hours to Complete Total Job	Part of Job Completed in 1 Hour
1st Pipe	12	$\frac{1}{12}$
2nd Pipe	15	$\frac{1}{15}$
Together	x	$\frac{1}{x}$

$$\frac{1}{12} + \frac{1}{15} = \frac{1}{x}$$
$$60x\left(\frac{1}{12}\right) + 60x\left(\frac{1}{15}\right) = 60x\left(\frac{1}{x}\right)$$
$$5x + 4x = 60$$
$$9x = 60$$
$$x = \frac{60}{9} = \frac{20}{3} = 6\frac{2}{3}$$

Together, the pipes can fill the tank in $6\frac{2}{3}$ hours.

27.
$$\frac{8}{x} = \frac{10}{15}$$
$$8(15) = 10x$$
$$120 = 10x$$
$$12 = x$$
The missing length is 12.

Chapter 7 Cumulative Review

1. a. $\frac{15}{x} = 4$

 b. $12 - 3 = x$

 c. $4x + 17 \neq 21$

 d. $3x < 48$

2. a. $12 - x = -45$

 b. $12x = -45$

 c. $x - 10 = 2x$

3. Let x = the amount invested at 9% for one year.

	Principal ·	Rate =	Interest
9%	x	0.09	$0.09x$
7%	$20{,}000 - x$	0.07	$0.07(20{,}000 - x)$
Total	20,000		1550

$$0.09x + 0.07(20{,}000 - x) = 1550$$
$$0.09x + 1400 - 0.07x = 1550$$
$$0.02x + 1400 = 1550$$
$$0.02x = 150$$
$$x = 7500$$

$20{,}000 - x = 20{,}000 - 7500 = 12{,}500$
He invested \$7500 at 9% and \$12,500 at 7%.

4. Let x be the number of bankruptcies in 1994 then
$2x - 80,000$ is the number in 2002.
$$x + 2x - 80,000 = 2,290,000$$
$$3x - 80,000 = 2,290,000$$
$$3x = 2,370,000$$
$$x = 790,000$$
$2x - 80,000 = 2(790,000) - 80,000 = 1,500,000$
There were 790,000 bankruptcies in 1994 and
1,500,000 in 2002.

5. $x - 3y = 6$

x	y
0	-2
6	0

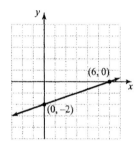

6. $7x + 2y = 9$
$$2y = -7x + 9$$
$$y = -\frac{7}{2}x + \frac{9}{2}$$
$$y = mx + b$$
$$m = -\frac{7}{2}$$

7. a. $4^2 \cdot 4^5 = 4^{2+5} = 4^7$

b. $x^4 \cdot x^6 = x^{4+6} = x^{10}$

c. $y^3 \cdot y = y^{3+1} = y^4$

d. $y^3 \cdot y^2 \cdot y^7 = y^{3+2+7} = y^{12}$

e. $(-5)^7 \cdot (-5)^8 = (-5)^{7+8} = (-5)^{15}$

f. $a^2 \cdot b^2 = a^2 b^2$

8. a. $\dfrac{x^9}{x^7} = x^{9-7} = x^2$

b. $\dfrac{x^{19} y^5}{xy} = x^{19-1} \cdot y^{5-1} = x^{18} y^4$

c. $(x^5 y^2)^3 = x^{5 \cdot 3} y^{2 \cdot 3} = x^{15} y^6$

d. $(-3a^2 b)(5a^3 b) = -15a^{2+3} b^{1+1} = -15a^5 b^2$

9. $[(8z + 11) + (9z - 2)] - (5z - 7)$
$$= 8z + 11 + 9z - 2 - 5z + 7$$
$$= 12z + 16$$

10. $(x + 1) - (9x^2 - 6x + 2) = x + 1 - 9x^2 + 6x - 2$
$$= -9x^2 + 7x - 1$$

11. $(3a + b)^3$
$$= (3a + b)(3a + b)^2$$
$$= (3a + b)[(3a)^2 + 2(3a)(b) + (b)^2]$$
$$= (3a + b)(9a^2 + 6ab + b^2)$$
$$= 27a^3 + 18a^2 b + 3ab^2 + 9a^2 b + 6ab^2 + b^3$$
$$= 27a^3 + 27a^2 b + 9ab^2 + b^3$$

12. $(2x + 1)(5x^2 - x + 2)$
$$= 2x(5x^2 - x + 2) + 1(5x^2 - x + 2)$$
$$= 10x^3 - 2x^2 + 4x + 5x^2 - x + 2$$
$$= 10x^3 + 3x^2 + 3x + 2$$

13. a. $(t + 2)^2 = (t)^2 + 2(t)(2) + (2)^2 = t^2 + 4t + 4$

b. $(p - q)^2 = (p)^2 - 2(p)(q) + (q)^2$
$$= p^2 - 2pq + q^2$$

c. $(2x + 5)^2 = (2x)^2 + 2(2x)(5) + (5)^2$
$$= 4x^2 + 20x + 25$$

d. $(x^2 - 7y)^2 = (x^2)^2 - 2(x^2)(7y) + (7y)^2$
$$= x^4 - 14x^2 y + 49y^2$$

14. a. $(x + 9)^2 = (x)^2 + 2(x)(9) + (9)^2$
$$= x^2 + 18x + 81$$

b. $(2x + 1)(2x - 1) = (2x)^2 - (1)^2 = 4x^2 - 1$

c. $8x(x^2 + 1)(x^2 - 1) = 8x[(x^2)^2 - (1)^2]$
$$= 8x[x^4 - 1]$$
$$= 8x^5 - 8x$$

15. a. $\dfrac{1}{x^{-3}} = x^3$

b. $\dfrac{1}{3^{-4}} = 3^4 = 81$

c. $\dfrac{p^{-4}}{q^{-9}} = \dfrac{q^9}{p^4}$

d. $\dfrac{5^{-3}}{2^{-5}} = \dfrac{2^5}{5^3} = \dfrac{32}{125}$

16. a. $5^{-3} = \dfrac{1}{5^3} = \dfrac{1}{125}$

b. $\dfrac{9}{x^{-7}} = 9x^7$

c. $\dfrac{11^{-1}}{7^{-2}} = \dfrac{7^2}{11^1} = \dfrac{49}{11}$

17.

$$
\begin{array}{r}
4x^2 - 4x + 6 \\
2x+3\overline{\smash{\big)}\,8x^3 + 4x^2 + 0x + 7} \\
\underline{8x^3 + 12x^2} \\
-8x^2 + 0x \\
\underline{-8x^2 - 12x} \\
12x + 7 \\
\underline{12x + 18} \\
-11
\end{array}
$$

$$\dfrac{4x^2 + 7 + 8x^3}{2x+3} = 4x^2 - 4x + 6 - \dfrac{11}{2x+3}$$

18.

$$
\begin{array}{r}
4x^2 + 16x + 55 \\
x-4\overline{\smash{\big)}\,4x^3 + 0x^2 - 9x + 2} \\
\underline{4x^3 - 16x^2} \\
16x^2 - 9x \\
\underline{16x^2 - 64x} \\
55x + 2 \\
\underline{55x - 220} \\
222
\end{array}
$$

$$\dfrac{4x^3 - 9x + 2}{x-4} = 4x^2 + 16x + 55 + \dfrac{222}{x-4}$$

19. a. $28 = 2 \cdot 2 \cdot 7$
$40 = 2 \cdot 2 \cdot 2 \cdot 5$
$\text{GCF} = 2^2 = 4$

b. $55 = 5 \cdot 11$
$21 = 3 \cdot 7$
$\text{GCF} = 1$

c. $15 = 3 \cdot 5$
$18 = 2 \cdot 3 \cdot 3$
$66 = 2 \cdot 3 \cdot 11$
$\text{GCF} = 3$

20. $9x^2 = 3 \cdot 3 \cdot x^2$
$6x^3 = 2 \cdot 3 \cdot x^3$
$21x^5 = 3 \cdot 7 \cdot x^5$
$\text{GCF} = 3x^2$

21. $-9a^5 + 18a^2 - 3a = -3a(3a^4 - 6a + 1)$

22. $7x^6 - 7x^5 + 7x^4 = 7x^4(x^2 - x + 1)$

23. $3m^2 - 24m - 60 = 3(m^2 - 8m - 20)$
$= 3(m^2 - 10m + 2m - 20)$
$= 3[m(m-10) + 2(m-10)]$
$= 3(m-10)(m+2)$

24. $-2a^2 + 10a + 12 = -2(a^2 - 5a - 6)$
$= -2(a+1)(a-6)$

25. $3x^2 + 11x + 6 = 3x^2 + 2x + 9x + 6$
$= x(3x+2) + 3(3x+2)$
$= (3x+2)(x+3)$

26. $10m^2 - 7m + 1 = 10m^2 - 2m - 5m + 1$
$= 2m(5m-1) - 1(5m-1)$
$= (2m-1)(5m-1)$

27. $x^2 + 12x + 36 = x^2 + 2 \cdot x \cdot 6 + 6^2 = (x+6)^2$

28. $4x^2 + 12x + 9 = (2x)^2 + 2(2x)(3) + (3)^2$
$= (2x+3)^2$

29. $x^2 + 4$ is a prime polynomial.

30. $x^2 - 4 = (x)^2 - (2)^2 = (x+2)(x-2)$

31. $x^3 + 8 = x^3 + 2^3$

$$= (x+2)(x^2 - x \cdot 2 + 2^2)$$
$$= (x+2)(x^2 - 2x + 4)$$

32. $27y^3 - 1 = (3y)^3 - (1)^3$

$$= (3y-1)[(3y)^2 + 3y(1) + (1)^2]$$
$$= (3y-1)(9y^2 + 3y + 1)$$

33. $2x^3 + 3x^2 - 2x - 3 = x^2(2x+3) - 1(2x+3)$

$$= (2x+3)(x^2 - 1)$$
$$= (2x+3)(x^2 - 1^2)$$
$$= (2x+3)(x+1)(x-1)$$

34. $3x^3 + 5x^2 - 12x - 20 = x^2(3x+5) - 4(3x+5)$

$$= (3x+5)(x^2 - 4)$$
$$= (3x+5)(x^2 - 2^2)$$
$$= (3x+5)(x+2)(x-2)$$

35. $12m^2 - 3n^2 = 3(4m^2 - n^2)$

$$= 3[(2m)^2 - (n)^2]$$
$$= 3(2m+n)(2m-n)$$

36. $x^5 - x = x(x^4 - 1)$

$$= x[(x^2)^2 - 1^2]$$
$$= x(x^2+1)(x^2-1)$$
$$= x(x^2+1)(x+1)(x-1)$$

37.
$$x(2x-7) = 4$$
$$2x^2 - 7x = 4$$
$$2x^2 - 7x - 4 = 0$$
$$2x^2 - 8x + x - 4 = 0$$
$$2x(x-4) + 1(x-4) = 0$$
$$(x-4)(2x+1) = 0$$
$$2x+1 = 0 \quad \text{or} \quad x-4 = 0$$
$$2x = -1 \qquad\qquad x = 4$$
$$x = -\frac{1}{2}$$

38.
$$3x^2 + 5x = 2$$
$$3x^2 + 5x - 2 = 0$$
$$3x^2 + 6x - x - 2 = 0$$
$$3x(x+2) - 1(x+2) = 0$$
$$(x+2)(3x-1) = 0$$

$$3x - 1 = 0 \quad \text{or} \quad x + 2 = 0$$
$$3x = 1 \qquad\qquad x = -2$$
$$x = \frac{1}{3}$$

39. $y = x^2 - 5x + 4$

$$0 = x^2 - 5x + 4$$
$$0 = (x-4)(x-1)$$
$$x - 1 = 0 \quad \text{or} \quad x - 4 = 0$$
$$x = 1 \qquad\qquad x = 4$$

The x-intercepts are $(1, 0)$ and $(4, 0)$.

40. $y = x^2 - x - 6$

$$0 = x^2 - x - 6$$
$$0 = (x-3)(x+2)$$
$$x + 2 = 0 \quad \text{or} \quad x - 3 = 0$$
$$x = -2 \qquad\qquad x = 3$$

The x-intercepts are $(-2, 0)$ and $(3, 0)$.

41. Let x = the base and $2x - 2$ = the height.

$$A = \frac{1}{2}bh$$
$$30 = \frac{1}{2}x(2x-2)$$
$$30 = \frac{1}{2}(2x)(x-1)$$
$$30 = x(x-1)$$
$$30 = x^2 - x$$
$$0 = x^2 - x - 30$$
$$0 = (x+5)(x-6)$$
$$x - 6 = 0 \quad \text{or} \quad x + 5 = 0$$
$$x = 6 \qquad\qquad x = -5$$

Length cannot be negative, so $x = 6$.
$2x - 2 = 2(6) - 2 = 10$
The base is 6 meters and the height is 10 meters.

42. Let x = the base and $3x + 5$ = the height.

$$A = bh$$
$$182 = x(3x+5)$$
$$182 = 3x^2 + 5x$$
$$0 = 3x^2 + 5x - 182$$
$$0 = 3x^2 + 26x - 21x - 182$$
$$0 = x(3x+26) - 7(3x+26)$$
$$0 = (x-7)(3x+26)$$

$$x - 7 = 0 \quad \text{or} \quad 3x + 26 = 0$$
$$x = 7 \qquad\qquad x = -\frac{26}{3}$$

Length cannot be negative so $x = 7$.
$3x + 5 = 3(7) + 5 = 26$
The base is 7 ft and the height is 26 ft.

43. $\dfrac{18 - 2x^2}{x^2 - 2x - 3} = \dfrac{2(9 - x^2)}{(x+1)(x-3)}$

$\qquad = \dfrac{2(3+x)(3-x)}{(x+1)(x-3)}$

$\qquad = \dfrac{-2(3+x)(x-3)}{(x+1)(x-3)}$

$\qquad = -\dfrac{2(3+x)}{x+1}$

44. $\dfrac{2x^2 - 50}{4x^4 - 20x^3} = \dfrac{2(x^2 - 25)}{4x^3(x-5)}$

$\qquad = \dfrac{2(x+5)(x-5)}{4x^3(x-5)}$

$\qquad = \dfrac{x+5}{2x^3}$

45. $\dfrac{6x+2}{x^2-1} \div \dfrac{3x^2+x}{x-1} = \dfrac{6x+2}{x^2-1} \cdot \dfrac{x-1}{3x^2+x}$

$\qquad = \dfrac{2(3x+1)}{(x+1)(x-1)} \cdot \dfrac{x-1}{x(3x+1)}$

$\qquad = \dfrac{2}{x(x+1)}$

46. $\dfrac{6x^2 - 18x}{3x^2 - 2x} \cdot \dfrac{15x - 10}{x^2 - 10} = \dfrac{6x(x-3) \cdot 5(3x-2)}{x(3x-2) \cdot (x+3)(x-3)}$

$\qquad\qquad\qquad\qquad = \dfrac{30}{x+3}$

47. $\dfrac{(2x)^{-1} + 1}{2x^{-1} - 1} = \dfrac{\frac{1}{2x} + 1}{\frac{2}{x} - 1}$

$\qquad = \dfrac{2x\left(\frac{1}{2x} + 1\right)}{2x\left(\frac{2}{x} - 1\right)}$

$\qquad = \dfrac{1 + 2x}{4 - 2x}$

$\qquad = \dfrac{1 + 2x}{2(2 - x)}$

48. $\dfrac{\frac{m}{3} + \frac{n}{6}}{\frac{m+n}{12}} = \dfrac{12}{12} \cdot \dfrac{\frac{m}{3} + \frac{n}{6}}{\frac{m+n}{12}}$

$\qquad = \dfrac{12\left(\frac{m}{3}\right) + 12\left(\frac{n}{6}\right)}{12\left(\frac{m+n}{12}\right)}$

$\qquad = \dfrac{4m + 2n}{m + n} \text{ or } \dfrac{2(2m + n)}{m + n}$

Chapter 8

Practice Exercises

1. $f(x) = 4x$, $g(x) = 4x - 3$

x	$f(x)$	$g(x)$
0	0	-3
-1	-4	-7
1	4	1

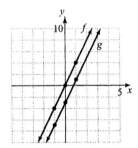

2. $f(x) = -2x$, $g(x) = -2x + 5$

x	$f(x)$	$g(x)$
0	0	5
-1	2	7
1	-2	3
2	-4	1

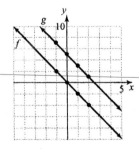

3. Use the slope-intercept form with $m = -4$ and $b = -3$.
$$y = mx + b$$
$$y = -4x + (-3)$$
$$y = -4x - 3$$
$$f(x) = -4x - 3$$

4. First find the slope.
$$m = \frac{0 - 2}{2 - (-1)} = \frac{-2}{3} = -\frac{2}{3}$$
Use the slope and one of the points in the point-slope form. We use (2, 0).
$$y - y_1 = m(x - x_1)$$
$$y - 0 = -\frac{2}{3}(x - 2)$$
$$y = -\frac{2}{3}x + \frac{4}{3}$$
$$f(x) = -\frac{2}{3}x + \frac{4}{3}$$

5. A horizontal line has an equation of the form $y = b$. Since the line contains the point (6, -2), the equation is $y = -2$ or $f(x) = -2$.

6. Solve the given equation for y.
$$3x + 4y = 1$$
$$4y = -3x + 1$$
$$y = -\frac{3}{4}x + \frac{1}{4}$$

The slope of this line is $-\frac{3}{4}$, so the slope of any line parallel to it is also $-\frac{3}{4}$. Use this slope and the point (8, -3) in the point-slope form.
$$y - y_1 = m(x - x_1)$$
$$y - (-3) = -\frac{3}{4}(x - 8)$$
$$4(y + 3) = -3(x - 8)$$
$$4y + 12 = -3x + 24$$
$$3x + 4y = 12$$

7. Solve the given equation for y.
$$3x + 4y = 1$$
$$4y = -3x + 1$$
$$y = -\frac{3}{4}x + \frac{1}{4}$$

The slope of this line is $-\frac{3}{4}$, so the slope of any line perpendicular to it is the negative reciprocal of $-\frac{3}{4}$, or $\frac{4}{3}$. Use this slope and the point

(8, −3) in the point-slope form.

$$y - y_1 = m(x - x_1)$$
$$y - (-3) = \frac{4}{3}(x - 8)$$
$$3(y + 3) = 4(x - 8)$$
$$3y + 9 = 4x - 32$$
$$3y = 4x - 41$$
$$y = \frac{4}{3}x - \frac{41}{3}$$
$$f(x) = \frac{4}{3}x - \frac{41}{3}$$

Graphing Calculator Explorations

1. $x = 3.5y$

$$y = \frac{x}{3.5}$$

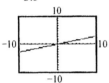

2. $-2.7y = x$

$$y = \frac{x}{-2.7} = -\frac{x}{2.7}$$

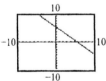

3. $5.78x + 2.31y = 10.98$

$$2.31y = -5.78x + 10.98$$
$$y = -\frac{5.78}{2.31}x + \frac{10.98}{2.31}$$

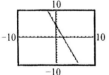

4. $-7.22x + 3.89y = 12.57$

$$3.89y = 7.22x + 12.57$$
$$y = \frac{7.22}{3.89}x + \frac{12.57}{3.89}$$

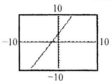

5. $y - |x| = 3.78$

$$y = |x| + 3.78$$

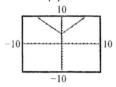

6. $3y - 5x^2 = 6x - 4$

$$3y = 5x^2 + 6x - 4$$
$$y = \frac{5}{3}x^2 + 2x - \frac{4}{3}$$

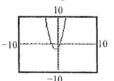

7. $y - 5.6x^2 = 7.7x + 1.5$

$$y = 5.6x^2 + 7.7x + 1.5$$

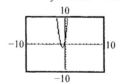

8. $y + 2.6|x| = -3.2$

$$y = -2.6|x| - 3.2$$

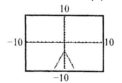

Vocabulary and Readiness Check

1. A <u>linear</u> function can be written in the form
   $f(x) = mx + b$.

2. In the form $f(x) = mx + b$, the y-intercept is (0, b) and the slope is m.

3. $m = -4$, $b = 12$ so y-intercept is (0, 12).

4. $m = \dfrac{2}{3}$, $b = -\dfrac{7}{2}$ so y-intercept is $\left(0, -\dfrac{7}{2}\right)$.

5. $m = 5$, $b = 0$ so y-intercept is (0, 0).

6. $m = -1$, $b = 0$ so y-intercept is (0, 0).

7. The lines both have slope 12 and they have different y-intercepts, (0, 6) and (0, −2), so they are parallel.

8. The lines both have slope −5 and they have different y-intercepts, (0, 8) and (0, −8), so they are parallel.

9. The line have slopes −9 and $\dfrac{3}{2}$. The slopes are not equal and their product is not −1, so the lines are neither parallel nor perpendicular.

10. The line have slopes 2 and $\dfrac{1}{2}$. The slopes are not equal and their product is not −1, so the lines are neither parallel nor perpendicular.

Exercise Set 8.1

2. $f(x) = 2x$

x	0	−1	1
y	0	−2	2

Plot the points to obtain the graph.

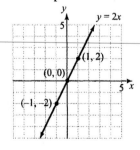

4. $f(x) = 2x + 6$

x	0	−1	−2
y	6	4	2

Plot the points to obtain the graph.

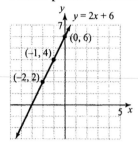

6. $f(x) = \dfrac{1}{3}x$

x	0	3	−3
y	0	1	−1

Plot the points to obtain the graph.

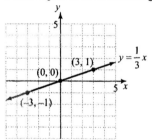

8. $f(x) = \dfrac{1}{3}x - 2$

x	0	3	−3
y	−2	−1	−3

Plot the points to obtain the graph.

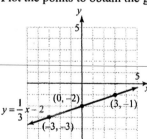

10. The graph of $f(x) = 5x - 2$ is the graph of $f(x) = 5x$ shifted down 2 units. The correct graph is A.

12. The graph of $f(x) = 5x + 3$ is the graph of $f(x) = 5x$ shifted up 3 units. The correct graph is B.

14. $m = \dfrac{1}{2}, \; b = -6$

$y = mx + b$

$y = \dfrac{1}{2}x - 6$

$f(x) = \dfrac{1}{2}x - 6$

16. $m = -3, \; b = -\dfrac{1}{5}$

$y = mx + b$

$y = -3x - \dfrac{1}{5}$

$f(x) = -3x - \dfrac{1}{5}$

18. $m = -\dfrac{4}{5}, \; b = 0$

$y = mx + b$

$y = -\dfrac{4}{5}x + 0$

$y = -\dfrac{4}{5}x$

$f(x) = -\dfrac{4}{5}x$

20. $y - y_1 = m(x - x_1)$

$y - 1 = 4(x - 5)$

$y - 1 = 4x - 20$

$y = 4x - 19$

$f(x) = 4x - 19$

22. $y - y_1 = m(x - x_1)$

$y - (-4) = -4(x - 2)$

$y + 4 = -4x + 8$

$y = -4x + 4$

$f(x) = -4x + 4$

24. $y - y_1 = m(x - x_1)$

$y - 4 = \dfrac{2}{3}[x - (-9)]$

$y - 4 = \dfrac{2}{3}(x + 9)$

$y - 4 = \dfrac{2}{3}x + 6$

$y = \dfrac{2}{3}x + 10$

$f(x) = \dfrac{2}{3}x + 10$

26. $y - y_1 = m(x - x_1)$

$y - (-6) = -\dfrac{1}{5}(x - 4)$

$y + 6 = -\dfrac{1}{5}x + \dfrac{4}{5}$

$y = -\dfrac{1}{5}x - \dfrac{26}{5}$

$f(x) = -\dfrac{1}{5}x - \dfrac{26}{5}$

28. $m = \dfrac{8 - 0}{7 - 3} = \dfrac{8}{4} = 2$

$y - 0 = 2(x - 3)$

$y = 2x - 6$

$f(x) = 2x - 6$

30. $m = \dfrac{6 - (-4)}{2 - 7} = \dfrac{10}{-5} = -2$

$y - 6 = -2(x - 2)$

$y - 6 = -2x + 4$

$y = -2x + 10$

$f(x) = -2x + 10$

32. $m = \dfrac{10 - (-2)}{-3 - (-9)} = \dfrac{12}{6} = 2$

$y - 10 = 2[x - (-3)]$

$y - 10 = 2(x + 3)$

$y - 10 = 2x + 6$

$y = 2x + 16$

$f(x) = 2x + 16$

34. $m = \dfrac{-8-(-3)}{4-8} = \dfrac{-5}{-4} = \dfrac{5}{4}$

$y - (-3) = \dfrac{5}{4}(x-8)$

$y + 3 = \dfrac{5}{4}x - 10$

$y = \dfrac{5}{4}x - 13$

$f(x) = \dfrac{5}{4}x - 13$

36. $m = \dfrac{\frac{3}{4} - \left(-\frac{1}{4}\right)}{\frac{3}{2} - \frac{1}{2}} = \dfrac{1}{1} = 1$

$y - \dfrac{3}{4} = 1\left(x - \dfrac{3}{2}\right)$

$y - \dfrac{3}{4} = x - \dfrac{3}{2}$

$y = x - \dfrac{3}{4}$

$f(x) = x - \dfrac{3}{4}$

38. Every horizontal line is in the form $y = c$. Since the line passes through the point $(-3, 1)$, its equation is $y = 1$ or $f(x) = 1$.

40. $y = mx + b$

$23 = 0(-10) + b$

$23 = b$

$y = 23$

$f(x) = 23$

42. $y = 3x - 4$ so $m = 3$

$y - 5 = 3(x - 1)$

$y - 5 = 3x - 3$

$y = 3x + 2$

$f(x) = 3x + 2$

44. $2x - 3y = 1$ or $y = \dfrac{2}{3}x - \dfrac{1}{3}$ so

$m = \dfrac{2}{3}$ and $m_\perp = -\dfrac{3}{2}$

$y - 8 = -\dfrac{3}{2}(x + 4)$

$y - 8 = -\dfrac{3}{2}x - 6$

$y = -\dfrac{3}{2}x + 2$

$f(x) = -\dfrac{3}{2}x + 2$

46. $3x + 2y = 5$

$2y = -3x + 5$

$y = -\dfrac{3}{2}x + \dfrac{5}{2}$ so $m_\perp = \dfrac{2}{3}$

$y + 3 = \dfrac{2}{3}(x + 2)$

$y + 3 = \dfrac{2}{3}x + \dfrac{4}{3}$

$y = \dfrac{2}{3}x - \dfrac{5}{3}$

$f(x) = \dfrac{2}{3}x - \dfrac{5}{3}$

48. $y - 2 = 3[x - (-4)]$

$y - 2 = 3(x + 4)$

$y - 2 = 3x + 12$

$3x - y = -14$

50. $m = \dfrac{6-9}{8-2} = \dfrac{-3}{6} = -\dfrac{1}{2}$

$y - 9 = -\dfrac{1}{2}(x - 2)$

$y - 9 = -\dfrac{1}{2}x + 1$

$y = -\dfrac{1}{2}x + 10$

$f(x) = -\dfrac{1}{2}x + 10$

52. $y = -4x + \dfrac{2}{9}$

$f(x) = -4x + \dfrac{2}{9}$

54. $m = \dfrac{-3-(-8)}{-4-2} = \dfrac{5}{-6} = -\dfrac{5}{6}$

$$y+8 = -\dfrac{5}{6}(x-2)$$
$$6y+48 = -5x+10$$
$$5x+6y = -38$$

56. $\quad y+1 = -\dfrac{3}{5}(x-4)$

$$5y+5 = -3x+12$$
$$3x+5y = 7$$

58. Every horizontal line is in the form $y = c$. Since the line passes through the point $(1, 0)$, its equation is $y = 0$ or $f(x) = 0$.

60. $6x+2y = 5$

$$y = -3x+\dfrac{5}{2} \quad \text{so} \quad m = -3$$
$$y+3 = -3(x-8)$$
$$y+3 = -3x+24$$
$$3x+y = 21$$

62. Lines with slopes of 0 are horizontal lines. Every horizontal line is in the form $y = c$. Since the line passes through the point $(10, -8)$, its equation is $y = -8$ or $f(x) = -8$.

64. $2x-y = 8$

$$y = 2x-8 \quad \text{so} \quad m = 2 \text{ and } m_\perp = -\dfrac{1}{2}$$
$$y-5 = -\dfrac{1}{2}(x-3)$$
$$2y-10 = -x+3$$
$$x+2y = 13$$

66. A line parallel to $y = 9$ will have the form $y = c$. Since the line passes through $(-3, -5)$, its equation is $y = -5$.

68. $m = \dfrac{5-(-2)}{-6-(-4)} = \dfrac{7}{-2} = -\dfrac{7}{2}$

$$y+2 = -\dfrac{7}{2}(x+4)$$
$$y+2 = -\dfrac{7}{2}x-14$$
$$y = -\dfrac{7}{2}x-16$$
$$f(x) = -\dfrac{7}{2}x-16$$

70. $-3x+1 > 0$

$$-3x > -1$$
$$x < \dfrac{1}{3}$$
$$\left(-\infty, \dfrac{1}{3}\right)$$

72. $-2(x+1) \le -x+10$

$$-2x-2 \le -x+10$$
$$-x \le 12$$
$$x \ge -12$$
$$[-12, \infty)$$

74. $\dfrac{x}{5} - \dfrac{3}{10} \ge \dfrac{x}{2} - 1$

$$2x-3 \ge 5x-10$$
$$-3x \ge -7$$
$$x \le \dfrac{7}{3}$$
$$\left(-\infty, \dfrac{7}{3}\right]$$

76. $(0, -2), (2, 2)$

$$m = \dfrac{2-(-2)}{2-0} = \dfrac{4}{2} = 2 \text{ and } b = -2$$
$$y = 2x-2$$
$$f(x) = 2x-2$$

78. $(-4, 0), (3, -1)$

$$m = \dfrac{-1-0}{3-(-4)} = -\dfrac{1}{7} \text{ and}$$
$$y-0 = -\dfrac{1}{7}(x+4)$$
$$y = -\dfrac{1}{7}x - \dfrac{4}{7}$$
$$f(x) = -\dfrac{1}{7}x - \dfrac{4}{7}$$

80. a. We have two ordered pairs, $(2, 2000)$ and $(4, 800)$. Find the slope.

$$m = \dfrac{800-2000}{4-2} = \dfrac{-1200}{2} = -600$$

Use the slope and one of the ordered pairs, $(2, 2000)$, to write the equation.

$$y-2000 = -600(x-2)$$
$$y-2000 = -600x+1200$$
$$y = -600x+3200$$

b. The year 2008 corresponds to $x = 5$.

$y = -600(5) + 3200$

$= -3000 + 3200$

$= 200$

We estimate that the computer was worth $200 in 2008.

82. a. $(7, 165,000)$, $(12, 180,000)$

$m = \dfrac{180,000 - 165,000}{12 - 7} = 3000$

$y - 165,000 = 3000(x - 7)$

$y - 165,000 = 3000x - 21,000$

$y = 3000x + 144,000$

b. $x = 2010 - 1990 = 20$

$y = 3000(20) + 144,000 = \$204,000$

84. a. $(4, 4116)$, $(0, 4060)$

$m = \dfrac{4060 - 4116}{0 - 4} = 14$

$y - 4060 = 14(x - 0)$

$y = 14x + 4060$

b. $x = 2013 - 2000 = 13$

$y = 14(13) + 4060$

$= 4242$ thousand births

c. The number of births increases by 14 thousand every year

86. a. $(0, 487)$, $(10, 640)$

$m = \dfrac{640 - 487}{10 - 0} = \dfrac{153}{10} = 15.3$

$y - 487 = 15.3(x - 0)$

$y = 15.3x + 487$

b. $x = 2012 - 2004 = 8$

$y = 15.3(8) + 487$

$= 609.4$ thousand people

88. Since two distinct vertical lines will never intersect, they are parallel. The statement is true.

90. $m = \dfrac{-1 - (-3)}{-8 - (-6)} = \dfrac{2}{-2} = -1$ so $m_\perp = 1$

$M((-6, -3), (-8, -1)) = \left(\dfrac{-14}{2}, \dfrac{-4}{2} \right)$

$= (-7, -2)$

$y + 2 = 1(x + 7)$

$y + 2 = x + 7$

$x - y = -5$

92. $m = \dfrac{2 - 8}{7 - 5} = \dfrac{-6}{2} = -3$ so $m_\perp = \dfrac{1}{3}$

$M((5, 8), (7, 2)) = \left(\dfrac{12}{2}, \dfrac{10}{2} \right) = (6, 5)$

$y - 5 = \dfrac{1}{3}(x - 6)$

$3y - 15 = x - 6$

$x - 3y = -9$

94. $m = \dfrac{-2 - 8}{-4 - (-6)} = \dfrac{-10}{2} = -5$ so $m_\perp = \dfrac{1}{5}$

$M((-6, 8), (-4, -2)) = \left(\dfrac{-10}{2}, \dfrac{6}{2} \right)$

$= (-5, 3)$

$y - 3 = \dfrac{1}{5}(x + 5)$

$5y - 15 = x + 5$

$x - 5y = -20$

Section 8.2

Practice Exercises

1. a. To find $f(1)$, find the y-value when $x = 1$. We see from the graph that when $x = 1$, y or $f(x) = -3$. Thus, $f(1) = -3$.

b. $f(0) = -2$ from the ordered pair $(0, -2)$.

c. $g(-2) = 3$ from the ordered pair $(-2, 3)$.

d. $g(0) = 1$ from the ordered pair $(0, 1)$.

e. To find x-values such that $f(x) = 1$, we are looking for any ordered pairs on the graph of f whose $f(x)$ or y-value is 1. They are $(-1, 1)$ and $(3, 1)$. Thus, $f(-1) = 1$ and $f(3) = 1$. The x-values are -1 and 3.

f. Find ordered pairs on the graph of g whose $g(x)$ or y-value is -2. There is one such ordered pair, $(-3, -2)$. Thus, $g(-3) = -2$. The only x-value is -3.

2. Find the year 2003 and move upward until you reach the graph. From the point on the graph, move horizontally to the left until the other axis is reached. In 2003, approximately \$35 billion was spent.

3. Find $f(2012)$.
$$f(x) = 2.602x - 5178$$
$$f(2012) = 2.602(2012) - 5178$$
$$= 57.224$$
We predict that \$57.224 billion will be spent in 2012.

4. a. $\sqrt{121} = 11$ since 11 is positive and $11^2 = 121$.

b. $\sqrt{\dfrac{1}{16}} = \dfrac{1}{4}$ since $\left(\dfrac{1}{4}\right)^2 = \dfrac{1}{16}$.

c. $-\sqrt{64} = -8$

d. $\sqrt{-64}$ is not a real number.

e. $\sqrt{100} = 10$ since $10^2 = 100$.

5. $f(x) = 2x^2$

This equation is not linear because of the x^2 term. Its graph is not a line.

If $x = -3$, then $f(-3) = 2(-3)^2$, or 18.

If $x = -2$, then $f(-2) = 2(-2)^2$, or 8.

If $x = -1$, then $f(-1) = 2(-1)^2$, or 2.

If $x = 0$, then $f(0) = 2(0)^2$, or 0.

If $x = 1$, then $f(1) = 2(1)^2$, or 2.

If $x = 2$, then $f(2) = 2(2)^2$, or 8.

If $x = 3$, then $f(3) = 2(3)^2$, or 18.

x	y or $f(x)$
-3	18
-2	8
-1	2
0	0
1	2
2	8
3	18

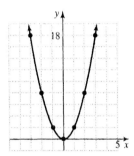

6. $f(x) = -|x|$

This equation is not linear because it cannot be written in the form $Ax + By = C$. Its graph is not a line.

If $x = -3$, then $f(-3) = -|-3|$, or -3.

If $x = -2$, then $f(-2) = -|-2|$, or -2.

If $x = -1$, then $f(-1) = -|-1|$, or -1.

If $x = 0$, then $f(0) = -|0|$, or 0.

If $x = 1$, then $f(1) = -|1|$, or -1.

If $x = 2$, then $f(2) = -|2|$, or -2.

If $x = 3$, then $f(3) = -|3|$, or -3.

x	y or $f(x)$
-3	-3
-2	-2
-1	-1
0	0
1	-1
2	-2
3	-3

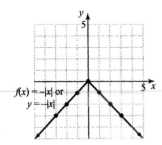

7. $f(x) = \sqrt{x} + 1$

    This equation is not linear because it cannot be
    written in the form $Ax + By = C$. Its graph is not
    a line.

    If $x = 0$, then $f(0) = \sqrt{0} + 1$, or 1.

    If $x = 1$, then $f(1) = \sqrt{1} + 1$, or 2.

    If $x = 4$, then $f(4) = \sqrt{4} + 1$, or 3.

    If $x = 9$, then $f(9) = \sqrt{9} + 1$, or 4.

x	y or $f(x)$
0	1
1	2
4	3
9	4

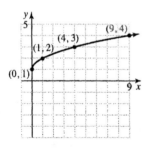

Graphing Calculator Explorations

1.
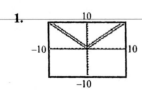

2.
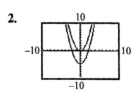

3.
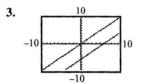

4.
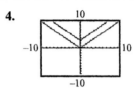

5.
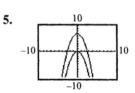

6.
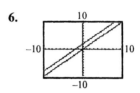

Vocabulary and Readiness Check

1. The graph of $y = |x|$ looks <u>V-shaped</u>.

2. The graph of $y = x^2$ is a <u>parabola</u>.

3. If $f(-2) = 1.7$, the corresponding ordered pair is
    <u>(−2, 1.7)</u>.

4. If $f(x) = x^2$, then $f(-3) = \underline{9}$.

Exercise Set 8.2

2. To find $f(0)$, find the y-value when $x = 0$. We see
    from the graph that when $x = 0$, y or $f(x)$ is −2.
    Thus, $f(0) = -2$.

4. To find $f(2)$, find the y-value when $x = 2$. We see
    from the graph that when $x = 2$, y or $f(x)$ is 2.
    Thus, $f(2) = 2$.

6. To find x-values such that $f(x) = -6$, find any
    ordered pairs on the graph with $f(x)$- or y-value
    of −6. The only such point is (−2, −6). Thus
    $f(-2) = -6$ and the x-value is −2.

8. If $f(-5) = -10$, then $y = -10$ when $x = -5$. The
    ordered pair is (−5, −10).

10. If $g(-2) = 8$, then $y = 8$ when $x = -2$. The ordered pair is $(-2, 8)$.

12. The ordered pair $(-2, -1)$ is on the graph of f. Thus, $f(-2) = -1$.

14. The ordered pair $(-4, -5)$ is on the graph of g. Thus, $g(-4) = -5$.

16. There are two ordered pairs on the graph of f with a y-value of -2, $(-3, -2)$ and $(-1, -2)$. The x-values are -3 and -1.

18. Since $g(x) = 0$ for values of x where the graph crosses the x-axis, the x-values are -3, 0, and 2.

20. $\sqrt{81} = 9$, since $9^2 = 81$.

22. $-\sqrt{\dfrac{4}{25}} = -\dfrac{2}{5}$, since $\left(\dfrac{2}{5}\right)^2 = \dfrac{4}{25}$.

24. $\sqrt{4} = 2$, since $2^2 = 4$.

26. $\sqrt{1} = 1$, since $1^2 = 1$.

28. $\sqrt{-25}$ is not a real number.

30. $g(x) = (x + 2)^2$

x	-4	-3	-2	-1	0
y or $g(x)$	4	1	0	1	4

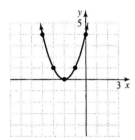

32. $f(x) = |x - 2|$

x	0	1	2	3	4
y or $f(x)$	2	1	0	1	2

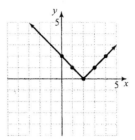

34. $h(x) = 5x^2$

x	-1	0	1
y or $h(x)$	5	0	5

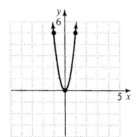

36. $g(x) = -3x + 2$

x	-1	0	1
y or $g(x)$	5	2	-1

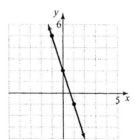

38. $f(x) = \sqrt{x} - 1$

x	0	1	4	9
y or $f(x)$	-1	0	1	2

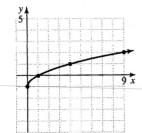

40. $g(x) = -3|x|$

x	-2	-1	0	1	2
y or $g(x)$	-6	-3	0	-3	-6

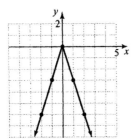

42. $h(x) = \sqrt{x+2}$

x	-2	-1	2	7
y or $h(x)$	0	1	2	3

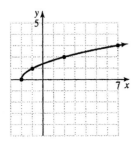

44. a. Find the year 1999 and move upward until you reach the graph. From the point on the graph, move horizontally to the left until the other axis is reached. In 1999, approximately $23 billion was spent.

b. Find $f(1999)$.
$$f(x) = 2.602x - 5178$$
$$f(1999) = 2.602(1999) - 5178 = 23.398$$
Approximately $23.398 billion was spent in 1999.

46. Since 2015 is 15 years after 2000, find $f(15)$.
$$f(x) = 0.42x + 10.5$$
$$f(15) = 0.42(15) + 10.5 = 16.8$$
We predict that diamond production will be $16.8 billion in 2015.

48. $A(r) = \pi r^2$
$$A(8) = \pi(8)^2 = 64\pi \text{ square feet}$$

50. $V(x) = x^3$
$$V(1.7) = (1.7)^3 = 4.913 \text{ cubic cm}$$

52. $H(t) = 2.72t + 61.28$
$$H(35) = 2.72(35) + 61.28$$
$$= 156.48 \text{ centimeters}$$

54. $D(x) = \dfrac{136}{25}x$
$$D(50) = \dfrac{136}{25}(50) = 272 \text{ milligrams}$$

56. 1; otherwise, it would fail the vertical line test.

58. $5 + 7(x+1) = 12 + 10x$
$$5 + 7x + 7 = 12 + 10x$$
$$7x + 12 = 12 + 10x$$
$$-3x = 0$$
$$x = 0$$
The solution is 0.

60. $\dfrac{1}{6} + 2x = \dfrac{2}{3}$
$$1 + 12x = 4$$
$$12x = 3$$
$$x = \dfrac{1}{4}$$

The solution is $\dfrac{1}{4}$.

62. Look for the graph where the decrease in y-values from 40 to 0 and increase from 0 to 60 is gradual. The answer is d.

64. Look for the graph that ends in February. The answer is a.

66. The first segment in the graph with y-coordinate greater than 0.30 begins in January 1995. Thus, 1995 is the first year that the price of a first-class stamp rose above $0.30.

68. The price increased to \$0.41 in 2007. The difference is \$0.41 − \$0.02 or \$0.39.

70. $y = x^2 + 2x + 3$

x	y
−3	6
−2	3
−1	2
0	3
1	6

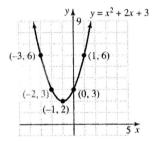

Integrated Review

1. $f(x) = 3x - 5$
$$y = 3x - 5$$
$$y = mx + b$$
The slope is $m = 3$; the y-intercept is $(0, b) = (0, -5)$.

2. $f(x) = \dfrac{5}{2}x - \dfrac{7}{2}$
$$y = \dfrac{5}{2}x - \dfrac{7}{2}$$
$$y = mx + b$$
The slope is $m = \dfrac{5}{2}$; the y-intercept is
$$(0, b) = \left(0, -\dfrac{7}{2}\right).$$

3. $f(x) = 8x - 6$: slope 8; y-intercept $(0, -6)$
$g(x) = 8x + 6$: slope 8; y-intercept $(0, 6)$
The lines have the same slope and different y-intercepts, so they are parallel.

4. $f(x) = \dfrac{2}{3}x + 1$: slope $\dfrac{2}{3}$; y-intercept $(0, 1)$
$$2y + 3x = 1$$
$$2y = -3x + 1$$
$$y = -\dfrac{3}{2}x + \dfrac{1}{2}$$
slope $-\dfrac{3}{2}$; y-intercept $\left(0, \dfrac{1}{2}\right)$
The slopes of the lines are not equal and their product is −1, so the lines are perpendicular.

5. $(1, 6), (5, 2)$
$$m = \dfrac{2 - 6}{5 - 1} = \dfrac{-4}{4} = -1$$
$$y - y_1 = m(x - x_1)$$
$$y - 6 = -1(x - 1)$$
$$y - 6 = -x + 1$$
$$y = -x + 7$$
$$f(x) = -x + 7$$

6. $(2, -8), (-6, -5)$
$$m = \dfrac{-5 - (-8)}{-6 - 2} = \dfrac{3}{-8} = -\dfrac{3}{8}$$
$$y - y_1 = m(x - x_1)$$
$$y - (-8) = -\dfrac{3}{8}(x - 2)$$
$$y + 8 = -\dfrac{3}{8}x + \dfrac{3}{4}$$
$$y = -\dfrac{3}{8}x - \dfrac{29}{4}$$
$$f(x) = -\dfrac{3}{8}x - \dfrac{29}{4}$$

7. $3x - y = 5$
$$3x - 5 = y$$
The line $3x - y = 5$ has slope 3. A parallel line will also have slope 3.
$$y - y_1 = m(x - x_1); (-1, -5)$$
$$y - (-5) = 3[x - (-1)]$$
$$y + 5 = 3(x + 1)$$
$$y + 5 = 3x + 3$$
$$y = 3x - 2$$
$$f(x) = 3x - 2$$

8. $4x - 5y = 10$

$$-5y = -4x + 10$$

$$y = \frac{4}{5}x - 2$$

The line $4x - 5y = 10$ has slope $\frac{4}{5}$.

A perpendicular line has slope $-\frac{5}{4}$.

$$y = mx + b;\ (0, 4)$$

$$y = -\frac{5}{4}x + 4$$

$$f(x) = -\frac{5}{4}x + 4$$

9. $4x + y = \frac{2}{3}$

$$y = -4x + \frac{2}{3}$$

The line $4x + y = \frac{2}{3}$ has slope -4. A

perpendicular line has slope $\frac{1}{4}$.

$$y - y_1 = m(x - x_1);\ (2, -3)$$

$$y - (-3) = \frac{1}{4}(x - 2)$$

$$y + 3 = \frac{1}{4}x - \frac{1}{2}$$

$$y = \frac{1}{4}x - \frac{7}{2}$$

$$f(x) = \frac{1}{4}x - \frac{7}{2}$$

10. $5x + 2y = 2$

$$2y = -5x + 2$$

$$y = -\frac{5}{2}x + 1$$

The line $5x + 2y = 2$ has slope $-\frac{5}{2}$. A parallel

line will also have slope $-\frac{5}{2}$.

$$y - y_1 = m(x - x_1);\ (-1, 0)$$

$$y - 0 = -\frac{5}{2}[x - (-1)]$$

$$y = -\frac{5}{2}(x + 1)$$

$$y = -\frac{5}{2}x - \frac{5}{2}$$

$$f(x) = -\frac{5}{2}x - \frac{5}{2}$$

11. $f(x) = 4x - 2$
Linear

x	0	$\frac{1}{2}$	1
y or $f(x)$	-2	0	2

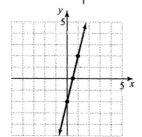

12. $f(x) = 6x - 5$
Linear

x	0	$\frac{1}{2}$	1
y or $f(x)$	-5	-2	1

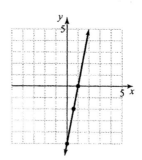

13. $g(x) = |x| + 3$
Not linear

x	-2	-1	0	1	2
y or $g(x)$	5	4	3	4	5

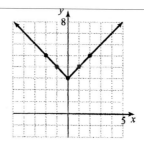

14. $h(x) = |x| + 2$
Not linear

x	-2	-1	0	1	2
y or $h(x)$	4	3	2	3	4

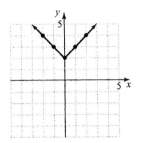

15. $f(x) = 2x^2$
Not linear

x	-2	-1	0	1	2
y or $f(x)$	8	2	0	2	8

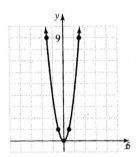

16. $F(x) = 3x^2$
Not linear

x	-2	-1	0	1	2
y or $F(x)$	12	3	0	3	12

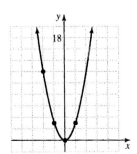

17. $h(x) = x^2 - 3$
Not linear

x	-2	-1	0	1	2
y or $h(x)$	1	-2	-3	-2	1

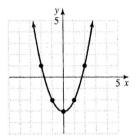

18. $G(x) = x^2 + 3$
Not linear

x	-2	-1	0	1	2
y or $G(x)$	7	4	3	4	7

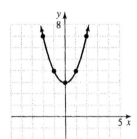

19. $F(x) = -2x$
Linear

x	-1	0	1
y or $F(x)$	2	0	-2

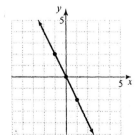

20. $H(x) = -3x$
Linear

x	-1	0	1
y or $H(x)$	3	0	-3

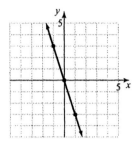

21. $G(x) = |x + 2|$
Not linear

x	-4	-3	-2	-1	0
y or $G(x)$	2	1	0	1	2

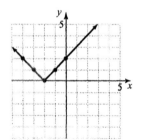

22. $g(x) = |x - 1|$
Not linear

x	-1	0	1	2	3
y or $g(x)$	2	1	0	1	2

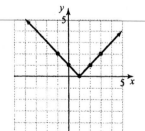

23. $f(x) = \dfrac{1}{3}x - 1$
Linear

x	-3	0	3
y or $f(x)$	-2	-1	0

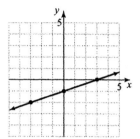

24. $f(x) = \dfrac{1}{2}x - 3$
Linear

x	-2	0	2
y or $f(x)$	-4	-3	-2

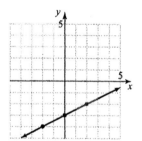

25. $g(x) = -\dfrac{3}{2}x + 1$
Linear

x	-2	0	2
y or $g(x)$	4	1	-2

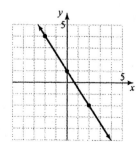

26. $G(x) = -\dfrac{2}{3}x + 1$

Linear

x	-3	0	3
y or $G(x)$	3	1	-1

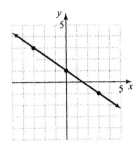

Section 8.3

Practice Exercises

1. $f(x) = \begin{cases} -4x - 2 & \text{if } x \le 0 \\ x + 1 & \text{if } x > 0 \end{cases}$

Since $4 > 0$, $f(4) = 4 + 1 = 5$.

Since $-2 \le 0$, $f(-2) = -4(-2) - 2 = 8 - 2 = 6$.

Since $0 \le 0$, $f(0) = -4(0) - 2 = 0 - 2 = -2$.

2. $f(x) = \begin{cases} -4x - 2 & \text{if } x \le 0 \\ x + 1 & \text{if } x > 0 \end{cases}$

For $x \le 0$:

x	$f(x)$
-2	6
-1	2
0	-2

For $x > 0$:

x	$f(x)$
1	2
2	3
3	4

Graph a closed circle at $(0, -2)$. Graph an open circle at $(0, 1)$, which is found by substituting 0 for x in $f(x) = x + 1$.

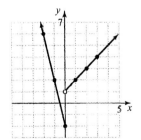

3. $f(x) = x^2$ and $g(x) = x^2 - 3$

The graph of $g(x) = x^2 - 3$ is the graph of $f(x) = x^2$ moved downward 3 units.

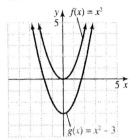

4. $f(x) = \sqrt{x}$ and $g(x) = \sqrt{x} + 1$

The graph of $g(x) = \sqrt{x} + 1$ is the graph of $f(x) = \sqrt{x}$ moved upward 1 unit.

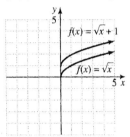

5. $f(x) = |x|$ and $g(x) = |x - 3|$

x	$f(x)$	$g(x)$
-2	2	5
-1	1	4
0	0	3
1	1	2
2	2	1
3	3	0
4	4	1
5	5	2

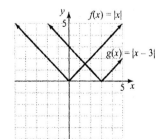

6. $f(x) = |x|$ and $g(x) = |x-2|+3$

The graph of $g(x)$ is the same as the graph of $f(x)$ shifted 2 units to the right and 3 units up.

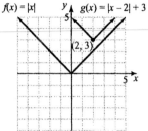

7. $h(x) = -(x+2)^2 - 1$

The graph of $h(x) = -(x+2)^2 - 1$ is the same as the graph of $f(x) = x^2$ reflected about the x-axis, then moved 2 units to the left and 1 unit downward.

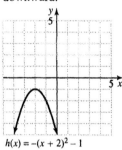

$h(x) = -(x + 2)^2 - 1$

Vocabulary and Readiness Check

1. The graph that corresponds to $y = \sqrt{x}$ is C.

2. The graph that corresponds to $y = x^2$ is B.

3. The graph that corresponds to $y = x$ is D.

4. The graph that corresponds to $y = |x|$ is A.

Exercise Set 8.3

2. $f(x) = \begin{cases} 3x & \text{if } x < 0 \\ x+2 & \text{if } x \geq 0 \end{cases}$

For $x < 0$:

x	$f(x)$
-2	-6
-1	-3

For $x \geq 0$:

x	$f(x)$
0	2
1	3
2	4

Graph a closed circle at (0, 2). Graph an open circle at (0, 0), which is found by substituting 0 for x in $f(x) = 3x$.

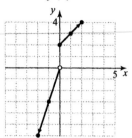

4. $f(x) = \begin{cases} 5x+4 & \text{if } x \leq 0 \\ \frac{1}{3}x-1 & \text{if } x > 0 \end{cases}$

For $x \leq 0$:

x	$f(x)$
-2	-6
-1	-1
0	4

For $x > 0$:

x	$f(x)$
1	$-\frac{2}{3}$
2	$-\frac{1}{3}$
3	0

Graph a closed circle at (0, 4). Graph an open circle at (0, –1), which is found by substituting 0 for x in $f(x) = \frac{1}{3}x - 1$.

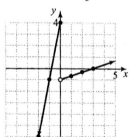

6. $g(x) = \begin{cases} 3x-1 & \text{if } x \leq 2 \\ -x & \text{if } x > 2 \end{cases}$

For $x \leq 2$:

x	$g(x)$
0	-1
1	2
2	5

For $x > 2$:

x	$g(x)$
3	-3
4	-4
5	-5

Graph a closed circle at (2, 5). Graph an open circle at (2, −2), which is found by substituting 2 for x in $g(x) = -x$.

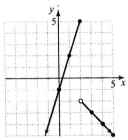

8. $f(x) = \begin{cases} 4 & \text{if } x < -3 \\ -2 & \text{if } x \ge -3 \end{cases}$

For $x < -3$:   For $x \ge -3$:

x	$f(x)$
−6	4
−5	4
−4	4

x	$f(x)$
−3	−2
−2	−2
−1	−2

Graph a closed circle at (−3, −2). Graph an open circle at (−3, 4), which is found by substituting −3 for x in $f(x) = 4$.

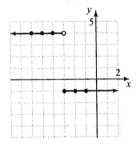

10. $f(x) = \begin{cases} -3x & \text{if } x \le 0 \\ 3x+2 & \text{if } x > 0 \end{cases}$

For $x \le 0$:   For $x > 0$:

x	$f(x)$
−1	3
0	0

x	$f(x)$
1	5
2	8

Graph a closed circle at (0, 0). Graph an open circle at (0, 2), which is found by substituting 0 for x in $f(x) = 3x + 2$.

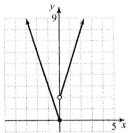

The function is defined for all real numbers, so the domain is $(-\infty, \infty)$. The function takes on all y-values greater than or equal to 0, so the range is $[0, \infty)$.

12. $f(x) = \begin{cases} 4x-4 & \text{if } x < 2 \\ -x+1 & \text{if } x \ge 2 \end{cases}$

For $x < 2$:   For $x \ge 2$:

x	$f(x)$
0	−4
1	0

x	$f(x)$
2	−1
3	−2

Graph a closed circle at (2, −1). Graph an open circle at (2, 4), which is found by substituting 2 for x in $f(x) = 4x - 4$.

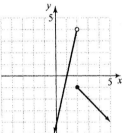

The function is defined for all real numbers, so the domain is $(-\infty, \infty)$. The function takes on all y-values less than 4, so the range is $(-\infty, 4)$.

14. $h(x) = \begin{cases} x+2 & \text{if } x < 1 \\ 2x+1 & \text{if } x \ge 1 \end{cases}$

For $x < 1$:   For $x \ge 1$:

x	$h(x)$
−2	0
−1	1
0	2

x	$h(x)$
1	3
2	5
3	7

Graph a closed circle at (1, 3). The graph of $h(x) = x + 2$ for $x < 1$ also approaches the point

(1, 3).

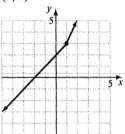

The function is defined for all real numbers, so the domain is $(-\infty, \infty)$. The function takes on all y-values, so the range is $(-\infty, \infty)$.

16. $f(x) = \begin{cases} -1 & \text{if } x \le 0 \\ -3 & \text{if } x \ge 2 \end{cases}$

For $x \le 0$:   For $x \ge 2$:

x	$f(x)$
-2	-1
-1	-1
0	-1

x	$f(x)$
2	-3
3	-3
4	-3

Graph closed circles at $(0, -1)$ and $(2, -3)$.

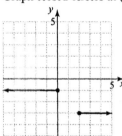

The function is defined for $x \le 0$ or $x \ge 2$, so the domain is $(-\infty, 0] \cup [2, \infty)$. The function takes on two y-values, -1 and -3, so the range is $\{-3, -1\}$.

18. $f(x) = |x| - 2$

The graph of $f(x) = |x| - 2$ is the same as the graph of $y = |x|$ shifted down 2 units.

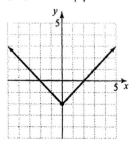

20. $f(x) = \sqrt{x} + 3$

The graph of $f(x) = \sqrt{x} + 3$ is the same as the graph of $y = \sqrt{x}$ shifted up 3 units.

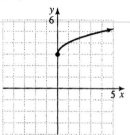

22. $f(x) = |x + 3|$

The graph of $f(x) = |x + 3|$ is the same as the graph of $y = |x|$ shifted left 3 units.

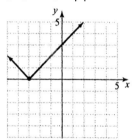

24. $f(x) = \sqrt{x - 2}$

The graph of $f(x) = \sqrt{x - 2}$ is the same as the graph of $y = \sqrt{x}$ shifted right 2 units.

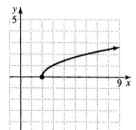

26. $y = (x + 4)^2$

The graph of $y = (x + 4)^2$ is the same as the graph of $y = x^2$ shifted left 4 units.

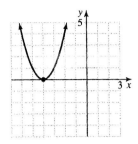

28. $f(x) = x^2 - 4$

The graph of $f(x) = x^2 - 4$ is the same as the graph of $y = x^2$ shifted down 4 units.

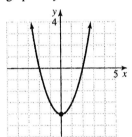

30. $f(x) = \sqrt{x-1} + 3$

The graph of $f(x) = \sqrt{x-1} + 3$ is the same as the graph of $y = \sqrt{x}$ shifted right 1 unit and up 3 units.

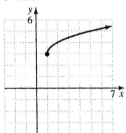

32. $f(x) = |x-3| + 2$

The graph of $f(x) = |x-3| + 2$ is the same as the graph of $y = |x|$ shifted right 3 units and up 2 units.

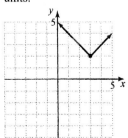

34. $f(x) = \sqrt{x+3} + 2$

The graph of $f(x) = \sqrt{x+3} + 2$ is the same as the graph of $y = \sqrt{x}$ shifted left 3 units and up 2 units.

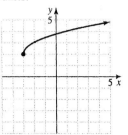

36. $f(x) = |x+1| - 4$

The graph of $f(x) = |x+1| - 4$ is the same as the graph of $y = |x|$ shifted left 1 unit and down 4 units.

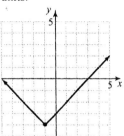

38. $h(x) = (x+2)^2 + 2$

The graph of $h(x) = (x+2)^2 + 2$ is the same as the graph of $y = x^2$ shifted left 2 units and up 2 units.

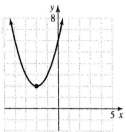

40. $f(x) = (x+2)^2 + 4$

The graph of $f(x) = (x+2)^2 + 4$ is the same as the graph of $y = x^2$ shifted left 2 units and up 4 units.

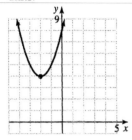

42. $g(x) = -(x+2)^2$

The graph of $g(x) = -(x+2)^2$ is the same as the graph of $y = x^2$ reflected about the x-axis and then shifted left 2 units.

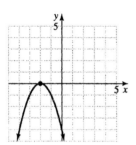

44. $f(x) = -\sqrt{x+3}$

The graph of $f(x) = -\sqrt{x+3}$ is the same as the graph of $y = \sqrt{x}$ reflected about the x-axis and then shifted left 3 units.

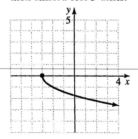

46. $g(x) = -|x+1| + 1$

The graph of $g(x) = -|x+1| + 1$ is the same as the graph of $y = |x|$ reflected about the x-axis and then shifted left 1 unit and up 1 unit.

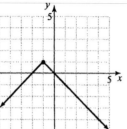

48. $f(x) = (x-1) + 4$

Since the function can be simplified to $f(x) = x + 3$, we see that its graph is a line with slope $m = 1$ and y-intercept $(0, 3)$.

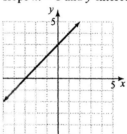

50. The graph of $x = -1$ is a vertical line with x-intercept $(-1, 0)$. The correct graph is C.

52. The graph of $y = 3$ is a horizontal line with y-intercept $(0, 3)$. The correct graph is B.

54. Answers may vary

56. $f(x) = \begin{cases} -\frac{1}{3}x & \text{if } x \le 0 \\ x+2 & \text{if } 0 < x \le 4 \\ 3x - 4 & \text{if } x > 4 \end{cases}$

Some points for $x \le 0$: $(-6, 2)$, $(-3, 1)$, $(0, 0)$
Closed dot at $(0, 0)$
Some points for $0 < x \le 4$: $(1, 3)$, $(2, 4)$, $(4, 6)$
Open dot at $(0, 2)$, closed dot at $(4, 6)$
Some points for $x > 4$: $(5, 11)$, $(6, 14)$
Open dot at $(4, 8)$

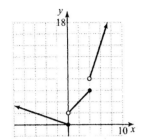

58. $f(x) = \sqrt{x-1} + 3$

The function is defined when $x - 1 \geq 0$, or $x \geq 1$, so the domain is $[1, \infty)$. The function takes on all y-values greater than or equal to 3, so the range is $[3, \infty)$.

60. $g(x) = -|x+1| + 1$

The function is defined for all real numbers, so the domain is $(-\infty, \infty)$. The function takes on all y-values less than or equal to 1, so the range is $(-\infty, 1]$.

62. $g(x) = -3\sqrt{x+5}$

The function is defined when $x + 5 \geq 0$, or $x \geq -5$, so the domain is $[-5, \infty)$.

64. $f(x) = -3|x+5.7|$

The function is defined for all real numbers, so the domain is $(-\infty, \infty)$.

66. $h(x) = \sqrt{x-17} - 3$

The function is defined when $x - 17 \geq 0$, or $x \geq 17$, so the domain is $[17, \infty)$.

68. $f(x) = \begin{cases} x^2 & \text{if } x < 0 \\ \sqrt{x} & \text{if } x \geq 0 \end{cases}$

For $x < 0$:   For $x \geq 0$:

x	$f(x)$
-3	9
-2	4
-1	1

x	$f(x)$
0	0
1	1
4	2

Graph a closed circle at $(0, 0)$. The graph of $f(x) = x^2$ for $x < 0$ also approaches the point $(0, 0)$.

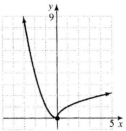

The function is defined for all real numbers, so the domain is $(-\infty, \infty)$. The function takes on all y-values greater than or equal to 0, so the range is $[0, \infty)$.

70. $g(x) = \begin{cases} -|x+1| - 1 & \text{if } x < -2 \\ \sqrt{x+2} - 4 & \text{if } x \geq -2 \end{cases}$

For $x < -2$:   For $x \geq -2$:

x	$g(x)$
-5	-5
-4	-4
-3	-3

x	$g(x)$
-2	-4
-1	-3
2	-2

Graph an open circle at $(-2, -2)$. Graph a closed circle at $(-2, -4)$.

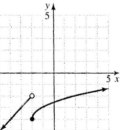

The function is defined for all real numbers, so the domain is $(-\infty, \infty)$. The function takes on all y-values, so the range is $(-\infty, \infty)$.

Section 8.4

Practice Exercises

1. $y = kx$
$20 = k(15)$
$\dfrac{4}{3} = k$
$k = \dfrac{4}{3}; \; y = \dfrac{4}{3}x$

2. $d = kw$

   $9 = k(36)$

   $\dfrac{1}{4} = k$

   $d = \dfrac{1}{4}w$

   $d = \dfrac{1}{4}(75)$

   $d = \dfrac{75}{4}$ inches or $18\dfrac{3}{4}$ inches

3. $b = \dfrac{k}{a}$

   $5 = \dfrac{k}{9}$

   $k = 45;\ b = \dfrac{45}{a}$

4. $P = \dfrac{k}{V}$

   $350 = \dfrac{k}{2.8}$

   $980 = k$

   $P = \dfrac{980}{V}$

   $P = \dfrac{980}{1.5}$

   $P = 653\dfrac{1}{3}$ kilopascals

5. $A = kap$

6. $y = \dfrac{k}{x^3}$

   $\dfrac{1}{2} = \dfrac{k}{2^3}$

   $\dfrac{1}{2} = \dfrac{k}{8}$

   $4 = k$

   $k = 4;\ y = \dfrac{4}{x^3}$

7. $y = \dfrac{kz}{x^3}$

   $15 = \dfrac{k \cdot 5}{3^3}$

   $81 = k$

   $k = 81;\ y = \dfrac{81z}{x^3}$

Vocabulary and Readiness Check

1. $y = 5x$ represents direct variation.

2. $y = \dfrac{700}{x}$ represents inverse variation.

3. $y = 5xz$ represents joint variation.

4. $y = \dfrac{1}{2}abc$ represents joint variation.

5. $y = \dfrac{9.1}{x}$ represents inverse variation.

6. $y = 2.3x$ represents direct variation.

7. $y = \dfrac{2}{3}x$ represents direct variation.

8. $y = 3.1st$ represents joint variation.

Exercise Set 8.4

2. $y = kx$

   $5 = k(30)$

   $k = \dfrac{1}{6}$

   $y = \dfrac{1}{6}x$

4. $y = kx$

   $12 = k(8)$

   $y = \dfrac{3}{2}$

   $y = \dfrac{3}{2}x$

6. $y = kx$

   $11 = k\left(\dfrac{1}{3}\right)$

   $k = 33$

   $y = 33x$

8. $y = kx$

   $0.4 = k(2.5)$

   $k = 0.16$

   $y = 0.16x$

10. $d = k\sqrt{e}$

$7.4 = k\sqrt{36}$

$7.4 = k \cdot 6$

$k = \dfrac{37}{30}$

$d = \dfrac{37}{30}\sqrt{e} = \dfrac{37}{30}\sqrt{64} \approx 9.9$

The person can see 9.9 miles.

12. $V = kT$

$20 = k(300)$

$k = \dfrac{20}{300} = \dfrac{1}{15}$

$V = \dfrac{1}{15}T = \dfrac{1}{15}(360) = 24$

The new volume is 24 cubic meters.

14. $y = \dfrac{k}{x}$

$20 = \dfrac{k}{9}$

$k = 180$

$y = \dfrac{180}{x}$

16. $y = \dfrac{k}{x}$

$63 = \dfrac{k}{3}$

$k = 189$

$y = \dfrac{189}{x}$

18. $y = \dfrac{k}{x}$

$\dfrac{1}{10} = \dfrac{k}{40}$

$k = 4$

$y = \dfrac{4}{x}$

20. $y = \dfrac{k}{x}$

$0.6 = \dfrac{k}{0.3}$

$k = 0.18$

$y = \dfrac{0.18}{x}$

22. $w = \dfrac{k}{d^2}$

$160 = \dfrac{k}{(4000)^2}$

$k = 2{,}560{,}000{,}000$

$w = \dfrac{2{,}560{,}000{,}000}{d^2} = \dfrac{2{,}560{,}000{,}000}{(4200)^2} \approx 145$

The person will weigh 145 pounds.

24. $C = \dfrac{k}{n}$

$1.20 = \dfrac{k}{4000}$

$k = 4800$

$C = \dfrac{4800}{n} = \dfrac{4800}{6000} = 0.8 = 0.80$

The cost per disk is $0.80.

26. $W = \dfrac{k}{h^2}$

$2 = \dfrac{k}{8^2}$

$k = 128$

$W = \dfrac{128}{h^2} = \dfrac{128}{10^2} = 1.28$

It can hold 1.28 tons.

28. $P = kRS^2$

30. $a = kbc$

32. $y = kx^3$

$32 = k(4)^3$

$32 = 64k$

$k = \dfrac{1}{2}$

$y = \dfrac{1}{2}x^3$

34. $y = k\sqrt{x}$

$2.1 = k\sqrt{9}$

$2.1 = 3k$

$k = 0.7$

$y = 0.7\sqrt{x}$

36. $y = \dfrac{k}{x^2}$

$0.011 = \dfrac{k}{10^2}$

$k = 1.1$

$y = \dfrac{1.1}{x^2}$

38. $y = kxz^2$

$360 = k(4)(3)^2$

$360 = k \cdot 4 \cdot 9$

$360 = 36k$

$k = 10$

$y = 10xz^2$

40. $C = kwt$

$60 = k(200)(2)$

$60 = 400k$

$k = 0.15$

$C = 0.15wt = 0.15(240)(3) = 108$

The workers can make 108 cars.

42. $F = kAs$

$20 = k(12)(10)$

$20 = 120k$

$k = \dfrac{1}{6}$

$F = \dfrac{1}{6}As = \dfrac{1}{6}(8)(12) = 16$

The force is 16 pounds.

44. $h = ksd^3$

$40 = k(120)(2)^3$

$40 = k(120)(8)$

$40 = 960k$

$k = \dfrac{40}{960} = \dfrac{1}{24}$

$h = \dfrac{1}{24}sd^3 = \dfrac{1}{24}(80)(3)^3 = \dfrac{1}{24} \cdot 80 \cdot 27 = 90$

It can transmit 90 horsepower.

46. p varies directly as q is written as $p = kq$.

48. y varies inversely as x is written as $y = \dfrac{k}{x}$.

50. y varies jointly as q, r, and t is written as $y = kqrt$.

52. y varies inversely as a^4 is written as $y = \dfrac{k}{a^4}$.

54. y varies directly as a^5 and inversely as b is written as $y = \dfrac{ka^5}{b}$.

56. $r = 6$ cm

$C = 2\pi r = 2\pi(6) = 12\pi$ cm

$A = \pi r^2 = \pi(6)^2 = 36\pi$ sq cm

58. $r = 7$ m

$C = 2\pi r = 2\pi(7) = 14\pi$ m

$A = \pi r^2 = \pi(7)^2 = 49\pi$ sq m

60. $|-3| = 3$

62. $|0| = 0$

64. $-\left|\dfrac{1}{5}\right| = -\dfrac{1}{5}$

66. $\left(\dfrac{5}{11}\right)^2 = \left(\dfrac{5}{11}\right)\left(\dfrac{5}{11}\right) = \dfrac{25}{121}$

68. $y = \dfrac{0.6}{x}$ is an example of inverse variation; b.

70. $xy = \dfrac{2}{11}$ or $y = \dfrac{2}{11x}$ is an example of inverse variation; b.

72. $V_1 = khr^2$

$V_2 = k\left(\dfrac{1}{2}h\right)(2r)^2$

$\quad = k\left(\dfrac{1}{2}h\right)(4r^2)$

$\quad = 2(khr^2)$

$\quad = 2V_1$

It is multiplied by 2.

74. $y_1 = kx^2$

$y_2 = k(2x)^2 = k(4x^2) = 4(kx^2) = 4y_1$

It is multiplied by 4.

76.

x	$\frac{1}{4}$	$\frac{1}{2}$	1	2	4
$y = \frac{1}{x}$	4	2	1	$\frac{1}{2}$	$\frac{1}{4}$

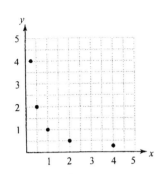

78.

x	$\frac{1}{4}$	$\frac{1}{2}$	1	2	4
$y = \frac{5}{x}$	20	10	5	$\frac{5}{2}$	$\frac{5}{4}$

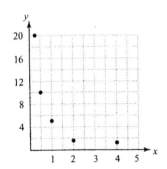

Chapter 8 Vocabulary Check

1. <u>Parallel</u> lines have the same slope and different y-intercepts.

2. <u>Slope-intercept</u> form of a linear equation in two variables is $y = mx + b$.

3. A <u>function</u> is a relation in which each first component in the ordered pairs corresponds to exactly one second component.

4. In the equation $y = 4x - 2$, the coefficient of x is the <u>slope</u> of its corresponding graph.

5. Two lines are <u>perpendicular</u> if the product of their slopes is -1.

6. A <u>linear function</u> is a function that can be written in the form $f(x) = mx + b$.

7. In the equation $y = kx$, y varies <u>directly</u> as x.

8. In the equation $y = \dfrac{k}{x}$, y varies <u>inversely</u> as x.

9. In the equation $y = kxz$, y varies <u>jointly</u> as x and z.

Chapter 8 Review

1. $f(x) = x$ or $y = x$
   $m = 1, \ b = 0$

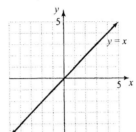

2. $f(x) = -\dfrac{1}{3}x$ or $y = -\dfrac{1}{3}x$
   $m = -\dfrac{1}{3}, \ b = 0$

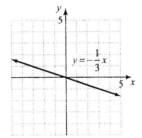

3. $g(x) = 4x - 1$ or $y = 4x - 1$
   $m = 4, \ b = -1$

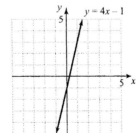

4. $F(x) = -\dfrac{2}{3}x + 2$ or $y = -\dfrac{2}{3}x + 2$

$m = -\dfrac{2}{3},\ b = 2$

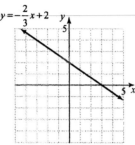

$y = -\dfrac{2}{3}x + 2$

5. $f(x) = 3x + 1$

The y-intercept should be $(0, 1)$. The correct graph is C.

6. $f(x) = 3x - 2$

The y-intercept should be $(0, -2)$. The correct graph is A.

7. $f(x) = 3x + 2$

The y-intercept should be $(0, 2)$. The correct graph is B.

8. $f(x) = 3x - 5$

The y-intercept should be $(0, -5)$. The correct graph is D.

9. $f(x) = \dfrac{2}{5}x - \dfrac{4}{3}$

slope $m = \dfrac{2}{5}$; y-intercept $(0, b) = \left(0, -\dfrac{4}{3}\right)$

10. $f(x) = -\dfrac{2}{7}x + \dfrac{3}{2}$

slope $m = -\dfrac{2}{7}$; y-intercept $(0, b) = \left(0, \dfrac{3}{2}\right)$

11. $y - y_1 = m(x - x_1)$
$y - (-2) = 2(x - 5)$
$y + 2 = 2x - 10$
$2x - y = 12$

12. $y - y_1 = m(x - x_1)$
$y - 5 = 3[x - (-3)]$
$y - 5 = 3(x + 3)$
$y - 5 = 3x + 9$
$3x - y = -14$

13. $m = \dfrac{-8 - 3}{-4 - (-5)} = \dfrac{-11}{1} = -11$
$y - y_1 = m(x - x_1)$
$y - 3 = -11[x - (-5)]$
$y - 3 = -11(x + 5)$
$y - 3 = -11x - 55$
$11x + y = -52$

14. $m = \dfrac{-2 - (-1)}{-4 - (-6)} = \dfrac{-1}{2} = -\dfrac{1}{2}$
$y - y_1 = m(x - x_1)$
$y - (-1) = -\dfrac{1}{2}[x - (-6)]$
$2(y + 1) = -(x + 6)$
$2y + 2 = -x - 6$
$x + 2y = -8$

15. $y = 8$ has slope $= 0$
A line parallel to $y = 8$ has slope $= 0$.
$y = -5$

16. $x = 4$ has undefined slope.
A line perpendicular to $x = 4$ has slope $= 0$ and is therefore horizontal.
$y = 3$

17. Every horizontal line is in the form $y = c$. Since the line passes through the point $(3, -1)$, its equation is $y = -1$ or $f(x) = -1$.

18. $y = mx + b$
$y = -\dfrac{2}{3}x + 4$
$f(x) = -\dfrac{2}{3}x + 4$

19. $y = mx + b$
$y = -x - 2$
$f(x) = -x - 2$

20. $6x + 3y = 5$
$3y = -6x + 5$
$y = -2x + \dfrac{5}{3}$ so $m = -2$
$y - y_1 = m(x - x_1)$
$y - (-6) = -2(x - 2)$
$y + 6 = -2x + 4$
$y = -2x - 2$
$f(x) = -2x - 2$

21. $3x + 2y = 8$
$$2y = -3x + 8$$
$$y = -\frac{3}{2}x + 4 \text{ so } m = -\frac{3}{2}$$
$$y - y_1 = m(x - x_1)$$
$$y - (-2) = -\frac{3}{2}[x - (-4)]$$
$$2(y + 2) = -3(x + 4)$$
$$2y + 4 = -3x - 12$$
$$2y = -3x - 16$$
$$y = -\frac{3}{2}x - 8$$
$$f(x) = -\frac{3}{2}x - 8$$

22. $4x + 3y = 5$
$$3y = -4x + 5$$
$$y = -\frac{4}{3}x + \frac{5}{3}$$
$$\text{so } m = -\frac{4}{3} \text{ and } m_\perp = \frac{3}{4}$$
$$y - y_1 = m(x - x_1)$$
$$y - (-1) = \frac{3}{4}[x - (-6)]$$
$$4(y + 1) = 3(x + 6)$$
$$4y + 4 = 3x + 18$$
$$4y = 3x + 14$$
$$y = \frac{3}{4}x + \frac{7}{2}$$
$$f(x) = \frac{3}{4}x + \frac{7}{2}$$

23. $2x - 3y = 6$
$$-3y = -2x + 6$$
$$y = \frac{2}{3}x - 2$$
$$\text{so } m = \frac{2}{3} \text{ and } m_\perp = -\frac{3}{2}$$
$$y - y_1 = m(x - x_1)$$
$$y - 5 = -\frac{3}{2}[x - (-4)]$$
$$2(y - 5) = -3(x + 4)$$
$$2y - 10 = -3x - 12$$
$$2y = -3x - 2$$
$$y = -\frac{3}{2}x - 1$$
$$f(x) = -\frac{3}{2}x - 1$$

24. a. Use ordered pairs (0, 71) and (5, 82)
$$m = \frac{82 - 71}{5 - 0} = \frac{11}{5} = 2.2 \text{ and } b = 71$$
$$y = 2.2x + 71$$

b. $x = 2009 - 2000 = 9$
$y = 2.2(9) + 71 = 90.8$
About 91% of US drivers will be wearing seat belts.

25. a. Use ordered pairs (0, 43) and (22, 60)
$$m = \frac{60 - 43}{22 - 0} = \frac{17}{22} \text{ and } b = 43$$
$$y = \frac{17}{22}x + 43$$

b. $x = 2010 - 1998 = 12$
$$y = \frac{17}{22}(12) + 43 \approx 52.3$$
There will be about 52 million people reporting arthritis.

26. $-x + 3y = 2$
$$3y = x + 2$$
$$y = \frac{1}{3}x + \frac{2}{3}$$
$$m = \frac{1}{3}, \; b = \frac{2}{3}$$
$$6x - 18y = 3$$
$$-18y = -6x + 3$$
$$y = \frac{1}{3}x - \frac{1}{6}$$
$$m = \frac{1}{3}, \; b = -\frac{1}{6}$$
The slopes are the same and the y-intercepts are different, so the lines are parallel.

27. When $x = -1$, y or $f(x)$ is 0, so $f(-1) = 0$.

28. When $x = 1$, y or $f(x)$ is -2, so $f(1) = -2$.

29. The x-values that correspond to a y-value of 1 are -2 and 4, so $f(x) = 1$ for $x = -2$ and $x = 4$.

30. The x-values that correspond to a y-value of -1 are 0 and 2, so $f(x) = -1$ for $x = 0$ and $x = 2$.

31. $f(x) = 3x$; Linear

x	-1	0	1
y	-3	0	3

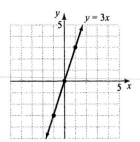

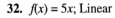

32. $f(x) = 5x$; Linear

x	-1	0	1
y	-5	0	5

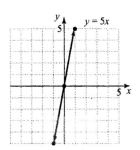

33. $g(x) = |x| + 4$; Nonlinear

x	-3	-2	-1	0	1	2	3
y	7	6	5	4	5	6	7

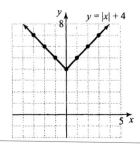

34. $h(x) = x^2 + 4$; Nonlinear

x	-3	-2	-1	0	1	2	3
y	13	8	5	4	5	8	13

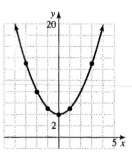

35. $F(x) = -\dfrac{1}{2}x + 2$; Linear

Find three ordered pair solutions, or find x- and y-intercepts, or find m and b.

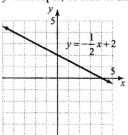

36. $G(x) = -x + 5$; Linear

Find three ordered pair solutions, or find x- and y-intercepts, or find m and b.

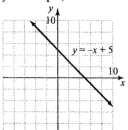

37. $y = -1.36x$; Linear

Find three ordered pair solutions, or find x- and y-intercepts, or find m and b.

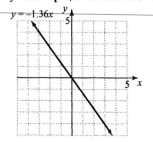

38. $y = 2.1x + 5.9$; Linear

Find three ordered pair solutions, or find *x*- and *y*-intercepts, or find *m* and *b*.

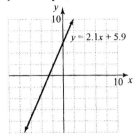

39. $H(x) = (x-2)^2$; Nonlinear

x	0	1	2	3	4
y	4	1	0	1	4

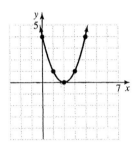

40. $f(x) = -|x - 3|$; Nonlinear

x	1	2	3	4	5
y	-2	-1	0	-1	-2

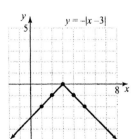

41. $g(x) = \begin{cases} -\dfrac{1}{5}x & \text{if } x \le -1 \\ -4x + 2 & \text{if } x > -1 \end{cases}$

For $x \le -1$:   For $x > -1$:

x	$g(x)$
-5	1
-3	$\frac{3}{5}$
-1	$\frac{1}{5}$

x	$g(x)$
0	2
1	-2
2	-6

Graph a closed circle at $\left(-1, \dfrac{1}{5}\right)$. Graph an open circle at $(-1, 6)$, which is found by substituting -1 for *x* in $g(x) = -4x + 2$.

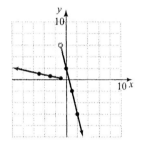

42. $f(x) = \begin{cases} -3x & \text{if } x < 0 \\ x - 3 & \text{if } x \ge 0 \end{cases}$

For $x < 0$:   For $x \ge 0$:

x	$f(x)$
-3	9
-2	6
-1	3

x	$f(x)$
0	-3
1	-2
2	-1

Graph a closed circle at $(0, -3)$. Graph an open circle at $(0, 0)$, which is found by substituting 0 for *x* in $f(x) = -3x$.

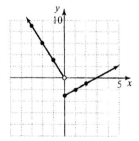

43. $f(x) = \sqrt{x-4}$

The graph of $f(x) = \sqrt{x-4}$ is the same as the graph of $y = \sqrt{x}$ shifted right 4 units.

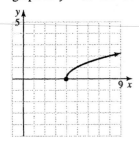

44. $y = \sqrt{x} - 4$

The graph of $f(x) = \sqrt{x} - 4$ is the same as the graph of $y = \sqrt{x}$ shifted down 4 units.

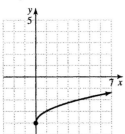

45. $h(x) = -(x+3)^2 - 1$

The graph of $h(x) = -(x+3)^2 - 1$ is the same as the graph of $y = x^2$ reflected about the x-axis and then shifted left 3 units and down 1 unit.

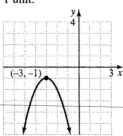

46. $g(x) = |x-2| - 2$

The graph of $g(x) = |x-2| - 2$ is the same as the graph of $y = |x|$ shifted right 2 units and down 2 units.

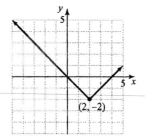

47. $A = kB$

$6 = k(14)$

$k = \dfrac{6}{14} = \dfrac{3}{7}$

$A = \dfrac{3}{7}B$

$A = \dfrac{3}{7}(21) = 9$

48. $C = \dfrac{k}{D}$

$12 = \dfrac{k}{8}$

$96 = k$

$C = \dfrac{96}{D}$

$C = \dfrac{96}{24} = 4$

49. $P = \dfrac{k}{V}$

$1250 = \dfrac{k}{2}$

$k = 2500$

$P = \dfrac{2500}{V}$

$800 = \dfrac{2500}{V}$

$800V = 2500$

$V = 3.125$

When the pressure is 800 kilopascals, the volume is 3.125 cubic meters.

50. $A = kr^2$

$36\pi = k(3)^2$

$36\pi = 9k$

$4\pi = k$

$A = 4\pi r^2$

$A = 4\pi(4)^2 = 64\pi$

When the radius is 4 inches, the surface area is 64π square inches.

51. Slope 0; through $\left(-4, \dfrac{9}{2}\right)$

A line with slope 0 is horizontal, and a horizontal line has an equation of the form $y = b$, where b is the y-coordinate of any point on the line. The equation is $y = \dfrac{9}{2}$ or $f(x) = \dfrac{9}{2}$.

52. Slope $\dfrac{3}{4}$; through $(-8, -4)$

$y - y_1 = m(x - x_1)$

$y - (-4) = \dfrac{3}{4}(x - (-8))$

$y + 4 = \dfrac{3}{4}(x + 8)$

$4(y + 4) = 3(x + 8)$

$4y + 16 = 3x + 24$

$4y = 3x + 8$

$y = \dfrac{3}{4}x + 2$

$f(x) = \dfrac{3}{4}x + 2$

53. Through $(-3, 8)$ and $(-2, 3)$

Find the slope.

$m = \dfrac{3 - 8}{-2 - (-3)} = \dfrac{-5}{1} = -5$

Use the slope and one of the points in the point-slope form. We use $(-2, 3)$.

$y - y_1 = m(x - x_1)$

$y - 3 = -5(x - (-2))$

$y - 3 = -5(x + 2)$

$y - 3 = -5x - 10$

$y = -5x - 7$

$f(x) = -5x - 7$

54. Through $(-6, 1)$; parallel to $y = -\dfrac{3}{2}x + 11$

The slope of a line parallel to $y = -\dfrac{3}{2}x + 11$ will have the same slope, $-\dfrac{3}{2}$.

$y - y_1 = m(x - x_1)$

$y - 1 = -\dfrac{3}{2}(x - (-6))$

$y - 1 = -\dfrac{3}{2}(x + 6)$

$2(y - 1) = -3(x + 6)$

$2y - 2 = -3x - 18$

$2y = -3x - 16$

$y = -\dfrac{3}{2}x - 8$

$f(x) = -\dfrac{3}{2}x - 8$

55. Through $(-5, 7)$; perpendicular to $5x - 4y = 10$

Find the slope of $5x - 4y = 10$.

$5x - 4y = 10$

$-4y = -5x + 10$

$y = \dfrac{5}{4}x - \dfrac{5}{2}$

The slope is $\dfrac{5}{4}$. The slope of any line perpendicular to this line is the negative reciprocal of $\dfrac{5}{4}$, or $-\dfrac{4}{5}$.

$y - y_1 = m(x - x_1)$

$y - 7 = -\dfrac{4}{5}(x - (-5))$

$y - 7 = -\dfrac{4}{5}(x + 5)$

$5(y - 7) = -4(x + 5)$

$5y - 35 = -4x - 20$

$5y = -4x + 15$

$y = -\dfrac{4}{5}x + 3$

$f(x) = -\dfrac{4}{5}x + 3$

56. $g(x) = \begin{cases} 4x - 3 & \text{if } x \le 1 \\ 2x & \text{if } x > 1 \end{cases}$

For $x \le 1$:   For $x > 1$:

x	$g(x)$
-1	-7
0	-3
1	1

x	$g(x)$
2	4
3	6
4	8

Graph a closed circle at (1, 1). Graph an open circle at (1, 2), which is found by substituting 1 for x in $g(x) = 2x$.

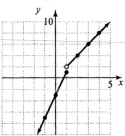

57. $f(x) = \begin{cases} x-2 & \text{if } x \leq 0 \\ -\frac{x}{3} & \text{if } x \geq 3 \end{cases}$

For $x \leq 0$:   For $x \geq 3$:

x	$f(x)$
-2	-4
-1	-3
0	-2

x	$f(x)$
3	-1
4	$-\frac{4}{3}$
6	-2

Graph closed circles at (0, –2) and (3, –1).

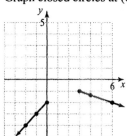

58. $f(x) = |x+1| - 3$

The graph of $f(x) = |x+1| - 3$ is the same as the graph of $y = |x|$ shifted left 1 unit and down 3 units.

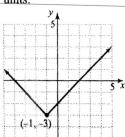

59. $f(x) = \sqrt{x-2}$

The graph of $f(x) = \sqrt{x-2}$ is the same as the graph of $y = \sqrt{x}$ shifted right 2 units.

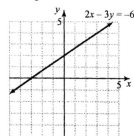

60. $y = \dfrac{k}{x}$

$14 = \dfrac{k}{6}$

$84 = k$

$y = \dfrac{84}{x}$

$y = \dfrac{84}{21} = 4$

Chapter 8 Test

1. When $x = 1$, y or $f(x)$ is 3, so $f(1) = 3$.

2. When $x = -3$, y or $f(x)$ is –5, so $f(-3) = -5$.

3. The x-values that correspond to a y-value of 0 are –2 and 2, so $f(x) = 0$ for $x = -2$ and $x = 2$.

4. The x-value that corresponds to a y-value of 4 is 0, so $f(x) = 4$ for $x = 0$.

5. $2x - 3y = -6$

   $-3y = -2x - 6$

   $y = \dfrac{2}{3}x + 2$

   $m = \dfrac{2}{3},\ b = 2$

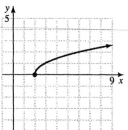

6. $f(x) = \dfrac{2}{3}x$ or $y = \dfrac{2}{3}x$

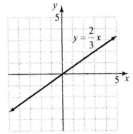

7. Horizontal; through $(2, -8)$
A horizontal line has an equation of the form $y = b$, where b is the y-coordinate of any point on the line. The equation is $y = -8$.

8.
$$y - y_1 = m(x - x_1)$$
$$y - (-1) = -3(x - 4)$$
$$y + 1 = -3x + 12$$
$$3x + y = 11$$

9.
$$y - y_1 = m(x - x_1)$$
$$y - (-2) = 5(x - 0)$$
$$y + 2 = 5x$$
$$5x - y = 2$$

10. $m = \dfrac{-3 - (-2)}{6 - 4} = \dfrac{-1}{2} = -\dfrac{1}{2}$
$$y - y_1 = m(x - x_1)$$
$$y - (-2) = -\dfrac{1}{2}(x - 4)$$
$$2(y + 2) = -(x - 4)$$
$$2y + 4 = -x + 4$$
$$2y = -x$$
$$y = -\dfrac{1}{2}x$$
$$f(x) = -\dfrac{1}{2}x$$

11. $3x - y = 4$
$$y = 3x - 4$$
$$m = 3 \text{ so } m_\perp = -\dfrac{1}{3}$$
$$y - y_1 = m(x - x_1)$$
$$y - 2 = -\dfrac{1}{3}[x - (-1)]$$
$$3(y - 2) = -(x + 1)$$
$$3y - 6 = -x - 1$$
$$3y = -x + 5$$
$$y = -\dfrac{1}{3}x + \dfrac{5}{3}$$
$$f(x) = -\dfrac{1}{3}x + \dfrac{5}{3}$$

12. $2y + x = 3$
$$2y = -x + 3$$
$$y = -\dfrac{1}{2}x + 3 \text{ so } m = -\dfrac{1}{2}$$
$$y - y_1 = m(x - x_1)$$
$$y - (-2) = -\dfrac{1}{2}(x - 3)$$
$$2(y + 2) = -(x - 3)$$
$$2y + 4 = -x + 3$$
$$2y = -x - 1$$
$$y = -\dfrac{1}{2}x - \dfrac{1}{2}$$
$$f(x) = -\dfrac{1}{2}x - \dfrac{1}{2}$$

13. $2x - 5y = 8$
$$-5y = -2x + 8$$
$$y = \dfrac{2}{5}x - \dfrac{8}{5} \text{ so } m_1 = \dfrac{2}{5}$$
$$m_2 = \dfrac{-1 - 4}{-1 - 1} = \dfrac{-5}{-2} = \dfrac{5}{2}$$
Therefore, lines L_1 and L_2 are neither parallel nor perpendicular since their slopes are not equal and the product of their slopes is not -1.

14. Domain: $(-\infty, \infty)$
Range: $\{5\}$
Function since it passes the vertical line test.

15. Domain: $\{-2\}$
Range: $(-\infty, \infty)$
Not a function since it fails the vertical line test.

16. Domain: $(-\infty, \infty)$
Range: $[0, \infty)$
Function since it passes the vertical line test.

17. Domain: $(-\infty, \infty)$
Range: $(-\infty, \infty)$
Function since it passes the vertical line test.

18. $f(x) = 1031x + 25{,}193$

    a. $x = 0$
$$f(0) = 1031(0) + 25{,}193 = 25{,}193$$
The average earnings in 2000 were \$25,193.

    b. $x = 2007 - 2000 = 7$
$$f(7) = 1031(7) + 25{,}193 = 32{,}410$$
The average earnings in 2007 were \$32,410.

c. $40,000 \leq 1031x + 25,193$
$14,807 \leq 1031x$
$14.4 \leq x$
$2000 + 15 = 2015$
The average earnings will be greater than $40,000 in 2015.

d. slope = 1031; the yearly earnings for high school graduates increases $1031 per year.

e. (0, 25,193); the yearly earnings for a high school graduate in 2000 were $25,193.

19. $f(x) = \begin{cases} -\frac{1}{2}x & \text{if } x \leq 0 \\ 2x - 3 & \text{if } x > 0 \end{cases}$

For $x \leq 0$:   For $x > 0$:

x	$f(x)$
−4	2
−2	1
0	0

x	$f(x)$
1	−1
2	1
3	3

Graph a closed circle at (0, 0). Graph an open circle at (0, −3), which is found by substituting 0 for x in $f(x) = 2x - 3$.

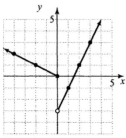

Domain: $(-\infty, \infty)$;
range: $(-3, \infty)$

20. $f(x) = (x - 4)^2$

The graph of $f(x) = (x - 4)^2$ is the same as the graph of $y = x^2$ shifted right 4 units.

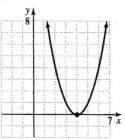

21. $g(x) = -|x + 2| - 1$

The graph of $g(x) = -|x + 2| - 1$ is the same as the graph of $y = |x|$ reflected about the x-axis and then shifted left 2 units and down 1 unit.

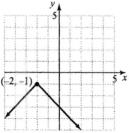

Domain: $(-\infty, \infty)$;
range: $(-\infty, -1]$

22. $h(x) = \sqrt{x} - 1$

The graph of $h(x) = \sqrt{x} - 1$ is the same as the graph of $y = \sqrt{x}$ shifted down 1 unit.

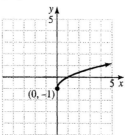

23. $W = \frac{k}{V}$

$20 = \frac{k}{12}$

$240 = k$

$W = \frac{240}{V}$

$W = \frac{240}{15} = 16$

24. $Q = kRS^2$

$24 = k(3)(4)^2$

$24 = 48k$

$\frac{1}{2} = k$

$Q = \frac{1}{2}RS^2$

$Q = \frac{1}{2}(2)(3)^2 = \frac{1}{2}(2)(9) = 9$

25.
$$s = k\sqrt{d}$$
$$160 = k\sqrt{400}$$
$$160 = 20k$$
$$8 = k$$
$$s = 8\sqrt{d}$$
$$128 = 8\sqrt{d}$$
$$16 = \sqrt{d}$$
$$16^2 = \left(\sqrt{d}\right)^2$$
$$256 = d$$
The cliff is 256 feet tall.

Chapter 8 Cumulative Review

1. $3[4 + 2(10-1)] = 3[4 + 2(9)]$
$$= 3[4 + 18]$$
$$= 3[22]$$
$$= 66$$

2. $5[3 + 6(8 - 5)] = 5[3 + 6(3)]$
$$= 5[3 + 18]$$
$$= 5[21]$$
$$= 105$$

3. Let $x = 2$ and $y = -5$.

   a. $\dfrac{x-y}{12+x} = \dfrac{2-(-5)}{12+2} = \dfrac{2+5}{14} = \dfrac{7}{14} = \dfrac{1}{2}$

   b. $x^2 - 3y = 2^2 - 3(-5) = 4 + 15 = 19$

4. Let $x = 2$ and $y = -5$.

   a. $\dfrac{x+y}{3y} = \dfrac{2+(-5)}{3(-5)} = \dfrac{-3}{-15} = \dfrac{1}{5}$

   b. $y^2 - x = (-5)^2 - 2 = 25 - 2 = 23$

5. $-3x = 33$
$$\frac{-3x}{-3} = \frac{33}{-3}$$
$$x = -11$$

6. $\dfrac{2}{3}y = 7$
$$\frac{3}{2}\left(\frac{2}{3}y\right) = \frac{3}{2}(7)$$
$$y = \frac{21}{2}$$

7. $8(2 - t) = -5t$
$$16 - 8t = -5t$$
$$16 - 8t + 8t = -5t + 8t$$
$$16 = 3t$$
$$\frac{16}{3} = \frac{3t}{3}$$
$$\frac{16}{3} = t$$

8. $5x - 9 = 5x - 29$
$$5x - 5x - 9 = 5x - 5x - 29$$
$$-9 = -29$$
This is a false statement, so the equation has no solution.

9. $y = mx + b$
$$y - b = mx$$
$$\frac{y-b}{m} = x \quad \text{or} \quad x = \frac{y-b}{m}$$

10. $y = 7x - 2$
$$y + 2 = 7x$$
$$\frac{y+2}{7} = x \quad \text{or} \quad x = \frac{y+2}{7}$$

11. $-4x + 7 \geq -9$
$$-4x + 7 - 7 \geq -9 - 7$$
$$-4x \geq -16$$
$$\frac{-4x}{-4} \leq \frac{-16}{-4}$$
$$x \leq 4$$
$(-\infty, 4]$

12. $-5x - 6 < 3x + 1$
$$-5x - 3x - 6 < 3x - 3x + 1$$
$$-8x - 6 < 1$$
$$-8x - 6 + 6 < 1 + 6$$
$$-8x < 7$$
$$\frac{-8x}{-8} > \frac{7}{-8}$$
$$x > -\frac{7}{8}$$
$\left(-\dfrac{7}{8}, \infty\right)$

13. $(-1, 7), (2, 2)$
$$m = \frac{2-7}{2-(-1)} = \frac{-5}{3} = -\frac{5}{3}$$

The slope of a perpendicular line is $\dfrac{3}{5}$.

14. $(0, 7), (-1, 0)$

$$m = \frac{0-7}{-1-0} = \frac{-7}{-1} = 7$$

The slope of a parallel line is 7.

15. $g(x) = x^2 - 3$

　a. $g(2) = 2^2 - 3 = 4 - 3 = 1$

　b. $g(-2) = (-2)^2 - 3 = 4 - 3 = 1$

　c. $g(0) = 0^2 - 3 = 0 - 3 = -3$

16. $f(x) = 3 - x^2$

　a. $f(2) = 3 - 2^2 = 3 - 4 = -1$

　b. $f(-2) = 3 - (-2)^2 = 3 - 4 = -1$

　c. $f(0) = 3 - 0^2 = 3 - 0 = 3$

17. $\begin{cases} 2x + y = 10 \\ x = y + 2 \end{cases}$

Substitute $y + 2$ for x in the first equation.

$$2(y+2) + y = 10$$
$$2y + 4 + y = 10$$
$$4 + 3y = 10$$
$$3y = 6$$
$$y = 2$$

Let $y = 2$ in the second equation.

$x = 2 + 2 = 4$

The solution is $(4, 2)$.

18. $\begin{cases} 3y = x + 10 \\ 2x + 5y = 24 \end{cases}$

Solve the first equation for x.

$x = 3y - 10$

Substitute $3y - 10$ for x in the second equation.

$$2(3y - 10) + 5y = 24$$
$$6y - 20 + 5y = 24$$
$$11y - 20 = 24$$
$$11y = 44$$
$$y = 4$$

Let $y = 4$ in $x = 3y - 10$.

$x = 3(4) - 10 = 12 - 10 = 2$

The solution is $(2, 4)$.

19. $\begin{cases} -x - \dfrac{y}{2} = \dfrac{5}{2} \\ -\dfrac{x}{2} + \dfrac{y}{4} = 0 \end{cases}$

Multiply the first equation by 2 and the second equation by 4, then add.

$$-2x - y = 5$$
$$\underline{-2x + y = 0}$$
$$-4x = 5$$
$$x = -\frac{5}{4}$$

Let $x = -\dfrac{5}{4}$ in the first equation.

$$-\left(-\frac{5}{4}\right) - \frac{y}{2} = \frac{5}{2}$$
$$\frac{5}{4} - \frac{y}{2} = \frac{5}{2}$$
$$-\frac{y}{2} = \frac{10}{4} - \frac{5}{4}$$
$$-\frac{y}{2} = \frac{5}{4}$$
$$-2\left(-\frac{y}{2}\right) = -2\left(\frac{5}{4}\right)$$
$$y = -\frac{5}{2}$$

The solution is $\left(-\dfrac{5}{4}, -\dfrac{5}{2}\right)$.

20. $\begin{cases} \dfrac{x}{2} + y = \dfrac{5}{6} \\ 2x - y = \dfrac{5}{6} \end{cases}$

Multiply both equations by 6, then add.

$$3x + 6y = 5$$
$$\underline{12x - 6y = 5}$$
$$15x = 10$$
$$x = \frac{2}{3}$$

Let $x = \dfrac{2}{3}$ in the first equation.

$$\frac{\frac{2}{3}}{2} + y = \frac{5}{6}$$
$$\frac{1}{3} + y = \frac{5}{6}$$
$$y = \frac{5}{6} - \frac{2}{6}$$
$$y = \frac{3}{6} = \frac{1}{2}$$

The solution is $\left(\frac{2}{3}, \frac{1}{2}\right)$.

21.
$$\begin{array}{r} x+4 \\ x+3 \overline{\smash{\big)}\, x^2+7x+12} \\ \underline{x^2+3x} \\ 4x+12 \\ \underline{4x+12} \\ 0 \end{array}$$

$$\frac{x^2+7x+12}{x+3} = x+4$$

22. $\dfrac{5x^2y - 6xy + 2}{6xy} = \dfrac{5x^2y}{6xy} - \dfrac{6xy}{6xy} + \dfrac{2}{6xy}$

$$= \frac{5x}{6} - 1 + \frac{1}{3xy}$$

23. a. $6t + 18 = 6 \cdot t + 6 \cdot 3 = 6(t+3)$

b. $y^5 - y^7 = y^5 \cdot 1 - y^5 \cdot y^2 = y^5(1 - y^2)$

24. a. $5y - 20 = 5 \cdot y - 5 \cdot 4 = 5(y-4)$

b. $z^{10} - z^3 = z^3 \cdot z^7 - z^3 \cdot 1 = z^3(z^7 - 1)$

25. $x^2 + 4x - 12 = (x-2)(x+6)$

26. $x^2 - 10x + 21 = (x-7)(x-3)$

27. $10x^2 - 13xy - 3y^2 = 10x^2 - 15xy + 2xy - 3y^2$
$$= 5x(2x - 3y) + y(2x - 3y)$$
$$= (2x - 3y)(5x + y)$$

28. $12a^2 + 5ab - 2b^2 = 12a^2 - 3ab + 8ab - 2b^2$
$$= 3a(4a - b) + 2b(4a - b)$$
$$= (4a - b)(3a + 2b)$$

29. $x^3 + 8 = x^3 + 2^3$
$$= (x+2)(x^2 - x \cdot 2 + 2^2)$$
$$= (x+2)(x^2 - 2x + 4)$$

30. $y^3 - 27 = y^3 - 3^3$
$$= (y-3)(y^2 + y \cdot 3 + 3^2)$$
$$= (y-3)(y^2 + 3y + 9)$$

31. $x^2 - 9x - 22 = 0$
$$(x+2)(x-11) = 0$$
$$x+2 = 0 \quad \text{or} \quad x-11 = 0$$
$$x = -2 \qquad\qquad x = 11$$
The solutions are -2 and 11.

32. $\qquad y^2 - 5y = -6$
$$y^2 - 5y + 6 = 0$$
$$(y-2)(y-3) = 0$$
$$y-2 = 0 \quad \text{or} \quad y-3 = 0$$
$$y = 2 \qquad\qquad y = 3$$
The solutions are 2 and 3.

33. a. $\dfrac{2x^2}{10x^3 - 2x^2} = \dfrac{2x^2}{2x^2(5x-1)} = \dfrac{1}{5x-1}$

b. $\dfrac{9x^2 + 13x + 4}{8x^2 + x - 7} = \dfrac{(9x+4)(x+1)}{(8x-7)(x+1)} = \dfrac{9x+4}{8x-7}$

34. a. $\dfrac{33x^4y^2}{3xy} = \dfrac{33}{3}x^{4-1}y^{2-1} = 11x^3y^1 = 11x^3y$

b. $\dfrac{9y}{90y^2 + 9y} = \dfrac{9y}{9y(10y+1)} = \dfrac{1}{10y+1}$

35. $\dfrac{3x+3}{5x - 5x^2} \cdot \dfrac{2x^2 + x - 3}{4x^2 - 9}$
$$= \frac{3(x+1) \cdot (2x+3)(x-1)}{-5x(x-1) \cdot (2x+3)(2x-3)}$$
$$= -\frac{3(x+1)}{5x(2x-3)}$$

36. $\dfrac{2x}{x-6} - \dfrac{x+6}{x-6} = \dfrac{2x-(x+6)}{x-6}$

$\qquad = \dfrac{2x-x-6}{x-6}$

$\qquad = \dfrac{x-6}{x-6}$

$\qquad = 1$

37. $\dfrac{3x^2+2x}{x-1} - \dfrac{10x-5}{x-1} = \dfrac{3x^2+2x-(10x-5)}{x-1}$

$\qquad = \dfrac{3x^2+2x-10x+5}{x-1}$

$\qquad = \dfrac{3x^2-8x+5}{x-1}$

$\qquad = \dfrac{(3x-5)(x-1)}{x-1}$

$\qquad = 3x-5$

38. $\dfrac{9}{y^2} - 4y = \dfrac{9}{y^2} - \dfrac{4y}{1} \cdot \dfrac{y^2}{y^2} = \dfrac{9}{y^2} - \dfrac{4y^3}{y^2} = \dfrac{9-4y^3}{y^2}$

39. $3 - \dfrac{6}{x} = x+8$

$x\left(3 - \dfrac{6}{x}\right) = x(x+8)$

$3x - 6 = x^2 + 8x$

$0 = x^2 + 5x + 6$

$0 = (x+3)(x+2)$

$x+3 = 0 \quad \text{or} \quad x+2 = 0$

$x = -3 \qquad\qquad x = -2$

The solutions are -3 and -2.

40. $\dfrac{x}{2} + \dfrac{x}{5} = \dfrac{x-7}{20}$

$20\left(\dfrac{x}{2} + \dfrac{x}{5}\right) = 20\left(\dfrac{x-7}{20}\right)$

$10x + 4x = x - 7$

$14x = x - 7$

$13x = -7$

$x = -\dfrac{7}{13}$

The solution is $-\dfrac{7}{13}$.

41. $(4, 0), (-4, -5)$

$m = \dfrac{-5-0}{-4-4} = \dfrac{-5}{-8} = \dfrac{5}{8}$

$y - y_1 = m(x - x_1)$

$y - 0 = \dfrac{5}{8}(x-4)$

$y = \dfrac{5}{8}x - \dfrac{5}{2}$

$f(x) = \dfrac{5}{8}x - \dfrac{5}{2}$

42. $(-1, 3), (-2, 7)$

$m = \dfrac{7-3}{-2-(-1)} = \dfrac{4}{-2+1} = \dfrac{4}{-1} = -4$

$y - y_1 = m(x - x_1)$

$y - 3 = -4[x-(-1)]$

$y - 3 = -4(x+1)$

$y - 3 = -4x - 4$

$y = -4x - 1$

$f(x) = -4x - 1$

Chapter 9

Section 9.1

Practice Exercises

1. $A = \{1, 3, 5, 7, 9\}$ and $B = \{1, 2, 3, 4\}$
   The numbers 1 and 3 are in sets A and B.
   The intersection is $\{1, 3\}$. $A \cap B = \{1, 3\}$.

2. $x + 3 < 8$ and $2x - 1 < 3$
   $x < 5$ and $2x < 4$
   $x < 5$ and $x < 2$
   $\{x | x < 5\}, (-\infty, 5)$

   $\{x | x < 2\}, (-\infty, 2)$

   $\{x | x < 5 \text{ and } x < 2\} = \{x | x < 2\}$

   The solution set is $(-\infty, 2)$.

3. $4x \leq 0$ and $3x + 2 > 8$
   $x \leq 0$ and $3x > 6$
   $x \leq 0$ and $x > 2$
   $\{x | x \leq 0\}, (-\infty, 0]$

   $\{x | x > 2\}, (2, \infty)$

   $\{x | 4x \leq 0 \text{ and } 3x + 2 > 8\} = \{\ \}$ or $\varnothing$

4. $3 < 5 - x < 9$
   $3 - 5 < 5 - x - 5 < 9 - 5$
   $-2 < -x < 4$
   $\dfrac{-2}{-1} > \dfrac{-x}{-1} > \dfrac{4}{-1}$
   $2 > x > -4$
   or $-4 < x < 2$
   The solution set is $(-4, 2)$.

5. $-4 \leq \dfrac{x}{2} - 1 \leq 3$
   $2(-4) \leq 2\left(\dfrac{x}{2} - 1\right) \leq 2(3)$
   $-8 \leq x - 2 \leq 6$
   $-8 + 2 \leq x - 2 + 2 \leq 6 + 2$
   $-6 \leq x \leq 8$
   The solution set is $[-6, 8]$.

6. $A = \{1, 3, 5, 7, 9\}$ and $B = \{2, 3, 4, 5, 6\}$.
   The numbers that are in either set or both sets are
   $\{1, 2, 3, 4, 5, 6, 7, 9\}$. This set is the union,
   $A \cup B$.

7. $8x + 5 \leq 8$ or $x - 1 \geq 2$
   $8x \leq 3$ or $x \geq 3$
   $x \leq \dfrac{3}{8}$ or $x \geq 3$
   $\left\{x | x \leq \dfrac{3}{8}\right\}, \left(-\infty, \dfrac{3}{8}\right]$

   $\{x | x \geq 3\}, [3, \infty)$

   $\left\{x | x \leq \dfrac{3}{8} \text{ or } x \geq 3\right\} = \left(-\infty, \dfrac{3}{8}\right] \cup [3, \infty)$

   The solution set is $\left(-\infty, \dfrac{3}{8}\right] \cup [3, \infty)$.

8. $-3x - 2 > -8$ or $5x > 0$
   $-3x > -6$ or $x > 0$
   $x < 2$ or $x > 0$
   $\{x | x < 2\}, (-\infty, 2)$

   $\{x | x > 0\}, (0, \infty)$

   $\{x | x < 2 \text{ or } x > 0\}, (-\infty, \infty)$

   The solution set is $(-\infty, \infty)$.

Vocabulary and Readiness Check

1. Two inequalities joined by the words "and" or "or" are called <u>compound</u> inequalities.

2. The word <u>and</u> means intersection.

3. The word <u>or</u> means union.

4. The symbol $\cap$ means intersection.

5. The symbol $\cup$ represents union.

6. The symbol $\varnothing$ is the empty set.

7. The inequality $-2 \le x < 1$ means $-2 \le x$ <u>and</u> $x < 1$.

8. $\{x | x < 0 \text{ and } x > 0\} = \varnothing$.

Exercise Set 9.1

2. $C \cap D = \{4, 5\}$

4. $A \cup D = \{x | x \text{ is an even integer or } x = 5 \text{ or } x = 7\}$

6. $A \cap B = \varnothing$

8. $B \cup D = \{x | x \text{ is an odd integer or } x = 4 \text{ or } x = 6\}$

10. $B \cap C = \{3, 5\}$

12. $A \cup C = \{x | x \text{ is an even integer or } x = 3 \text{ or } x = 5\}$

14. $x \le 0$ and $x \ge -2$
$-2 \le x \le 0$
$[-2, 0]$

16. $x < 2$ and $x > 4$
$\varnothing$

18. $x \ge -4$ and $x > 1$
$x > 1$
$(1, \infty)$

20. $x + 2 \ge 3$ and $5x - 1 \ge 9$
$\quad x \ge 1$ and $\quad 5x \ge 10$
$\qquad\qquad\qquad x \ge 2$
$x \ge 2$
$[2, \infty)$

22. $2x + 4 > 0$ and $4x > 0$
$\quad 2x > -4$ and $\quad x > 0$
$\quad x > -2$
$(0, \infty)$

24. $-7x \le -21$ and $x - 20 \le -15$
$\quad x \ge 3$ and $\quad x \le 5$
$3 \le x \le 5$
$[3, 5]$

26. $-2 \le x + 3 \le 0$
$-5 \le x \le -3$
$[-5, -3]$

28. $1 < 4 + 2x < 7$
$1 - 4 < 4 + 2x - 4 < 7 - 4$
$-3 < 2x < 3$
$\dfrac{-3}{2} < x < \dfrac{3}{2}$
$\left(-\dfrac{3}{2}, \dfrac{3}{2}\right)$

30. $-2 < \dfrac{1}{2}x - 5 < 1$
$3 < \dfrac{1}{2}x < 6$
$6 < x < 12$
$(6, 12)$

32. $-4 \le \dfrac{-2x+5}{3} \le 1$
$3(-4) \le 3\left(\dfrac{-2x+5}{3}\right) \le 3(1)$
$-12 \le -2x + 5 \le 3$
$-17 \le -2x \le -2$
$\dfrac{17}{2} \ge x \ge 1$
$1 \le x \le \dfrac{17}{2}$
$\left[1, \dfrac{17}{2}\right]$

34. $x \ge -2$ or $x \le 2$
$(-\infty, \infty)$

36. $x < 0$ or $x < 1$
$(-\infty, 1)$

38. $x \ge -3$ or $x \le -4$
$(-\infty, -4] \cup [-3, \infty)$

40. $-5x \le 10$ or $3x - 5 \ge 1$
$\quad x \ge -2$ or $\quad 3x \ge 6$
$\qquad\qquad\qquad x \ge 2$
$x \ge -2$
$[-2, \infty)$

42. $x + 9 < 0$ or $4x > -12$

     $x < -9$ or $x > -3$

    $(-\infty, -9) \cup (-3, \infty)$

44. $5(x - 1) \geq -5$ or $5 - x \leq 11$

     $x - 1 \geq -1$ or $-x \leq 6$

       $x \geq 0$ or $x \geq -6$

   $x \geq -6$

   $[-6, \infty)$

46. $x < \dfrac{5}{7}$ and $x < 1$

   $x < \dfrac{5}{7}$

   $\left(-\infty, \dfrac{5}{7}\right)$

48. $x < \dfrac{5}{7}$ or $x < 1$

   $x < 1$

   $(-\infty, 1)$

50. $3 < 5x + 1 < 11$

   $2 < 5x < 10$

   $\dfrac{2}{5} < x < 2$

   $\left(\dfrac{2}{5}, 2\right)$

52. $\dfrac{2}{3} < x + \dfrac{1}{2} < 4$

   $6\left(\dfrac{2}{3}\right) < 6\left(x + \dfrac{1}{2}\right) < 6(4)$

     $4 < 6x + 3 < 24$

     $1 < 6x < 21$

     $\dfrac{1}{6} < x < \dfrac{7}{2}$

   $\left(\dfrac{1}{6}, \dfrac{7}{2}\right)$

54. $2x - 1 \geq 3$ and $-x > 2$

     $2x \geq 4$ and $x < -2$

      $x \geq 2$ and $x < -2$

   $\varnothing$

56. $\dfrac{3}{8}x + 1 \leq 0$ or $-2x < -4$

     $\dfrac{3}{8}x \leq -1$ or $x > 2$

       $x \leq -\dfrac{8}{3}$ or $x > 2$

   $\left(-\infty, -\dfrac{8}{3}\right] \cup (2, \infty)$

58. $-2 < \dfrac{-2x - 1}{3} < 2$

   $3(-2) < 3\left(\dfrac{-2x - 1}{3}\right) < 3(2)$

      $-6 < -2x - 1 < 6$

       $-5 < -2x < 7$

      $\dfrac{-5}{-2} > x > \dfrac{7}{-2}$

      $-\dfrac{7}{2} < x < \dfrac{5}{2}$

   $\left(-\dfrac{7}{2}, \dfrac{5}{2}\right)$

60. $-5 < 2(x + 4) < 8$

     $-5 < 2x + 8 < 8$

     $-13 < 2x < 0$

     $-\dfrac{13}{2} < x < 0$

   $\left(-\dfrac{13}{2}, 0\right)$

62. $5x \leq 0$ and $-x + 5 < 8$

     $x \leq 0$ and $-x < 3$

     $x \leq 0$ and $x > -3$

   $(-3, 0]$

64. $-x < 7$ or $3x + 1 < -20$

     $x > -7$ or $3x < -21$

     $x > -7$ or $x < -7$

   $(-\infty, -7) \cup (-7, \infty)$

66. $-2x < -6$ or $1 - x > -2$

     $x > 3$ or $-x > -3$

     $x > 3$ or $x < 3$

   $(-\infty, 3) \cup (3, \infty)$

68.

$$-\frac{1}{2} \le \frac{3x-1}{10} < \frac{1}{2}$$

$$10\left(-\frac{1}{2}\right) \le 10\left(\frac{3x-1}{10}\right) < 10\left(\frac{1}{2}\right)$$

$$-5 \le 3x-1 < 5$$

$$-4 \le 3x < 6$$

$$-\frac{4}{3} \le x < 2$$

$$\left[-\frac{4}{3}, 2\right)$$

70.

$$-\frac{1}{4} < \frac{6-x}{12} < -\frac{1}{6}$$

$$12\left(-\frac{1}{4}\right) < 12\left(\frac{6-x}{12}\right) < 12\left(-\frac{1}{6}\right)$$

$$-3 < 6-x < -2$$

$$-9 < -x < -8$$

$$9 > x > 8$$

$$(8, 9)$$

72. $-0.7 \le 0.4x + 0.8 < 0.5$

$$-1.5 \le 0.4x < -0.3$$

$$-3.75 \le x < -0.75$$

$$[-3.75, -0.75)$$

74. $|-7 - 19| = |-26| = 26$

76. $|-4| - (-4) + |-20| = 4 + 4 + 20 = 28$

78. $|x| = 5$

$$x = -5, 5$$

80. $|x| = -2$

$$\varnothing$$

82. The years that consumption of bottled water were less than 15 gallons per person were 1998 and 1999. The years that consumption of diet soda were greater than 14 gallons per person were 2003, 2004, and 2005. The union of the years is 1998, 1999, 2003, 2004, and 2005.

84. The number of jobs in 2000 was greater than 1800 thousand for registered nurses. The predicted number of jobs in 2012 is greater than 1800 thousand for post secondary teachers and registered nurses. The union of these is registered nurses and post secondary teachers.

86.

$$-10 \le C \le 18$$

$$-10 \le \frac{5}{9}(F - 32) \le 18$$

$$\frac{9}{5}(-10) \le \frac{9}{5}\left(\frac{5}{9}(F - 32)\right) \le \frac{9}{5}(18)$$

$$-18 \le F - 32 \le \frac{162}{5}$$

$$14 \le F \le 64.4$$

$$14° \le F \le 64.4°$$

88. Let x be Wendy's grade on the final exam.

$$80 \le \frac{1}{6}(2x + 80 + 90 + 82 + 75) \le 89$$

$$480 \le 2x + 327 \le 534$$

$$153 \le 2x \le 207$$

$$76.5 \le x \le 103.5$$

$$76.5 \le x \le 100$$

If Wendy scores between 76.5 and 100 inclusive on her final exam, she will receive a B in the course.

90. $x + 3 < 2x + 1 < 4x + 6$

$x + 3 < 2x + 1$	and	$2x + 1 < 4x + 6$
$2 < x$	and	$-5 < 2x$
$x > 2$	and	$-\dfrac{5}{2} < x$
$x > 2$	and	$x > -\dfrac{5}{2}$

$$(2, \infty)$$

92. $7x - 1 \le 7 + 5x \le 3(1 + 2x)$

$7x - 1 \le 7 + 5x$	and	$7 + 5x \le 3 + 6x$
$2x \le 8$	and	$4 \le x$
$x \le 4$	and	$x \ge 4$

$$\{4\}$$

94. $1 + 2x < 3(2 + x) < 1 + 4x$

$1 + 2x < 6 + 3x$	and	$6 + 3x < 1 + 4x$
$-5 < x$	and	$5 < x$
$x > -5$	and	$x > 5$

$$(5, \infty)$$

The Bigger Picture

1. $-\dfrac{1}{2} - \left(-\dfrac{3}{8}\right) = -\dfrac{1}{2} + \dfrac{3}{8} = -\dfrac{4}{8} + \dfrac{3}{8} = -\dfrac{1}{8}$

2. $(8xy - 7y^2) - (4xy - y^2) = 8xy - 7y^2 - 4xy + y^2$

$$= 4xy - 6y^2$$

3. $\dfrac{x+2}{xy-z^2} - \dfrac{x+1}{xy-z^2} = \dfrac{x+2-(x+1)}{xy-z^2}$

$\qquad\qquad\qquad = \dfrac{x+2-x-1}{xy-z^2}$

$\qquad\qquad\qquad = \dfrac{1}{xy-z^2}$

4. $\dfrac{x^3-8}{x-2} \cdot \dfrac{x^2-4}{x-2}$

$\qquad = \dfrac{(x-2)(x^2+2x+4)\cdot(x+2)(x-2)}{(x-2)\cdot(x-2)}$

$\qquad = (x+2)(x^2+2x+4)$

5. $x-2 \le 1$ and $3x-1 \ge -4$

$\qquad x \le 3$ and $3x \ge -3$

$\qquad\qquad\qquad\qquad\qquad x \ge -1$

$-1 \le x \le 3$

$[-1, 3]$

6. $\qquad -2 < x-1 < 5$

$\qquad -2+1 < x-1+1 < 5+1$

$\qquad\qquad -1 < x < 6$

$\qquad (-1, 6)$

7. $-2x+2.5 = -7.7$

$\qquad -2x = -10.2$

$\qquad\quad x = 5.1$

8. $-5x > 20$

$\qquad \dfrac{-5x}{-5} < \dfrac{20}{-5}$

$\qquad\quad x < -4$

$\qquad (-\infty, -4)$

9. $x \le -3$ or $x \le -5$

$\qquad x \le -3$

$\qquad (-\infty, -3]$

10. $5x < -10$ or $3x-4 > 2$

$\qquad x < -2$ or $3x > 6$

$\qquad\qquad\qquad\qquad\qquad x > 2$

$\qquad (-\infty, -2) \cup (2, \infty)$

11. $\qquad \dfrac{5t}{2} - \dfrac{3t}{4} = 7$

$\qquad 4\left(\dfrac{5t}{2} - \dfrac{3t}{4}\right) = 4(7)$

$\qquad\qquad 2(5t) - 3t = 28$

$\qquad\qquad\quad 10t - 3t = 28$

$\qquad\qquad\qquad\quad 7t = 28$

$\qquad\qquad\qquad\quad\; t = 4$

12. $5(x-3) + x + 2 \ge 3(x+2) + 2x$

$\qquad 5x - 15 + x + 2 \ge 3x + 6 + 2x$

$\qquad\qquad 6x - 13 \ge 5x + 6$

$\qquad\qquad 6x - 5x \ge 13 + 6$

$\qquad\qquad\qquad x \ge 19$

$[19, \infty)$

Section 9.2

Practice Exercises

1. $|q| = 7$

$\qquad q = 7$ or $q = -7$

The solution set is $\{-7, 7\}$.

2. $|2x-3| = 5$

$\qquad 2x-3 = 5$ or $2x-3 = -5$

$\qquad\quad 2x = 8$ or $2x = -2$

$\qquad\qquad x = 4$ or $x = -1$

The solution set is $\{-1, 4\}$.

3. $\left|\dfrac{x}{5} + 1\right| = 15$

$\qquad \dfrac{x}{5} + 1 = 15$ or $\dfrac{x}{5} + 1 = -15$

$\qquad\quad \dfrac{x}{5} = 14$ or $\dfrac{x}{5} = -16$

$\qquad\quad x = 70$ or $x = -80$

The solutions are -80 and 70.

4. $|3x| + 8 = 14$

$\qquad |3x| = 6$

$\qquad 3x = 6$ or $3x = -6$

$\qquad\; x = 2$ or $x = -2$

The solutions are -2 and 2.

5. $|z| = 0$

The solution is 0.

6. $3|z| + 9 = 7$

$3|z| = -2$

$|z| = -\dfrac{2}{3}$

The absolute value of a number is never negative, so there is no solution. The solution set is { } or $\varnothing$.

7. $\left|\dfrac{5x+3}{4}\right| = -8$

The absolute value of a number is never negative, so there is no solution. The solution set is { } or $\varnothing$.

8. $|2x + 4| = |3x - 1|$

$\begin{array}{ll} 2x+4 = 3x-1 & \text{or} \quad 2x+4 = -(3x-1) \\ -x+4 = -1 & 2x+4 = -3x+1 \\ \quad -x = -5 & 5x+4 = 1 \\ \quad\ \ x = 5 & 5x = -3 \\ & x = -\dfrac{3}{5} \end{array}$

The solutions are $-\dfrac{3}{5}$ and 5.

9. $|x - 2| = |8 - x|$

$\begin{array}{ll} x-2 = 8-x & \text{or} \quad x-2 = -(8-x) \\ 2x-2 = 8 & x-2 = -8+x \\ 2x = 10 & -2 = -8 \quad \text{False} \\ \ \ x = 5 & \end{array}$

The solution is 5.

Vocabulary and Readiness Check

1. $|x - 2| = 5$
C. $x - 2 = 5$ or $x - 2 = -5$

2. $|x - 2| = 0$
A. $x - 2 = 0$

3. $|x - 2| = |x + 3|$
B. $x - 2 = x + 3$ or $x - 2 = -(x + 3)$

4. $|x + 3| = 5$
E. $x + 3 = 5$ or $x + 3 = -5$

5. $|x + 3| = -5$
D. $\varnothing$

Exercise Set 9.2

2. $|y| = 15$
$y = -15$ or $y = 15$

4. $|6n| = 12.6$
$\begin{array}{ll} 6n = 12.6 & \text{or} \quad 6n = -12.6 \\ n = 2.1 & \text{or} \quad\ \ n = -2.1 \end{array}$

6. $|6 + 2n| = 4$
$\begin{array}{ll} 6+2n = -4 & \text{or} \quad 6+2n = 4 \\ 2n = -10 & \text{or} \quad\ \ 2n = -2 \\ n = -5 & \text{or} \quad\ \ \ \ n = -1 \end{array}$

8. $\left|\dfrac{n}{3} + 2\right| = 4$

$\begin{array}{ll} \dfrac{n}{3}+2 = -4 & \text{or} \quad \dfrac{n}{3}+2 = 4 \\[2mm] \dfrac{n}{3} = -6 & \text{or} \quad \dfrac{n}{3} = 2 \\[2mm] n = -18 & \text{or} \quad\ \ n = 6 \end{array}$

10. $|x| + 1 = 3$
$|x| = 2$
$x = -2$ or $x = 2$

12. $|2x| - 6 = 4$
$|2x| = 10$
$\begin{array}{ll} 2x = -10 & \text{or} \quad 2x = 10 \\ x = -5 & \text{or} \quad\ \ x = 5 \end{array}$

14. $|7z| = 0$
$7z = 0$
$z = 0$

16. $|3z - 2| + 8 = 1$
$|3z - 2| = -7$
which is impossible.
The solution set is $\varnothing$.

18. $|3y + 2| = 0$
$3y + 2 = 0$
$3y = -2$
$y = -\dfrac{2}{3}$

20. $|x| = 2$

22. $|9y + 1| = |6y + 4|$
$\begin{array}{ll} 9y+1 = -(6y+4) & \text{or} \quad 9y+1 = 6y+4 \\ 9y+1 = -6y-4 & \text{or} \quad\ \ 3y = 3 \\ 15y = -5 & \text{or} \quad\ \ \ \ y = 1 \\ y = -\dfrac{1}{3} & \text{or} \quad\ \ \ \ y = 1 \end{array}$

24. $|2x - 5| = |2x + 5|$

$2x - 5 = -(2x + 5)$ or $2x - 5 = 2x + 5$

$2x - 5 = -2x - 5$ or $\quad -5 = 5$

$\quad 4x = 0$ or $\quad\quad$ false

$\quad\quad x = 0$

The only solution is 0.

26. Answers may vary

28. $|x| = 1$

$x = 1$ or $x = -1$

30. $|y| = 8$

$y = 8$ or $y = -8$

32. The absolute value of any expression is never negative, so no solution exists. The solution set is $\varnothing$.

34. $|4m + 5| = 5$

$4m + 5 = 5$ or $4m + 5 = -5$

$\quad 4m = 0$ or $\quad 4m = -10$

$\quad\quad m = 0$ or $\quad\quad m = -\dfrac{10}{4}$

$\quad\quad m = 0$ or $\quad\quad m = -\dfrac{5}{2}$

36. $|7z| + 1 = 22$

$|7z| = 21$

$7z = 21$ or $7z = -21$

$z = 3$ or $z = -3$

38. The absolute value of any expression is never negative, so no solution exists. The solution set is $\varnothing$.

40. $|x + 4| - 4 = 1$

$|x + 4| = 5$

$x + 4 = 5$ or $x + 4 = -5$

$\quad x = 1$ or $\quad x = -9$

42. The absolute value of any expression is never negative, so no solution exists. The solution set is $\varnothing$.

44. The absolute value of any expression is never negative, so no solution exists. The solution set is $\varnothing$.

46. $|5x - 2| = 0$

$5x - 2 = 0$

$5x = 2$

$x = \dfrac{2}{5}$

48. $|2 + 3m| - 9 = -7$

$|2 + 3m| = 2$

$2 + 3m = 2$ or $2 + 3m = -2$

$\quad 3m = 0$ or $\quad 3m = -4$

$\quad\quad m = 0$ or $\quad\quad m = -\dfrac{4}{3}$

50. $|8 - 6c| = 1$

$8 - 6c = 1$ or $8 - 6c = -1$

$\quad -6c = -7$ or $\quad -6c = -9$

$\quad\quad c = \dfrac{-7}{-6}$ or $\quad\quad c = \dfrac{-9}{-6}$

$\quad\quad c = \dfrac{7}{6}$ or $\quad\quad c = \dfrac{3}{2}$

52. $|3x + 5| = |-4|$

$|3x + 5| = 4$

$3x + 5 = 4$ or $3x + 5 = -4$

$\quad 3x = -1$ or $\quad 3x = -9$

$\quad\quad x = -\dfrac{1}{3}$ or $\quad\quad x = -3$

54. $|3 + 6n| = |4n + 11|$

$3 + 6n = 4n + 11$ or $3 + 6n = -(4n + 11)$

$\quad 2n = 8$ or $3 + 6n = -4n - 11$

$\quad\quad n = 4$ or $\quad 10n = -14$

$\quad\quad n = 4$ or $\quad\quad n = -\dfrac{7}{5}$

56. $|4 - 5y| = -|-3|$

$|4 - 5y| = -3$

The absolute value of any expression is never negative, so no solution exists. The solution set is $\varnothing$.

58. $|4n + 5| = |4n + 3|$

$4n + 5 = -(4n + 3)$ or $4n + 5 = 4n + 3$

$4n + 5 = -4n - 3$ or $\quad\quad 5 = 3$

$\quad 8n = -8$ or $\quad\quad$ false

$\quad\quad n = -1$

The only solution is -1.

60. $\left|\dfrac{1+3n}{4}\right| = 4$

$\dfrac{1+3n}{4} = 4$ or $\dfrac{1+3n}{4} = -4$

$1+3n = 16$ or $1+3n = -16$

$3n = 15$ or $3n = -17$

$n = 5$ or $n = -\dfrac{17}{3}$

62. $8 + |4m| = 24$

$|4m| = 16$

$4m = 16$ or $4m = -16$

$m = 4$ or $m = -4$

64. $\left|\dfrac{5x+2}{2}\right| = |-6|$

$\left|\dfrac{5x+2}{2}\right| = 6$

$\dfrac{5x+2}{2} = 6$ or $\dfrac{5x+2}{2} = -6$

$5x+2 = 12$ or $5x+2 = -12$

$5x = 10$ or $5x = -14$

$x = 2$ or $x = -\dfrac{14}{5}$

66. $|5z - 1| = |7 - z|$

$5z - 1 = -(7 - z)$ or $5z - 1 = 7 - z$

$5z - 1 = -7 + z$ or $6z = 8$

$4z = -6$ or $z = \dfrac{4}{3}$

$z = -\dfrac{3}{2}$

68. $\left|\dfrac{2r-6}{5}\right| = |-2|$

$\left|\dfrac{2r-6}{5}\right| = 2$

$\dfrac{2r-6}{5} = 2$ or $\dfrac{2r-6}{5} = -2$

$2r-6 = 10$ or $2r-6 = -10$

$2r = 16$ or $2r = -4$

$r = 8$ or $r = -2$

70. $|8 - y| = |y + 2|$

$8 - y = -(y+2)$ or $8 - y = y + 2$

$8 - y = -y - 2$ or $6 = 2y$

$8 = -2$ or $3 = y$

false or $3 = y$

The only solution is 3.

72. $\left|\dfrac{5d+1}{6}\right| = -|-9|$

$\left|\dfrac{5d+1}{6}\right| = -9$

The absolute value of any expression is never negative, so no solution exists. The solution set is $\varnothing$.

74. Answers may vary. Possible answer: In some cases, one of the equations yields no solution. One example is problem 70 above. The equation $8 = -2$ is false.

76. $3\%(360°) = 0.03(360°) = 10.8°$

78. $|x| \le 3$
Answers may vary
3, 2, 1, 0, −1, for example

80. $|y| > -10$
Answers may vary
0, 1, 2, 3, 4, for example

82. $|x - 1| = 5$

84. $|x| = 6$

86. $|x - 2| = |3x - 4|$

Section 9.3

Practice Exercises

1. $|x| < 2$
The solution set of this inequality contains all numbers whose distance from 0 is less than 2. The solution set is $(-2, 2)$.

2. $|b + 1| < 3$

$-3 < b + 1 < 3$

$-3 - 1 < b + 1 - 1 < 3 - 1$

$-4 < b < 2$

$(-4, 2)$

3. $|3x - 2| + 5 \le 9$

$\qquad |3x - 2| \le 9 - 5$

$\qquad |3x - 2| \le 4$

$\qquad -4 \le 3x - 2 \le 4$

$\qquad -4 + 2 \le 3x - 2 + 2 \le 4 + 2$

$\qquad -2 \le 3x \le 6$

$\qquad -\dfrac{2}{3} \le x \le 2$

$\left[-\dfrac{2}{3}, 2 \right]$

4. $\left| 3x + \dfrac{5}{8} \right| < -4$

The absolute value of a number is always nonnegative and can never be less than –4. The solution set is { } or $\varnothing$.

5. $|y + 4| \ge 6$

$\qquad y + 4 \le -6 \qquad\text{or}\qquad y + 4 \ge 6$

$\qquad y + 4 - 4 \le -6 - 4 \quad\text{or}\quad y + 4 - 4 \ge 6 - 4$

$\qquad\qquad y \le -10 \qquad\text{or}\qquad\qquad y \ge 2$

$(-\infty, -10] \cup [2, \infty)$

6. $\qquad |4x + 3| + 5 > 3$

$\qquad |4x + 3| + 5 - 5 > 3 - 5$

$\qquad\qquad |4x + 3| > -2$

The absolute value of any number is always nonnegative and thus is always greater than –2.

$(-\infty, \infty)$

7. $\qquad \left| \dfrac{x}{2} - 3 \right| - 5 > -2$

$\qquad \left| \dfrac{x}{2} - 3 \right| - 5 + 5 > -2 + 5$

$\qquad\qquad \left| \dfrac{x}{2} - 3 \right| > 3$

$\qquad \dfrac{x}{2} - 3 < -3 \qquad\text{or}\qquad \dfrac{x}{2} - 3 > 3$

$\qquad 2\left(\dfrac{x}{2} - 3 \right) < 2(-3) \quad\text{or}\quad 2\left(\dfrac{x}{2} - 3 \right) > 2(3)$

$\qquad\quad x - 6 < -6 \qquad\text{or}\qquad x - 6 > 6$

$\qquad\qquad x < 0 \qquad\text{or}\qquad\qquad x > 12$

$(-\infty, 0) \cup (12, \infty)$

8. $\left| \dfrac{3(x - 2)}{5} \right| \le 0$

$\qquad \dfrac{3(x - 2)}{5} = 0$

$\qquad 5\left[\dfrac{3(x - 2)}{5} \right] = 5(0)$

$\qquad\qquad 3(x - 2) = 0$

$\qquad\qquad 3x - 6 = 0$

$\qquad\qquad\quad 3x = 6$

$\qquad\qquad\quad\; x = 2$

The solution set is {2}.

Vocabulary and Readiness Check

1. D

2. E

3. C

4. B

5. A

Exercise Set 9.3

2. $|x| < 6$

$\qquad -6 < x < 6$

The solution set is (–6, 6).

4. $|y - 7| \le 5$

$\qquad -5 \le y - 7 \le 5$

$\qquad\;\; 2 \le y \le 12$

The solution set is [2, 12].

6. $|x + 4| < 6$

$\qquad -6 < x + 4 < 6$

$\qquad -10 < x < 2$

The solution set is (–10, 2).

8. $|5x - 3| \le 18$

$\qquad -18 \le 5x - 3 \le 18$

$\qquad -15 \le 5x \le 21$

$\qquad -3 \le x \le \dfrac{21}{5}$

The solution set is $\left[-3, \dfrac{21}{5} \right]$.

10. $|x| + 6 \le 7$

$\quad\quad |x| \le 1$

$-1 \le x \le 1$

The solution set is $[-1, 1]$.

12. $|8x - 3| < -2$

The absolute value of an expression is never negative, so no solution exists. The solution set is $\varnothing$.

14. $|z + 2| - 7 < -3$

$\quad\quad |z + 2| < 4$

$\quad -4 < z + 2 < 4$

$-4 - 2 < z + 2 - 2 < 4 - 2$

$\quad\quad -6 < z < 2$

The solution set is $(-6, 2)$.

16. $|y| \ge 4$

$y \le -4$ or $y \ge 4$

The solution set is $(-\infty, -4] \cup [4, \infty)$.

18. $|x - 9| \ge 2$

$x - 9 \le -2$ or $x - 9 \ge 2$

$\quad x \le 7$ or $\quad\quad x \ge 11$

The solution set is $(-\infty, 7] \cup [11, \infty)$.

20. $|x| - 1 > 3$

$\quad\quad |x| > 4$

$x < -4$ or $x > 4$

The solution set is $(-\infty, -4) \cup (4, \infty)$.

22. $|4x - 11| > -1$

An absolute value is always greater than a negative number. Thus, the answer is $(-\infty, \infty)$.

24. $|10 + 3x| + 1 > 2$

$\quad\quad |10 + 3x| > 1$

$10 + 3x < -1$ or $10 + 3x > 1$

$\quad 3x < -11$ or $\quad\quad 3x > -9$

$\quad x < -\dfrac{11}{3}$ or $\quad\quad\quad x > -3$

The solution set is $\left(-\infty, -\dfrac{11}{3}\right) \cup (-3, \infty)$.

26. $|x| \ge 0$

An absolute value is always greater than or equal to 0. Thus, the answer is $(-\infty, \infty)$.

28. $|5x - 6| < 0$

The absolute value of an expression is never negative, so no solution exists. The solution set is $\varnothing$.

30. $|z| < 8$

$-8 < z < 8$

$(-8, 8)$

32. $|x| \ge 10$

$x \le -10$ or $x \ge 10$

$(-\infty, -10] \cup [10, \infty)$

34. $|-3 + x| \le 10$

$-10 \le -3 + x \le 10$

$\quad -7 \le x \le 13$

$[-7, 13]$

36. $|1 + 0.3x| \ge 0.1$

$1 + 0.3x \le -0.1$ or $1 + 0.3x \ge 0.1$

$\quad 0.3x \le -1.1$ or $\quad\quad 0.3x \ge -0.9$

$\dfrac{0.3x}{0.3} \le -\dfrac{1.1}{0.3}$ or $\dfrac{0.3x}{0.3} \ge -\dfrac{0.9}{0.3}$

$\quad x \le -\dfrac{11}{3}$ or $\quad\quad\quad x \ge -3$

$\left(-\infty, -\dfrac{11}{3}\right] \cup [-3, \infty)$

38. $8 + |x| < 1$

$|x| < -7$

An absolute value is never negative, so no solution exists. The solution set is $\varnothing$.

40. $|x| \le -7$

An absolute value is never negative, so no solution exists. The solution set is $\varnothing$.

42. $|5x + 2| < 8$

$-8 < 5x + 2 < 8$

$-10 < 5x < 6$

$-2 < x < \dfrac{6}{5}$

The solution set is $\left(-2, \dfrac{6}{5}\right)$.

44. $|-1 + x| - 6 > 2$

$|-1 + x| - 6 + 6 > 2 + 6$

$|-1 + x| > 8$

$-1 + x < -8 \quad$ or $\quad -1 + x > 8$

$x < -7 \quad$ or $\qquad x > 9$

$(-\infty, -7) \cup (9, \infty)$

46. $|x| < 0$

An absolute value is never negative, so no solution exists. The solution set is $\varnothing$.

48. $5 + |x| \ge 4$

$|x| \ge -1$

An absolute value is always greater than or equal to 0. Thus, the answer is $(-\infty, \infty)$.

50. $-3 + |5x - 2| \le 4$

$|5x - 2| \le 7$

$-7 \le 5x - 2 \le 7$

$-5 \le 5x \le 9$

$-1 \le x \le \dfrac{9}{5}$

The solution set is $\left[-1, \dfrac{9}{5}\right]$.

52. $\left|\dfrac{3}{4}x - 1\right| \ge 2$

$\dfrac{3}{4}x - 1 \le -2 \quad$ or $\quad \dfrac{3}{4}x - 1 \ge 2$

$\dfrac{3}{4}x \le -1 \quad$ or $\quad \dfrac{3}{4}x \ge 3$

$x \le -\dfrac{4}{3} \quad$ or $\qquad x \ge 4$

$\left(-\infty, -\dfrac{4}{3}\right] \cup [4, \infty)$

54. $|4 + 9x| \ge -6$

An absolute value is always greater than or equal to 0. Thus, the answer is $(-\infty, \infty)$.

56. $\left|\dfrac{5x + 6}{2}\right| \le 0$

$\dfrac{5x + 6}{2} = 0$

$5x + 6 = 0$

$5x = -6$

$x = -\dfrac{6}{5}$

$\left\{-\dfrac{6}{5}\right\}$

58. $|7x-3|-1 \le 10$

$\quad |7x-3| \le 11$

$\quad -11 \le 7x-3 \le 11$

$\quad -8 \le 7x \le 14$

$\quad -\dfrac{8}{7} \le x \le 2$

$$\left[-\dfrac{8}{7}, 2\right]$$

60. $\left|\dfrac{7+x}{2}\right| \ge 4$

$\dfrac{7+x}{2} \le -4 \quad$ or $\quad \dfrac{7+x}{2} \ge 4$

$7+x \le -8 \quad$ or $\quad 7+x \ge 8$

$\quad x \le -15 \quad$ or $\quad\quad x \ge 1$

The solution set is $(-\infty, -15] \cup (1, \infty]$.

62. $\quad -9 + |3+4x| < -4$

$-9 + |3+4x| + 9 < -4 + 9$

$\quad\quad\quad |3+4x| < 5$

$\quad -5 < 3+4x < 5$

$\quad -8 < 4x < 2$

$\quad -2 < x < \dfrac{2}{4}$

$\quad -2 < x < \dfrac{1}{2}$

$$\left(-2, \dfrac{1}{2}\right)$$

64. $\left|\dfrac{3}{5}+4x\right| - 6 < -1$

$\quad \left|\dfrac{3}{5}+4x\right| < 5$

$\quad -5 < \dfrac{3}{5}+4x < 5$

$\quad -25 < 3+20x < 25$

$\quad -28 < 20x < 22$

$\quad -\dfrac{28}{20} < \dfrac{20x}{20} < \dfrac{22}{20}$

$\quad -\dfrac{7}{5} < x < \dfrac{11}{10}$

$$\left(-\dfrac{7}{5}, \dfrac{11}{10}\right)$$

66. $|2x-3| > 7$

$2x-3 < -7 \quad$ or $\quad 2x-3 > 7$

$\quad 2x < -4 \quad$ or $\quad\quad 2x > 10$

$\quad x < -2 \quad$ or $\quad\quad x > 5$

$(-\infty, -2) \cup (5, \infty)$

68. $|5-6x| = 29$

$5-6x = -29 \quad$ or $\quad 5-6x = 29$

$\quad -6x = -34 \quad$ or $\quad -6x = 24$

$\quad x = \dfrac{17}{3} \quad$ or $\quad\quad x = -4$

The solution set is $\left\{-4, \dfrac{17}{3}\right\}$.

70. $|x+4| \ge 20$

$x+4 \le -20 \quad$ or $\quad x+4 \ge 20$

$\quad x \le -24 \quad$ or $\quad\quad x \ge 16$

The solution set is $(-\infty, -24] \cup [16, \infty)$.

72. $|9+4x| \ge 0$

An absolute value is always greater than or equal to 0. Thus, the answer is $(-\infty, \infty)$.

74. $8 + |5x-3| \ge 11$

$\quad |5x-3| \ge 3$

$5x-3 \le -3 \quad$ or $\quad 5x-3 \ge 3$

$\quad 5x \le 0 \quad$ or $\quad\quad 5x \ge 6$

$\quad x \le 0 \quad$ or $\quad\quad x \ge \dfrac{6}{5}$

The solution set is $(-\infty, 0] \cup \left[\dfrac{6}{5}, \infty\right)$.

76. $|5x-3| + 2 = 4$

$\quad |5x-3| = 2$

$5x-3 = -2 \quad$ or $\quad 5x-3 = 2$

$\quad 5x = 1 \quad$ or $\quad\quad 5x = 5$

$\quad x = \dfrac{1}{5} \quad$ or $\quad\quad x = 1$

The solution set is $\left\{\dfrac{1}{5}, 1\right\}$.

78. $|4x - 4| = -3$

An absolute value is never negative, so no solution exists. The solution set is $\varnothing$.

80. $\left|\dfrac{6 - x}{4}\right| = 5$

$\dfrac{6 - x}{4} = -5$ or $\dfrac{6 - x}{4} = 5$

$6 - x = -20$ or $6 - x = 20$

$26 = x$ or $-14 = x$

The solution set is $\{-14, 26\}$.

82. $\left|\dfrac{4x - 7}{5}\right| < 2$

$-2 < \dfrac{4x - 7}{5} < 2$

$-10 < 4x - 7 < 10$

$-3 < 4x < 17$

$-\dfrac{3}{4} < x < \dfrac{17}{4}$

The solution set is $\left(-\dfrac{3}{4}, \dfrac{17}{4}\right)$.

84. $3x - 4y = 12$

$3x - 4(-1) = 12$

$3x + 4 = 12$

$3x = 8$

$x = \dfrac{8}{3}$

86. $3x - 4y = 12$

$3(4) - 4y = 12$

$12 - 4y = 12$

$-4y = 0$

$y = 0$

88. $|x| > 4$

90. $|x| > 1$

92. Answers may vary

94. $\left|0.2 - \dfrac{51}{256}\right| = |0.2 - 0.19921875|$

$= |0.00078125|$

$= 0.00078125$

The absolute error is 0.00078125.

The Bigger Picture

1. $9x - 14 = 11x + 2$

$9x - 11x = 14 + 2$

$-2x = 16$

$x = -8$

2. $|x - 4| = 17$

$x - 4 = -17$ or $x - 4 = 17$

$x = -13$ or $x = 21$

3. $x - 1 \le 5$ or $3x - 2 \le 10$

     $x \le 6$ or $3x \le 12$

     $x \le 6$ or $x \le 4$

$(-\infty, 6]$

4. $-x < 7$ and $4x \le 20$

     $x > -7$ and $x \le 5$

$(-7, 5]$

5. $|x - 2| = |x + 15|$

$x - 2 = x + 15$ or $x - 2 = -(x + 15)$

$-2 = 15$ False $x - 2 = -x - 15$

                     $2x - 2 = -15$

                        $2x = -13$

                         $x = -\dfrac{13}{2}$

The only solution is $-\dfrac{13}{2}$.

6. $9y - 6y + 1 = 4y + 10 - y + 3$

     $3y + 1 = 3y + 13$

        $1 = 13$

$\varnothing$

7. $1.5x - 3 = 1.2x - 18$

$1.5x - 1.2x = 3 - 18$

$0.3x = -15$

$x = -50$

8. $\dfrac{7x + 1}{8} - 3 = x + \dfrac{2x + 1}{4}$

$8\left(\dfrac{7x + 1}{8} - 3\right) = 8\left(x + \dfrac{2x + 1}{4}\right)$

$7x + 1 - 8 \cdot 3 = 8x + 2(2x + 1)$

$7x + 1 - 24 = 8x + 4x + 2$

$7x - 23 = 12x + 2$

$7x - 12x = 2 + 23$

$-5x = 25$

$x = -5$

9. $|5x+2|-10 \le -3$

$|5x+2| \le 7$

$-7 \le 5x+2 \le 7$

$-9 \le 5x \le 5$

$-\dfrac{9}{5} \le x \le 1$

$\left[-\dfrac{9}{5}, 1\right]$

10. $|x+11| > 2$

$x+11 > 2$ or $x+11 < -2$

$x > -9$ or $x < -13$

$(-\infty, -13) \cup (-9, \infty)$

11. $|9x+2|-1 = 24$

$|9x+2| = 25$

$9x+2 = -25$ or $9x+2 = 25$

$9x = -27$ or $9x = 23$

$x = -3$ or $x = \dfrac{23}{9}$

12. $\left|\dfrac{3x-1}{2}\right| = |2x+5|$

$\dfrac{3x-1}{2} = -(2x+5)$ or $\dfrac{3x-1}{2} = 2x+5$

$2\left(\dfrac{3x-1}{2}\right) = 2[-(2x+5)]$ or $2\left[\dfrac{3x-1}{2}\right] = 2(2x+5)$

$3x-1 = -4x-10$ or $3x-1 = 4x+10$

$3x+4x = -10+1$ or $3x-4x = 10+1$

$7x = -9$ or $-x = 11$

$x = -\dfrac{9}{7}$ or $x = -11$

Integrated Review

1. $x < 7$ and $x > -5$ is $-5 < x < 7$. The solution set is $(-5, 7)$.

2. $x < 7$ or $x > -5$

The solution set is $(-\infty, \infty)$.

3. $|4x - 3| = 1$

$4x - 3 = 1 \quad$ or $\quad 4x - 3 = -1$

$4x = 4 \quad$ or $\qquad 4x = 2$

$x = 1 \quad$ or $\qquad x = \dfrac{1}{2}$

The solutions are 1 and $\dfrac{1}{2}$.

4. $|2x + 1| < 5$

$-5 < 2x + 1 < 5$

$-6 < 2x < 4$

$-3 < x < 2$

The solution set is $(-3, 2)$.

5. $|6x| - 9 \geq -3$

$|6x| \geq 6$

$6x \leq -6 \quad$ or $\quad 6x \geq 6$

$x \leq -1 \quad$ or $\quad x \geq 1$

The solution set is $(-\infty, -1] \cup [1, \infty)$.

6. $|x - 7| = |2x + 11|$

$x - 7 = 2x + 11 \quad$ or $\qquad x - 7 = -(2x + 11)$

$-7 = x + 11 \quad$ or $\qquad x - 7 = -2x - 11$

$-18 = x \qquad$ or $\quad 3x - 7 = -11$

$\qquad\qquad\qquad\qquad\quad 3x = -4$

$-18 = x \qquad\quad$ or $\qquad x = -\dfrac{4}{3}$

The solutions are -18 and $-\dfrac{4}{3}$.

7. $-5 \leq \dfrac{3x - 8}{2} \leq 2$

$-10 \leq 3x - 8 \leq 4$

$-2 \leq 3x \leq 12$

$-\dfrac{2}{3} \leq x \leq 4$

The solution set is $\left[-\dfrac{2}{3}, 4 \right]$.

8. $|9x - 1| = -3$

The absolute value of a number cannot be negative. There is no solution, or $\varnothing$.

9. $3x + 2 \leq 5 \quad$ or $\quad -3x \geq 0$

$3x \leq 3 \quad$ or $\quad \dfrac{-3x}{-3} \leq \dfrac{0}{-3}$

$x \leq 1 \quad$ or $\qquad x \leq 0$

The solution set is $(-\infty, 1]$.

10. $3x + 2 \leq 5 \quad$ and $\quad -3x \geq 0$

$3x \leq 3 \quad$ and $\quad \dfrac{-3x}{-3} \leq \dfrac{0}{-3}$

$x \leq 1 \quad$ and $\qquad x \leq 0$

The solution set is $(-\infty, 0]$.

11. $|3 - x| - 5 \leq -2$

$|3 - x| \leq 3$

$-3 \leq 3 - x \leq 3$

$-6 \leq -x \leq 0$

$\dfrac{-6}{-1} \geq \dfrac{-x}{-1} \geq \dfrac{0}{-1}$

$6 \geq x \geq 0$

$0 \leq x \leq 6$

The solution set is $[0, 6]$.

12. $\left| \dfrac{4x + 1}{5} \right| = |-1|$

$\dfrac{4x + 1}{5} = 1 \quad$ or $\quad \dfrac{4x + 1}{5} = -1$

$4x + 1 = 5 \quad$ or $\quad 4x + 1 = -5$

$4x = 4 \quad$ or $\qquad 4x = -6$

$x = 1 \quad$ or $\qquad x = \dfrac{-6}{4} = -\dfrac{3}{2}$

The solutions are 1 and $-\dfrac{3}{2}$.

13. $|2x + 1| = 5$

$2x + 1 = 5 \quad$ or $\quad 2x + 1 = -5$

This is statement B.

14. $|2x + 1| < 5$

$-5 < 2x + 1 < 5$

This is statement E.

15. $|2x + 1| > 5$

$2x + 1 < -5 \quad$ or $\quad 2x + 1 > 5$

This is statement A.

16. $x < 3$ or $x < 5$ is $x < 5$. This is statement C.

17. $x < 3$ and $x < 5$ is $x < 3$. This is statement D.

Section 9.4

Practice Exercises

1.

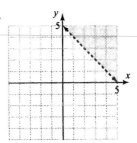

2.

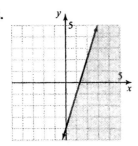

3.

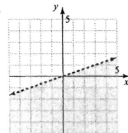

4.

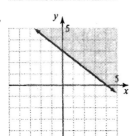

5.

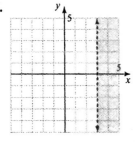

6. $\begin{cases} 4x \le y \\ x + 3y \ge 9 \end{cases}$

Graph $4x \le y$ with a solid line.
Test $(1, 0)$

$$4(1) \overset{?}{\le} 0$$

False
Shade above.
Graph $x + 3y \ge 9$ with a solid line.
Test $(0, 0)$

$$0 + 3(0) \overset{?}{\ge} 9$$

False
Shade above.
The solution of the system is the darker shaded region and includes parts of both boundary lines.

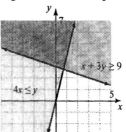

7. $\begin{cases} x - y > 4 \\ x + 3y < -4 \end{cases}$

Graph both inequalities using dashed lines. The solution of the system is the darker shaded region which does not include any of the boundary lines.

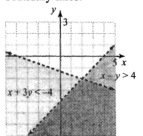

8. $\begin{cases} y \le 6 \\ -2x + 5y > 10 \end{cases}$

Graph both inequalities. The solution of the system is the darker shaded region.

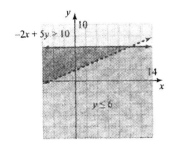

Vocabulary and Readiness Check

1. The statement $5x - 6y < 7$ is an example of a linear inequality in two variables.

2. A boundary line divides a plane into two regions called half-planes.

3. The graph of $5x - 6y < 7$ does not include its corresponding boundary line. The statement is false.

4. When graphing a linear inequality to determine which side of the boundary line to shade, choose a point *not* on the boundary line. The statement is true.

5. The boundary line for the inequality $5x - 6y < 7$ is the graph of $5x - 6y = 7$. The statement is true.

6. The graph of $y \leq 3$ is

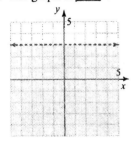

7. Yes, since the inequality is $\geq$, the graph includes the boundary line.

8. No, since the inequality is $>$, the graph does not include the boundary line.

9. Yes, since the inequality is $\geq$, the graph includes the boundary line.

10. No, since the inequality is $>$, the graph does not include the boundary line.

11. $x + y > -5,\ (0, 0)$
$$0 + 0 \overset{?}{>} -5$$
$$0 \overset{?}{>} -5$$
Yes, $(0, 0)$ is a solution.

12. $2x + 3y < 10,\ (0, 0)$
$$2(0) + 3(0) \overset{?}{<} 10$$
$$0 \overset{?}{<} 10$$
Yes, $(0, 0)$ is a solution.

13. $x - y \leq -1,\ (0,)$
$$0 - 0 \overset{?}{\leq} -1$$
$$0 \overset{?}{\leq} -1$$
No, $(0, 0)$ is not a solution.

14. $\dfrac{2}{3}x + \dfrac{5}{6}y > 4,\ (0, 0)$
$$\dfrac{2}{3}(0) + \dfrac{5}{6}(0) \overset{?}{>} 4$$
$$0 \overset{?}{>} 4$$
No, $(0, 0)$ is not a solution.

Exercise Set 9.4

2. $y - x < -2$
$$(2, 1),\ 1 - 2 \overset{?}{<} -2$$
$$-1 \overset{?}{<} -2,\ \text{False}$$
$(2, 1)$ is not a solution.

$$(5, -1),\ -1 - 5 \overset{?}{<} -2$$
$$-6 \overset{?}{<} -2,\ \text{True}$$
$(5, -1)$ is a solution.

4. $2x + y \geq 10$
$$(-1, -4),\ 2(-1) + (-4) \overset{?}{\geq} 10$$
$$-6 \overset{?}{\geq} 10,\ \text{False}$$
$(-1, -4)$ is not a solution.

$$(5, 0),\ 2(5) + 0 \overset{?}{\geq} 10$$
$$10 \overset{?}{\geq} 10,\ \text{True}$$
$(5, 0)$ is a solution.

6. $y > 3x$

$(0, 0),\ 0 \overset{?}{>} 3(0),\ $ False

$(0, 0)$ is not a solution.

$(-1, -4),\ -4 \overset{?}{>} 3(-1),\ $ False

$(-1, -4)$ is not a solution.

8. $x + y \geq -2$

Test $(0, 0)$

$0 + 0 \overset{?}{\geq} -2$

True

Shade above.

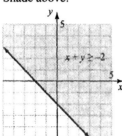

10. $x + 3y \leq 3$

Test $(0, 0)$

$0 + 3(0) \overset{?}{\leq} 3$

True

Shade below.

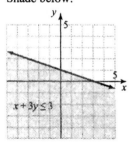

12. $7x + y > -14$

Test $(0, 0)$

$7(0) + 0 \overset{?}{>} -14$

True

Shade above.

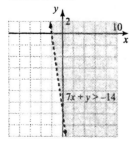

14. $5x + 2y \leq 10$

Test $(0, 0)$

$5(0) + 2(0) \overset{?}{\leq} 10$

True

Shade below.

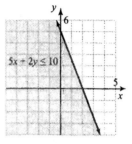

16. $2x + 3y > -5$

Test $(0, 0)$

$2(0) + 3(0) \overset{?}{>} -5$

True

Shade above.

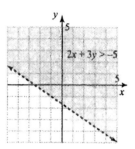

18. $3x + 5y \leq -2$

Test $(0, 0)$

$3(0) + 5(0) \overset{?}{\leq} -2$

False

Shade below.

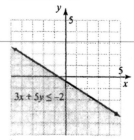

20. $4x + y \le 2$
Test $(0, 0)$
$$4(0) + 0 \overset{?}{\le} 2$$
True
Shade below.

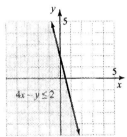

22. $x + 2y > -7$
Test $(0, 0)$
$$(0) + 2(0) \overset{?}{>} -7$$
True
Shade above.

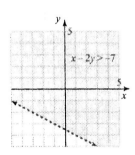

24. $9x + 2y \ge -9$
Test $(0, 0)$
$$9(0) + 2(0) \overset{?}{\ge} -9$$
True
Shade above.

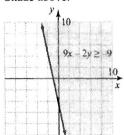

26. $x < 5y$
Test $(1, 0)$
$$1 \overset{?}{<} 5(0)$$
False
Shade above.

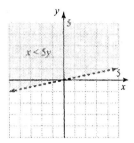

28. $y \le 0$
Shade below.

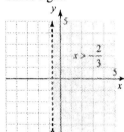

30. $x > -\dfrac{2}{3}$
Shade right.

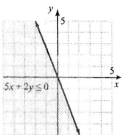

32. $5x + 2y \le 0$
Test $(1, 0)$
$$5(1) + 2(0) \overset{?}{\le} 0$$
False
Shade below.

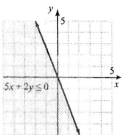

34. $-2x - 9y > 0$
Test $(1, 0)$

$$-2(1) - 9(0) \overset{?}{>} 0$$

False
Shade below.

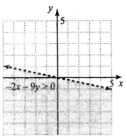

36. $x \leq y$
Test $(0, 1)$

$$0 \overset{?}{\leq} -1$$

False
Shade below.

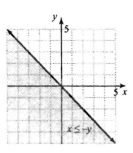

38. $x - y > 10$
Test $(0, 0)$

$$0 - 0 \overset{?}{>} 10$$

False
Shade below.

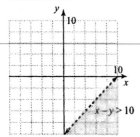

40. $\dfrac{1}{2}x - \dfrac{1}{3}y \leq -1$
Test $(0, 0)$

$$\dfrac{1}{2}(0) - \dfrac{1}{3}(0) \overset{?}{\leq} -1$$

False
Shade above.

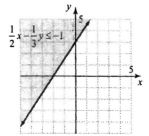

42. $0.3x \geq 0.1y$
Test $(1, 0)$

$$0.3(1) \overset{?}{\geq} 0.1(0)$$

True
Shade below.

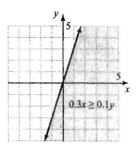

44. a

46. b

48. d

50. $\begin{cases} y \geq x - 3 \\ y \geq -1 - x \end{cases}$

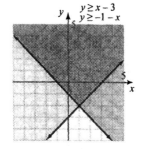

52. $\begin{cases} y \le 2x + 1 \\ y > x + 2 \end{cases}$

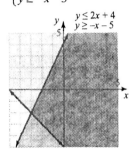

54. $\begin{cases} y \le 2x + 4 \\ y \ge -x - 5 \end{cases}$

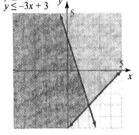

56. $\begin{cases} y \ge x - 5 \\ y \le -3x + 3 \end{cases}$

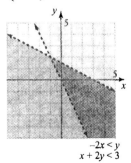

58. $\begin{cases} -3x < y \\ x + 2y < 3 \end{cases}$

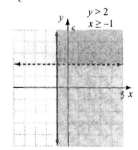

60. $\begin{cases} y + 2x \le 0 \\ 5x + 3y \ge -2 \end{cases}$

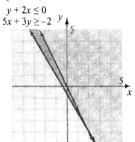

62. $\begin{cases} 4x - y \ge -2 \\ 2x + 3y \le -8 \end{cases}$

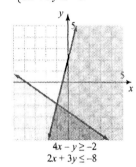

64. $\begin{cases} x \ge -3 \\ y \ge -2 \end{cases}$

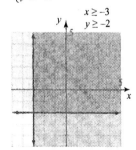

66. $\begin{cases} y > 2 \\ x \ge -1 \end{cases}$

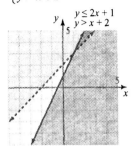

68. $\begin{cases} 3x + 2y \le 6 \\ \quad\quad x < 2 \end{cases}$

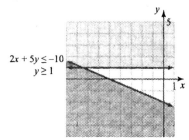

70. $\begin{cases} 2x + 5y \le -10 \\ \quad\quad y \ge 1 \end{cases}$

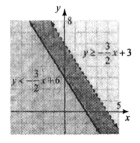

72. $\begin{cases} y \ge \dfrac{-3}{2}x + 3 \\ y < \dfrac{-3}{2}x + 6 \end{cases}$

74. Let $x = -5$.

$x^3 = (-5)(-5)(-5) = -125$

76. Let $x = -1$.

$3x^2 = 3(-1)(-1) = 3$

78. $y > 5x$; $(1, 1)$

$1 > 5(1)$

$1 > 5$ False

$(1, 1)$ is not included in the graph of $y > 5x$.

80. $x > 3$; $(1, 1)$

$1 > 3$ False

$(1, 1)$ is not included in the graph of $x > 3$.

82. The inequality is $x + y \le -4$.

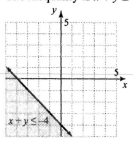

84. Answers may vary

86. $22x + 15y \le 100$

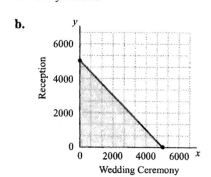

88. a. $x + y \le 5000$

b.

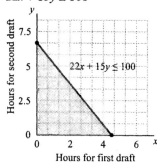

c. Answers may vary

90. Answers may vary

92. A

94. B

96. $\begin{cases} x + y < 5 \\ y < 2x \\ x \geq 0 \\ y \geq 0 \end{cases}$

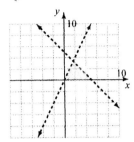

Chapter 9 Vocabulary Check

1. The statement "$x < 5$ or $x > 7$" is called a compound inequality.

2. The intersection of two sets is the set of all elements common to both sets.

3. The union of two sets is the set of all elements that belong to either of the sets.

4. A number's distance from 0 is called its absolute value.

5. When a variable in an equation is replaced by a number and the resulting equation is true, then that number is called a solution of the equation.

6. Two or more linear inequalities are called a system of linear inequalities.

Chapter 9 Review

1. $-3 < 4(2x - 1) < 12$
   $-3 < 8x - 4 < 12$
   $1 < 8x < 16$
   $\dfrac{1}{8} < x < 2$
   $\left(\dfrac{1}{8}, 2 \right)$

2. $-2 \leq 8 + 5x < -1$
   $-10 \leq 5x \leq -9$
   $-2 \leq x \leq -\dfrac{9}{5}$
   $\left[-2, \dfrac{9}{5} \right)$

3. $\dfrac{1}{6} < \dfrac{4x - 3}{3} \leq \dfrac{4}{5}$
   $30\left(\dfrac{1}{6} \right) < 30\left(\dfrac{4x - 3}{3} \right) \leq 30\left(\dfrac{4}{5} \right)$
   $5 < 10(4x - 3) \leq 24$
   $5 < 40x - 30 \leq 24$
   $35 < 40x < 54$
   $\dfrac{7}{8} < x \leq \dfrac{27}{20}$
   $\left(\dfrac{7}{8}, \dfrac{27}{20} \right]$

4. $-6 < x - (3 - 4x) < -3$
   $-6 < x - 3 + 4x < -3$
   $-6 < 5x - 3 < -3$
   $-3 < 5x < 0$
   $-\dfrac{3}{5} < x < 0$
   $\left(-\dfrac{3}{5}, 0 \right)$

5. $3x - 5 > 6$ or $-x < -5$
   $\quad 3x > 11$ or $x > 5$
   $\qquad x > \dfrac{11}{3}$ or $x > 5$
   $x > \dfrac{11}{3}$
   $\left(\dfrac{11}{3}, \infty \right)$

6. $x \leq 2$ and $x > -5$
   $-5 < x \leq 2$
   $(-5, 2]$

7. $|8 - x| = 3$
   $8 - x = 3$ or $8 - x = -3$
   $\quad -x = -5$ or $-x = -11$
   $\qquad x = 5$ or $x = 11$

8. $|x - 7| = 9$
   $x - 7 = 9$ or $x - 7 = -9$
   $\quad x = 16$ or $x = -2$

9. $|-3x + 4| = 7$
   $-3x + 4 = 7$ or $-3x + 4 = -7$
   $\quad -3x = 3$ or $-3x = -11$
   $\qquad x = -1$ or $x = \dfrac{11}{3}$

10. $|2x+9|=9$
$2x+9=9$ or $2x+9=-9$
$2x=0$ or $2x=-18$
$x=0$ or $x=-9$

11. $5+|6x+1|=5$
$|6x+1|=0$
$6x+1=0$
$6x=-1$
$x=-\dfrac{1}{6}$

12. $|3x-2|+6=10$
$|3x-2|=4$
$3x-2=4$ or $3x-2=-4$
$3x=6$ or $3x=-2$
$x=2$ or $x=-\dfrac{2}{3}$

13. $|5-6x|+8=3$
$|5-6x|=-5$
The solution set is $\varnothing$.

14. $-5=|4x-3|$
The solution set is $\varnothing$.

15. $\left|\dfrac{3x-7}{4}\right|=2$

$\dfrac{3x-7}{4}=2$ or $\dfrac{3x-7}{4}=-2$
$3x-7=8$ or $3x-7=-8$
$3x=15$ or $3x=-1$
$x=5$ or $x=-\dfrac{1}{3}$

16. $-8=|x-3|-10$
$2=|x-3|$
$x-3=2$ or $x-3=-2$
$x=5$ or $x=1$

17. $|6x+1|=|15+4x|$
$6x+1=15+4x$ or $6x+1=-(15+4x)$
$2x=14$ or $6x+1=-15-4x$
$x=7$ or $10x=-16$
$x=-\dfrac{8}{5}$

18. $|x-3|=|x+5|$
$x-3=x+5$ or $x-3=-(x+5)$
$-3=5$ False   or $x-3=-x-5$
$2x-3=-5$
$2x=-2$
$x=-1$

19. $|5x-1|<9$
$-9<5x-1<9$
$-8<5x<10$
$-\dfrac{8}{5}<x<2$
$\left(-\dfrac{8}{5},\,2\right)$

20. $|6+4x|\ge 10$
$6+4x\le -10$ or $6+4x\ge 10$
$4x\le -16$ or $4x\ge 4$
$x\le -4$ or $x\ge 1$
$(-\infty,\,-4]\cup[1,\,\infty)$

21. $|3x|-8>1$
$|3x|>9$
$3x<-9$ or $3x>9$
$x<-3$ or $x>3$
$(-\infty,\,-3)\cup(3,\,\infty)$

22. $9+|5x|<24$
$|5x|<15$
$-15<5x<15$
$-3<x<3$
$(-3,\,3)$

23. $|6x-5|\le -1$
The solution set is $\varnothing$.

24. $|6x - 5| \le 5$

$-5 \le 6x - 5 \le 5$

$0 \le 6x \le 10$

$\dfrac{0}{6} \le x \le \dfrac{10}{6}$

$0 \le x \le \dfrac{5}{3}$

$\left[0, \dfrac{5}{3}\right]$

25. $\left|3x + \dfrac{2}{5}\right| \ge 4$

$3x + \dfrac{2}{5} \le -4$ or $3x + \dfrac{2}{5} \ge 4$

$5\left(3x + \dfrac{2}{5}\right) \le 5(-4)$ or $5\left(3x + \dfrac{2}{5}\right) \ge 5(4)$

$15x + 2 \le -20$ or $15x + 2 \ge 20$

$15x \le -22$ or $15x \ge 18$

$x \le -\dfrac{22}{15}$ or $x \ge \dfrac{6}{5}$

$\left(-\infty, -\dfrac{22}{15}\right] \cup \left[\dfrac{6}{5}, \infty\right)$

26. $|5x - 3| > 2$

$5x - 3 < -2$ or $5x - 3 > 2$

$5x < 1$ or $5x > 5$

$x < \dfrac{1}{5}$ or $x > 1$

$\left(-\infty, \dfrac{1}{5}\right) \cup (1, \infty)$

27. $\left|\dfrac{x}{3} + 6\right| - 8 > -5$

$\left|\dfrac{x}{3} + 6\right| > 3$

$\dfrac{x}{3} + 6 < -3$ or $\dfrac{x}{3} + 6 > 3$

$\dfrac{x}{3} < -9$ or $\dfrac{x}{3} > -3$

$x < -27$ or $x > -9$

$(-\infty, -27) \cup (-9, \infty)$

28. $\left|\dfrac{4(x-1)}{7}\right| + 10 < 2$

$\left|\dfrac{4(x-1)}{7}\right| < -8$

The solution set is $\varnothing$.

29. $3x - 4y \le 0$

Test $(1, 0)$.

$3 - 0 \overset{?}{\le} 0$

False

Shade above.

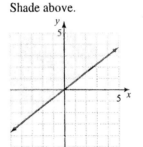

30. $3x - 4y \ge 0$

Test $(1, 0)$.

$3 - 0 \overset{?}{\ge} 0$

True

Shade below.

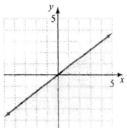

31. $x + 6y < 6$

Test $(0, 0)$

$0 + 6(0) \overset{?}{<} 6$

True

Shade below.

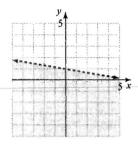

32. $y \leq -4$
Shade below.

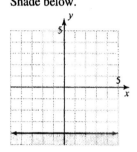

33. $y \geq -7$
Shade above.

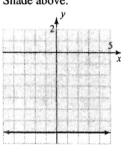

34. $x \geq -y$
Test $(1, 0)$

$$1 \overset{?}{\geq} 0$$

True
Shade above.

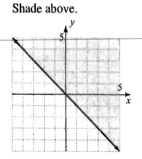

35. $\begin{cases} y \geq 2x - 3 \\ y \leq -2x + 1 \end{cases}$

$y \geq 2x - 3$
$y \leq -2x + 1$

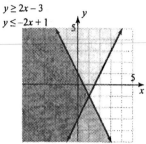

36. $\begin{cases} y \leq -3x - 3 \\ y \leq 2x + 7 \end{cases}$

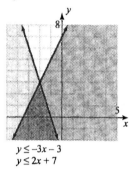

$y \leq -3x - 3$
$y \leq 2x + 7$

37. $\begin{cases} x + 2y > 0 \\ x - y \leq 6 \end{cases}$

$x + 2y > 0$
$x - y \leq 6$

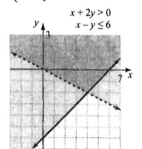

38. $\begin{cases} 4x - y \leq 0 \\ 3x - 2y \geq -5 \end{cases}$

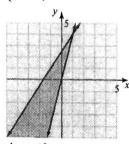

$4x - y \leq 0$
$3x - 2y \geq -5$

39. $\begin{cases} 3x - 2y \le 4 \\ 2x + y \ge 5 \end{cases}$

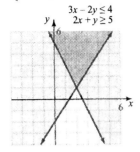

40. $\begin{cases} -2x + 3y > -7 \\ x \ge -2 \end{cases}$

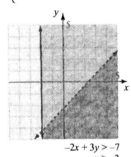

41. $0 \le \dfrac{2(3x+4)}{5} \le 3$

$5(0) \le 5\left[\dfrac{2(3x+4)}{5}\right] \le 5(3)$

$0 \le 2(3x+4) \le 15$

$0 \le 6x + 8 \le 15$

$-8 \le 6x \le 7$

$-\dfrac{4}{3} \le x \le \dfrac{7}{6}$

$\left[-\dfrac{4}{3}, \dfrac{7}{6}\right]$

42. $x \le 2$ or $x > -5$

$(-\infty, \infty)$

43. $-2x \le 6$ and $-2x + 3 < -7$

     $x \ge -3$ and $-2x < -10$

     $x \ge -3$ and $x > 5$

$x > 5$

$(5, \infty)$

44. $|7x| - 26 = -5$

     $|7x| = 21$

$7x = 21$ or $7x = -21$

 $x = 3$ or $x = -3$

45. $\left|\dfrac{9 - 2x}{5}\right| = -3$

The solution set is $\varnothing$.

46. $|x - 3| = |7 + 2x|$

$x - 3 = 7 + 2x$ or $x - 3 = -(7 + 2x)$

   $-10 = x$ or $x - 3 = -7 - 2x$

                              $3x = -4$

                                $x = -\dfrac{4}{3}$

47. $|6x - 5| \ge -1$

Since $|6x - 5|$ is nonnegative for all numbers x, the solution set is $(-\infty, \infty)$.

48. $\left|\dfrac{4x - 3}{5}\right| < 1$

$-1 < \dfrac{4x - 3}{5} < 1$

$-5 < 4x - 3 < 5$

$-2 < 4x < 8$

$-\dfrac{1}{2} < x < 2$

$\left(-\dfrac{1}{2}, 2\right)$

49. $-x \le y$

Test $(1, 0)$

$-1 \overset{?}{\le} 0$

True

Shade above.

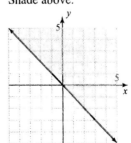

50. $x + y > -2$

Test $(0, 0)$

$$0 + 0 \overset{?}{>} -2$$

True

Shade above.

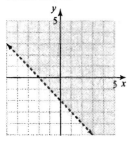

51. $\begin{cases} -3x + 2y > -1 \\ y < -2 \end{cases}$

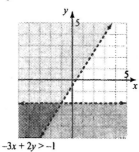

$-3x + 2y > -1$
$y < -2$

52. $\begin{cases} x - 2y \geq 7 \\ x + y \leq -5 \end{cases}$

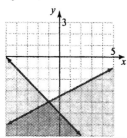

$x - 2y \geq 7$
$x + y \leq -5$

Chapter 9 Test

1. $|6x - 5| - 3 = -2$

$\quad\;\; |6x - 5| = 1$

$6x - 5 = 1 \quad$ or $\quad 6x - 5 = -1$

$\quad\; 6x = 6 \quad$ or $\quad\quad 6x = 4$

$\quad\quad x = 1 \quad$ or $\quad\quad\quad x = \dfrac{2}{3}$

2. $|8 - 2t| = -6$

No solution, $\varnothing$

3. $|x - 5| = |x + 2|$

$x - 5 = x + 2 \quad$ or $\quad x - 5 = -(x + 2)$

$\quad -5 = 2 \;$ False $\;$ or $\quad x - 5 = -x - 2$

$\quad\quad\quad\quad\quad\quad\quad\quad\quad\; 2x = 3$

$\quad\quad\quad\quad\quad\quad\quad\quad\quad\;\; x = \dfrac{3}{2}$

Since $-5 = 2$ is not possible, the only solution is

$\dfrac{3}{2}$.

4. $-3 < 2(x - 3) \leq 4$

$-3 < 2x - 6 \leq 4$

$\;\; 3 < 2x \leq 10$

$\dfrac{3}{2} < x \leq 5$

$\left(\dfrac{3}{2}, 5 \right]$

5. $|3x + 1| > 5$

$3x + 1 < -5 \quad$ or $\quad 3x + 1 > 5$

$\quad 3x < -6 \quad$ or $\quad\quad 3x > 4$

$\quad\;\; x < -2 \quad$ or $\quad\quad\; x > \dfrac{4}{3}$

$(-\infty, -2) \cup \left(\dfrac{4}{3}, \infty \right)$

6. $|x - 5| - 4 < -2$

$\quad |x - 5| < 2$

$-2 < x - 5 < 2$

$\;\; 3 < x < 7$

$(3, 7)$

7. $x \leq -2 \;$ and $\; x \leq -5$

$(-\infty, -5]$

8. $x \leq -2 \;$ or $\; x \leq -5$

$(-\infty, -2]$

9. $-x > 1 \quad\quad$ and $\quad 3x + 3 \geq x - 3$

$\dfrac{-x}{-1} < \dfrac{1}{-1} \quad$ and $\quad\quad 2x \geq -6$

$\quad x < -1 \quad$ and $\quad\quad\; x \geq -3$

$-3 \leq x < -1$

$[-3, -1)$

10. $6x + 1 > 5x + 4$ or $1 - x > -4$
$\qquad\quad x > 3$ or $5 > x$

$(-\infty, \infty)$

11. $\left| \dfrac{5x - 7}{2} \right| = 4$

$\dfrac{5x - 7}{2} = 4$ or $\dfrac{5x - 7}{2} = -4$

$5x - 7 = 8$ or $5x - 7 = -8$

$5x = 15$ or $5x = -1$

$x = 3$ or $x = -\dfrac{1}{5}$

12. $\left| 17x - \dfrac{1}{5} \right| > -2$

The solution set is $(-\infty, \infty)$ since an absolute value is never negative.

13. $-1 \le \dfrac{2x - 5}{3} < 2$

$3(-1) \le 3\left(\dfrac{2x - 5}{3} \right) < 3(2)$

$-3 \le 2x - 5 < 6$

$-3 + 5 \le 2x - 5 + 5 < 6 + 5$

$2 \le 2x < 11$

$\dfrac{2}{2} \le \dfrac{2x}{2} < \dfrac{11}{2}$

$1 \le x < \dfrac{11}{2}$

$\left[1, \dfrac{11}{2} \right)$

14. $y > -4x$
Test $(1, 0)$
$\overset{?}{}$
$0 > -4(1)$
True
Shade above.

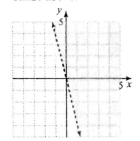

15. $2x - 3y > -6$
Test $(0, 0)$
$2(0) - 3(0) \overset{?}{>} -6$
True
Shade below.

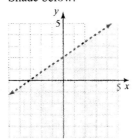

16. $\begin{cases} y + 2x \le 4 \\ y \ge 2 \end{cases}$

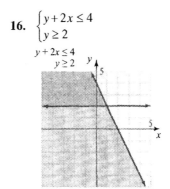

17. $\begin{cases} 2y - x \ge 1 \\ x + y \ge -4 \end{cases}$

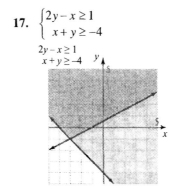

Chapter 9 Cumulative Review

1. Let $x = 2$ and $y = -5$.

  a. $\dfrac{x - y}{12 + x} = \dfrac{2 - (-5)}{12 + 2} = \dfrac{2 + 5}{14} = \dfrac{7}{14} = \dfrac{1}{2}$

  b. $x^2 - 3y = 2^2 - 3(-5) = 4 + 15 = 19$

2. Let $x = -4$ and $y = 7$.

    a. $\dfrac{x-y}{7-x} = \dfrac{-4-7}{7-(-4)} = \dfrac{-11}{7+4} = \dfrac{-11}{11} = -1$

    b. $x^2 + 2y = (-4)^2 + 2 \cdot 7 = 16 + 14 = 30$

3. **a.** $\dfrac{(-12)(-3)+3}{-7-(-2)} = \dfrac{36+3}{-7+2} = \dfrac{39}{-5} = -\dfrac{39}{5}$

    b. $\dfrac{2(-3)^2 - 20}{-5+4} = \dfrac{2 \cdot 9 - 20}{-1} = \dfrac{18-20}{-1} = \dfrac{-2}{-1} = 2$

4. **a.** $\dfrac{4(-3)-(-6)}{-8+4} = \dfrac{-12+6}{-8+4} = \dfrac{-6}{-4} = \dfrac{3}{2}$

    b. $\dfrac{3+(-3)(-2)^3}{-1-(-4)} = \dfrac{3+(-3)(-8)}{-1+4}$

$$= \dfrac{3+24}{3}$$
$$= \dfrac{27}{3}$$
$$= 9$$

5. **a.** $2x + 3x + 5 + 2 = (2+3)x + (5+2) = 5x + 7$

    b. $-5a - 3 + a + 2 = -5a + a - 3 + 2 = -4a - 1$

    c. $4y - 3y^2$ cannot be simplified.

    d. $2.3x + 5x - 6 = 7.3x - 6$

    e. $-\dfrac{1}{2}b + b = \left(-\dfrac{1}{2}+1\right)b = \dfrac{1}{2}b$

6. **a.** $4x - 3 + 7 - 5x = 4x - 5x - 3 + 7 = -x + 4$

    b. $-6y + 3y - 8 + 8y = -6y + 3y + 8y - 8$
$$= 5y - 8$$

    c. $2 + 8.1a + a - 6 = 8.1a + a + 2 - 6 = 9.1a - 4$

    d. $2x^2 - 2x$ cannot be simplified.

7. $2x + 3x - 5 + 7 = 10x + 3 - 6x - 4$
$$5x + 2 = 4x - 1$$
$$x + 2 = -1$$
$$x = -3$$

8. $6y - 11 + 4 + 2y = 8 + 15y - 8y$
$$8y - 7 = 7y + 8$$
$$y - 7 = 8$$
$$y = 15$$

9. $y = 3x$
$x = -1: \ y = 3(-1) = -3$
$y = 0: \ 0 = 3x$
$$\dfrac{0}{3} = \dfrac{3x}{3}$$
$$0 = x$$
$y = -9: \ -9 = 3x$
$$\dfrac{-9}{3} = \dfrac{3x}{3}$$
$$-3 = x$$

x	y
-1	-3
0	0
-3	-9

10. $2x + y = 6$
$x = 0: \ 2(0) + y = 6$
$$y = 6$$
$y = -2: \ 2x + (-2) = 6$
$$2x - 2 = 6$$
$$2x = 8$$
$$x = 4$$
$x = 3: \ 2(3) + y = 6$
$$6 + y = 6$$
$$y = 0$$

x	y
0	6
4	-2
3	0

11. **a.** x-intercept: $(-3, 0)$; y-intercept: $(0, 2)$

    b. x-intercepts: $(-4, 0)$ and $(-1, 0)$; y-intercept: $(0, 1)$

    c. x-intercept: $(0, 0)$; y-intercept: $(0, 0)$

    d. x-intercept: $(2, 0)$; no y-intercept

   e. x-intercepts: $(-1, 0)$ and $(3, 0)$;
       y-intercepts: $(0, -1)$ and $(0, 2)$

12. a. x-intercept: $(4, 0)$; y-intercept: $(0, 1)$

    b. x-intercepts: $(-2, 0)$, $(0, 0)$, and $(3, 0)$;
        y-intercept: $(0, 0)$

    c.   no x-intercept; y-intercept: $(0, -3)$

    d. x-intercepts: $(-3, 0)$ and $(3, 0)$;
        y-intercepts: $(0, -3)$ and $(0, 3)$

13. $y = -\dfrac{1}{5}x + 1: \ m = -\dfrac{1}{5}, \ b = 1$

$$2x + 10y = 30$$
$$10y = -2x + 30$$
$$y = -\frac{1}{5}x + 3: \ m = -\frac{1}{5}, \ b = 3$$

The slopes are the same, but the y-intercepts are different, so the lines are parallel.

14. $y = 3x + 7: \ m = 3, \ b = 7$

$$x + 3y = -15$$
$$3y = -x - 15$$
$$y = -\frac{1}{3}x - 5: \ m = -\frac{1}{3}, \ b = -5$$

The product of the slopes is -1, so the lines are perpendicular.

15. y-intercept $(0, -3)$: $b = -3$; $m = \dfrac{1}{4}$

$$y = mx + b$$
$$y = \frac{1}{4}x + (-3) \text{ or } y = \frac{1}{4}x - 3$$

16. y-intercept $(0, 4)$: $b = 4$; $m = -2$
       $y = mx + b$
       $y = -2x + 4$

17.   The line $y = 5$ is vertical. A parallel line will also be vertical. The vertical line passing through $(-2, -3)$ has equation $y = -3$.

18. $y = 2x + 4: \ m = 2$

A perpendicular line has slope $m = -\dfrac{1}{2}$.

$$(x_1, y_1) = (1, 5)$$
$$y - y_1 = m(x - x_1)$$
$$y - 5 = -\frac{1}{2}(x - 1)$$
$$y - 5 = -\frac{1}{2}x + \frac{1}{2}$$
$$y = -\frac{1}{2}x + \frac{11}{2}$$

19.   a, b, and c are functions since they represent non-vertical lines.

20.   a, c, and d are functions since they represent non-vertical lines.

21. $\begin{cases} 2x - 3y = 6 \\ \quad\ x = 2y \end{cases}$

    a.   Let $x = 12$ and $y = 6$.

$2x - 3y = 6$	$x = 2y$
$2(12) - 3(6) \overset{?}{=} 6$	$12 \overset{?}{=} 2(6)$
$24 - 18 \overset{?}{=} 6$	$12 = 12 \ \ $ True
$6 = 6 \ \ $ True	

       $(12, 6)$ is a solution.

    b.   Let $x = 0$ and $y = -2$.

$2x - 3y = 6$	$x = 2y$
$2(0) - 3(-2) \overset{?}{=} 6$	$0 \overset{?}{=} 2(-2)$
$0 + 6 \overset{?}{=} 6$	$0 = -4 \ \ $ False
$6 = 6 \ \ $ True	

       $(0, -2)$ is not a solution.

22. $\begin{cases} 2x + y = 4 \\ \ x + y = 2 \end{cases}$

    a.   Let $x = 1$ and $y = 1$.
       $2x + y = 4$
       $2(1) + 1 \overset{?}{=} 4$
       $2 + 1 \overset{?}{=} 4$
         $3 = 4 \ \ $ False
       $(1, 1)$ is not a solution.

    b.   Let $x = 2$ and $y = 0$.

$2x + y = 4$	$x + y = 2$
$2(2) + 0 \overset{?}{=} 4$	$2 + 0 \overset{?}{=} 2$
$4 + 0 \overset{?}{=} 4$	$2 = 2 \ \ $ True
$4 = 4 \ \ $ True	

       $(2, 0)$ is a solution.

23. $(11x^3 - 12x^2 + x - 3) + (x^3 - 10x + 5)$
$= 11x^3 + x^3 - 12x^2 + x - 10x - 3 + 5$
$= 12x^3 - 12x^2 - 9x + 2$

24. $4a^2 + 3a - 2a^2 + 7a - 5$
$= 4a^2 - 2a^2 + 3a + 7a - 5$
$= 2a^2 + 10a - 5$

25. $x^2 + 7yx + 6y^2 = (x + 6y)(x + y)$

26. $3x^2 + 15x + 18 = 3(x^2 + 5x + 6) = 3(x + 2)(x + 3)$

27. $\dfrac{3x^3 y^7}{40} \div \dfrac{4x^3}{y^2} = \dfrac{3x^3 y^7}{40} \cdot \dfrac{y^2}{4x^3} = \dfrac{3y^9}{160}$

28. $\dfrac{12x^2 y^3}{5} \div \dfrac{3y^2}{x} = \dfrac{12x^2 y^3}{5} \cdot \dfrac{x}{3y^2} = \dfrac{4x^3 y}{5}$

29. $\dfrac{2y}{2y-7} - \dfrac{7}{2y-7} = \dfrac{2y-7}{2y-7} = 1$

30. $\dfrac{-4x^2}{x+1} - \dfrac{4x}{x+1} = \dfrac{-4x^2 - 4x}{x+1} = \dfrac{-4x(x+1)}{x+1} = -4x$

31. $\dfrac{2x}{x^2 + 2x + 1} + \dfrac{x}{x^2 - 1} = \dfrac{2x}{(x+1)^2} + \dfrac{x}{(x+1)(x-1)}$
$= \dfrac{2x(x-1) + x(x+1)}{(x+1)^2 (x-1)}$
$= \dfrac{2x^2 - 2x + x^2 + x}{(x+1)^2 (x-1)}$
$= \dfrac{3x^2 - x}{(x+1)^2 (x-1)}$
$= \dfrac{x(3x-1)}{(x+1)^2 (x-1)}$

32. $\dfrac{3x}{x^2 + 5x + 6} + \dfrac{1}{x^2 + 2x - 3}$
$= \dfrac{3x}{(x+2)(x+3)} + \dfrac{1}{(x+3)(x-1)}$
$= \dfrac{3x(x-1) + 1(x+2)}{(x+2)(x+3)(x-1)}$
$= \dfrac{3x^2 - 3x + x + 2}{(x+2)(x+3)(x-1)}$
$= \dfrac{3x^2 - 2x + 2}{(x+2)(x+3)(x-1)}$

33. $\dfrac{x}{2} + \dfrac{8}{3} = \dfrac{1}{6}$
$6\left(\dfrac{x}{2} + \dfrac{8}{3}\right) = 6\left(\dfrac{1}{6}\right)$
$3x + 16 = 1$
$3x = -15$
$x = -5$

34. $\dfrac{1}{21} + \dfrac{x}{7} = \dfrac{5}{3}$
$21\left(\dfrac{1}{21} + \dfrac{x}{7}\right) = 21\left(\dfrac{5}{3}\right)$
$1 + 3x = 35$
$3x = 34$
$x = \dfrac{34}{3}$

35. $\begin{cases} 2x + y = 7 \\ 2y = -4x \end{cases}$

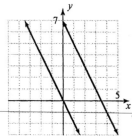

The system has no solution.

36. $\begin{cases} y = x + 2 \\ 2x + y = 5 \end{cases}$

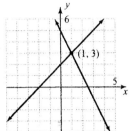

The solution is $(1, 3)$.

37. $\begin{cases} 7x - 3y = -14 \\ -3x + y = 6 \end{cases}$

Solve the second equation for y.

$y = 3x + 6$

Substitute $3x + 6$ for y in the first equation.

$7x - 3(3x + 6) = -14$

$7x - 9x - 18 = -14$

$-2x - 18 = -14$

$-2x = 4$

$x = -2$

Let $x = -2$ in $y = 3x + 6$.

$y = 3(-2) + 6 = -6 + 6 = 0$

The solution is $(-2, 0)$.

38. $\begin{cases} 5x + y = 3 \\ y = -5x \end{cases}$

Substitute $-5x$ for y in the first equation.

$5x + (-5x) = 3$

$0 = 3$

This is a false statement, so the system has no solution.

39. $\begin{cases} 3x - 2y = 2 \\ -9x + 6y = -6 \end{cases}$

Multiply the first equation by 3, then add.

$9x - 6y = 6$

$\underline{-9x + 6y = -6}$

$0 = 0$

This is a true statement, so the system has an infinite number of solutions.

40. $\begin{cases} -2x + y = 7 \\ 6x - 3y = -21 \end{cases}$

Multiply the first equation by 3, then add.

$-6x + 3y = 21$

$\underline{6x - 3y = -21}$

$0 = 0$

This is a true statement, so the system has an infinite number of solutions.

41. $\begin{cases} -3x + 4y < 12 \\ x \geq 2 \end{cases}$

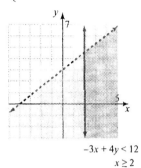

$-3x + 4y < 12$
$x \geq 2$

42. $\begin{cases} 2x - y \leq 6 \\ y \geq 2 \end{cases}$

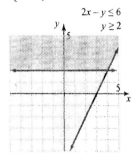

43. a. $\left(\dfrac{st}{2}\right)^4 = \dfrac{s^4 t^4}{2^4} = \dfrac{s^4 t^4}{16}$

b. $(9y^5 z^7)^2 = 9^2 (y^5)^2 (z^7)^2 = 81 y^{10} z^{14}$

c. $\left(\dfrac{-5x^2}{y^3}\right)^2 = \dfrac{(-5)^2 (x^2)^2}{(y^3)^2} = \dfrac{25x^4}{y^6}$

44. a. $\left(\dfrac{-6x}{y^3}\right)^3 = \dfrac{(-6)^3 x^3}{(y^3)^3} = \dfrac{-216x^3}{y^9} = -\dfrac{216x^3}{y^9}$

b. $\dfrac{a^2 b^7}{(2b^2)^5} = \dfrac{a^2 b^7}{2^5 (b^2)^5}$

   $= \dfrac{a^2 b^7}{32 b^{10}}$

   $= \dfrac{a^2}{32} b^{7-10}$

   $= \dfrac{a^2}{32} b^{-3}$

   $= \dfrac{a^2}{32 b^3}$

c. $\dfrac{(3y)^2}{y^2} = \dfrac{3^2 y^2}{y^2} = 9 y^{2-2} = 9 y^0 = 9$

d. $\dfrac{(x^2 y^4)^2}{x y^3} = \dfrac{(x^2)^2 (y^4)^2}{x y^3}$

   $= \dfrac{x^4 y^8}{x y^3}$

   $= x^{4-1} y^{8-3}$

   $= x^3 y^5$

45. $(5x-1)(2x^2 + 15x + 18) = 0$

  $(5x-1)(2x+3)(x+6) = 0$

  $5x - 1 = 0$ or $2x + 3 = 0$ or $x + 6 = 0$

   $5x = 1$ $2x = -3$ $x = -6$

   $x = \dfrac{1}{5}$ $x = -\dfrac{3}{2}$

  The solutions are -6, $-\dfrac{3}{2}$, and $\dfrac{1}{5}$.

46. $(x+1)(2x^2 - 3x - 5) = 0$

  $(x+1)(2x-5)(x+1) = 0$

  $x + 1 = 0$ or $2x - 5 = 0$

   $x = -1$ $2x = 5$

          $x = \dfrac{5}{2}$

  The solutions are -1 and $\dfrac{5}{2}$.

47. $\dfrac{45}{x} = \dfrac{5}{7}$

  $45 \cdot 7 = 5x$

  $315 = 5x$

  $\dfrac{315}{5} = \dfrac{5x}{5}$

  $63 = x$

48. $\dfrac{2x+7}{3} = \dfrac{x-6}{2}$

  $2(2x+7) = 3(x-6)$

  $4x + 14 = 3x - 18$

  $x + 14 = -18$

  $x = -32$

Chapter 10

Section 10.1

Practice Exercises

1. a. $\sqrt{49} = 7$ because $7^2 = 49$ and 7 is not negative.

b. $\sqrt{\dfrac{0}{1}} = \sqrt{0} = 0$ because $0^2 = 0$ and 0 is not negative.

c. $\sqrt{\dfrac{16}{81}} = \dfrac{4}{9}$ because $\left(\dfrac{4}{9}\right)^2 = \dfrac{16}{81}$ and $\dfrac{4}{9}$ is not negative.

d. $\sqrt{0.64} = 0.8$ because $(0.8)^2 = 0.64$.

e. $\sqrt{z^8} = z^4$ because $(z^4)^2 = z^8$.

f. $\sqrt{16b^4} = 4b^2$ because $(4b^2)^2 = 16b^4$.

g. $-\sqrt{36} = -6$. The negative in front of the radical indicates the negative square root of 36.

h. $\sqrt{-36}$ is not a real number.

2. $\sqrt{45} \approx 6.708$

Since $36 < 45 < 49$, then $\sqrt{36} < \sqrt{45} < \sqrt{49}$, or $6 < \sqrt{45} < 7$. The approximation is between 6 and 7 and thus is reasonable.

3. a. $\sqrt[3]{-1} = -1$ because $(-1)^3 = -1$.

b. $\sqrt[3]{27} = 3$ because $3^3 = 27$.

c. $\sqrt[3]{\dfrac{27}{64}} = \dfrac{3}{4}$ because $\left(\dfrac{3}{4}\right)^3 = \dfrac{27}{64}$.

d. $\sqrt[3]{x^{12}} = x^4$ because $(x^4)^3 = x^{12}$.

e. $\sqrt[3]{-8x^3} = -2x$ because $(-2x)^3 = -8x^3$.

4. a. $\sqrt[4]{10,000} = 10$ because $10^4 = 10,000$ and 10 is positive.

b. $\sqrt[5]{-1} = -1$ because $(-1)^5 = -1$.

c. $-\sqrt{81} = -9$ because -9 is the opposite of $\sqrt{81}$.

d. $\sqrt[4]{-625}$ is not a real number. There is no real number that, when raised to the fourth power, is -625.

e. $\sqrt[3]{27x^9} = 3x^3$ because $(3x^3)^3 = 27x^9$.

5. a. $\sqrt{(-4)^2} = |-4| = 4$

b. $\sqrt{x^{14}} = \left|x^7\right|$

c. $\sqrt[4]{(x+7)^4} = |x+7|$

d. $\sqrt[3]{(-7)^3} = -7$

e. $\sqrt[5]{(3x-5)^5} = 3x-5$

f. $\sqrt{49x^2} = 7|x|$

g. $\sqrt{x^2 + 4x + 4} = \sqrt{(x+2)^2} = |x+2|$

6. $f(x) = \sqrt{x+5}$, $g(x) = \sqrt[3]{x-3}$

a. $f(11) = \sqrt{11+5} = \sqrt{16} = 4$

b. $f(-1) = \sqrt{-1+5} = \sqrt{4} = 2$

c. $g(11) = \sqrt[3]{11-3} = \sqrt[3]{8} = 2$

d. $g(-5) = \sqrt[3]{-5-3} = \sqrt[3]{-8} = -2$

7. $h(x) = \sqrt{x+2}$
Find the domain.
$x + 2 \geq 0$
$x \geq -2$
The domain of $h(x)$ is $\{x \mid x \geq -2\}$.

x	$h(x) = \sqrt{x+2}$
-2	0
-1	1
1	$\sqrt{1+2} = \sqrt{3} \approx 1.7$
2	2
7	3

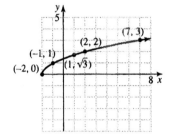

8. $f(x) = \sqrt[3]{x} - 4$

The domain is the set of all real numbers.

x	$f(x) = \sqrt[3]{x} - 4$
0	-4
1	-3
-1	-5
6	$\sqrt[3]{6} - 4 \approx 1.8 - 4 = -2.2$
-6	$\sqrt[3]{-6} - 4 \approx -1.8 - 4 = -5.8$
8	-2
-8	-6

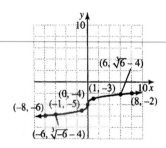

Vocabulary and Readiness Check

1. In the expression $\sqrt[n]{a}$, the n is called the <u>index</u>, the $\sqrt{}$ is called the <u>radical sign</u>, and a is called the <u>radicand</u>.

2. If $\sqrt{a}$ is the positive square root of a, $a \neq 0$, then $-\sqrt{a}$ is the negative square root of a.

3. The square root of a negative number <u>is not</u> a real number.

4. Numbers such as 1, 4, 9, and 25 are called perfect <u>squares</u> where numbers such as 1, 8, 27, and 125 are called perfect <u>cubes</u>.

5. The domain of the function $f(x) = \sqrt{x}$ is $[0, \infty)$.

6. The domain of the function $f(x) = \sqrt[3]{x}$ is $(-\infty, \infty)$.

7. If $f(16) = 4$, the corresponding ordered pair is $(16, 4)$.

8. If $g(-8) = -2$, the corresponding ordered pair is $(-8, -2)$.

9. The radical that is not a real number is $\sqrt{-10}$, choice d.

10. The radicals that simplify to 3 are $\sqrt{9}$ and $\sqrt[3]{27}$, choices a and c.

11. The radical that simplifies to -3 is $\sqrt[3]{-27}$, choice d.

12. The radical that does not simplify to a whole number is $\sqrt{8}$, choice c.

Exercise Set 10.1

2. $\sqrt{400} = 20$ because $20^2 = 400$.

4. $\sqrt{\dfrac{9}{25}} = \dfrac{3}{5}$ because $\left(\dfrac{3}{5}\right)^2 = \dfrac{9}{25}$.

6. $\sqrt{0.04} = 0.2$ because $(0.2)^2 = 0.04$.

8. $-\sqrt{9} = -3$ because $3^2 = 9$.

10. $\sqrt{x^{16}} = x^8$ because $(x^8)^2 = x^{16}$.

12. $\sqrt{64y^{20}} = 8y^{10}$ because $(8y^{10})^2 = 64y^{20}$.

14. $\sqrt{11} \approx 3.317$

Since $9 < 11 < 16$, then $\sqrt{9} < \sqrt{11} < \sqrt{16}$, or $3 < \sqrt{11} < 4$. The approximation is between 3 and 4 and thus is reasonable.

16. $\sqrt{56} \approx 7.483$

Since $49 < 56 < 64$, then $\sqrt{49} < \sqrt{56} < \sqrt{64}$; or $7 < \sqrt{56} < 8$. The approximation is between 7 and 8 and thus is reasonable.

18. $\sqrt{300} \approx 17.321$

Since $289 < 300 < 324$, then $\sqrt{289} < \sqrt{300} < \sqrt{324}$, or $17 < \sqrt{300} < 18$. The approximation is between 17 and 18 and thus is reasonable.

20. $\sqrt[3]{27} = 3$ because $3^3 = 27$.

22. $\sqrt[3]{\dfrac{27}{64}} = \dfrac{3}{4}$ because $\left(\dfrac{3}{4}\right)^3 = \dfrac{27}{64}$.

24. $\sqrt[3]{-125} = -5$ because $(-5)^3 = -125$.

26. $\sqrt[3]{x^{15}} = x^5$ because $(x^5)^3 = x^{15}$.

28. $\sqrt[3]{-64x^6} = -4x^2$ because $(-4x^2)^3 = -64x^6$.

30. $\sqrt[5]{-243} = -3$ because $(-3)^5 = -243$.

32. $\sqrt{-16}$ is not a real number. There is no real number that, when squared, is -16.

34. $\sqrt[5]{-1} = -1$ because $(-1)^5 = -1$.

36. $\sqrt[4]{x^{20}} = x^5$ because $(x^5)^4 = x^{20}$.

38. $\sqrt[5]{-32x^{15}} = -2x^3$ because $(-2x^3)^5 = -32x^{15}$.

40. $\sqrt[4]{81x^4} = 3x$ because $(3x)^4 = 81x^4$.

42. $\sqrt{256x^8} = 16x^4$ because $(16x^4)^2 = 256x^8$.

44. $\sqrt{(-7)^2} = |-7| = 7$

46. $\sqrt[5]{(-7)^5} = -7$

48. $\sqrt[4]{16x^4} = 4|x|$

50. $\sqrt[5]{x^5} = x$

52. $\sqrt{(y-6)^2} = |y-6|$

54. $\sqrt{x^2 - 8x + 16} = \sqrt{(x-4)^2} = |x-4|$

56. $-\sqrt[3]{125} = -5$

58. $\sqrt{16x^8} = 4x^4$

60. $\sqrt[3]{y^{12}} = y^4$

62. $\sqrt{9x^4y^6} = 3x^2y^3$

64. $\sqrt[3]{-8a^{21}b^6} = -2a^7b^2$

66. $\sqrt[4]{x^8y^{12}} = x^2y^3$

68. $\sqrt[5]{-243z^{15}} = -3z^3$

70. $\sqrt{\dfrac{4}{81}} = \dfrac{2}{9}$

72. $\sqrt{\dfrac{y^{10}}{9x^6}} = \dfrac{y^5}{3x^3}$

74. $-\sqrt[3]{\dfrac{64a^3}{b^9}} = -\dfrac{4a}{b^3}$

76. $\sqrt[4]{\dfrac{y^4}{81x^4}} = \dfrac{y}{3x}$

78. $g(x) = \sqrt[3]{x-8}$

$g(0) = \sqrt[3]{0-8} = \sqrt[3]{-8} = -2$

80. $f(x) = \sqrt{2x+3}$

$f(-1) = \sqrt{2(-1)+3} = \sqrt{1} = 1$

82. $f(x) = \sqrt{2x+3}$

$f(3) = \sqrt{2(3)+3} = \sqrt{9} = 3$

84. $g(x) = \sqrt[3]{x-8}$

$g(1) = \sqrt[3]{1-8} = \sqrt[3]{-7}$

86. $f(x) = \sqrt{x} - 2$

$x \geq 0$

Domain: $[0, \infty)$

x	$f(x) = \sqrt{x} - 2$
0	$\sqrt{0} - 2 = -2$
1	$\sqrt{1} - 2 = -1$
3	$\sqrt{3} - 2 \approx -0.3$
4	$\sqrt{4} - 2 = 0$

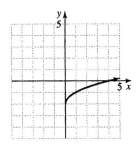

88. $f(x) = \sqrt{x+1}$

$x + 1 \geq 0$

$x \geq -1$

Domain: $[-1, \infty)$

x	$f(x) = \sqrt{x+1}$
-1	$\sqrt{-1+1} = \sqrt{0} = 0$
0	$\sqrt{0+1} = \sqrt{1} = 1$
3	$\sqrt{3+1} = \sqrt{4} = 2$
8	$\sqrt{8+1} = \sqrt{9} = 3$

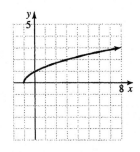

90. $f(x) = \sqrt[3]{x} - 2$

Domain: $(-\infty, \infty)$

x	$f(x) = \sqrt[3]{x} - 2$
-4	$\sqrt[3]{-4} - 2 \approx -3.6$
-1	$\sqrt[3]{-1} - 2 = -3$
0	$\sqrt[3]{0} - 2 = -2$
1	$\sqrt[3]{1} - 2 = -1$
4	$\sqrt[3]{4} - 2 \approx -0.4$

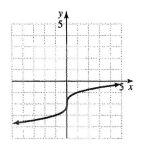

92. $g(x) = \sqrt[3]{x+1}$

Domain: $(-\infty, \infty)$

x	$g(x) = \sqrt[3]{x+1}$
-1	$\sqrt[3]{-1+1} = \sqrt[3]{0} = 0$
0	$\sqrt[3]{0+1} = \sqrt[3]{1} = 1$
-2	$\sqrt[3]{-2+1} = \sqrt[3]{-1} = -1$
7	$\sqrt[3]{7+1} = \sqrt[3]{8} = 2$
-9	$\sqrt[3]{-9+1} = \sqrt[3]{-8} = -2$

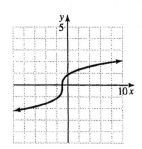

94. $(4y^6 z^7)^3 = 4^3 y^{6\cdot3} z^{7\cdot3} = 64 y^{18} z^{21}$

96. $(-14a^5bc^2)(2abc^4) = -14(2)a^{5+1}b^{1+1}c^{2+4}$
$$= -28a^6b^2c^6$$

98. $\dfrac{(2a^{-1}b^2)^3}{(8a^2b)^{-2}} = \dfrac{8a^{-3}b^6}{8^{-2}a^{-4}b^{-2}}$
$$= \dfrac{8^2 \cdot 8ab^8}{1}$$
$$= 64(8)ab^8$$
$$= 512ab^8$$

100. $\sqrt[3]{-17}$ is a real number.

102. $\sqrt[15]{-17}$ is a real number.

104. Answers may vary

106. $900 < 1000 < 1600$ so $\sqrt{900} < \sqrt{1000} < \sqrt{1600}$, or $30 < \sqrt{1000} < 40$. Thus $\sqrt{1000}$ is between 30 and 40. Therefore, the answer is **b.**

108. $\sqrt{20} \approx 4$ and $\sqrt{8} \approx 3$ so the length is $\sqrt{20} + \sqrt{8} \approx 4 + 3 = 7$. Therefore, the answer is **c.**

110. $B = \sqrt{\dfrac{hw}{3131}} = \sqrt{\dfrac{74 \cdot 225}{3131}}$
$$= \sqrt{\dfrac{16,650}{3131}}$$
$$\approx 2.31 \text{ sq meters}$$

112. $v = \sqrt{\dfrac{2Gm}{r}}$
$$= \sqrt{\dfrac{2(6.67 \times 10^{-11})(5.97 \times 10^{24})}{6.37 \times 10^6}}$$
$$= \sqrt{\dfrac{2(6.67)(5.97)}{6.37} \times 10^{-11+24-6}}$$
$$= \sqrt{12.50232339 \times 10^7}$$
$$= \sqrt{125,023,233.9} = 11,181 \text{ m per sec}$$

114. $f(x) = \sqrt{x} - 2$

Domain: $[0, \infty)$

116. $f(x) = \sqrt[3]{x} - 2$

Domain: $(-\infty, \infty)$

Section 10.2

Practice Exercises

1. a. $36^{1/2} = \sqrt{36} = 6$

b. $1000^{1/3} = \sqrt[3]{1000} = 10$

c. $x^{1/5} = \sqrt[5]{x}$

d. $1^{1/4} = \sqrt[4]{1} = 1$

e. $-64^{1/2} = -\sqrt{64} = -8$

f. $(125x^9)^{1/3} = \sqrt[3]{125x^9} = 5x^3$

g. $(3x)^{1/4} = \sqrt[4]{3x}$

2. a. $16^{3/2} = \left(\sqrt{16}\right)^3 = 4^3 = 64$

b. $-1^{3/5} = -\left(\sqrt[5]{1}\right)^3 = -(1)^3 = -1$

c. $-(81)^{3/4} = -\left(\sqrt[4]{81}\right)^3 = -(3)^3 = -27$

d. $\left(\dfrac{1}{25}\right)^{3/2} = \left(\sqrt{\dfrac{1}{25}}\right)^3 = \left(\dfrac{1}{5}\right)^3 = \dfrac{1}{125}$

e. $(3x+2)^{5/9} = \sqrt[9]{(3x+2)^5}$

3. a. $9^{-3/2} = \dfrac{1}{9^{3/2}} = \dfrac{1}{\left(\sqrt{9}\right)^3} = \dfrac{1}{3^3} = \dfrac{1}{27}$

b. $(-64)^{-2/3} = \dfrac{1}{(-64)^{2/3}} = \dfrac{1}{\left(\sqrt[3]{-64}\right)^2} = \dfrac{1}{(-4)^2} = \dfrac{1}{16}$

4. a. $y^{2/3} \cdot y^{8/3} = y^{(2/3+8/3)} = y^{10/3}$

b. $x^{3/5} \cdot x^{1/4} = x^{3/5+1/4} = x^{12/20+5/20} = x^{17/20}$

c. $\dfrac{9^{2/7}}{9^{9/7}} = 9^{2/7-9/7} = 9^{-7/7} = 9^{-1} = \dfrac{1}{9}$

d. $b^{4/9} \cdot b^{-2/9} = b^{4/9+(-2/9)} = b^{2/9}$

e. $\dfrac{\left(3x^{1/4}y^{-2/3}\right)^4}{x^4 y} = \dfrac{3^4 (x^{1/4})^4 (y^{-2/3})^4}{x^4 y}$

$= \dfrac{81xy^{-8/3}}{x^4 y}$

$= 81x^{1-4}y^{-8/3-3/3}$

$= 81x^{-3}y^{-11/3}$

$= \dfrac{81}{x^3 y^{11/3}}$

5. a. $x^{3/5}(x^{1/3} - x^2) = x^{3/5}x^{1/3} - x^{3/5}x^2$

$= x^{(3/5+1/3)} - x^{(3/5+2)}$

$= x^{(9/15+5/15)} - x^{(3/5+10/5)}$

$= x^{14/15} - x^{13/5}$

b. $(x^{1/2} + 6)(x^{1/2} - 2)$

$= x^{2/2} - 2x^{1/2} + 6x^{1/2} - 12$

$= x + 4x^{1/2} - 12$

6. $2x^{-1/5} - 7x^{4/5} = (x^{-1/5})(2) - (x^{-1/5})(7x^{5/5})$

$= x^{-1/5}(2 - 7x)$

7. a. $\sqrt[9]{x^3} = x^{3/9} = x^{1/3} = \sqrt[3]{x}$

b. $\sqrt[4]{36} = 36^{1/4} = (6^2)^{1/4} = 6^{2/4} = 6^{1/2} = \sqrt{6}$

c. $\sqrt[8]{a^4 b^2} = (a^4 b^2)^{1/8}$

$= a^{4/8} b^{2/8}$

$= a^{2/4} b^{1/4}$

$= (a^2 b)^{1/4}$

$= \sqrt[4]{a^2 b}$

8. a. $\sqrt[3]{x} \cdot \sqrt[4]{x} = x^{1/3} \cdot x^{1/4}$

$= x^{1/3+1/4}$

$= x^{4/12+3/12}$

$= x^{7/12}$

$= \sqrt[12]{x^7}$

b. $\dfrac{\sqrt[3]{y}}{\sqrt[5]{y}} = \dfrac{y^{1/3}}{y^{1/5}}$

$= y^{1/3-1/5}$

$= y^{5/15-3/15}$

$= y^{2/15}$

$= \sqrt[15]{y^2}$

c. $\sqrt[3]{5} \cdot \sqrt{3} = 5^{1/3} \cdot 3^{1/2}$

$= 5^{2/6} \cdot 3^{3/6}$

$= (5^2 \cdot 3^3)^{1/6}$

$= \sqrt[6]{5^2 \cdot 3^3}$

$= \sqrt[6]{675}$

Vocabulary and Readiness Check

1. It is true that $9^{-1/2}$ is a positive number.

2. It is false that $9^{-1/2}$ is a whole number.

3. It is true that $\dfrac{1}{a^{-m/n}} = a^{m/n}$ (where $a^{m/n}$ is a nonzero real number).

4. To simplify $x^{2/3} \cdot x^{1/5}$, <u>add</u> the exponents.

5. To simplify $(x^{2/3})^{1/5}$, <u>multiply</u> the exponents.

6. To simplify $\dfrac{x^{2/3}}{x^{1/5}}$, <u>subtract</u> the exponents.

7. $4^{1/2} = 2$, A

8. $-4^{1/2} = -2$, B

9. $(-4)^{1/2}$ is not a real number, C

10. $8^{1/3} = 2$, A

11. $-8^{1/3} = -2$, B

12. $(-8)^{1/3} = -2$, B

Exercise Set 10.2

2. $64^{1/3} = \sqrt[3]{64} = 4$

4. $8^{1/3} = \sqrt[3]{8} = 2$

6. $\left(\dfrac{1}{64}\right)^{1/2} = \sqrt{\dfrac{1}{64}} = \dfrac{1}{8}$

8. $81^{1/4} = \sqrt[4]{81} = 3$

10. $(2m)^{1/3} = \sqrt[3]{2m}$

12. $(16x^8)^{1/2} = \sqrt{16x^8} = 4x^4$

14. $-64^{1/2} = -\sqrt{64} = -8$

16. $(-32)^{1/5} = \sqrt[5]{-32} = -2$

18. $4^{5/2} = \left(\sqrt{4}\right)^5 = 2^5 = 32$

20. $(-8)^{4/3} = \left(\sqrt[3]{-8}\right)^4 = (-2)^4 = 16$

22. $(-9)^{3/2} = \left(\sqrt{-9}\right)^3$ is not a real number.

24. $2x^{3/5} = 2\sqrt[5]{x^3}$

26. $(x-4)^{3/4} = \sqrt[4]{(x-4)^3}$ or $\left(\sqrt[4]{x-4}\right)^3$

28. $\left(\dfrac{49}{25}\right)^{3/2} = \left(\sqrt{\dfrac{49}{25}}\right)^3 = \left(\dfrac{7}{5}\right)^3 = \dfrac{343}{125}$

30. $64^{-2/3} = \dfrac{1}{64^{2/3}} = \dfrac{1}{\left(\sqrt[3]{64}\right)^2} = \dfrac{1}{4^2} = \dfrac{1}{16}$

32. $(-8)^{-4/3} = \dfrac{1}{(-8)^{4/3}}$

$= \dfrac{1}{\left(\sqrt[3]{-8}\right)^4}$

$= \dfrac{1}{(-2)^4}$

$= \dfrac{1}{16}$

34. $(-16)^{-5/4} = \dfrac{1}{(-16)^{5/4}} = \dfrac{1}{\left(\sqrt[4]{-16}\right)^5}$ is not a real

number.

36. $y^{-1/6} = \dfrac{1}{y^{1/6}}$

38. $\dfrac{1}{n^{-8/9}} = n^{8/9}$

40. $\dfrac{2}{3y^{-5/7}} = \dfrac{2y^{5/7}}{3}$

42. $b^{9/5}b^{8/5} = b^{9/5+8/5} = b^{17/5}$

44. $y^{4/3} \cdot y^{-1/3} = y^{\frac{4}{3}+\left(-\frac{1}{3}\right)} = y^{3/3} = y$

46. $5^{1/2} \cdot 5^{1/6} = 5^{\frac{1}{2}+\frac{1}{6}} = 5^{\frac{3}{6}+\frac{1}{6}} = 5^{4/6} = 5^{2/3}$

48. $\dfrac{x^{3/4}}{x^{1/8}} = x^{\frac{3}{4}-\frac{1}{8}} = x^{\frac{6}{8}-\frac{1}{8}} = x^{5/8}$

50. $(32^{1/5}x^{2/3})^3 = 32^{3/5}x^{6/3}$

$= \left(\sqrt[5]{32}\right)^3 x^2$

$= 2^3 x^2$

$= 8x^2$

52. $\dfrac{a^{1/4}a^{-1/2}}{a^{2/3}} = a^{\frac{1}{4}-\frac{1}{2}-\frac{2}{3}}$

$= a^{\frac{3}{12}-\frac{6}{12}-\frac{8}{12}}$

$= a^{-11/12}$

$= \dfrac{1}{a^{11/12}}$

54. $\dfrac{y^{11/3}}{(y^5)^{1/3}} = \dfrac{y^{11/3}}{y^{5/3}} = y^{\frac{11}{3}-\frac{5}{3}} = y^{6/3} = y^2$

56. $\dfrac{(2x^{1/5})^4}{x^{3/10}} = \dfrac{2^4 x^{4/5}}{x^{3/10}}$

$= 16x^{\frac{4}{5}-\frac{3}{10}}$

$= 16x^{\frac{8}{10}-\frac{3}{10}}$

$= 16x^{5/10}$

$= 16x^{1/2}$

58. $\dfrac{(m^2 n)^{1/4}}{m^{-1/2}n^{5/8}} = \dfrac{m^{1/2}n^{1/4}}{m^{-1/2}n^{5/8}}$

$= m^{\frac{1}{2}-\left(-\frac{1}{2}\right)}n^{\frac{1}{4}-\frac{5}{8}}$

$= m^{\frac{2}{2}}n^{-\frac{3}{8}}$

$= \dfrac{m}{n^{3/8}}$

60. $\dfrac{(a^{-2}b^3)^{1/8}}{(a^{-3}b)^{-1/4}} = \dfrac{a^{-2/8}b^{3/8}}{a^{3/4}b^{-1/4}}$

$= a^{-\frac{2}{8}-\frac{3}{4}}b^{\frac{3}{8}-\left(-\frac{1}{4}\right)}$

$= a^{-\frac{2}{8}-\frac{6}{8}}b^{\frac{3}{8}+\frac{2}{8}}$

$= a^{-8/8}b^{5/8}$

$= \dfrac{b^{5/8}}{a}$

62. $x^{1/2}(x^{1/2}+x^{3/2}) = x^{1/2+1/2}+x^{1/2+3/2}$

$= x^1 + x^2$

$= x + x^2$

64. $3x^{1/2}(x+y) = 3x^{1/2+1}+3x^{1/2}y$

$= 3x^{3/2}+3x^{1/2}y$

66. $(y^{1/2}+5)(y^{1/2}+5) = (y^{1/2})^2 + 2(y^{1/2}\cdot 5)+5^2$

$= y+10y^{1/2}+25$

68. $x^{5/2}-x^{3/2} = x^{3/2}\cdot x^{2/2}-x^{3/2}\cdot 1 = x^{3/2}(x-1)$

70. $x^{3/7}-2x^{2/7} = x^{2/7}\cdot x^{1/7}-x^{2/7}\cdot 2$

$= x^{2/7}(x^{1/7}-2)$

72. $x^{-3/4}+3x^{1/4} = x^{-3/4}(1)+x^{-3/4}(3x^{4/4})$

$= x^{-3/4}(1+3x)$

74. $\sqrt[9]{a^3} = a^{3/9} = a^{1/3} = \sqrt[3]{a}$

76. $\sqrt[4]{36} = 36^{1/4} = (6^2)^{1/4} = 6^{1/2} = \sqrt{6}$

78. $\sqrt[8]{4y^2} = (4y^2)^{1/8}$

$= (2^2)^{1/8}(y^{2/8})$

$= 2^{1/4}y^{1/4}$

$= (2y)^{1/4}$

$= \sqrt[4]{2y}$

80. $\sqrt[9]{y^6 z^3} = (y^6 z^3)^{1/9}$

$= y^{2/3}z^{1/3}$

$= (y^2 z^1)^{1/3}$

$= \sqrt[3]{y^2 z}$

82. $\sqrt[10]{a^5 b^5} = (a^5 b^5)^{1/10}$

$= a^{5/10}b^{5/10}$

$= a^{1/2}b^{1/2}$

$= (ab)^{1/2}$

$= \sqrt{ab}$

84. $\sqrt[8]{(y+1)^4} = (y+1)^{4/8} = (y+1)^{1/2} = \sqrt{y+1}$

86. $\sqrt[3]{y^2}\cdot\sqrt[6]{y} = y^{2/3}\cdot y^{1/6}$

$= y^{\frac{2}{3}+\frac{1}{6}}$

$= y^{\frac{4}{6}+\frac{1}{6}}$

$= y^{5/6}$

$= \sqrt[6]{y^5}$

88. $\dfrac{\sqrt[4]{a}}{\sqrt[5]{b}} = \dfrac{a^{1/4}}{a^{1/5}} = a^{\frac{1}{4}-\frac{1}{5}} = a^{\frac{5}{20}-\frac{4}{20}} = a^{1/20} = \sqrt[20]{a}$

90. $\sqrt[6]{y} \cdot \sqrt[3]{y} \cdot \sqrt[5]{y^2} = y^{1/6} y^{1/3} y^{2/5}$
$= y^{5/30} y^{10/30} y^{12/30}$
$= y^{27/30}$
$= y^{9/10}$
$= \sqrt[10]{y^9}$

92. $\dfrac{\sqrt[5]{b^2}}{\sqrt[10]{b^3}} = \dfrac{b^{2/5}}{b^{3/10}} = b^{\frac{2}{5}-\frac{3}{10}} = b^{\frac{4}{10}-\frac{3}{10}} = b^{1/10} = \sqrt[10]{b}$

94. $\sqrt[3]{5} \cdot \sqrt{2} = 5^{1/3} \cdot 2^{1/2}$
$= 5^{2/6} \cdot 2^{3/6}$
$= (5^2 \cdot 2^3)^{1/6}$
$= (200)^{1/6}$
$= \sqrt[6]{200}$

96. $\sqrt[4]{5} \cdot \sqrt[3]{x} = 5^{1/4} \cdot x^{1/3}$
$= 5^{3/12} \cdot x^{4/12}$
$= (5^3 \cdot x^4)^{1/12}$
$= (125x^4)^{1/12}$
$= \sqrt[12]{125x^4}$

98. $\sqrt[3]{b} \cdot \sqrt[5]{4a} = b^{1/3}(4a)^{1/5}$
$= b^{1/3} 4^{1/5} a^{1/5}$
$= b^{5/15} 4^{3/15} a^{3/15}$
$= (4^3 a^3 b^5)^{1/15}$
$= (64a^3 b^5)^{1/15}$
$= \sqrt[15]{64a^3 b^5}$

100. $20 = 4 \cdot 5$ where 4 is a perfect square.

102. $45 = 9 \cdot 5$ where 9 is a perfect square.

104. $56 = 8 \cdot 7$ where 8 is a perfect cube.

106. $80 = 8 \cdot 10$ where 8 is a perfect cube.

108. $B(w) = 70w^{3/4}$
$B(90) = 70(90)^{3/4}$
≈ 2045 calories

110. $f(x) = 33.3x^{4/5}$
$f(14) = 33.3(14)^{4/5}$
≈ 275.0 million subscriptions

112. $\Box \cdot x^{1/8} = x^{4/8}$
$$\Box = \dfrac{x^{4/8}}{x^{1/8}}$$
$\Box = x^{4/8 - 1/8}$
$\Box = x^{3/8}$

114.
$$\dfrac{\Box}{y^{-3/4}} = y^{4/4}$$
$y^{-3/4}\left(\dfrac{\Box}{y^{-3/4}}\right) = y^{4/4} \cdot y^{-3/4}$
$\Box = y^{4/4 - 3/4}$
$\Box = y^{1/4}$

116. $20^{1/5} \approx 1.8206$

118. $76^{5/7} \approx 22.0515$

120. $(LC)^{-1/2} = \dfrac{1}{(LC)^{1/2}} = \dfrac{1}{\sqrt{LC}}$

Section 10.3

Practice Exercises

1. a. $\sqrt{5} \cdot \sqrt{7} = \sqrt{5 \cdot 7} = \sqrt{35}$

b. $\sqrt{13} \cdot \sqrt{z} = \sqrt{13z}$

c. $\sqrt[4]{125} \cdot \sqrt[4]{5} = \sqrt[4]{125 \cdot 5} = \sqrt[4]{625} = 5$

d. $\sqrt[3]{5y} \cdot \sqrt[3]{3x^2} = \sqrt[3]{5y \cdot 3x^2} = \sqrt[3]{15x^2 y}$

e. $\sqrt{\dfrac{5}{m}} \cdot \sqrt{\dfrac{t}{2}} = \sqrt{\dfrac{5}{m} \cdot \dfrac{t}{2}} = \sqrt{\dfrac{5t}{2m}}$

2. a. $\sqrt{\dfrac{36}{49}} = \dfrac{\sqrt{36}}{\sqrt{49}} = \dfrac{6}{7}$

b. $\sqrt{\dfrac{z}{16}} = \dfrac{\sqrt{z}}{\sqrt{16}} = \dfrac{\sqrt{z}}{4}$

c. $\sqrt[3]{\dfrac{125}{8}} = \dfrac{\sqrt[3]{125}}{\sqrt[3]{8}} = \dfrac{5}{2}$

d. $\sqrt[4]{\dfrac{5}{81x^8}} = \dfrac{\sqrt[4]{5}}{\sqrt[4]{81x^8}} = \dfrac{\sqrt[4]{5}}{3x^2}$

3. a. $\sqrt{98} = \sqrt{49 \cdot 2} = \sqrt{49} \cdot \sqrt{2} = 7\sqrt{2}$

b. $\sqrt[3]{54} = \sqrt[3]{27 \cdot 2} = \sqrt[3]{27} \cdot \sqrt[3]{2} = 3\sqrt[3]{2}$

c. The largest perfect square factor of 35 is 1, so $\sqrt{35}$ cannot be simplified further.

d. $\sqrt[4]{243} = \sqrt[4]{81 \cdot 3} = \sqrt[4]{81} \cdot \sqrt[4]{3} = 3\sqrt[4]{3}$

4. a. $\sqrt{36z^7} = \sqrt{36z^6 \cdot z} = \sqrt{36z^6} \cdot \sqrt{z} = 6z^3\sqrt{z}$

b. $\sqrt[3]{32p^4q^7} = \sqrt[3]{8 \cdot 4 \cdot p^3 \cdot p \cdot q^6 \cdot q}$
$= \sqrt[3]{8p^3q^6 \cdot 4pq}$
$= \sqrt[3]{8p^3q^6} \cdot \sqrt[3]{4pq}$
$= 2pq^2\sqrt[3]{4pq}$

c. $\sqrt[4]{16x^{15}} = \sqrt[4]{16 \cdot x^{12} \cdot x^3}$
$= \sqrt[4]{16x^{12}} \cdot \sqrt[4]{x^3}$
$= 2x^3\sqrt[4]{x^3}$

5. a. $\dfrac{\sqrt{80}}{\sqrt{5}} = \sqrt{\dfrac{80}{5}} = \sqrt{16} = 4$

b. $\dfrac{\sqrt{98z}}{3\sqrt{2}} = \dfrac{1}{3} \cdot \sqrt{\dfrac{98z}{2}}$
$= \dfrac{1}{3} \cdot \sqrt{49z}$
$= \dfrac{1}{3} \cdot \sqrt{49} \cdot \sqrt{z}$
$= \dfrac{1}{3} \cdot 7 \cdot \sqrt{z}$
$= \dfrac{7}{3}\sqrt{z}$

c. $\dfrac{5\sqrt[3]{40x^5y^7}}{\sqrt[3]{5y}} = 5 \cdot \sqrt[3]{\dfrac{40x^5y^7}{5y}}$
$= 5 \cdot \sqrt[3]{8x^5y^6}$
$= 5 \cdot \sqrt[3]{8x^3y^6 \cdot x^2}$
$= 5 \cdot \sqrt[3]{8x^3y^6} \cdot \sqrt[3]{x^2}$
$= 5 \cdot 2xy^2 \cdot \sqrt[3]{x^2}$
$= 10xy^2\sqrt[3]{x^2}$

d. $\dfrac{3\sqrt[5]{64x^9y^8}}{\sqrt[5]{x^{-1}y^2}} = 3 \cdot \sqrt[5]{\dfrac{64x^9y^8}{x^{-1}y^2}}$
$= 3 \cdot \sqrt[5]{64x^{10}y^6}$
$= 3 \cdot \sqrt[5]{32 \cdot x^{10} \cdot y^5 \cdot 2 \cdot y}$
$= 3 \cdot \sqrt[5]{32x^{10}y^5} \cdot \sqrt[5]{2y}$
$= 3 \cdot 2x^2y \cdot \sqrt[5]{2y}$
$= 6x^2y\sqrt[5]{2y}$

6. Let $(x_1, y_1) = (-3, 7)$ and $(x_2, y_2) = (-2, 3)$.
$d = \sqrt{(x_2 - x_1)^2 + (y_2 - y_1)^2}$
$= \sqrt{[-2 - (-3)]^2 + (3 - 7)^2}$
$= \sqrt{(1)^2 + (-4)^2}$
$= \sqrt{1 + 16}$
$= \sqrt{17} \approx 4.123$
The distance between the two points is exactly $\sqrt{17}$ units, or approximately 4.123 units.

7. Let $(x_1, y_1) = (5, -2)$ and $(x_2, y_2) = (8, -6)$.
$\text{midpoint} = \left(\dfrac{x_1 + x_2}{2}, \dfrac{y_1 + y_2}{2}\right)$
$= \left(\dfrac{5 + 8}{2}, \dfrac{-2 + (-6)}{2}\right)$
$= \left(\dfrac{13}{2}, \dfrac{-8}{2}\right)$
$= \left(\dfrac{13}{2}, -4\right)$

The midpoint of the segment is $\left(\dfrac{13}{2}, -4\right)$.

Vocabulary and Readiness Check

1. The <u>midpoint</u> of a line segment is a <u>point</u> exactly halfway between the two endpoints of the line segment.

2. The <u>distance</u> formula is
$$d = \sqrt{(x_2 - x_1)^2 + (y_2 - y_1)^2}.$$

3. The <u>midpoint</u> formula is $\left(\dfrac{x_1 + x_2}{2}, \dfrac{y_1 + y_2}{2} \right)$.

4. The statement $\sqrt[n]{a} \cdot \sqrt[n]{b} = \sqrt[n]{ab}$ is <u>true</u>.

5. The statement $\sqrt[3]{7} \cdot \sqrt[3]{11} = \sqrt[3]{18}$ is <u>false</u>.

6. The statement $\sqrt[3]{7} \cdot \sqrt{11} = \sqrt{77}$ is <u>false</u>.

7. The statement $\sqrt{x^7 y^8} = \sqrt{x^7} \cdot \sqrt{y^8}$ is <u>true</u>.

8. The statement $\dfrac{\sqrt[n]{a}}{\sqrt[n]{b}} = \sqrt[n]{\dfrac{a}{b}}$ is <u>true</u>.

9. The statement $\dfrac{\sqrt[3]{12}}{\sqrt[3]{4}} = \sqrt[3]{8}$ is <u>false</u>.

10. The statement $\dfrac{\sqrt[n]{x^7}}{\sqrt[n]{x}} = \sqrt[n]{x^6}$ is <u>true</u>.

Exercise Set 10.3

2. $\sqrt{11} \cdot \sqrt{10} = \sqrt{11 \cdot 10} = \sqrt{110}$

4. $\sqrt[4]{27} \cdot \sqrt[4]{3} = \sqrt[4]{27 \cdot 3} = \sqrt[4]{81} = 3$

6. $\sqrt[3]{10} \cdot \sqrt[3]{5} = \sqrt[3]{10 \cdot 5} = \sqrt[3]{50}$

8. $\sqrt{3y} \cdot \sqrt{5x} = \sqrt{3y \cdot 5x} = \sqrt{15xy}$

10. $\sqrt{\dfrac{6}{m}} \cdot \sqrt{\dfrac{n}{5}} = \sqrt{\dfrac{6}{m} \cdot \dfrac{n}{5}} = \sqrt{\dfrac{6n}{5m}}$

12. $\sqrt[4]{ab^2} \cdot \sqrt[4]{27ab} = \sqrt[4]{ab^2 \cdot 27ab} = \sqrt[4]{27a^2 b^3}$

14. $\sqrt{\dfrac{8}{81}} = \dfrac{\sqrt{8}}{\sqrt{81}} = \dfrac{\sqrt{4 \cdot 2}}{9} = \dfrac{\sqrt{4} \cdot \sqrt{2}}{9} = \dfrac{2\sqrt{2}}{9}$

16. $\sqrt{\dfrac{5}{121}} = \dfrac{\sqrt{5}}{\sqrt{121}} = \dfrac{\sqrt{5}}{11}$

18. $\sqrt[4]{\dfrac{y}{81x^4}} = \dfrac{\sqrt[4]{y}}{\sqrt[4]{81x^4}} = \dfrac{\sqrt[4]{y}}{3x}$

20. $\sqrt[3]{\dfrac{3}{64}} = \dfrac{\sqrt[3]{3}}{\sqrt[3]{64}} = \dfrac{\sqrt[3]{3}}{4}$

22. $\sqrt[4]{\dfrac{a^3}{81}} = \dfrac{\sqrt[4]{a^3}}{\sqrt[4]{81}} = \dfrac{\sqrt[4]{a^3}}{3}$

24. $\sqrt[3]{\dfrac{3}{8x^6}} = \dfrac{\sqrt[3]{3}}{\sqrt[3]{8x^6}} = \dfrac{\sqrt[3]{3}}{2x^2}$

26. $\sqrt{\dfrac{y^2 z}{36}} = \dfrac{\sqrt{y^2 z}}{\sqrt{36}} = \dfrac{\sqrt{y^2} \sqrt{z}}{6} = \dfrac{y\sqrt{z}}{6}$

28. $\sqrt{\dfrac{y^{10}}{9x^6}} = \dfrac{\sqrt{y^{10}}}{\sqrt{9x^6}} = \dfrac{y^5}{3x^3}$

30. $-\sqrt[3]{\dfrac{64a}{b^9}} = -\dfrac{\sqrt[3]{64a}}{\sqrt[3]{b^9}} = -\dfrac{\sqrt[3]{64} \cdot \sqrt[3]{a}}{b^3} = -\dfrac{4\sqrt[3]{a}}{b^3}$

32. $\sqrt{27} = \sqrt{9 \cdot 3} = \sqrt{9} \cdot \sqrt{3} = 3\sqrt{3}$

34. $\sqrt[3]{108} = \sqrt[3]{27 \cdot 4} = \sqrt[3]{27} \cdot \sqrt[3]{4} = 3\sqrt[3]{4}$

36. $3\sqrt{8} = 3\sqrt{4 \cdot 2} = 3\sqrt{4} \cdot \sqrt{2} = 3(2)\sqrt{2} = 6\sqrt{2}$

38. $\sqrt{20} = \sqrt{4 \cdot 5} = \sqrt{4} \cdot \sqrt{5} = 2\sqrt{5}$

40. $\sqrt{64y^9} = \sqrt{64y^8 \cdot y} = \sqrt{64y^8} \cdot \sqrt{y} = 8y^4 \sqrt{y}$

42. $\sqrt[3]{64y^9} = 4y^3$

44. $\sqrt[5]{32z^{12}} = \sqrt[5]{32z^{10} \cdot z^2}$
$= \sqrt[5]{32z^{10}} \cdot \sqrt[5]{z^2}$
$= 2z^2 \sqrt[5]{z^2}$

46. $\sqrt[3]{y^5} = \sqrt[3]{y^3 \cdot y^2} = y\sqrt[3]{y^2}$

48. $\sqrt{9x^5 y^7} = \sqrt{9x^4 y^6 \cdot xy}$
$= \sqrt{9x^4 y^6} \cdot \sqrt{xy}$
$= 3x^2 y^3 \sqrt{xy}$

50. $\sqrt[5]{-243z^9} = \sqrt[5]{-243z^5 \cdot z^4}$
$= \sqrt[5]{-243z^5} \cdot \sqrt[5]{z^4}$
$= -3z\sqrt[5]{z^4}$

52. $\sqrt[3]{40y^{10}} = \sqrt[3]{8y^9 \cdot 5y} = \sqrt[3]{8y^9} \cdot \sqrt[3]{5y} = 2y^3\sqrt[3]{5y}$

54. $-\sqrt{20ab^6} = -\sqrt{4b^6 \cdot 5a}$
$= -\sqrt{4b^6} \cdot \sqrt{5a}$
$= -2b^3\sqrt{5a}$

56. $\sqrt{12r^9s^{12}} = \sqrt{4r^8s^{12} \cdot 3r}$
$= \sqrt{4r^8s^{12}} \cdot \sqrt{3r}$
$= 2r^4s^6\sqrt{3r}$

58. $\sqrt[3]{8a^6b^9} = 2a^2b^3$

60. $\dfrac{\sqrt{45}}{\sqrt{9}} = \sqrt{\dfrac{45}{9}} = \sqrt{5}$

62. $\dfrac{\sqrt[3]{10}}{\sqrt[3]{2}} = \sqrt[3]{\dfrac{10}{2}} = \sqrt[3]{5}$

64. $\dfrac{7\sqrt[4]{162}}{\sqrt[4]{2}} = 7\sqrt[4]{\dfrac{162}{2}} = 7\sqrt[4]{81} = 7(3) = 21$

66. $\dfrac{\sqrt{a^7b^6}}{\sqrt{a^3b^2}} = \sqrt{\dfrac{a^7b^6}{a^3b^2}} = \sqrt{a^4b^4} = a^2b^2$

68. $\dfrac{\sqrt[3]{128x^3}}{-3\sqrt[3]{2x}} = -\dfrac{1}{3}\sqrt[3]{\dfrac{128x^3}{2x}} = -\dfrac{1}{3}\sqrt[3]{64x^2} = -\dfrac{4}{3}\sqrt[3]{x^2}$

70. $\dfrac{\sqrt{270y^2}}{5\sqrt{3y^{-4}}} = \dfrac{1}{5}\sqrt{\dfrac{270y^2}{3y^{-4}}}$
$= \dfrac{1}{5}\sqrt{90y^6}$
$= \dfrac{1}{5}\sqrt{9y^6 \cdot 10}$
$= \dfrac{1}{5}(3y^3)\sqrt{10}$
$= \dfrac{3y^3}{5}\sqrt{10}$ or $\dfrac{3y^3\sqrt{10}}{5}$

72. $\dfrac{\sqrt[5]{64x^{10}y^3}}{\sqrt[5]{2x^3y^{-7}}} = \sqrt[5]{\dfrac{64x^{10}y^3}{2x^3y^{-7}}}$
$= \sqrt[5]{32x^7y^{10}}$
$= \sqrt[5]{32x^5y^{10} \cdot x^2}$
$= \sqrt[5]{32x^5y^{10}} \cdot \sqrt[5]{x^2}$
$= 2xy^2\sqrt[5]{x^2}$

74. $(2, 3), (14, 8)$
$d = \sqrt{(14-2)^2 + (8-3)^2}$
$= \sqrt{12^2 + 5^2}$
$= \sqrt{144 + 25}$
$= \sqrt{169}$
$= 13$ units

76. $(3, -2), (-4, 1)$
$d = \sqrt{(-4-3)^2 + [1-(-2)]^2}$
$= \sqrt{(-7)^2 + 3^2}$
$= \sqrt{49+9}$
$= \sqrt{58} \approx 7.616$ units

78. $(-5, -2), (-6, -6)$
$d = \sqrt{[-6-(-5)]^2 + [-6-(-2)]^2}$
$= \sqrt{(-1)^2 + (-4)^2}$
$= \sqrt{1+16}$
$= \sqrt{17} \approx 4.123$ units

80. $\left(-\sqrt{5}, 0\right), \left(0, \sqrt{7}\right)$
$d = \sqrt{\left[0-\left(-\sqrt{5}\right)\right]^2 + \left(\sqrt{7}-0\right)^2}$
$= \sqrt{\left(\sqrt{5}\right)^2 + \left(\sqrt{7}\right)^2}$
$= \sqrt{5+7}$
$= \sqrt{12}$
$= 2\sqrt{3} \approx 3.464$ units

82. $(9.6, 2.5), (-1.9, -3.7)$
$d = \sqrt{(-1.9-9.6)^2 + (-3.7-2.5)^2}$
$= \sqrt{(-11.5)^2 + (-6.2)^2}$
$= \sqrt{170.69} \approx 13.065$ units

84. $(3, 9)$, $(7, 11)$

$$\left(\frac{3+7}{2}, \frac{9+11}{2}\right) = \left(\frac{10}{2}, \frac{20}{2}\right) = (5, 10)$$

The midpoint of the segment is $(5, 10)$.

86. $(-3, -4)$, $(6, -8)$

$$\left(\frac{-3+6}{2}, \frac{-4+(-8)}{2}\right) = \left(\frac{3}{2}, \frac{-12}{2}\right) = \left(\frac{3}{2}, -6\right)$$

The midpoint of the segment is $\left(\frac{3}{2}, -6\right)$.

88. $(-2, 5)$, $(-1, 6)$

$$\left(\frac{-2+(-1)}{2}, \frac{5+6}{2}\right) = \left(-\frac{3}{2}, \frac{11}{2}\right)$$

The midpoint of the segment is $\left(-\frac{3}{2}, \frac{11}{2}\right)$.

90. $\left(-\frac{2}{5}, \frac{7}{15}\right)$, $\left(-\frac{2}{5}, -\frac{4}{15}\right)$

$$\left(\frac{-\frac{2}{5}+\left(-\frac{2}{5}\right)}{2}, \frac{\frac{7}{15}+\left(-\frac{4}{15}\right)}{2}\right) = \left(\frac{-\frac{4}{5}}{2}, \frac{\frac{3}{15}}{2}\right)$$

$$= \left(-\frac{2}{5}, \frac{1}{10}\right)$$

The midpoint of the segment is $\left(-\frac{2}{5}, \frac{1}{10}\right)$.

92. $\left(\sqrt{8}, -\sqrt{12}\right)$, $\left(3\sqrt{2}, 7\sqrt{3}\right)$

$$\left(\frac{\sqrt{8}+3\sqrt{2}}{2}, \frac{-\sqrt{12}+7\sqrt{3}}{2}\right)$$

$$= \left(\frac{2\sqrt{2}+3\sqrt{2}}{2}, \frac{-2\sqrt{3}+7\sqrt{3}}{2}\right)$$

$$= \left(\frac{5\sqrt{2}}{2}, \frac{5\sqrt{3}}{2}\right)$$

The midpoint of the segment is $\left(\frac{5\sqrt{2}}{2}, \frac{5\sqrt{3}}{2}\right)$.

94. $(-4.6, 2.1)$, $(-6.7, 1.9)$

$$\left(\frac{-4.6+(-6.7)}{2}, \frac{2.1+1.9}{2}\right) = \left(\frac{-11.3}{2}, \frac{4}{2}\right)$$

$$= (-5.65, 2)$$

The midpoint of the segment is $(-5.65, 2)$.

96. $(6x)(8x) = (6)(8)x \cdot x = 48x^2$

98. $(2x+3)+(x-5) = 2x+3+x-5$

$$= (2x+x)+(3-5)$$

$$= 3x+(-2)$$

$$= 3x-2$$

100. $(9y^2)(-8y^2) = 9(-8)y^2 \cdot y^2 = -72y^4$

102. $-3+x+5 = x+(-3+5) = x+2$

104. $(2x+1)^2 = (2x)^2 + 2(2x)(1) + 1^2$

$$= 4x^2 + 4x + 1$$

106. $\dfrac{\sqrt[4]{16}}{\sqrt{4}} = \dfrac{2}{2} = 1$

108. $\sqrt[6]{y^{48}} = y^8$

110. $\sqrt[3]{a^9 b^{21} c^3} = a^3 b^7 c$

112. $\sqrt[5]{x^{49}} = \sqrt[5]{x^{45} \cdot x^4} = \sqrt[5]{x^{45}} \cdot \sqrt[5]{x^4} = x^9 \sqrt[5]{x^4}$

114. $\sqrt[4]{p^{11} q^4 r^{45}} = \sqrt[4]{p^8 \cdot p^3 \cdot q^4 \cdot r^{44} \cdot r}$

$$= \sqrt[4]{p^8 q^4 r^{44} \cdot p^3 r}$$

$$= p^2 q r^{11} \sqrt[4]{p^3 r}$$

116. $A = \pi r \sqrt{r^2 + h^2}$

a. $A = \pi(4)\sqrt{4^2 + 3^2}$

$$= 4\pi\sqrt{16+9}$$

$$= 4\pi\sqrt{25}$$

$$= 4\pi(5)$$

$$= 20\pi \text{ sq centimeters}$$

b. $A = \pi(6.8)\sqrt{(6.8)^2 + (7.2)^2}$

$$= 6.8\pi\sqrt{46.24+51.84}$$

$$= 6.8\pi\sqrt{98.08}$$

$$\approx 211.57 \text{ sq feet}$$

118. $A = \pi r \sqrt{r^2 + h^2}$

$$= \pi(25,200)\sqrt{(25,200)^2 + (4190)^2}$$

$$= 25,200\pi\sqrt{652,596,100}$$

$$\approx 2,022,426,050 \text{ sq feet}$$

Section 10.4

Practice Exercises

1. **a.** $3\sqrt{17} + 5\sqrt{17} = (3+5)\sqrt{17} = 8\sqrt{17}$

   b. $7\sqrt[3]{5z} - 12\sqrt[3]{5z} = (7-12)\sqrt[3]{5z} = -5\sqrt[3]{5z}$

   c. $3\sqrt{2} + 5\sqrt[3]{2}$
   This expression cannot be simplified since
   $3\sqrt{2}$ and $5\sqrt[3]{2}$ do not contain like radicals.

2. **a.** $\sqrt{24} + 3\sqrt{54} = \sqrt{4\cdot 6} + 3\sqrt{9\cdot 6}$
   $= \sqrt{4}\cdot\sqrt{6} + 3\cdot\sqrt{9}\cdot\sqrt{6}$
   $= 2\cdot\sqrt{6} + 3\cdot 3\cdot\sqrt{6}$
   $= 2\sqrt{6} + 9\sqrt{6}$
   $= 11\sqrt{6}$

   b. $\sqrt[3]{24} - 4\sqrt[3]{81} + \sqrt[3]{3}$
   $= \sqrt[3]{8}\cdot\sqrt[3]{3} - 4\cdot\sqrt[3]{27}\cdot\sqrt[3]{3} + \sqrt[3]{3}$
   $= 2\cdot\sqrt[3]{3} - 4\cdot 3\cdot\sqrt[3]{3} + \sqrt[3]{3}$
   $= 2\sqrt[3]{3} - 12\sqrt[3]{3} + \sqrt[3]{3}$
   $= -9\sqrt[3]{3}$

   c. $\sqrt{75x} - 3\sqrt{27x} + \sqrt{12x}$
   $= \sqrt{25}\cdot\sqrt{3x} - 3\cdot\sqrt{9}\cdot\sqrt{3x} + \sqrt{4}\cdot\sqrt{3x}$
   $= 5\cdot\sqrt{3x} - 3\cdot 3\cdot\sqrt{3x} + 2\cdot\sqrt{3x}$
   $= 5\sqrt{3x} - 9\sqrt{3x} + 2\sqrt{3x}$
   $= -2\sqrt{3x}$

   d. $\sqrt{40} + \sqrt[3]{40} = \sqrt{4}\cdot\sqrt{10} + \sqrt[3]{8}\cdot\sqrt[3]{5}$
   $= 2\sqrt{10} + 2\sqrt[3]{5}$

   e. $\sqrt[3]{81x^4} + \sqrt[3]{3x^4} = \sqrt[3]{27x^3}\cdot\sqrt[3]{3x} + \sqrt[3]{x^3}\cdot\sqrt[3]{3x}$
   $= 3x\sqrt[3]{3x} + x\sqrt[3]{3x}$
   $= 4x\sqrt[3]{3x}$

3. **a.** $\dfrac{\sqrt{28}}{3} - \dfrac{\sqrt{7}}{4} = \dfrac{2\sqrt{7}}{3} - \dfrac{\sqrt{7}}{4}$
   $= \dfrac{2\sqrt{7}\cdot 4}{3\cdot 4} - \dfrac{\sqrt{7}\cdot 3}{4\cdot 3}$
   $= \dfrac{8\sqrt{7}}{12} - \dfrac{3\sqrt{7}}{12}$
   $= \dfrac{5\sqrt{7}}{12}$

b. $\sqrt[3]{\dfrac{6y}{64}} + 3\sqrt[3]{6y} = \dfrac{\sqrt[3]{6y}}{\sqrt[3]{64}} + 3\sqrt[3]{6y}$
   $= \dfrac{\sqrt[3]{6y}}{4} + 3\sqrt[3]{6y}$
   $= \dfrac{\sqrt[3]{6y}}{4} + \dfrac{3\sqrt[3]{6y}\cdot 4}{4}$
   $= \dfrac{\sqrt[3]{6y}}{4} + \dfrac{12\sqrt[3]{6y}}{4}$
   $= \dfrac{13\sqrt[3]{6y}}{4}$

4. **a.** $\sqrt{5}(2 + \sqrt{15}) = \sqrt{5}(2) + \sqrt{5}(\sqrt{15})$
   $= 2\sqrt{5} + \sqrt{5\cdot 15}$
   $= 2\sqrt{5} + \sqrt{5\cdot 5\cdot 3}$
   $= 2\sqrt{5} + 5\sqrt{3}$

   b. $(\sqrt{2} - \sqrt{5})(\sqrt{6} + 2)$
   $= \sqrt{2}\cdot\sqrt{6} + \sqrt{2}\cdot 2 - \sqrt{5}\cdot\sqrt{6} - \sqrt{5}\cdot 2$
   $= \sqrt{2\cdot 2\cdot 3} + 2\sqrt{2} - \sqrt{30} - 2\sqrt{5}$
   $= 2\sqrt{3} + 2\sqrt{2} - \sqrt{30} - 2\sqrt{5}$

   c. $(3\sqrt{z} - 4)(2\sqrt{z} + 3)$
   $= 3\sqrt{z}(2\sqrt{z}) + 3\sqrt{z}(3) - 4(2\sqrt{z}) - 4(3)$
   $= 6\cdot z + 9\sqrt{z} - 8\sqrt{z} - 12$
   $= 6z + \sqrt{z} - 12$

   d. $(\sqrt{6} - 3)^2 = (\sqrt{6} - 3)(\sqrt{6} - 3)$
   $= \sqrt{6}(\sqrt{6}) - \sqrt{6}(3) - 3(\sqrt{6}) - 3(-3)$
   $= 6 - 3\sqrt{6} - 3\sqrt{6} + 9$
   $= 6 - 6\sqrt{6} + 9$
   $= 15 - 6\sqrt{6}$

   e. $(\sqrt{5x} + 3)(\sqrt{5x} - 3)$
   $= \sqrt{5x}\cdot\sqrt{5x} - 3\sqrt{5x} + 3\sqrt{5x} - 3\cdot 3$
   $= 5x - 9$

   f. $(\sqrt{x+2} + 3)^2 = (\sqrt{x+2})^2 + 2\cdot\sqrt{x+2}\cdot 3 + 3^2$
   $= x + 2 + 6\sqrt{x+2} + 9$
   $= x + 11 + 6\sqrt{x+2}$

Vocabulary and Readiness Check

1. The terms $\sqrt{7}$ and $\sqrt[3]{7}$ are <u>unlike</u> terms.

2. The terms $\sqrt[3]{x^2 y}$ and $\sqrt[3]{yx^2}$ are <u>like</u> terms.

3. The terms $\sqrt[3]{abc}$ and $\sqrt[3]{cba}$ are <u>like</u> terms.

4. The terms $2x\sqrt{5}$ and $2x\sqrt{10}$ are <u>unlike</u> terms.

5. $2\sqrt{3} + 4\sqrt{3} = \underline{6\sqrt{3}}$

6. $5\sqrt{7} + 3\sqrt{7} = \underline{8\sqrt{7}}$

7. $8\sqrt{x} - \sqrt{x} = \underline{7\sqrt{x}}$

8. $3\sqrt{y} - \sqrt{y} = \underline{2\sqrt{y}}$

9. $7\sqrt[3]{x} + \sqrt[3]{x} = \underline{8\sqrt[3]{x}}$

10. $8\sqrt[3]{z} + \sqrt[3]{z} = \underline{9\sqrt[3]{z}}$

11. $\sqrt{11} + \sqrt[3]{11} = \underline{\sqrt{11} + \sqrt[3]{11}}$

12. $9\sqrt{13} - \sqrt[4]{13} = \underline{9\sqrt{13} - \sqrt[4]{13}}$

13. $8\sqrt[3]{2x} + 3\sqrt[3]{2x} - \sqrt[3]{2x} = \underline{10\sqrt[3]{2x}}$

14. $8\sqrt[3]{2x} + 3\sqrt[3]{2x^2} - \sqrt[3]{2x} = \underline{7\sqrt[3]{2x} + 3\sqrt[3]{2x^2}}$

Exercise Set 10.4

2. $\sqrt{27} - \sqrt{75} = \sqrt{9 \cdot 3} - \sqrt{25 \cdot 3}$
$= \sqrt{9} \cdot \sqrt{3} - \sqrt{25} \cdot \sqrt{3}$
$= 3\sqrt{3} - 5\sqrt{3}$
$= -2\sqrt{3}$

4. $3\sqrt{45x^3} + x\sqrt{5x} = 3\sqrt{9x^2 \cdot 5x} + x\sqrt{5x}$
$= 3\sqrt{9x^2} \cdot \sqrt{5x} + x\sqrt{5x}$
$= 3(3x)\sqrt{5x} + x\sqrt{5x}$
$= 9x\sqrt{5x} + x\sqrt{5x}$
$= 10x\sqrt{5x}$

6. $4\sqrt{32} - \sqrt{18} + 2\sqrt{128}$
$= 4\sqrt{16 \cdot 2} - \sqrt{9 \cdot 2} + 2\sqrt{64 \cdot 2}$
$= 4\sqrt{16} \cdot \sqrt{2} - \sqrt{9} \cdot \sqrt{2} + 2\sqrt{64} \cdot \sqrt{2}$
$= 4(4)\sqrt{2} - 3\sqrt{2} + 2(8)\sqrt{2}$
$= 16\sqrt{2} - 3\sqrt{2} + 16\sqrt{2}$
$= 29\sqrt{2}$

8. $2\sqrt[3]{3a^4} - 3a\sqrt[3]{81a} = 2\sqrt[3]{a^3 \cdot 3a} - 3a\sqrt[3]{27 \cdot 3a}$
$= 2\sqrt[3]{a^3} \cdot \sqrt[3]{3a} - 3a\sqrt[3]{27} \cdot \sqrt[3]{3a}$
$= 2a\sqrt[3]{3a} - 3a(3)\sqrt[3]{3a}$
$= 2a\sqrt[3]{3a} - 9a\sqrt[3]{3a}$
$= -7a\sqrt[3]{3a}$

10. $\sqrt{4x^7} + 9x^2\sqrt{x^3} - 5x\sqrt{x^5}$
$= \sqrt{4x^6 \cdot x} + 9x^2\sqrt{x^2 \cdot x} - 5x\sqrt{x^4 \cdot x}$
$= \sqrt{4x^6} \cdot \sqrt{x} + 9x^2\sqrt{x^2} \cdot \sqrt{x} - 5x\sqrt{x^4} \cdot \sqrt{x}$
$= 2x^3\sqrt{x} + 9x^2(x)\sqrt{x} - 5x(x^2)\sqrt{x}$
$= 2x^3\sqrt{x} + 9x^3\sqrt{x} - 5x^3\sqrt{x}$
$= 6x^3\sqrt{x}$

12. $\dfrac{\sqrt{3}}{2} + \dfrac{4\sqrt{3}}{3} = \dfrac{3\left(\sqrt{3}\right) + 2\left(4\sqrt{3}\right)}{6}$
$= \dfrac{3\sqrt{3} + 8\sqrt{3}}{6}$
$= \dfrac{11\sqrt{3}}{6}$

14. $\dfrac{2\sqrt[3]{4}}{7} - \dfrac{\sqrt[3]{4}}{14} = \dfrac{2\left(2\sqrt[3]{4}\right) - \sqrt[3]{4}}{14}$
$= \dfrac{4\sqrt[3]{4} - \sqrt[3]{4}}{14}$
$= \dfrac{3\sqrt[3]{4}}{14}$

16. $\dfrac{3x\sqrt{7}}{5} + \sqrt{\dfrac{7x^2}{100}} = \dfrac{3x\sqrt{7}}{5} + \dfrac{\sqrt{7x^2}}{\sqrt{100}}$
$= \dfrac{3x\sqrt{7}}{5} + \dfrac{x\sqrt{7}}{10}$
$= \dfrac{2\left(3x\sqrt{7}\right) + x\sqrt{7}}{10}$
$= \dfrac{6x\sqrt{7} + x\sqrt{7}}{10}$
$= \dfrac{7x\sqrt{7}}{10}$

18. $\sqrt{16} - 5\sqrt{10} + 7 = 4 - 5\sqrt{10} + 7 = 11 - 5\sqrt{10}$

20. $3\sqrt{7} - \sqrt[3]{x} + 4\sqrt{7} - 3\sqrt[3]{x} = 7\sqrt{7} - 4\sqrt[3]{x}$

22. $-\sqrt{75}+\sqrt{12}-3\sqrt{3}=-\sqrt{25\cdot3}+\sqrt{4\cdot3}-3\sqrt{3}$
$$=-5\sqrt{3}+2\sqrt{3}-3\sqrt{3}$$
$$=-6\sqrt{3}$$

24. $-2\sqrt[3]{108}-\sqrt[3]{32}=-2\sqrt[3]{27\cdot4}-\sqrt[3]{8\cdot4}$
$$=-2(3)\sqrt[3]{4}-2\sqrt[3]{4}$$
$$=-6\sqrt[3]{4}-2\sqrt[3]{4}$$
$$=-8\sqrt[3]{4}$$

26. $\sqrt{4x^7y^5}+9x^2\sqrt{x^3y^5}-5xy\sqrt{x^5y^3}$
$$=\sqrt{4x^6y^4\cdot xy}+9x^2\sqrt{x^2y^4\cdot xy}$$
$$\quad-5xy\sqrt{x^4y^2\cdot xy}$$
$$=2x^3y^2\sqrt{xy}+9x^2(xy^2)\sqrt{xy}-5xy(x^2y)\sqrt{xy}$$
$$=2x^3y^2\sqrt{xy}+9x^3y^2\sqrt{xy}-5x^3y^2\sqrt{xy}$$
$$=6x^3y^2\sqrt{xy}$$

28. $3\sqrt{8x^2y^3}-2x\sqrt{32y^3}$
$$=3\sqrt{4x^2y^2\cdot2y}-2x\sqrt{16y^2\cdot2y}$$
$$=3(2xy)\sqrt{2y}-2x(4y)\sqrt{2y}$$
$$=6xy\sqrt{2y}-8xy\sqrt{2y}$$
$$=-2xy\sqrt{2y}$$

30. $2\sqrt[3]{24x^3y^4}+4x\sqrt[3]{81y^4}$
$$=2\sqrt[3]{8x^3y^3\cdot3y}+4x\sqrt[3]{27y^3\cdot3y}$$
$$=2(2xy)\sqrt[3]{3y}+4x(3y)\sqrt[3]{3y}$$
$$=4xy\sqrt[3]{3y}+12xy\sqrt[3]{3y}$$
$$=16xy\sqrt[3]{3y}$$

32. $3\sqrt[3]{5}+4\sqrt{5}=3\sqrt[3]{5}+4\sqrt{5}$

34. $6\sqrt[3]{24x^3}-2\sqrt[3]{81x^3}-x\sqrt[3]{3}$
$$=6\sqrt[3]{8x^3\cdot3}-2\sqrt[3]{27x^3\cdot3}-x\sqrt[3]{3}$$
$$=6(2x)\sqrt[3]{3}-2(3x)\sqrt[3]{3}-x\sqrt[3]{3}$$
$$=12x\sqrt[3]{3}-6x\sqrt[3]{3}-x\sqrt[3]{3}$$
$$=5x\sqrt[3]{3}$$

36. $\dfrac{\sqrt{45}}{10}+\dfrac{7\sqrt{5}}{10}=\dfrac{\sqrt{9\cdot5}}{10}+\dfrac{7\sqrt{5}}{10}$
$$=\dfrac{3\sqrt{5}+7\sqrt{5}}{10}$$
$$=\dfrac{10\sqrt{5}}{10}$$
$$=\sqrt{5}$$

38. $\dfrac{\sqrt[4]{48}}{5x}-\dfrac{2\sqrt[4]{3}}{10x}=\dfrac{\sqrt[4]{16\cdot3}}{5x}-\dfrac{2\sqrt[4]{3}}{10x}$
$$=\dfrac{2\sqrt[4]{3}}{5x}-\dfrac{\sqrt[4]{3}}{5x}$$
$$=\dfrac{2\sqrt[4]{3}-\sqrt[4]{3}}{5x}$$
$$=\dfrac{\sqrt[4]{3}}{5x}$$

40. $\dfrac{\sqrt{99}}{5x}-\sqrt{\dfrac{44}{x^2}}=\dfrac{\sqrt{9\cdot11}}{5x}-\dfrac{\sqrt{4\cdot11}}{x}$
$$=\dfrac{3\sqrt{11}}{5x}-\dfrac{2\sqrt{11}}{x}$$
$$=\dfrac{3\sqrt{11}-5\left(2\sqrt{11}\right)}{5x}$$
$$=\dfrac{3\sqrt{11}-10\sqrt{11}}{5x}$$
$$=-\dfrac{7\sqrt{11}}{5x}$$

42. $\dfrac{\sqrt[3]{3}}{10}+\sqrt[3]{\dfrac{24}{125}}=\dfrac{\sqrt[3]{3}}{10}+\dfrac{\sqrt[3]{8\cdot3}}{\sqrt[3]{125}}$
$$=\dfrac{\sqrt[3]{3}}{10}+\dfrac{2\sqrt[3]{3}}{5}$$
$$=\dfrac{\sqrt[3]{3}+2\left(2\sqrt[3]{3}\right)}{10}$$
$$=\dfrac{\sqrt[3]{3}+4\sqrt[3]{3}}{10}$$
$$=\dfrac{5\sqrt[3]{3}}{10}$$
$$=\dfrac{\sqrt[3]{3}}{2}$$

44. $\dfrac{\sqrt[3]{y^5}}{8} + \dfrac{5y\sqrt[3]{y^2}}{4} = \dfrac{\sqrt[3]{y^3 \cdot y^2}}{8} + \dfrac{5y\sqrt[3]{y^2}}{4}$

$\qquad = \dfrac{y\sqrt[3]{y^2}}{8} + \dfrac{5y\sqrt[3]{y^2}}{4}$

$\qquad = \dfrac{y\sqrt[3]{y^2} + 2\left(5y\sqrt[3]{y^2}\right)}{8}$

$\qquad = \dfrac{y\sqrt[3]{y^2} + 10y\sqrt[3]{y^2}}{8}$

$\qquad = \dfrac{11y\sqrt[3]{y^2}}{8}$

46. $P = \sqrt{8} + \sqrt{32} + \sqrt{45}$

$\qquad = \sqrt{4 \cdot 2} + \sqrt{16 \cdot 2} + \sqrt{9 \cdot 5}$

$\qquad = 2\sqrt{2} + 4\sqrt{2} + 3\sqrt{5}$

$\qquad = 6\sqrt{2} + 3\sqrt{5}$

$\qquad = \left(6\sqrt{2} + 3\sqrt{5}\right)$ meters

48. $\sqrt{5}\left(\sqrt{15} - \sqrt{35}\right) = \sqrt{5}\sqrt{15} - \sqrt{5}\sqrt{35}$

$\qquad = \sqrt{75} - \sqrt{175}$

$\qquad = \sqrt{25 \cdot 3} - \sqrt{25 \cdot 7}$

$\qquad = 5\sqrt{3} - 5\sqrt{7}$

50. $\left(3x - \sqrt{2}\right)\left(3x - \sqrt{2}\right) = \left(3x - \sqrt{2}\right)^2$

$\qquad = (3x)^2 - 2(3x)\sqrt{2} + \left(\sqrt{2}\right)^2$

$\qquad = 9x^2 - 6x\sqrt{2} + 2$

52. $\sqrt{5y}\left(\sqrt{y} + \sqrt{5}\right) = \sqrt{5y}\sqrt{y} + \sqrt{5y}\sqrt{5}$

$\qquad = \sqrt{5y^2} + \sqrt{25y}$

$\qquad = y\sqrt{5} + 5\sqrt{y}$

54. $\left(8\sqrt{y} + z\right)\left(4\sqrt{y} - 1\right)$

$\qquad = 8\sqrt{y}\left(4\sqrt{y}\right) - 8\sqrt{y} + z\left(4\sqrt{y}\right) - z$

$\qquad = 32y - 8\sqrt{y} + 4z\sqrt{y} - z$

56. $\left(\sqrt[3]{a} + 2\right)\left(\sqrt[3]{a} + 7\right)$

$\qquad = \sqrt[3]{a}\left(\sqrt[3]{a}\right) + \sqrt[3]{a} \cdot 7 + 2\sqrt[3]{a} + 2(7)$

$\qquad = \sqrt[3]{a^2} + 7\sqrt[3]{a} + 2\sqrt[3]{a} + 14$

$\qquad = \sqrt[3]{a^2} + 9\sqrt[3]{a} + 14$

58. $\sqrt{5}\left(6 - \sqrt{5}\right) = \sqrt{5} \cdot 6 - \sqrt{5}\left(\sqrt{5}\right) = 6\sqrt{5} - 5$

60. $\sqrt{3}\left(\sqrt{3} - 2\sqrt{5x}\right) = \sqrt{3}\sqrt{3} - \sqrt{3}\left(2\sqrt{5x}\right)$

$\qquad = 3 - 2\sqrt{15x}$

62. $(\sqrt{6} - 4\sqrt{2})(3\sqrt{6} + \sqrt{2})$

$\qquad = \sqrt{6}(3\sqrt{6}) + \sqrt{6}\sqrt{2} - 4\sqrt{2}(3\sqrt{6}) - 4\sqrt{2}(\sqrt{2})$

$\qquad = 3 \cdot 6 + \sqrt{12} - 12\sqrt{12} - 4 \cdot 2$

$\qquad = 18 - 11\sqrt{12} - 8$

$\qquad = 10 - 11\sqrt{4 \cdot 3}$

$\qquad = 10 - 22\sqrt{3}$

64. $(\sqrt{3x} + 2)(\sqrt{3x} - 2) = \left(\sqrt{3x}\right)^2 - 2^2 = 3x - 4$

66. $\left(\sqrt{y} - 3x\right)^2 = \left(\sqrt{y}\right)^2 - 2\sqrt{y} \cdot (3x) + (3x)^2$

$\qquad = y - 6x\sqrt{y} + 9x^2$

68. $(5\sqrt{7x} - \sqrt{2x})(4\sqrt{7x} + 6\sqrt{2x})$

$\qquad = 5\sqrt{7x}(4\sqrt{7x}) + 5\sqrt{7x}(6\sqrt{2x})$

$\qquad \qquad - \sqrt{2x}(4\sqrt{7x}) - \sqrt{2x}(6\sqrt{2x})$

$\qquad = 20 \cdot 7x + 30\sqrt{14x^2} - 4\sqrt{14x^2} - 6 \cdot 2x$

$\qquad = 140x + 30x\sqrt{14} - 4x\sqrt{14} - 12x$

$\qquad = 128x + 26x\sqrt{14}$

70. $\left(\sqrt[3]{3} + \sqrt[3]{2}\right)\left(\sqrt[3]{9} - \sqrt[3]{4}\right)$

$\qquad = \sqrt[3]{3}\left(\sqrt[3]{9}\right) + \sqrt[3]{3}\left(-\sqrt[3]{4}\right) + \sqrt[3]{2}\left(\sqrt[3]{9}\right) + \sqrt[3]{2}\left(-\sqrt[3]{4}\right)$

$\qquad = \sqrt[3]{27} - \sqrt[3]{12} + \sqrt[3]{18} - \sqrt[3]{8}$

$\qquad = 3 - \sqrt[3]{12} + \sqrt[3]{18} - 2$

$\qquad = 1 - \sqrt[3]{12} + \sqrt[3]{18}$

72. $\left(\sqrt[3]{3x} + 2\right)\left(\sqrt[3]{9x^2} - 2\sqrt[3]{3x} + 4\right)$

$\qquad = \sqrt[3]{3x}\left(\sqrt[3]{9x^2}\right) - \sqrt[3]{3x}\left(2\sqrt[3]{3x}\right) + \sqrt[3]{3x}(4)$

$\qquad \qquad + 2\left(\sqrt[3]{9x^2}\right) - 2\left(2\sqrt[3]{3x}\right) + 2(4)$

$\qquad = \sqrt[3]{27x^3} - 2\sqrt[3]{9x^2} + 4\sqrt[3]{3x} + 2\sqrt[3]{9x^2} - 4\sqrt[3]{3x} + 8$

$\qquad = 3x + 8$

74. $\left(\sqrt{3x+1} + 2\right)^2 = \left(\sqrt{3x+1}\right)^2 + 2\sqrt{3x+1} \cdot 2 + 2^2$

$\qquad = (3x+1) + 4\sqrt{3x+1} + 4$

$\qquad = 3x + 4\sqrt{3x+1} + 5$

76. $\left(\sqrt{x-6}-7\right)^2 = \left(\sqrt{x-6}\right)^2 - 2\sqrt{x-6}\cdot 7 + 7^2$

$\qquad = (x-6) - 14\sqrt{x-6} + 49$

$\qquad = x - 14\sqrt{x-6} + 43$

78. $\dfrac{8x-24y}{4} = \dfrac{8(x-3y)}{4} = 2(x-3y)$

80. $\dfrac{x^3-8}{4x-8} = \dfrac{(x-2)(x^2+2x+4)}{4(x-2)} = \dfrac{x^2+2x+4}{4}$

82. $\dfrac{14r-28r^2s^2}{7rs} = \dfrac{14r(1-2rs^2)}{7rs} = \dfrac{2(1-2rs^2)}{s}$

84. $\dfrac{-5+10\sqrt{7}}{5} = \dfrac{5\left(-1+2\sqrt{7}\right)}{5} = -1+2\sqrt{7}$

86. $A = \dfrac{1}{2}h(b+B)$

$\qquad = \dfrac{1}{2}\left(6\sqrt{3}\right)\left(2\sqrt{63}+7\sqrt{7}\right)$

$\qquad = 3\sqrt{3}\left(2\sqrt{9\cdot 7}+7\sqrt{7}\right)$

$\qquad = 3\sqrt{3}\left(6\sqrt{7}+7\sqrt{7}\right)$

$\qquad = 3\sqrt{3}\left(13\sqrt{7}\right)$

$\qquad = 39\sqrt{21}$ square meters

$P = 2\sqrt{63}+6\sqrt{3}+7\sqrt{7}+2\sqrt{27}$

$\qquad = 2\sqrt{9\cdot 7}+6\sqrt{3}+7\sqrt{7}+2\sqrt{9\cdot 3}$

$\qquad = 6\sqrt{7}+6\sqrt{3}+7\sqrt{7}+6\sqrt{3}$

$\qquad = 13\sqrt{7}+12\sqrt{3}$

$\qquad = \left(13\sqrt{7}+12\sqrt{3}\right)$ meters

88. $\left(\sqrt{2}+\sqrt{3}-1\right)^2$

$\qquad = \left[\left(\sqrt{2}+\sqrt{3}\right)-1\right]^2$

$\qquad = \left(\sqrt{2}+\sqrt{3}\right)^2 - 2\left(\sqrt{2}+\sqrt{3}\right)+1^2$

$\qquad = \left(\sqrt{2}\right)^2 + 2\sqrt{2}\sqrt{3} + \left(\sqrt{3}\right)^2 - 2\sqrt{2} - 2\sqrt{3} + 1$

$\qquad = 2 + 2\sqrt{6} + 3 - 2\sqrt{2} - 2\sqrt{3} + 1$

$\qquad = 6 + 2\sqrt{6} - 2\sqrt{2} - 2\sqrt{3}$

90. Answers may vary

Section 10.5

Practice Exercises

1. a. $\dfrac{5}{\sqrt{3}} = \dfrac{5\cdot\sqrt{3}}{\sqrt{3}\cdot\sqrt{3}} = \dfrac{5\sqrt{3}}{3}$

b. $\dfrac{3\sqrt{25}}{\sqrt{4x}} = \dfrac{3(5)}{2\sqrt{x}} = \dfrac{15}{2\sqrt{x}} = \dfrac{15\cdot\sqrt{x}}{2\sqrt{x}\cdot\sqrt{x}} = \dfrac{15\sqrt{x}}{2x}$

c. $\sqrt[3]{\dfrac{2}{9}} = \dfrac{\sqrt[3]{2}}{\sqrt[3]{9}} = \dfrac{\sqrt[3]{2}\cdot\sqrt[3]{3}}{\sqrt[3]{3^2}\cdot\sqrt[3]{3}} = \dfrac{\sqrt[3]{6}}{3}$

2. $\sqrt{\dfrac{3z}{5y}} = \dfrac{\sqrt{3z}}{\sqrt{5y}} = \dfrac{\sqrt{3z}\cdot\sqrt{5y}}{\sqrt{5y}\cdot\sqrt{5y}} = \dfrac{\sqrt{15yz}}{5y}$

3. $\dfrac{\sqrt[3]{z^2}}{\sqrt[3]{27x^4}} = \dfrac{\sqrt[3]{z^2}}{\sqrt[3]{27x^3}\cdot\sqrt[3]{x}}$

$\qquad = \dfrac{\sqrt[3]{z^2}}{3x\sqrt[3]{x}}$

$\qquad = \dfrac{\sqrt[3]{z^2}\cdot\sqrt[3]{x^2}}{3x\sqrt[3]{x}\cdot\sqrt[3]{x^2}}$

$\qquad = \dfrac{\sqrt[3]{z^2x^2}}{3x\sqrt[3]{x^3}}$

$\qquad = \dfrac{\sqrt[3]{x^2z^2}}{3x^2}$

4. a. $\dfrac{5}{3\sqrt{5}+2} = \dfrac{5\left(3\sqrt{5}-2\right)}{\left(3\sqrt{5}+2\right)\left(3\sqrt{5}-2\right)}$

$\qquad = \dfrac{5\left(3\sqrt{5}-2\right)}{\left(3\sqrt{5}\right)^2 - 2^2}$

$\qquad = \dfrac{5\left(3\sqrt{5}-2\right)}{45-4}$

$\qquad = \dfrac{5\left(3\sqrt{5}-2\right)}{41}$

b. $\dfrac{\sqrt{2}+5}{\sqrt{3}-\sqrt{5}} = \dfrac{\left(\sqrt{2}+5\right)\left(\sqrt{3}+\sqrt{5}\right)}{\left(\sqrt{3}-\sqrt{5}\right)\left(\sqrt{3}+\sqrt{5}\right)}$

$= \dfrac{\sqrt{2}\sqrt{3}+\sqrt{2}\sqrt{5}+5\sqrt{3}+5\sqrt{5}}{\left(\sqrt{3}\right)^2-\left(\sqrt{5}\right)^2}$

$= \dfrac{\sqrt{6}+\sqrt{10}+5\sqrt{3}+5\sqrt{5}}{3-5}$

$= \dfrac{\sqrt{6}+\sqrt{10}+5\sqrt{3}+5\sqrt{5}}{-2}$

c. $\dfrac{3\sqrt{x}}{2\sqrt{x}+\sqrt{y}} = \dfrac{3\sqrt{x}\left(2\sqrt{x}-\sqrt{y}\right)}{\left(2\sqrt{x}+\sqrt{y}\right)\left(2\sqrt{x}-\sqrt{y}\right)}$

$= \dfrac{6\sqrt{x^2}-3\sqrt{xy}}{\left(2\sqrt{x}\right)^2-\left(\sqrt{y}\right)^2}$

$= \dfrac{6x-3\sqrt{xy}}{4x-y}$

5. $\dfrac{\sqrt{32}}{\sqrt{80}} = \dfrac{\sqrt{16\cdot2}}{\sqrt{16\cdot5}} = \dfrac{4\sqrt{2}}{4\sqrt{5}} = \dfrac{\sqrt{2}}{\sqrt{5}} = \dfrac{\sqrt{2}\cdot\sqrt{2}}{\sqrt{5}\cdot\sqrt{2}} = \dfrac{2}{\sqrt{10}}$

6. $\dfrac{\sqrt[3]{5b}}{\sqrt[3]{2a}} = \dfrac{\sqrt[3]{5b}\cdot\sqrt[3]{25b^2}}{\sqrt[3]{2a}\cdot\sqrt[3]{25b^2}} = \dfrac{\sqrt[3]{125b^3}}{\sqrt[3]{50ab^2}} = \dfrac{5b}{\sqrt[3]{50ab^2}}$

7. $\dfrac{\sqrt{x}-3}{4} = \dfrac{\left(\sqrt{x}-3\right)\left(\sqrt{x}+3\right)}{4\left(\sqrt{x}+3\right)}$

$= \dfrac{\left(\sqrt{x}\right)^2-(3)^2}{4\left(\sqrt{x}+3\right)}$

$= \dfrac{x-9}{4\left(\sqrt{x}+3\right)}$

Vocabulary and Readiness Check

1. The <u>conjugate</u> of $a+b$ is $a-b$.

2. The process of writing an equivalent expression, but without a radical in the denominator is called <u>rationalizing the denominator</u>.

3. The process of writing an equivalent expression, but without a radical in the numerator is called <u>rationalizing the numerator</u>.

4. To rationalize the denominator of $\dfrac{5}{\sqrt{3}}$, we multiply by $\dfrac{\sqrt{3}}{\sqrt{3}}$.

5. The conjugate of $\sqrt{2}+x$ is $\sqrt{2}-x$.

6. The conjugate of $\sqrt{3}+y$ is $\sqrt{3}-y$.

7. The conjugate of $5-\sqrt{a}$ is $5+\sqrt{a}$.

8. The conjugate of $6-\sqrt{b}$ is $6+\sqrt{b}$.

9. The conjugate of $-7\sqrt{5}+8\sqrt{x}$ is $-7\sqrt{5}-8\sqrt{x}$.

10. The conjugate of $-9\sqrt{2}-6\sqrt{y}$ is $-9\sqrt{2}+6\sqrt{y}$.

Exercise Set 10.5

2. $\dfrac{\sqrt{3}}{\sqrt{2}} = \dfrac{\sqrt{3}\cdot\sqrt{2}}{\sqrt{2}\cdot\sqrt{2}} = \dfrac{\sqrt{6}}{\sqrt{4}} = \dfrac{\sqrt{6}}{2}$

4. $\sqrt{\dfrac{1}{2}} = \dfrac{\sqrt{1}}{\sqrt{2}} = \dfrac{1\cdot\sqrt{2}}{\sqrt{2}\cdot\sqrt{2}} = \dfrac{\sqrt{2}}{\sqrt{4}} = \dfrac{\sqrt{2}}{2}$

6. $\sqrt{\dfrac{25}{y}} = \dfrac{\sqrt{25}}{\sqrt{y}} = \dfrac{5}{\sqrt{y}} = \dfrac{5\cdot\sqrt{y}}{\sqrt{y}\cdot\sqrt{y}} = \dfrac{5\sqrt{y}}{\sqrt{y^2}} = \dfrac{5\sqrt{y}}{y}$

8. $\dfrac{6}{\sqrt[3]{9}} = \dfrac{6\cdot\sqrt[3]{3}}{\sqrt[3]{3^2}\cdot\sqrt[3]{3}} = \dfrac{6\sqrt[3]{3}}{\sqrt[3]{3^3}} = \dfrac{6\sqrt[3]{3}}{3} = 2\sqrt[3]{3}$

10. $\dfrac{5}{\sqrt{27a}} = \dfrac{5}{3\sqrt{3a}} = \dfrac{5\cdot\sqrt{3a}}{3\sqrt{3a}\cdot\sqrt{3a}} = \dfrac{5\sqrt{3a}}{3\cdot3a} = \dfrac{5\sqrt{3a}}{9a}$

12. $\dfrac{5}{\sqrt[3]{3y}} = \dfrac{5\cdot\sqrt[3]{9y^2}}{\sqrt[3]{3y}\cdot\sqrt[3]{9y^2}} = \dfrac{5\sqrt[3]{9y^2}}{\sqrt[3]{27y^3}} = \dfrac{5\sqrt[3]{9y^2}}{3y}$

14. $\dfrac{x}{\sqrt{5}} = \dfrac{x\cdot\sqrt{5}}{\sqrt{5}\cdot\sqrt{5}} = \dfrac{x\sqrt{5}}{5}$

16. $\dfrac{5}{\sqrt[3]{9}} = \dfrac{5\cdot\sqrt[3]{3}}{\sqrt[3]{9}\cdot\sqrt[3]{3}} = \dfrac{5\sqrt[3]{3}}{\sqrt[3]{27}} = \dfrac{5\sqrt[3]{3}}{3}$

18. $\dfrac{-5\sqrt{2}}{\sqrt{11}} = \dfrac{-5\sqrt{2}\cdot\sqrt{11}}{\sqrt{11}\cdot\sqrt{11}} = \dfrac{-5\sqrt{22}}{11}$

20. $\sqrt{\dfrac{13a}{2b}} = \dfrac{\sqrt{13a}}{\sqrt{2b}} = \dfrac{\sqrt{13a}\cdot\sqrt{2b}}{\sqrt{2b}\cdot\sqrt{2b}} = \dfrac{\sqrt{26ab}}{2b}$

22. $\sqrt[3]{\dfrac{7}{10}} = \dfrac{\sqrt[3]{7}}{\sqrt[3]{10}}\cdot\dfrac{\sqrt[3]{100}}{\sqrt[3]{100}} = \dfrac{\sqrt[3]{700}}{10}$

24. $\sqrt{\dfrac{11y}{45}} = \dfrac{\sqrt{11y}}{\sqrt{45}} = \dfrac{\sqrt{11y}}{3\sqrt{5}}\cdot\dfrac{\sqrt{5}}{\sqrt{5}} = \dfrac{\sqrt{55y}}{15}$

26. $\dfrac{1}{\sqrt{32x}} = \dfrac{1}{4\sqrt{2x}}\cdot\dfrac{\sqrt{2x}}{\sqrt{2x}} = \dfrac{\sqrt{2x}}{8x}$

28. $\dfrac{\sqrt[3]{3x}}{\sqrt[3]{4y^4}} = \dfrac{\sqrt[3]{3x}}{y\sqrt[3]{4y}}\cdot\dfrac{\sqrt[3]{2y^2}}{\sqrt[3]{2y^2}} = \dfrac{\sqrt[3]{6xy^2}}{y\cdot 2y} = \dfrac{\sqrt[3]{6xy^2}}{2y^2}$

30. $\sqrt[4]{\dfrac{1}{9}} = \dfrac{\sqrt[4]{1}}{\sqrt[4]{9}} = \dfrac{1}{\sqrt[4]{9}} = \dfrac{1\cdot\sqrt[4]{3^2}}{\sqrt[4]{3^2}\cdot\sqrt[4]{3^2}} = \dfrac{\sqrt[4]{9}}{3}$

32. $\sqrt[5]{\dfrac{32}{m^6 n^{13}}} = \dfrac{\sqrt[5]{32}}{\sqrt[5]{m^6 n^{13}}}$

$= \dfrac{2}{mn^2\sqrt[5]{mn^3}}$

$= \dfrac{2\cdot\sqrt[5]{m^4 n^2}}{mn^2\sqrt[5]{mn^3}\cdot\sqrt[5]{m^4 n^2}}$

$= \dfrac{2\sqrt[5]{m^4 n^2}}{mn^2\cdot mn}$

$= \dfrac{2\sqrt[5]{m^4 n^2}}{m^2 n^3}$

34. $\dfrac{9y}{\sqrt[4]{4y^9}} = \dfrac{9y}{y^2\sqrt[4]{4y}}$

$= \dfrac{9y\cdot\sqrt[4]{2^2 y^3}}{y^2\sqrt[4]{2^2 y}\cdot\sqrt[4]{2^2 y^3}}$

$= \dfrac{9y\sqrt[4]{4y^3}}{y^2\cdot 2y}$

$= \dfrac{9\sqrt[4]{4y^3}}{2y^2}$

36. $\dfrac{3}{\sqrt{7}-4} = \dfrac{3(\sqrt{7}+4)}{(\sqrt{7}-4)(\sqrt{7}+4)}$

$= \dfrac{3(\sqrt{7}+4)}{7-16}$

$= \dfrac{3(\sqrt{7}+4)}{-9}$

$= -\dfrac{\sqrt{7}+4}{3}$

38. $\dfrac{-8}{\sqrt{y}+4} = \dfrac{-8(\sqrt{y}-4)}{(\sqrt{y}+4)(\sqrt{y}-4)}$

$= \dfrac{-8(\sqrt{y}-4)}{y-16}$ or $\dfrac{32-8\sqrt{y}}{y-16}$

40. $\dfrac{\sqrt{3}+\sqrt{4}}{\sqrt{2}-\sqrt{3}} = \dfrac{\sqrt{3}+2}{\sqrt{2}-\sqrt{3}}$

$= \dfrac{(\sqrt{3}+2)(\sqrt{2}+\sqrt{3})}{(\sqrt{2}-\sqrt{3})(\sqrt{2}+\sqrt{3})}$

$= \dfrac{\sqrt{6}+3+2\sqrt{2}+2\sqrt{3}}{2-3}$

$= \dfrac{\sqrt{6}+3+2\sqrt{2}+2\sqrt{3}}{-1}$

$= -3-\sqrt{6}-2\sqrt{2}-2\sqrt{3}$

42. $\dfrac{2\sqrt{a}-3}{2\sqrt{a}+\sqrt{b}} = \dfrac{(2\sqrt{a}-3)(2\sqrt{a}-\sqrt{b})}{(2\sqrt{a}+\sqrt{b})(2\sqrt{a}-\sqrt{b})}$

$= \dfrac{4a-2\sqrt{ab}-6\sqrt{a}+3\sqrt{b}}{4a-b}$

44. $\dfrac{-3}{\sqrt{6}-2} = \dfrac{-3(\sqrt{6}+2)}{(\sqrt{6}-2)(\sqrt{6}+2)}$

$= \dfrac{-3(\sqrt{6}+2)}{6-4}$

$= \dfrac{-3(\sqrt{6}+2)}{2}$ or $\dfrac{-3\sqrt{6}-6}{2}$

46. $\dfrac{2\sqrt{a}}{2\sqrt{x}-\sqrt{y}}=\dfrac{2\sqrt{a}\left(2\sqrt{x}+\sqrt{y}\right)}{\left(2\sqrt{x}-\sqrt{y}\right)\left(2\sqrt{x}+\sqrt{y}\right)}$

$\qquad\qquad = \dfrac{2\sqrt{a}\left(2\sqrt{x}+\sqrt{y}\right)}{4x-y}$

$\qquad\qquad = \dfrac{4\sqrt{ax}+2\sqrt{ay}}{4x-y}$

48. $\dfrac{4\sqrt{5}+\sqrt{2}}{2\sqrt{5}-\sqrt{2}}=\dfrac{\left(4\sqrt{5}+\sqrt{2}\right)\left(2\sqrt{5}+\sqrt{2}\right)}{\left(2\sqrt{5}-\sqrt{2}\right)\left(2\sqrt{5}+\sqrt{2}\right)}$

$\qquad\qquad = \dfrac{8(5)+4\sqrt{10}+2\sqrt{10}+2}{4(5)-2}$

$\qquad\qquad = \dfrac{42+6\sqrt{10}}{18}$

$\qquad\qquad = \dfrac{6\left(7+\sqrt{10}\right)}{18}$

$\qquad\qquad = \dfrac{7+\sqrt{10}}{3}$

50. $\sqrt{\dfrac{3}{2}}=\dfrac{\sqrt{3}}{\sqrt{2}}=\dfrac{\sqrt{3}\cdot\sqrt{3}}{\sqrt{2}\cdot\sqrt{3}}=\dfrac{3}{\sqrt{6}}$

52. $\sqrt{\dfrac{12}{7}}=\dfrac{\sqrt{12}}{\sqrt{7}}=\dfrac{2\sqrt{3}}{\sqrt{7}}=\dfrac{2\sqrt{3}\cdot\sqrt{3}}{\sqrt{7}\cdot\sqrt{3}}=\dfrac{2\cdot3}{\sqrt{21}}=\dfrac{6}{\sqrt{21}}$

54. $\dfrac{\sqrt{3x^5}}{6}=\dfrac{x^2\sqrt{3x}}{6}$

$\qquad\quad = \dfrac{x^2\sqrt{3x}\cdot\sqrt{3x}}{6\cdot\sqrt{3x}}$

$\qquad\quad = \dfrac{x^2\cdot3x}{6\sqrt{3x}}$

$\qquad\quad = \dfrac{3x^3}{6\sqrt{3x}}$

$\qquad\quad = \dfrac{x^3}{2\sqrt{3x}}$

56. $\dfrac{\sqrt[3]{4x}}{\sqrt[3]{z^4}}=\dfrac{\sqrt[3]{4x}}{z\sqrt[3]{z}}=\dfrac{\sqrt[3]{2^2 x}\cdot\sqrt[3]{2x^2}}{z\sqrt[3]{z}\cdot\sqrt[3]{2x^2}}=\dfrac{2x}{z\sqrt[3]{2x^2 z}}$

58. $\sqrt{\dfrac{3}{7}}=\dfrac{\sqrt{3}}{\sqrt{7}}=\dfrac{\sqrt{3}\cdot\sqrt{3}}{\sqrt{7}\cdot\sqrt{3}}=\dfrac{3}{\sqrt{21}}$

60. $\dfrac{\sqrt{y}}{7}=\dfrac{\sqrt{y}\cdot\sqrt{y}}{7\cdot\sqrt{y}}=\dfrac{y}{7\sqrt{y}}$

62. $\sqrt[3]{\dfrac{25}{2}}=\dfrac{\sqrt[3]{25}}{\sqrt[3]{2}}=\dfrac{\sqrt[3]{5^2}\cdot\sqrt[3]{5}}{\sqrt[3]{2}\cdot\sqrt[3]{5}}=\dfrac{5}{\sqrt[3]{10}}$

64. $\sqrt[3]{\dfrac{9y}{7}}=\dfrac{\sqrt[3]{9y}}{\sqrt[3]{7}}=\dfrac{\sqrt[3]{3^2 y}\cdot\sqrt[3]{3y^2}}{\sqrt[3]{7}\cdot\sqrt[3]{3y^2}}=\dfrac{3y}{\sqrt[3]{21y^2}}$

66. $\sqrt{\dfrac{8x^5 y}{2z}}=\sqrt{\dfrac{4x^5 y}{z}}=\dfrac{\sqrt{4x^5 y}}{\sqrt{z}}$

$\qquad\qquad = \dfrac{2x^2\sqrt{xy}}{\sqrt{z}}$

$\qquad\qquad = \dfrac{2x^2\sqrt{xy}\cdot\sqrt{xy}}{\sqrt{z}\cdot\sqrt{xy}}$

$\qquad\qquad = \dfrac{2x^2\cdot xy}{\sqrt{xyz}}$

$\qquad\qquad = \dfrac{2x^3 y}{\sqrt{xyz}}$

68. Answers may vary

70. $\dfrac{\sqrt{15}+1}{2}=\dfrac{\left(\sqrt{15}+1\right)\left(\sqrt{15}-1\right)}{2\left(\sqrt{15}-1\right)}$

$\qquad\qquad = \dfrac{15-1}{2\left(\sqrt{15}-1\right)}$

$\qquad\qquad = \dfrac{14}{2\left(\sqrt{15}-1\right)}$

$\qquad\qquad = \dfrac{7}{\sqrt{15}-1}$

72. $\dfrac{\sqrt{5}+2}{\sqrt{2}}=\dfrac{\left(\sqrt{5}+2\right)\left(\sqrt{5}-2\right)}{\sqrt{2}\left(\sqrt{5}-2\right)}$

$\qquad\qquad = \dfrac{5-4}{\sqrt{10}-2\sqrt{2}}$

$\qquad\qquad = \dfrac{1}{\sqrt{10}-2\sqrt{2}}$

74. $\dfrac{5+\sqrt{2}}{\sqrt{2x}} = \dfrac{\left(5+\sqrt{2}\right)\left(5-\sqrt{2}\right)}{\sqrt{2x}\left(5-\sqrt{2}\right)}$

$= \dfrac{25-2}{5\sqrt{2x}-\sqrt{4x}}$

$= \dfrac{23}{5\sqrt{2x}-2\sqrt{x}}$

76. $\dfrac{\sqrt{8}-\sqrt{3}}{\sqrt{2}+\sqrt{3}} = \dfrac{\left(\sqrt{8}-\sqrt{3}\right)\left(\sqrt{8}+\sqrt{3}\right)}{\left(\sqrt{2}+\sqrt{3}\right)\left(\sqrt{8}+\sqrt{3}\right)}$

$= \dfrac{8-3}{\sqrt{16}+\sqrt{6}+\sqrt{24}+3}$

$= \dfrac{5}{4+\sqrt{6}+2\sqrt{6}+3}$

$= \dfrac{5}{7+3\sqrt{6}}$

78. $\dfrac{\sqrt{x}+\sqrt{y}}{\sqrt{x}-\sqrt{y}} = \dfrac{\left(\sqrt{x}+\sqrt{y}\right)\left(\sqrt{x}-\sqrt{y}\right)}{\left(\sqrt{x}-\sqrt{y}\right)\left(\sqrt{x}-\sqrt{y}\right)}$

$= \dfrac{x-y}{x-2\sqrt{xy}+y}$

80. $9x-4 = 7(x-2)$
$9x-4 = 7x-14$
$2x = -10$
$x = -5$
The solution is –5.

82. $(y+2)(5y+4) = 0$
$y+2 = 0 \quad \text{or} \quad 5y+4 = 0$
$y = -2 \quad \text{or} \qquad 5y = -4$
$$y = -\dfrac{4}{5}$$
The solutions are $-2, -\dfrac{4}{5}$.

84. $x^3 = x$
$x^3 - x = 0$
$x(x^2-1) = 0$
$x(x+1)(x-1) = 0$
$x = 0 \quad \text{or} \quad x+1 = 0 \quad \text{or} \quad x-1 = 0$
$\qquad\qquad\qquad x = -1 \quad \text{or} \qquad x = 1$
The solutions are –1, 0, 1.

86. $\dfrac{5}{\sqrt{27}} = \dfrac{5}{\sqrt{27}} \cdot \dfrac{\sqrt{3}}{\sqrt{3}} = \dfrac{5\sqrt{3}}{\sqrt{81}} = \dfrac{5\sqrt{3}}{9}$
The smallest number is $\sqrt{3}$.

88. $r = \sqrt{\dfrac{3V}{7\pi}} = \dfrac{\sqrt{3V}}{\sqrt{7\pi}} = \dfrac{\sqrt{3V}\cdot\sqrt{3V}}{\sqrt{7\pi}\cdot\sqrt{3V}} = \dfrac{3V}{\sqrt{21\pi V}}$

90. Answers may vary

The Bigger Picture

1. $\sqrt{56} = \sqrt{4\cdot14} = \sqrt{4}\cdot\sqrt{14} = 2\sqrt{14}$

2. $\sqrt{\dfrac{20x^5}{49}} = \dfrac{\sqrt{20x^5}}{\sqrt{49}}$

$= \dfrac{\sqrt{4x^4\cdot5x}}{7}$

$= \dfrac{\sqrt{4x^4}\cdot\sqrt{5x}}{7}$

$= \dfrac{2x^2\sqrt{5x}}{7}$

3. $(-5x^{12}y^{-3})(3x^{-7}y^{14}) = -5\cdot3x^{12-7}y^{-3+14}$
$\qquad\qquad\qquad\qquad\qquad = -15x^5y^{11}$

4. $\sqrt{\dfrac{10}{11}} = \dfrac{\sqrt{10}}{\sqrt{11}} = \dfrac{\sqrt{10}\cdot\sqrt{11}}{\sqrt{11}\cdot\sqrt{11}} = \dfrac{\sqrt{110}}{11}$

5. $\dfrac{8}{\sqrt{5}-1} = \dfrac{8\left(\sqrt{5}+1\right)}{\left(\sqrt{5}-1\right)\left(\sqrt{5}+1\right)}$

$= \dfrac{8\left(\sqrt{5}+1\right)}{5-1}$

$= \dfrac{8\left(\sqrt{5}+1\right)}{4}$

$= 2\left(\sqrt{5}+1\right) \text{ or } 2\sqrt{5}+2$

6. $\dfrac{1}{2}(6x^2-4)+\dfrac{1}{3}(6x^2-9)-14$
$= 3x^2-2+2x^2-3-14$
$= 5x^2-19$

7. $\dfrac{\sqrt{13}}{\sqrt{2x^5}} = \dfrac{\sqrt{13}}{\sqrt{x^4 \cdot 2x}}$

$\qquad = \dfrac{\sqrt{13}}{x^2\sqrt{2x}}$

$\qquad = \dfrac{\sqrt{13}}{x^2\sqrt{2x}} \cdot \dfrac{\sqrt{2x}}{\sqrt{2x}}$

$\qquad = \dfrac{\sqrt{26x}}{2x^3}$

8. $\dfrac{y}{y^2+1} - \dfrac{2y-6}{y^2+1} = \dfrac{y-(2y-6)}{y^2+1}$

$\qquad = \dfrac{y-2y+6}{y^2+1}$

$\qquad = \dfrac{-y+6}{y^2+1}$

9. $\dfrac{5x^3+20x}{10x-10y} \div \dfrac{2x^2+8}{x^2-y^2} = \dfrac{5x^3+20x}{10x-10y} \cdot \dfrac{x^2-y^2}{2x^2+8}$

$\qquad = \dfrac{5x(x^2+4)\cdot(x+y)(x-y)}{2\cdot5(x-y)\cdot2(x^2+4)}$

$\qquad = \dfrac{x(x+y)}{4}$

10. $\sqrt[3]{16y^{20}} = \sqrt[3]{8y^{18}\cdot2y^2}$

$\qquad = \sqrt[3]{2^3y^{18}}\,\sqrt[3]{2y^2}$

$\qquad = 2y^6\sqrt[3]{2y^2}$

Integrated Review

1. $\sqrt{81} = 9$ because $9^2 = 81$.

2. $\sqrt[3]{-8} = -2$ because $(-2)^3 = -8$.

3. $\sqrt[4]{\dfrac{1}{16}} = \dfrac{1}{2}$ because $\left(\dfrac{1}{2}\right)^4 = \dfrac{1}{16}$.

4. $\sqrt{x^6} = x^3$ because $(x^3)^2 = x^6$.

5. $\sqrt[3]{y^9} = y^3$ because $(y^3)^3 = y^9$.

6. $\sqrt{4y^{10}} = 2y^5$ because $(2y^5)^2 = 4y^{10}$.

7. $\sqrt[5]{-32y^5} = -2y$ because $(-2y)^5 = -32y^5$.

8. $\sqrt[4]{81b^{12}} = 3b^3$ because $(3b^3)^4 = 81b^{12}$.

9. $36^{1/2} = \sqrt{36} = 6$

10. $(3y)^{1/4} = \sqrt[4]{3y}$

11. $64^{-2/3} = \dfrac{1}{\left(\sqrt[3]{64}\right)^2} = \dfrac{1}{4^2} = \dfrac{1}{16}$

12. $(x+1)^{3/5} = \sqrt[5]{(x+1)^3}$

13. $y^{-1/6} \cdot y^{7/6} = y^{-\frac{1}{6}+\frac{7}{6}} = y^{6/6} = y$

14. $\dfrac{(2x^{1/3})^4}{x^{5/6}} = 16x^{4/3}x^{-5/6}$

$\qquad = 16x^{\frac{8}{6}-\frac{5}{6}}$

$\qquad = 16x^{3/6}$

$\qquad = 16x^{1/2}$

15. $\dfrac{x^{1/4}x^{3/4}}{x^{-1/4}} = x^{\frac{1}{4}+\frac{3}{4}+\frac{1}{4}} = x^{5/4}$

16. $4^{1/3} \cdot 4^{2/5} = 4^{\frac{1}{3}+\frac{2}{5}} = 4^{\frac{5}{15}+\frac{6}{15}} = 4^{11/15}$

17. $\sqrt[3]{8x^6} = (8x^6)^{1/3} = (2^3x^6)^{1/3} = 2^{3/3}x^{6/3} = 2x^2$

18. $\sqrt[12]{a^9b^6} = (a^9b^6)^{1/12}$

$\qquad = a^{9/12}b^{6/12}$

$\qquad = a^{3/4}b^{1/2}$

$\qquad = a^{3/4}b^{2/4}$

$\qquad = (a^3b^2)^{1/4}$

$\qquad = \sqrt[4]{a^3b^2}$

19. $\sqrt[4]{x} \cdot \sqrt{x} = x^{1/4} \cdot x^{1/2} = x^{\frac{1}{4}+\frac{2}{4}} = x^{3/4} = \sqrt[4]{x^3}$

20. $\sqrt{5} \cdot \sqrt[3]{2} = 5^{1/2} \cdot 2^{1/3}$

$\qquad = 5^{3/6} \cdot 2^{2/6}$

$\qquad = (5^3 \cdot 2^2)^{1/6}$

$\qquad = \sqrt[6]{5^3 \cdot 2^2}$

$\qquad = \sqrt[6]{500}$

21. $\sqrt{40} = \sqrt{4}\sqrt{10} = 2\sqrt{10}$

22. $\sqrt[4]{16x^7y^{10}} = \sqrt[4]{16x^4y^8}\sqrt[4]{x^3y^2} = 2xy^2\sqrt[4]{x^3y^2}$

23. $\sqrt[3]{54x^4} = \sqrt[3]{27x^3}\sqrt[3]{2x} = 3x\sqrt[3]{2x}$

24. $\sqrt[5]{-64b^{10}} = \sqrt[5]{-32b^{10}}\sqrt[5]{2} = -2b^2\sqrt[5]{2}$

25. $\sqrt{5}\cdot\sqrt{x} = \sqrt{5x}$

26. $\sqrt[3]{8x}\cdot\sqrt[3]{8x^2} = \sqrt[3]{64x^3} = 4x$

27. $\dfrac{\sqrt{98y^6}}{\sqrt{2y}} = \sqrt{\dfrac{98y^6}{2y}}$
$= \sqrt{49y^5}$
$= \sqrt{49y^4}\cdot\sqrt{y}$
$= 7y^2\sqrt{y}$

28. $\dfrac{\sqrt[4]{48a^9b^3}}{\sqrt[4]{ab^3}} = \sqrt[4]{\dfrac{48a^9b^3}{ab^3}}$
$= \sqrt[4]{48a^8}$
$= \sqrt[4]{16a^8}\cdot\sqrt[4]{3}$
$= 2a^2\sqrt[4]{3}$

29. $\sqrt{20} - \sqrt{75} + 5\sqrt{7} = \sqrt{4}\sqrt{5} - \sqrt{25}\sqrt{3} + 5\sqrt{7}$
$= 2\sqrt{5} - 5\sqrt{3} + 5\sqrt{7}$

30. $\sqrt[3]{54y^4} - y\sqrt[3]{16y} = \sqrt[3]{27y^3}\sqrt[3]{2y} - y\sqrt[3]{8}\sqrt[3]{2y}$
$= 3y\sqrt[3]{2y} - 2y\sqrt[3]{2y}$
$= y\sqrt[3]{2y}$

31. $\sqrt{3}\left(\sqrt{5} - \sqrt{2}\right) = \sqrt{3}\sqrt{5} - \sqrt{3}\sqrt{2} = \sqrt{15} - \sqrt{6}$

32. $\left(\sqrt{7} + \sqrt{3}\right)^2 = \left(\sqrt{7}\right)^2 + 2\sqrt{7}\sqrt{3} + \left(\sqrt{3}\right)^2$
$= 7 + 2\sqrt{21} + 3$
$= 10 + 2\sqrt{21}$

33. $\left(2x - \sqrt{5}\right)\left(2x + \sqrt{5}\right) = (2x)^2 - \left(\sqrt{5}\right)^2$
$= 4x^2 - 5$

34. $\left(\sqrt{x+1} - 1\right)^2 = \left(\sqrt{x+1}\right)^2 - 2\left(\sqrt{x+1}\right) + 1^2$
$= x + 1 - 2\sqrt{x+1} + 1$
$= x + 2 - 2\sqrt{x+1}$

35. $\sqrt{\dfrac{7}{3}} = \dfrac{\sqrt{7}}{\sqrt{3}} = \dfrac{\sqrt{7}}{\sqrt{3}}\cdot\dfrac{\sqrt{3}}{\sqrt{3}} = \dfrac{\sqrt{21}}{3}$

36. $\dfrac{5}{\sqrt[3]{2x^2}} = \dfrac{5}{\sqrt[3]{2x^2}}\cdot\dfrac{\sqrt[3]{4x}}{\sqrt[3]{4x}} = \dfrac{5\sqrt[3]{4x}}{\sqrt[3]{8x^3}} = \dfrac{5\sqrt[3]{4x}}{2x}$

37. $\dfrac{\sqrt{3} - \sqrt{7}}{2\sqrt{3} + \sqrt{7}}$

$= \dfrac{\sqrt{3} - \sqrt{7}}{2\sqrt{3} + \sqrt{7}}\cdot\dfrac{\left(2\sqrt{3} - \sqrt{7}\right)}{\left(2\sqrt{3} - \sqrt{7}\right)}$

$= \dfrac{\sqrt{3}\left(2\sqrt{3}\right) - \sqrt{3}\sqrt{7} - \sqrt{7}\left(2\sqrt{3}\right) + \sqrt{7}\sqrt{7}}{\left(2\sqrt{3}\right)^2 - \left(\sqrt{7}\right)^2}$

$= \dfrac{6 - \sqrt{21} - 2\sqrt{21} + 7}{12 - 7}$

$= \dfrac{13 - 3\sqrt{21}}{5}$

38. $\sqrt{\dfrac{7}{3}} = \dfrac{\sqrt{7}}{\sqrt{3}} = \dfrac{\sqrt{7}}{\sqrt{3}}\cdot\dfrac{\sqrt{7}}{\sqrt{7}} = \dfrac{7}{\sqrt{21}}$

39. $\sqrt[3]{\dfrac{9y}{11}} = \dfrac{\sqrt[3]{9y}}{\sqrt[3]{11}} = \dfrac{\sqrt[3]{9y}}{\sqrt[3]{11}}\cdot\dfrac{\sqrt[3]{3y^2}}{\sqrt[3]{3y^2}} = \dfrac{\sqrt[3]{27y^3}}{\sqrt[3]{31y^2}} = \dfrac{3y}{\sqrt[3]{33y^2}}$

40. $\dfrac{\sqrt{x} - 2}{\sqrt{x}} = \dfrac{\sqrt{x} - 2}{\sqrt{x}}\cdot\dfrac{\sqrt{x} + 2}{\sqrt{x} + 2}$

$= \dfrac{\left(\sqrt{x}\right)^2 - 2^2}{\sqrt{x}\sqrt{x} + 2\sqrt{x}}$

$= \dfrac{x - 4}{x + 2\sqrt{x}}$

Section 10.6

Practice Exercises

1. $\sqrt{3x - 5} = 7$
$\left(\sqrt{3x - 5}\right)^2 = 7^2$
$3x - 5 = 49$
$3x = 54$
$x = 18$

Check:
$$\sqrt{3x-5}=7$$
$$\sqrt{3(18)-5}\overset{?}{=}7$$
$$\sqrt{54-5}\overset{?}{=}7$$
$$\sqrt{49}\overset{?}{=}7$$
$$7=7$$
The solution is 18.

2. $$\sqrt{3-2x}-4x=0$$
$$\sqrt{3-2x}-4x+4x=0+4x$$
$$\sqrt{3-2x}=4x$$
$$\left(\sqrt{3-2x}\right)^2=\left(4x\right)^2$$
$$3-2x=16x^2$$
$$16x^2+2x-3=0$$
$$(8x-3)(2x+1)=0$$
$$8x-3=0 \text{ or } 2x+1=0$$
$$x=\frac{3}{8} \text{ or } x=-\frac{1}{2}$$

Check $\frac{3}{8}$:
$$\sqrt{3-2x}-4x=0$$
$$\sqrt{3-2\left(\frac{3}{8}\right)}-4\left(\frac{3}{8}\right)\overset{?}{=}0$$
$$\sqrt{\frac{24}{8}-\frac{6}{8}}-\frac{3}{2}\overset{?}{=}0$$
$$\sqrt{\frac{9}{4}}-\frac{3}{2}\overset{?}{=}0$$
$$\frac{3}{2}-\frac{3}{2}=0$$

Check $-\frac{1}{2}$:
$$\sqrt{3-2x}-4x=0$$
$$\sqrt{3-2\left(-\frac{1}{2}\right)}-4\left(-\frac{1}{2}\right)\overset{?}{=}0$$
$$\sqrt{3+1}+2\overset{?}{=}0$$
$$2+2\overset{?}{=}0$$
$$4\ne 0$$

$-\frac{1}{2}$ does not check, so the only solution is $\frac{3}{8}$.

3. $$\sqrt[3]{x-2}+1=3$$
$$\sqrt[3]{x-2}=2$$
$$\left(\sqrt[3]{x-2}\right)^3=2^3$$
$$x-2=8$$
$$x=10$$
Check:
$$\sqrt[3]{x-2}+1=3$$
$$\sqrt[3]{10-2}+1\overset{?}{=}3$$
$$\sqrt[3]{8}+1\overset{?}{=}3$$
$$2+1=3$$
The solution is 10.

4. $$\sqrt{16+x}=x-4$$
$$\left(\sqrt{16+x}\right)^2=\left(x-4\right)^2$$
$$16+x=x^2-8x+16$$
$$x^2-9x=0$$
$$x(x-9)=0$$
$$x=0 \text{ or } x-9=0$$
$$x=9$$

Check 0:
$$\sqrt{16+x}=x-4$$
$$\sqrt{16+0}\overset{?}{=}0-4$$
$$\sqrt{16}\overset{?}{=}-4$$
$$4\ne -4$$
Check 9:
$$\sqrt{16+x}=x-4$$
$$\sqrt{16+9}\overset{?}{=}9-4$$
$$\sqrt{25}\overset{?}{=}5$$
$$5=5$$
0 does not check, so the only solution is 9.

5. $$\sqrt{8x+1}+\sqrt{3x}=2$$
$$\sqrt{8x+1}=2-\sqrt{3x}$$
$$\left(\sqrt{8x+1}\right)^2=\left(2-\sqrt{3x}\right)^2$$
$$8x+1=4-4\sqrt{3x}+3x$$
$$4\sqrt{3x}=3-5x$$
$$\left(4\sqrt{3x}\right)^2=\left(3-5x\right)^2$$
$$16(3x)=9-30x+25x^2$$
$$25x^2-78x+9=0$$
$$(25x-3)(x-3)=0$$
$$25x-3=0 \text{ or } x-3=0$$
$$x=\frac{3}{25} \text{ or } x=3$$

Check $\dfrac{3}{25}$:

$$\sqrt{8x+1}+\sqrt{3x}=2$$

$$\sqrt{8\left(\dfrac{3}{25}\right)+1}+\sqrt{3\left(\dfrac{3}{25}\right)}\overset{?}{=}2$$

$$\sqrt{\dfrac{24}{25}+\dfrac{25}{25}}+\sqrt{\dfrac{9}{25}}\overset{?}{=}2$$

$$\sqrt{\dfrac{49}{25}}+\sqrt{\dfrac{9}{25}}\overset{?}{=}2$$

$$\dfrac{7}{5}+\dfrac{3}{5}\overset{?}{=}2$$

$$\dfrac{10}{5}=2$$

Check 3:

$$\sqrt{8x+1}+\sqrt{3x}=2$$

$$\sqrt{8(3)+1}+\sqrt{3(3)}\overset{?}{=}2$$

$$\sqrt{25}+\sqrt{9}\overset{?}{=}2$$

$$5+3\neq 2$$

3 does not check, so the only solution is $\dfrac{3}{25}$.

6. $\quad a^2+b^2=c^2$

$\quad a^2+6^2=12^2$

$\quad a^2+36=144$

$\quad a^2=108$

$\quad a=\pm\sqrt{108}=\pm\sqrt{36\cdot 3}=\pm 6\sqrt{3}$

Since a is a length, we will use the positive value only. The unknown leg is $6\sqrt{3}$ meters long.

7. Consider the base of the tank, and the plastic divider in the diagonal. Use the Pythagorean theorem to find l.

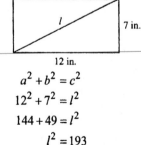

$$a^2+b^2=c^2$$

$$12^2+7^2=l^2$$

$$144+49=l^2$$

$$l^2=193$$

$$l=\pm\sqrt{193}$$

We will use the positive value because l represents length. The divider must be $\sqrt{193}\approx 13.89$ inches long.

Graphing Calculator Explorations

1.

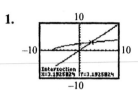

The solution is 3.19.

2.

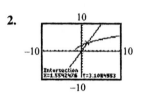

The solution is 1.55.

3.

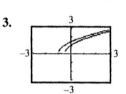

There is no solution. The solution set is $\varnothing$.

4.

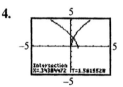

The solution is 0.34.

5.

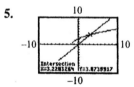

The solution is 3.23.

6.

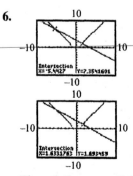

The solutions are −5.44 and 7.35.

Vocabulary and Readiness Check

1. A proposed solution that is not a solution of the original equation is called an <u>extraneous solution</u>.

2. The Pythagorean Theorem states that $a^2 + b^2 = c^2$ where a and b are the lengths of the <u>legs</u> of a <u>right</u> triangle and c is the length of the <u>hypotenuse</u>.

3. The square of $x - 5$, or $(x-5)^2 = \underline{x^2 - 10x + 25}$.

4. The square of $4 - \sqrt{7x}$, or
$$\left(4 - \sqrt{7x}\right)^2 = \underline{16 - 8\sqrt{7x} + 7x}.$$

Exercise Set 10.6

2.
$$\sqrt{3x} = 3$$
$$\left(\sqrt{3x}\right)^2 = 3^2$$
$$3x = 9$$
$$x = 3$$
The solution is 3.

4.
$$\sqrt{x+1} = 5$$
$$\left(\sqrt{x+1}\right)^2 = 5^2$$
$$x + 1 = 25$$
$$x = 24$$
The solution is 24.

6. $\sqrt{5x} = -5$
No solution since a principle square root does not yield a negative number.

8.
$$\sqrt{x-3} - 1 = 0$$
$$\sqrt{x-3} = 1$$
$$\left(\sqrt{x-3}\right)^2 = 1^2$$
$$x - 3 = 1$$
$$x = 4$$
The solution is 4.

10.
$$\sqrt{3x+3} - 4 = 8$$
$$\sqrt{3x+3} = 12$$
$$\left(\sqrt{3x+3}\right)^2 = 12^2$$
$$3x + 3 = 144$$
$$3x = 141$$
$$x = 47$$
The solution is 47.

12.
$$\sqrt[3]{4x} = -2$$
$$\left(\sqrt[3]{4x}\right)^3 = (-2)^3$$
$$4x = -8$$
$$x = -2$$
The solution is –2.

14.
$$\sqrt[3]{2x-6} - 4 = 0$$
$$\sqrt[3]{2x-6} = 4$$
$$\left(\sqrt[3]{2x-6}\right)^3 = 4^3$$
$$2x - 6 = 64$$
$$2x = 70$$
$$x = 35$$
The solution is 35.

16.
$$\sqrt{2x-3} = 3 - x$$
$$\left(\sqrt{2x-3}\right)^2 = (3-x)^2$$
$$2x - 3 = 9 - 6x + x^2$$
$$0 = x^2 - 8x + 12$$
$$0 = (x-6)(x-2)$$
$$x - 6 = 0 \text{ or } x - 2 = 0$$
$$x = 6 \text{ or } \qquad x = 2$$
We discard 6 as extraneous. The solution is 2.

18.
$$2x + \sqrt{x+1} = 8$$
$$\sqrt{x+1} = 8 - 2x$$
$$\left(\sqrt{x+1}\right)^2 = (8-2x)^2$$
$$x + 1 = 64 - 32x + 4x^2$$
$$0 = 4x^2 - 33x + 63$$
$$0 = (4x - 21)(x - 3)$$
$$4x - 21 = 0 \quad \text{ or } x - 3 = 0$$
$$x = \frac{21}{4} \text{ or } \qquad x = 3$$

We discard $\dfrac{21}{4}$ as extraneous. The solution is 3.

20. $\sqrt{x+3}+\sqrt{x-5}=3$

$$\left(\sqrt{x+3}\right)^2=\left(3-\sqrt{x-5}\right)^2$$
$$x+3=9-6\sqrt{x-5}+(x-5)$$
$$x+3=x+4-6\sqrt{x-5}$$
$$-1=-6\sqrt{x-5}$$
$$(-1)^2=\left(-6\sqrt{x-5}\right)^2$$
$$1=36(x-5)$$
$$1=36x-180$$
$$181=36x$$
$$\frac{181}{36}=x$$

The solution is $\frac{181}{36}$.

22. $\sqrt{2x-4}-\sqrt{3x+4}=-2$

$$\sqrt{2x-4}+2=\sqrt{3x+4}$$
$$\left(\sqrt{2x-4}+2\right)^2=\left(\sqrt{3x+4}\right)^2$$
$$(2x-4)+4\sqrt{2x-4}+4=3x+4$$
$$2x+4\sqrt{2x-4}=3x+4$$
$$4\sqrt{2x-4}=x+4$$
$$\left(4\sqrt{2x-4}\right)^2=(x+4)^2$$
$$16(2x-4)=x^2+8x+16$$
$$32x-64=x^2+8x+16$$
$$0=x^2-24x+80$$
$$0=(x-4)(x-20)$$

$x=4$ or $x=20$
The solutions are 4 and 20.

24. $\sqrt{5x-4}=9$

$$\left(\sqrt{5x-4}\right)^2=9^2$$
$$5x-4=81$$
$$5x=85$$
$$x=17$$

The solution is 17.

26. $-\sqrt{3x+9}=-12$

$$\left(-\sqrt{3x+9}\right)^2=(-12)^2$$
$$3x+9=144$$
$$3x=135$$
$$x=45$$

The solution is 45.

28. $\sqrt{3x+1}-2=0$

$$\sqrt{3x+1}=2$$
$$\left(\sqrt{3x+1}\right)^2=2^2$$
$$3x+1=4$$
$$3x=3$$
$$x=1$$

The solution is 1.

30. $\sqrt[4]{2x-9}-3=0$

$$\sqrt[4]{2x-9}=3$$
$$\left(\sqrt[4]{2x-9}\right)^4=3^4$$
$$2x-9=81$$
$$2x=90$$
$$x=45$$

The solution is 45.

32. $\sqrt{3x+9}=6$

$$\left(\sqrt{3x+9}\right)^2=6^2$$
$$3x+9=36$$
$$3x=27$$
$$x=9$$

The solution is 9.

34. $\sqrt[3]{3x}+4=7$

$$\sqrt[3]{3x}=3$$
$$\left(\sqrt[3]{3x}\right)^3=3^3$$
$$3x=27$$
$$x=9$$

The solution is 9.

36. $\sqrt[3]{x-4}-5=-7$

$$\sqrt[3]{x-4}=-2$$
$$\left(\sqrt[3]{x-4}\right)^3=(-2)^3$$
$$x-4=-8$$
$$x=-4$$

The solution is -4.

38. $\sqrt{3y+6}=\sqrt{7y-6}$

$$\left(\sqrt{3y+6}\right)^2=\left(\sqrt{7y-6}\right)^2$$
$$3y+6=7y-6$$
$$-4y=-12$$
$$x=3$$

The solution is 3.

40.
$$x - \sqrt{x-2} = 4$$
$$x - 4 = \sqrt{x-2}$$
$$(x-4)^2 = \left(\sqrt{x-2}\right)^2$$
$$x^2 - 8x + 16 = x - 2$$
$$x^2 - 9x + 18 = 0$$
$$(x-6)(x-3) = 0$$
$$x = 6 \ \text{or} \ x = 3$$
We discard 3 as extraneous. The solution is 6.

42.
$$\sqrt[3]{-4x-3} = \sqrt[3]{-x-15}$$
$$\left(\sqrt[3]{-4x-3}\right)^3 = \left(\sqrt[3]{-x-15}\right)^3$$
$$-4x - 3 = -x - 15$$
$$-3x = -12$$
$$x = 4$$
The solution is 4.

44.
$$\sqrt{2x-1} - 4 = -\sqrt{x-4}$$
$$\left(\sqrt{2x-1} - 4\right)^2 = \left(-\sqrt{x-4}\right)^2$$
$$(2x-1) - 8\sqrt{2x-1} + 16 = x - 4$$
$$x + 19 = 8\sqrt{2x-1}$$
$$(x+19)^2 = \left(8\sqrt{2x-1}\right)^2$$
$$x^2 + 38x + 361 = 64(2x-1)$$
$$x^2 + 38x + 361 = 128x - 64$$
$$x^2 - 90x + 425 = 0$$
$$(x-5)(x-85) = 0$$
$$x = 5 \ \text{or} \ x = 85$$
We discard 85 as extraneous. The solution is 5.

46.
$$\sqrt{7x-4} = \sqrt{4-7x}$$
$$\left(\sqrt{7x-4}\right)^2 = \left(\sqrt{4-7x}\right)^2$$
$$7x - 4 = 4 - 7x$$
$$14x = 8$$
$$x = \frac{8}{14} = \frac{4}{7}$$
The solution is $\frac{4}{7}$.

48.
$$\sqrt{x-2} + 3 = \sqrt{4x+1}$$
$$\left(\sqrt{x-2} + 3\right)^2 = \left(\sqrt{4x+1}\right)^2$$
$$(x-2) + 6\sqrt{x-2} + 9 = 4x + 1$$
$$6\sqrt{x-2} = 3x - 6$$
$$2\sqrt{x-2} = x - 2$$
$$\left(2\sqrt{x-2}\right)^2 = (x-2)^2$$
$$4(x-2) = x^2 - 4x + 4$$
$$4x - 8 = x^2 - 4x + 4$$
$$0 = x^2 - 8x + 12$$
$$0 = (x-6)(x-2)$$
$$x = 6 \ \text{or} \ x = 2$$
The solutions are 2 and 6.

50.
$$\sqrt{x+1} - \sqrt{x-1} = 2$$
$$\sqrt{x+1} = 2 + \sqrt{x-1}$$
$$\left(\sqrt{x+1}\right)^2 = \left(2 + \sqrt{x-1}\right)^2$$
$$x + 1 = 4 + 4\sqrt{x-1} + (x-1)$$
$$-2 = 4\sqrt{x-1}$$
$$(-2)^2 = \left(4\sqrt{x-1}\right)^2$$
$$4 = 16(x-1)$$
$$4 = 16x - 16$$
$$20 = 16x$$
$$x = \frac{20}{16} = \frac{5}{4}$$
We discard $\frac{5}{4}$ as extraneous so there is no solution.

52. Let c = length of the hypotenuse.
$$7^2 + 8^2 = c^2$$
$$49 + 64 = c^2$$
$$113 = c^2$$
$$\sqrt{113} = \sqrt{c^2}$$
$$\sqrt{113} = c$$
$$c = \sqrt{113} \ \text{inches}$$

54. Let b = length of the unknown leg.
$$4^2 + b^2 = 7^2$$
$$16 + b^2 = 49$$
$$b^2 = 33$$
$$\sqrt{b^2} = \sqrt{33}$$
$$b = \sqrt{33} \ \text{cm}$$

56. Let c = length of the hypotenuse.

$$\left(5\sqrt{3}\right)^2 + 10^2 = c^2$$
$$25(3) + 100 = c^2$$
$$175 = c^2$$
$$\sqrt{175} = \sqrt{c^2}$$
$$\sqrt{25 \cdot 7} = c$$
$$c = 5\sqrt{7} \approx 13.2 \text{ cm}$$

58. Let c = length of the hypotenuse.

$$(2.7)^2 + (2.3)^2 = c^2$$
$$7.29 + 5.29 = c^2$$
$$12.58 = c^2$$
$$\sqrt{12.58} = \sqrt{c^2}$$
$$c = \sqrt{12.58} \text{ in.} \approx 3.5 \text{ in.}$$

60. Let a = distance from base.

$$a^2 + (2063)^2 = (2382)^2$$
$$a^2 = (2382)^2 - (2063)^2$$
$$a^2 = 1,417,955$$
$$\sqrt{a^2} = \sqrt{1,417,955}$$
$$a \approx 1191 \text{ feet}$$

62. Let b = distance up the pole.

$$(15)^2 + b^2 = (30 - 2)^2$$
$$225 + b^2 = (28)^2$$
$$b^2 = 784 - 225$$
$$b^2 = 559$$
$$b = \sqrt{559} \text{ ft} \approx 23.64 \text{ ft}$$

64. $S(x) = \sqrt{10.5x}$

$$= \sqrt{10.5(280)}$$
$$= \sqrt{2940}$$
$$= 14\sqrt{15} \text{ mph}$$
$$\approx 54.22 \text{ mph}$$

66. $R = \sqrt{A^2 + B^2}$

$$850 = \sqrt{600^2 + B^2}$$
$$850^2 = \left(\sqrt{600^2 + B^2}\right)^2$$
$$850^2 = 600^2 + B^2$$
$$B^2 = 850^2 - 600^2$$
$$= 722,500 - 360,000$$
$$= 362,500$$
$$B = \sqrt{362,500} = 50\sqrt{145} \approx 602.08 \text{ lb}$$

Tractor B is exerting approximately 602 pounds of force.

68. $S = 2\sqrt{I} - 9$

$$15 = 2\sqrt{I} - 9$$
$$24 = 2\sqrt{I}$$
$$12 = \sqrt{I}$$
$$12^2 = \left(\sqrt{I}\right)^2$$
$$144 = I$$

The estimated IQ is 144.

70. $l = \dfrac{43 \text{ in.}}{1} \cdot \dfrac{1 \text{ ft}}{12 \text{ in.}} = \dfrac{43}{12} \text{ ft}$

$$P = 2\pi\sqrt{\frac{l}{32}} = 2\pi\sqrt{\frac{\frac{43}{12}}{32}} = 2\pi\sqrt{\frac{43}{384}} \approx 2.10 \text{ sec}$$

72. $P = 2\pi\sqrt{\dfrac{l}{32}}$

$$3 = 2\pi\sqrt{\frac{l}{32}}$$
$$\frac{3}{2\pi} = \sqrt{\frac{l}{32}}$$
$$\left(\frac{3}{2\pi}\right)^2 = \left(\sqrt{\frac{l}{32}}\right)^2$$
$$\frac{9}{4\pi^2} = \frac{l}{32}$$
$$l = 32\left(\frac{9}{4\pi^2}\right) \approx 7.30 \text{ feet}$$

74. Answers may vary

76. $s = \dfrac{1}{2}(2+3+3) = \dfrac{1}{2}(8) = 4$

$\begin{aligned} A &= \sqrt{s(s-a)(s-b)(s-c)} \\ &= \sqrt{4(4-2)(4-3)(4-3)} \\ &= \sqrt{4(2)(1)(1)} \\ &= \sqrt{8} \\ &= 2\sqrt{2} \text{ sq cm} \approx 2.83 \text{ sq cm} \end{aligned}$

78. Answers may vary

80.
$\begin{aligned} D(h) &= 111.7\sqrt{h} \\ 40 &= 111.7\sqrt{h} \\ \dfrac{40}{111.7} &= \sqrt{h} \\ \left(\dfrac{40}{111.7}\right)^2 &= \left(\sqrt{h}\right)^2 \\ 0.1282370847 &\approx h \\ h &\approx 0.13 \text{ km} \end{aligned}$

82. Not a function; any vertical line to the right of the *y*-axis intersects the graph more than one time.

84. Not a function; the graph itself is a vertical line that intersects the graph more than one time.

86. Not a function; the *y*-axis is an example of a vertical line that intersects the graph more than one time.

88. $\dfrac{\frac{1}{y}+\frac{4}{5}}{\frac{-3}{20}} = \dfrac{\left(\frac{1}{y}+\frac{4}{5}\right)\cdot 20y}{\left(\frac{-3}{20}\right)\cdot 20y}$

$\qquad = \dfrac{20+16y}{-3y}$

$\qquad = -\dfrac{16y+20}{3y}$

90. $\dfrac{\frac{1}{y}+\frac{1}{x}}{\frac{1}{y}-\frac{1}{x}} = \dfrac{\left(\frac{1}{y}+\frac{1}{x}\right)\cdot xy}{\left(\frac{1}{y}-\frac{1}{x}\right)\cdot xy} = \dfrac{x+y}{x-y}$

92. Answers may vary

94. $\begin{aligned} C(x) &= 80\sqrt[3]{x}+500 \\ 1620 &= 80\sqrt[3]{x}+500 \\ 1120 &= 80\sqrt[3]{x} \\ 14 &= \sqrt[3]{x} \\ 14^3 &= \left(\sqrt[3]{x}\right)^3 \\ 2744 &= x \end{aligned}$

Thus, 2743 deliveries will keep overhead below $1620.

96. $3\sqrt{x^2-8x} = x^2 - 8x$

Let $t = x^2 - 8x$. Then

$\begin{aligned} 3\sqrt{t} &= t \\ \left(3\sqrt{t}\right)^2 &= t^2 \\ 9t &= t^2 \\ 0 &= t^2 - 9t \\ 0 &= t(t-9) \end{aligned}$

$t = 0 \quad \text{or} \quad t = 9$

Replace *t* with $x^2 - 8x$.

$\begin{array}{ll} x^2 - 8x = 0 & \text{or} \quad x^2 - 8x = 9 \\ x(x-8) = 0 & \qquad x^2 - 8x - 9 = 0 \\ x = 0 \text{ or } x = 8 & \qquad (x-9)(x+1) = 0 \\ & \qquad x = 9 \text{ or } x = -1 \end{array}$

The solutions are –1, 0, 8, and 9.

98. $7 - (x^2 - 3x) = \sqrt{(x^2-3x)+5}$

Let $t = x^2 - 3x$. Then

$\begin{aligned} 7 - t &= \sqrt{t+5} \\ (7-t)^2 &= \left(\sqrt{t+5}\right)^2 \\ 49 - 14t + t^2 &= t + 5 \\ t^2 - 15t + 44 &= 0 \\ (t-11)(t-4) &= 0 \end{aligned}$

$t = 11 \text{ or } t = 4$

Replace *t* with $x^2 - 3x$.

$\begin{array}{ll} x^2 - 3x = 11 & \text{or} \quad x^2 - 3x = 4 \\ x^2 - 3x - 11 = 0 & \qquad x^2 - 3x - 4 = 0 \\ \text{Can't factor} & \qquad (x-4)(x+1) = 0 \\ & \qquad x = 4 \text{ or } x = -1 \end{array}$

The solutions are –1 and 4.

The Bigger Picture

1. $$\frac{x}{4} + \frac{x+18}{20} = \frac{x-5}{5}$$

    $$20\left(\frac{x}{4}\right) + 20\left(\frac{x+18}{20}\right) = 20\left(\frac{x-5}{5}\right)$$

    $$5x + (x+18) = 4(x-5)$$
    $$6x + 18 = 4x - 20$$
    $$2x = -38$$
    $$x = -19$$

    The solution set is $\{-19\}$.

2. $|3x - 5| = 10$

    $3x - 5 = -10$ or $3x - 5 = 10$

    $3x = -5$ $\qquad$ $3x = 15$

    $x = -\dfrac{5}{3}$ $\qquad$ $x = 5$

    The solution set is $\left\{-\dfrac{5}{3}, 5\right\}$.

3. $$2x^2 - x = 45$$
    $$2x^2 - x - 45 = 0$$
    $$(2x + 9)(x - 5) = 0$$

    $2x + 9 = 0$ or $x - 5 = 0$

    $x = -\dfrac{9}{2}$ $\qquad$ $x = 5$

    The solution set is $\left\{-\dfrac{9}{2}, 5\right\}$.

4. $-6 \le -5x - 1 \le 10$

    $-5 \le -5x \le 11$

    $1 \ge x \ge -\dfrac{11}{5}$

    $-\dfrac{11}{5} \le x \le 1$

    The solution is $\left[-\dfrac{11}{5}, 1\right]$.

5. $4(x-1) + 3x > 1 + 2(x-6)$

    $4x - 4 + 3x > 1 + 2x - 12$

    $7x - 4 > 2x - 11$

    $5x > -7$

    $x > -\dfrac{7}{5}$

    The solution is $\left(-\dfrac{7}{5}, \infty\right)$.

6. $\sqrt{x} + 14 = x - 6$

    $\sqrt{x} = x - 20$

    $\left(\sqrt{x}\right)^2 = (x-20)^2$

    $x = x^2 - 40x + 400$

    $0 = x^2 - 41x + 400$

    $0 = (x - 25)(x - 16)$

    $x - 25 = 0$ or $x - 16 = 0$

    $x = 25$ $\qquad$ $x = 16$

    Discard 16 as an extraneous solution. The solution set is $\{25\}$.

7. $x \ge 10$ or $-x < 5$

    $x \ge 10$ or $x > -5$

    The solution is $(-5, \infty)$.

8. $\sqrt{3x - 1} + 4 = 1$

    $\sqrt{3x - 1} = -3$

    There is no real number whose square root is negative. The solution set is $\varnothing$.

9. $|x - 2| > 15$

    $x - 2 < -15$ or $x - 2 > 15$

    $x < -13$ or $x > 17$

    The solution is $(-\infty, -13) \cup (17, \infty)$.

10. $5x - 4[x - 2(3x+1)] = 25$

    $5x - 4(x - 6x - 2) = 25$

    $5x - 4(-5x - 2) = 25$

    $5x + 20x + 8 = 25$

    $25x = 17$

    $x = \dfrac{17}{25}$

    The solution set is $\left\{\dfrac{17}{25}\right\}$.

Section 10.7

Practice Exercises

1. a. $\sqrt{-4} = \sqrt{-1 \cdot 4} = \sqrt{-1} \cdot \sqrt{4} = i \cdot 2$, or $2i$

    b. $\sqrt{-7} = \sqrt{-1(7)} = \sqrt{-1} \cdot \sqrt{7} = i\sqrt{7}$

    c. $-\sqrt{-18} = -\sqrt{-1 \cdot 18}$
    $= -\sqrt{-1} \cdot \sqrt{9 \cdot 2}$
    $= -i \cdot 3\sqrt{2}$
    $= -3i\sqrt{2}$

2. a. $\sqrt{-5} \cdot \sqrt{-6} = i\sqrt{5}\left(i\sqrt{6}\right)$
$= i^2\sqrt{30}$
$= -1\sqrt{30}$
$= -\sqrt{30}$

b. $\sqrt{-9} \cdot \sqrt{-1} = 3i \cdot i = 3i^2 = 3(-1) = -3$

c. $\sqrt{125} \cdot \sqrt{-5} = 5\sqrt{5}\left(i\sqrt{5}\right)$
$= 5i\left(\sqrt{5}\sqrt{5}\right)$
$= 5i(5)$
$= 25i$

d. $\dfrac{\sqrt{-27}}{\sqrt{3}} = \dfrac{i\sqrt{27}}{\sqrt{3}} = i\sqrt{9} = 3i$

3. a. $(3 - 5i) + (-4 + i) = (3 - 4) + (-5 + 1)i$
$= -1 - 4i$

b. $4i - (3 - i) = 4i - 3 + i$
$= -3 + (4 + 1)i$
$= -3 + 5i$

c. $(-5 - 2i) - (-8) = -5 - 2i + 8$
$= (-5 + 8) - 2i$
$= 3 - 2i$

4. a. $-4i \cdot 5i = -20i^2 = -20(-1) = 20$

b. $5i(2 + i) = 5i \cdot 2 + 5i \cdot i$
$= 10i + 5i^2$
$= 10i + 5(-1)$
$= 10i - 5$
$= -5 + 10i$

c. $(2 + 3i)(6 - i) = 2(6) - 2(i) + 3i(6) - 3i(i)$
$= 12 - 2i + 18i - 3i^2$
$= 12 + 16i - 3(-1)$
$= 12 + 16i + 3$
$= 15 + 16i$

d. $(3 - i)^2 = (3 - i)(3 - i)$
$= 3(3) - 3(i) - 3(i) + i^2$
$= 9 - 6i + (-1)$
$= 8 - 6i$

e. $(9 + 2i)(9 - 2i) = 9(9) - 9(2i) + 2i(9) - 2i(2i)$
$= 81 - 18i + 18i - 4i^2$
$= 81 - 4(-1)$
$= 81 + 4$
$= 85$

5. a. $\dfrac{4 - i}{3 + i} = \dfrac{(4 - i)(3 - i)}{(3 + i)(3 - i)}$
$= \dfrac{4(3) - 4(i) - 3(i) + i^2}{3^2 - i^2}$
$= \dfrac{12 - 7i - 1}{9 + 1}$
$= \dfrac{11 - 7i}{10}$
$= \dfrac{11}{10} - \dfrac{7i}{10} \text{ or } \dfrac{11}{10} - \dfrac{7}{10}i$

b. $\dfrac{5}{2i} = \dfrac{5(-2i)}{2i(-2i)}$
$= \dfrac{-10i}{-4i^2}$
$= \dfrac{-10i}{-4(-1)}$
$= \dfrac{-10i}{4}$
$= \dfrac{-5i}{2}$
$= 0 - \dfrac{5i}{2} \text{ or } 0 - \dfrac{5}{2}i$

6. a. $i^9 = i^4 \cdot i^4 \cdot i = 1 \cdot 1 \cdot i = i$

b. $i^{16} = (i^4)^4 = 1^4 = 1$

c. $i^{34} = i^{32} \cdot i^2 = (i^4)^8 \cdot i^2 = 1^8(-1) = -1$

d. $i^{-24} = \dfrac{1}{i^{24}} = \dfrac{1}{(i^4)^6} = \dfrac{1}{(1)^6} = \dfrac{1}{1} = 1$

Vocabulary and Readiness Check

1. A <u>complex</u> number is one that can be written in the form $a + bi$ where a and b are real numbers.

2. In the complex number system, i denotes the <u>imaginary unit</u>.

3. $i^2 = \underline{-1}$

4. $i = \sqrt{-1}$

5. A complex number, $a + bi$, is a <u>real</u> number if $b = 0$.

6. A complex number, $a + bi$, is a <u>pure imaginary</u> number if $a = 0$ and $b \neq 0$.

7. $\sqrt{-81} = 9i$

8. $\sqrt{-49} = 7i$

9. $\sqrt{-7} = i\sqrt{7}$

10. $\sqrt{-3} = i\sqrt{3}$

11. $-\sqrt{16} = -4$

12. $-\sqrt{4} = -2$

13. $\sqrt{-64} = 8i$

14. $\sqrt{-100} = 10i$

Exercise Set 10.7

2. $\sqrt{-32} = \sqrt{-1 \cdot 16 \cdot 2} = i \cdot 4\sqrt{2} = 4i\sqrt{2}$

4. $-\sqrt{-121} = -\sqrt{-1 \cdot 121} = -11i$

6. $4\sqrt{-20} = 4\sqrt{-1 \cdot 4 \cdot 5} = 4 \cdot i \cdot 2\sqrt{5} = 8i\sqrt{5}$

8. $\sqrt{-63} = \sqrt{-1 \cdot 9 \cdot 7} = 3i\sqrt{7}$

10. $\sqrt{-11} \cdot \sqrt{-3} = i\sqrt{11} \cdot i\sqrt{3} = i^2\sqrt{33} = -\sqrt{33}$

12. $\sqrt{-2} \cdot \sqrt{-6} = i\sqrt{2} \cdot i\sqrt{6} = i^2\sqrt{12} = -2\sqrt{3}$

14. $\sqrt{3} \cdot \sqrt{-27} = \sqrt{3} \cdot i\sqrt{27} = i\sqrt{81} = 9i$

16. $\dfrac{\sqrt{49}}{\sqrt{-10}} = \dfrac{7}{i\sqrt{10}}$

$$= \dfrac{7\left(-i\sqrt{10}\right)}{i\sqrt{10}\left(-i\sqrt{10}\right)}$$

$$= \dfrac{-7i\sqrt{10}}{-i^2 \cdot 10}$$

$$= \dfrac{-7i\sqrt{10}}{-(-1) \cdot 10}$$

$$= -\dfrac{7i\sqrt{10}}{10}$$

18. $\dfrac{\sqrt{-40}}{\sqrt{-8}} = \dfrac{i\sqrt{40}}{i\sqrt{8}} = \sqrt{\dfrac{40}{8}} = \sqrt{5}$

20. $(2 - 4i) - (2 - i) = 2 - 4i - 2 + i$
$$= (2 - 2) + (-4i + i)$$
$$= -3i$$

22. $(8 - 3i) + (-8 + 3i) = 8 - 3i - 8 + 3i$
$$= (8 - 8) + (-3i + 3i)$$
$$= 0$$

24. $(9 - 4i) - 9 = 9 - 4i - 9$
$$= (9 - 9) - 4i$$
$$= -4i$$

26. $-2i \cdot -11i = 22i^2 = 22(-1) = -22$

28. $5i(4 - 7i) = 20i - 35i^2$
$$= 20i - 35(-1)$$
$$= 20i + 35$$
$$= 35 + 20i$$

30. $\left(\sqrt{5} - 5i\right)\left(\sqrt{5} + 5i\right) = \left(\sqrt{5}\right)^2 - (5i)^2$
$$= 5 - 25i^2$$
$$= 5 + 25$$
$$= 30$$

32. $(6 - 3i)^2 = 36 - 2(6)(3i) + (3i)^2$
$$= 36 - 36i + 9i^2$$
$$= 36 - 36i - 9$$
$$= 27 - 36i$$

34. $\dfrac{5}{6i} = \dfrac{5(-6i)}{6i(-6i)} = \dfrac{-30i}{-36i^2} = \dfrac{-30i}{36} = -\dfrac{5}{6}i$

36. $\dfrac{9}{1-2i} = \dfrac{9(1+2i)}{(1-2i)(1+2i)}$

$= \dfrac{9+18i}{1^2 - 4i^2}$

$= \dfrac{9+18i}{1+4}$

$= \dfrac{9+18i}{5}$

$= \dfrac{9}{5} + \dfrac{18}{5}i$

38. $\dfrac{6+2i}{4-3i} = \dfrac{(6+2i)(4+3i)}{(4-3i)(4+3i)}$

$= \dfrac{24+18i+8i+6i^2}{4^2 - 9i^2}$

$= \dfrac{24+26i-6}{16+9}$

$= \dfrac{18+26i}{25}$

$= \dfrac{18}{25} + \dfrac{26}{25}i$

40. $\dfrac{6-i}{2+i} = \dfrac{(6-i)(2-i)}{(2+i)(2-i)}$

$= \dfrac{12-6i-2i+i^2}{2^2 - i^2}$

$= \dfrac{12-8i-1}{4+1}$

$= \dfrac{11-8i}{5}$

$= \dfrac{11}{5} - \dfrac{8}{5}i$

42. $(-6i)(-4i) = 24i^2 = 24(-1) = -24$

44. $(-2-4i)-(6-8i) = -2-4i-6+8i$

$= -8+4i$

46. $-5i(-2+i) = 10i - 5i^2 = 10i - 5(-1) = 5 + 10i$

48. $\dfrac{6+8i}{3i} = \dfrac{6+8i}{3i} \cdot \dfrac{-3i}{-3i}$

$= \dfrac{-18i - 24i^2}{-9i^2}$

$= \dfrac{24-18i}{9}$

$= \dfrac{24}{9} - \dfrac{18}{9}i$

$= \dfrac{8}{3} - 2i$

50. $(3+i)(2+4i) = 6+12i+2i+4i^2$

$= 6+14i+4(-1)$

$= 2+14i$

52. $(2-4i)(2-i) = 4-2i-8i+4i^2$

$= 4-10i-4$

$= -10i$

54. $(7+4i)+(4-4i) = 7+4i+4-4i = 11$

56. $(6+2i)(6-2i) = 6^2 - (2i)^2$

$= 36 - 4i^2$

$= 36 + 4$

$= 40$

58. $\dfrac{2-3i}{-7i} = \dfrac{(2-3i)(7i)}{-7i(7i)}$

$= \dfrac{14i - 21i^2}{-49i^2}$

$= \dfrac{14i + 21}{49}$

$= \dfrac{21}{49} + \dfrac{14}{49}i$

$= \dfrac{3}{7} + \dfrac{2}{7}i$

60. $(4-7i)^2 = 4^2 - 2(4)(7i) + (7i)^2$

$= 16 - 56i + 49i^2$

$= 16 - 56i - 49$

$= -33 - 56i$

62. $\dfrac{5}{3-2i} = \dfrac{5(3+2i)}{(3-2i)(3+2i)}$

$\qquad = \dfrac{15+10i}{3^2 - 4i^2}$

$\qquad = \dfrac{15+10i}{9+4}$

$\qquad = \dfrac{15+10i}{13}$

$\qquad = \dfrac{15}{13} + \dfrac{10}{13}i$

64. $(6-2i)+7i = 6-2i+7i = 6+5i$

66. $\dfrac{6+5i}{6-5i} = \dfrac{(6+5i)(6+5i)}{(6-5i)(6+5i)}$

$\qquad = \dfrac{36+30i+30i+25i^2}{6^2 - 25i^2}$

$\qquad = \dfrac{36+60i-25}{36+25}$

$\qquad = \dfrac{11+60i}{61}$

$\qquad = \dfrac{11}{61} + \dfrac{60}{61}i$

68. $(5-3i)+(7-8i) = 5-3i+7-8i$

$\qquad\qquad = 12-11i$

70. $\left(\sqrt{5} - 5i\right)\left(\sqrt{5} + 5i\right) = \left(\sqrt{5}\right)^2 - (5i)^2$

$\qquad\qquad = 5 - 25i^2$

$\qquad\qquad = 5 - 25(-1)$

$\qquad\qquad = 30$

72. $(6-3i)^2 = 6^2 - 2 \cdot 6 \cdot 3i + (3i)^2$

$\qquad\qquad = 36 - 36i + 9i^2$

$\qquad\qquad = 36 - 36i + 9(-1)$

$\qquad\qquad = 27 - 36i$

74. $i^{10} = (i^2)^5 = (-1)^5 = -1$

76. $i^{15} = i^{12} \cdot i^3 = (i^4)^3 \cdot (-i) = 1^4(-i) = -i$

78. $i^{40} = (i^4)^{10} = 1^{10} = 1$

80. $i^{-9} = \dfrac{1}{i^9} = \dfrac{1}{i^8 \cdot i} = \dfrac{1}{1 \cdot i} = \dfrac{1}{i} = \dfrac{1 \cdot i}{i \cdot i} = \dfrac{i}{i^2} = \dfrac{i}{-1} = -i$

82. $(5i)^4 = 5^4 i^4 = 625 \cdot 1 = 625$

84. $(-2i)^7 = (-2)^7 i^7$

$\qquad\quad = -128 i^4 \cdot i^3$

$\qquad\quad = -128(1)(-i)$

$\qquad\quad = 128i$

86. $x + 57° + 90° = 180°$

$\qquad x + 147° = 180°$

$\qquad\qquad x = 33°$

88.

$$\begin{array}{r|rrrrr} -2 & 5 & 0 & -3 & 0 & 2 \\ & & -10 & 20 & -34 & 68 \\ \hline & 5 & -10 & 17 & -34 & 70 \end{array}$$

Answer: $5x^3 - 10x^2 + 17x - 34 + \dfrac{70}{x+2}$

90. 5 people

92. $6 + 2 + 3 = 11$ people

94. $\dfrac{5 \text{ people}}{30 \text{ people}} = \dfrac{1}{6} \approx 0.1666$

About 16.7% of the people reported an average checking balance of \$201 to \$300.

96. $i^8 - i^7 = (i^4)^2 - i^4 i^3 = 1^2 - 1(-i) = 1 + i$

98. $i^4 + i^{12} = i^4 + (i^4)^3 = 1 + 1^3 = 2$

100. $5 - \sqrt{-16} = 5 - i\sqrt{16} = 5 - 4i$

102. $\dfrac{4 - \sqrt{-8}}{2} = \dfrac{4 - i\sqrt{4 \cdot 2}}{2}$

$\qquad\qquad = \dfrac{4 - 2i\sqrt{2}}{2}$

$\qquad\qquad = \dfrac{4}{2} - \dfrac{2i\sqrt{2}}{2}$

$\qquad\qquad = 2 - i\sqrt{2}$

104. Answers may vary

106. $\left(8 - \sqrt{-3}\right) - \left(2 + \sqrt{-12}\right)$

$\qquad = 8 - i\sqrt{3} - 2 - 2i\sqrt{3}$

$\qquad = 6 - 3i\sqrt{3}$

108. $x^2 + 4 = 0$

$(2i)^2 + 4 = 0$

$4i^2 + 4 = 0$

$4(-1) + 4 = 0$

$-4 + 4 = 0$, which is true.

Yes, $2i$ is a solution.

Chapter 10 Vocabulary Check

1. The <u>conjugate</u> of $\sqrt{3} + 2$ is $\sqrt{3} - 2$.

2. The <u>principal square root</u> of a nonnegative number a is written as $\sqrt{a}$.

3. The process of writing a radical expression as an equivalent expression but without a radical in the denominator is called <u>rationalizing</u> the denominator.

4. The <u>imaginary unit</u> written i, is the number whose square is -1.

5. The <u>cube root</u> of a number is written as $\sqrt[3]{a}$.

6. In the notation $\sqrt[n]{a}$, n is called the <u>index</u> and a is called the <u>radicand</u>.

7. Radicals with the same index and the same radicand are called <u>like radicals</u>.

8. A <u>complex number</u> is a number that can be written in the form $a + bi$, where a and b are real numbers.

9. The <u>distance</u> formula is
$d = \sqrt{(x_2 - x_1)^2 + (y_2 - y_1)^2}$.

10. The <u>midpoint</u> formula is $\left(\dfrac{x_1 + x_2}{2}, \dfrac{y_1 + y_2}{2} \right)$.

Chapter 10 Review

1. $\sqrt{81} = 9$ because $9^2 = 81$.

2. $\sqrt[4]{81} = 3$ because $3^4 = 81$.

3. $\sqrt[3]{-8} = -2$ because $(-2)^3 = -8$.

4. $\sqrt[4]{-16}$ is not a real number.

5. $-\sqrt{\dfrac{1}{49}} = -\dfrac{1}{7}$ because $\left(\dfrac{1}{7} \right)^2 = \dfrac{1}{49}$.

6. $\sqrt{x^{64}} = x^{32}$ because $(x^{32})^2 = x^{32 \cdot 2} = x^{64}$.

7. $-\sqrt{36} = -6$ because $6^2 = 36$.

8. $\sqrt[3]{64} = 4$ because $4^3 = 64$.

9. $\sqrt[3]{-a^6 b^9} = \sqrt[3]{-1} \sqrt[3]{a^6} \sqrt[3]{b^9}$
$= -1 a^2 b^3$
$= -a^2 b^3$

10. $\sqrt{16 a^4 b^{12}} = \sqrt{16} \sqrt{a^4} \sqrt{b^{12}} = 4 a^2 b^6$

11. $\sqrt[5]{32 a^5 b^{10}} = \sqrt[5]{32} \sqrt[5]{a^5} \sqrt[5]{b^{10}} = 2ab^2$

12. $\sqrt[5]{-32 x^{15} y^{20}} = \sqrt[5]{-32} \sqrt[5]{x^{15}} \sqrt[5]{y^{20}} = -2x^3 y^4$

13. $\sqrt{\dfrac{x^{12}}{36 y^2}} = \dfrac{\sqrt{x^{12}}}{\sqrt{36 y^2}} = \dfrac{x^6}{6y}$

14. $\sqrt[3]{\dfrac{27 y^3}{z^{12}}} = \dfrac{\sqrt[3]{27 y^3}}{\sqrt[3]{z^{12}}} = \dfrac{3y}{z^4}$

15. $\sqrt{(-x)^2} = |-x|$

16. $\sqrt[4]{(x^2 - 4)^4} = |x^2 - 4|$

17. $\sqrt[3]{(-27)^3} = -27$

18. $\sqrt[5]{(-5)^5} = -5$

19. $-\sqrt[5]{x^5} = -x$

20. $\sqrt[4]{16(2y + z)^{12}} = \sqrt[4]{16} \sqrt[4]{(2y + z)^{12}} = 2 \left| (2y + z)^3 \right|$

21. $\sqrt{25(x - y)^{10}} = \sqrt{25} \sqrt{(x - y)^{10}}$
$= 5 \left| (x - y)^5 \right|$

22. $\sqrt[5]{-y^5} = \sqrt[5]{-1} \sqrt[5]{y^5} = -1y = -y$

23. $\sqrt[9]{-x^9} = \sqrt[9]{-1}\sqrt[9]{x^9} = -1x = -x$

24. $f(x) = \sqrt{x} + 3$

$x \geq 0$

Domain: $[0, \infty)$

x	0	1	4	9
$f(x)$	3	4	5	6

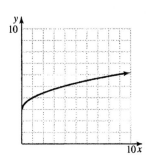

25. $g(x) = \sqrt[3]{x} - 3$

Domain: $(-\infty, \infty)$

x	-5	2	3	4	11
$g(x)$	-2	-1	0	1	2

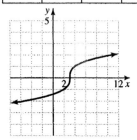

26. $\left(\dfrac{1}{81}\right)^{1/4} = \dfrac{1}{81^{1/4}} = \dfrac{1}{\sqrt[4]{81}} = \dfrac{1}{3}$

27. $\left(-\dfrac{1}{27}\right)^{1/3} = -\dfrac{1}{27^{1/3}} = -\dfrac{1}{\sqrt[3]{27}} = -\dfrac{1}{3}$

28. $(-27)^{-1/3} = \dfrac{1}{(-27)^{1/3}} = \dfrac{1}{\sqrt[3]{-27}} = \dfrac{1}{-3} = -\dfrac{1}{3}$

29. $(-64)^{-1/3} = \dfrac{1}{(-64)^{1/3}} = \dfrac{1}{\sqrt[3]{-64}} = \dfrac{1}{-4} = -\dfrac{1}{4}$

30. $-9^{3/2} = -\left(\sqrt{9}\right)^3 = -3^3 = -27$

31. $64^{-1/3} = \dfrac{1}{64^{1/3}} = \dfrac{1}{\sqrt[3]{64}} = \dfrac{1}{4}$

32. $(-25)^{5/2} = \left(\sqrt{-25}\right)^5$ is not a real number, since there is no real number whose square is -25.

33. $\left(\dfrac{25}{49}\right)^{-3/2} = \dfrac{1}{\left(\frac{25}{49}\right)^{3/2}}$

$= \dfrac{1}{\left(\sqrt{\frac{25}{49}}\right)^3}$

$= \dfrac{1}{\left(\frac{5}{7}\right)^3}$

$= \dfrac{1}{\frac{125}{343}}$

$= \dfrac{343}{125}$

34. $\left(\dfrac{8}{27}\right)^{-2/3} = \dfrac{1}{\left(\frac{8}{27}\right)^{2/3}} = \dfrac{1}{\left(\sqrt[3]{\frac{8}{27}}\right)^2} = \dfrac{1}{\left(\frac{2}{3}\right)^2} = \dfrac{1}{\frac{4}{9}} = \dfrac{9}{4}$

35. $\left(-\dfrac{1}{36}\right)^{-1/4} = \dfrac{1}{\left(-\frac{1}{36}\right)^{1/4}} = \dfrac{1}{\sqrt[4]{-\frac{1}{36}}}$ is not a real number, since there is no real number whose 4th power is $-\dfrac{1}{36}$.

36. $\sqrt[3]{x^2} = (x^2)^{1/3} = x^{2/3}$

37. $\sqrt[5]{5x^2 y^3} = (5x^2 y^3)^{1/5}$
$= 5^{1/5}(x^2)^{1/5}(y^3)^{1/5}$
$= 5^{1/5} x^{2/5} y^{3/5}$

38. $y^{4/5} = (y^4)^{1/5} = \sqrt[5]{y^4}$

39. $5(xy^2 z^5)^{1/3} = 5\sqrt[3]{xy^2 z^5}$

40. $(x+2y)^{-1/2} = \dfrac{1}{(x+2y)^{1/2}} = \dfrac{1}{\sqrt{x+2y}}$

41. $a^{1/3}a^{4/3}a^{1/2} = a^{\frac{1}{3}+\frac{4}{3}+\frac{1}{2}} = a^{\frac{2}{6}+\frac{8}{6}+\frac{3}{6}} = a^{13/6}$

42. $\dfrac{b^{1/3}}{b^{4/3}} = b^{1/3-4/3} = b^{-3/3} = b^{-1} = \dfrac{1}{b}$

43. $(a^{1/2}a^{-2})^3 = (a^{1/2-2})^3$
$= (a^{1/2-4/2})^3$
$= (a^{-3/2})^3$
$= a^{-9/2}$
$= \dfrac{1}{a^{9/2}}$

44. $(x^{-3}y^6)^{1/3} = (x^{-3})^{1/3}(y^6)^{1/3} = x^{-1}y^2 = \dfrac{y^2}{x}$

45. $\left(\dfrac{b^{3/4}}{a^{-1/2}}\right)^8 = (a^{1/2}b^{3/4})^8$
$= (a^{1/2})^8(b^{3/4})^8$
$= a^4b^6$

46. $\dfrac{x^{1/4}x^{-1/2}}{x^{2/3}} = x^{1/4+(-1/2)-2/3}$
$= x^{\frac{3}{12}-\frac{6}{12}-\frac{8}{12}}$
$= x^{-11/12}$
$= \dfrac{1}{x^{11/12}}$

47. $\left(\dfrac{49c^{5/3}}{a^{-1/4}b^{5/6}}\right)^{-1} = \dfrac{49^{-1}c^{-5/3}}{a^{1/4}b^{-5/6}} = \dfrac{b^{5/6}}{49a^{1/4}c^{5/3}}$

48. $a^{-1/4}(a^{5/4} - a^{9/4}) = a^{-1/4}(a^{5/4}) - a^{-1/4}(a^{9/4})$
$= a^{-1/4+5/4} - a^{-1/4+9/4}$
$= a^{4/4} - a^{8/4}$
$= a - a^2$

49. $\sqrt{20} \approx 4.472$

50. $\sqrt[3]{-39} \approx -3.391$

51. $\sqrt[4]{726} \approx 5.191$

52. $56^{1/3} \approx 3.826$

53. $-78^{3/4} \approx -26.246$

54. $105^{-2/3} \approx 0.045$

55. $\sqrt[3]{2} \cdot \sqrt{7} = 2^{1/3} \cdot 7^{1/2}$
$= 2^{2/6} \cdot 7^{3/6}$
$= (2^2 \cdot 7^3)^{1/6}$
$= \sqrt[6]{4 \cdot 343}$
$= \sqrt[6]{1372}$

56. $\sqrt[3]{3} \cdot \sqrt[4]{x} = 3^{1/3} \cdot x^{1/4}$
$= 3^{4/12} \cdot x^{3/12}$
$= (3^4 \cdot x^3)^{1/12}$
$= \sqrt[12]{81x^3}$

57. $\sqrt{3} \cdot \sqrt{8} = \sqrt{24} = \sqrt{4 \cdot 6} = 2\sqrt{6}$

58. $\sqrt[3]{7y} \cdot \sqrt[3]{x^2z} = \sqrt[3]{7y \cdot x^2z} = \sqrt[3]{7x^2yz}$

59. $\dfrac{\sqrt{44x^3}}{\sqrt{11x}} = \sqrt{\dfrac{44x^3}{11x}} = \sqrt{4x^2} = 2x$

60. $\dfrac{\sqrt[4]{a^6b^{13}}}{\sqrt[4]{a^2b}} = \sqrt[4]{\dfrac{a^6b^{13}}{a^2b}} = \sqrt[4]{a^4b^{12}} = ab^3$

61. $\sqrt{60} = \sqrt{4 \cdot 15} = 2\sqrt{15}$

62. $-\sqrt{75} = -\sqrt{25 \cdot 3} = -5\sqrt{3}$

63. $\sqrt[3]{162} = \sqrt[3]{27 \cdot 6} = 3\sqrt[3]{6}$

64. $\sqrt[3]{-32} = \sqrt[3]{-8 \cdot 4} = -2\sqrt[3]{4}$

65. $\sqrt{36x^7} = \sqrt{36x^6 \cdot x} = 6x^3\sqrt{x}$

66. $\sqrt[3]{24a^5b^7} = \sqrt[3]{8a^3b^6 \cdot 3a^2b} = 2ab^2\sqrt[3]{3a^2b}$

67. $\sqrt{\dfrac{p^{17}}{121}} = \dfrac{\sqrt{p^{17}}}{\sqrt{121}} = \dfrac{\sqrt{p^{16} \cdot p}}{11} = \dfrac{p^8\sqrt{p}}{11}$

68. $\sqrt[3]{\dfrac{y^5}{27x^6}} = \dfrac{\sqrt[3]{y^5}}{\sqrt[3]{27x^6}} = \dfrac{\sqrt[3]{y^3y^2}}{\sqrt[3]{27x^6}} = \dfrac{y\sqrt[3]{y^2}}{3x^2}$

69. $\sqrt[4]{\dfrac{xy^6}{81}} = \dfrac{\sqrt[4]{xy^6}}{\sqrt[4]{81}} = \dfrac{\sqrt[4]{y^4 \cdot xy^2}}{3} = \dfrac{y\sqrt[4]{xy^2}}{3}$

70. $\sqrt{\dfrac{2x^3}{49y^4}} = \dfrac{\sqrt{2x^3}}{\sqrt{49y^4}} = \dfrac{\sqrt{x^2 \cdot 2x}}{7y^2} = \dfrac{x\sqrt{2x}}{7y^2}$

71. $r = \sqrt{\dfrac{A}{\pi}}$

  a. $r = \sqrt{\dfrac{25}{\pi}} = \dfrac{\sqrt{25}}{\sqrt{\pi}} = \dfrac{5}{\sqrt{\pi}}$ meters, or

  $r = \dfrac{5}{\sqrt{\pi}} = \dfrac{5\sqrt{\pi}}{\sqrt{\pi}\sqrt{\pi}} = \dfrac{5\sqrt{\pi}}{\pi}$ meters

  b. $r = \sqrt{\dfrac{104}{\pi}} \approx 5.75$ inches

72. $(x_1, y_1) = (-6, 3), (x_2, y_2) = (8, 4)$

$d = \sqrt{(x_2 - x_1)^2 + (y_2 - y_1)^2}$
$= \sqrt{(8+6)^2 + (4-3)^2}$
$= \sqrt{196+1}$
$= \sqrt{197} \approx 14.036$ units

73. $(x_1, y_1) = (-4, -6), (x_2, y_2) = (-1, 5)$

$d = \sqrt{(x_2 - x_1)^2 + (y_2 - y_1)^2}$
$= \sqrt{(-1+4)^2 + (5+6)^2}$
$= \sqrt{9+121}$
$= \sqrt{130} \approx 11.402$ units

74. $(x_1, y_1) = (-1, 5), (x_2, y_2) = (2, -3)$

$d = \sqrt{(x_2 - x_1)^2 + (y_2 - y_1)^2}$
$= \sqrt{(2+1)^2 + (-3-5)^2}$
$= \sqrt{9+64}$
$= \sqrt{73} \approx 8.544$ units

75. $(x_1, y_1) = \left(-\sqrt{2}, 0\right), (x_2, y_2) = \left(0, -4\sqrt{6}\right)$

$d = \sqrt{(x_2 - x_1)^2 + (y_2 - y_1)^2}$
$= \sqrt{\left(0+\sqrt{2}\right)^2 + \left(-4\sqrt{6}-0\right)^2}$
$= \sqrt{2+96}$
$= \sqrt{98}$
$= 7\sqrt{2} \approx 9.899$ units

76. $(x_1, y_1) = \left(-\sqrt{5}, -\sqrt{11}\right),$
$(x_2, y_2) = \left(-\sqrt{5}, -3\sqrt{11}\right)$

$d = \sqrt{(x_2 - x_1)^2 + (y_2 - y_1)^2}$
$= \sqrt{\left(-\sqrt{5}+\sqrt{5}\right)^2 + \left(-3\sqrt{11}+\sqrt{11}\right)^2}$
$= \sqrt{0+44}$
$= \sqrt{44}$
$= 2\sqrt{11} \approx 6.633$ units

77. $(x_1, y_1) = (7.4, -8.6), (x_2, y_2) = (-1.2, 5.6)$

$d = \sqrt{(-1.2-7.4)^2 + (5.6+8.6)^2}$
$= \sqrt{(-8.6)^2 + (14.2)^2}$
$= \sqrt{73.96+201.64}$
$= \sqrt{275.6} \approx 16.601$ units

78. $(x_1, y_1) = (2, 6), (x_2, y_2) = (-12, 4)$

$\text{midpoint} = \left(\dfrac{x_1+x_2}{2}, \dfrac{y_1+y_2}{2}\right)$
$= \left(\dfrac{2-12}{2}, \dfrac{6+4}{2}\right)$
$= \left(\dfrac{-10}{2}, \dfrac{10}{2}\right)$
$= (-5, 5)$

79. $(x_1, y_1) = (-6, -5), (x_2, y_2) = (-9, 7)$

$\text{midpoint} = \left(\dfrac{x_1+x_2}{2}, \dfrac{y_1+y_2}{2}\right)$
$= \left(\dfrac{-6-9}{2}, \dfrac{-5+7}{2}\right)$
$= \left(\dfrac{-15}{2}, \dfrac{2}{2}\right)$
$= \left(-\dfrac{15}{2}, 1\right)$

80. $(x_1, y_1) = (4, -6), (x_2, y_2) = (-15, 2)$

$\text{midpoint} = \left(\dfrac{x_1+x_2}{2}, \dfrac{y_1+y_2}{2}\right)$
$= \left(\dfrac{4-15}{2}, \dfrac{-6+2}{2}\right)$
$= \left(\dfrac{-11}{2}, \dfrac{-4}{2}\right)$
$= \left(-\dfrac{11}{2}, -2\right)$

81. $(x_1, y_1) = \left(0, -\dfrac{3}{8}\right), (x_2, y_2) = \left(\dfrac{1}{10}, 0\right)$

$$\text{midpoint} = \left(\dfrac{x_1 + x_2}{2}, \dfrac{y_1 + y_2}{2}\right)$$

$$= \left(\dfrac{0 + \frac{1}{10}}{2}, \dfrac{-\frac{3}{8} + 0}{2}\right)$$

$$= \left(\dfrac{1}{20}, -\dfrac{3}{16}\right)$$

82. $(x_1, y_1) = \left(\dfrac{3}{4}, -\dfrac{1}{7}\right), (x_2, y_2) = \left(-\dfrac{1}{4}, -\dfrac{3}{7}\right)$

$$\text{midpoint} = \left(\dfrac{x_1 + x_2}{2}, \dfrac{y_1 + y_2}{2}\right)$$

$$= \left(\dfrac{\frac{3}{4} - \frac{1}{4}}{2}, \dfrac{-\frac{1}{7} - \frac{3}{7}}{2}\right)$$

$$= \left(\dfrac{\frac{1}{2}}{2}, \dfrac{-\frac{4}{7}}{2}\right)$$

$$= \left(\dfrac{1}{4}, -\dfrac{2}{7}\right)$$

83. $(x_1, y_1) = \left(\sqrt{3}, -2\sqrt{6}\right), (x_2, y_2) = \left(\sqrt{3}, -4\sqrt{6}\right)$

$$\text{midpoint} = \left(\dfrac{x_1 + x_2}{2}, \dfrac{y_1 + y_2}{2}\right)$$

$$= \left(\dfrac{\sqrt{3} + \sqrt{3}}{2}, \dfrac{-2\sqrt{6} - 4\sqrt{6}}{2}\right)$$

$$= \left(\dfrac{2\sqrt{3}}{2}, \dfrac{-6\sqrt{6}}{2}\right)$$

$$= \left(\sqrt{3}, -3\sqrt{6}\right)$$

84. $2\sqrt{50} - 3\sqrt{125} + \sqrt{98}$

$$= 2\sqrt{25 \cdot 2} - 3\sqrt{25 \cdot 5} + \sqrt{49 \cdot 2}$$

$$= 2 \cdot 5\sqrt{2} - 3 \cdot 5\sqrt{5} + 7\sqrt{2}$$

$$= 10\sqrt{2} - 15\sqrt{5} + 7\sqrt{2}$$

$$= 17\sqrt{2} - 15\sqrt{5}$$

85. $x\sqrt{75xy} - \sqrt{27x^3 y} = x\sqrt{25 \cdot 3xy} - \sqrt{9x^2 \cdot 3xy}$

$$= x \cdot 5\sqrt{3xy} - 3x\sqrt{3xy}$$

$$= 2x\sqrt{3xy}$$

86. $\sqrt[3]{128} + \sqrt[3]{250} = \sqrt[3]{64 \cdot 2} + \sqrt[3]{125 \cdot 2}$

$$= 4\sqrt[3]{2} + 5\sqrt[3]{2}$$

$$= 9\sqrt[3]{2}$$

87. $3\sqrt[4]{32a^5} - a\sqrt[4]{162a} = 3\sqrt[4]{16a^4 \cdot 2a} - a\sqrt[4]{81 \cdot 2a}$

$$= 3 \cdot 2a\sqrt[4]{2a} - 3a\sqrt[4]{2a}$$

$$= 6a\sqrt[4]{2a} - 3a\sqrt[4]{2a}$$

$$= 3a\sqrt[4]{2a}$$

88. $\dfrac{5}{\sqrt{4}} + \dfrac{\sqrt{3}}{3} = \dfrac{5}{2} + \dfrac{\sqrt{3}}{3} = \dfrac{5 \cdot 3 + 2\sqrt{3}}{6} = \dfrac{15 + 2\sqrt{3}}{6}$

89. $\sqrt{\dfrac{8}{x^2}} - \sqrt{\dfrac{50}{16x^2}} = \dfrac{\sqrt{8}}{\sqrt{x^2}} - \dfrac{\sqrt{50}}{\sqrt{16x^2}}$

$$= \dfrac{\sqrt{4 \cdot 2}}{x} - \dfrac{\sqrt{25 \cdot 2}}{4x}$$

$$= \dfrac{2\sqrt{2} \cdot 4}{x \cdot 4} - \dfrac{5\sqrt{2}}{4x}$$

$$= \dfrac{8\sqrt{2} - 5\sqrt{2}}{4x}$$

$$= \dfrac{3\sqrt{2}}{4x}$$

90. $2\sqrt{32x^2 y^3} - xy\sqrt{98y}$

$$= 2\sqrt{16x^2 y^2 \cdot 2y} - xy\sqrt{49 \cdot 2y}$$

$$= 2 \cdot 4xy\sqrt{2y} - xy \cdot 7\sqrt{2y}$$

$$= 8xy\sqrt{2y} - 7xy\sqrt{2y}$$

$$= xy\sqrt{2y}$$

91. $2a\sqrt[4]{32b^5} - 3b\sqrt[4]{162a^4 b} + \sqrt[4]{2a^4 b^5}$

$$= 2a\sqrt[4]{16b^4 \cdot 2b} - 3b\sqrt[4]{81a^4 \cdot 2b} + \sqrt[4]{a^4 b^4 \cdot 2b}$$

$$= 2a \cdot 2b\sqrt[4]{2b} - 3b \cdot 3a\sqrt[4]{2b} + ab\sqrt[4]{2b}$$

$$= 4ab\sqrt[4]{2b} - 9ab\sqrt[4]{2b} + ab\sqrt[4]{2b}$$

$$= -4ab\sqrt[4]{2b}$$

92. $\sqrt{3}\left(\sqrt{27} - \sqrt{3}\right) = \sqrt{3}\left(\sqrt{9 \cdot 3} - \sqrt{3}\right)$

$$= \sqrt{3}\left(3\sqrt{3} - \sqrt{3}\right)$$

$$= \sqrt{3}\left(2\sqrt{3}\right)$$

$$= 2\sqrt{9}$$

$$= 2(3)$$

$$= 6$$

93. $\left(\sqrt{x}-3\right)^2 = \left(\sqrt{x}\right)^2 - 2\cdot\sqrt{x}\cdot 3 + 3^2 = x - 6\sqrt{x} + 9$

94. $\left(\sqrt{5}-5\right)\left(2\sqrt{5}+2\right) = 2\sqrt{25} + 2\sqrt{5} - 10\sqrt{5} - 10$
$$= 2(5) - 8\sqrt{5} - 10$$
$$= 10 - 8\sqrt{5} - 10$$
$$= -8\sqrt{5}$$

95. $\left(2\sqrt{x}-3\sqrt{y}\right)\left(2\sqrt{x}+3\sqrt{y}\right)$
$$= \left(2\sqrt{x}\right)^2 - \left(3\sqrt{y}\right)^2$$
$$= 2^2\left(\sqrt{x}\right)^2 - 3^2\left(\sqrt{y}\right)^2$$
$$= 4x - 9y$$

96. $\left(\sqrt{a}+3\right)\left(\sqrt{a}-3\right) = \left(\sqrt{a}\right)^2 - (3)^2 = a - 9$

97. $\left(\sqrt[3]{a}+2\right)^2 = \left(\sqrt[3]{a}\right)^2 + 2\cdot\sqrt[3]{a}\cdot 2 + 2^2$
$$= \sqrt[3]{a^2} + 4\sqrt[3]{a} + 4$$

98. $\left(\sqrt[3]{5x}+9\right)\left(\sqrt[3]{5x}-9\right) = \left(\sqrt[3]{5x}\right)^2 - 9^2$
$$= \sqrt[3]{(5x)^2} - 81$$
$$= \sqrt[3]{25x^2} - 81$$

99. $\left(\sqrt[3]{a}+4\right)\left(\sqrt[3]{a^2}-4\sqrt[3]{a}+16\right)$
$$= \left(\sqrt[3]{a}\right)\left(\sqrt[3]{a^2}\right) - 4\cdot\left(\sqrt[3]{a}\right)^2 + 16\sqrt[3]{a} + 4\sqrt[3]{a^2}$$
$$\quad - 16\sqrt[3]{a} + 64$$
$$= \sqrt[3]{a^3} - 4\sqrt[3]{a^2} + 4\sqrt[3]{a^2} + 64$$
$$= a + 64$$

100. $\dfrac{3}{\sqrt{7}} = \dfrac{3\cdot\sqrt{7}}{\sqrt{7}\cdot\sqrt{7}} = \dfrac{3\sqrt{7}}{7}$

101. $\sqrt{\dfrac{x}{12}} = \dfrac{\sqrt{x}}{\sqrt{12}}$
$$= \dfrac{\sqrt{x}}{\sqrt{4\cdot 3}}$$
$$= \dfrac{\sqrt{x}}{2\sqrt{3}}$$
$$= \dfrac{\sqrt{x}\cdot\sqrt{3}}{2\sqrt{3}\cdot\sqrt{3}}$$
$$= \dfrac{\sqrt{3x}}{2\cdot 3}$$
$$= \dfrac{\sqrt{3x}}{6}$$

102. $\dfrac{5}{\sqrt[3]{4}} = \dfrac{5\cdot\sqrt[3]{2}}{\sqrt[3]{4}\cdot\sqrt[3]{2}} = \dfrac{5\sqrt[3]{2}}{\sqrt[3]{8}} = \dfrac{5\sqrt[3]{2}}{2}$

103. $\sqrt{\dfrac{24x^5}{3y^2}} = \sqrt{\dfrac{8x^5}{y^2}}$
$$= \dfrac{\sqrt{8x^5}}{\sqrt{y^2}}$$
$$= \dfrac{\sqrt{4x^4\cdot 2x}}{y}$$
$$= \dfrac{2x^2\sqrt{2x}}{y}$$

104. $\sqrt[3]{\dfrac{15x^6y^7}{z^2}} = \dfrac{\sqrt[3]{15x^6y^7}}{\sqrt[3]{z^2}}$
$$= \dfrac{\sqrt[3]{15x^6y^7}\cdot\sqrt[3]{z}}{\sqrt[3]{z^2}\cdot\sqrt[3]{z}}$$
$$= \dfrac{\sqrt[3]{15x^6y^7z}}{\sqrt[3]{z^3}}$$
$$= \dfrac{\sqrt[3]{15x^6y^6\cdot yz}}{z}$$
$$= \dfrac{x^2y^2\sqrt[3]{15yz}}{z}$$

105. $\dfrac{5}{2-\sqrt{7}} = \dfrac{5\left(2+\sqrt{7}\right)}{\left(2-\sqrt{7}\right)\left(2+\sqrt{7}\right)}$

$= \dfrac{5\left(2+\sqrt{7}\right)}{2^2 - \left(\sqrt{7}\right)^2}$

$= \dfrac{10+5\sqrt{7}}{4-7}$

$= \dfrac{10+5\sqrt{7}}{-3}$

$= -\dfrac{10+5\sqrt{7}}{3}$

106. $\dfrac{3}{\sqrt{y}-2} = \dfrac{3\left(\sqrt{y}+2\right)}{\left(\sqrt{y}-2\right)\left(\sqrt{y}+2\right)}$

$= \dfrac{3\left(\sqrt{y}+2\right)}{\left(\sqrt{y}\right)^2 - 2^2}$

$= \dfrac{3\sqrt{y}+6}{y-4}$

107. $\dfrac{\sqrt{2}-\sqrt{3}}{\sqrt{2}+\sqrt{3}} = \dfrac{\left(\sqrt{2}-\sqrt{3}\right)\left(\sqrt{2}-\sqrt{3}\right)}{\left(\sqrt{2}+\sqrt{3}\right)\left(\sqrt{2}-\sqrt{3}\right)}$

$= \dfrac{2-\sqrt{2}\sqrt{3}-\sqrt{3}\sqrt{2}+3}{\left(\sqrt{2}\right)^2-\left(\sqrt{3}\right)^2}$

$= \dfrac{5-\sqrt{6}-\sqrt{6}}{2-3}$

$= \dfrac{5-2\sqrt{6}}{-1}$

$= -5+2\sqrt{6}$

108. $\dfrac{\sqrt{11}}{3} = \dfrac{\sqrt{11}\cdot\sqrt{11}}{3\cdot\sqrt{11}} = \dfrac{11}{3\sqrt{11}}$

109. $\sqrt{\dfrac{18}{y}} = \dfrac{\sqrt{18}}{\sqrt{y}} = \dfrac{3\sqrt{2}}{\sqrt{y}} = \dfrac{3\sqrt{2}\cdot\sqrt{2}}{\sqrt{y}\cdot\sqrt{2}} = \dfrac{3\cdot 2}{\sqrt{2y}} = \dfrac{6}{\sqrt{2y}}$

110. $\dfrac{\sqrt[3]{9}}{7} = \dfrac{\sqrt[3]{9}\cdot\sqrt[3]{3}}{7\cdot\sqrt[3]{3}} = \dfrac{\sqrt[3]{27}}{7\sqrt[3]{3}} = \dfrac{3}{7\sqrt[3]{3}}$

111. $\sqrt{\dfrac{24x^5}{3y^2}} = \sqrt{\dfrac{8x^5}{y^2}}$

$= \dfrac{\sqrt{4x^4\cdot 2x}}{\sqrt{y^2}}$

$= \dfrac{2x^2\sqrt{2x}}{y}$

$= \dfrac{2x^2\sqrt{2x}\cdot\sqrt{2x}}{y\cdot\sqrt{2x}}$

$= \dfrac{2x^2\cdot 2x}{y\sqrt{2x}} = \dfrac{4x^3}{y\sqrt{2x}}$

112. $\sqrt[3]{\dfrac{xy^2}{10z}} = \dfrac{\sqrt[3]{xy^2}}{\sqrt[3]{10z}}$

$= \dfrac{\sqrt[3]{xy^2}\cdot\sqrt[3]{x^2y}}{\sqrt[3]{10z}\cdot\sqrt[3]{x^2y}}$

$= \dfrac{\sqrt[3]{x^3y^3}}{\sqrt[3]{10x^2yz}}$

$= \dfrac{xy}{\sqrt[3]{10x^2yz}}$

113. $\dfrac{\sqrt{x}+5}{-3} = \dfrac{\left(\sqrt{x}+5\right)\left(\sqrt{x}-5\right)}{-3\left(\sqrt{x}-5\right)}$

$= \dfrac{\left(\sqrt{x}\right)^2-5^2}{-3\sqrt{x}+15}$

$= \dfrac{x-25}{-3\sqrt{x}+15}$

114. $\sqrt{y-7} = 5$

$\left(\sqrt{y-7}\right)^2 = 5^2$

$y-7 = 25$

$y = 32$

The solution is 32.

115. $\sqrt{2x}+10 = 4$

$\sqrt{2x} = -6$

No solution exists since the principle square root of a number is not negative.

116. $\sqrt[3]{2x-6} = 4$

$\left(\sqrt[3]{2x-6}\right)^3 = 4^3$

$2x - 6 = 64$

$2x = 70$

$x = 35$

The solution is 35.

117. $\sqrt{x+6} = \sqrt{x+2}$

$\left(\sqrt{x+6}\right)^2 = \left(\sqrt{x+2}\right)^2$

$x + 6 = x + 2$

$6 = 2$, which is false.

There is no solution.

118. $2x - 5\sqrt{x} = 3$

$2x - 3 = 5\sqrt{x}$

$(2x - 3)^2 = \left(5\sqrt{x}\right)^2$

$4x^2 - 12x + 9 = 25x$

$4x^2 - 37x + 9 = 0$

$(4x - 1)(x - 9) = 0$

$4x - 1 = 0$ or $x - 9 = 0$

$4x = 1$ or $\qquad x = 9$

$x = \dfrac{1}{4}$

Discard the solution $\dfrac{1}{4}$ as extraneous. The solution is 9.

119. $\sqrt{x+9} = 2 + \sqrt{x-7}$

$\left(\sqrt{x+9}\right)^2 = \left(2 + \sqrt{x-7}\right)^2$

$x + 9 = 4 + 4\sqrt{x-7} + (x-7)$

$x + 9 = x - 3 + 4\sqrt{x-7}$

$12 = 4\sqrt{x-7}$

$3 = \sqrt{x-7}$

$3^2 = \left(\sqrt{x-7}\right)^2$

$9 = x - 7$

$16 = x$

The solution is 16.

120. Let c = length of the hypotenuse.

$3^2 + 3^2 = c^2$

$18 = c^2$

$\sqrt{18} = \sqrt{c^2}$

$3\sqrt{2} = c$

The length is $3\sqrt{2}$ centimeters.

121. Let c = length of the hypotenuse.

$7^2 + \left(8\sqrt{3}\right)^2 = c^2$

$49 + 64 \cdot 3 = c^2$

$241 = c^2$

$\sqrt{241} = \sqrt{c^2}$

$\sqrt{241} = c$

The length is $\sqrt{241}$ feet.

122. Let b = width of the lake.

$a^2 + b^2 = c^2$

$40^2 + b^2 = 65^2$

$1600 + b^2 = 4225$

$b^2 = 2625$

$\sqrt{b^2} = \sqrt{2625}$

$b = 51.23475$

The width is about 51.2 feet.

123. Let c = length of the shortest pipe.

$a^2 + b^2 = c^2$

$3^2 + 3^2 = c^2$

$18 = c^2$

$\sqrt{18} = \sqrt{c^2}$

$4.24264 = c$

The shortest possible pipe is 4.24 feet.

124. $\sqrt{-8} = i\sqrt{4 \cdot 2} = 2i\sqrt{2}$

125. $-\sqrt{-6} = -i\sqrt{6}$

126. $\sqrt{-4} + \sqrt{-16} = 2i + 4i = 6i$

127. $\sqrt{-2} \cdot \sqrt{-5} = i\sqrt{2} \cdot i\sqrt{5}$

$= i^2\sqrt{10}$

$= -1 \cdot \sqrt{10}$

$= -\sqrt{10}$

128.
$$
\begin{aligned}
(12 - 6i) + (3 + 2i) &= (12 + 3) + (-6 + 2)i \\
&= 15 + (-4)i \\
&= 15 - 4i
\end{aligned}
$$

129.
$$
\begin{aligned}
(-8 - 7i) - (5 - 4i) &= -8 - 7i - 5 + 4i \\
&= -13 - 3i
\end{aligned}
$$

130. $(2i)^6 = 2^6 i^6 = 64i^4 \cdot i^2 = 64(1)(-1) = -64$

131.
$$
\begin{aligned}
-3i(6 - 4i) &= -18i + 12i^2 \\
&= -18i + 12(-1) \\
&= -12 - 18i
\end{aligned}
$$

132.
$$
\begin{aligned}
(3 + 2i)(1 + i) &= 3 + 3i + 2i + 2i^2 \\
&= 3 + 5i + 2(-1) \\
&= 1 + 5i
\end{aligned}
$$

133.
$$
\begin{aligned}
(2 - 3i)^2 &= 2^2 + 2 \cdot 2 \cdot (-3i) + (3i)^2 \\
&= 4 - 12i + 9i^2 \\
&= 4 - 12i + 9(-1) \\
&= -5 - 12i
\end{aligned}
$$

134.
$$
\begin{aligned}
\left(\sqrt{6} - 9i\right)\left(\sqrt{6} + 9i\right) &= \left(\sqrt{6}\right)^2 - (9i)^2 \\
&= 6 - 81i^2 \\
&= 6 + 81 \\
&= 87
\end{aligned}
$$

135.
$$
\begin{aligned}
\frac{2 + 3i}{2i} &= \frac{(2 + 3i) \cdot (-2i)}{2i \cdot (-2i)} \\
&= \frac{-4i - 6i^2}{-4i^2} \\
&= \frac{-4i + 6}{4} \\
&= \frac{6}{4} - \frac{4}{4}i \\
&= \frac{3}{2} - i
\end{aligned}
$$

136.
$$
\begin{aligned}
\frac{1 + i}{-3i} &= \frac{(1 + i) \cdot (3i)}{-3i \cdot (3i)} \\
&= \frac{3i + 3i^2}{-9i^2} \\
&= \frac{3i - 3}{9} \\
&= \frac{-3}{9} - \frac{3}{9}i \\
&= -\frac{1}{3} + \frac{1}{3}i
\end{aligned}
$$

137. $\sqrt[3]{x^3} = x$

138. $\sqrt{(x + 2)^2} = |x + 2|$

139. $-\sqrt{100} = -10$

140. $\sqrt[3]{-x^{12}y^3} = -x^4 y$

141. $\sqrt[4]{\dfrac{y^{20}}{16x^{12}}} = \dfrac{\sqrt[4]{y^{20}}}{\sqrt[4]{16x^{12}}} = \dfrac{y^5}{2x^3}$

142. $9^{1/2} = \sqrt{9} = 3$

143. $64^{-1/2} = \dfrac{1}{64^{1/2}} = \dfrac{1}{\sqrt{64}} = \dfrac{1}{8}$

144.
$$
\begin{aligned}
\left(\frac{27}{64}\right)^{-2/3} &= \left(\frac{64}{27}\right)^{2/3} \\
&= \left(\sqrt[3]{\frac{64}{27}}\right)^2 \\
&= \left(\frac{4}{3}\right)^2 \\
&= \frac{16}{9}
\end{aligned}
$$

145.
$$
\begin{aligned}
\frac{(x^{2/3} x^{-3})^3}{x^{-1/2}} &= \frac{x^{6/3} x^{-9}}{x^{-1/2}} \\
&= x^{2 - 9 + \frac{1}{2}} \\
&= x^{-13/2} \\
&= \frac{1}{x^{13/2}}
\end{aligned}
$$

146. $\sqrt{200x^9} = \sqrt{100x^8 \cdot 2x} = 10x^4 \sqrt{2x}$

147. $\sqrt{\dfrac{3n^3}{121m^{10}}} = \dfrac{\sqrt{3n^3}}{\sqrt{121m^{10}}} = \dfrac{\sqrt{n^2 \cdot 3n}}{\sqrt{121m^{10}}} = \dfrac{n\sqrt{3n}}{11m^5}$

148.
$$
\begin{aligned}
3\sqrt{20} - 7x\sqrt[3]{40} + 3\sqrt[3]{5x^3} &= 3\sqrt{4}\sqrt{5} - 7x\sqrt[3]{8}\sqrt[3]{5} + 3\sqrt[3]{x^3}\sqrt[3]{5} \\
&= 6\sqrt{5} - 14x\sqrt[3]{5} + 3x\sqrt[3]{5} \\
&= 6\sqrt{5} - 11x\sqrt[3]{5}
\end{aligned}
$$

149. $\left(2\sqrt{x}-5\right)^2 = \left(2\sqrt{x}\right)^2 - 2(5)\left(2\sqrt{x}\right)+5^2$
$$= 4x - 20\sqrt{x} + 25$$

150. $(x_1, y_1) = (-3, 5)$, $(x_2, y_2) = (-8, 9)$
$$d = \sqrt{(x_2 - x_1)^2 + (y_2 - y_1)^2}$$
$$= \sqrt{(-8+3)^2 + (9-5)^2}$$
$$= \sqrt{(-5)^2 + (4)^2}$$
$$= \sqrt{25+16}$$
$$= \sqrt{41}$$
The distance is $\sqrt{41}$ units.

151. $(x_1, y_1) = (-3, 8)$, $(x_2, y_2) = (11, 24)$
$$\text{midpoint} = \left(\frac{x_1 + x_2}{2}, \frac{y_1 + y_2}{2}\right)$$
$$= \left(\frac{-3+11}{2}, \frac{8+24}{2}\right)$$
$$= \left(\frac{8}{2}, \frac{32}{2}\right)$$
$$= (4, 16)$$

152. $\dfrac{7}{\sqrt{13}} = \dfrac{7}{\sqrt{13}} \cdot \dfrac{\sqrt{13}}{\sqrt{13}} = \dfrac{7\sqrt{13}}{13}$

153. $\dfrac{2}{\sqrt{x}+3} = \dfrac{2}{\sqrt{x}+3} \cdot \dfrac{\sqrt{x}-3}{\sqrt{x}-3} = \dfrac{2\sqrt{x}-6}{x-9}$

154. $\sqrt{x}+2 = x$
$$\sqrt{x} = x - 2$$
$$\left(\sqrt{x}\right)^2 = (x-2)^2$$
$$x = x^2 - 4x + 4$$
$$0 = x^2 - 5x + 4$$
$$0 = (x-4)(x-1)$$
$$x - 4 = 0 \quad \text{or} \quad x - 1 = 0$$
$$x = 4 \qquad\qquad x = 1$$
Discard the extraneous solution 1. The solution set is $\{4\}$.

Chapter 10 Test

1. $\sqrt{216} = \sqrt{36 \cdot 6} = 6\sqrt{6}$

2. $-\sqrt[4]{x^{64}} = -x^{16}$

3. $\left(\dfrac{1}{125}\right)^{1/3} = \dfrac{1}{125^{1/3}} = \dfrac{1}{\sqrt[3]{125}} = \dfrac{1}{5}$

4. $\left(\dfrac{1}{125}\right)^{-1/3} = \dfrac{1}{\left(\frac{1}{125}\right)^{1/3}} = \dfrac{1}{\frac{1}{5}} = 5$

5. $\left(\dfrac{8x^3}{27}\right)^{2/3} = \dfrac{(8x^3)^{2/3}}{27^{2/3}}$
$$= \dfrac{\left(\sqrt[3]{8x^3}\right)^2}{\left(\sqrt[3]{27}\right)^2}$$
$$= \dfrac{(2x)^2}{3^2}$$
$$= \dfrac{4x^2}{9}$$

6. $\sqrt[3]{-a^{18}b^9} = \sqrt[3]{-1a^{18}b^9} = (-1)a^6 b^3 = -a^6 b^3$

7. $\left(\dfrac{64c^{4/3}}{a^{-2/3}b^{5/6}}\right)^{1/2} = \left(\dfrac{64a^{2/3}c^{4/3}}{b^{5/6}}\right)^{1/2}$
$$= \dfrac{64^{1/2}(a^{2/3})^{1/2}(c^{4/3})^{1/2}}{(b^{5/6})^{1/2}}$$
$$= \dfrac{\sqrt{64}\,a^{1/3}c^{2/3}}{b^{5/12}}$$
$$= \dfrac{8a^{1/3}c^{2/3}}{b^{5/12}}$$

8. $a^{-2/3}(a^{5/4} - a^3) = a^{-2/3}a^{5/4} - a^{-2/3}a^3$
$$= a^{-\frac{2}{3}+\frac{5}{4}} - a^{-\frac{2}{3}+3}$$
$$= a^{-\frac{8}{12}+\frac{15}{12}} - a^{-\frac{2}{3}+\frac{9}{3}}$$
$$= a^{7/12} - a^{7/3}$$

9. $\sqrt[4]{(4xy)^4} = |4xy| = 4|xy|$

10. $\sqrt[3]{(-27)^3} = -27$

11. $\sqrt{\dfrac{9}{y}} = \dfrac{\sqrt{9}}{\sqrt{y}} = \dfrac{3}{\sqrt{y}} = \dfrac{3 \cdot \sqrt{y}}{\sqrt{y} \cdot \sqrt{y}} = \dfrac{3\sqrt{y}}{y}$

12. $\dfrac{4-\sqrt{x}}{4+2\sqrt{x}} = \dfrac{4-\sqrt{x}}{2\left(2+\sqrt{x}\right)}$

$= \dfrac{\left(4-\sqrt{x}\right)\left(2-\sqrt{x}\right)}{2\left(2+\sqrt{x}\right)\left(2-\sqrt{x}\right)}$

$= \dfrac{8-4\sqrt{x}-2\sqrt{x}+x}{2\left[2^2-\left(\sqrt{x}\right)^2\right]}$

$= \dfrac{8-6\sqrt{x}+x}{2(4-x)}$ or $\dfrac{8-6\sqrt{x}+x}{8-2x}$

13. $\dfrac{\sqrt[3]{ab}}{\sqrt[3]{ab^2}} = \sqrt[3]{\dfrac{ab}{ab^2}}$

$= \sqrt[3]{\dfrac{1}{b}}$

$= \dfrac{1}{\sqrt[3]{b}}$

$= \dfrac{1 \cdot \sqrt[3]{b^2}}{\sqrt[3]{b} \cdot \sqrt[3]{b^2}}$

$= \dfrac{\sqrt[3]{b^2}}{b}$

14. $\dfrac{\sqrt{6}+x}{8} = \dfrac{\left(\sqrt{6}+x\right)\left(\sqrt{6}-x\right)}{8\left(\sqrt{6}-x\right)}$

$= \dfrac{\left(\sqrt{6}\right)^2-x^2}{8\left(\sqrt{6}-x\right)}$

$= \dfrac{6-x^2}{8\left(\sqrt{6}-x\right)}$

15. $\sqrt{125x^3}-3\sqrt{20x^3} = \sqrt{25x^2 \cdot 5x}-3\sqrt{4x^2 \cdot 5x}$

$= 5x\sqrt{5x}-3 \cdot 2x\sqrt{5x}$

$= 5x\sqrt{5x}-6x\sqrt{5x}$

$= -x\sqrt{5x}$

16. $\sqrt{3}\left(\sqrt{16}-\sqrt{2}\right) = \sqrt{3}\left(4-\sqrt{2}\right)$

$= 4\sqrt{3}-\sqrt{3}\sqrt{2}$

$= 4\sqrt{3}-\sqrt{6}$

17. $\left(\sqrt{x}+1\right)^2 = \left(\sqrt{x}\right)^2+2\sqrt{x}+1^2$

$= x+2\sqrt{x}+1$

18. $\left(\sqrt{2}-4\right)\left(\sqrt{3}+1\right) = \sqrt{2}\sqrt{3}+1 \cdot \sqrt{2}-4\sqrt{3}-4$

$= \sqrt{6}+\sqrt{2}-4\sqrt{3}-4$

19. $\left(\sqrt{5}+5\right)\left(\sqrt{5}-5\right) = \left(\sqrt{5}\right)^2-5^2$

$= 5-25$

$= -20$

20. $\sqrt{561} \approx 23.685$

21. $386^{-2/3} \approx 0.019$

22. $x = \sqrt{x-2}+2$

$x-2 = \sqrt{x-2}$

$(x-2)^2 = \left(\sqrt{x-2}\right)^2$

$x^2-4x+4 = x-2$

$x^2-5x+6 = 0$

$(x-2)(x-3) = 0$

$x = 2$ or $x = 3$

The solutions are 2 and 3.

23. $\sqrt{x^2-7}+3 = 0$

$\sqrt{x^2-7} = -3$

No solution exists since the principle square root of a number is not negative.

24. $\sqrt[3]{x+5} = \sqrt[3]{2x-1}$

$\left(\sqrt[3]{x+5}\right)^3 = \left(\sqrt[3]{2x-1}\right)^3$

$x+5 = 2x-1$

$-x = -6$

$x = 6$

The solution is 6.

25. $\sqrt{-2} = i\sqrt{2}$

26. $-\sqrt{-8} = -i\sqrt{4 \cdot 2} = -2i\sqrt{2}$

27. $(12-6i)-(12-3i) = 12-6i-12+3i = -3i$

28. $(6-2i)(6+2i) = 6^2-(2i)^2$

$= 36-4i^2$

$= 36+4$

$= 40$

29. $(4+3i)^2 = 4^2 + 2 \cdot 4 \cdot 3i + (3i)^2$

$\qquad = 16 + 24i + 9i^2$

$\qquad = 16 + 24i - 9$

$\qquad = 7 + 24i$

30. $\dfrac{1+4i}{1-i} = \dfrac{(1+4i)(1+i)}{(1-i)(1+i)}$

$\qquad = \dfrac{1+i+4i+4i^2}{1^2 - i^2}$

$\qquad = \dfrac{1+5i-4}{1-(-1)}$

$\qquad = \dfrac{-3+5i}{2}$

$\qquad = -\dfrac{3}{2} + \dfrac{5}{2}i$

31. $x^2 + x^2 = 5^2$

$\qquad 2x^2 = 25$

$\qquad x^2 = \dfrac{25}{2}$

$\qquad \sqrt{x^2} = \sqrt{\dfrac{25}{2}}$

$\qquad x = \dfrac{5}{\sqrt{2}} = \dfrac{5 \cdot \sqrt{2}}{\sqrt{2} \cdot \sqrt{2}} = \dfrac{5\sqrt{2}}{2}$

32. $g(x) = \sqrt{x+2}$

$\quad x + 2 \ge 0$

$\qquad x \ge -2$

Domain: $[-2, \infty)$

x	-2	-1	2	7
$g(x)$	0	1	2	3

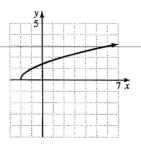

33. $(x_1, y_1) = (-6, 3)$, $(x_2, y_2) = (-8, -7)$

$d = \sqrt{(-8-(-6))^2 + (-7-3)^2}$

$\quad = \sqrt{(-2)^2 + (-10)^2}$

$\quad = \sqrt{4 + 100}$

$\quad = \sqrt{104}$

$\quad = \sqrt{4 \cdot 26}$

$\quad = 2\sqrt{26}$

The distance is $2\sqrt{26}$ units.

34. $(x_1, y_1) = \left(-2\sqrt{5}, \sqrt{10}\right)$,

$\quad (x_2, y_2) = \left(-\sqrt{5}, 4\sqrt{10}\right)$

$d = \sqrt{(x_2 - x_1)^2 + (y_2 - y_1)^2}$

$\quad = \sqrt{\left(-\sqrt{5} + 2\sqrt{5}\right)^2 + \left(4\sqrt{10} - \sqrt{10}\right)^2}$

$\quad = \sqrt{\left(\sqrt{5}\right)^2 + \left(3\sqrt{10}\right)^2}$

$\quad = \sqrt{5 + 90}$

$\quad = \sqrt{95}$

The distance is $\sqrt{95}$ units.

35. $(x_1, y_1) = (-2, -5)$, $(x_2, y_2) = (-6, 12)$

$\text{midpoint} = \left(\dfrac{x_1 + x_2}{2}, \dfrac{y_1 + y_2}{2}\right)$

$\quad = \left(\dfrac{-2-6}{2}, \dfrac{-5+12}{2}\right)$

$\quad = \left(-\dfrac{8}{2}, \dfrac{7}{2}\right)$

$\quad = \left(-4, \dfrac{7}{2}\right)$

36. $(x_1, y_1) = \left(-\dfrac{2}{3}, -\dfrac{1}{5}\right)$, $(x_2, y_2) = \left(-\dfrac{1}{3}, \dfrac{4}{5}\right)$

$\text{midpoint} = \left(\dfrac{x_1 + x_2}{2}, \dfrac{y_1 + y_2}{2}\right)$

$\quad = \left(\dfrac{-\frac{2}{3} - \frac{1}{3}}{2}, \dfrac{-\frac{1}{5} + \frac{4}{5}}{2}\right)$

$\quad = \left(\dfrac{-\frac{3}{3}}{2}, \dfrac{\frac{3}{5}}{2}\right)$

$\quad = \left(-\dfrac{1}{2}, \dfrac{3}{10}\right)$

37. $V(r) = \sqrt{2.5r}$

$V(300) = \sqrt{2.5(300)} = \sqrt{750} \approx 27$ mph

38. $V(r) = \sqrt{2.5r}$

$30 = \sqrt{2.5r}$

$30^2 = \left(\sqrt{2.5r}\right)^2$

$900 = 2.5r$

$r = \dfrac{900}{2.5} = 360$ feet

Chapter 10 Cumulative Review

1. a. $\dfrac{(-12)(-3)+3}{-7-(-2)} = \dfrac{36+3}{-7+2} = \dfrac{39}{-5} = -\dfrac{39}{5}$

b. $\dfrac{2(-3)^2 - 20}{-5+4} = \dfrac{2 \cdot 9 - 20}{-1} = \dfrac{18-20}{-1} = \dfrac{-2}{-1} = 2$

2. a. $2(x-3)+(5x+3) = 2x-6+5x+3$
$\qquad\qquad\qquad\qquad = 7x-3$

b. $4(3x+2)-3(5x-1) = 12x+8-15x+3$
$\qquad\qquad\qquad\qquad\qquad = -3x+11$

c. $7x+2(x-7)-3x = 7x+2x-14-3x$
$\qquad\qquad\qquad\qquad\quad = 6x-14$

3. $\dfrac{x}{2}-1 = \dfrac{2}{3}x-3$

$6\left(\dfrac{x}{2}-1\right) = 6\left(\dfrac{2}{3}x-3\right)$

$\quad 3x-6 = 4x-18$

$\quad\; -6 = x-18$

$\quad\; 12 = x$

4. $\dfrac{a-1}{2}+a = 2-\dfrac{2a+7}{8}$

$8\left(\dfrac{a-1}{2}+a\right) = 8\left(2-\dfrac{2a+7}{8}\right)$

$4(a-1)+8a = 16-(2a+7)$

$\quad 4a-4+8a = 16-2a-7$

$\qquad 12a-4 = 9-2a$

$\qquad\quad 14a = 13$

$\qquad\qquad a = \dfrac{13}{14}$

5. Let $x =$ the length of the shorter board. Then the longer board has length $3x$.

$x+3x = 48$

$\quad 4x = 48$

$\quad \dfrac{4x}{4} = \dfrac{48}{4}$

$\quad\; x = 12$

$3x = 3(12) = 36$

The pieces are 12 inches and 36 inches long.

6. Let $r =$ their average speed.

$t_{\text{going}} + t_{\text{returning}} = 4.5$ hr

$\dfrac{121.5}{r} + \dfrac{121.5}{r} = 4.5$

$\qquad \dfrac{243}{r} = 4.5$

$\qquad 243 = 4.5r$

$\qquad\;\; r = \dfrac{243}{4.5} = 54$

Their average speed was 54 mph.

7. $\begin{cases} 3x-y=4 \\ x+2y=8 \end{cases}$

$3x-y=4$

$\quad -y = -3x+4$

$\qquad y = 3x-4\!: m = 3$

$x+2y=8$

$\quad 2y = -x+8$

$\qquad y = -\dfrac{1}{2}x+4\!: m = -\dfrac{1}{2}$

Since the slopes are different, the lines intersect in one point. The system has one solution.

8. $|3x-2|+5 = 5$

$\quad |3x-2| = 0$

$\quad\; 3x-2 = 0$

$\qquad 3x = 2$

$\qquad\; x = \dfrac{2}{3}$

9. $\begin{cases} x+2y=7 \\ 2x+2y=13 \end{cases}$

Solve the first equation for x.

$x = -2y+7$

Substitute $-2y+7$ for x in the second equation.

$2(-2y+7)+2y = 13$

$\quad -4y+14+2y = 13$

$\qquad -2y+14 = 13$

$\qquad\quad -2y = -1$

$\qquad\qquad y = \dfrac{1}{2}$

Let $y = \frac{1}{2}$ in the equation $x = -2y + 7$.

$x = -2y + 7 = -2\left(\frac{1}{2}\right) + 7 = -1 + 7 = 6$

The solution is $\left(6, \frac{1}{2}\right)$.

10. $\left|\frac{x}{2} - 1\right| \le 0$

$\frac{x}{2} - 1 = 0$

$\frac{x}{2} = 1$

$x = 2$

11. $\begin{cases} 2x - y = 7 \\ 8x - 4y = 1 \end{cases}$

Multiply the first equation by –4, then add.

$-8x + 4y = -28$

$\underline{8x - 4y = 1}$

$0 = -27$

This is a false statement, so the system has no solution.

12. $y = |x - 2|$

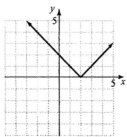

13. Let x be the amount of 30% alcohol solution and y the amount of 80% solution.

$\begin{cases} x + y = 70 \\ 0.30x + 0.80y = 0.50(70) \end{cases}$

$\begin{cases} x + y = 70 \\ 3x + 8y = 350 \end{cases}$

Multiply the first equation by –3, then add.

$-3x - 3y = -210$

$\underline{3x + 8y = 350}$

$5y = 140$

$y = 28$

Let $y = 28$ in the first equation.

$x + y = 70$

$x + 28 = 70$

$x = 42$

She should mix 42 liters of 30% solution with 28 liters of 80% solution.

14. a. Domain: $(-\infty, 0]$, Range: $(-\infty, \infty)$

not a function

b. Domain: $(-\infty, \infty)$, Range: $(-\infty, \infty)$

function

c. Domain: $(-\infty, -2] \cup [2, \infty)$

Range: $(-\infty, \infty)$

not a function

15. $P(x) = 3x^2 - 2x - 5$

a. $P(1) = 3(1)^2 - 2(1) - 5$
$= 3(1) - 2(1) - 5$
$= 3 - 2 - 5$
$= -4$

b. $P(-2) = 3(-2)^2 - 2(-2) - 5$
$= 3(4) - (-4) - 5$
$= 12 + 4 - 5$
$= 11$

16. $f(x) = -2$

This is a horizontal line passing through $(0, -2)$.

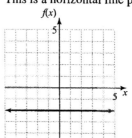

17. $\dfrac{6m^2 + 2m}{2m} = \dfrac{2m(3m+1)}{2m} = 3m + 1$

18. $y = -3$ is a horizontal line. The slope is 0.

19.

$$3\,\overline{)\begin{array}{rrrr} 2 & -1 & -13 & 1 \\ & 6 & 15 & 6 \end{array}}$$
$$\begin{array}{rrrr} 2 & 5 & 2 & 7 \end{array}$$

Answer: $2x^2 + 5x + 2 + \dfrac{7}{x-3}$

20. $\begin{cases} \dfrac{x}{6} - \dfrac{y}{2} = 1 \\ \dfrac{x}{3} - \dfrac{y}{4} = 2 \end{cases}$ or $\begin{cases} x - 3y = 6 & (1) \\ 4x - 3y = 24 & (2) \end{cases}$

Solve equation (1) for x.
$x - 3y = 6$
$\quad x = 3y + 6$

Replace x with $3y + 6$ in equation (2).
$4(3y + 6) - 3y = 24$
$12y + 24 - 3y = 24$
$\quad\quad 9y + 24 = 24$
$\quad\quad\quad 9y = 0$
$\quad\quad\quad\quad y = 0$

Substitute 0 for y in $x = 3y + 6$.
$x = 3(0) + 6 = 0 + 6 = 6$
The solution is $(6, 0)$.

21. $x^2 + 7yx + 6y^2 = (x + 6y)(x + y)$

22. Let x = number of tee-shirts and
y = number of shorts.
$\begin{cases} x + y = 9 & (1) \\ 3.50x + 4.25y = 33.75 & (2) \end{cases}$

Solve equation (1) for y.
$x + y = 9$
$\quad y = 9 - x$

Substitute $9 - x$ for y in equation (2).
$3.50x + 4.25(9 - x) = 33.75$
$3.50x + 38.25 - 4.25x = 33.75$
$\quad -0.75x + 38.25 = 33.75$
$\quad\quad\quad -0.75x = -4.5$
$\quad\quad\quad\quad x = \dfrac{-4.5}{-0.75} = 6$

Replace x with 6 in $y = 9 - x$.
$y = 9 - 6 = 3$
Nana bought 6 shirts and 3 shorts.

23. a. $\dfrac{x^3 + 8}{2 + x} = \dfrac{x^3 + 2^3}{x + 2}$

$\quad = \dfrac{(x + 2)(x^2 - 2x + 4)}{x + 2}$

$\quad = x^2 - 2x + 4$

b. $\dfrac{2y^2 + 2}{y^3 - 5y^2 + y - 5} = \dfrac{2(y^2 + 1)}{y^2(y - 5) + 1(y - 5)}$

$\quad = \dfrac{2(y^2 + 1)}{(y - 5)(y^2 + 1)}$

$\quad = \dfrac{2}{y - 5}$

24. $\dfrac{0.0000035 \times 4000}{0.28} = \dfrac{(3.5 \times 10^{-6}) \times (4 \times 10^3)}{2.8 \times 10^{-1}}$

$\quad = \dfrac{3.5 \times 4}{2.8} \times 10^{-6 + 3 - (-1)}$

$\quad = 5 \times 10^{-2}$

25. $\dfrac{3x^3 y^7}{40} \div \dfrac{4x^3}{y^2} = \dfrac{3x^3 y^7}{40} \cdot \dfrac{y^2}{4x^3} = \dfrac{3y^9}{160}$

26. $[(5x^2 - 3x + 6) + (4x^2 + 5x - 3)] - (2x - 5)$
$\quad = 5x^2 - 3x + 6 + 4x^2 + 5x - 3 - 2x + 5$
$\quad = 9x^2 + 8$

27. $\dfrac{2y}{2y - 7} - \dfrac{7}{2y - 7} = \dfrac{2y - 7}{2y - 7} = 1$

28. a. $(y - 2)(3y + 4) = 3y^2 + 4y - 6y - 8$
$\quad\quad\quad\quad\quad\quad\quad = 3y^2 - 2y - 8$

b. $(3y - 1)(2y^2 + 3y - 1)$
$\quad = 6y^3 + 9y^2 - 3y - 2y^2 - 3y + 1$
$\quad = 6y^3 + 7y^2 - 6y + 1$

29. $\dfrac{2x}{x^2 + 2x + 1} + \dfrac{x}{x^2 - 1} = \dfrac{2x}{(x+1)^2} + \dfrac{x}{(x+1)(x-1)}$

$\quad = \dfrac{2x(x-1) + x(x+1)}{(x+1)^2(x-1)}$

$\quad = \dfrac{2x^2 - 2x + x^2 + x}{(x+1)^2(x-1)}$

$\quad = \dfrac{3x^2 - x}{(x+1)^2(x-1)}$

$\quad = \dfrac{x(3x - 1)}{(x+1)^2(x-1)}$

30. $x^3 - x^2 + 4x - 4 = (x^3 - x^2) + (4x - 4)$
$$= x^2(x-1) + 4(x-1)$$
$$= (x-1)(x^2+4)$$

31. a. $\dfrac{\frac{5x}{x+2}}{\frac{10}{x-2}} = \dfrac{5x}{x+2} \cdot \dfrac{x-2}{10} = \dfrac{x(x-2)}{2(x+2)}$

b. $\dfrac{\frac{x}{y^2} + \frac{1}{y}}{\frac{y}{x^2} + \frac{1}{x}} = \dfrac{\left(\frac{x}{y^2} + \frac{1}{y}\right)x^2 y^2}{\left(\frac{y}{x^2} + \frac{1}{x}\right)x^2 y^2}$

$$= \dfrac{x^3 + x^2 y}{y^3 + xy^2}$$

$$= \dfrac{x^2(x+y)}{y^2(y+x)}$$

$$= \dfrac{x^2}{y^2}$$

32. a. $\dfrac{a^3 - 8}{2-a} = \dfrac{a^3 - 2^3}{2-a}$

$$= \dfrac{(a-2)(a^2 + 2a + 4)}{-1(a-2)}$$

$$= -1(a^2 + 2a + 4)$$

$$= -a^2 - 2a - 4$$

b. $\dfrac{3a^2 - 3}{a^3 + 5a^2 - a - 5} = \dfrac{3(a^2 - 1)}{a^2(a+5) - 1(a+5)}$

$$= \dfrac{3(a^2 - 1)}{(a+5)(a^2 - 1)}$$

$$= \dfrac{3}{a+5}$$

33. $\dfrac{x}{2} + \dfrac{8}{3} = \dfrac{1}{6}$

$$6\left(\dfrac{x}{2} + \dfrac{8}{3}\right) = 6\left(\dfrac{1}{6}\right)$$

$$3x + 16 = 1$$
$$3x = -15$$
$$x = -5$$

34. a. $\dfrac{3}{xy^2} - \dfrac{2}{3x^2 y} = \dfrac{3 \cdot 3x}{xy^2 \cdot 3x} - \dfrac{2 \cdot y}{3x^2 y \cdot y}$

$$= \dfrac{9x - 2y}{3x^2 y^2}$$

b. $\dfrac{5x}{x+3} - \dfrac{2x}{x-3} = \dfrac{5x(x-3) - 2x(x+3)}{(x+3)(x-3)}$

$$= \dfrac{5x^2 - 15x - 2x^2 - 6x}{(x+3)(x-3)}$$

$$= \dfrac{3x^2 - 21x}{(x+3)(x-3)}$$

$$\text{or } \dfrac{3x(x-7)}{(x+3)(x-3)}$$

c. $\dfrac{x}{x-2} - \dfrac{5}{2-x} = \dfrac{x}{x-2} + \dfrac{5}{x-2} = \dfrac{x+5}{x-2}$

35. $\dfrac{x}{10} = \dfrac{3}{2}$
$$2x = 10 \cdot 3$$
$$2x = 30$$
$$x = 15$$
The missing length is 15 yards.

36. a. $\dfrac{\frac{y-2}{16}}{\frac{2y+3}{12}} = \dfrac{y-2}{16} \cdot \dfrac{12}{2y+3} = \dfrac{3(y-2)}{4(2y+3)}$

b. $\dfrac{\frac{x}{16} - \frac{1}{x}}{1 - \frac{4}{x}} = \dfrac{\left(\frac{x}{16} - \frac{1}{x}\right)16x}{\left(1 - \frac{4}{x}\right)16x}$

$$= \dfrac{x^2 - 16}{16x - 64}$$

$$= \dfrac{(x+4)(x-4)}{16(x-4)}$$

$$= \dfrac{x+4}{16}$$

37. a. $\sqrt[3]{1} = 1$, since $1^3 = 1$.

b. $\sqrt[3]{-64} = \sqrt[3]{(-4)^3} = -4$

c. $\sqrt[3]{\dfrac{8}{125}} = \sqrt[3]{\left(\dfrac{2}{5}\right)^3} = \dfrac{2}{5}$

d. $\sqrt[3]{x^6} = \sqrt[3]{(x^2)^3} = x^2$

e. $\sqrt[3]{-27x^9} = \sqrt[3]{(-3x^3)^3} = -3x^3$

38.

$$\begin{array}{r} x^2 + 3 \\ x-2 \overline{\smash{\big)}\, x^3 - 2x^2 + 3x - 6} \\ \underline{x^3 - 2x^2} \\ 3x - 6 \\ \underline{3x - 6} \\ 0 \end{array}$$

Answer: $x^2 + 3$

39. a. $16^{-3/4} = \dfrac{1}{16^{3/4}} = \dfrac{1}{\left(\sqrt[4]{16}\right)^3} = \dfrac{1}{(2)^3} = \dfrac{1}{8}$

b. $(-27)^{-2/3} = \dfrac{1}{(-27)^{2/3}}$

$$= \dfrac{1}{\left(\sqrt[3]{-27}\right)^2}$$

$$= \dfrac{1}{(-3)^2}$$

$$= \dfrac{1}{9}$$

40.

$$\begin{array}{r|rrrr} 3 & 4 & -12 & -1 & 12 \\ & & 12 & 0 & -3 \\ \hline & 4 & 0 & -1 & 9 \end{array}$$

Answer: $4y^2 - 1 + \dfrac{9}{y-3}$

41. $\dfrac{\sqrt{x}+2}{5} = \dfrac{\left(\sqrt{x}+2\right)\left(\sqrt{x}-2\right)}{5\left(\sqrt{x}-2\right)}$

$$= \dfrac{\left(\sqrt{x}\right)^2 - 2^2}{5\left(\sqrt{x}-2\right)}$$

$$= \dfrac{x-4}{5\left(\sqrt{x}-2\right)}$$

42.

$$\frac{28}{9-a^2} = \frac{2a}{a-3} + \frac{6}{a+3}$$

$$\frac{28}{-(a^2-9)} = \frac{2a}{a-3} + \frac{6}{a+3}$$

$$\frac{-28}{(a+3)(a-3)} = \frac{2a}{a-3} + \frac{6}{a+3}$$

$$(a+3)(a-3)\cdot\frac{-28}{(a+3)(a-3)} = (a+3)(a-3)\cdot\left(\frac{2a}{a-3} + \frac{6}{a+3}\right)$$

$$-28 = 2a(a+3) + 6(a-3)$$

$$-28 = 2a^2 + 6a + 6a - 18$$

$$0 = 2a^2 + 12a + 10$$

$$0 = 2(a^2 + 6a + 5)$$

$$0 = 2(a+5)(a+1)$$

$a = -5$ or $a = -1$

The solutions are -5 and -1.

43. $u = \dfrac{k}{w}$

$3 = \dfrac{k}{5}$

$k = 3(5) = 15$

$u = \dfrac{15}{w}$

44. $y = kx$

$0.51 = k(3)$

$k = \dfrac{0.51}{3} = 0.17$

$y = 0.17x$

Chapter 11

Practice Exercises

1. $x^2 = 18$

   $x = \pm\sqrt{18}$

   $x = \pm 3\sqrt{2}$

   Check:

   Let $x = 3\sqrt{2}$.   Let $x = -3\sqrt{2}$.

   $\quad x^2 = 18$ $\quad\quad x^2 = 18$

   $\left(3\sqrt{2}\right)^2 \stackrel{?}{=} 18$ $\left(-3\sqrt{2}\right)^2 \stackrel{?}{=} 18$

   $\quad 9 \cdot 2 \stackrel{?}{=} 18$ $\quad\quad 9 \cdot 2 \stackrel{?}{=} 18$

   $\quad 18 = 18$ True $\quad 18 = 18$ True

   The solutions are $3\sqrt{2}$ and $-3\sqrt{2}$, or the

   solution set is $\left\{-3\sqrt{2},\, 3\sqrt{2}\right\}$.

2. First we get the squared variable alone on one
   side of the equation.

   $3x^2 - 30 = 0$

   $\quad 3x^2 = 30$

   $\quad\; x^2 = 10$

   $\quad\quad x = \pm\sqrt{10}$

   The solutions are $\sqrt{10}$ and $-\sqrt{10}$, or the

   solution set is $\left\{-\sqrt{10},\, \sqrt{10}\right\}$.

3. $(x+3)^2 = 20$

   $x + 3 = \pm\sqrt{20}$

   $x + 3 = \pm 2\sqrt{5}$

   $\quad\;\; x = -3 \pm 2\sqrt{5}$

   Check:

   $\quad\quad (x+3)^2 = 20$

   $\left(-3+2\sqrt{5}+3\right)^2 \stackrel{?}{=} 20$

   $\quad\quad \left(2\sqrt{5}\right)^2 \stackrel{?}{=} 20$

   $\quad\quad\quad 4 \cdot 5 \stackrel{?}{=} 20$

   $\quad\quad\quad 20 = 20$ True

$\quad\quad\quad\quad (x+3)^2 = 20$

$\quad\left(-3-2\sqrt{5}+3\right)^2 \stackrel{?}{=} 20$

$\quad\quad\quad\quad \left(-2\sqrt{5}\right)^2 \stackrel{?}{=} 20$

$\quad\quad\quad\quad\quad 4 \cdot 5 \stackrel{?}{=} 20$

$\quad\quad\quad\quad\quad 20 = 20$ True

The solutions are $-3+2\sqrt{5}$ and $-3-2\sqrt{5}$.

4. $(5x-2)^2 = -9$

   $5x - 2 = \pm\sqrt{-9}$

   $5x - 2 = \pm 3i$

   $\quad 5x = 2 \pm 3i$

   $\quad\; x = \dfrac{2 \pm 3i}{5}$

   The solutions are $\dfrac{2+3i}{5}$ and $\dfrac{2-3i}{5}$.

5. $b^2 + 4b = 3$

   Add the square of half the coefficient of b to
   both sides.

   $b^2 + 4b + \left(\dfrac{4}{2}\right)^2 = 3 + \left(\dfrac{4}{2}\right)^2$

   $\quad b^2 + 4b + 4 = 7$

   $\quad\quad (b+2)^2 = 7$

   $\quad\quad\; b + 2 = \pm\sqrt{7}$

   $\quad\quad\quad\; b = -2 \pm\sqrt{7}$

   The solutions are $-2+\sqrt{7}$ and $-2-\sqrt{7}$.

6. $p^2 - 3p + 1 = 0$

   Subtract 1 from both sides.

   $p^2 - 3p = -1$

   Add the square of half the coefficient of p to
   both sides.

$$p^2 - 3p + \left(\frac{-3}{2}\right)^2 = -1 + \left(\frac{-3}{2}\right)^2$$

$$p^2 - 3p + \frac{9}{4} = -1 + \frac{9}{4} = \frac{5}{4}$$

$$\left(p - \frac{3}{2}\right)^2 = \frac{5}{4}$$

$$p - \frac{3}{2} = \pm\frac{\sqrt{5}}{2}$$

$$p = \frac{3 \pm \sqrt{5}}{2}$$

The solutions are $\dfrac{3+\sqrt{5}}{2}$ and $\dfrac{3-\sqrt{5}}{2}$.

7. $3x^2 - 12x + 1 = 0$
Divide both sides by 3.

$$3x^2 - 12x + 1 = 0$$

$$x^2 - 4x + \frac{1}{3} = 0$$

$$x^2 - 4x = -\frac{1}{3}$$

Find the square of half of -4.

$$\left(\frac{-4}{2}\right)^2 = (-2)^2 = 4$$

Add 4 to both sides of the equation.

$$x^2 - 4x + 4 = -\frac{1}{3} + 4$$

$$(x-2)^2 = -\frac{1}{3} + \frac{12}{3} = \frac{11}{3}$$

$$x - 2 = \pm\sqrt{\frac{11}{3}} = \pm\frac{\sqrt{33}}{3}$$

$$x = \frac{6}{3} \pm \frac{\sqrt{33}}{3} = \frac{6 \pm \sqrt{33}}{3}$$

The solutions are $\dfrac{6+\sqrt{33}}{3}$ and $\dfrac{6-\sqrt{33}}{3}$.

8. $2x^2 - 5x + 7 = 0$

$$2x^2 - 5x = -7$$

$$x^2 - \frac{5}{2}x = -\frac{7}{2}$$

Since $\dfrac{1}{2}\left(-\dfrac{5}{2}\right) = -\dfrac{5}{4}$ and $\left(-\dfrac{5}{4}\right)^2 = \dfrac{25}{16}$, we add

$\dfrac{25}{16}$ to both sides of the equation.

$$x^2 - \frac{5}{2}x + \frac{25}{16} = -\frac{7}{2} + \frac{25}{16}$$

$$\left(x - \frac{5}{4}\right)^2 = -\frac{56}{16} + \frac{25}{16} = -\frac{31}{16}$$

$$x - \frac{5}{4} = \pm\sqrt{-\frac{31}{16}}$$

$$x = \frac{5}{4} \pm \frac{i\sqrt{31}}{4} = \frac{5 \pm i\sqrt{31}}{4}$$

The solutions are $\dfrac{5+i\sqrt{31}}{4}$ and $\dfrac{5-i\sqrt{31}}{4}$.

9. $A = P(1+r)^t$; $A = 5618$, $P = 5000$, $t = 2$

$$A = P(1+r)^t$$

$$5618 = 5000(1+r)^2$$

$$1.1236 = (1+r)^2$$

$$\pm\sqrt{1.1236} = 1 + r$$

$$-1 \pm 1.06 = r$$

$$0.06 = r \text{ or } -2.06 = r$$

The rate cannot be negative, so we reject -2.06.

Check: $A = 5000(1+0.06)^2$

$$= 5000(1.06)^2$$

$$= 5000 \cdot 1.1236$$

$$= 5618$$

The interest rate is 6% compounded annually.

Graphing Calculator Explorations

1. $-1.27, 6.27$

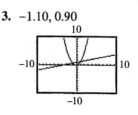

2. $-3.45, 1.45$

3. $-1.10, 0.90$

4. $-1.54, 1.94$

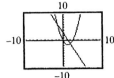

5. No real solutions, or $\varnothing$

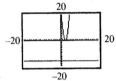

6. Answers may vary

Vocabulary and Readiness Check

1. By the square root property, if b is a real number, and $a^2 = b$, then $a = \underline{\pm\sqrt{b}}$.

2. A <u>quadratic</u> equation can be written in the form $ax^2 + bx + c = 0$, $a \neq 0$.

3. The process of writing a quadratic equation so that one side is a perfect square trinomial is called <u>completing the square</u>.

4. A perfect square trinomial is one that can be factored as a <u>binomial</u> squared.

5. To solve $x^2 + 6x = 10$ by completing the square, add $\underline{9}$ to both sides.

6. To solve $x^2 + bx = c$ by completing the square, add $\underline{\left(\dfrac{b}{2}\right)^2}$ to both sides.

7. $m^2 + 2m + \underline{1}$

8. $m^2 - 2m + \underline{1}$

9. $y^2 - 14y + \underline{49}$

10. $z^2 + z + \underline{\dfrac{1}{4}}$

Exercise Set 11.1

2. $x^2 = 49$
$x = \pm\sqrt{49}$
$x = \pm 7$

4. $x^2 - 11 = 0$
$x^2 = 11$
$x = \pm\sqrt{11}$

6. $y^2 = 20$
$y = \pm\sqrt{20}$
$y = \pm 2\sqrt{5}$

8. $2x^2 - 4 = 0$
$2x^2 = 4$
$x^2 = 2$
$x = \pm\sqrt{2}$

10. $(y-3)^2 = 4$
$y - 3 = \pm\sqrt{4}$
$y - 3 = \pm 2$
$y = 3 \pm 2$
$y = 1 \text{ or } y = 5$

12. $(y+4)^2 = 27$
$y + 4 = \pm\sqrt{27}$
$y + 4 = \pm 3\sqrt{3}$
$y = -4 \pm 3\sqrt{3}$

14. $(4x+9)^2 = 6$
$4x + 9 = \pm\sqrt{6}$
$4x = -9 \pm \sqrt{6}$
$x = \dfrac{-9 \pm \sqrt{6}}{4}$

16. $x^2 + 4 = 0$
$x^2 = -4$
$x = \pm\sqrt{-4}$
$x = \pm 2i$

18. $y^2 - 10 = 0$
$y^2 = 10$
$y = \pm\sqrt{10}$

20. $3p^2 + 36 = 0$

$3p^2 = -36$

$p^2 = -12$

$p = \pm\sqrt{-12}$

$p = \pm 2i\sqrt{3}$

22. $(y+2)^2 = -25$

$y + 2 = \pm\sqrt{-25}$

$y + 2 = \pm 5i$

$y = -2 \pm 5i$

24. $(x+10)^2 = 11$

$x + 10 = \pm\sqrt{11}$

$x = -10 \pm \sqrt{11}$

26. $(y-4)^2 = -18$

$y - 4 = \pm\sqrt{-18}$

$y - 4 = \pm 3i\sqrt{2}$

$y = 4 \pm 3i\sqrt{2}$

28. $y^2 + 2y + \left(\dfrac{2}{2}\right)^2 = y^2 + 2y + 1$

$= (y+1)^2$

30. $x^2 - 8x + \left(\dfrac{-8}{2}\right)^2 = x^2 - 8x + 16$

$= (x-4)^2$

32. $n^2 + 5n + \left(\dfrac{5}{2}\right)^2 = n^2 + 5n + \dfrac{25}{4}$

$= \left(n + \dfrac{5}{2}\right)^2$

34. $y^2 - y + \left(\dfrac{-1}{2}\right)^2 = y^2 - y + \dfrac{1}{4}$

$= \left(y - \dfrac{1}{2}\right)^2$

36. $y^2 + 6y = -8$

$y^2 + 6y + \left(\dfrac{6}{2}\right)^2 = -8 + 9$

$y^2 + 6y + 9 = 1$

$(y+3)^2 = 1$

$y + 3 = \pm\sqrt{1}$

$y = -3 \pm 1$

$y = -4 \ \text{ or } \ y = -2$

38. $x^2 - 2x - 2 = 0$

$x^2 - 2x = 2$

$x^2 - 2x + \left(\dfrac{-2}{2}\right)^2 = 2 + 1$

$x^2 - 2x + 1 = 3$

$(x-1)^2 = 3$

$x - 1 = \pm\sqrt{3}$

$x = 1 \pm \sqrt{3}$

40. $x^2 + 3x - 2 = 0$

$x^2 + 3x = 2$

$x^2 + 3x + \left(\dfrac{3}{2}\right)^2 = 2 + \dfrac{9}{4}$

$x^2 + 3x + \dfrac{9}{4} = \dfrac{17}{4}$

$\left(x + \dfrac{3}{2}\right)^2 = \dfrac{17}{4}$

$x + \dfrac{3}{2} = \pm\sqrt{\dfrac{17}{4}}$

$x = -\dfrac{3}{2} \pm \dfrac{\sqrt{17}}{2} = \dfrac{-3 \pm \sqrt{17}}{2}$

42. $y^2 + y - 7 = 0$

$y^2 + y = 7$

$y^2 + y + \left(\dfrac{1}{2}\right)^2 = 7 + \dfrac{1}{4}$

$y^2 + y + \dfrac{1}{4} = \dfrac{29}{4}$

$\left(y + \dfrac{1}{2}\right)^2 = \dfrac{29}{4}$

$y + \dfrac{1}{2} = \pm\sqrt{\dfrac{29}{4}}$

$y = -\dfrac{1}{2} \pm \dfrac{\sqrt{29}}{2} = \dfrac{-1 \pm \sqrt{29}}{2}$

44.
$$2x^2 + 14x - 1 = 0$$
$$2x^2 + 14x = 1$$
$$x^2 + 7x = \frac{1}{2}$$
$$x^2 + 7x + \left(\frac{7}{2}\right)^2 = \frac{1}{2} + \frac{49}{4}$$
$$\left(x + \frac{7}{2}\right)^2 = \frac{51}{4}$$
$$x + \frac{7}{2} = \pm\sqrt{\frac{51}{4}}$$
$$x = -\frac{7}{2} \pm \frac{\sqrt{51}}{2} = \frac{-7 \pm \sqrt{51}}{2}$$

46.
$$6x^2 - 3 = 6x$$
$$6x^2 - 6x = 3$$
$$x^2 - x = \frac{1}{2}$$
$$x^2 - x + \left(\frac{-1}{2}\right)^2 = \frac{1}{2} + \frac{1}{4}$$
$$x^2 - x + \frac{1}{4} = \frac{3}{4}$$
$$\left(x - \frac{1}{2}\right)^2 = \frac{3}{4}$$
$$x - \frac{1}{2} = \pm\sqrt{\frac{3}{4}}$$
$$x = \frac{1}{2} \pm \frac{\sqrt{3}}{2} = \frac{1 \pm \sqrt{3}}{2}$$

48.
$$3x^2 - 4x = 4$$
$$x^2 - \frac{4}{3}x = \frac{4}{3}$$
$$x^2 - \frac{4}{3}x + \left(\frac{\frac{4}{3}}{2}\right)^2 = \frac{4}{3} + \frac{4}{9}$$
$$x^2 - \frac{4}{3}x + \frac{4}{9} = \frac{16}{9}$$
$$\left(x - \frac{2}{3}\right)^2 = \frac{16}{9}$$
$$x - \frac{2}{3} = \pm\sqrt{\frac{16}{9}}$$
$$x = \frac{2}{3} \pm \frac{4}{3}$$
$$x = -\frac{2}{3}, 2$$

50.
$$y^2 + 6y - 8 = 0$$
$$y^2 + 6y = 8$$
$$y^2 + 6y + \left(\frac{6}{2}\right)^2 = 8 + 9$$
$$y^2 + 6y + 9 = 17$$
$$(y + 3)^2 = 17$$
$$y + 3 = \pm\sqrt{17}$$
$$y = -3 \pm \sqrt{17}$$

52.
$$x^2 - 10x + 2 = 0$$
$$x^2 - 10x = -2$$
$$x^2 - 10 + \left(\frac{-10}{2}\right)^2 = -2 + 25$$
$$x^2 - 10x + 25 = 23$$
$$(x - 5)^2 = 23$$
$$x - 5 = \pm\sqrt{23}$$
$$x = 5 \pm \sqrt{23}$$

54.
$$2y^2 + 12y + 3 = 0$$
$$2y^2 + 12y = -3$$
$$y^2 + 6y = -\frac{3}{2}$$
$$y^2 + 6y + \left(\frac{6}{2}\right)^2 = -\frac{3}{2} + 9$$
$$y^2 + 6y + 9 = \frac{15}{2}$$
$$(y + 3)^2 = \frac{15}{2}$$
$$y + 3 = \pm\sqrt{\frac{15}{2}}$$
$$y + 3 = \pm\frac{\sqrt{15} \cdot \sqrt{2}}{\sqrt{2} \cdot \sqrt{2}}$$
$$y + 3 = \pm\frac{\sqrt{30}}{2}$$
$$y = -3 \pm \frac{\sqrt{30}}{2} = \frac{-6 \pm \sqrt{30}}{2}$$

56.
$$5x^2 + 3x - 2 = 0$$
$$5x^2 + 3x = 2$$
$$x^2 + \frac{3}{5}x = \frac{2}{5}$$
$$x^2 + \frac{3}{5}x + \left(\frac{\frac{3}{5}}{2}\right)^2 = \frac{2}{5} + \frac{9}{100}$$
$$x^2 + \frac{3}{5}x + \frac{9}{100} = \frac{49}{100}$$
$$\left(x + \frac{3}{10}\right)^2 = \frac{49}{100}$$
$$x + \frac{3}{10} = \pm\sqrt{\frac{49}{100}}$$
$$x = -\frac{3}{10} \pm \frac{7}{10}$$
$$x = \frac{-3 \pm 7}{10} = -1, \frac{2}{5}$$

58.
$$x^2 + 4x + 6 = 0$$
$$x^2 + 4x = -6$$
$$x^2 + 4x + \left(\frac{4}{2}\right)^2 = -6 + 4$$
$$x^2 + 4x + 4 = -2$$
$$(x+2)^2 = -2$$
$$x + 2 = \pm\sqrt{-2}$$
$$x = -2 \pm i\sqrt{2}$$

60.
$$x^2 - 7x - 1 = 0$$
$$x^2 - 7x = 1$$
$$x^2 - 7x + \left(\frac{-7}{2}\right)^2 = 1 + \frac{49}{4}$$
$$x^2 - 7x + \frac{49}{4} = \frac{53}{4}$$
$$\left(x - \frac{7}{2}\right)^2 = \frac{53}{4}$$
$$x - \frac{7}{2} = \pm\sqrt{\frac{53}{4}}$$
$$x = \frac{7}{2} \pm \frac{\sqrt{53}}{2} = \frac{7 \pm \sqrt{53}}{2}$$

62.
$$3x^2 + 12x = -14$$
$$x^2 + 4x = -\frac{14}{3}$$
$$x^2 + 4x + \left(\frac{4}{2}\right)^2 = -\frac{14}{3} + 4$$
$$x^2 + 4x + 4 = -\frac{2}{3}$$
$$(x+2)^2 = -\frac{2}{3}$$
$$x + 2 = \pm\sqrt{-\frac{2}{3}}$$
$$x + 2 = \pm\frac{i\sqrt{2} \cdot \sqrt{3}}{\sqrt{3} \cdot \sqrt{3}}$$
$$x = -2 \pm i\frac{\sqrt{6}}{3} = -\frac{6 \pm i\sqrt{6}}{3}$$

64.
$$16y^2 + 16y - 1 = 0$$
$$16y^2 + 16y = 1$$
$$y^2 + y = \frac{1}{16}$$
$$y^2 + y + \left(\frac{1}{2}\right)^2 = \frac{1}{16} + \frac{1}{4}$$
$$y^2 + y + \frac{1}{4} = \frac{5}{16}$$
$$\left(y + \frac{1}{2}\right)^2 = \frac{5}{16}$$
$$y + \frac{1}{2} = \pm\sqrt{\frac{5}{16}}$$
$$y = -\frac{1}{2} \pm \frac{\sqrt{5}}{4} = \frac{-2 \pm \sqrt{5}}{4}$$

66.
$$4x^2 - 2x + 5 = 0$$
$$4x^2 - 2x = -5$$
$$x^2 - \frac{1}{2}x = -\frac{5}{4}$$
$$x^2 - \frac{1}{2}x + \left(\frac{-\frac{1}{2}}{2}\right)^2 = -\frac{5}{4} + \frac{1}{16}$$
$$x^2 - \frac{1}{2}x + \frac{1}{16} = -\frac{19}{16}$$
$$\left(x - \frac{1}{4}\right)^2 = -\frac{19}{16}$$
$$x - \frac{1}{4} = \pm\sqrt{-\frac{19}{16}}$$
$$x - \frac{1}{4} = \pm i\frac{\sqrt{19}}{4}$$
$$x = \frac{1}{4} \pm i\frac{\sqrt{19}}{4} = \frac{1 \pm i\sqrt{19}}{4}$$

68.
$$y^2 + 8y + 18 = 0$$
$$y^2 + 8y = -18$$
$$y^2 + 8y + \left(\frac{8}{2}\right)^2 = -18 + 16$$
$$(y + 4)^2 = -2$$
$$y + 4 = \pm\sqrt{-2}$$
$$y = -4 \pm i\sqrt{2}$$

70.
$$y^2 + y - 2 = 0$$
$$y^2 + y = 2$$
$$y^2 + y + \left(\frac{1}{2}\right)^2 = 2 + \frac{1}{4}$$
$$y^2 + y + \frac{1}{4} = \frac{9}{4}$$
$$\left(y + \frac{1}{2}\right)^2 = \frac{9}{4}$$
$$y + \frac{1}{2} = \pm\sqrt{\frac{9}{4}}$$
$$y = -\frac{1}{2} \pm \frac{3}{2}$$
$$y = -2, 1$$

72.
$$9x^2 - 36x = -40$$
$$x^2 - 4x = -\frac{40}{9}$$
$$x^2 - 4x + \left(\frac{-4}{2}\right)^2 = -\frac{40}{9} + 4$$
$$x^2 - 4x + 4 = -\frac{4}{9}$$
$$(x - 2)^2 = -\frac{4}{9}$$
$$x - 2 = \pm\sqrt{-\frac{4}{9}}$$
$$x - 2 = \pm\frac{2}{3}i$$
$$x = 2 \pm \frac{2}{3}i = \frac{6 \pm 2i}{3}$$

74.
$$5y^2 - 15y = 1$$
$$y^2 - 3y = \frac{1}{5}$$
$$y^2 - 3y + \left(\frac{-3}{2}\right)^2 = \frac{1}{5} + \frac{9}{4}$$
$$y^2 - 3y + \frac{9}{4} = \frac{49}{20}$$
$$\left(y - \frac{3}{2}\right)^2 = \frac{49}{20}$$
$$y - \frac{3}{2} = \pm\sqrt{\frac{49}{20}}$$
$$y - \frac{3}{2} = \pm\frac{7}{2\sqrt{5}}$$
$$y - \frac{3}{2} = \pm\frac{7 \cdot \sqrt{5}}{2\sqrt{5} \cdot \sqrt{5}}$$
$$y - \frac{3}{2} = \pm\frac{7\sqrt{5}}{10}$$
$$y = \frac{3}{2} \pm \frac{7\sqrt{5}}{10} = \frac{15 \pm 7\sqrt{5}}{10}$$

76.
$$A = P(1 + r)^t$$
$$882 = 800(1 + r)^2$$
$$\frac{882}{800} = (1 + r)^2$$
$$1.1025 = (1 + r)^2$$
$$\pm\sqrt{1.1025} = 1 + r$$
$$\pm 1.05 = 1 + r$$
$$-1 \pm 1.05 = r$$
$$-2.05 = r \text{ or } 0.05 = r$$
Rate cannot be negative, so the rate is 0.05 or 5%.

78.
$$A = P(1+r)^t$$
$$2880 = 2000(1+r)^2$$
$$\frac{2880}{2000} = (1+r)^2$$
$$1.44 = (1+r)^2$$
$$\pm\sqrt{1.44} = 1+r$$
$$-1 \pm 1.2 = r$$
$$-2.2 = r \text{ or } 0.2 = r$$

Rate cannot be negative, so the rate is 0.2 or 20%.

80.
$$s(t) = 16t^2$$
$$1483 = 16t^2$$
$$t^2 = \frac{1483}{16}$$
$$t = \pm\sqrt{\frac{1483}{16}}$$
$$t \approx 9.63 \text{ or } -9.63 \text{ (disregard)}$$

It would take 9.63 seconds.

82.
$$s(t) = 16t^2$$
$$984 = 16t^2$$
$$t^2 = \frac{984}{16}$$
$$t = \pm\sqrt{\frac{984}{16}}$$
$$t \approx 7.84 \text{ or } -7.84 \text{ (disregard)}$$

It would take 7.84 seconds.

84. Compound; answers may vary.

86. $\dfrac{3}{4} - \sqrt{\dfrac{25}{16}} = \dfrac{3}{4} - \dfrac{5}{4} = -\dfrac{2}{4} = -\dfrac{1}{2}$

88. $\dfrac{1}{2} - \sqrt{\dfrac{9}{4}} = \dfrac{1}{2} - \dfrac{3}{2} = -\dfrac{2}{2} = -1$

90. $\dfrac{6+4\sqrt{5}}{2} = \dfrac{6}{2} + \dfrac{4\sqrt{5}}{2} = 3 + 2\sqrt{5}$

92. $\dfrac{3-9\sqrt{2}}{6} = \dfrac{3}{6} - \dfrac{9\sqrt{2}}{6} = \dfrac{1}{2} - \dfrac{3\sqrt{2}}{2} = \dfrac{1-3\sqrt{2}}{2}$

94.
$$\sqrt{b^2 - 4ac} = \sqrt{(4)^2 - 4(2)(-1)}$$
$$= \sqrt{16+8}$$
$$= \sqrt{24}$$
$$= 2\sqrt{6}$$

96.
$$\sqrt{b^2 - 4ac} = \sqrt{(-1)^2 - 4(3)(-2)}$$
$$= \sqrt{1+24}$$
$$= \sqrt{25}$$
$$= 5$$

98. The solutions of $(x+1)^2 = -1$ are complex, but not real numbers; answers may vary.

100. The solutions of $3z^2 = 10$ are real; answers may vary.

102. The solutions of $(2y-5)^2 + 7 = 3$ are complex, but not real numbers; answers may vary.

104. $x^2 + \underline{\quad} + 16$
$$\left(\frac{b}{2}\right)^2 = 16$$
$$\frac{b}{2} = \pm\sqrt{16}$$
$$\frac{b}{2} = \pm 4$$
$$b = \pm 8$$

Answer: $\pm 8x$

106. $z^2 + \underline{\quad} + \dfrac{25}{4}$
$$\left(\frac{b}{2}\right)^2 = \frac{25}{4}$$
$$\frac{b}{2} = \pm\sqrt{\frac{25}{4}}$$
$$\frac{b}{2} = \pm\frac{5}{2}$$
$$b = \pm 5$$

Answer: $\pm 5z$

108.
$$A = s^2$$
$$225 = s^2$$
$$\pm\sqrt{225} = s^2$$
$$s = 15 \text{ or } -15 \text{ (disregard)}$$

The dimensions are 15 ft by 15 ft.

110.
$$a^2 + b^2 = c^2$$
$$x^2 + x^2 = 20^2$$
$$2x^2 = 400$$
$$x^2 = 200$$
$$x = \pm\sqrt{200}$$
$$x = \pm 10\sqrt{2}$$
$$x = 10\sqrt{2} \text{ or } -10\sqrt{2} \text{ (disregard)}$$

The side of each leg is $10\sqrt{2}$ cm.

112.
$$p = -x^2 + 47$$
$$11 = -x^2 + 47$$
$$x^2 = 36$$
$$x = \pm\sqrt{36}$$
$$x = \pm 6$$

Demand cannot be negative. Therefore, the demand is 6 thousand scissors.

Section 11.2

Practice Exercises

1.
$$3x^2 - 5x - 2 = 0$$
$$a = 3, \, b = -5, \, c = -2$$
$$x = \frac{-b \pm \sqrt{b^2 - 4ac}}{2a}$$
$$= \frac{-(-5) \pm \sqrt{(-5)^2 - 4(3)(-2)}}{2(3)}$$
$$= \frac{5 \pm \sqrt{25 + 24}}{6}$$
$$= \frac{5 \pm \sqrt{49}}{6}$$
$$= \frac{5 \pm 7}{6}$$
$$x = \frac{5 + 7}{6} = \frac{12}{6} = 2 \text{ or } x = \frac{5 - 7}{6} = \frac{-2}{6} = -\frac{1}{3}$$

The solutions are $-\dfrac{1}{3}$ and 2, or the solution set is $\left\{-\dfrac{1}{3}, 2\right\}$.

2.
$$3x^2 - 8x = 2$$
Write in standard form.
$$3x^2 - 8x - 2 = 0$$
$$a = 3, \, b = -8, \, c = -2$$
$$x = \frac{-b \pm \sqrt{b^2 - 4ac}}{2a}$$
$$= \frac{-(-8) \pm \sqrt{(-8)^2 - 4(3)(-2)}}{2(3)}$$
$$= \frac{8 \pm \sqrt{64 + 24}}{6}$$
$$= \frac{8 \pm \sqrt{88}}{6}$$
$$= \frac{8 \pm 2\sqrt{22}}{6}$$
$$= \frac{4 \pm \sqrt{22}}{3}$$

The solutions are $\dfrac{4 + \sqrt{22}}{3}$ and $\dfrac{4 - \sqrt{22}}{3}$, or the solution set is $\left\{\dfrac{4 + \sqrt{22}}{3}, \dfrac{4 - \sqrt{22}}{3}\right\}$.

3.
$$\frac{1}{8}x^2 - \frac{1}{4}x - 2 = 0$$
Multiply both sides of the equation by 8.
$$8\left(\frac{1}{8}x^2 - \frac{1}{4}x - 2\right) = 8 \cdot 0$$
$$x^2 - 2x - 16 = 0$$
Substitute $a = 1$, $b = -2$, and $c = -16$ into the quadratic formula and simplify.
$$x = \frac{-(-2) \pm \sqrt{(-2)^2 - 4(1)(-16)}}{2(1)}$$
$$= \frac{2 \pm \sqrt{4 + 64}}{2}$$
$$= \frac{2 \pm \sqrt{68}}{2}$$
$$= \frac{2 \pm 2\sqrt{17}}{2}$$
$$= 1 \pm \sqrt{17}$$

The solutions are $1 + \sqrt{17}$ or $1 - \sqrt{17}$.

4. $x = -2x^2 - 2$

   The equation in standard form is

   $2x^2 + x + 2 = 0$. Thus, let $a = 2$, $b = 1$, and $c = 2$ in the quadratic formula.

   $x = \dfrac{-1 \pm \sqrt{1^2 - 4(2)(2)}}{2(2)}$

   $= \dfrac{-1 \pm \sqrt{1 - 16}}{4}$

   $= \dfrac{-1 \pm \sqrt{-15}}{4}$

   $= \dfrac{-1 \pm i\sqrt{15}}{4}$

   The solutions are $\dfrac{-1 + i\sqrt{15}}{4}$ and $\dfrac{-1 - i\sqrt{15}}{4}$.

5. **a.** $x^2 - 6x + 9 = 0$

   In $x^2 - 6x + 9$, $a = 1$, $b = -6$, and $c = 9$. Thus,

   $b^2 - 4ac = (-6)^2 - 4(1)(9) = 36 - 36 = 0$

   Since $b^2 - 4ac = 0$, this equation has one real solution.

   b. $x^2 - 3x - 1 = 0$

   In this equation, $a = 1$, $b = -3$, and $c = -1$.

   $b^2 - 4ac = (-3)^2 - 4(1)(-1) = 9 + 4 = 13 > 0$

   Since $b^2 - 4ac$ is positive, this equation has two real solutions.

   c. $7x^2 + 11 = 0$

   In this equation, $a = 7$, $b = 0$, and $c = 11$.

   $b^2 - 4ac = 0^2 - 4(7)(11) = -308 < 0$

   Since $b^2 - 4ac$ is negative, this equation has two complex but not real solutions.

6. By the Pythagorean theorem, we have

   $x^2 + (x + 3)^2 = 15^2$

   $x^2 + x^2 + 6x + 9 = 225$

   $2x^2 + 6x - 216 = 0$

   $x^2 + 3x - 108 = 0$

   Here, $a = 1$, $b = 3$, and $c = -108$. By the quadratic formula,

   $x = \dfrac{-3 \pm \sqrt{3^2 - 4(1)(-108)}}{2(1)}$

   $= \dfrac{-3 \pm \sqrt{9 + 432}}{2}$

   $= \dfrac{-3 \pm \sqrt{441}}{2}$

   $= \dfrac{-3 \pm 21}{2}$

   $x = \dfrac{-3 + 21}{2} = \dfrac{18}{2} = 9$ or

   $x = \dfrac{-3 - 21}{2} = \dfrac{-24}{2} = -12$

   The length can't be negative, so reject -12. The distance along the sidewalk is

   $x + (x + 3) = 2x + 3 = 2(9) + 3 = 18 + 3 = 21$ feet

   A person can save $21 - 15 = 6$ feet by cutting across the lawn.

7. $h = -16t^2 + 20t + 45$

   At the ground, $h = 0$.

   $0 = -16t^2 + 20t + 45$

   Here, $a = -16$, $b = 20$, and $c = 45$. By the quadratic formula,

   $t = \dfrac{-20 \pm \sqrt{20^2 - 4(-16)(45)}}{2(-16)}$

   $= \dfrac{-20 \pm \sqrt{400 + 2880}}{-32}$

   $= \dfrac{-20 \pm \sqrt{3280}}{-32}$

   $= \dfrac{20 \pm \sqrt{16 \cdot 205}}{32}$

   $= \dfrac{20 \pm 4\sqrt{205}}{32}$

   $= \dfrac{5 \pm \sqrt{205}}{8}$

   $t = \dfrac{5 + \sqrt{205}}{8} \approx 2.4$ or $t = \dfrac{5 - \sqrt{205}}{8} \approx -1.2$

   Since the time won't be negative, we reject -1.2. The rocket will strike the ground 2.4 seconds after launch.

Vocabulary and Readiness Check

1. The quadratic formula is $x = \dfrac{-b \pm \sqrt{b^2 - 4ac}}{2a}$.

2. For $2x^2 + x + 1 = 0$, if $a = 2$, then $b = \underline{1}$ and $c = \underline{1}$.

3. For $5x^2 - 5x - 7 = 0$, if $a = 5$, then $b = \underline{-5}$ and $c = \underline{-7}$.

4. For $7x^2 - 4 = 0$, if $a = 7$, then $b = \underline{0}$ and $c = \underline{-4}$.

5. For $x^2 + 9 = 0$, if $c = 9$, then $a = \underline{1}$ and $b = \underline{0}$.

6. The correct simplified form of $\dfrac{5 \pm 10\sqrt{2}}{5}$ is $\underline{1 \pm 2\sqrt{2}}$. The answer is **c**.

Exercise Set 11.2

2. $p^2 + 11p - 12 = 0$
$a = 1, b = 11, c = -12$
$$p = \frac{-11 \pm \sqrt{(11)^2 - 4(1)(-12)}}{2(1)}$$
$$= \frac{-11 \pm \sqrt{169}}{2}$$
$$= \frac{-11 \pm 13}{2} = -12 \text{ or } 1$$
The solutions are -12 and 1.

4. $5x^2 - 3 = 14x$
$5x^2 - 14x - 3 = 0$
$a = 5, b = -14, c = -3$
$$x = \frac{14 \pm \sqrt{(-14)^2 - 4(5)(-3)}}{2(5)}$$
$$= \frac{14 \pm \sqrt{256}}{10}$$
$$= \frac{14 \pm 16}{10} = -\frac{1}{5} \text{ or } 3$$
The solutions are $-\dfrac{1}{5}$ and 3.

6. $y^2 + 10y + 25 = 0$
$a = 1, b = 10, c = 25$
$$y = \frac{-10 \pm \sqrt{(10)^2 - 4(1)(25)}}{2(1)}$$
$$= \frac{-10 \pm \sqrt{0}}{2}$$
$$= \frac{-10}{2} = -5$$
The solution is -5.

8. $y^2 + 5y + 3 = 0$
$a = 1, b = 5, c = 3$
$$y = \frac{-5 \pm \sqrt{(5)^2 - 4(1)(3)}}{2(1)} = \frac{-5 \pm \sqrt{13}}{2}$$
The solutions are $\dfrac{-5 + \sqrt{13}}{2}$ and $\dfrac{-5 - \sqrt{13}}{2}$.

10. $11n^2 - 9n = 1$
$11n^2 - 9n - 1 = 0$
$a = 11, b = -9, c = -1$
$$n = \frac{9 \pm \sqrt{(-9)^2 - 4(11)(-1)}}{2(11)}$$
$$= \frac{9 \pm \sqrt{125}}{22}$$
$$= \frac{9 \pm 5\sqrt{5}}{22}$$
The solutions are $\dfrac{9 + 5\sqrt{5}}{22}$ and $\dfrac{9 - 5\sqrt{5}}{22}$.

12. $x^2 - 13 = 5x$
$x^2 - 5x - 13 = 0$
$a = 1, b = -5, c = -13$
$$x = \frac{5 \pm \sqrt{(-5)^2 - 4(1)(-13)}}{2(1)}$$
$$= \frac{5 \pm \sqrt{77}}{2}$$
The solutions are $\dfrac{5 + \sqrt{77}}{2}$ and $\dfrac{5 - \sqrt{77}}{2}$.

14. $\frac{1}{6}x^2 + x + \frac{1}{3} = 0$

$x^2 + 6x + 2 = 0$

$a = 1, b = 6, c = 2$

$x = \dfrac{-6 \pm \sqrt{(6)^2 - 4(1)(2)}}{2(1)}$

$= \dfrac{-6 \pm \sqrt{28}}{2}$

$= \dfrac{-6 \pm 2\sqrt{7}}{2}$

$= -3 \pm \sqrt{7}$

The solutions are $-3 + \sqrt{7}$ and $-3 - \sqrt{7}$.

16. $\frac{1}{8}x^2 + x = \frac{5}{2}$

$x^2 + 8x - 20 = 0$

$a = 1, b = 8, c = -20$

$x = \dfrac{-8 \pm \sqrt{(-8)^2 - 4(1)(-20)}}{2(1)}$

$= \dfrac{-8 \pm \sqrt{144}}{2}$

$= \dfrac{-8 \pm 12}{2} = -10 \text{ or } 2$

The solutions are -10 and 2.

18. $\frac{1}{2}y^2 = y + \frac{1}{2}$

$y^2 - 2y - 1 = 0$

$a = 1, b = -2, c = -1$

$y = \dfrac{2 \pm \sqrt{(-2)^2 - 4(1)(-1)}}{2(1)}$

$= \dfrac{2 \pm \sqrt{8}}{2}$

$= \dfrac{2 \pm 2\sqrt{2}}{2} = 1 \pm \sqrt{2}$

The solutions are $1 + \sqrt{2}$ and $1 - \sqrt{2}$.

20. $y^2 - 8 = 4y$

$y^2 - 4y - 8 = 0$

$a = 1, b = -4, c = -8$

$y = \dfrac{4 \pm \sqrt{(-4)^2 - 4(1)(-8)}}{2(1)}$

$= \dfrac{4 \pm \sqrt{48}}{2}$

$= \dfrac{4 \pm 4\sqrt{3}}{2} = 2 \pm 2\sqrt{3}$

The solutions are $2 + 2\sqrt{3}$ and $2 - 2\sqrt{3}$.

22. $7p(p - 2) + 2(p + 4) = 3$

$7p^2 - 14p + 2p + 8 = 3$

$7p^2 - 12p + 5 = 0$

$a = 7, b = -12, c = 5$

$p = \dfrac{12 \pm \sqrt{(-12)^2 - 4(7)(5)}}{2(7)}$

$= \dfrac{12 \pm \sqrt{4}}{14}$

$= \dfrac{12 \pm 2}{14} = \dfrac{5}{7} \text{ or } 1$

The solutions are $\dfrac{5}{7}$ and 1.

24. $x^2 + 2x + 2 = 0$

$a = 1, b = 2, c = 2$

$x = \dfrac{-2 \pm \sqrt{(2)^2 - 4(1)(2)}}{2(1)}$

$= \dfrac{-2 \pm \sqrt{-4}}{2}$

$= \dfrac{-2 \pm 2i}{2} = -1 \pm i$

The solutions are $-1 + i$ and $-1 - i$.

26. $x(x + 6) = 2$

$x^2 + 6x - 2 = 0$

$a = 1, b = 6, c = -2$

$x = \dfrac{-6 \pm \sqrt{(6)^2 - 4(1)(-2)}}{2(1)}$

$= \dfrac{-6 \pm \sqrt{44}}{2}$

$= \dfrac{-6 \pm 2\sqrt{11}}{2} = -3 \pm \sqrt{11}$

The solutions are $-3 + \sqrt{11}$ and $-3 - \sqrt{11}$.

28.
$$2 = -9x^2 - x$$
$$9x^2 + x + 2 = 0$$
$$a = 9, \, b = 1, \, c = 2$$
$$x = \frac{-1 \pm \sqrt{(1)^2 - 4(9)(2)}}{2(9)}$$
$$= \frac{-1 \pm \sqrt{-71}}{18}$$
$$= \frac{-1 \pm i\sqrt{71}}{18}$$

The solutions are $\dfrac{-1 + i\sqrt{71}}{18}$ and $\dfrac{-1 - i\sqrt{71}}{18}$.

30.
$$\frac{x^2}{2} - 3 = -\frac{9}{2}x$$
$$x^2 + 9x - 6 = 0$$
$$a = 1, \, b = 9, \, c = -6$$
$$x = \frac{-9 \pm \sqrt{(9)^2 - 4(1)(-6)}}{2(1)}$$
$$= \frac{-9 \pm \sqrt{105}}{2}$$

The solutions are $\dfrac{-9 + \sqrt{105}}{2}$ and $\dfrac{-9 - \sqrt{105}}{2}$.

32.
$$3y^2 + 6y + 5 = 0$$
$$a = 3, \, b = 6, \, c = 5$$
$$y = \frac{-6 \pm \sqrt{(6)^2 - 4(3)(5)}}{2(3)}$$
$$= \frac{-6 \pm \sqrt{-24}}{6}$$
$$= \frac{-6 \pm 2i\sqrt{6}}{6}$$
$$= \frac{-3 \pm i\sqrt{6}}{3}$$

The solutions are $\dfrac{-3 + i\sqrt{6}}{3}$ and $\dfrac{-3 - i\sqrt{6}}{3}$.

34.
$$x(7x + 1) = 2$$
$$7x^2 + x - 2 = 0$$
$$a = 7, \, b = 1, \, c = -2$$
$$x = \frac{-1 \pm \sqrt{(1)^2 - 4(7)(-2)}}{2(7)}$$
$$= \frac{-1 \pm \sqrt{57}}{14}$$

The solutions are $\dfrac{-1 + \sqrt{57}}{14}$ and $\dfrac{-1 - \sqrt{57}}{14}$.

36.
$$\frac{1}{8}x^2 + x + \frac{5}{2} = 0$$
$$x^2 + 8x + 20 = 0$$
$$a = 1, \, b = 8, \, c = 20$$
$$x = \frac{-8 \pm \sqrt{(8)^2 - 4(1)(20)}}{2(1)}$$
$$= \frac{-8 \pm \sqrt{-16}}{2}$$
$$= \frac{-8 \pm 4i}{2} = -4 \pm 2i$$

The solutions are $-4 + 2i$ and $-4 - 2i$.

38.
$$\frac{2}{3}x^2 - \frac{20}{3}x = -\frac{100}{6}$$
$$4x^2 - 40x + 100 = 0$$
$$x^2 - 10x + 25 = 0$$
$$a = 1, \, b = -10, \, c = 25$$
$$x = \frac{10 \pm \sqrt{(-10)^2 - 4(1)(25)}}{2(1)}$$
$$= \frac{10 \pm \sqrt{0}}{2} = \frac{10}{2} = 5$$

The solution is 5.

40.
$$\left(p - \frac{1}{2}\right)^2 = \frac{p}{2}$$
$$p^2 - p + \frac{1}{4} = \frac{p}{2}$$
$$4p^2 - 4p + 1 = 2p$$
$$4p^2 - 6p + 1 = 0$$
$$a = 4, \, b = -6, \, c = 1$$

$$p = \frac{6 \pm \sqrt{(-6)^2 - 4(4)(1)}}{2(4)}$$

$$= \frac{6 \pm \sqrt{20}}{8}$$

$$= \frac{6 \pm 2\sqrt{5}}{8} = \frac{3 \pm \sqrt{5}}{4}$$

The solutions are $\dfrac{3+\sqrt{5}}{4}$ and $\dfrac{3-\sqrt{5}}{4}$.

42. $x^2 - 7 = 0$

$a = 1, b = 0, c = -7$

$b^2 - 4ac = 0^2 - 4(1)(-7) = 0 + 28 = 28 > 0$

Therefore, there are two real solutions.

44. $9x^2 + 1 = 6x$

$9x^2 - 6x + 1 = 0$

$a = 9, b = -6, c = 1$

$b^2 - 4ac = (-6)^2 - 4(9)(1)$

$\quad\quad = 36 - 36$

$\quad\quad = 0$

Therefore, there is one real solution.

46. $3x^2 = 5 - 7x$

$3x^2 + 7x - 5 = 0$

$a = 3, b = 7, c = -5$

$b^2 - 4ac = 7^2 - 4(3)(-5)$

$\quad\quad = 49 + 60$

$\quad\quad = 109 > 0$

Therefore, there are two real solutions.

48. $8x = 3 - 9x^2$

$9x^2 + 8x - 3 = 0$

$a = 9, b = 8, c = -3$

$b^2 - 4ac = 8^2 - 4(9)(-3)$

$\quad\quad = 64 + 108$

$\quad\quad = 172 > 0$

Therefore, there are two real solutions.

50. $5 - 4x + 12x^2 = 0$

$12x^2 - 4x + 5 = 0$

$a = 12, b = -4, c = 5$

$b^2 - 4ac = (-4)^2 - 4(12)(5)$

$\quad\quad = 16 - 240$

$\quad\quad = -224 < 0$

Therefore, there are two complex but not real solutions.

52. $\quad (x+10)^2 + x^2 = 40^2$

$(x^2 + 20x + 100) + x^2 = 1600$

$2x^2 + 20x - 1500 = 0$

$x^2 + 10x - 750 = 0$

$a = 1, b = 10, c = -750$

$$x = \frac{-10 \pm \sqrt{(10)^2 - 4(1)(-750)}}{2(1)}$$

$$= \frac{-10 \pm \sqrt{3100}}{2}$$

$x \approx 23$ or $x \approx -33$ (disregard)

$x + (x + 10) = 23 + 23 + 10 = 56$

$56 - 40 = 16$

They saved about 16 feet of walking distance.

54. Let x = length of leg. Then $x + 1$ = length of hypotenuse.

$$x^2 + x^2 = (x+1)^2$$

$$2x^2 = x^2 + 2x + 1$$

$x^2 - 2x - 1 = 0$

$a = 1, b = -2, c = -1$

$$x = \frac{2 \pm \sqrt{(-2)^2 - 4(1)(-1)}}{2(1)}$$

$$= \frac{2 \pm \sqrt{8}}{2}$$

$$= \frac{2 \pm 2\sqrt{2}}{2}$$

$= 1 \pm \sqrt{2}$ (disregard the negative)

$= 1 + \sqrt{2}$

The sides measure $1 + \sqrt{2}$ m, $1 + \sqrt{2}$ m, and $2 + \sqrt{2}$ m.

56. Let x = width; then $x + 20$ = length.

Area = length · width

$1200 = (x + 20)x$

$0 = x^2 + 20x - 1200$

$a = 1, b = 20, c = -1200$

$$x = \frac{-20 \pm \sqrt{(20)^2 - 4(1)(-1200)}}{2(1)}$$

$$= \frac{-20 \pm \sqrt{5200}}{2}$$

$$= \frac{-20 \pm 20\sqrt{13}}{2}$$

$= -10 \pm 10\sqrt{13}$

Disregard the negative length. The width is $-10 + 10\sqrt{13}$ in. and the length is $10 + 10\sqrt{13}$ in.

58. a. Let x = width. Then $3x$ = length.

$$x^2 + (3x)^2 = 50^2$$
$$x^2 + 9x^2 = 2500$$
$$10x^2 - 2500 = 0$$
$$x^2 - 250 = 0$$
$$a = 1, b = 0, c = -250$$
$$x = \frac{0 \pm \sqrt{(0)^2 - 4(1)(-250)}}{2(1)}$$
$$= \frac{\pm\sqrt{1000}}{2}$$
$$= \frac{\pm 10\sqrt{10}}{2} = \pm 5\sqrt{10}$$

Disregard the negative width. The width is $5\sqrt{10}$ cm and the length is $15\sqrt{10}$ cm.

b. Perimeter = $2l + 2w$
$$= 2\left(15\sqrt{10}\right) + 2\left(5\sqrt{10}\right)$$
$$= 40\sqrt{10} \text{ cm}$$

60. Let w = width; then $w + 7.3$ = length.

Area = length $\cdot$ width
$$569.9 = (w + 7.3)w$$
$$0 = w^2 + 7.3w - 569.9$$
$$a = 1, b = 7.3, c = -569.9$$
$$w = \frac{-7.3 \pm \sqrt{(7.3)^2 - 4(1)(-569.9)}}{2(1)}$$
$$= \frac{-7.3 \pm \sqrt{2332.89}}{2}$$
$$= 20.5 \text{ or } -27.8 \text{ (disregard)}$$

Its width is 20.5 inches and its height is 27.8 inches.

62.
$$\frac{x-1}{1} = \frac{1}{x}$$
$$x(x-1) = 1$$
$$x^2 - x - 1 = 0$$
$$a = 1, b = -1, c = -1$$
$$x = \frac{1 \pm \sqrt{(-1)^2 - 4(1)(-1)}}{2(1)}$$
$$= \frac{1 \pm \sqrt{5}}{2} \text{ (disregard the negative)}$$

The value is $\frac{1 + \sqrt{5}}{2}$.

64.
$$h = -16t^2 + 20t + 1100$$
$$550 = -16t^2 + 20t + 1100$$
$$0 = -16t^2 + 20t + 550$$
$$a = -16, b = 20, c = 550$$
$$t = \frac{-20 \pm \sqrt{(20)^2 - 4(-16)(550)}}{2(-16)}$$
$$= \frac{-20 \pm \sqrt{35,600}}{-32}$$
$$\approx 6.5 \text{ or } -5.3 \text{ (disregard)}$$

It will take about 6.5 seconds.

66.
$$h = -16t^2 - 20t + 180$$
$$50 = -16t^2 - 20t + 180$$
$$0 = -16t^2 - 20t + 130$$
$$a = -16, b = -20, c = 130$$
$$t = \frac{20 \pm \sqrt{(-20)^2 - 4(-16)(130)}}{2(-16)}$$
$$= \frac{20 \pm \sqrt{8720}}{-32}$$
$$\approx 2.3 \text{ or } -3.5 \text{ (disregard)}$$

It will take about 2.3 seconds.

68.
$$\sqrt{y+2} + 7 = 12$$
$$\sqrt{y+2} = 5$$
$$y + 2 = 5^2$$
$$y + 2 = 25$$
$$y = 23$$

70.
$$\frac{10}{z} = \frac{5}{z} - \frac{1}{3}$$
$$3z\left(\frac{10}{z}\right) = 3z\left(\frac{5}{z} - \frac{1}{3}\right)$$
$$30 = 15 - z$$
$$z = -15$$

72. $2y^4 + 11y^2 - 6 = (2y^2 - 1)(y^2 + 6)$

74. $x^4 - 1 = (x^2 + 1)(x^2 - 1)$
$$= (x^2 + 1)(x + 1)(x - 1)$$

76. $x^2 + 5 = -x$
$$x^2 + x + 5 = 0$$
$$a = 1, b = 1, c = 5$$

The correct substitution is **d**.

78. $p^2 + 11p - 12 = 0$
$(p+12)(p-1) = 0$
$p+12 = 0 \quad$ or $\quad p-1 = 0$
$\quad p = -12 \quad$ or $\quad p = 1$
The results are the same. Answers may vary.

80. $3.6x^2 + 1.8x - 4.3 = 0$
$a = 3.6, b = 1.8, c = -4.3$
$x = \dfrac{-1.8 \pm \sqrt{(1.8)^2 - 4(3.6)(-4.3)}}{2(3.6)}$
$= \dfrac{-1.8 \pm \sqrt{65.16}}{7.2}$
≈ -1.4 or 0.9

82. From Friday to Saturday

84. $33°F$

86. $f(x) = 3x^2 - 18x + 56$
$35 = 3x^2 - 18x + 56$
$0 = 3x^2 - 18x + 21$
$0 = x^2 - 6x + 7$
$a = 1, b = -6, c = 7$
$x = \dfrac{6 \pm \sqrt{(-6)^2 - 4(1)(7)}}{2(1)}$
$= \dfrac{6 \pm \sqrt{8}}{2} \approx 4.4$ or 1.6

This means the temperature was $35°$ on Monday and Thursday. This agrees with the graph.

88. $v(x) = 0.25x^2 + 2.6x + 315.6$

a. $x = 2005 - 2000 = 5$
$v(5) = 0.25(5)^2 + 2.6(5) + 315.6$
$= 334.85 \approx 335$
There were approximately 335 million visitors.

b. $x = 2010 - 2000 = 10$
$v(10) = 0.25(10)^2 + 2.6(10) + 315.6$
$= 366.6 \approx 367$
There will be approximately 367 million visitors.

90. $\dfrac{-b + \sqrt{b^2 - 4ac}}{2a} \cdot \dfrac{-b - \sqrt{b^2 - 4ac}}{2a}$
$= \dfrac{\left(-b + \sqrt{b^2 - 4ac}\right)\left(-b - \sqrt{b^2 - 4ac}\right)}{4a^2}$
$= \dfrac{b^2 - (b^2 - 4ac)}{4a^2}$
$= \dfrac{4ac}{4a^2}$
$= \dfrac{c}{a}$

92. $5x^2 + \sqrt{20}x + 1 = 0$
$a = 5, b = \sqrt{20}, c = 1$
$x = \dfrac{-\sqrt{20} \pm \sqrt{\left(\sqrt{20}\right)^2 - 4(5)(1)}}{2(5)}$
$= \dfrac{-\sqrt{20} \pm \sqrt{0}}{10}$
$= \dfrac{-2\sqrt{5}}{10} = -\dfrac{\sqrt{5}}{5}$
The solution is $-\dfrac{\sqrt{5}}{5}$.

94. $x^2 - \sqrt{2}x + 1 = 0$
$a = 1, b = -\sqrt{2}, c = 1$
$x = \dfrac{\sqrt{2} \pm \sqrt{\left(-\sqrt{2}\right)^2 - 4(1)(1)}}{2(1)}$
$= \dfrac{\sqrt{2} \pm \sqrt{-2}}{2}$
$= \dfrac{\sqrt{2} \pm i\sqrt{2}}{2}$
The solutions are $\dfrac{\sqrt{2} + i\sqrt{2}}{2}$ and $\dfrac{\sqrt{2} - i\sqrt{2}}{2}$.

96. $7x^2 + \sqrt{7}x - 2 = 0$

$a = 7, b = \sqrt{7}, c = -2$

$$x = \frac{-\sqrt{7} \pm \sqrt{\left(\sqrt{7}\right)^2 - 4(7)(-2)}}{2(7)}$$

$$= \frac{-\sqrt{7} \pm \sqrt{63}}{14}$$

$$= \frac{-\sqrt{7} \pm 3\sqrt{7}}{14} = \frac{\sqrt{7}}{7} \text{ or } -\frac{2\sqrt{7}}{7}$$

The solutions are $\dfrac{\sqrt{7}}{7}$ and $-\dfrac{2\sqrt{7}}{7}$.

98. Exercise 64:

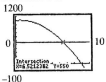

Exercise 66:

100. $y = 5 - 4x + 12x^2$

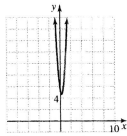

There are no *x*-intercepts. There are two complex but not real solutions.

Section 11.3

Practice Exercises

1. $x - \sqrt{x+1} - 5 = 0$

Get the radical alone on one side of the equation. Then square both sides.

$$x - \sqrt{x+1} - 5 = 0$$

$$x - 5 = \sqrt{x+1}$$

$$(x-5)^2 = x+1$$

$$x^2 - 10x + 25 = x+1$$

$$x^2 - 11x + 24 = 0$$

$$(x-8)(x-3) = 0$$

$$x-8=0 \quad \text{or} \quad x-3=0$$
$$x=8 \quad \text{or} \quad x=3$$

Check:

Let $x = 3$.
$$x-\sqrt{x+1}-5=0$$
$$3-\sqrt{3+1}-5 \overset{?}{=} 0$$
$$-2-\sqrt{4} \overset{?}{=} 0$$
$$-2-2 \overset{?}{=} 0$$
$$-4=0 \quad \text{False}$$

Let $x = 8$.
$$x-\sqrt{x+1}-5=0$$
$$8-\sqrt{8+1}-5 \overset{?}{=} 0$$
$$3-\sqrt{9} \overset{?}{=} 0$$
$$3-3 \overset{?}{=} 0$$
$$0=0 \quad \text{True}$$

The solution is 8 or the solution set is $\{8\}$.

2. $\dfrac{5x}{x+1} - \dfrac{x+4}{x} = \dfrac{3}{x(x+1)}$

x cannot be either -1 or 0, because these values cause denominators to equal zero. Multiply both sides of the equation by $x(x + 1)$.

$$x(x+1)\left(\frac{5x}{x+1}\right) - x(x+1)\left(\frac{x+4}{x}\right) = x(x+1)\left[\frac{3}{x(x+1)}\right]$$
$$5x^2 - (x+1)(x+4) = 3$$
$$5x^2 - x^2 - 5x - 4 = 3$$
$$4x^2 - 5x - 7 = 0$$

Use the quadratic formula with $a = 4$, $b = -5$, and $c = -7$.

$$x = \frac{-(-5) \pm \sqrt{(-5)^2 - 4(4)(-7)}}{2(4)} = \frac{5 \pm \sqrt{25+112}}{8} = \frac{5 \pm \sqrt{137}}{8}$$

Neither proposed solution will make denominators 0. The solutions are $\dfrac{5+\sqrt{137}}{8}$ and $\dfrac{5-\sqrt{137}}{8}$ or the solution

set is $\left\{ \dfrac{5+\sqrt{137}}{8}, \dfrac{5-\sqrt{137}}{8} \right\}$.

3. $\quad p^4 - 7p^2 - 144 = 0$
$$(p^2+9)(p^2-16)=0$$
$$(p^2+9)(p+4)(p-4)=0$$
$$p^2+9=0 \quad \text{or} \quad p+4=0 \quad \text{or} \quad p-4=0$$
$$p^2=-9 \qquad\qquad p=-4 \qquad\quad p=4$$
$$p=\pm\sqrt{-9}$$
$$p=\pm 3i$$

The solutions are 4, -4, $3i$, and $-3i$.

4. $(x+2)^2 - 2(x+2) - 3 = 0$

Let $y = x + 2$.

$y^2 - 2y - 3 = 0$

$(y-3)(y+1) = 0$

$y - 3 = 0$ or $y + 1 = 0$

    $y = 3$ $y = -1$

Substitute $x + 2$ for y.

$x + 2 = 3$ or $x + 2 = -1$

    $x = 1$ $x = -3$

Both 1 and −3 check. The solutions are 1 and −3.

5. $x^{2/3} - 5x^{1/3} + 4 = 0$

Let $m = x^{1/3}$.

$m^2 - 5m + 4 = 0$

$(m-4)(m-1) = 0$

$m - 4 = 0$ or $m - 1 = 0$

    $m = 4$ $m = 1$

Since $m = x^{1/3}$, we have

$x^{1/3} = 4$ or $x^{1/3} = 1$

    $x = 4^3 = 64$ $x = 1^3 = 1$

Both 64 and 1 check. The solutions are 64 and 1.

6. Let x = the time in hours it takes Steve to groom all the dogs. Then,

$x - 1$ = the time it takes Katy to groom all the dogs.

The part of the job completed in one hour by Steve is $\dfrac{1}{x}$, and the part completed by Katy in one hour is $\dfrac{1}{x-1}$. In

one hour, $\dfrac{1}{4}$ of the job is completed. We have,

$$\frac{1}{x} + \frac{1}{x-1} = \frac{1}{4}$$

$$4x(x-1)\left(\frac{1}{x}\right) + 4x(x-1)\left(\frac{1}{x-1}\right) = 4x(x-1)\left(\frac{1}{4}\right)$$

$$4(x-1) + 4x = x(x-1)$$

$$4x - 4 + 4x = x^2 - x$$

$$0 = x^2 - 9x + 4$$

Use the quadratic formula with $a = 1$, $b = -9$, and $c = 4$.

$$x = \frac{-(-9) \pm \sqrt{(-9)^2 - 4(1)(4)}}{2(1)}$$

$$x = \frac{9 \pm \sqrt{81-16}}{2} = \frac{9 \pm \sqrt{65}}{2}$$

$x \approx 8.53$ or $x \approx 0.47$

Since $x - 1 = 0.47 - 1 = -0.53 < 0$, representing negative time worked, we reject 0.47. It takes Steve

$\dfrac{9+\sqrt{65}}{2} \approx 8.5$ hours and Katy $\dfrac{9+\sqrt{65}}{2} - 1 = \dfrac{7+\sqrt{65}}{2} \approx 7.5$ hours to groom all the dogs when working alone.

7. Let x = the speed driven to Shanghai. Then $x + 50$ = the speed driven to Ningbo.

	distance =	rate ·	time
To Shanghai	36	x	$\frac{36}{x}$
To Ningbo	36	$x + 50$	$\frac{36}{x+50}$

The total travel time was 1.3 hours, so

$$\frac{36}{x} + \frac{36}{x+50} = 1.3$$

$$x(x+50)\left(\frac{36}{x}\right) + x(x+50)\left(\frac{36}{x+50}\right) = 1.3x(x+50)$$

$$36(x+50) + 36x = 1.3x^2 + 65x$$

$$36x + 1800 + 36x = 1.3x^2 + 65x$$

$$0 = 1.3x^2 - 7x - 1800$$

Use the quadratic formula with $a = 1.3$, $b = -7$, and $c = -1800$.

$$x = \frac{-(-7) \pm \sqrt{(-7)^2 - 4(1.3)(-1800)}}{2(1.3)} = \frac{7 \pm \sqrt{9409}}{2.6}$$

$$x = \frac{7 + \sqrt{9409}}{2.6} = 40 \quad \text{or} \quad x = \frac{7 - \sqrt{9409}}{2.6} \approx -34.6$$

The speed is not negative, so reject -34.6. The speed to Shanghai was 40 km/hr and to Ningbo it was $40 + 50 = 90$ km/hr.

Exercise Set 11.3

2.
$$3x = \sqrt{8x+1}$$
$$9x^2 = 8x + 1$$
$$9x^2 - 8x - 1 = 0$$
$$(9x+1)(x-1) = 0$$
$$9x + 1 = 0 \quad \text{or} \quad x - 1 = 0$$
$$x = -\frac{1}{9} \quad \text{or} \quad x = 1$$

Discard $-\frac{1}{9}$. The solution is 1.

4.
$$x - \sqrt{2x} = 4$$
$$x - 4 = \sqrt{2x}$$
$$(x-4)^2 = 2x$$
$$x^2 - 8x + 16 = 2x$$
$$x^2 - 10x + 16 = 0$$
$$(x-8)(x-2) = 0$$
$$x - 8 = 0 \quad \text{or} \quad x - 2 = 0$$
$$x = 8 \quad \text{or} \quad x = 2 \text{ (discard)}$$

The solution is 8.

6. $\sqrt{16x} = x + 3$

$16x = (x+3)^2$

$16x = x^2 + 6x + 9$

$0 = x^2 - 10x + 9$

$0 = (x-9)(x-1)$

$x - 9 = 0$ or $x - 1 = 0$

$x = 9$ or $x = 1$

The solutions are 1 and 9.

8. $\dfrac{6}{x^2} = \dfrac{3}{x+1}$

$3x^2 = 6(x+1)$

$3x^2 - 6x - 6 = 0$

$x^2 - 2x - 2 = 0$

$x = \dfrac{2 \pm \sqrt{(-2)^2 - 4(1)(-2)}}{2(1)}$

$= \dfrac{2 \pm \sqrt{12}}{2}$

$= \dfrac{2 \pm 2\sqrt{3}}{2} = 1 \pm \sqrt{3}$

The solutions are $1 + \sqrt{3}$ and $1 - \sqrt{3}$.

10. $\dfrac{5}{x-2} + \dfrac{4}{x-2} = 1$

$5(x+2) + 4(x-2) = 1(x+2)(x-2)$

$5x + 10 + 4x - 8 = x^2 - 4$

$0 = x^2 - 9x - 6$

$x = \dfrac{9 \pm \sqrt{(-9)^2 - 4(1)(-6)}}{2(1)} = \dfrac{9 \pm \sqrt{105}}{2}$

The solutions are $\dfrac{9 + \sqrt{105}}{2}$ and $\dfrac{9 - \sqrt{105}}{2}$.

12. $\dfrac{11}{2x^2 + x - 15} = \dfrac{5}{2x-5} - \dfrac{x}{x+3}$

$\dfrac{11}{(2x-5)(x+3)} = \dfrac{5}{2x-5} - \dfrac{x}{x+3}$

$11 = 5(x+3) - x(2x-5)$

$11 = -2x^2 + 10x + 15$

$2x^2 - 10x - 4 = 0$

$x^2 - 5x - 2 = 0$

$x = \dfrac{5 \pm \sqrt{(-5)^2 - 4(1)(-2)}}{2(1)} = \dfrac{5 \pm \sqrt{33}}{2}$

The solutions are $\dfrac{5 + \sqrt{33}}{2}$ and $\dfrac{5 - \sqrt{33}}{2}$.

14. $x^4 + 2x^2 - 3 = 0$

$(x^2 - 1)(x^2 + 3) = 0$

$(x+1)(x-1)(x^2 + 3) = 0$

$x + 1 = 0$ or $x - 1 = 0$ or $x^2 + 3 = 0$

$x = -1$ or $x = 1$ or $x^2 = -3$

$x = \pm i\sqrt{3}$

The solutions are -1, 1, $-i\sqrt{3}$, and $i\sqrt{3}$.

16. $z^4 = 81$

$z^4 - 81 = 0$

$(z^2 - 9)(z^2 + 9) = 0$

$(z+3)(z-3)(z^2 + 9) = 0$

$z + 3 = 0$ or $z - 3 = 0$ or $z^2 + 9 = 0$

$z = -3$ or $z = 3$ or $z^2 = -9$

$z = \pm 3i$

The solutions are -3, 3, $-3i$, and $3i$.

18. $9x^4 + 5x^2 - 4 = 0$

$(9x^2 - 4)(x^2 + 1) = 0$

$(3x+2)(3x-2)(x^2 + 1) = 0$

$3x + 2 = 0$ or $3x - 2 = 0$ or $x^2 + 1 = 0$

$x = -\dfrac{2}{3}$ or $x = \dfrac{2}{3}$ or $x^2 = -1$

$x = \pm i$

The solutions are $-\dfrac{2}{3}, \dfrac{2}{3}, -i$, and i.

20. $x^{2/3} + 2x^{1/3} + 1 = 0$

Let $y = x^{1/3}$. Then $y^2 = x^{2/3}$ and

$y^2 + 2y + 1 = 0$
$(y+1)^2 = 0$
$y + 1 = 0$
$y = -1$
$x^{1/3} = -1$
$x = (-1)^3 = -1$

The solution is –1.

22. $(m-6)^2 + 5(m-6) + 4 = 0$

Let $y = m - 6$. Then $y^2 = (m-6)^2$ and

$y^2 + 5y + 4 = 0$
$(y+4)(y+1) = 0$
$y + 4 = 0$ or $y + 1 = 0$
$y = -4$ or $y = -1$
$m - 6 = -4$ or $m - 6 = -1$
$m = 2$ or $m = 5$

The solutions are 2 and 5.

24. $3x^{2/3} + 11x^{1/3} = 4$

Let $y = x^{1/3}$. Then $y^2 = x^{2/3}$ and

$3y^2 + 11y = 4$
$3y^2 + 11y - 4 = 0$
$(3y-1)(y+4) = 0$
$3y - 1 = 0$ or $y + 4 = 0$
$y = \dfrac{1}{3}$ or $y = -4$
$x^{1/3} = \dfrac{1}{3}$ or $x^{1/3} = -4$
$x = \dfrac{1}{27}$ or $x = -64$

The solutions are –64 and $\dfrac{1}{27}$.

26. $2 - \dfrac{7}{x+6} = \dfrac{15}{(x+6)^2}$

$2(x+6)^2 - 7(x+6) - 15 = 0$

Let $y = x + 6$. Then $y^2 = (x+6)^2$ and

$2y^2 - 7y - 15 = 0$
$(2y+3)(y-5) = 0$

$2y + 3 = 0$ or $y - 5 = 0$
$y = -\dfrac{3}{2}$ or $y = 5$
$x + 6 = -\dfrac{3}{2}$ or $x + 6 = 5$
$x = -\dfrac{15}{2}$ or $x = -1$

The solutions are $-\dfrac{15}{2}$ and -1.

28. $4x^{2/3} + 16x^{1/3} = -15$

$4x^{2/3} + 16x^{1/3} + 15 = 0$

Let $y = x^{1/3}$. Then $y^2 = x^{2/3}$ and

$4y^2 + 16y + 15 = 0$
$(2y+5)(2y+3) = 0$
$2y + 5 = 0$ or $2y + 3 = 0$
$y = -\dfrac{5}{2}$ or $y = -\dfrac{3}{2}$
$x^{1/3} = -\dfrac{5}{2}$ or $x^{1/3} = -\dfrac{3}{2}$
$x = -\dfrac{125}{8}$ or $x = -\dfrac{27}{8}$

The solutions are $-\dfrac{125}{8}$ and $-\dfrac{27}{8}$.

30. $x^4 - 12x^2 + 11 = 0$

$(x^2 - 11)(x^2 - 1) = 0$

$x^2 - 11 = 0$ or $x^2 - 1 = 0$
$x^2 = 11$ or $x^2 = 1$
$x = \pm\sqrt{11}$ or $x = \pm 1$

The solutions are $-\sqrt{11}$, $\sqrt{11}$, -1, and 1.

32. $\dfrac{5}{x-3} + \dfrac{x}{x+3} = \dfrac{19}{x^2-9}$

$\dfrac{5}{x-3} + \dfrac{x}{x+3} = \dfrac{19}{(x+3)(x-3)}$

$5(x+3) + x(x-3) = 19$

$x^2 + 2x - 4 = 0$

$$x = \frac{-2 \pm \sqrt{(2)^2 - 4(1)(-4)}}{2(1)}$$

$$= \frac{-2 \pm \sqrt{20}}{2}$$

$$= \frac{-2 \pm 2\sqrt{5}}{2}$$

$$= -1 \pm \sqrt{5}$$

The solutions are $-1 + \sqrt{5}$ and $-1 - \sqrt{5}$.

34. $2(4m-3)^2 - 9(4m-3) = 5$

Let $x = 4m - 3$. Then $x^2 = (4m-3)^2$ and

$$2x^2 - 9x - 5 = 0$$
$$(2x+1)(x-5) = 0$$
$$2x+1 = 0 \quad \text{or} \quad x - 5 = 0$$
$$x = -\frac{1}{2} \quad \text{or} \quad x = 5$$
$$4m - 3 = -\frac{1}{2} \quad \text{or} \quad 4m - 3 = 5$$
$$4m = \frac{5}{2} \quad \text{or} \quad 4m = 8$$
$$m = \frac{5}{8} \quad \text{or} \quad m = 2$$

The solutions are $\frac{5}{8}$ and 2.

36.
$$4x = \sqrt{2x+3}$$
$$16x^2 - 2x - 3 = 0$$
$$(8x+3)(2x-1) = 0$$
$$x = -\frac{3}{8} \text{ (discard)} \quad \text{or} \quad x = \frac{1}{2}$$

The solution is $\frac{1}{2}$.

38. $x^{2/3} - 2x^{1/3} - 8 = 0$

Let $y = x^{1/3}$. Then $y^2 = x^{2/3}$ and

$$y^2 - 2y - 8 = 0$$
$$(y-4)(y+2) = 0$$
$$y = 4 \quad \text{or} \quad y = -2$$
$$x^{1/3} = 4 \quad \text{or} \quad x^{1/3} = -2$$
$$x = 64 \quad \text{or} \quad x = -8$$

The solutions are -8 and 64.

40.
$$x^3 + x - 3x^2 - 3 = 0$$
$$x(x^2+1) - 3(x^2+1) = 0$$
$$(x^2+1)(x-3) = 0$$
$$x^2 + 1 = 0 \quad \text{or} \quad x - 3 = 0$$
$$x^2 = -1 \quad \text{or} \quad x = 3$$
$$x = \pm i$$

The solutions are $3, -i,$ and i.

42. $6x^{2/3} - 25x^{1/3} - 25 = 0$

Let $y = x^{1/3}$. Then $y^2 = x^{2/3}$ and

$$6y^2 - 25y - 25 = 0$$
$$(6y+5)(y-5) = 0$$
$$y = -\frac{5}{6} \quad \text{or} \quad y = 5$$
$$x^{1/3} = -\frac{5}{6} \quad \text{or} \quad x^{1/3} = 5$$
$$x = -\frac{125}{216} \quad \text{or} \quad x = 125$$

The solutions are $-\frac{125}{216}$ and 125.

44. $y^{-2} - 8y^{-1} + 7 = 0$

Let $x = y^{-1}$. Then $x^2 = y^{-2}$ and

$$x^2 - 8x + 7 = 0$$
$$(x-7)(x-1) = 0$$
$$x = 7 \quad \text{or} \quad x = 1$$
$$y^{-1} = 7 \quad \text{or} \quad y^{-1} = 1$$
$$\frac{1}{y} = 7 \quad \text{or} \quad \frac{1}{y} = 1$$
$$y = \frac{1}{7} \quad \text{or} \quad y = 1$$

The solutions are $\frac{1}{7}$ and 1.

46.
$$x - \sqrt{3x} = 6$$
$$x - 6 = \sqrt{3x}$$
$$(x-6)^2 = 3x$$
$$x^2 - 12x + 36 = 3x$$
$$x^2 - 15x + 36 = 0$$
$$(x-12)(x-3) = 0$$
$$x = 12 \text{ or } x = 3 \text{ (discard)}$$

The solution is 12.

48.
$$\frac{x}{x-5}+\frac{5}{x+5}=-\frac{1}{x^2-25}$$
$$\frac{x}{x-5}+\frac{5}{x+5}=-\frac{1}{(x+5)(x-5)}$$
$$x(x+5)+5(x-5)=-1$$
$$x^2+10x-24=0$$
$$(x+12)(x-2)=0$$
$$x=-12 \text{ or } x=2$$
The solutions are -12 and 2.

50.
$$x^4-10x^2+9=0$$
$$(x^2-9)(x^2-1)=0$$
$$(x+3)(x-3)(x+1)(x-1)=0$$
$$x=-3 \text{ or } x=3 \text{ or } x=-1 \text{ or } x=1$$
The solutions are -3, 3, -1, 1.

52. $(x-6)(x^2+6x+36)=0$

$x-6=0$ or $x^2+6x+36=0$

$$x=6 \text{ or } x=\frac{-6\pm\sqrt{(6)^2-4(1)(36)}}{2(1)}$$
$$=\frac{-6\pm\sqrt{-108}}{2}$$
$$=\frac{-6\pm6i\sqrt{3}}{2}$$
$$=-3\pm3i\sqrt{3}$$

The solutions are 6, $-3+3i\sqrt{3}$, and $-3-3i\sqrt{3}$.

54.
$$3+\frac{1}{2p+4}=\frac{10}{(2p+4)^2}$$
$$3(2p+4)^2+(2p+4)-10=0$$

Let $y=2p+4$. Then $y^2=(2p+4)^2$ and

$$3y^2+y-10=0$$
$$(3y-5)(y+2)=0$$
$$y=\frac{5}{3} \text{ or } y=-2$$
$$2p+4=\frac{5}{3} \text{ or } 2p+4=-2$$
$$2p=-\frac{7}{3} \text{ or } 2p=-6$$
$$p=-\frac{7}{6} \text{ or } p=-3$$

The solutions are $-\frac{7}{6}$ and -3.

56.
$$8z^4+14z^2=-5$$
$$8z^4+14z^2+5=0$$
$$(4z^2+5)(2z^2+1)=0$$
$$z^2=-\frac{5}{4} \text{ or } z^2=-\frac{1}{2}$$
$$z=\pm\frac{i\sqrt{5}}{2} \text{ or } z=\pm\frac{i}{\sqrt{2}}=\pm\frac{i\sqrt{2}}{2}$$

The solutions are $-\frac{i\sqrt{5}}{2}, \frac{i\sqrt{5}}{2}, -\frac{i\sqrt{2}}{2},$

and $\frac{i\sqrt{2}}{2}$.

58. Let x = his jogging speed. Then
$x+4$ = his biking speed.

$$d=rt \Rightarrow t=\frac{d}{r}$$

$$t_{\text{jogging}}+t_{\text{biking}}=1$$
$$\frac{3}{x}+\frac{5}{x+4}=1$$
$$3(x+4)+5x=x(x+4)$$
$$3x+12+5x=x^2+4x$$
$$0=x^2-4x-12$$
$$0=(x-6)(x+2)$$

$x=6$ or $x=-2$

Discard -2. His jogging speed is 6 mph and his biking speed is 10 mph.

60. Let x = time for the small pipe. Then
$x-2$ = time for the large pipe.
$$\frac{1}{x}+\frac{1}{x-2}=\frac{1}{3}$$
$$3(x-2)+3x=x(x-2)$$
$$3x-6+3x=x^2-2x$$
$$0=x^2-8x+6$$
$$x=\frac{8\pm\sqrt{(-8)^2-4(1)(6)}}{2(1)}$$
$$=\frac{8\pm\sqrt{40}}{2}$$
$x\approx0.8$ (discard) or $x\approx7.2$
$$x-2\approx5.2$$
Large pipe: 5.2 hrs; small pipe: 7.2 hrs

62. Let x = original speed. Then
$x-15$ = rainfall speed.
$$d=rt \Rightarrow t=\frac{d}{r}$$

$$t_{\text{before rain}} + t_{\text{after rain}} = 6$$

$$\frac{220}{x} + \frac{80}{x-15} = 6$$

$$220(x-15) + 80(x) = 6x(x-15)$$

$$220x - 3300 + 80x = 6x^2 - 90x$$

$$0 = 6x^2 - 390x + 3300$$

$$0 = x^2 - 65x + 550$$

$$0 = (x-55)(x-10)$$

$$x = 55 \text{ or } x = 10 \text{ (discard)}$$

$$x - 15 = 55 - 15 = 40$$

Original speed: 55 mph
Rainfall speed: 40 mph

64. Let x = days for Freckels to eat the food
$x - 14$ = days for Noodles to eat the food.

$$\frac{1}{x} + \frac{1}{x-14} = \frac{1}{30}$$

$$30(x-14) + 30x = x(x-14)$$

$$30x - 420 + 30x = x^2 - 14x$$

$$0 = x^2 - 74x + 420$$

$$x = \frac{74 \pm \sqrt{(-74)^2 - 4(1)(420)}}{2(1)}$$

$$= \frac{74 \pm \sqrt{3796}}{2}$$

$$\approx 6 \text{ (discard) or } 68$$

It would take Freckels about 68 days to eat the dog food.

66. Let x = the number.

$$x + x^2 = 2x + 2$$

$$x^2 - x - 2 = 0$$

$$(x-2)(x+1) = 0$$

$$x = 2 \text{ or } x = -1 \text{ (discard)}$$

The number is 2.

68. a. length $= x - 4$

b. $V = lwh$

$$128 = (x-4)(x-4) \cdot 2$$

c. $128 = 2(x-4)^2$

$$64 = x^2 - 8x + 16$$

$$0 = x^2 - 8x - 48$$

$$0 = (x-12)(x+4)$$

$$x = 12 \text{ or } x = -4 \text{ (discard)}$$

The sheet is 12 in. by 12 in.

70. Let x = length of the side of the square.

$$\text{Area} = x^2$$

$$6270 = x^2$$

$$\sqrt{6270} = x$$

Adding another radial line to a different corner would yield a right triangle with legs r and hypotenuse x.

$$r^2 + r^2 = x^2$$

$$2r^2 = \left(\sqrt{6270}\right)^2$$

$$2r^2 = 6270$$

$$r^2 = 3135$$

$$r = \pm\sqrt{3135} = \pm 55.99107$$

Disregard the negative. The smallest radius would be 56 feet.

72.

$$\frac{2x}{3} + \frac{1}{6} \geq 2$$

$$6\left(\frac{2x}{3} + \frac{1}{6}\right) \geq 6(2)$$

$$4x + 1 \geq 12$$

$$4x \geq 11$$

$$x \geq \frac{11}{4}$$

$$\left[\frac{11}{4}, \infty\right)$$

74.

$$\frac{z-2}{12} < \frac{1}{4}$$

$$z - 2 < 3$$

$$z < 5$$

$$(-\infty, 5)$$

76. Domain: $\{x \mid -3 \leq x \leq 3\}$ or $[-3, 3]$
Range: $\{y \mid -2 \leq y \leq 2\}$ or $[-2, 2]$
It is not a function.

78. Domain: $\{x \mid x \leq -1\}$ or $(-\infty, -1]$
Range: $\{y \mid y \leq 2\}$ or $(-\infty, 2]$
It is a function.

80.

$$x^3 + x - 3x^2 - 3 = 0$$

$$x(x^2 + 1) - 3(x^2 + 1) = 0$$

$$(x-3)(x^2 + 1) = 0$$

$x - 3 = 0$ or $x^2 + 1 = 0$
$x = 3$ $x^2 = -1$
                $x = \pm\sqrt{-1} = \pm i$

The solutions are 3, $-i$, and i.

82. $y^{-2} - 8y^{-1} + 7 = 0$
$1 - 8y + 7y^2 = 0$
$(1 - y)(1 - 7y) = 0$
$1 - y = 0$ or $1 - 7y = 0$
$1 = y$ $1 = 7y$
                $\dfrac{1}{7} = y$

The solutions are 1 and $\dfrac{1}{7}$.

84. $y^3 - 216 = 0$
$(y - 6)(y^2 + 6y + 36) = 0$
$y - 6 = 0$ or $y^2 + 6y + 36 = 0$
$y = 6$ or $y = \dfrac{-6 \pm \sqrt{(6)^2 - 4(1)(36)}}{2(1)}$
$= \dfrac{-6 \pm \sqrt{-108}}{2}$
$= \dfrac{-6 \pm 6i\sqrt{3}}{2}$
$= -3 \pm 3i\sqrt{3}$

The solutions are 6, $-3 + 3i\sqrt{3}$, and $-3 - 3i\sqrt{3}$.

86. Answers may vary

88. Answers may vary

Integrated Review

1. $x^2 - 10 = 0$
$x^2 = 10$
$x = \pm\sqrt{10}$

2. $x^2 - 14 = 0$
$x^2 = 14$
$x = \pm\sqrt{14}$

3. $(x - 1)^2 = 8$
$x - 1 = \pm\sqrt{8}$
$x - 1 = \pm 2\sqrt{2}$
$x = 1 \pm 2\sqrt{2}$

4. $(x + 5)^2 = 12$
$x + 5 = \pm\sqrt{12}$
$x + 5 = \pm 2\sqrt{3}$
$x = -5 \pm 2\sqrt{3}$

5. $x^2 + 2x - 12 = 0$
$x^2 + 2x + \left(\dfrac{2}{2}\right)^2 = 12 + 1$
$x^2 + 2x + 1 = 13$
$(x + 1)^2 = 13$
$x + 1 = \pm\sqrt{13}$
$x = -1 \pm \sqrt{13}$

6. $x^2 - 12x + 11 = 0$
$x^2 - 12x + \left(\dfrac{-12}{2}\right)^2 = -11 + 36$
$x^2 - 12x + 36 = 25$
$(x - 6)^2 = \pm\sqrt{25}$
$x - 6 = \pm 5$
$x = 6 \pm 5$
$x = 1 \text{ or } x = 11$

7.
$3x^2 + 3x = 5$
$x^2 + x = \dfrac{5}{3}$
$x^2 + x + \left(\dfrac{1}{2}\right)^2 = \dfrac{5}{3} + \dfrac{1}{4}$
$x^2 + x + \dfrac{1}{4} = \dfrac{23}{12}$
$\left(x + \dfrac{1}{2}\right)^2 = \dfrac{23}{12}$
$x + \dfrac{1}{2} = \pm\sqrt{\dfrac{23}{12}}$
$x + \dfrac{1}{2} = \pm\dfrac{\sqrt{23}}{2\sqrt{3}}$
$x + \dfrac{1}{2} = \pm\dfrac{\sqrt{23} \cdot \sqrt{3}}{2\sqrt{3} \cdot \sqrt{3}}$
$x + \dfrac{1}{2} = \pm\dfrac{\sqrt{69}}{6}$
$x = -\dfrac{1}{2} \pm \dfrac{\sqrt{69}}{6} = \dfrac{-3 \pm \sqrt{69}}{6}$

8. $16y^2 + 16y = 1$

$$y^2 + y = \frac{1}{16}$$

$$y^2 + y + \left(\frac{1}{2}\right)^2 = \frac{1}{16} + \frac{1}{4}$$

$$y^2 + y + \frac{1}{4} = \frac{5}{16}$$

$$\left(y + \frac{1}{2}\right)^2 = \frac{5}{16}$$

$$y + \frac{1}{2} = \pm\sqrt{\frac{5}{16}}$$

$$y + \frac{1}{2} = \pm\frac{\sqrt{5}}{4}$$

$$y = -\frac{1}{2} \pm \frac{\sqrt{5}}{4} = \frac{-2 \pm \sqrt{5}}{4}$$

9. $2x^2 - 4x + 1 = 0$

$a = 2, b = -4, c = 1$

$$x = \frac{4 \pm \sqrt{(-4)^2 - 4(2)(1)}}{2(2)}$$

$$= \frac{4 \pm \sqrt{8}}{4}$$

$$= \frac{4 \pm 2\sqrt{2}}{4} = \frac{2 \pm \sqrt{2}}{2}$$

10. $\frac{1}{2}x^2 + 3x + 2 = 0$

$$x^2 + 6x + 4 = 0$$

$a = 1, b = 6, c = 4$

$$x = \frac{-6 \pm \sqrt{(6)^2 - 4(1)(4)}}{2(1)}$$

$$= \frac{-6 \pm \sqrt{20}}{2}$$

$$= \frac{-6 \pm 2\sqrt{5}}{2} = -3 \pm \sqrt{5}$$

11. $x^2 + 4x = -7$

$$x^2 + 4x + 7 = 0$$

$a = 1, b = 4, c = 7$

$$x = \frac{-4 \pm \sqrt{(4)^2 - 4(1)(7)}}{2(1)}$$

$$= \frac{-4 \pm \sqrt{-12}}{2}$$

$$= \frac{-4 \pm i\sqrt{4 \cdot 3}}{2}$$

$$= \frac{-4 \pm 2i\sqrt{3}}{2} = -2 \pm i\sqrt{3}$$

12. $x^2 + x = -3$

$$x^2 + x + 3 = 0$$

$a = 1, b = 1, c = 3$

$$x = \frac{-1 \pm \sqrt{(1)^2 - 4(1)(3)}}{2(1)}$$

$$= \frac{-1 \pm \sqrt{-11}}{2}$$

$$= \frac{-1 \pm i\sqrt{11}}{2}$$

13. $x^2 + 3x + 6 = 0$

$a = 1, b = 3, c = 6$

$$x = \frac{-3 \pm \sqrt{(3)^2 - 4(1)(6)}}{2(1)}$$

$$= \frac{-3 \pm \sqrt{-15}}{2}$$

$$= \frac{-3 \pm i\sqrt{15}}{2}$$

14. $2x^2 + 18 = 0$

$$2x^2 = -18$$

$$x^2 = -9$$

$$x = \pm\sqrt{-9}$$

$$x = \pm 3i$$

15. $x^2 + 17x = 0$

$$x(x + 17) = 0$$

$$x = 0 \text{ or } x + 17 = 0$$

$$x = -17$$

$$x = 0, -17$$

16. $4x^2 - 2x - 3 = 0$

$a = 4, b = -2, c = -3$

$$x = \frac{2 \pm \sqrt{(-2)^2 - 4(4)(-3)}}{2(4)}$$

$$= \frac{2 \pm \sqrt{52}}{8}$$

$$= \frac{2 \pm 2\sqrt{13}}{8}$$

$$= \frac{1 \pm \sqrt{13}}{4}$$

17. $(x - 2)^2 = 27$

$x - 2 = \pm\sqrt{27}$

$x - 2 = \pm 3\sqrt{3}$

$x = 2 \pm 3\sqrt{3}$

18. $\frac{1}{2}x^2 - 2x + \frac{1}{2} = 0$

$x^2 - 4x + 1 = 0$

$x^2 - 4x + \left(\frac{-4}{2}\right)^2 = -1 + 4$

$x^2 - 4x + 4 = 3$

$(x - 2)^2 = 3$

$x - 2 = \pm\sqrt{3}$

$x = 2 \pm \sqrt{3}$

19. $3x^2 + 2x = 8$

$3x^2 + 2x - 8 = 0$

$(3x - 4)(x + 2) = 0$

$3x - 4 = 0$ or $x + 2 = 0$

$x = \frac{4}{3}$ or $x = -2$

20. $2x^2 = -5x - 1$

$2x^2 + 5x + 1 = 0$

$a = 2, b = 5, c = 1$

$$x = \frac{-5 \pm \sqrt{(5)^2 - 4(2)(1)}}{2(2)}$$

$$= \frac{-5 \pm \sqrt{17}}{4}$$

21. $x(x - 2) = 5$

$x^2 - 2x = 5$

$x^2 - 2x + \left(\frac{-2}{2}\right)^2 = 5 + 1$

$x^2 - 2x + 1 = 6$

$(x - 1)^2 = 6$

$x - 1 = \pm\sqrt{6}$

$x = 1 \pm \sqrt{6}$

22. $x^2 - 31 = 0$

$x^2 = 31$

$x = \pm\sqrt{31}$

23. $5x^2 - 55 = 0$

$5x^2 = 55$

$x^2 = 11$

$x = \pm\sqrt{11}$

24. $5x^2 + 55 = 0$

$5x^2 = -55$

$x^2 = -11$

$x = \pm\sqrt{-11}$

$x = \pm i\sqrt{11}$

25. $x(x + 5) = 66$

$x^2 + 5x = 66$

$x^2 + 5x - 66 = 0$

$(x + 11)(x - 6) = 0$

$x + 11 = 0$ or $x - 6 = 0$

$x = -11$ or $x = 6$

26. $5x^2 + 6x - 2 = 0$

$a = 5, b = 6, c = -2$

$$x = \frac{-6 \pm \sqrt{(6)^2 - 4(5)(-2)}}{2(5)}$$

$$= \frac{-6 \pm \sqrt{76}}{10}$$

$$= \frac{-6 \pm \sqrt{4 \cdot 19}}{10}$$

$$= \frac{-6 \pm 2\sqrt{19}}{10}$$

$$= \frac{-3 \pm \sqrt{19}}{5}$$

27.
$$2x^2 + 3x = 1$$
$$2x^2 + 3x - 1 = 0$$
$$a = 2, b = 3, c = -1$$
$$x = \frac{-3 \pm \sqrt{(3)^2 - 4(2)(-1)}}{2(2)}$$
$$= \frac{-3 \pm \sqrt{17}}{4}$$

28.
$$a^2 + b^2 = c^2$$
$$x^2 + x^2 = 20^2$$
$$2x^2 = 400$$
$$x^2 = 200$$
$$x = \pm\sqrt{200}$$
$$= \pm 10\sqrt{2} \approx 14.1421$$
Disregard the negative. A side of the room is $10\sqrt{2}$ feet ≈ 14.1 feet.

29. Let x = time for Jack alone. Then $x - 2$ = time for Lucy alone.
$$\frac{1}{x} + \frac{1}{x-2} = \frac{1}{4}$$
$$4(x-2) + 4x = x(x-2)$$
$$4x - 8 + 4x = x^2 - 2x$$
$$0 = x^2 - 10x + 8$$
$$x = \frac{10 \pm \sqrt{(-10)^2 - 4(1)(8)}}{2(1)}$$
$$= \frac{10 \pm \sqrt{68}}{2}$$
$$\approx 9.1 \text{ or } 0.9 \text{ (disregard)}$$
$$x - 2 = 9.1 - 2 = 7.1$$
It would take Jack 9.1 hours and Lucy 7.1 hours.

30. Let x = initial speed on treadmill. Then $x + 1$ = speed increased.
$$t_{\text{initial}} + t_{\text{increased}} = \frac{4}{3}$$
$$\frac{5}{x} + \frac{2}{x+1} = \frac{4}{3}$$
$$5 \cdot 3(x+1) + 2 \cdot 3x = 4x(x+1)$$
$$15x + 15 + 6x = 4x^2 + 4x$$
$$0 = 4x^2 - 17x - 15$$
$$0 = (4x+3)(x-5)$$
$$x = -\frac{4}{3} \text{ (disregard) or } x = 5$$
$$x + 1 = 5 + 1 = 6$$
Initial speed: 5 mph
Increased speed: 6 mph

Section 11.4

Practice Exercises

1. $(x-4)(x+3) > 0$

Solve the related equation, $(x-4)(x+3) = 0$.
$$(x-4)(x+3) = 0$$
$$x - 4 = 0 \quad \text{or} \quad x + 3 = 0$$
$$x = 4 \qquad\qquad x = -3$$
Test points in the three regions separated by $x = 4$ and $x = -3$.

Region	Test Point	$(x-4)(x+3) > 0$ Result
A: $(-\infty, -3)$	-4	$(-8)(-1) > 0$ True
B: $(-3, 4)$	0	$(-4)(3) > 0$ False
C: $(4, \infty)$	5	$(1)(8) > 0$ True

The points in regions A and C satisfy the inequality. The numbers 4 and -3 are not included in the solution since the inequality symbol is $>$. The solution set is $(-\infty, -3) \cup (4, \infty)$.

2. $x^2 - 8x \le 0$

Solve the related equation, $x^2 - 8x = 0$.
$$x^2 - 8x = 0$$
$$x(x-8) = 0$$
$$x = 0 \quad \text{or} \quad x - 8 = 0$$
$$x = 8$$
The numbers 0 and 8 separate the number line into three regions, A, B, and C. Test a point in each region.

Region	Test Point	$x^2 - 8x \le 0$ Result
A: $(-\infty, 0]$	-1	$1 + 8 \le 0$ False
B: $[0, 8]$	1	$1 - 8 \le 0$ True
C: $[8, \infty)$	9	$81 - 72 \le 0$ False

Values in region B satisfy the inequality. The numbers 0 and 8 are included in the solution since the inequality symbol is $\le$. The solution set is $[0, 8]$.

3. $(x+3)(x-2)(x+1) \le 0$

Solve $(x+3)(x-2)(x+1) = 0$ by inspection.

$x = -3$ or $x = 2$ or $x = -1$

These separate the number line into four regions. Test points in each region.

Region	Test Point	$(x+3)(x-2)(x+1) \le 0$ Result
$A: (-\infty, -3]$	-4	$(-1)(-6)(-3) \le 0$ True
$B: [-3, -1]$	-2	$(1)(-4)(-1) \le 0$ False
$C: [-1, 2]$	0	$(3)(-2)(1) \le 0$ True
$D: [2, \infty)$	3	$(6)(1)(4) \le 0$ False

The solution set is $(-\infty, -3] \cup [-1, 2]$. We include the numbers $-3, -1$, and 2 because the inequality symbol is $\le$.

4. $\dfrac{x-5}{x+4} \le 0$

$x + 4 = 0$

$x = -4$

$x = -4$ makes the denominator zero. Solve the related equation $\dfrac{x-5}{x+4} = 0$.

$\dfrac{x-5}{x+4} = 0$

$x - 5 = 0$

$x = 5$

Test points in the three regions separated by $x = -4$ and $x = 5$.

Region	Test Point	$\dfrac{x-5}{x+4} \le 0$ Result
$A: (-\infty, -4)$	-5	$\dfrac{-10}{-1} \le 0$ False
$B: (-4, 5]$	0	$\dfrac{-5}{4} \le 0$ True
$C: [5, \infty)$	6	$\dfrac{1}{10} \le 0$ False

The solution set is $(-4, 5]$. The interval includes 5 because 5 satisfies the original inequality. This interval does not include -4, because -4 would make the denominator zero.

5. $\dfrac{7}{x+3} < 5$

$x + 3 = 0$

$x = -3$

$x = -3$ makes the denominator zero.

Solve $\dfrac{7}{x+3} = 5$.

$(x+3)\left(\dfrac{7}{x+3}\right) = 5(x+3)$

$7 = 5x + 15$

$-8 = 5x$

$-\dfrac{8}{5} = x$

We use these two solutions to divide the number line into three regions and choose test points.

Region	Test Point	$\dfrac{7}{x+3} < 5$ Result
$A: (-\infty, -3)$	-4	$\dfrac{7}{-1} < 5$ True
$B: \left(-3, -\dfrac{8}{5}\right)$	-2	$\dfrac{7}{1} < 5$ False
$C: \left(-\dfrac{8}{5}, \infty\right)$	0	$\dfrac{7}{3} < 5$ True

The solution set is $(-\infty, -3) \cup \left(-\dfrac{8}{5}, \infty\right)$.

Vocabulary and Readiness Check

1. $[-7, 3)$

2. $(-1, 5]$

3. $(-\infty, 0]$

4. $(-\infty, -8]$

5. $(-\infty, -12) \cup [-10, \infty)$

6. $(-\infty, -3] \cup (4, \infty)$

Exercise Set 11.4

2. $(x+1)(x+5) \le 0$
$\quad x = -1 \ \text{ or } \ x = -5$

Region	Test Point	$(x+1)(x+5) \le 0$ Result
A: $(-\infty, -5]$	-6	$(-5)(-1) \le 0$ False
B: $[-5, -1]$	-2	$(-1)(3) \le 0$ True
C: $[-1, \infty)$	0	$(1)(5) \le 0$ False

    Solution: $[-5, -1]$

4. $(x+4)(x-1) > 0$
$\quad x = -4 \ \text{ or } \ x = 1$

Region	Test Point	$(x+4)(x-1) > 0$ Result
A: $(-\infty, -4)$	-5	$(-1)(-6) > 0$ True
B: $(-4, 1)$	0	$(4)(-1) > 0$ False
C: $(1, \infty)$	2	$(6)(1) > 0$ True

    Solution: $(-\infty, -4) \cup (1, \infty)$

6. $x^2 + 8x + 15 \ge 0$
$\quad (x+5)(x+3) \ge 0$
$\quad x = -5 \ \text{ or } \ x = -3$

Region	Test Point	$(x+5)(x+3) \ge 0$ Result
A: $(-\infty, -5]$	-6	$(-1)(-3) \ge 0$ True
B: $[-5, -3]$	-4	$(1)(-1) \ge 0$ False
C: $[-3, \infty)$	0	$(5)(3) \ge 0$ True

    Solution: $(-\infty, -5] \cup [-3, \infty)$

8. $\quad 2x^2 - 5x < 7$
$\quad 2x^2 - 5x - 7 < 0$
$\quad (2x - 7)(x + 1) < 0$
$\quad x = \dfrac{7}{2} \ \text{ or } \ x = -1$

Region	Test Point	$(2x - 7)(x + 1) < 0$ Result
A: $(-\infty, -1)$	-2	$(-11)(-1) < 0$ False
B: $\left(-1, \dfrac{7}{2}\right)$	0	$(-7)(1) < 0$ True
C: $\left(\dfrac{7}{2}, \infty\right)$	4	$(1)(5) < 0$ False

Solution: $\left(-1, \dfrac{7}{2}\right)$

10. $(x-6)(x-4)(x-2) \le 0$
$\quad x = 6 \ \text{ or } \ x = 4 \ \text{ or } \ x = 2$

Region	Test Point	$(x-6)(x-4)(x-2) \le 0$ Result
A: $(-\infty, 2]$	0	$(-6)(-4)(-2) \le 0$ True
B: $[2, 4]$	3	$(-3)(-1)(1) \le 0$ False
C: $[4, 6]$	5	$(-1)(1)(3) \le 0$ True
D: $[6, \infty)$	7	$(1)(3)(5) \le 0$ False

Solution: $(-\infty, 2] \cup [4, 6]$

12. $x(x-6)(x+2) > 0$

$x = 0$ or $x = 6$ or $x = -2$

Region	Test Point	$x(x-6)(x+2) > 0$ Result
A: $(-\infty, -2)$	-5	$-5(-11)(-3) > 0$ False
B: $(-2, 0)$	-1	$-1(-7)(1) > 0$ True
C: $(0, 6)$	1	$1(-5)(3) > 0$ False
D: $(6, \infty)$	7	$7(1)(9) > 0$ True

Solution: $(-2, 0) \cup (6, \infty)$

14. $(x^2 - 16)(x^2 - 1) \le 0$

$(x+4)(x-4)(x+1)(x-1) \le 0$

$x = -4$ or $x = 4$ or $x = -1$ or $x = 1$

Region	Test Point	$(x+4)(x-4)(x+1)(x-1) \le 0$ Result
A: $(-\infty, -4]$	-5	$(-1)(-9)(-4)(-6) \le 0$ False
B: $[-4, -1]$	-2	$(2)(-6)(-1)(-3) \le 0$ True
C: $[-1, 1]$	0	$(4)(-4)(1)(-1) \le 0$ False
D: $[1, 4]$	2	$(6)(-2)(3)(1) \le 0$ True
E: $[4, \infty)$	5	$(9)(1)(6)(4) \le 0$ False

Solution: $[-4, -1] \cup [1, 4]$

16. $\dfrac{x-5}{x-6} > 0$

$x = 5$ or $x = 6$

Region	Test Point	$\dfrac{x-5}{x-6} > 0$; Result
$A: (-\infty, 5)$	0	$\dfrac{-5}{-6} > 0$; True
$B: (5, 6)$	5.5	$\dfrac{0.5}{-0.5} > 0$; False
$C: (6, \infty)$	7	$\dfrac{2}{1} > 0$; True

Solution: $(-\infty, 5) \cup (6, \infty)$

18. $\dfrac{3}{y-5} < 0$

$y = 5$

Region	Test Point	$\dfrac{3}{y-5} < 0$; Result
$A: (-\infty, 5)$	0	$\dfrac{3}{-5} < 0$; True
$B: (5, \infty)$	6	$\dfrac{3}{1} < 0$; False

Solution: $(-\infty, 5)$

20. $\dfrac{x+1}{x-4} \le 0$

$x = -1$ or $x = 4$

Region	Test Point	$\dfrac{x+1}{x-4} \le 0$; Result
$A: (-\infty, -1]$	-2	$\dfrac{-1}{-6} \le 0$; False
$B: [-1, 4)$	0	$\dfrac{1}{-4} \le 0$; True
$C: (4, \infty)$	5	$\dfrac{6}{1} \le 0$; False

Solution: $[-1, 4)$

22. $\dfrac{-2}{y+3} > 2$

The denominator is equal to 0 when

$y + 3 = 0$, or $y = -3$.

$\dfrac{-2}{y+3} = 2$

$-2 = 2y + 6$

$-8 = 2y$

$-4 = y$

Region	Test Point	$\dfrac{-2}{y+3} > 2$; Result
$A: (-\infty, -4)$	-5	$\dfrac{-2}{-2} > 2$; False
$B: (-4, -3)$	-3.5	$\dfrac{-2}{-0.5} = 4 > 2$; True
$C: (-3, \infty)$	4	$\dfrac{-2}{7} > 2$; False

Solution: $(-4, -3)$

24. $\dfrac{y^2 + 15}{8y} \le 1$

The denominator is equal to 0 when $8y = 0$, or $y = 0$.

$\dfrac{y^2 + 15}{8y} = 1$

$y^2 + 15 = 8y$

$y^2 - 8y + 15 = 0$

$(y - 5)(y - 3) = 0$

$y = 5$ or $y = 3$

Region	Test Point	$\dfrac{y^2 + 15}{8y} \le 1$; Result
$A: (-\infty, 0)$	-1	$\dfrac{16}{-8} \le 1$; True
$B: (0, 3]$	1	$\dfrac{16}{8} \le 1$; False
$C: [3, 5]$	4	$\dfrac{31}{32} \le 1$; True
$D: [5, \infty)$	6	$\dfrac{51}{48} \le 1$; False

Solution: $(-\infty, 0) \cup [3, 5]$

26. $(x-5)(x+1) < 0$

$x = 5$ or $x = -1$

Region	Test Point	$(x-5)(x+1) < 0$ Result
A: $(-\infty, -1)$	-2	$(-7)(-1) < 0$ False
B: $(-1, 5)$	0	$(-5)(1) < 0$ True
C: $(5, \infty)$	6	$(1)(7) < 0$ False

Solution: $(-1, 5)$

28. $(6x+7)(7x-12) > 0$

$6x+7 = 0$ or $7x-12 = 0$

$x = -\dfrac{7}{6}$ or $\quad x = \dfrac{12}{7}$

Region	Test Point	$(6x+7)(7x-12) > 0$ Result
A: $\left(-\infty, -\dfrac{7}{6}\right)$	-2	$(-5)(-26) > 0$ True
B: $\left(-\dfrac{7}{6}, \dfrac{12}{7}\right)$	0	$(7)(-12) > 0$ False
C: $\left(\dfrac{12}{7}, \infty\right)$	2	$(19)(2) > 0$ True

Solution: $\left(-\infty, -\dfrac{7}{6}\right) \cup \left(\dfrac{12}{7}, \infty\right)$

30. $\quad\quad x^2 < 25$

$x^2 - 25 < 0$

$(x+5)(x-5) < 0$

$x = -5$ or $x = 5$

Region	Test Point	$(x+5)(x-5) < 0$ Result
A: $(-\infty, -5)$	-6	$(-1)(-11) < 0$ False
B: $(-5, 5)$	0	$(5)(-5) < 0$ True
C: $(5, \infty)$	6	$(11)(1) < 0$ False

Solution: $(-5, 5)$

32. $(3x-12)(x+5)(2x-3) \geq 0$

$3x-12 = 0$ or $x+5 = 0$ or $2x-3 = 0$

$x = 4$ $x = -5$ or $x = \dfrac{3}{2}$

Region	Test Point	$(3x - 12)(x + 5)(2x - 3) \geq 0$ Result
A: $(-\infty, -5]$	-6	$(-30)(-1)(-15) \geq 0$ False
B: $\left[-5, \dfrac{3}{2}\right]$	0	$(-12)(5)(-3) \geq 0$ True
C: $\left[\dfrac{3}{2}, 4\right]$	2	$(-6)(7)(1) \geq 0$ False
D: $[4, \infty)$	5	$(3)(10)(7) \geq 0$ True

Solution: $\left[-5, \dfrac{3}{2}\right] \cup [4, \infty)$

34. $12x^2 + 11x \leq 15$

        $12x^2 + 11x - 15 \leq 0$

        $(3x + 5)(4x - 3) \leq 0$

$x = -\dfrac{5}{3}$ or $x = \dfrac{3}{4}$

Region	Test Point	$(3x + 5)(4x - 3) \leq 0$ Result
A: $\left(-\infty, -\dfrac{5}{3}\right]$	-2	$(-1)(-11) \leq 0$ False
B: $\left[-\dfrac{5}{3}, \dfrac{3}{4}\right]$	0	$(5)(-3) \leq 0$ True
C: $\left[\dfrac{3}{4}, \infty\right)$	1	$(8)(1) \leq 0$ False

Solution: $\left[-\dfrac{5}{3}, \dfrac{3}{4}\right]$

36. $x^3 + 2x^2 - 4x - 8 < 0$

$x^2(x+2) - 4(x+2) < 0$

$(x+2)(x^2 - 4) < 0$

$(x+2)^2(x-2) < 0$

$x = -2 \quad \text{or} \quad x = 2$

Region	Test Point	$(x+2)^2(x-2) < 0$ Result
A: $(-\infty, -2)$	-3	$(1)(-5) < 0$ True
B: $(-2, 2)$	0	$(4)(-2) < 0$ True
C: $(2, \infty)$	3	$(25)(1) < 0$ False

Solution: $(-\infty, -2) \cup (-2, 2)$

38. $16x^4 - 40x^2 + 9 \le 0$

$(4x^2 - 9)(4x^2 - 1) \le 0$

$(2x+3)(2x-3)(2x+1)(2x-1) \le 0$

$x = -\dfrac{3}{2} \quad \text{or} \quad x = \dfrac{3}{2} \quad \text{or} \quad x = -\dfrac{1}{2} \quad \text{or} \quad x = \dfrac{1}{2}$

Region	Test Point	$(2x+3)(2x-3)(2x+1)(2x-1) \le 0$ Result
A: $\left(-\infty, -\dfrac{3}{2}\right]$	-2	$(-1)(-7)(-3)(-5) \le 0$ False
B: $\left[-\dfrac{3}{2}, -\dfrac{1}{2}\right]$	-1	$(1)(-5)(-1)(-3) \le 0$ True
C: $\left[-\dfrac{1}{2}, \dfrac{1}{2}\right]$	0	$(3)(-3)(1)(-1) \le 0$ False
D: $\left[\dfrac{1}{2}, \dfrac{3}{2}\right]$	1	$(5)(-1)(3)(1) \le 0$ True
E: $\left[\dfrac{3}{2}, \infty\right)$	2	$(7)(1)(5)(3) \le 0$ False

Solution: $\left[-\dfrac{3}{2}, -\dfrac{1}{2}\right] \cup \left[\dfrac{1}{2}, \dfrac{3}{2}\right]$

40. $(4x-9)(2x+5) < 0$

$x = \dfrac{9}{4}$ or $x = -\dfrac{5}{2}$

Region	Test Point	$(4x-9)(2x+5) < 0$ Result
$A: \left(-\infty, -\dfrac{5}{2}\right)$	-3	$(-21)(-1) < 0$ False
$B: \left(-\dfrac{5}{2}, \dfrac{9}{4}\right)$	0	$(-9)(5) < 0$ True
$C: \left(\dfrac{9}{4}, \infty\right)$	3	$(3)(11) < 0$ False

Solution: $\left(-\dfrac{5}{2}, \dfrac{9}{4}\right)$

42. $\dfrac{x+10}{x-10} > 0$

$x = -10$ or $x = 10$

Region	Test Point	$\dfrac{x+10}{x-10} > 0$ Result
$A: (-\infty, -10)$	-11	$\dfrac{-1}{-21} > 0$ True
$B: (-10, 10)$	0	$\dfrac{10}{-10} > 0$ False
$C: (10, \infty)$	11	$\dfrac{21}{1} > 0$ True

Solution: $(-\infty, -10) \cup (10, \infty)$

44. $\dfrac{x-3}{x+2} \le 0$

$x = 3$ or $x = -2$

Region	Test Point	$\dfrac{x-3}{x+2} \le 0$ Result
$A: (-\infty, -2)$	-3	$\dfrac{-6}{-1} \le 0$ False
$B: (-2, 3]$	0	$\dfrac{-3}{2} \le 0$ True
$C: [3, \infty)$	4	$\dfrac{1}{6} \le 0$ False

Solution: $(-2, 3]$

46. $\dfrac{(x-2)(x+2)}{(x+1)(x-4)} \le 0$

$x = 2$ or $x = -2$ or $x = -1$ or $x = 4$

Region	Test Point	$\dfrac{(x-2)(x+2)}{(x+1)(x-4)} \le 0$ Result
$A: (-\infty, -2]$	-3	$\dfrac{(-5)(-1)}{(-2)(-7)} \le 0$ False
$B: [-2, -1)$	-1.5	$\dfrac{(-3.5)(0.5)}{(-0.5)(-5.5)} \le 0$ True
$C: (-1, 2]$	0	$\dfrac{(-2)(2)}{(1)(-4)} \le 0$ False
$D: [2, 4)$	3	$\dfrac{(1)(5)}{(4)(-1)} \le 0$ True
$E: (4, \infty)$	5	$\dfrac{(3)(7)}{(6)(1)} \le 0$ False

Solution: $[-2, -1) \cup [2, 4)$

48. $\dfrac{4}{y+2} < -2$

The denominator is equal to 0 when $y + 2 = 0$, or $y = -2$.

$$\dfrac{4}{y+2} = -2$$
$$4 = -2y - 4$$
$$2y = -8$$
$$y = -4$$

Region	Test Point	$\dfrac{4}{y+2} < -2$ Result
A: $(-\infty, -4)$	-5	$\dfrac{4}{-3} < -2$ False
B: $(-4, -2)$	-3	$\dfrac{4}{-1} < -2$ True
C: $(-2, \infty)$	0	$\dfrac{4}{2} < -2$ False

Solution: $(-4, -2)$

50. $\dfrac{4x}{x-3} \geq 5$

The denominator is equal to 0 when $x - 3 = 0$, or $x = 3$.

$$\dfrac{4x}{x-3} = 5$$
$$4x = 5x - 15$$
$$x = 15$$

Region	Test Point	$\dfrac{4x}{x-3} \geq 5$ Result
A: $(-\infty, 3)$	0	$\dfrac{4(0)}{-3} \geq 5$ False
B: $(3, 15]$	4	$\dfrac{4(4)}{1} \geq 5$ True
C: $[15, \infty)$	16	$\dfrac{4(16)}{13} \geq 5$ False

Solution: $(3, 15]$

52. $\dfrac{p}{p+4} \leq 3p$

The denominator is equal to 0 when $p + 4 = 0$, or $p = -4$.

$$\dfrac{p}{p+4} = 3p$$
$$p = 3p^2 + 12p$$
$$0 = 3p^2 + 11p$$
$$0 = p(3p + 11)$$
$$p = 0 \ \text{ or } \ p = -\dfrac{11}{3}$$

Region	Test Point	$\dfrac{p}{p+4} \leq 3p$ Result
A: $(-\infty, -4)$	-5	$\dfrac{-5}{-1} \leq 3(-5)$ False
B: $\left(-4, -\dfrac{11}{3}\right]$	-3.9	$\dfrac{-3.9}{0.1} \leq 3(-3.9)$ True
C: $\left[-\dfrac{11}{3}, 0\right]$	-1	$\dfrac{-1}{3} \leq 3(-1)$ False
D: $[0, \infty)$	1	$\dfrac{1}{5} \leq 3(1)$ True

Solution: $\left(-4, -\dfrac{11}{3}\right] \cup [0, \infty)$

54. $\dfrac{(2x-3)^2}{x} < 0$

$$x = \dfrac{3}{2} \ \text{ or } \ x = 0$$

Region	Test Point	$\dfrac{(2x-3)^2}{x} < 0$ Result
$A: (-\infty, 0)$	-1	$\dfrac{25}{-1} < 0$ True
$B: \left(0, \dfrac{3}{2}\right)$	1	$\dfrac{1}{1} < 0$ False
$C: \left(\dfrac{3}{2}, \infty\right)$	2	$\dfrac{1}{2} < 0$ False

Solution: $(-\infty, 0)$

56. $H(x) = |x| - 2$

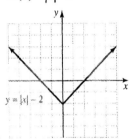

58. $h(x) = |x| + 5$

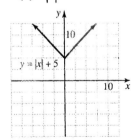

60. $h(x) = x^2 - 4$

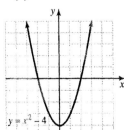

62. $g(x) = x^2 + 3$

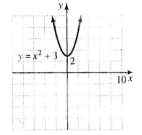

64. Answers may vary

66. Let $x =$ the number. Then

$\dfrac{1}{x} =$ the reciprocal of the number.

$2x + \dfrac{1}{x} \geq 0$

$\dfrac{2x^2 + 1}{x} \geq 0$

$x = 0$

Region	Test Point	$\dfrac{2x^2 + 1}{x} \geq 0$ Result
$A: (-\infty, 0)$	-1	$\dfrac{3}{-1} \geq 0$ False
$B: (0, \infty)$	1	$\dfrac{3}{1} \geq 0$ True

Any number greater than 0 and its reciprocal satisfy the conditions.

68. $s(t) = -16t^2 + 80t$

$-16t^2 + 80t > 96$

$-16(t^2 - 5t + 6) > 0$

$-16(t - 2)(t - 3) > 0$

$t = 2 \ \text{ or } \ t = 3$

Region	Test Point	$-16(t-2)(t-3) > 0$ Result
$A: (0, 2)$	1	$-16(-1)(-2) > 0$ False
$B: (2, 3)$	2.5	$-16(0.5)(-0.5) > 0$ True
$C: (3, \infty)$	4	$-16(2)(1) > 0$ False

The height of the projectile is greater than 96 feet between 2 and 3 seconds.

70.

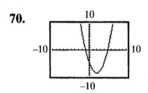

72.

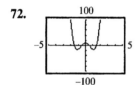

The Bigger Picture

1. $|x-8| = |2x+1|$

$x-8 = 2x+1$ or $x-8 = -(2x+1)$

$-9 = x$ $\qquad\qquad$ $x-8 = -2x-1$

$\qquad\qquad\qquad$ $3x = 7$

$\qquad\qquad\qquad$ $x = \dfrac{7}{3}$

2. $0 < -x+7 < 3$

$-7 < -x < -4$

$7 > x > 4$

$4 < x < 7$

Solution: $(4, 7)$

3. $\sqrt{3x-11} + 3 = x$

$\sqrt{3x-11} = x-3$

$3x-11 = (x-3)^2$

$3x-11 = x^2 - 6x + 9$

$0 = x^2 - 9x + 20$

$0 = (x-4)(x-5)$

$x-4 = 0$ or $x-5 = 0$

$x = 4$ $\qquad\qquad$ $x = 5$

The solutions are 4 and 5.

4. $x(3x+1) = 1$

$3x^2 + x - 1 = 0$

$a = 3, b = 1, c = -1$

$x = \dfrac{-1 \pm \sqrt{1^2 - 4(3)(-1)}}{2(3)}$

$= \dfrac{-1 \pm \sqrt{1+12}}{6}$

$= \dfrac{-1 \pm \sqrt{13}}{6}$

The solutions are $\dfrac{-1+\sqrt{13}}{6}$ and $\dfrac{-1-\sqrt{13}}{6}$.

5. $\dfrac{x+2}{x-7} \le 0$

$x - 7 = 0$, so $x = 7$ makes the denominator 0.

$\dfrac{x+2}{x-7} = 0$

$x + 2 = 0$

$x = -2$

Region	Test Point	$\dfrac{x+2}{x-7} \le 0$ Result
$A: (-\infty, -2]$	-3	$\dfrac{-1}{-10} \le 0$ False
$B: [-2, 7)$	0	$\dfrac{2}{-7} \le 0$ True
$C: (7, \infty)$	8	$\dfrac{10}{1} \le 0$ False

Solution: $[-2, 7)$

6. $x(x-6) + 4 = x^2 - 2(3-x)$

$x^2 - 6x + 4 = x^2 - 6 + 2x$

$-6x + 4 = -6 + 2x$

$10 = 8x$

$\dfrac{5}{4} = x$

The solution is $\dfrac{5}{4}$.

7. $x(5x - 36) = -7$

$5x^2 - 36x + 7 = 0$

$a = 5, b = -36, c = 7$

$x = \dfrac{-(-36) \pm \sqrt{(-36)^2 - 4(5)(7)}}{2(5)}$

$= \dfrac{36 \pm \sqrt{1156}}{10}$

$= \dfrac{36 \pm 34}{10}$

$x = \dfrac{36 + 34}{10} = \dfrac{70}{10} = 7$ or $x = \dfrac{36 - 34}{10} = \dfrac{2}{10} = \dfrac{1}{5}$

The solutions are 7 and $\dfrac{1}{5}$.

8. $2x^2 - 4 \geq 7x$

Solve $2x^2 - 4 = 7x$.

$2x^2 - 7x - 4 = 0$

$(2x + 1)(x - 4) = 0$

$2x + 1 = 0$ or $x - 4 = 0$

$2x = -1$ $x = 4$

$x = -\dfrac{1}{2}$

Region	Test Point	$2x^2 - 4 \geq 7x$ Result
$A: \left(-\infty, -\dfrac{1}{2}\right]$	-1	$2 - 4 \geq -7$ True
$B: \left[-\dfrac{1}{2}, 4\right]$	0	$-4 \geq 0$ False
$C: [4, \infty)$	5	$50 - 4 \geq 35$ True

Solution: $\left(-\infty, -\dfrac{1}{2}\right] \cup [4, \infty)$

9. $\left|\dfrac{x - 7}{3}\right| > 5$

$\dfrac{x - 7}{3} > 5$ or $\dfrac{x - 7}{3} < -5$

$x - 7 > 15$ or $x - 7 < -15$

$x > 22$ or $x < -8$

Solution: $(-\infty, -8) \cup (22, \infty)$

10. $2(x - 5) + 4 < 1 + 7(x - 5) - x$

$2x - 10 + 4 < 1 + 7x - 35 - x$

$2x - 6 < 6x - 34$

$28 < 4x$

$7 < x$

Solution: $(7, \infty)$

Section 11.5

Practice Exercises

1. $f(x) = x^2$ and $g(x) = x^2 - 4$

Construct a table of values for $f(x)$ and $g(x)$.

x	$f(x) = x^2$	$g(x) = x^2 - 4$
-2	4	0
-1	1	-3
0	0	-4
1	1	-3
2	4	0

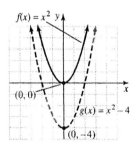

2. a. $f(x) = x^2 - 5$

The graph of $f(x)$ is obtained by shifting the graph of $y = x^2$ downward 5 units.

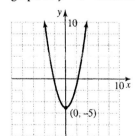

b. $g(x) = x^2 + 3$

The graph of $g(x)$ is obtained by shifting the graph of $y = x^2$ upward 3 units.

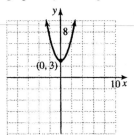

3. $f(x) = x^2$ and $g(x) = (x + 6)^2$

Plot points. Notice that the graph of $g(x)$ is the graph of $f(x)$ shifted 6 units to the left.

x	$f(x) = x^2$	x	$g(x) = (x+6)^2$
-2	4	-8	4
-1	1	-7	1
0	0	-6	0
1	1	-5	1
2	4	-4	4

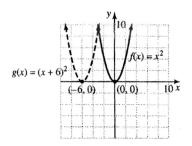

4. a. $G(x) = (x + 4)^2$

The graph of $G(x)$ is obtained by shifting the graph of $y = x^2$ to the left 4 units.

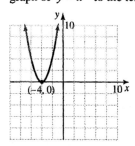

b. $H(x) = (x - 7)^2$

The graph of $H(x)$ is obtained by shifting the graph of $y = x^2$ to the right 7 units.

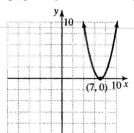

5. $f(x) = (x + 2)^2 + 2$

The graph of $f(x)$ is the graph of $y = x^2$ shifted 2 units to the left and 2 units upward. The vertex is then $(-2, 2)$, and the axis of symmetry is $x = -2$.

x	$f(x) = (x+2)^2 + 2$
-4	6
-3	3
-1	3
0	6

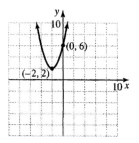

6. $f(x) = x^2$, $g(x) = 4x^2$, and $h(x) = \dfrac{1}{4}x^2$

Comparing tables of values, we see that for each x-value, the corresponding value of $g(x)$ is four times that of $f(x)$. Similarly, the value of $h(x)$ is one quarter the value of $f(x)$.

x	$f(x) = x^2$	$g(x) = 4x^2$	$h(x) = \frac{1}{4}x^2$
-2	4	16	1
-1	1	4	$\frac{1}{4}$
0	0	0	0
1	1	4	$\frac{1}{4}$
2	4	16	1

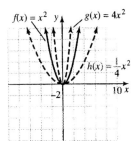

7. $f(x) = -\dfrac{1}{2}x^2$

Because $a = -\dfrac{1}{2}$, a negative value, this parabola

opens downward. Since $\left| -\dfrac{1}{2} \right| = \dfrac{1}{2} < 1$, the

parabola is wider than the graph of $y = x^2$. The

vertex is $(0, 0)$, and the axis of symmetry is the

y-axis.

x	$f(x) = -\frac{1}{2}x^2$
-2	-2
-1	$-\frac{1}{2}$
0	0
1	$-\frac{1}{2}$
2	-2

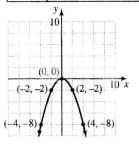

8. $h(x) = \dfrac{1}{3}(x-4)^2 - 3$

This graph is the same as $y = x^2$ shifted 4 units

to the right and 3 units downward, and it is wider

because a is $\dfrac{1}{3}$. The vertex is $(4, -3)$, and the

axis of symmetry is $x = 4$.

x	$h(x) = \frac{1}{3}(x-4)^2 - 3$
2	$-\frac{5}{3}$
3	$-\frac{8}{3}$
4	-3
5	$-\frac{8}{3}$
6	$-\frac{5}{3}$

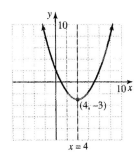

Graphing Calculator Explorations

1.

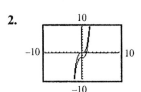

2.

3.

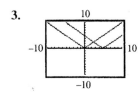

4.

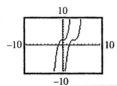

5.

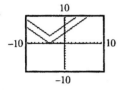

6.

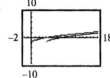

Vocabulary and Readiness Check

1. A <u>quadratic</u> function is one that can be written in the form $f(x) = ax^2 + bx + c$, $a \neq 0$.

2. The graph of a quadratic function is a <u>parabola</u> opening <u>upward</u> or <u>downward</u>.

3. If $a > 0$, the graph of the quadratic function opens <u>upward</u>.

4. If $a < 0$, the graph of the quadratic function opens <u>downward</u>.

5. The vertex of a parabola is the <u>lowest</u> point if $a > 0$.

6. The vertex of a parabola is the <u>highest</u> point if $a < 0$.

7. $f(x) = x^2$; vertex: $(0, 0)$

8. $f(x) = -5x^2$; vertex: $(0, 0)$

9. $g(x) = (x-2)^2$; vertex: $(2, 0)$

10. $g(x) = (x+5)^2$; vertex: $(-5, 0)$

11. $f(x) = 2x^2 + 3$; vertex: $(0, 3)$

12. $h(x) = x^2 - 1$; vertex: $(0, -1)$

13. $g(x) = (x+1)^2 + 5$; vertex: $(-1, 5)$

14. $h(x) = (x-10)^2 - 7$; vertex: $(10, -7)$

Exercise Set 11.5

2. The graph of $g(x) = x^2 + 3$ is the graph of $y = x^2$ shifted up 3 units. The vertex is then $(0, 3)$, and the axis of symmetry is $x = 0$.

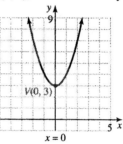

4. The graph of $h(x) = x^2 - 4$ is the graph of $y = x^2$ shifted down 4 units. The vertex is then $(0, -4)$, and the axis of symmetry is $x = 0$.

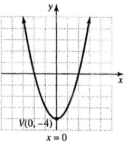

6. The graph of $f(x) = x^2 - 2$ is the graph of $y = x^2$ shifted down 2 units. The vertex is then $(0, -2)$, and the axis of symmetry is $x = 0$.

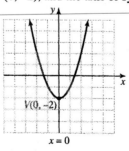

8. The graph of $g(x) = (x+5)^2$ is the graph of $y = x^2$ shifted left 5 units. The vertex is then $(-5, 0)$, and the axis of symmetry is $x = -5$.

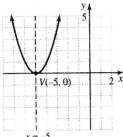

10. The graph of $H(x) = (x-1)^2$ is the graph of $y = x^2$ shifted right 1 unit. The vertex is then $(1, 0)$, and the axis of symmetry is $x = 1$.

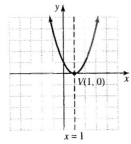

12. The graph of $f(x) = (x-6)^2$ is the graph of $y = x^2$ shifted right 6 units. The vertex is then $(6, 0)$, and the axis of symmetry is $x = 6$.

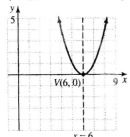

14. The graph of $g(x) = (x-6)^2 + 1$ is the graph of $y = x^2$ shifted right 6 units and up 1 unit. The vertex is then $(6, 1)$, and the axis of symmetry is $x = 6$.

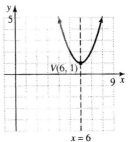

16. The graph of $G(x) = (x+3)^2 + 3$ is the graph of $y = x^2$ shifted left 3 units and up 3 units. The vertex is then $(-3, 3)$, and the axis of symmetry is $x = -3$.

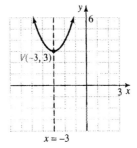

18. The graph of $h(x) = (x+4)^2 - 6$ is the graph of $y = x^2$ shifted left 4 units and down 6 units. The vertex is then $(-4, -6)$, and the axis of symmetry is $x = -4$.

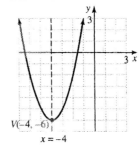

20. The graph of $f(x) = 5x^2$ is the graph of $y = x^2$ but made narrower. The vertex is then (0, 0), and the axis of symmetry is $x = 0$.

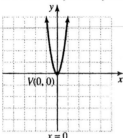

22. The graph of $f(x) = -\dfrac{1}{4}x^2$ is the graph of

$y = x^2$ but opening down and made wider. The vertex is then (0, 0), and the axis of symmetry is $x = 0$.

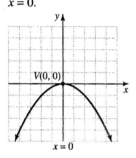

24. The graph of $g(x) = -3x^2$ is the graph of

$y = x^2$ but opening down and made narrower. The vertex is then (0, 0), and the axis of symmetry is $x = 0$.

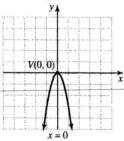

26. The graph of $g(x) = 4(x-4)^2 + 2$ is the graph of

$y = x^2$ shifted right 4 units, made narrower, and shifted up 2 units. The vertex is then (4, 2), and the axis of symmetry is $x = 4$.

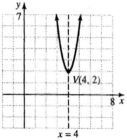

28. The graph of $f(x) = -(x-2)^2 - 6$ is the graph

of $y = x^2$ shifted right 2 units, opening down, and shifted down 6 units. The vertex is then (2, −6), and the axis of symmetry is $x = 2$.

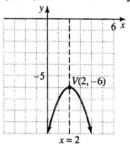

30. The graph of $G(x) = \dfrac{1}{5}(x+4)^2 + 3$ is the graph

of $y = x^2$ shifted left 4 units, made wider, and shifted up 3 units. The vertex is then (−4, 3), and the axis of symmetry is $x = -4$.

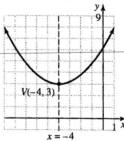

32. The graph of $g(x) = -(x+6)^2$ is the graph of $y = x^2$ shifted left 6 units and opening down. The vertex is then $(-6, 0)$, and the axis of symmetry is $x = -6$.

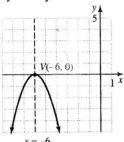

34. The graph of $H(x) = -x^2 + 10$ is the graph of $y = x^2$ opening down and then shifted up 10 units. The vertex is then $(0, 10)$, and the axis of symmetry is $x = 0$.

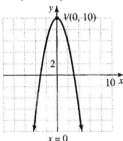

36. The graph of $g(x) = \frac{1}{2}x^2 - 2$ is the graph of $y = x^2$ made wider and then shifted down 2 units. The vertex is then $(0, -2)$, and the axis of symmetry is $x = 0$.

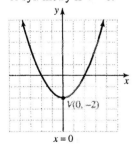

38. The graph of $f(x) = (x-5)^2 + 2$ is the graph of $y = x^2$ shifted right 5 units and up 2 units. The vertex is then $(5, 2)$, and the axis of symmetry is $x = 5$.

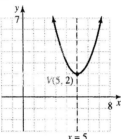

40. The graph of $H(x) = \left(x + \frac{1}{2}\right)^2 - 3$ is the graph of $y = x^2$ shifted left $\frac{1}{2}$ unit and down 3 units. The vertex is then $\left(-\frac{1}{2}, -3\right)$, and the axis of symmetry is $x = -\frac{1}{2}$.

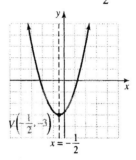

42. The graph of $g(x) = -\frac{3}{2}(x-1)^2 - 5$ is the graph of $y = x^2$ shifted right 1 unit, made narrower, opening down, and shifted down 5 units. The vertex is then $(1, -5)$, and the axis of symmetry is $x = 1$.

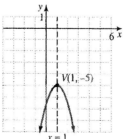

44. The graph of $H(x) = \frac{3}{4}x^2 - 2$ is the graph of

$y = x^2$ made wider and shifted down 2 units.
The vertex is then $(0, -2)$, and the axis of
symmetry is $x = 0$.

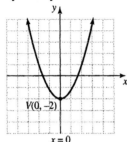

46. The graph of $F(x) = 3\left(x - \frac{3}{2}\right)^2$ is the graph of

$y = x^2$ shifted right $\frac{3}{2}$ units and made narrower.

The vertex is then $\left(\frac{3}{2}, 0\right)$, and the axis of

symmetry is $x = \frac{3}{2}$.

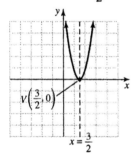

48. The graph of $f(x) = -3(x + 2)^2 + 2$ is the graph

of $y = x^2$ shifted left 2 units, made narrower,
opening down, and shifted up 2 units. The vertex
is then $(-2, 2)$, and the axis of symmetry is
$x = -2$.

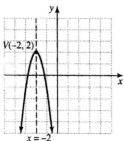

50. The graph of $G(x) = \sqrt{5}(x - 7)^2 - \frac{1}{2}$ is the graph

of $y = x^2$ shifted right 7 units, made narrower,

and shifted down $\frac{1}{2}$ unit. The vertex is then

$\left(7, -\frac{1}{2}\right)$, and the axis of symmetry is $x = 7$.

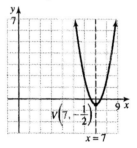

52. The graph of $h(x) = 8(x + 1)^2 + 9$ is the graph of

$y = x^2$ shifted left 1 unit, made narrower, and
shifted up 9 units. The vertex is then $(-1, 9)$, and
the axis of symmetry is $x = -1$.

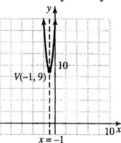

54. The graph of $G(x) = -4(x + 9)^2 - 1$ is the graph

of $y = x^2$ shifted left 9 units, made narrower,
opening down, and shifted down 1 unit. The
vertex is then $(-9, -1)$, and the axis of symmetry
is $x = -9$.

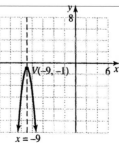

56. $y^2 + 4y$

$$\left[\frac{1}{2}(4)\right]^2 = (2)^2 = 4$$

$$y^2 + 4y + 4$$

58. $x^2 - 10x$

$$\left[\frac{1}{2}(-10)\right]^2 = (-5)^2 = 25$$

$$x^2 - 10x + 25$$

60. $z^2 - 3z$

$$\left[\frac{1}{2}(-3)\right]^2 = \left(-\frac{3}{2}\right)^2 = \frac{9}{4}$$

$$z^2 - 3z + \frac{9}{4}$$

62.

$$y^2 + 6y = -5$$

$$y^2 + 6y + \left(\frac{6}{2}\right)^2 = -5 + 9$$

$$(y+3)^2 = 4$$

$$y + 3 = \pm 2$$

$$y = -3 \pm 2$$

$$y = -5 \text{ or } -1$$

The solutions are –5 and –1.

64.

$$x^2 + 14x + 20 = 0$$

$$x^2 + 14x = -20$$

$$x^2 + 14x + \left(\frac{14}{2}\right)^2 = -20 + 49$$

$$(x+7)^2 = 29$$

$$x + 7 = \pm\sqrt{29}$$

$$x = -7 \pm \sqrt{29}$$

The solutions are $-7 + \sqrt{29}$ and $-7 - \sqrt{29}$.

66.

$$y^2 - 10y = 3$$

$$y^2 - 10y + \left(\frac{-10}{2}\right)^2 = 3 + 25$$

$$(y-5)^2 = 28$$

$$y - 5 = \pm 2\sqrt{7}$$

$$y = 5 \pm 2\sqrt{7}$$

The solutions are $5 + 2\sqrt{7}$ and $5 - 2\sqrt{7}$.

68. $f(x) = 5\left(x + \frac{1}{2}\right)^2 + \frac{1}{2}$

Since $5 > 0$, the graph opens upward.

$x - h = x + \frac{1}{2}$, so $h = -\frac{1}{2}$, and $k = \frac{1}{2}$.

$(h, k) = \left(-\frac{1}{2}, \frac{1}{2}\right)$

The correct description is **b**.

70. We need a function with the form:

$$f(x) = 5(x - h)^2 + k$$

Since the vertex is $(h, k) = (1, 6)$, we get:

$$f(x) = 5(x-1)^2 + 6$$

72. We need a function with the form:

$$f(x) = 5(x - h)^2 + k$$

Since the vertex is $(h, k) = (4, -1)$, we get:

$$f(x) = 5(x-4)^2 + (-1)$$

$$= 5(x-4)^2 - 1$$

74. $y = f(x) - 2$

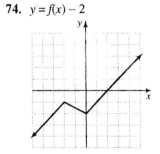

76. $h = f(x + 3)$

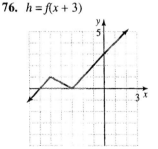

78. $y = f(x - 1) + 1$

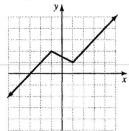

80. $f(x) = 668.7x^2 - 2990.7x + 938$

    a. $x = 2010 - 1985 = 25$

$$f(25) = 668.7(25)^2 - 2990.7(25) + 938$$
$$= 344,108$$

        There will be 344,108 thousand subscribers.

    b. Answers may vary—around 300,000,000.

    c. Answers may vary

Section 11.6

Practice Exercises

1. $g(x) = x^2 - 2x - 3$

Write in the form $y = (x - h)^2 + k$ by completing the square.

$$y = x^2 - 2x - 3$$
$$y + 3 = x^2 - 2x$$
$$y + 3 + \left(\frac{-2}{2}\right)^2 = x^2 - 2x + \left(\frac{-2}{2}\right)^2$$
$$y + 4 = x^2 - 2x + 1$$
$$y = (x - 1)^2 - 4$$

The vertex is at $(1, -4)$.
Let $g(x) = 0$.

$$0 = x^2 - 2x - 3$$
$$0 = (x - 3)(x + 1)$$
$$x - 3 = 0 \quad \text{or} \quad x + 1 = 0$$
$$x = 3 \qquad\qquad x = -1$$

The x-intercepts are $(3, 0)$ and $(-1, 0)$.
Let $x = 0$.

$$g(0) = 0^2 - 2(0) - 3 = -3$$

The y-intercept is $(0, -3)$.

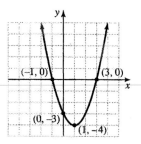

2. $g(x) = 4x^2 + 4x + 3$

Replace $g(x)$ with y and complete the square to write the equation in the form $y = a(x - h)^2 + k$.

$$y = 4x^2 + 4x + 3$$
$$y - 3 = 4x^2 + 4x = 4(x^2 + x)$$
$$y - 3 + 4\left(\frac{1}{2}\right)^2 = 4\left[x^2 + x + \left(\frac{1}{2}\right)^2\right]$$
$$y - 3 + 1 = 4\left(x^2 + x + \frac{1}{4}\right)$$
$$y = 4\left(x + \frac{1}{2}\right)^2 + 2$$

$a = 4$, $h = -\dfrac{1}{2}$, and $k = 2$.
The parabola opens upward with vertex $\left(-\dfrac{1}{2}, 2\right)$, and has an axis of symmetry $x = -\dfrac{1}{2}$.
Let $x = 0$.

$$g(0) = 4(0)^2 + 4(0) + 3 = 3$$

The y-intercept is $(0, 3)$. There are no x-intercepts.

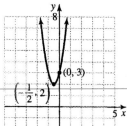

3. $g(x) = -x^2 + 5x + 6$

Write $g(x)$ in the form $a(x-h)^2 + k$ by completing the square. Replace $g(x)$ with y.

$$y = -x^2 + 5x + 6$$
$$y - 6 = -x^2 + 5x$$
$$y - 6 = -1(x^2 - 5x)$$
$$y - 6 - \left(\frac{-5}{2}\right)^2 = -1\left[x^2 - 5x + \left(\frac{-5}{2}\right)^2\right]$$
$$y - 6 - \frac{25}{4} = -1\left(x^2 - 5x + \frac{25}{4}\right)$$
$$y - \frac{49}{4} = -\left(x - \frac{5}{2}\right)^2$$
$$y = -\left(x - \frac{5}{2}\right)^2 + \frac{49}{4}$$

Since $a = -1$, the parabola opens downward with vertex $\left(\frac{5}{2}, \frac{49}{4}\right)$ and axis of symmetry $x = \frac{5}{2}$.

Let $x = 0$.

$$y = -0^2 + 5(0) + 6 = 6$$

The y-intercept is $(0, 6)$. Let $y = 0$.

$$0 = -x^2 + 5x + 6$$
$$0 = x^2 - 5x - 6$$
$$0 = (x - 6)(x + 1)$$
$$x - 6 = 0 \quad \text{or} \quad x + 1 = 0$$
$$x = 6 \qquad\qquad x = -1$$

The x-intercepts are $(6, 0)$ and $(-1, 0)$.

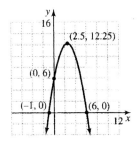

4. $g(x) = x^2 - 2x - 3$

$a = 1$, $b = -2$, and $c = -3$

$$\frac{-b}{2a} = \frac{-(-2)}{2(1)} = \frac{2}{2} = 1$$

The x-value of the vertex is 1.

$$g(1) = 1^2 - 2(1) - 3 = 1 - 2 - 3 = -4$$

The vertex is $(1, -4)$.

5. $h(t) = -16t^2 + 24t$

Find the vertex of $h(t)$ to find its maximum value.

$a = -16$, $b = 24$, and $c = 0$

$$\frac{-b}{2a} = \frac{-24}{2(-16)} = \frac{3}{4}$$

The t-value of the vertex is $\frac{3}{4}$.

$$h\left(\frac{3}{4}\right) = -16\left(\frac{3}{4}\right)^2 + 24\left(\frac{3}{4}\right)$$
$$= -16\left(\frac{9}{16}\right) + 18$$
$$= -9 + 18$$
$$= 9$$

The vertex is $\left(\frac{3}{4}, 9\right)$. Thus, the ball reaches its maximum height of 9 feet in $\frac{3}{4}$ second.

Vocabulary and Readiness Check

1. If a quadratic function is in the form $f(x) = a(x-h)^2 + k$, the vertex of its graph is $\underline{(h, k)}$.

2. The graph of $f(x) = ax^2 + bx + c$, $a \neq 0$ is a parabola whose vertex has x-value of $\underline{\dfrac{-b}{2a}}$.

	Parabola Opens	Vertex Location	Number of x-intercept(s)	Number of y-intercept(s)
3.	up	Q I	0	1
4.	up	Q III	2	1
5.	down	Q II	2	1
6.	down	Q IV	0	1
7.	up	x-axis	1	1
8.	down	x-axis	1	1
9.	down	Q III	0	
10.	down	Q I	2	
11.	up	Q IV	2	
12.	up	Q II	0	

Exercise Set 11.6

2. $f(x) = x^2 + 6x + 5$

$-\dfrac{b}{2a} = \dfrac{-6}{2(1)} = -3$ and

$f(-3) = (-3)^2 + 6(-3) + 5 = -4$

Thus, the vertex is $(-3, -4)$.

4. $f(x) = -x^2 - 8x + 2$

$-\dfrac{b}{2a} = \dfrac{-(-8)}{2(-1)} = -4$ and

$f(-4) = -(-4)^2 - 8(-4) + 2 = 18$

Thus, the vertex is $(-4, 18)$.

6. $f(x) = -3x^2 + 6x + 4$

$-\dfrac{b}{2a} = \dfrac{-6}{2(-3)} = 1$ and

$f(1) = -3(1)^2 + 6(1) + 4 = 7$

Thus, the vertex is $(1, 7)$.

8. $f(x) = x^2 - 9x + 8$

$-\dfrac{b}{2a} = \dfrac{-(-9)}{2(1)} = \dfrac{9}{2}$ and

$f\left(\dfrac{9}{2}\right) = \left(\dfrac{9}{2}\right)^2 - 9\left(\dfrac{9}{2}\right) + 8 = -\dfrac{49}{4}$

Thus, the vertex is $\left(\dfrac{9}{2}, -\dfrac{49}{4}\right)$.

10. $f(x) = x^2 + 2x - 3$

$-\dfrac{b}{2a} = \dfrac{-2}{2(1)} = -1$ and

$f(-1) = (-1)^2 + 2(-1) - 3 = -4$

The vertex is $(-1, -4)$, so the graph is A.

12. $f(x) = x^2 + 4x + 3$

$-\dfrac{b}{2a} = \dfrac{-4}{2(1)} = -2$ and

$f(-2) = (-2)^2 + 4(-2) + 3 = -1$

The vertex is $(-2, -1)$, so the graph is C.

14. $f(x) = x^2 + 2x - 3$

$-\dfrac{b}{2a} = \dfrac{-2}{2(1)} = -1$ and

$f(-1) = (-1)^2 + 2(-1) - 3 = -4$

Thus, the vertex is $(-1, -4)$.

The graph opens upward ($a = 1 > 0$).

$x^2 + 2x - 3 = 0$

$(x + 3)(x - 1) = 0$

$x = -3$ or $x = 1$

x-intercepts: $(-3, 0)$ and $(1, 0)$.

$f(0) = -3$; y-intercept is $(0, -3)$.

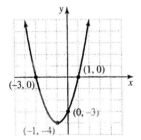

16. $f(x) = -x^2 + 4x - 4$

$-\dfrac{b}{2a} = \dfrac{-4}{2(-1)} = 2$ and

$f(2) = -(2)^2 + 4(2) - 4 = 0$

Thus, the vertex is $(2, 0)$.

The graph opens downward ($a = -1 < 0$).

$-x^2 + 4x - 4 = 0$

$x^2 - 4x + 4 = 0$

$(x - 2)^2 = 0$

$x = 2$

x-intercept: $(2, 0)$.

$f(0) = -4$; y-intercept is $(0, -4)$.

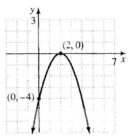

18. $f(x) = x^2 - 1$

$-\dfrac{b}{2a} = \dfrac{-0}{2(1)} = 0$ and

$f(0) = (0)^2 - 1 = -1$

Thus, the vertex is $(0, -1)$.

The graph opens upward ($a = 1 > 0$).

$x^2 - 1 = 0$

$(x + 1)(x - 1) = 0$

$x = -1$ or $x = 1$

x-intercepts: $(-1, 0)$ and $(1, 0)$.

$f(0) = -1$; y-intercept is $(0, -1)$.

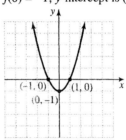

20. $f(x) = 2x^2 - x - 3$

$-\dfrac{b}{2a} = \dfrac{-(-1)}{2(2)} = \dfrac{1}{4}$ and

$f\left(\dfrac{1}{4}\right) = 2\left(\dfrac{1}{4}\right)^2 - \left(\dfrac{1}{4}\right) - 3 = -\dfrac{25}{8}$

Thus, the vertex is $\left(\dfrac{1}{4}, -\dfrac{25}{8}\right)$.

The graph opens upward ($a = 2 > 0$).

$2x^2 - x - 3 = 0$

$(2x - 3)(x + 1) = 0$

$x = \dfrac{3}{2}$ or $x = -1$

x-intercepts: $\left(\dfrac{3}{2}, 0\right)$ and $(-1, 0)$.

$f(0) = -3$, so the y-intercept is $(0, -3)$.

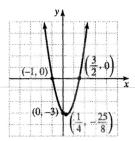

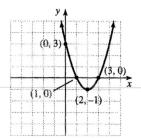

22.
$$f(x) = x^2 + 10x + 9$$
$$y = x^2 + 10x + 9$$
$$y - 9 = x^2 + 10x$$
$$y - 9 + 25 = x^2 + 10x + 25$$
$$y + 16 = (x + 5)^2$$
$$f(x) = (x + 5)^2 - 16$$

Thus, the vertex is $(-5, -16)$.
The graph opens upward ($a = 1 > 0$).
$$x^2 + 10x + 9 = 0$$
$$(x + 9)(x + 1) = 0$$
$$x = -9 \text{ or } x = -1$$
x-intercepts: $(-9, 0)$ and $(-1, 0)$.
$f(0) = 9$; y-intercept is $(0, 9)$.

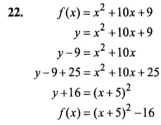

26.
$$f(x) = x^2 - 6x + 11$$
$$y - 11 = x^2 - 6x$$
$$y - 11 + 9 = x^2 - 6x + 9$$
$$y - 2 = (x - 3)^2$$
$$f(x) = (x - 3)^2 + 2$$

Thus, the vertex is $(3, 2)$.
The graph opens upward ($a = 1 > 0$).
$$x^2 - 6x + 11 = 0$$
$$x = \frac{6 \pm \sqrt{(-6)^2 - 4(1)(11)}}{2(1)} = \frac{6 \pm \sqrt{-8}}{2}$$

which give non-real solutions.
Hence, there are no x-intercepts.
$f(0) = 11$; y-intercept is $(0, 11)$.

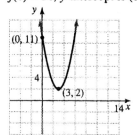

24.
$$f(x) = x^2 - 4x + 3$$
$$y - 3 = x^2 - 4x$$
$$y - 3 + 4 = x^2 - 4x + 4$$
$$y + 1 = (x - 2)^2$$
$$f(x) = (x - 2)^2 - 1$$

Thus, the vertex is $(2, -1)$.
The graph opens upward ($a = 1 > 0$).
$$x^2 - 4x + 3 = 0$$
$$(x - 3)(x - 1) = 0$$
$$x = 3 \text{ or } x = 1$$
x-intercepts: $(3, 0)$ and $(1, 0)$.
$f(0) = 3$; y-intercept is $(0, 3)$.

28.
$$f(x) = 3x^2 + 12x + 16$$
$$y - 16 = 3(x^2 + 4x)$$
$$y - 16 + 3(4) = 3(x^2 + 4x + 4)$$
$$y - 4 = 3(x + 2)^2$$
$$f(x) = 3(x + 2)^2 + 4$$

Thus, the vertex is $(-2, 4)$.
The graph opens upward ($a = 3 > 0$).
$$3x^2 + 12x + 16 = 0$$
$$x = \frac{-12 \pm \sqrt{(12)^2 - 4(3)(16)}}{2(3)}$$
$$= \frac{-12 \pm \sqrt{-48}}{6}$$

which give non-real solutions.
Hence, there are no x-intercepts.
$f(0) = 16$; y-intercept is $(0, 16)$.

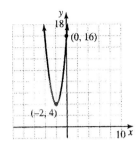

30. $f(x) = -4x^2 + 8x$

$$y = -4(x^2 - 2x)$$

$$y + [-4(1)] = -4(x^2 - 2x + 1)$$

$$y - 4 = -4(x - 1)^2$$

$$f(x) = -4(x - 1)^2 + 4$$

Thus, the vertex is (1, 4).

The graph opens downward ($a = -4 < 0$).

$$-4x^2 + 8x = 0$$

$$-4x(x - 2) = 0$$

$$x = 0 \text{ or } x = 2$$

x-intercepts: (0, 0) and (2, 0)

$f(0) = 0$; y-intercept is (0, 0).

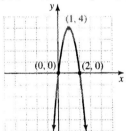

32. $f(x) = x^2 + 4$

$$x = -\frac{b}{2a} = -\frac{0}{2(1)} = 0$$

$$f(0) = (0)^2 + 4 = 4$$

Thus, the vertex is (0, 4).

The graph opens upward ($a = 1 > 0$).

$$x^2 + 4 = 0$$

$$x^2 = -4$$

which give non-real solutions.

Hence, there are no x-intercepts.

$f(0) = 4$ so the y-intercept is (0, 4).

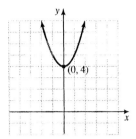

34. $f(x) = x^2 - x - 12$

$$y + 12 = x^2 - x$$

$$y + 12 + \frac{1}{4} = x^2 - x + \frac{1}{4}$$

$$y + \frac{49}{4} = \left(x - \frac{1}{2}\right)^2$$

$$f(x) = \left(x - \frac{1}{2}\right)^2 - \frac{49}{4}$$

Thus, the vertex is $\left(\frac{1}{2}, -\frac{49}{4}\right)$. The graph opens

upward ($a = 1 > 0$).

$$x^2 - x - 12 = 0$$

$$(x - 4)(x + 3) = 0$$

$$x = 4 \text{ or } x = -3$$

x-intercepts: (4, 0) and (−3, 0).

$f(0) = -12$, so the y-intercept is (0, −12)

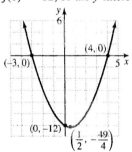

36. $f(x) = 3x^2 - 12x$

$$x = -\frac{b}{2a} = \frac{-(-12)}{2(3)} = 2 \text{ and}$$

$$f(2) = 3(2)^2 - 12(2) = -12$$

Thus, the vertex is (2, −12).

The graph opens upward ($a = 3 > 0$).

$$3x^2 - 12x = 0$$

$$3x(x - 4) = 0$$

$$x = 0 \text{ or } x = 4$$

x-intercepts: (0, 0) and (4, 0)

$f(0) = 0$; y-intercept is (0, 0).

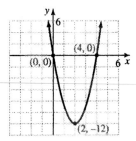

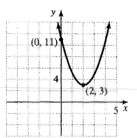

38. $f(x) = -x^2 + 8x - 17$

$x = -\dfrac{b}{2a} = \dfrac{-8}{2(-1)} = 4$ and

$f(4) = -(4)^2 + 8(4) - 17 = -1$

Thus, the vertex is $(4, -1)$.

The graph opens downward ($a = -1 < 0$).

$-x^2 + 8x - 17 = 0$

$x^2 - 8x + 17 = 0$

$x = \dfrac{8 \pm \sqrt{(-8)^2 - 4(1)(17)}}{2(1)} = \dfrac{8 \pm \sqrt{-4}}{2}$

which yields non-real solutions.

Hence, there are no x-intercepts.

$f(0) = -17$; y-intercept is $(0, -17)$.

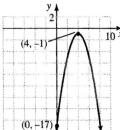

40. $f(x) = 2x^2 - 8x + 11$

$x = -\dfrac{b}{2a} = \dfrac{-(-8)}{2(2)} = 2$ and

$f(2) = 2(2)^2 - 8(2) + 11 = 3$

Thus, the vertex is $(2, 3)$.

The graph opens upward ($a = 2 > 0$).

$2x^2 - 8x + 11 = 0$

$x = \dfrac{8 \pm \sqrt{(-8)^2 - 4(2)(11)}}{2(2)} = \dfrac{8 \pm \sqrt{-24}}{4}$

which yields non-real solutions.

Hence, there are no x-intercepts.

$f(0) = 11$; so the y-intercept is $(0, 11)$.

42. $f(x) = x^2 + 3x - 18$

$x = -\dfrac{b}{2a} = \dfrac{-3}{2(1)} = -\dfrac{3}{2}$ and

$f\left(-\dfrac{3}{2}\right) = \left(-\dfrac{3}{2}\right)^2 + 3\left(-\dfrac{3}{2}\right) - 18 = -\dfrac{81}{4}$

Thus, the vertex is $\left(-\dfrac{3}{2}, -\dfrac{81}{4}\right)$.

The graph opens upward ($a = 1 > 0$).

$x^2 + 3x - 18 = 0$

$(x + 6)(x - 3) = 0$

$x = -6$ or $x = 3$

x-intercepts: $(-6, 0)$ and $(3, 0)$.

$f(0) = -18$; y-intercept is $(0, -18)$.

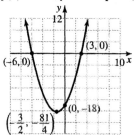

44. $f(x) = 3x^2 - 13x - 10$

$x = -\dfrac{b}{2a} = \dfrac{-(-13)}{2(3)} = \dfrac{13}{6}$ and

$f\left(\dfrac{13}{6}\right) = 3\left(\dfrac{13}{6}\right)^2 - 13\left(\dfrac{13}{6}\right) - 10 = -\dfrac{289}{12}$

Thus, the vertex is $\left(\dfrac{13}{6}, -\dfrac{289}{12}\right)$.

The graph opens upward ($a = 3 > 0$).

$3x^2 - 13x - 10 = 0$

$(3x + 2)(x - 5) = 0$

$x = -\dfrac{2}{3}$ or $x = 5$

x-intercepts: $(5, 0)$ and $\left(-\dfrac{2}{3}, 0\right)$.

$f(0) = -10$; y-intercept is $(0, -10)$.

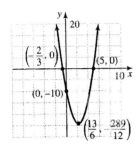

46. $h(t) = -16t^2 + 32t$

$t = -\dfrac{b}{2a} = \dfrac{-32}{2(-16)} = \dfrac{32}{32} = 1$ and

$h(1) = -16(1)^2 + 32(1)$

$\qquad = -16 + 32$

$\qquad = 16$

The maximum height is 16 feet.

48. $P(x) = 360x - x^2$

a. $x = -\dfrac{b}{2a} = \dfrac{-360}{2(-1)} = 180$

180 calendars are needed to maximize profit.

b. $P(180) = 360(180) - (180)^2 = 32,400$

The maximum profit is $32,400.

50. Let x = one number. Then

$11 - x$ = the other number.

$f(x) = x(11 - x) = -x^2 + 11x$

The maximum will occur at the vertex.

$x = -\dfrac{b}{2a} = \dfrac{-11}{2(-1)} = 5.5$

$11 - x = 11 - 5.5 = 5.5$

The two numbers are 5.5 and 5.5.

52. Let x = one number. Then

$8 + x$ = the other number.

$f(x) = x(8 + x) = x^2 + 8x$

The minimum will occur at the vertex.

$x = -\dfrac{b}{2a} = \dfrac{-8}{2(1)} = -4$

$8 + x = 8 + (-4) = 4$

The numbers are –4 and 4.

54. Let x = width. Then

$50 - x$ = the length.

Area = length · width

$A(x) = (50 - x)x = -x^2 + 50x$

The maximum will occur at the vertex.

$x = -\dfrac{b}{2a} = \dfrac{-50}{2(-1)} = 25$

$50 - x = 50 - 25 = 25$

The maximum area will occur when the length and width are 25 units each.

56. The graph of $f(x) = (x - 3)^2$ is the graph of $y = x^2$ shifted right 3 units. The vertex is then $(3, 0)$, and the axis of symmetry is $x = 3$.

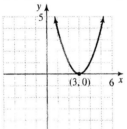

58. The graph of $h(x) = x - 3$ is the graph of $y = x$ shifted down 3 units.

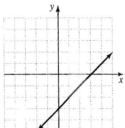

60. The graph of $f(x) = 2(x - 3)^2 + 2$ is the graph of $y = x^2$ shifted right 3 units, made narrower, and shifted up 2 units. The vertex is then $(3, 2)$, and the axis of symmetry is $x = 3$.

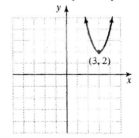

62. The graph of $f(x) = (x+1)^2 + 4$ is the graph of $y = x^2$ shifted left 1 unit and shifted up 4 units. The vertex is then $(-1, 4)$, and the axis of symmetry is $x = -1$.

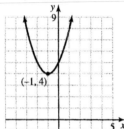

64. The graph of $f(x) = -2(x+7)^2 + \dfrac{1}{2}$ is the graph of $y = x^2$ shifted left 7 units, made narrower, opening down, and shifted up $\dfrac{1}{2}$ unit. The vertex is then $\left(-7, \dfrac{1}{2}\right)$, and the axis of symmetry is $x = -7$.

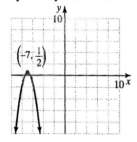

66. $g(x) = -7x^2 + x + 1$

Since $a = -7 < 0$, the graph opens downward; thus, $g(x)$ has a maximum value.

68. $G(x) = 3 - \dfrac{1}{2}x + 0.8x^2$

Since $a = 0.8 > 0$, the graph opens upward; thus, $G(x)$ has a minimum value.

70. $f(x) = x^2 - 6x + 4$

$x = -\dfrac{b}{2a} = \dfrac{-(-6)}{2(1)} = 3$ and

$f(3) = (3)^2 - 6(3) + 4 = -5$

Thus, the vertex is $(3, -5)$.

The graph opens upward ($a = 1 > 0$).

$f(0) = 4$; y-intercept is $(0, 4)$.

$x^2 - 6x + 4 = 0$

$x = \dfrac{6 \pm \sqrt{(-6)^2 - 4(1)(4)}}{2(1)}$

$= \dfrac{6 \pm \sqrt{20}}{2} \approx 5.2 \text{ or } 0.8$

The x-intercepts are approximately $(0.8, 0)$ and $(5.2, 0)$.

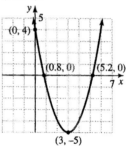

72. $f(x) = 2x^2 + 4x - 1$

$x = -\dfrac{b}{2a} = \dfrac{-4}{2(2)} = -1$ and

$f(-1) = 2(-1)^2 + 4(-1) - 1 = -3$

Thus, the vertex is $(-1, -3)$.

The graph opens upward ($a = 2 > 0$).

$f(0) = -1$; y-intercept is $(0, -1)$.

$2x^2 + 4x - 1 = 0$

$x = \dfrac{-4 \pm \sqrt{(4)^2 - 4(2)(-1)}}{2(2)}$

$= \dfrac{-4 \pm \sqrt{24}}{4} \approx -2.2 \text{ or } 0.2$

The x-intercepts are approximately $(-2.2, 0)$ and $(0.2, 0)$.

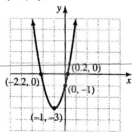

74. $f(x) = 7.6x^2 + 9.8x - 2.1$

$x = \dfrac{-9.8}{2(7.6)} \approx -0.64$

$f(-0.64) \approx -5.26$

minimum ≈ -5.26

Alternative solution:

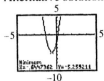

76. $f(x) = -5.2x^2 - 3.8x + 5.1$

$x = \dfrac{-(-3.8)}{2(-5.2)} \approx -0.37$

$f(-0.37) \approx 5.79$

maximum ≈ 5.79

Alternative solution:

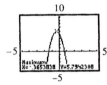

78. $f(x) = -0.072x^2 + 1.93x + 173.9$

a. $x = 2009 - 2000 = 9$

$f(9) = -0.072(9)^2 + 1.93(9) + 173.9$

$= 185.438$

According to the model, there will be about 185.44 million metric tons of methane emissions produced in the U.S. during 2009.

b. Since the coefficient of x^2 is negative, the graph will open down. Therefore, it will have a maximum.

c. $x = -\dfrac{b}{2a} = \dfrac{-1.93}{2(-0.072)} \approx 13.4$

$2000 + 13.4 = 2013.4$

According to the model, the methane emissions in the U.S. will reach a maximum in the year 2013.

d. $f(13) = -0.072(13)^2 + 1.93(13) + 173.9$

$= 186.822$

According to the model, the maximum methane emissions in the U.S. will be about 186.82 million metric tons.

80. The graphs are the same.

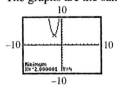

82. The graphs are the same.

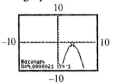

Chapter 11 Vocabulary Check

1. The <u>discriminant</u> helps us find the number and type of solutions of a quadratic equation.

2. If $a^2 = b$, then $a = \pm\sqrt{b}$.

3. The graph of $f(x) = ax^2 + bx + c$ where a is not 0 is a parabola whose vertex has x-value of $\dfrac{-b}{2a}$.

4. A <u>quadratic inequality</u> is an inequality that can be written so that one side is a quadratic expression and the other side is 0.

5. The process of writing a quadratic equation so that one side is a perfect square trinomial is called <u>completing the square</u>.

6. The graph of $f(x) = x^2 + k$ has vertex <u>(0, k)</u>.

7. The graph of $f(x) = (x - h)^2$ has vertex <u>(h, 0)</u>.

8. The graph of $f(x) = (x - h)^2 + k$ has vertex <u>(h, k)</u>.

9. The formula $x = \dfrac{-b \pm \sqrt{b^2 - 4ac}}{2a}$ is called the <u>quadratic formula</u>.

10. A <u>quadratic</u> equation is one that can be written in the form $ax^2 + bx + c = 0$ where a, b, and c are real numbers and a is not 0.

Chapter 11 Review

1. $x^2 - 15x + 14 = 0$

$(x - 14)(x - 1) = 0$

$x - 14 = 0$ or $x - 1 = 0$

$x = 14$ or $\quad x = 1$

The solutions are 1 and 14.

2.
$$7a^2 = 29a + 30$$
$$7a^2 - 29a - 30 = 0$$
$$(7a + 6)(a - 5) = 0$$
$$7a + 6 = 0 \quad \text{or} \quad a - 5 = 0$$
$$7a = -6 \quad \text{or} \quad a = 5$$
$$a = -\frac{6}{7}$$

The solutions are $-\frac{6}{7}$ and 5.

3. $4m^2 = 196$
$$m^2 = 49$$
$$m = \pm\sqrt{49}$$
$$m = \pm 7$$
The solutions are –7 and 7.

4. $(5x - 2)^2 = 2$
$$5x - 2 = \pm\sqrt{2}$$
$$5x = 2 \pm \sqrt{2}$$
$$x = \frac{2 \pm \sqrt{2}}{5}$$

The solutions are $\frac{2 + \sqrt{2}}{5}$ and $\frac{2 - \sqrt{2}}{5}$.

5.
$$z^2 + 3z + 1 = 0$$
$$z^2 + 3z = -1$$
$$z^2 + 3z + \left(\frac{3}{2}\right)^2 = -1 + \frac{9}{4}$$
$$\left(z + \frac{3}{2}\right)^2 = \frac{5}{4}$$
$$z + \frac{3}{2} = \pm\sqrt{\frac{5}{4}}$$
$$z + \frac{3}{2} = \pm\frac{\sqrt{5}}{2}$$
$$z = -\frac{3}{2} \pm \frac{\sqrt{5}}{2} = \frac{-3 \pm \sqrt{5}}{2}$$

The solutions are $\frac{-3 + \sqrt{5}}{2}$ and $\frac{-3 - \sqrt{5}}{2}$.

6.
$$(2x + 1)^2 = x$$
$$4x^2 + 4x + 1 = x$$
$$4x^2 + 3x = -1$$
$$x^2 + \frac{3}{4}x = -\frac{1}{4}$$
$$x^2 + \frac{3}{4}x + \left(\frac{\frac{3}{4}}{2}\right)^2 = -\frac{1}{4} + \frac{9}{64}$$
$$\left(x + \frac{3}{8}\right)^2 = -\frac{7}{64}$$
$$x + \frac{3}{8} = \pm\sqrt{-\frac{7}{64}}$$
$$x + \frac{3}{8} = \pm\frac{i\sqrt{7}}{8}$$
$$x = -\frac{3}{8} \pm \frac{i\sqrt{7}}{8} = \frac{-3 \pm i\sqrt{7}}{8}$$

The solutions are $\frac{-3 + i\sqrt{7}}{8}$ and $\frac{-3 - i\sqrt{7}}{8}$.

7.
$$A = P(1 + r)^2$$
$$2717 = 2500(1 + r)^2$$
$$\frac{2717}{2500} = (1 + r)^2$$
$$(1 + r)^2 = 1.0868$$
$$1 + r = \pm\sqrt{1.0868}$$
$$1 + r = \pm 1.0425$$
$$r = -1 \pm 1.0425$$
$$= 0.0425 \text{ or } -2.0425 \text{ (disregard)}$$
The interest rate is 4.25%.

8. Let x = distance traveled.
$$a^2 + b^2 = c^2$$
$$x^2 + x^2 = (150)^2$$
$$2x^2 = 22{,}500$$
$$x^2 = 11{,}250$$
$$x = \pm 75\sqrt{2} \approx \pm 106.1$$
Disregard the negative. The ships each traveled $75\sqrt{2} \approx 106.1$ miles.

9. Two complex but not real solutions exist.

10. Two real solutions exist.

11. Two real solutions exist.

12. One real solution exists.

13. $x^2 - 16x + 64 = 0$

$a = 1, b = -16, c = 64$

$$x = \frac{16 \pm \sqrt{(-16)^2 - 4(1)(64)}}{2(1)}$$

$$= \frac{16 \pm \sqrt{256 - 256}}{2}$$

$$= \frac{16 \pm \sqrt{0}}{2}$$

$$= 8$$

The solution is 8.

14. $x^2 + 5x = 0$

$a = 1, b = 5, c = 0$

$$x = \frac{-5 \pm \sqrt{(5)^2 - 4(1)(0)}}{2(1)}$$

$$= \frac{-5 \pm \sqrt{25}}{2}$$

$$= \frac{-5 \pm 5}{2}$$

$$= 0 \text{ or } -5$$

The solutions are −5 and 0.

15. $2x^2 + 3x = 5$

$2x^2 + 3x - 5 = 0$

$a = 2, b = 3, c = -5$

$$x = \frac{-3 \pm \sqrt{(3)^2 - 4(2)(-5)}}{2(2)}$$

$$= \frac{-3 \pm \sqrt{49}}{4}$$

$$= \frac{-3 \pm 7}{4}$$

$$= 1 \text{ or } -\frac{5}{2}$$

The solutions are $-\dfrac{5}{2}$ and 1.

16. $9a^2 + 4 = 2a$

$9a^2 - 2a + 4 = 0$

$$a = \frac{2 \pm \sqrt{(-2)^2 - 4(9)(4)}}{2(9)}$$

$$= \frac{2 \pm \sqrt{-140}}{18}$$

$$= \frac{2 \pm i\sqrt{4 \cdot 35}}{18}$$

$$= \frac{2 \pm 2i\sqrt{35}}{18}$$

$$= \frac{1 \pm i\sqrt{35}}{9}$$

The solutions are $\dfrac{1 + i\sqrt{35}}{9}$ and $\dfrac{1 - i\sqrt{35}}{9}$.

17. $6x^2 + 7 = 5x$

$6x^2 - 5x + 7 = 0$

$a = 6, b = -5, c = 7$

$$x = \frac{5 \pm \sqrt{(-5)^2 - 4(6)(7)}}{2(6)}$$

$$= \frac{5 \pm \sqrt{25 - 168}}{12}$$

$$= \frac{5 \pm \sqrt{-143}}{12}$$

$$= \frac{5 \pm i\sqrt{143}}{12}$$

The solutions are $\dfrac{5 + i\sqrt{143}}{12}$ and $\dfrac{5 - i\sqrt{143}}{12}$.

18.
$$(2x-3)^2 = x$$
$$4x^2 - 12x + 9 - x = 0$$
$$4x^2 - 13x + 9 = 0$$
$$a = 4, b = -13, c = 9$$

$$x = \frac{13 \pm \sqrt{(-13)^2 - 4(4)(9)}}{2(4)}$$
$$= \frac{13 \pm \sqrt{169 - 144}}{8}$$
$$= \frac{13 \pm \sqrt{25}}{8}$$
$$= \frac{13 \pm 5}{8}$$
$$= \frac{9}{4} \text{ or } 1$$

The solutions are 1 and $\frac{9}{4}$.

19. $d(t) = -16t^2 + 30t + 6$

a. $d(1) = -16(1)^2 + 30(1) + 6$
$$= -16 + 30 + 6$$
$$= 20 \text{ feet}$$

b. $-16t^2 + 30t + 6 = 0$
$$8t^2 - 15t - 3 = 0$$
$$a = 8, b = -15, c = -3$$
$$t = \frac{15 \pm \sqrt{(-15)^2 - 4(8)(-3)}}{2(8)}$$
$$= \frac{15 \pm \sqrt{225 + 96}}{16}$$
$$= \frac{15 \pm \sqrt{321}}{16}$$

Disregarding the negative, we have
$$t = \frac{15 + \sqrt{321}}{16} \text{ seconds}$$
$$\approx 2.1 \text{ seconds.}$$

20. Let x = length of the legs. Then
$x + 6$ = length of the hypotenuse.
$$x^2 + x^2 = (x+6)^2$$
$$2x^2 = x^2 + 12x + 36$$
$$x^2 - 12x - 36 = 0$$
$$a = 1, b = -12, c = -36$$

$$x = \frac{12 \pm \sqrt{(-12)^2 - 4(1)(-36)}}{2(1)}$$
$$= \frac{12 \pm \sqrt{144 + 144}}{2}$$
$$= \frac{12 \pm \sqrt{144 \cdot 2}}{2}$$
$$= \frac{12 \pm 12\sqrt{2}}{2}$$
$$= 6 \pm 6\sqrt{2}$$

Disregard the negative. The length of each leg is
$\left(6 + 6\sqrt{2}\right)$ cm.

21.
$$x^3 = 27$$
$$x^3 - 27 = 0$$
$$(x-3)(x^2 + 3x + 9) = 0$$
$$x - 3 = 0 \text{ or } x^2 + 3x + 9 = 0$$
$$x = 3 \qquad a = 1, b = 3, c = 9$$

$$x = \frac{-3 \pm \sqrt{(3)^2 - 4(1)(9)}}{2(1)}$$
$$= \frac{-3 \pm \sqrt{9 - 36}}{2}$$
$$= \frac{-3 \pm \sqrt{-27}}{2}$$
$$= \frac{-3 \pm 3i\sqrt{3}}{2}$$

The solutions are 3, $\dfrac{-3 + 3i\sqrt{3}}{2}$, and $\dfrac{-3 - 3i\sqrt{3}}{2}$.

22.
$$y^3 = -64$$
$$y^3 + 64 = 0$$
$$(y+4)(y^2 - 4y + 16) = 0$$
$$y + 4 = 0 \text{ or } y^2 - 4y + 16 = 0$$
$$y = -4 \qquad a = 1, b = -4, c = 16$$

$$y = \frac{4 \pm \sqrt{(-4)^2 - 4(1)(16)}}{2(1)}$$
$$= \frac{4 \pm \sqrt{16 - 64}}{2}$$
$$= \frac{4 \pm \sqrt{-48}}{2}$$
$$= \frac{4 \pm 4i\sqrt{3}}{2}$$
$$= 2 \pm 2i\sqrt{3}$$

The solutions are –4, $2 + 2i\sqrt{3}$, and $2 - 2i\sqrt{3}$.

23.

$$\frac{5}{x}+\frac{6}{x-2}=3$$

$$x(x-2)\left(\frac{5}{x}+\frac{6}{x-2}\right)=3x(x-2)$$

$$5(x-2)+6x=3x^2-6x$$

$$5x-10+6x=3x^2-6x$$

$$0=3x^2-17x+10$$

$$0=(3x-2)(x-5)$$

$$3x-2=0 \text{ or } x-5=0$$

$$x=\frac{2}{3} \text{ or } \quad x=5$$

The solutions are $\frac{2}{3}$ and 5.

24.

$$x^4-21x^2-100=0$$

$$(x^2-25)(x^2+4)=0$$

$$(x+5)(x-5)(x^2+4)=0$$

$$x+5=0 \quad \text{or } x-5=0 \text{ or } x^2+4=0$$

$$x=-5 \text{ or } \quad x=5 \text{ or } \quad x^2=-4$$

$$x=\pm 2i$$

The solutions are -5, 5 $-2i$, and $2i$.

25. $x^{2/3}-6x^{1/3}+5=0$

Let $y=x^{1/3}$. Then $y^2=x^{2/3}$ and

$$y^2-6y+5=0$$

$$(y-5)(y-1)=0$$

$$y-5=0 \quad \text{or } y-1=0$$

$$y=5 \quad \text{or} \quad y=1$$

$$x^{1/3}=5 \quad \text{or} \quad x^{1/3}=1$$

$$x=125 \text{ or} \quad x=1$$

The solutions are 1 and 125.

26. $5(x+3)^2-19(x+3)=4$

$$5(x+3)^2-19(x+3)-4=0$$

Let $y=x+3$. Then $y^2=(x+3)^2$ and

$$5y^2-19y-4=0$$

$$(5y+1)(y-4)=0$$

$$5y+1=0 \quad \text{or } y-4=0$$

$$y=-\frac{1}{5} \quad \text{or} \quad y=4$$

$$x+3=-\frac{1}{5} \quad \text{or } x+3=4$$

$$x=-\frac{16}{5} \quad \text{or} \quad x=1$$

The solutions are $-\frac{16}{5}$ and 1.

27.

$$a^6-a^2=a^4-1$$

$$a^6-a^4-a^2+1=0$$

$$a^4(a^2-1)-1(a^2-1)=0$$

$$(a^2-1)(a^4-1)=0$$

$$(a+1)(a-1)(a^2+1)(a^2-1)=0$$

$$(a+1)(a-1)(a^2+1)(a+1)(a-1)=0$$

$$(a+1)^2(a-1)^2(a^2+1)=0$$

$$(a+1)^2=0 \text{ or } (a-1)^2=0 \text{ or } a^2+1=0$$

$$a+1=0 \text{ or} \quad a-1=0 \text{ or} \quad a^2=-1$$

$$a=-1 \text{ or} \quad a=1 \text{ or} \quad a=\pm i$$

The solutions are -1, 1, $-i$, and i.

28. $y^{-2}+y^{-1}=20$

$$\frac{1}{y^2}+\frac{1}{y}=20$$

$$1+y=20y^2$$

$$0=20y^2-y-1$$

$$0=(5y+1)(4y-1)$$

$$5y+1=0 \quad \text{or } 4y-1=0$$

$$y=-\frac{1}{5} \text{ or} \quad y=\frac{1}{4}$$

The solutions are $-\frac{1}{5}$ and $\frac{1}{4}$.

29. Let x = time for Jerome alone. Then $x-1$ = time for Tim alone.

$$\frac{1}{x}+\frac{1}{x-1}=\frac{1}{5}$$

$$5(x-1)+5x=x(x-1)$$

$$5x-5+5x=x^2-x$$

$$0=x^2-11x+5$$

$a = 1, b = -11, c = 5$

$$x = \frac{11 \pm \sqrt{(-11)^2 - 4(1)(5)}}{2(1)}$$

$$= \frac{11 \pm \sqrt{101}}{2}$$

≈ 0.475 (disregard) or 10.525

Jerome: 10.5 hours

Tim: 9.5 hours

30. Let x = the number; then

$\dfrac{1}{x}$ = the reciprocal of the number.

$$x - \frac{1}{x} = -\frac{24}{5}$$

$$5x\left(x - \frac{1}{x}\right) = 5x\left(-\frac{24}{5}\right)$$

$$5x^2 - 5 = -24x$$

$$5x^2 + 24x - 5 = 0$$

$$(5x - 1)(x + 5) = 0$$

$$5x - 1 = 0 \text{ or } x + 5 = 0$$

$$x = \frac{1}{5} \text{ or } \quad x = -5$$

Disregard the positive value as extraneous.
The number is –5.

31. $2x^2 - 50 \le 0$

$$2(x^2 - 25) \le 0$$

$$2(x + 5)(x - 5) \le 0$$

$$x + 5 = 0 \text{ or } x - 5 = 0$$

$$x = -5 \text{ or } \quad x = 5$$

Region	Test Point	$2(x + 5)(x - 5) \le 0$ Result
A: $(-\infty, -5]$	–6	$2(-1)(-11) \le 0$ False
B: $[-5, 5]$	0	$2(5)(-5) \le 0$ True
C: $[5, \infty)$	6	$2(11)(1) \le 0$ False

Solution: $[-5, 5]$

32. $\dfrac{1}{4}x^2 < \dfrac{1}{16}$

$$x^2 < \frac{1}{4}$$

$$x^2 - \frac{1}{4} < 0$$

$$\left(x + \frac{1}{2}\right)\left(x - \frac{1}{2}\right) < 0$$

$$x + \frac{1}{2} = 0 \quad \text{or } x - \frac{1}{2} = 0$$

$$x = -\frac{1}{2} \text{ or } \quad x = \frac{1}{2}$$

Region	Test Point	$\left(x + \frac{1}{2}\right)\left(x - \frac{1}{2}\right) < 0$ Result
A: $\left(-\infty, -\frac{1}{2}\right)$	–1	$\left(-\frac{1}{2}\right)\left(-\frac{3}{2}\right) < 0$ False
B: $\left(-\frac{1}{2}, \frac{1}{2}\right)$	0	$\left(\frac{1}{2}\right)\left(-\frac{1}{2}\right) < 0$ True
C: $\left(\frac{1}{2}, \infty\right)$	1	$\left(\frac{3}{2}\right)\left(\frac{1}{2}\right) < 0$ False

Solution: $\left(-\dfrac{1}{2}, \dfrac{1}{2}\right)$

33. $\dfrac{x-5}{x-6} < 0$

$x - 5 = 0$ or $x - 6 = 0$

$x = 5$ or $\quad x = 6$

Region	Test Point	$\dfrac{x-5}{x-6} < 0$ Result
A: $(-\infty, 5)$	0	$\dfrac{-5}{-6} < 0$ False
B: $(5, 6)$	$\dfrac{11}{2}$	$\dfrac{\frac{1}{2}}{-\frac{1}{2}} < 0$ True
C: $(6, \infty)$	7	$\dfrac{2}{1} < 0$ False

Solution: $(5, 6)$

34. $\qquad (x^2 - 16)(x^2 - 1) > 0$

$(x + 4)(x - 4)(x + 1)(x - 1) > 0$

$x + 4 = 0 \quad$ or $\; x - 4 = 0 \;$ or $\; x + 1 = 0 \quad$ or $\; x - 1 = 0$

$\quad x = -4$ or $\quad x = 4$ or $\quad x = -1$ or $\quad x = 1$

Region	Test Point	$(x + 4)(x - 4)(x + 1)(x - 1) > 0$ Result
A: $(-\infty, -4)$	-5	$(-1)(-9)(-4)(-6) > 0$ True
B: $(-4, -1)$	-2	$(2)(-6)(-1)(-3) > 0$ False
C: $(-1, 1)$	0	$(4)(-4)(1)(-1) > 0$ True
D: $(1, 4)$	2	$(6)(-2)(3)(1) > 0$ False
E: $(4, \infty)$	5	$(9)(1)(6)(4) > 0$ True

Solution: $(-\infty, -4) \cup (-1, 1) \cup (4, \infty)$

35. $\dfrac{(4x+3)(x-5)}{x(x+6)} > 0$

$4x+3 = 0,\ x-5 = 0,\ x = 0,\ \text{or } x+6 = 0$

$x = -\dfrac{3}{4},\ x = 5,\ x = 0,\ \text{or } x = -6$

Region	Test Point	$\dfrac{(4x+3)(x-5)}{x(x+6)} > 0$ Result
$A: (-\infty, -6)$	-7	$\dfrac{(-25)(-12)}{-7(-1)} > 0$ True
$B: \left(-6, -\dfrac{3}{4}\right)$	-3	$\dfrac{(-9)(-8)}{-3(3)} > 0$ False
$C: \left(-\dfrac{3}{4}, 0\right)$	$-\dfrac{1}{2}$	$\dfrac{(1)\left(-\dfrac{11}{2}\right)}{-\dfrac{1}{2}\left(\dfrac{11}{2}\right)} > 0$ True
$D: (0, 5)$	1	$\dfrac{(7)(-4)}{1(7)} > 0$ False
$E: (5, \infty)$	6	$\dfrac{(27)(1)}{6(12)} > 0$ True

Solution: $(-\infty, -6) \cup \left(-\dfrac{3}{4}, 0\right) \cup (5, \infty)$

36. $(x+5)(x-6)(x+2) \le 0$

$x+5 = 0\ \text{ or } x-6 = 0\ \text{ or } x+2 = 0$

$x = -5\ \text{ or }\quad x = 6\ \text{ or }\quad x = -2$

Region	Test Point	$(x+5)(x-6)(x+2) \le 0$ Result
$A: (-\infty, -5]$	-6	$(-1)(-12)(-4) \le 0$ True
$B: [-5, -2]$	-3	$(2)(-9)(-1) \le 0$ False
$C: [-2, 6]$	0	$(5)(-6)(2) \le 0$ True
$D: [6, \infty)$	7	$(12)(1)(9) \le 0$ False

Solution: $(-\infty, -5] \cup [-2, 6]$

37. $x^3 + 3x^2 - 25x - 75 > 0$

$x^2(x+3) - 25(x+3) > 0$

$(x+3)(x^2 - 25) > 0$

$(x+3)(x+5)(x-5) > 0$

$x+3 = 0\ \text{ or } x+5 = 0\ \text{ or } x-5 = 0$

$x = -3\ \text{ or }\quad x = -5\ \text{ or }\quad x = 5$

Region	Test Point	$(x+3)(x+5)(x-5) > 0$ Result
$A: (-\infty, -5)$	-6	$(-3)(-1)(-11) > 0$ False
$B: (-5, -3)$	-4	$(-1)(1)(-9) > 0$ True
$C: (-3, 5)$	0	$(3)(5)(-5) > 0$ False
$D: (5, \infty)$	6	$(9)(11)(1) > 0$ True

Solution: $(-5, -3) \cup (5, \infty)$

38. $\dfrac{x^2 + 4}{3x} \le 1$

The denominator equals 0 when $3x = 0$, or $x = 0$.

$$\dfrac{x^2 + 4}{3x} = 1$$

$$x^2 + 4 = 3x$$

$$x^2 - 3x + 4 = 0$$

$$x = \frac{3 \pm \sqrt{(-3)^2 - 4(1)(4)}}{2(1)} = \frac{3 \pm \sqrt{-7}}{2}$$

which yields non-real solutions.

Region	Test Point	$\frac{x^2 + 4}{3x} \le 1$ Result
$A: (-\infty, 0)$	-1	$\frac{5}{-3} \le 1$ True
$B: (0, \infty)$	1	$\frac{5}{3} \le 1$ False

Solution: $(\infty, 0)$

39. $\frac{(5x + 6)(x - 3)}{x(6x - 5)} < 0$

$x = -\frac{6}{5}$ or $x = 3$ or $x = 0$ or $x = \frac{5}{6}$

Region	Test Point	$\frac{(5x + 6)(x - 3)}{x(6x - 5)} < 0$ Result
$A: \left(-\infty, -\frac{6}{5}\right)$	-2	$\frac{(-4)(-5)}{-2(-17)} < 0$ False
$B: \left(-\frac{6}{5}, 0\right)$	-1	$\frac{(1)(-4)}{-1(-11)} < 0$ True
$C: \left(0, \frac{5}{6}\right)$	$\frac{1}{2}$	$\frac{\left(\frac{17}{2}\right)\left(-\frac{5}{2}\right)}{\frac{1}{2}(-2)} < 0$ False
$D: \left(\frac{5}{6}, 3\right)$	2	$\frac{(16)(-1)}{2(7)} < 0$ True
$E: (3, \infty)$	4	$\frac{(26)(1)}{4(19)} < 0$ False

Solution: $\left(-\frac{6}{5}, 0\right) \cup \left(\frac{5}{6}, 3\right)$

40. $\frac{3}{x - 2} > 2$

The denominator is equal to 0 when $x - 2 = 0$, or $x = 2$.

$$\frac{3}{x - 2} = 2$$
$$3 = 2(x - 2)$$
$$3 = 2x - 4$$
$$7 = 2x$$
$$\frac{7}{2} = x$$

Region	Test Point	$\frac{3}{x - 2} > 2$ Result
$A: (-\infty, 2)$	0	$\frac{3}{-2} > 2$ False
$B: \left(2, \frac{7}{2}\right)$	3	$\frac{3}{1} > 2$ True
$C: \left(\frac{7}{2}, \infty\right)$	5	$\frac{3}{3} > 2$ False

Solution: $\left(2, \frac{7}{2}\right)$

41. $f(x) = x^2 - 4$

Vertex: $(0, -4)$

Axis of symmetry: $x = 0$

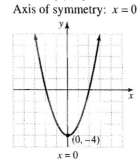

42. $g(x) = x^2 + 7$

Vertex: (0, 7)

Axis of symmetry: $x = 0$

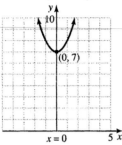

43. $H(x) = 2x^2$

Vertex: (0, 0)

Axis of symmetry: $x = 0$

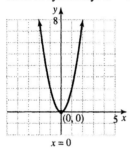

44. $h(x) = -\frac{1}{3}x^2$

Vertex: (0, 0)

Axis of symmetry: $x = 0$

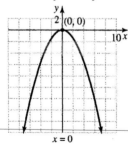

45. $F(x) = (x-1)^2$

Vertex: (1, 0)

Axis of symmetry: $x = 1$

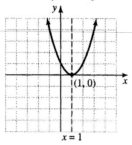

46. $G(x) = (x+5)^2$

Vertex: (−5, 0)

Axis of symmetry: $x = -5$

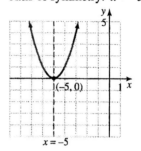

47. $f(x) = (x-4)^2 - 2$

Vertex: (4, −2)

Axis of symmetry: $x = 4$

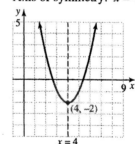

48. $f(x) = -3(x-1)^2 + 1$

Vertex: (1, 1)

Axis of symmetry: $x = 1$

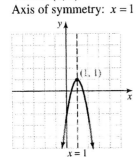

49. $f(x) = x^2 + 10x + 25$

$x = -\dfrac{b}{2a} = \dfrac{-10}{2(1)} = -5$

$f(-5) = (-5)^2 + 10(-5) + 25 = 0$

Vertex: (−5, 0)

$x^2 + 10x + 25 = 0$

$(x+5)^2 = 0$

$x + 5 = 0$

$x = -5$

x-intercept: (−5, 0)

$f(0) = 25$ so the y-intercept is (0, 25).

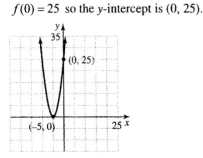

50. $f(x) = -x^2 + 6x - 9$

$x = -\dfrac{b}{2a} = \dfrac{-6}{2(-1)} = 3$

$f(3) = -(3)^2 + 6(3) - 9 = 0$

Vertex: (3, 0)

x-intercept: (3, 0)

$f(0) = -9$

y-intercept: (0, −9)

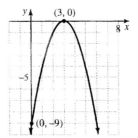

51. $f(x) = 4x^2 - 1$

$x = -\dfrac{b}{2a} = \dfrac{-0}{2(4)} = 0$

$f(0) = 4(0)^2 - 1 = -1$

Vertex: (0, −1)

$4x^2 - 1 = 0$

$(2x+1)(2x-1) = 0$

$x = -\dfrac{1}{2}$ or $x = \dfrac{1}{2}$

x-intercepts: $\left(-\dfrac{1}{2}, 0\right), \left(\dfrac{1}{2}, 0\right)$

$f(0) = -1$

y-intercept: (0, −1)

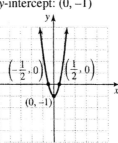

52. $f(x) = -5x^2 + 5$

$x = -\dfrac{b}{2a} = \dfrac{-0}{2(-5)} = 0$

$f(0) = -5(0)^2 + 5 = 5$

Vertex: (0, 5)

$-5x^2 + 5 = 0$

$-5x^2 = -5$

$x^2 = 1$

$x = \pm 1$

x-intercepts: (−1, 0), (1, 0)

$f(0) = 5$

y-intercept: (0, 5)

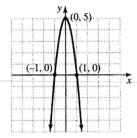

53. $f(x) = -3x^2 - 5x + 4$

$$x = -\frac{b}{2a} = \frac{-(-5)}{2(-3)} = -\frac{5}{6}$$

$$f\left(-\frac{5}{6}\right) = -3\left(-\frac{5}{6}\right)^2 - 5\left(-\frac{5}{6}\right) + 4 = \frac{73}{12}$$

Vertex: $\left(-\dfrac{5}{6}, \dfrac{73}{12}\right)$

The graph opens downward ($a = -3 < 0$).

$f(0) = 4 \Rightarrow$ y-intercept: $(0, 4)$

$$-3x^2 - 5x + 4 = 0$$

$$x = \frac{5 \pm \sqrt{(-5)^2 - 4(-3)(4)}}{2(-3)}$$

$$= \frac{5 \pm \sqrt{73}}{-6}$$

$$\approx -2.2573 \text{ or } 0.5907$$

x-intercepts: $(-2.3, 0)$, $(0.6, 0)$

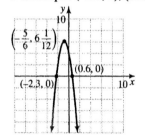

54. $h(t) = -16t^2 + 120t + 300$

a. $350 = -16t^2 + 120t + 300$

$$16t^2 - 120t + 50 = 0$$

$$8t^2 - 60t + 25 = 0$$

$$a = 8, b = -60, c = 25$$

$$t = \frac{60 \pm \sqrt{(-60)^2 - 4(8)(25)}}{2(8)}$$

$$= \frac{60 \pm \sqrt{2800}}{16}$$

$$\approx 0.4 \text{ second and } 7.1 \text{ seconds}$$

b. The object will be at 350 feet on the way up and on the way down.

55. Let $x =$ one number; then

$420 - x =$ the other number.

Let $f(x)$ represent their product.

$$f(x) = x(420 - x)$$

$$= 420x - x^2$$

$$= -x^2 + 420x$$

$$x = -\frac{b}{2a} = \frac{-420}{2(-1)} = 210;$$

$$420 - x = 420 - 210 = 210$$

Therefore, the numbers are both 210.

56. $y = a(x - h)^2 + k$

vertex $(-3, 7)$ gives $y = a(x + 3)^2 + 7$.

Passing through the origin gives

$$0 = a(0 + 3)^2 + 7$$

$$-7 = 9a$$

$$-\frac{7}{9} = a$$

Thus, $y = -\dfrac{7}{9}(x + 3)^2 + 7$.

57. $x^2 - x - 30 = 0$

$$(x + 5)(x - 6) = 0$$

$$x + 5 = 0 \quad \text{or} \quad x - 6 = 0$$

$$x = -5 \text{ or} \qquad x = 6$$

The solutions are -5 and 6.

58.
$$10x^2 = 3x + 4$$
$$10x^2 - 3x - 4 = 0$$
$$(5x - 4)(2x + 1) = 0$$
$$5x - 4 = 0 \text{ or } 2x + 1 = 0$$
$$5x = 4 \text{ or } 2x = -1$$
$$x = \frac{4}{5} \text{ or } x = -\frac{1}{2}$$

The solutions are $-\dfrac{1}{2}$ and $\dfrac{4}{5}$.

59.
$$9y^2 = 36$$
$$y^2 = 4$$
$$y = \pm\sqrt{4}$$
$$y = \pm 2$$

The solutions are -2 and 2.

60.
$$(9n + 1)^2 = 9$$
$$9n + 1 = \pm\sqrt{9}$$
$$9n + 1 = \pm 3$$
$$9n = -1 \pm 3$$
$$n = \frac{-1 \pm 3}{9} = \frac{2}{9}, -\frac{4}{9}$$

The solutions are $-\dfrac{4}{9}$ and $\dfrac{2}{9}$.

61.
$$x^2 + x + 7 = 0$$
$$x^2 + x = -7$$
$$x^2 + x + \left(\frac{1}{2}\right)^2 = -7 + \frac{1}{4}$$
$$\left(x + \frac{1}{2}\right)^2 = -\frac{27}{4}$$
$$x + \frac{1}{2} = \pm\sqrt{-\frac{27}{4}}$$
$$x + \frac{1}{2} = \pm\frac{i\sqrt{9 \cdot 3}}{2}$$
$$x + \frac{1}{2} = \pm\frac{3i\sqrt{3}}{2}$$
$$x = -\frac{1}{2} \pm \frac{3i\sqrt{3}}{2} = \frac{-1 \pm 3i\sqrt{3}}{2}$$

The solutions are $\dfrac{-1 + 3i\sqrt{3}}{2}$ and $\dfrac{-1 - 3i\sqrt{3}}{2}$.

62.
$$(3x - 4)^2 = 10x$$
$$9x^2 - 24x + 16 = 10x$$
$$9x^2 - 34x = -16$$
$$x^2 - \frac{34}{9}x = -\frac{16}{9}$$
$$x^2 - \frac{34}{9}x + \left(\frac{-\frac{34}{9}}{2}\right)^2 = -\frac{16}{9} + \frac{289}{81}$$
$$\left(x - \frac{17}{9}\right)^2 = \frac{145}{81}$$
$$x - \frac{17}{9} = \pm\sqrt{\frac{145}{81}}$$
$$x - \frac{17}{9} = \pm\frac{\sqrt{145}}{9}$$
$$x = \frac{17 \pm \sqrt{145}}{9}$$

The solutions are $\dfrac{17 + \sqrt{145}}{9}$ and $\dfrac{17 - \sqrt{145}}{9}$.

63.
$$x^2 + 11 = 0$$
$$a = 1, \, b = 0, \, c = 11$$
$$x = \frac{0 \pm \sqrt{(0)^2 - 4(1)(11)}}{2(1)}$$
$$= \frac{\pm\sqrt{-44}}{2}$$
$$= \frac{\pm 2i\sqrt{11}}{2}$$
$$= \pm i\sqrt{11}$$

The solutions are $-i\sqrt{11}$ and $i\sqrt{11}$.

64.
$$(5a - 2)^2 - a = 0$$
$$25a^2 - 20a + 4 - a = 0$$
$$25a^2 - 21a + 4 = 0$$
$$a = \frac{21 \pm \sqrt{(-21)^2 - 4(25)(4)}}{2(25)}$$
$$= \frac{21 \pm \sqrt{441 - 400}}{50}$$
$$= \frac{21 \pm \sqrt{41}}{50}$$

The solutions are $\dfrac{21 + \sqrt{41}}{50}$ and $\dfrac{21 - \sqrt{41}}{50}$.

65. $\dfrac{7}{8} = \dfrac{8}{x^2}$

$7x^2 = 64$

$x^2 = \dfrac{64}{7}$

$x = \pm\sqrt{\dfrac{64}{7}}$

$x = \pm\dfrac{8}{\sqrt{7}} = \pm\dfrac{8\cdot\sqrt{7}}{\sqrt{7}\cdot\sqrt{7}} = \pm\dfrac{8\sqrt{7}}{7}$

The solutions are $-\dfrac{8\sqrt{7}}{7}$ and $\dfrac{8\sqrt{7}}{7}$.

66. $x^{2/3} - 6x^{1/3} = -8$

$x^{2/3} - 6x^{1/3} + 8 = 0$

Let $y = x^{1/3}$. Then $y^2 = x^{2/3}$ and

$y^2 - 6y + 8 = 0$

$(y-4)(y-2) = 0$

$y - 4 = 0$ or $y - 2 = 0$

$y = 4$ or $y = 2$

$x^{1/3} = 4$ or $x^{1/3} = 2$

$x = 64$ or $x = 8$

The solutions are 8 and 64.

67. $(2x-3)(4x+5) \ge 0$

$2x - 3 = 0$ or $4x + 5 = 0$

$x = \dfrac{3}{2}$ or $x = -\dfrac{5}{4}$

Region	Test Point	$(2x-3)(4x+5) \ge 0$ Result
$A:\left(-\infty, -\dfrac{5}{4}\right]$	-2	$(-7)(-3) \ge 0$ True
$B:\left[-\dfrac{5}{4}, \dfrac{3}{2}\right]$	0	$(-3)(5) \ge 0$ False
$C:\left[\dfrac{3}{2}, \infty\right)$	3	$(3)(17) \ge 0$ True

Solution: $\left(-\infty, -\dfrac{5}{4}\right] \cup \left[\dfrac{3}{2}, \infty\right)$

68. $\dfrac{x(x+5)}{4x-3} \ge 0$

$x = 0$ or $x + 5 = 0$ or $4x - 3 = 0$

             $x = -5$ or $x = \dfrac{3}{4}$

Region	Test Point	$\dfrac{x(x+5)}{4x-3} \ge 0$ Result
$A: (-\infty, -5]$	-6	$\dfrac{-6(-1)}{-27} \ge 0$ False
$B: [-5, 0]$	-1	$\dfrac{-1(4)}{-7} \ge 0$ True
$C: \left[0, \dfrac{3}{4}\right)$	$\dfrac{1}{2}$	$\dfrac{\frac{1}{2}\left(\frac{11}{2}\right)}{-1} \ge 0$ False
$D: \left(\dfrac{3}{4}, \infty\right)$	1	$\dfrac{1(6)}{1} \ge 0$ True

Solution: $[-5, 0] \cup \left(\dfrac{3}{4}, \infty\right)$

69. $\dfrac{3}{x-2} > 2$

The denominator is equal to 0 when $x - 2 = 0$, or $x = 2$.

$\dfrac{3}{x-2} = 2$

$3 = 2(x-2)$

$3 = 2x - 4$

$7 = 2x$

$\dfrac{7}{2} = x$

Region	Test Point	$\dfrac{3}{x-2} > 2$ Result
$A: (-\infty, 2)$	0	$\dfrac{3}{-2} > 2$ False
$B: \left(2, \dfrac{7}{2}\right)$	3	$\dfrac{3}{1} > 2$ True
$C: \left(\dfrac{7}{2}, \infty\right)$	5	$\dfrac{3}{3} > 2$ False

Solution: $\left(2, \dfrac{7}{2}\right)$

70. $y = 6.46x^2 + 1236.5x + 7289$

    a. $x = 2000 - 1980 = 20$

$$y = 6.46(20)^2 + 1236.5(20) + 7289$$
$$= 34{,}603 \text{ thousand}$$

The passenger traffic was approximately 34,603,000.

    b. Let $y = 60{,}000$.

$$60{,}000 = 6.46x^2 + 1236.5x + 7289$$
$$0 = 6.46x^2 + 1236.5x - 52{,}711$$
$$x = \frac{-1236.5 \pm \sqrt{1236.5^2 - 4(6.46)(-52{,}711)}}{2(6.46)}$$

Choosing the positive root, $x \approx 36$, we see that there will be 60,000,000 passengers in $1980 + 36 = 2016$.

Chapter 11 Test

1.
$$5x^2 - 2x = 7$$
$$5x^2 - 2x - 7 = 0$$
$$(5x - 7)(x + 1) = 0$$
$$5x - 7 = 0 \quad \text{or} \quad x + 1 = 0$$
$$x = \frac{7}{5} \quad \text{or} \quad x = -1$$

The solutions are -1 and $\dfrac{7}{5}$.

2.
$$(x + 1)^2 = 10$$
$$x + 1 = \pm\sqrt{10}$$
$$x = -1 \pm \sqrt{10}$$

The solutions are $-1 + \sqrt{10}$ and $-1 - \sqrt{10}$.

3. $m^2 - m + 8 = 0$

$a = 1, b = -1, c = 8$

$$m = \frac{1 \pm \sqrt{(-1)^2 - 4(1)(8)}}{2(1)}$$
$$= \frac{1 \pm \sqrt{1 - 32}}{2}$$
$$= \frac{1 \pm \sqrt{-31}}{2}$$
$$= \frac{1 \pm i\sqrt{31}}{2}$$

The solutions are $\dfrac{1 + i\sqrt{31}}{2}$ and $\dfrac{1 - i\sqrt{31}}{2}$.

4. $u^2 - 6u + 2 = 0$

$a = 1, b = -6, c = 2$

$$u = \frac{-(-6) \pm \sqrt{(-6)^2 - 4(1)(2)}}{2(1)}$$
$$= \frac{6 \pm \sqrt{36 - 8}}{2}$$
$$= \frac{6 \pm \sqrt{28}}{2}$$
$$= \frac{6 \pm 2\sqrt{7}}{2}$$
$$= 3 \pm \sqrt{7}$$

The solutions are $3 + \sqrt{7}$ and $3 - \sqrt{7}$.

5.
$$7x^2 + 8x + 1 = 0$$
$$(7x + 1)(x + 1) = 0$$
$$7x + 1 = 0 \quad \text{or} \quad x + 1 = 0$$
$$7x = -1 \qquad\qquad x = -1$$
$$x = -\frac{1}{7}$$

The solutions are $-\dfrac{1}{7}$ and -1.

6. $y^2 - 3y = 5$

$y^2 - 3y - 5 = 0$

$a = 1, b = -3, c = -5$

$y = \dfrac{3 \pm \sqrt{(-3)^2 - 4(1)(-5)}}{2(1)}$

$= \dfrac{3 \pm \sqrt{9 + 20}}{2}$

$= \dfrac{3 \pm \sqrt{29}}{2}$

The solutions are $\dfrac{3 + \sqrt{29}}{2}$ and $\dfrac{3 - \sqrt{29}}{2}$.

7. $\dfrac{4}{x+2} + \dfrac{2x}{x-2} = \dfrac{6}{x^2 - 4}$

$\dfrac{4}{x+2} + \dfrac{2x}{x-2} = \dfrac{6}{(x+2)(x-2)}$

$4(x-2) + 2x(x+2) = 6$

$4x - 8 + 2x^2 + 4x = 6$

$2x^2 + 8x - 14 = 0$

$x^2 + 4x - 7 = 0$

$a = 1, b = 4, c = -7$

$x = \dfrac{-4 \pm \sqrt{(4)^2 - 4(1)(-7)}}{2(1)}$

$= \dfrac{-4 \pm \sqrt{16 + 28}}{2}$

$= \dfrac{-4 \pm \sqrt{44}}{2}$

$= \dfrac{-4 \pm 2\sqrt{11}}{2}$

$= -2 \pm \sqrt{11}$

The solutions are $-2 + \sqrt{11}$ and $-2 - \sqrt{11}$.

8. $x^5 + 3x^4 = x + 3$

$x^5 + 3x^4 - x - 3 = 0$

$x^4(x+3) - 1(x+3) = 0$

$(x+3)(x^4 - 1) = 0$

$(x+3)(x^2 + 1)(x^2 - 1) = 0$

$x + 3 = 0 \quad$ or $x^2 + 1 = 0 \quad$ or $x^2 - 1 = 0$

$x = -3$ or $\quad x^2 = -1$ or $\quad x^2 = 1$

$x = \pm i \quad$ or $\quad x = \pm 1$

The solutions are -3, -1, 1, $-i$, and i.

9. $x^6 + 1 = x^4 + x^2$

$x^6 - x^4 - x^2 + 1 = 0$

$x^4(x^2 - 1) - (x^2 - 1) = 0$

$(x^4 - 1)(x^2 - 1) = 0$

$(x^2 + 1)(x^2 - 1)(x + 1)(x - 1) = 0$

$(x^2 + 1)(x + 1)^2(x - 1)^2 = 0$

$x^2 + 1 = 0 \quad$ or $\quad x + 1 = 0 \quad$ or $\quad x - 1 = 0$

$x^2 = -1 \qquad\qquad x = -1 \qquad\qquad x = 1$

$x = \pm i$

The solutions are $-i$, i, -1, and 1.

10. $(x+1)^2 - 15(x+1) + 56 = 0$

Let $y = x + 1$. Then $y^2 = (x+1)^2$ and

$y^2 - 15y + 56 = 0$

$(y - 8)(y - 7) = 0$

$y = 8 \quad$ or $\quad y = 7$

$x + 1 = 8 \quad$ or $x + 1 = 7$

$x = 7 \quad$ or $\quad x = 6$

The solutions are 6 and 7.

11. $x^2 - 6x = -2$

$x^2 - 6x + \left(\dfrac{-6}{2}\right)^2 = -2 + 9$

$x^2 - 6x + 9 = 7$

$(x - 3)^2 = 7$

$x - 3 = \pm\sqrt{7}$

$x = 3 \pm \sqrt{7}$

The solutions are $3 + \sqrt{7}$ and $3 - \sqrt{7}$.

12.

$$2a^2 + 5 = 4a$$

$$2a^2 - 4a = -5$$

$$a^2 - 2a = -\frac{5}{2}$$

$$a^2 - 2a + \left(\frac{-2}{2}\right)^2 = -\frac{5}{2} + 1$$

$$a^2 - 2a + 1 = -\frac{3}{2}$$

$$(a-1)^2 = -\frac{3}{2}$$

$$a - 1 = \pm\sqrt{-\frac{3}{2}} = \pm\frac{i\sqrt{3}}{\sqrt{2}}$$

$$a - 1 = \pm\frac{i\sqrt{6}}{2}$$

$$a = 1 \pm \frac{i\sqrt{6}}{2} \quad \text{or} \quad \frac{2 \pm i\sqrt{6}}{2}$$

The solutions are $\dfrac{2 + i\sqrt{6}}{2}$ and $\dfrac{2 - i\sqrt{6}}{2}$.

13.

$$2x^2 - 7x > 15$$

$$2x^2 - 7x - 15 > 0$$

$$(2x + 3)(x - 5) > 0$$

$$2x + 3 = 0 \quad \text{or} \quad x - 5 = 0$$

$$x = -\frac{3}{2} \quad \text{or} \quad x = 5$$

Region	Test Point	$(2x + 3)(x - 5) > 0$ Result
A: $\left(-\infty, -\dfrac{3}{2}\right)$	-2	$(-1)(-7) > 0$ True
B: $\left(-\dfrac{3}{2}, 5\right)$	0	$(3)(-5) > 0$ False
C: $(5, \infty)$	6	$(15)(1) > 0$ True

Solution: $\left(-\infty, -\dfrac{3}{2}\right) \cup (5, \infty)$

14. $(x^2 - 16)(x^2 - 25) \geq 0$

$(x+4)(x-4)(x+5)(x-5) \geq 0$

$x+4=0$ or $x-4=0$ or $x+5=0$ or $x-5=0$

$x=-4$ or $x=4$ or $x=-5$ or $x=5$

Region	Test Point	$(x+4)(x-4)(x+5)(x-5) \geq 0$ Result
$A: (-\infty, -5]$	-6	$(-2)(-10)(-1)(-11) \geq 0$ True
$B: [-5, -4]$	$-\dfrac{9}{2}$	$\left(-\dfrac{1}{2}\right)\left(-\dfrac{17}{2}\right)\left(\dfrac{1}{2}\right)\left(-\dfrac{19}{2}\right) \geq 0$ False
$C: [-4, 4]$	0	$(4)(-4)(5)(-5) \geq 0$ True
$D: [4, 5]$	$\dfrac{9}{2}$	$\left(\dfrac{17}{2}\right)\left(\dfrac{1}{2}\right)\left(\dfrac{19}{2}\right)\left(-\dfrac{1}{2}\right) \geq 0$ False
$E: [5, \infty)$	6	$(10)(2)(11)(1) \geq 0$ True

Solution: $(-\infty, -5] \cup [-4, 4] \cup [5, \infty)$

15. $\dfrac{5}{x+3} < 1$

The denominator is equal to 0 when $x + 3 = 0$, or $x = -3$.

$\dfrac{5}{x+3} = 1$

$5 = x+3$ so $x = 2$

Region	Test Point	$\dfrac{5}{x+3} < 1$ Result
$A: (-\infty, -3)$	-4	$\dfrac{5}{-1} < 1$ True
$B: (-3, 2)$	0	$\dfrac{5}{3} < 1$ False
$C: (2, \infty)$	3	$\dfrac{5}{6} < 1$ True

Solution: $(-\infty, -3) \cup (2, \infty)$

16. $\dfrac{7x-14}{x^2-9} \leq 0$

$\dfrac{7(x-2)}{(x+3)(x-3)} \leq 0$

$x-2=0$ or $x+3=0$ or $x-3=0$

$\quad x=2$ or $\quad x=-3$ or $\quad x=3$

Region	Test Point	$\dfrac{7(x-2)}{(x+3)(x-3)} \leq 0$ Result
A: $(-\infty, -3)$	-4	$\dfrac{7(-6)}{(-1)(-7)} \leq 0$ True
B: $(-3, 2]$	0	$\dfrac{7(-2)}{(3)(-3)} \leq 0$ False
C: $[2, 3)$	$\dfrac{5}{2}$	$\dfrac{7\left(\frac{1}{2}\right)}{\left(\frac{11}{2}\right)\left(-\frac{1}{2}\right)} \leq 0$ True
D: $(3, \infty)$	4	$\dfrac{7(2)}{(7)(1)} \leq 0$ False

Solution: $(-\infty, -3) \cup [2, 3)$

17. $f(x) = 3x^2$

Vertex: $(0, 0)$

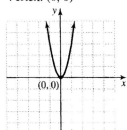

18. $G(x) = -2(x-1)^2 + 5$

Vertex: $(1, 5)$

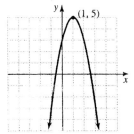

19. $h(x) = x^2 - 4x + 4$

$x = -\dfrac{b}{2a} = \dfrac{-(-4)}{2(1)} = 2$

$h(2) = (2)^2 - 4(2) + 4 = 0$

Vertex: $(2, 0)$

$h(0) = 4 \Rightarrow y\text{-intercept: } (0, 4)$

x-intercept: $(2, 0)$

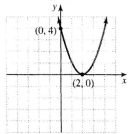

20. $F(x) = 2x^2 - 8x + 9$

$x = -\dfrac{b}{2a} = \dfrac{-(-8)}{2(2)} = 2$

$F(2) = 2(2)^2 - 8(2) + 9 = 1$

Vertex: $(2, 1)$

$F(0) = 9 \Rightarrow y\text{-intercept: } (0, 9)$

$2x^2 - 8x + 9 = 0$

$a = 2, b = -8, c = 9$

$x = \dfrac{8 \pm \sqrt{(-8)^2 - 4(2)(9)}}{2(2)}$

$\quad = \dfrac{8 \pm \sqrt{-8}}{4}$

which yields non-real solutons.

Therefore, there are no x-intercepts.

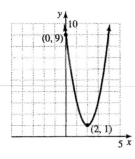

21. Let t = time for Sandy alone. Then $t - 2$ = time for Dave alone.

$$\frac{1}{t} + \frac{1}{t-2} = \frac{1}{4}$$

$$4(t-2) + 4t = t(t-2)$$

$$4t - 8 + 4t = t^2 - 2t$$

$$0 = t^2 - 10t + 8$$

$$a = 1, b = -10, c = 8$$

$$t = \frac{10 \pm \sqrt{(-10)^2 - 4(1)(8)}}{2(1)}$$

$$= \frac{10 \pm \sqrt{68}}{2}$$

$$= \frac{10 \pm 2\sqrt{17}}{2}$$

$$= 5 \pm \sqrt{17}$$

$$\approx 9.12 \text{ or } 0.88 \text{ (discard)}$$

It takes her about 9.12 hours.

22. $s(t) = -16t^2 + 32t + 256$

a. $t = -\dfrac{b}{2a} = \dfrac{-32}{2(-16)} = 1$

$s(1) = -16(1)^2 + 32(1) + 256 = 272$

Vertex: (1, 272)

The maximum height is 272 feet.

b. $-16t^2 + 32t + 256 = 0$

$$t^2 - 2t - 16 = 0$$

$$a = 1, b = -2, c = -16$$

$$t = \frac{2 \pm \sqrt{(-2)^2 - 4(1)(-16)}}{2(1)}$$

$$= \frac{2 \pm \sqrt{68}}{2}$$

$$= \frac{2 \pm 2\sqrt{17}}{2}$$

$$= 1 \pm \sqrt{17}$$

$$\approx -3.12 \text{ and } 5.12$$

Disregard the negative. The stone will hit the water in about 5.12 seconds.

23.

$$a^2 + b^2 = c^2$$

$$x^2 + (x+8)^2 = (20)^2$$

$$x^2 + (x^2 + 16x + 64) = 400$$

$$2x^2 + 16x - 336 = 0$$

$$x^2 + 8x - 168 = 0$$

$$a = 1, b = 8, c = -168$$

$$x = \frac{-8 \pm \sqrt{(8)^2 - 4(1)(-168)}}{2(1)}$$

$$= \frac{-8 \pm \sqrt{736}}{2}$$

$$\approx -17.565 \text{ or } 9.565$$

Disregard the negative.

$x \approx 9.6$

$x + 8 \approx 9.6 + 8 = 17.6$

$17.6 + 9.6 = 27.2$

$27.2 - 20 = 7.2$

They would save about 7 feet.

Chapter 11 Cumulative Review

1. Let $x = 2$ and $y = -5$.

a. $\dfrac{x-y}{12+x} = \dfrac{2-(-5)}{12+2} = \dfrac{2+5}{14} = \dfrac{7}{14} = \dfrac{1}{2}$

b. $x^2 - 3y = 2^2 - 3(-5) = 4 + 15 = 19$

2. $|3x - 2| = -5$ which is impossible. Thus, there is no solution, or $\varnothing$.

3. a. $2x + 3x + 5 + 2 = (2+3)x + (5+2) = 5x + 7$

b. $-5a - 3 + a + 2 = -5a + a - 3 + 2 = -4a - 1$

c. $4y - 3y^2$ cannot be simplified.

d. $2.3x + 5x - 6 = 7.3x - 6$

e. $-\dfrac{1}{2}b + b = \left(-\dfrac{1}{2} + 1\right)b = \dfrac{1}{2}b$

4. $\begin{cases} -6x + \ y = 5 \ \ (1) \\ \ \ 4x - 2y = 6 \ \ (2) \end{cases}$

Multiply E1 by 2 and add to E2.

$-12x + 2y = 10$
$\underline{\quad 4x - 2y = 6 \quad}$
$-8x \qquad = 16$
$\qquad \quad x = -2$

Replace x with –2 in E1.

$-6(-2) + y = 5$
$\quad 12 + y = 5$
$\qquad \quad y = -7$

The solution is $(-2, -7)$.

5. $\begin{cases} 2x + y = 7 \\ 2y = -4x \end{cases}$

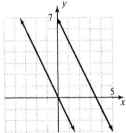

The system has no solution.

6. a. $(a^{-2}bc^3)^{-3} = (a^{-2})^{-3}b^{-3}(c^3)^{-3}$
$\qquad\qquad = a^6 b^{-3} c^{-9}$
$\qquad\qquad = \dfrac{a^6}{b^3 c^9}$

b. $\left(\dfrac{a^{-4}b^2}{c^3}\right)^{-2} = \dfrac{(a^{-4})^{-2}(b^2)^{-2}}{(c^3)^{-2}}$
$\qquad\qquad = \dfrac{a^8 b^{-4}}{c^{-6}}$
$\qquad\qquad = \dfrac{a^8 c^6}{b^4}$

c. $\left(\dfrac{3a^8 b^2}{12a^5 b^5}\right)^{-2} = \left(\dfrac{a^3}{4b^3}\right)^{-2}$
$\qquad\qquad = \dfrac{(a^3)^{-2}}{4^{-2}(b^3)^{-2}}$
$\qquad\qquad = \dfrac{4^2 a^{-6}}{b^{-6}}$
$\qquad\qquad = \dfrac{16b^6}{a^6}$

7. $\begin{cases} 7x - 3y = -14 \\ -3x + y = 6 \end{cases}$

Solve the second equation for y.

$y = 3x + 6$

Substitute $3x + 6$ for y in the first equation.

$7x - 3(3x + 6) = -14$
$\quad 7x - 9x - 18 = -14$
$\qquad \ -2x - 18 = -14$
$\qquad\qquad -2x = 4$
$\qquad\qquad \quad x = -2$

Let $x = -2$ in $y = 3x + 6$.

$y = 3x + 6 = 3(-2) + 6 = -6 + 6 = 0$

The solution is $(-2, 0)$.

8. a. $(4a - 3)(7a - 2) = 28a^2 - 8a - 21a + 6$
$\qquad\qquad\qquad\qquad = 28a^2 - 29a + 6$

b. $(2a + b)(3a - 5b)$
$\qquad = 6a^2 - 10ab + 3ab - 5b^2$
$\qquad = 6a^2 - 7ab - 5b^2$

9. a. $\dfrac{x^5}{x^2} = x^{5-2} = x^3$

b. $\dfrac{4^7}{4^3} = 4^{7-3} = 4^4 = 256$

c. $\dfrac{(-3)^5}{(-3)^2} = (-3)^{5-2} = (-3)^3 = -27$

d. $\dfrac{s^2}{t^3}$ cannot be simplified.

e. $\dfrac{2x^5 y^2}{xy} = 2x^{5-1}y^{2-1} = 2x^4 y^1 = 2x^4 y$

10. a. $9x^3 + 27x^2 - 15x = 3x(3x^2 + 9x - 5)$

b. $2x(3y-2) - 5(3y-2)$
$= (3y-2)(2x-5)$

c. $2xy + 6x - y - 3 = 2x(y+3) - 1(y+3)$
$= (y+3)(2x-1)$

11. $P(x) = 2x^3 - 4x^2 + 5$

a. $P(2) = 2(2)^3 - 4(2)^2 + 5$
$= 2(8) - 4(4) + 5$
$= 16 - 16 + 5$
$= 5$

b.
$$\begin{array}{r|rrrr} 2 & 2 & -4 & 0 & 5 \\ & & 4 & 0 & 0 \\ \hline & 2 & 0 & 0 & 5 \end{array}$$
Thus, $P(2) = 5$.

12. $x^2 - 2x - 48 = (x+6)(x-8)$

13. $(5x-1)(2x^2 + 15x + 18) = 0$
$(5x-1)(2x+3)(x+6) = 0$
$5x - 1 = 0 \quad$ or $\quad 2x + 3 = 0 \quad$ or $\quad x + 6 = 0$
$5x = 1 \qquad\qquad 2x = -3 \qquad\qquad x = -6$
$x = \dfrac{1}{5} \qquad\qquad x = -\dfrac{3}{2}$

The solutions are -6, $-\dfrac{3}{2}$, and $\dfrac{1}{5}$.

14. $2ax^2 - 12axy + 18ay^2 = 2a(x^2 - 6xy + 9y^2)$
$= 2a(x-3y)(x-3y)$
$= 2a(x-3y)^2$

15. $\dfrac{2x^2}{10x^3 - 2x^2} = \dfrac{2x^2}{2x^2(5x-1)} = \dfrac{1}{5x-1}$

16. $2(a^2 + 2) - 8 = -2a(a-2) - 5$
$2a^2 + 4 - 8 = -2a^2 + 4a - 5$
$4a^2 - 4a + 1 = 0$
$(2a-1)^2 = 0$
$2a - 1 = 0$
$2a = 1$
$a = \dfrac{1}{2}$

The solution is $\dfrac{1}{2}$.

17. $\dfrac{x^{-1} + 2xy^{-1}}{x^{-2} - x^{-2}y^{-1}} = \dfrac{\dfrac{1}{x} + \dfrac{2x}{y}}{\dfrac{1}{x^2} - \dfrac{1}{x^2 y}}$

$= \dfrac{\left(\dfrac{1}{x} + \dfrac{2x}{y}\right)x^2 y}{\left(\dfrac{1}{x^2} - \dfrac{1}{x^2 y}\right)x^2 y}$

$= \dfrac{xy + 2x^3}{y - 1}$

18. $f(x) = x^2 + x - 12$
$x = -\dfrac{b}{2a} = -\dfrac{1}{2(1)} = -\dfrac{1}{2}$

$f\left(-\dfrac{1}{2}\right) = \left(-\dfrac{1}{2}\right)^2 + \left(-\dfrac{1}{2}\right) - 12$
$= \dfrac{1}{4} - \dfrac{1}{2} - 12$
$= -\dfrac{49}{4}$

Vertex: $\left(-\dfrac{1}{2}, -\dfrac{49}{4}\right)$

$x^2 + x - 12 = 0$
$(x+4)(x-3) = 0$
$x + 4 = 0 \quad$ or $\quad x - 3 = 0$
$x = -4 \qquad\qquad x = 3$
x-intercepts: $(-4, 0)$, $(3, 0)$
$f(0) = 0^2 + 0 - 12 = -12$
y-intercept: $(0, -12)$

19. $4m^2 - 4m + 1 = (2m)^2 - 2 \cdot 2m \cdot 1 + 1^2 = (2m-1)^2$

20. $\dfrac{x^2 - 4x + 4}{2-x} = \dfrac{(x-2)^2}{-(x-2)} = \dfrac{x-2}{-1} = 2 - x$

21. Let x = the number.

$$x^2 + 3x = 70$$
$$x^2 + 3x - 70 = 0$$
$$(x+10)(x-7) = 0$$
$$x + 10 = 0 \quad \text{or} \quad x - 7 = 0$$
$$x = -10 \qquad\qquad x = 7$$

The number is -10 or 7.

22.
$$\frac{a+1}{a^2 - 6a + 8} - \frac{3}{16 - a^2}$$

$$= \frac{a+1}{(a-4)(a-2)} - \frac{3}{(4+a)(4-a)}$$

$$= \frac{a+1}{(a-4)(a-2)} + \frac{3}{(4+a)(a-4)}$$

$$= \frac{(a+1)(a+4) + 3(a-2)}{(a-4)(a-2)(a+4)}$$

$$= \frac{(a^2 + 4a + a + 4) + 3a - 6}{(a-4)(a-2)(a+4)}$$

$$= \frac{a^2 + 8a - 2}{(a-4)(a-2)(a+4)}$$

23. a. $\sqrt{25x^3} = \sqrt{25x^2 \cdot x} = 5x\sqrt{x}$

    b. $\sqrt[3]{54x^6 y^8} = \sqrt[3]{27x^6 y^6 \cdot 2y^2}$
$$= 3x^2 y^2 \sqrt[3]{2y^2}$$

    c. $\sqrt[4]{81z^{11}} = \sqrt[4]{81z^8 \cdot z^3} = 3z^2 \sqrt[4]{z^3}$

24. $\dfrac{(2a)^{-1} + b^{-1}}{a^{-1} + (2b)^{-1}} = \dfrac{\dfrac{1}{2a} + \dfrac{1}{b}}{\dfrac{1}{a} + \dfrac{1}{2b}}$

$$= \frac{\left(\dfrac{1}{2a} + \dfrac{1}{b}\right) 2ab}{\left(\dfrac{1}{a} + \dfrac{1}{2b}\right) 2ab}$$

$$= \frac{b + 2a}{2b + a}$$

$$= \frac{2a + b}{a + 2b}$$

25. a. $\dfrac{2}{\sqrt{5}} = \dfrac{2 \cdot \sqrt{5}}{\sqrt{5} \cdot \sqrt{5}} = \dfrac{2\sqrt{5}}{5}$

    b. $\dfrac{2\sqrt{16}}{\sqrt{9x}} = \dfrac{2 \cdot 4}{3\sqrt{x}} = \dfrac{8 \cdot \sqrt{x}}{3\sqrt{x} \cdot \sqrt{x}} = \dfrac{8\sqrt{x}}{3x}$

    c. $\sqrt[3]{\dfrac{1}{2}} = \dfrac{\sqrt[3]{1}}{\sqrt[3]{2}} = \dfrac{1}{\sqrt[3]{2}} = \dfrac{1 \cdot \sqrt[3]{2^2}}{\sqrt[3]{2} \cdot \sqrt[3]{2^2}} = \dfrac{\sqrt[3]{4}}{2}$

26.

$$\begin{array}{r} x^2 - 6x + 8 \\ x+3\overline{)x^3 - 3x^2 - 10x + 24} \\ \underline{x^3 + 3x^2} \\ -6x^2 - 10x \\ \underline{-6x^2 - 18x} \\ 8x + 24 \\ \underline{8x + 24} \\ 0 \end{array}$$

Answer: $x^2 - 6x + 8$

27.
$$\sqrt{2x+5} + \sqrt{2x} = 3$$
$$\sqrt{2x+5} = 3 - \sqrt{2x}$$
$$\left(\sqrt{2x+5}\right)^2 = \left(3 - \sqrt{2x}\right)^2$$
$$2x + 5 = 9 - 6\sqrt{2x} + 2x$$
$$-4 = -6\sqrt{2x}$$
$$(-4)^2 = \left(-6\sqrt{2x}\right)^2$$
$$16 = 36(2x)$$
$$16 = 72x$$
$$x = \frac{16}{72} = \frac{2}{9}$$

The solution is $\dfrac{2}{9}$.

28. $P(x) = 4x^3 - 2x^2 + 3$

    a. $P(-2) = 4(-2)^3 - 2(-2)^2 + 3$
$$= 4(-8) - 2(4) + 3$$
$$= -32 - 8 + 3$$
$$= -37$$

    b.
$$\begin{array}{r|rrrr} -2 & 4 & -2 & 0 & 3 \\ & & -8 & 20 & -40 \\ \hline & 4 & -10 & 20 & -37 \end{array}$$

Thus, $P(-2) = -37$.

29.

$$\frac{x}{2}+\frac{8}{3}=\frac{1}{6}$$

$$6\left(\frac{x}{2}+\frac{8}{3}\right)=6\left(\frac{1}{6}\right)$$

$$3x+16=1$$

$$3x=-15$$

$$x=-5$$

30.

$$\frac{x+3}{x^2+5x+6}=\frac{3}{2x+4}-\frac{1}{x+3}$$

$$\frac{x+3}{(x+3)(x+2)}=\frac{3}{2(x+2)}-\frac{1}{x+3}$$

$$2(x+3)=3(x+3)-2(x+2)$$

$$2x+6=3x+9-2x-4$$

$$2x+6=x+5$$

$$x=-1$$

31. Let x = the number.

$$\frac{x}{6}-\frac{5}{3}=\frac{x}{2}$$

$$6\left(\frac{x}{6}-\frac{5}{3}\right)=6\left(\frac{x}{2}\right)$$

$$x-10=3x$$

$$-10=2x$$

$$-5=x$$

The number is −5.

32. Let t = time to roof the house together.

$$\frac{1}{24}+\frac{1}{40}=\frac{1}{t}$$

$$120t\left(\frac{1}{24}+\frac{1}{40}\right)=120t\left(\frac{1}{t}\right)$$

$$5t+3t=120$$

$$8t=120$$

$$t=\frac{120}{8}=15$$

It would take them 15 hours to roof the house working together.

33. $y=kx$

$$5=k(30)$$

$$k=\frac{5}{30}=\frac{1}{6} \text{ and } y=\frac{1}{6}x$$

34. $y=\dfrac{k}{x}$

$$8=\frac{k}{14}$$

$$k=8(14)=112 \text{ and } y=\frac{112}{x}$$

35. a. $\sqrt{(-3)^2}=|-3|=3$

b. $\sqrt{x^2}=|x|$

c. $\sqrt[4]{(x-2)^4}=|x-2|$

d. $\sqrt[3]{(-5)^3}=-5$

e. $\sqrt[5]{(2x-7)^5}=2x-7$

f. $\sqrt{25x^2}=\sqrt{25}\cdot\sqrt{x^2}=5|x|$

g. $\sqrt{x^2+2x+1}=\sqrt{(x+1)^2}=|x+1|$

36. a. $\sqrt{(-2)^2}=|-2|=2$

b. $\sqrt{y^2}=|y|$

c. $\sqrt[4]{(a-3)^4}=|a-3|$

d. $\sqrt[3]{(-6)^3}=-6$

e. $\sqrt[5]{(3x-1)^5}=3x-1$

37. a. $\sqrt[8]{x^4}=x^{4/8}=x^{1/2}=\sqrt{x}$

b. $\sqrt[6]{25}=(25)^{1/6}$
$$=(5^2)^{1/6}=5^{2/6}=5^{1/3}=\sqrt[3]{5}$$

c. $\sqrt[4]{r^2s^6}=(r^2s^6)^{1/4}$
$$=r^{2/4}s^{6/4}$$
$$=r^{1/2}s^{3/2}$$
$$=(rs^3)^{1/2}=\sqrt{rs^3}$$

38. a. $\sqrt[4]{5^2}=5^{2/4}=5^{1/2}=\sqrt{5}$

b. $\sqrt[12]{x^3}=x^{3/12}=x^{1/4}=\sqrt[4]{x}$

c. $\sqrt[6]{x^2 y^4} = (x^2 y^4)^{1/6}$
$= x^{2/6} y^{4/6}$
$= x^{1/3} y^{2/3}$
$= (xy^2)^{1/3} = \sqrt[3]{xy^2}$

39. a. $\dfrac{2+i}{1-i} = \dfrac{(2+i) \cdot (1+i)}{(1-i) \cdot (1+i)}$
$= \dfrac{2+2i+1i+i^2}{1^2 - i^2}$
$= \dfrac{2+3i-1}{1+1}$
$= \dfrac{1+3i}{2}$ or $\dfrac{1}{2} + \dfrac{3}{2}i$

b. $\dfrac{7}{3i} = \dfrac{7 \cdot (-3i)}{3i \cdot (-3i)} = \dfrac{-21i}{-9i^2} = \dfrac{-21i}{9} = -\dfrac{7}{3}i$

40. a. $3i(5-2i) = 15i - 6i^2$
$= 15i + 6$
$= 6 + 15i$

b. $(6-5i)^2 = 6^2 - 2(6)(5i) + (5i)^2$
$= 36 - 60i + 25i^2$
$= 36 - 60i - 25$
$= 11 - 60i$

c. $\left(\sqrt{3}+2i\right)\left(\sqrt{3}-2i\right) = \left(\sqrt{3}\right)^2 - (2i)^2$
$= 3 - 4i^2$
$= 3 + 4$
$= 7$

41. $(x+1)^2 = 12$
$x+1 = \pm\sqrt{12}$
$x+1 = \pm 2\sqrt{3}$
$x = -1 \pm 2\sqrt{3}$
The solutions are $-1 + 2\sqrt{3}$ and $-1 - 2\sqrt{3}$.

42. $(y-1)^2 = 24$
$y-1 = \pm\sqrt{24}$
$y-1 = \pm 2\sqrt{6}$
$y = 1 \pm 2\sqrt{6}$
The solutions are $1 + 2\sqrt{6}$ and $1 - 2\sqrt{6}$.

43. $x - \sqrt{x} - 6 = 0$
Let $y = \sqrt{x}$. Then $y^2 = x$ and
$y^2 - y - 6 = 0$
$(y-3)(y+2) = 0$
$y - 3 = 0$ or $y + 2 = 0$
$y = 3$ or $\quad y = -2$
$\sqrt{x} = 3$ or $\sqrt{x} = -2$ (can't happen)
$x = 9$
The solution is 9.

44. $\qquad m^2 = 4m + 8$
$m^2 - 4m - 8 = 0$
$a = 1, b = -4, c = -8$
$x = \dfrac{4 \pm \sqrt{(-4)^2 - 4(1)(-8)}}{2(1)}$
$= \dfrac{4 \pm \sqrt{16 + 32}}{2}$
$= \dfrac{4 \pm \sqrt{48}}{2}$
$= \dfrac{4 \pm 4\sqrt{3}}{2}$
$= 2 \pm 2\sqrt{3}$
The solutions are $2 + 2\sqrt{3}$ and $2 - 2\sqrt{3}$.

Chapter 12

Practice Exercises

1. $f(x) = x + 2$; $g(x) = 3x + 5$

   a. $(f + g)(x) = f(x) + g(x)$
$$= (x + 2) + (3x + 5)$$
$$= 4x + 7$$

   b. $(f - g)(x) = f(x) - g(x)$
$$= (x + 2) - (3x + 5)$$
$$= x + 2 - 3x - 5$$
$$= -2x - 3$$

   c. $(f \cdot g)(x) = f(x) \cdot g(x)$
$$= (x + 2)(3x + 5)$$
$$= 3x^2 + 6x + 5x + 10$$
$$= 3x^2 + 11x + 10$$

   d. $\left(\dfrac{f}{g}\right)(x) = \dfrac{f(x)}{g(x)} = \dfrac{x+2}{3x+5}$, where $x \neq -\dfrac{5}{3}$.

2. $f(x) = x^2 + 1$; $g(x) = 3x - 5$

   a. $(f \circ g)(4) = f(g(4)) = f(7) = 50$
$$(g \circ f)(4) = g(f(4)) = g(17) = 46$$

   b. $(f \circ g)(x) = f(g(x))$
$$= f(3x - 5)$$
$$= (3x - 5)^2 + 1$$
$$= 9x^2 - 30x + 26$$
$$(g \circ f)(x) = g(f(x))$$
$$= g(x^2 + 1)$$
$$= 3(x^2 + 1) - 5$$
$$= 3x^2 - 2$$

3. $f(x) = x^2 + 5$; $g(x) = x + 3$

   a. $(f \circ g)(x) = f(g(x))$
$$= f(x + 3)$$
$$= (x + 3)^2 + 5$$
$$= x^2 + 6x + 14$$

   b. $(g \circ f)(x) = g(f(x))$
$$= g(x^2 + 5)$$
$$= (x^2 + 5) + 3$$
$$= x^2 + 8$$

4. $f(x) = 3x$; $g(x) = x - 4$; $h(x) = |x|$

   a. $F(x) = |x - 4|$
$$F(x) = (h \circ g)(x)$$
$$= h(g(x))$$
$$= h(x - 4)$$
$$= |x - 4|$$

   b. $G(x) = 3x - 4$
$$G(x) = (g \circ f)(x)$$
$$= g(f(x))$$
$$= g(3x)$$
$$= 3x - 4$$

Vocabulary and Readiness Check

1. C

2. E

3. F

4. A

5. D

6. B

Exercise Set 12.1

2. a. $(f + g)(x) = (x + 4) + (5x - 2)$
$$= 6x + 2$$

   b. $(f - g)(x) = (x + 4) - (5x - 2)$
$$= x + 4 - 5x + 2$$
$$= -4x + 6$$

   c. $(f \cdot g)(x) = (x + 4)(5x - 2)$
$$= 5x^2 + 18x - 8$$

   d. $\left(\dfrac{f}{g}\right)(x) = \dfrac{x+4}{5x-2}$, where $x \neq \dfrac{2}{5}$

4. a. $(f+g)(x) = (x^2-2)+(3x)$
$= x^2+3x-2$

b. $(f-g)(x) = (x^2-2)-(3x)$
$= x^2-3x-2$

c. $(f \cdot g)(x) = (x^2-2)(3x) = 3x^3-6x$

d. $\left(\dfrac{f}{g}\right)(x) = \dfrac{x^2-2}{3x}$, where $x \neq 0$

6. a. $(f+g)(x) = \sqrt[3]{x}+x-3$

b. $(f-g)(x) = \sqrt[3]{x}-(x-3) = \sqrt[3]{x}-x+3$

c. $(f \cdot g)(x) = \sqrt[3]{x} \cdot (x-3) = x\sqrt[3]{x}-3\sqrt[3]{x}$

d. $\left(\dfrac{f}{g}\right)(x) = \dfrac{\sqrt[3]{x}}{x-3}$, where $x \neq 3$

8. a. $(f+g)(x) = 4x^3+(-6x) = 4x^3-6x$

b. $(f-g)(x) = 4x^3-(-6x) = 4x^3+6x$

c. $(f \cdot g)(x) = 4x^3(-6x) = -24x^4$

d. $\left(\dfrac{f}{g}\right)(x) = \dfrac{4x^3}{-6x} = -\dfrac{2x^2}{3}$, where $x \neq 0$

10. $(h \circ f)(-2) = h(f(-2))$
$= h\left((-2)^2-6(-2)+2\right)$
$= h(18)$
$= \sqrt{18}$
$= 3\sqrt{2}$

12. $(f \circ h)(1) = f(h(1))$
$= f\left(\sqrt{1}\right)$
$= f(1)$
$= (1)^2-6(1)+2$
$= -3$

14. $(h \circ g)(0) = h(g(0))$
$= h\left(-2(0)\right)$
$= h(0)$
$= \sqrt{0}$
$= 0$

16. $(f \circ g)(x) = f(g(x))$
$= f\left(x^2\right)$
$= x^2-3$
$(g \circ f)(x) = g(f(x))$
$= g\left(x-3\right)$
$= (x-3)^2$
$= x^2-6x+9$

18. $(f \circ g)(x) = f(g(x))$
$= f\left(3x+1\right)$
$= (3x+1)+10 = 3x+11$
$(g \circ f)(x) = g(f(x))$
$= g\left(x+10\right)$
$= 3(x+10)+1 = 3x+31$

20. $(f \circ g)(x) = f(g(x))$
$= f\left(x^3+x^2-6\right)$
$= -4(x^3+x^2-6)$
$= -4x^3-4x^2+24$
$(g \circ f)(x) = g(f(x))$
$= g\left(-4x\right)$
$= (-4x)^3+(-4x)^2-6$
$= -64x^3+16x^2-6$

22. $(f \circ g)(x) = f(g(x)) = f(14x-8) = |14x-8|$
$(g \circ f)(x) = g(f(x)) = g\left(|x|\right) = 14|x|-8$

24. $(f \circ g)(x) = f(g(x))$
$= f\left(\sqrt[3]{x}\right)$
$= 7\sqrt[3]{x}-1$
$(g \circ f)(x) = g(f(x))$
$= g\left(7x-1\right)$
$= \sqrt[3]{7x-1}$

26. $G(x) = (g \circ f)(x)$
$= g(f(x))$
$= g(3x)$
$= \sqrt{3x}$

28. $H(x) = (f \circ h)(x)$
$\qquad = f(h(x))$
$\qquad = f(x^2 + 2)$
$\qquad = 3(x^2 + 2)$
$\qquad = 3x^2 + 6$

30. $F(x) = (h \circ g)(x)$
$\qquad = h(g(x))$
$\qquad = h\left(\sqrt{x}\right)$
$\qquad = \left(\sqrt{x}\right)^2 + 2$
$\qquad = x + 2$

32. Answers may vary; for example, $g(x) = x - 1$ and $f(x) = |x|$.

34. Answers may vary; for example, $g(x) = 3x + 4$ and $f(x) = x^2 + 3$.

36. Answers may vary; for example, $g(x) = x + 10$ and $f(x) = \dfrac{1}{x}$.

38. $\quad x = y - 5$
$\quad x + 5 = y$
$\qquad y = x + 5$

40. $\quad x = -6y$
$\quad \dfrac{x}{-6} = y$
$\qquad y = -\dfrac{x}{6}$

42. $\quad x = 4y + 7$
$\quad x - 7 = 4y$
$\quad \dfrac{x-7}{4} = y$
$\qquad y = \dfrac{x-7}{4}$

44. $(f - g)(7) = f(7) - g(7) = 1 - 4 = -3$

46. $(g \circ f)(2) = g(f(2)) = g(7) = 4$

48. $(f \cdot g)(0) = f(0) \cdot g(0) = 5(-3) = -15$

50. $\left(\dfrac{g}{f}\right)(-1) = \dfrac{g(-1)}{f(-1)} = \dfrac{-4}{4} = -1$

52. Answers may vary

54. $P(x) = R(x) - C(x)$
$$= 25x - (50 + x^2 + 4x)$$
$$= -x^2 + 21x - 50$$

Section 12.2

Practice Exercises

1. a. $f = \{(4, -3), (3, -4), (2, 7), (5, 0)\}$
  f is one-to-one since each y-value corresponds to only one x-value.

  b. $g = \{(8, 4), (-2, 0), (6, 4), (2, 6)\}$
  g is not one-to-one because the y-value 4 in (8, 4) and (6, 4) corresponds to two different x-values.

  c. $h = \{(2, 4), (1, 3), (4, 6), (-2, 4)\}$
  h is not one-to-one because the y-value 4 in (2, 4) and (-2, 4) corresponds to two different x-values.

  d.

Year	1950	1963	1968	1975	1997	2002
Federal Minimum Wage	$0.75	$1.25	$1.60	$2.10	$5.15	$5.15

  This function is not one-to-one because the wage $5.15 corresponds to two different years.

  e. The function represented by the graph is not one-to-one because the y-value 2 in (2, 2) and (3, 2) corresponds to two different x-values.

  f. The function represented by the diagram is not one-to-one because the score 509 corresponds to two different states.

2. Graphs **a**, **b**, and **c** all pass the vertical line test, so only these graphs are functions. But, of these, only **b** and **c** pass the horizontal line test, so only **b** and **c** are graphs of one-to-one functions.

3. $f(x) = \{(3, 4), (-2, 0), (2, 8), (6, 6)\}$
Switching the coordinates of each ordered pair gives $f^{-1}(x) = \{(4, 3), (0, -2), (8, 2), (6, 6)\}$

4. $f(x) = 6 - x$
Replace $f(x)$ with y.
$y = 6 - x$
Interchange x and y.
$x = 6 - y$
Solve for y.
$x = 6 - y$
$y = 6 - x$
Replace y with $f^{-1}(x)$.
$f^{-1}(x) = 6 - x$

5. $f(x) = 5x + 2$
Replace $f(x)$ with y.
$y = 5x + 2$
Interchange x and y.
$x = 5y + 2$
Solve for y.
$\quad x = 5y + 2$
$\quad x - 2 = 5y$
$\quad \dfrac{x-2}{5} = y$

Replace y with $f^{-1}(x)$.

$f^{-1}(x) = \dfrac{x-2}{5}$

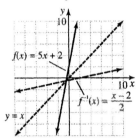

6. a. $f(x) = 2x - 3$
$\qquad y = 2x - 3$

$x = 2y - 3$
$x + 3 = 2y$
$\dfrac{x+3}{2} = y$
$f^{-1}(x) = \dfrac{x+3}{2}$

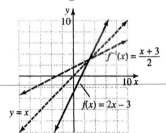

b. $f(x) = x^3$
$\quad y = x^3$

$x = y^3$
$\sqrt[3]{x} = y$
$f^{-1}(x) = \sqrt[3]{x}$

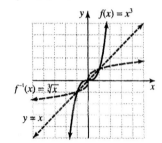

7. $f(x) = 4x - 1;\ f^{-1}(x) = \dfrac{x+1}{4}$

$(f \circ f^{-1})(x) = f(f^{-1}(x))$
$\qquad\qquad = f\left(\dfrac{x+1}{4}\right)$
$\qquad\qquad = 4\left(\dfrac{x+1}{4}\right) - 1$
$\qquad\qquad = x + 1 - 1$
$\qquad\qquad = x$

$(f^{-1} \circ f)(x) = f^{-1}(f(x))$
$\qquad\qquad = f^{-1}(4x - 1)$
$\qquad\qquad = \dfrac{(4x-1)+1}{4}$
$\qquad\qquad = \dfrac{4x-1+1}{4}$
$\qquad\qquad = \dfrac{4x}{4}$
$\qquad\qquad = x$

Since $f \circ f^{-1} = x$ and $f^{-1} \circ f = x$, if

$f(x) = 4x - 1,\ f^{-1}(x) = \dfrac{x+1}{4}.$

Vocabulary and Readiness Check

1. If $f(2) = 11$, the corresponding ordered pair is <u>(2, 11)</u>.

2. The symbol f^{-1} means <u>the inverse of f</u>.

3. If (7, 3) is an ordered pair solution of $f(x)$, and $f(x)$ has an inverse, then an ordered pair solution of $f^{-1}(x)$ is <u>(3, 7)</u>.

4. To tell whether a graph is the graph of a function, use the <u>vertical</u> line test.

5. To tell whether the graph of a function is also a one-to-one function, use the <u>horizontal</u> line test.

6. The graphs of f and f^{-1} are symmetric about the <u>$y = x$</u> line.

7. Two functions are inverse of each other if $(f \circ f^{-1})(x) = \underline{x}$ and $(f^{-1} \circ f)(x) = \underline{x}$.

Exercise Set 12.2

2. $g = \{(8, 6), (9, 6), (3, 4), (-4, 4)\}$ is not a one-to-one function. The y-values 6 and 4 are each assigned two different x-values.

4. $r = \{(1, 2), (3, 4), (5, 6), (6, 7)\}$ is a one-to-one function.
   $r^{-1} = \{(2, 1), (4, 3), (6, 5), (7, 6)\}$

6. $g = \{(0, 3), (3, 7), (6, 7), (-2, -2)\}$ is not a one-to-one function. The y-value 7 is assigned two different x-values.

8. This function is not one-to-one because the states Wisconsin and Arizona have the same output, 10.

10. This function is one-to-one.

No. of Sides (Input)	3	5	4	6	10
Shape (Output)	Triangle	Pentagon	Quadrilateral	Hexagon	Decagon

12. $f(x) = x^3 + 2$

   a. $f(0) = (0)^3 + 2 = 2$

   b. $f^{-1}(2) = 0$

14. $f(x) = x^3 + 2$

   a. $f(-2) = (-2)^3 + 2 = -6$

   b. $f^{-1}(-6) = -2$

16. The graph does not represent a one-to-one function because it does not pass the horizontal line test.

18. The graph does not represent a one-to-one function because it does not pass the horizontal line test.

20. The graph does not represent a one-to-one function because it does not pass the horizontal line test.

22. The graph represents a one-to-one function because it passes the horizontal line test.

24. $f(x) = x - 5$
$$y = x - 5$$
$$x = y - 5$$
$$x + 5 = y$$
$$f^{-1}(x) = x + 5$$

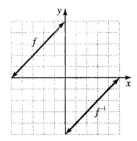

26. $f(x) = 4x + 9$
$$y = 4x + 9$$
$$x = 4y + 9$$
$$x - 9 = 4y$$
$$\frac{x - 9}{4} = y$$
$$f^{-1}(x) = \frac{x - 9}{4}$$

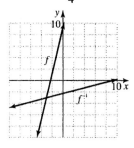

28. $f(x) = -\dfrac{1}{2}x + 2$
$$y = -\frac{1}{2}x + 2$$
$$x = -\frac{1}{2}y + 2$$
$$x - 2 = -\frac{1}{2}y$$
$$-2x + 4 = y$$
$$f^{-1}(x) = -2x + 4$$

30. $f(x) = x^3 - 1$
$$y = x^3 - 1$$
$$x = y^3 - 1$$
$$x + 1 = y^3$$
$$\sqrt[3]{x + 1} = y$$
$$f^{-1}(x) = \sqrt[3]{x + 1}$$

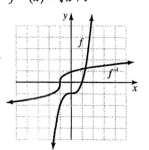

32. $f(x) = 6x - 1$
$$y = 6x - 1$$
$$x = 6y - 1$$
$$x + 1 = 6y$$
$$\frac{x + 1}{6} = y$$
$$f^{-1}(x) = \frac{x + 1}{6}$$

34. $f(x) = \dfrac{4x - 3}{2}$
$$y = \frac{4x - 3}{2}$$
$$x = \frac{4y - 3}{2}$$
$$2x = 4y - 3$$
$$2x + 3 = 4y$$
$$\frac{2x + 3}{4} = y$$
$$f^{-1}(x) = \frac{2x + 3}{4}$$

36. $f(x) = \sqrt[3]{x + 1}$
$$y = \sqrt[3]{x + 1}$$
$$x = \sqrt[3]{y + 1}$$
$$x^3 = y + 1$$
$$x^3 - 1 = y$$
$$f^{-1}(x) = x^3 - 1$$

38.
$$f(x) = \frac{7}{2x+4}$$
$$y = \frac{7}{2x+4}$$
$$x = \frac{7}{2y+4}$$
$$x(2y+4) = 7$$
$$2xy + 4x = 7$$
$$2xy = 7 - 4x$$
$$y = \frac{7-4x}{2x}$$
$$f^{-1}(x) = \frac{7-4x}{2x}$$

40.
$$f(x) = (x-5)^3$$
$$y = (x-5)^3$$
$$x = (y-5)^3$$
$$\sqrt[3]{x} = y - 5$$
$$\sqrt[3]{x} + 5 = y$$
$$f^{-1}(x) = \sqrt[3]{x} + 5$$

42.

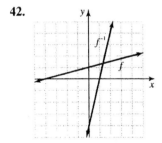

44.

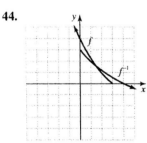

46.

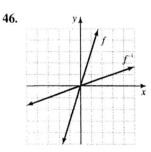

48.
$$(f^{-1} \circ f)(x) = f^{-1}(f(x))$$
$$= f^{-1}(3x-10)$$
$$= \frac{(3x-10)+10}{3}$$
$$= \frac{3x}{3}$$
$$= x$$
$$(f \circ f^{-1})(x) = f(f^{-1}(x))$$
$$= f\left(\frac{x+10}{3}\right)$$
$$= 3\left(\frac{x+10}{3}\right) - 10$$
$$= x + 10 - 10$$
$$= x$$

50.
$$(f^{-1} \circ f)(x) = f^{-1}(f(x))$$
$$= f^{-1}(x^3 - 5)$$
$$= \sqrt[3]{(x^3-5)+5}$$
$$= x$$
$$(f \circ f^{-1})(x) = f(f^{-1}(x))$$
$$= f\left(\sqrt[3]{x+5}\right)$$
$$= \left(\sqrt[3]{x+5}\right)^3 - 5$$
$$= x + 5 - 5$$
$$= x$$

52. $49^{1/2} = \sqrt{49} = 7$

54. $27^{2/3} = \left(\sqrt[3]{27}\right)^2 = 3^2 = 9$

56. $81^{-3/4} = \dfrac{1}{81^{3/4}} = \dfrac{1}{\left(\sqrt[4]{81}\right)^3} = \dfrac{1}{3^3} = \dfrac{1}{27}$

58. $f(x) = 3^x$
$f(0) = 3^0 = 1$

60. $f(x) = 3^x$
$f\left(\dfrac{2}{3}\right) = 3^{2/3} \approx 2.08$

62. $F\left(\dfrac{1}{2}\right) = -0.7$

a. $F(x) = y$, so $(x, y) = \left(\dfrac{1}{2}, -0.7\right)$.

b. One ordered pair is (y, x), or $\left(-0.7, \frac{1}{2}\right)$.

64. a. $(-2, -9), (-1, -2), (0, -1), (1, 0), (2, 7)$

b. $(-9, -2), (-2, -1), (-1, 0), (0, 1), (7, 2)$

c, d.

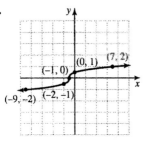

66. Answers may vary.

68.
$$f(x) = -2x - 6$$
$$y = -2x - 6$$
$$x = -2y - 6$$
$$2y = -x - 6$$
$$y = \frac{-x - 6}{2}$$
$$f^{-1}(x) = \frac{-x - 6}{2}$$

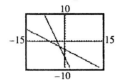

70.
$$f(x) = x^3 - 3$$
$$y = x^3 - 3$$
$$x = y^3 - 3$$
$$x + 3 = y^3$$
$$\sqrt[3]{x + 3} = y$$
$$f^{-1}(x) = \sqrt[3]{x + 3}$$

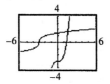

Section 12.3

Practice Exercises

1.

$f(x) = 2^x$	x	0	1	2	3	−1	−2
	$f(x)$	1	2	4	8	$\frac{1}{2}$	$\frac{1}{4}$

$g(x) = 7^x$	x	0	1	2	3	−1	−2
	$g(x)$	1	7	49	343	$\frac{1}{7}$	$\frac{1}{49}$

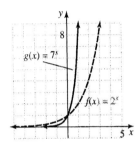

2.

$f(x) = \left(\frac{1}{3}\right)^x$	x	0	1	2	3	−1	−2
	$f(x)$	1	$\frac{1}{3}$	$\frac{1}{9}$	$\frac{1}{27}$	3	9

$g(x) = \left(\frac{1}{5}\right)^x$	x	0	1	2	3	−1	−2
	$g(x)$	1	$\frac{1}{5}$	$\frac{1}{25}$	$\frac{1}{125}$	5	25

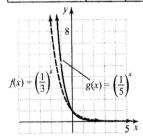

3. $f(x) = 2^{x+3}$

$y = 2^{x+3}$	x	0	−1	−2	−3	−4	−5
	y	8	4	2	1	$\frac{1}{2}$	$\frac{1}{4}$

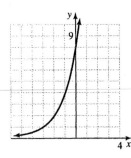

4. a. $3^x = 9$

Write 9 as a power of 3, $9 = 3^2$.

$3^x = 3^2$, thus, $x = 2$.

b. $8^x = 16$

Write 8 and 16 as powers of 2.

$8 = 2^3$ and $16 = 2^4$.

$8^x = 16$

$(2^3)^x = 2^4$

$2^{3x} = 2^4$

$3x = 4$

$x = \dfrac{4}{3}$

c. $125^x = 25^{x-2}$

Write 125 and 25 as powers of 5.

$125 = 5^3$ and $25 = 5^2$.

$125^x = 25^{x-2}$

$(5^3)^x = (5^2)^{x-2}$

$5^{3x} = 5^{2x-4}$

$3x = 2x - 4$

$x = -4$

5. $P = \$3000$, $r = 7\% = 0.07$, $n = 2$, and $t = 4$.

$A = P\left(1 + \dfrac{r}{n}\right)^{nt}$

$A = 3000\left(1 + \dfrac{0.07}{2}\right)^{2(4)}$

$= 3000(1.035)^8$

≈ 3950.43

Thus, the amount A owed is approximately $\$3950.43$.

6. $p(n) = 100(2.7)^{-0.05n}$, $n = 10$ sheets of glass.

$p(10) = 100(2.7)^{-0.05(10)} = 100(2.7)^{-0.5} \approx 60.86$

Thus, approximately 60.86% of the light passes through.

Graphing Calculator Explorations

1.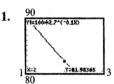

The expected percent after 2 days is 81.98%.

2.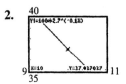

The expected percent after 10 days is 37.04%.

3.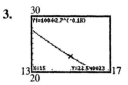

The expected percent after 15 days is 22.54%.

4.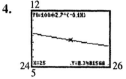

The expected percent after 25 days is 8.35%.

Vocabulary and Readiness Check

1. A function such as $f(x) = 2^x$ is an <u>exponential</u> function; **C.**

2. If $7^x = 7^y$, then <u>$x = y$</u>; **B.**

3. Yes, the function passes both the vertical- and horizontal-line tests.

4. The function has no x-intercept.

5. The function has a y-intercept of <u>(0, 1)</u>.

6. The domain of this function, in interval notation, is <u>$(-\infty, \infty)$</u>.

7. The range of this function, in interval notation, is <u>$(0, \infty)$</u>.

Exercise Set 12.3

2. $y = 5^x$

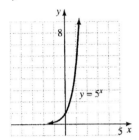

4. $y = 3^x - 1$

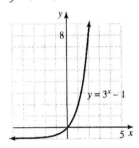

6. $y = \left(\dfrac{1}{5}\right)^x$

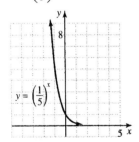

8. $y = \left(\dfrac{1}{3}\right)^x + 2$

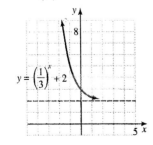

10. $y = -3^x$

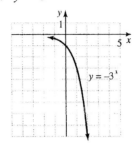

12. $y = -\left(\dfrac{1}{5}\right)^x$

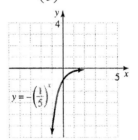

14. $f(x) = 3^{x-1}$

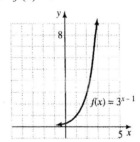

16. $f(x) = 2^{x+3}$

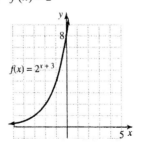

18. D

20. A

22. $6^x = 36$
$6^x = 6^2$
$x = 2$
The solution is 2.

24. $64^x = 16$
$(4^3)^x = 4^2$
$4^{3x} = 4^2$
$3x = 2$
$x = \dfrac{2}{3}$
The solution is $\dfrac{2}{3}$.

26. $9^{2x+1} = 81$
$9^{2x+1} = 9^2$
$2x + 1 = 2$
$2x = 1$
$x = \dfrac{1}{2}$
The solution is $\dfrac{1}{2}$.

28. $\dfrac{1}{27} = 3^{2x}$
$3^{-3} = 3^{2x}$
$-3 = 2x$
$-\dfrac{3}{2} = x$
The solution is $-\dfrac{3}{2}$.

30. $2^x = 64$
$2^x = 2^6$
$x = 6$
The solution is 6.

32. $32^x = 4$
$(2^5)^x = 2^2$
$2^{5x} = 2^2$
$5x = 2$
$x = \dfrac{2}{5}$
The solution is $\dfrac{2}{5}$.

34. $125^{x-2} = 25$
$(5^3)^{x-2} = 5^2$
$5^{3x-6} = 5^2$
$3x - 6 = 2$
$3x = 8$
$x = \dfrac{8}{3}$
The solution is $\dfrac{8}{3}$.

36. $4^{3x-7} = 32^{2x}$
$(2^2)^{3x-7} = (2^5)^{2x}$
$2^{6x-14} = 2^{10x}$
$6x - 14 = 10x$
$-14 = 4x$
$-\dfrac{7}{2} = x$
The solution is $-\dfrac{7}{2}$.

38. $y = 150(2.7)^{-0.03t}, \; t = 10$
$y = 150(2.7)^{-0.03(10)}$
$= 150(2.7)^{-0.3}$
≈ 111.3
Approximately 111.3 pounds of nuclear waste will be left after 10 centuries.

40. $y = 200(2.7)^{0.08t}, \; t = 12$
$y = 200(2.7)^{0.08(12)}$
$= 200(2.7)^{0.96}$
≈ 519
519 rats are expected by next January.

42. $y = 75(2.7)^{-0.04t}, \; t = 14$
$y = 75(2.7)^{-0.04(14)}$
$= 75(2.7)^{-0.56}$
≈ 43.0
After 14 days, 43 grams of debris remain.

44. $y = 200,000(2.7)^{0.08t}, \; t = 13$
$y = 200,000(2.7)^{0.08(13)}$
$= 200,000(2.7)^{1.04}$
$\approx 562,000$
There will be approximately 562,000 mosquitoes on May 25.

46. $y = 369.4(1.004)^t$

   a. $t = 2006 - 2000 = 6$

      $y = 369.4(1.004)^6 \approx 378.4$

      In 2006, the CO_2 concentration was
378.4 parts per million.

   b. $t = 2030 - 2000 = 30$

      $y = 369.4(1.004)^{30} \approx 416.4$

      In 2030, the CO_2 concentration is predicted
to be 416.4 parts per million.

48. $A = P\left(1 + \dfrac{r}{n}\right)^{nt}$

   $t = 5$, $P = 6000$, $r = 0.10$, and $n = 4$

   $A = 3000\left(1 + \dfrac{0.10}{4}\right)^{4(5)}$

      $= 3000(1.025)^{20}$

      ≈ 4915.85

   $4915.85 would be owed after 5 years.

50. $A = P\left(1 + \dfrac{r}{n}\right)^{nt}$

   $P = 500$, $r = 0.07$, $n = 4$, and $t = 4$

   $A = 500\left(1 + \dfrac{0.07}{12}\right)^{12(4)}$

      $= 500\left(1 + \dfrac{0.07}{12}\right)^{48}$

      ≈ 661.03

   $661.03 accrues after 4 years.

52. $y = 18(1.24)^x$

   $x = 2014 - 1994 = 20$

   $y = 18(1.24)^{20}$

      ≈ 1330

   There will be approximately 1330 million
cellular phone users in 2014.

54. $3x - 7 = 11$

      $3x = 18$

       $x = 6$

   The solution is 6.

56. $2 - 6x = 6(1 - x)$

    $2 - 6x = 6 - 6x$

       $2 = 6$

   This is a false statement. The solution set is $\varnothing$.

58. $18 = 11x - x^2$

   $x^2 - 11x + 18 = 0$

   $(x - 9)(x - 2) = 0$

   $x = 9$ or $x = 2$

   The solutions are 2 and 9.

60. $3^x = 9$

   $3^2 = 9$

   $x = 2$

62. $4^x = 1$

   $4^0 = 1$

   $x = 0$

64. Answers may vary

66. $y = \left|\left(\dfrac{1}{3}\right)^x\right|$

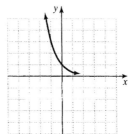

68. $y = \left(\dfrac{1}{3}\right)^{|x|}$

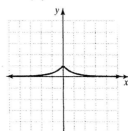

70. Answers may vary

72. $y = 30(2.7)^{-0.004x}$

20.16 pounds will be available after 100 days.

74. $y = 75(2.7)^{-0.04x}$

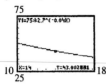

43.00 grams remain after 14 days.

76. $y = 75(2.7)^{-0.04x}$

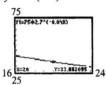

33.88 grams remain after 20 days.

Section 12.4

Practice Exercises

1.   **a.** $\log_3 81 = 4$ means $3^4 = 81$.

     b. $\log_5 \dfrac{1}{5} = -1$ means $5^{-1} = \dfrac{1}{5}$.

     c. $\log_7 \sqrt{7} = \dfrac{1}{2}$ means $7^{1/2} = \sqrt{7}$.

     d. $\log_{13} y = 4$ means $13^4 = y$.

2.   **a.** $4^3 = 64$ means $\log_4 64 = 3$.

     b. $6^{1/3} = \sqrt[3]{6}$ means $\log_6 \sqrt[3]{6} = \dfrac{1}{3}$.

     c. $5^{-3} = \dfrac{1}{125}$ means $\log_5 \dfrac{1}{125} = -3$.

     d. $\pi^7 = z$ means $\log_\pi z = 7$.

3.   **a.** $\log_3 9 = 2$ because $3^2 = 9$.

     b. $\log_2 \dfrac{1}{8} = -3$ because $2^{-3} = \dfrac{1}{8}$.

     c. $\log_{49} 7 = \dfrac{1}{2}$ because $49^{1/2} = 7$.

4.   **a.** $\log_5 \dfrac{1}{25} = x$

       $\log_5 \dfrac{1}{25} = x$ means $5^x = \dfrac{1}{25}$. Solve

       $5^x = \dfrac{1}{25}$.

       $5^x = \dfrac{1}{25}$

       $5^x = 5^{-2}$

       Since the bases are the same, by the uniqueness of b^x, we have that $x = -2$. The solution is -2 or the solution set is $\{-2\}$.

     b. $\log_x 8 = 3$

       $x^3 = 8$

       $x^3 = 2^3$

       $x = 2$

     c. $\log_6 x = 2$

       $6^2 = x$

       $36 = x$

     d. $\log_{13} 1 = x$

       $13^x = 1$

       $13^x = 13^0$

       $x = 0$

     e. $\log_h 1 = x$

       $h^x = 1$

       $h^x = h^0$

       $x = 0$

5.   **a.**   From Property 2, $\log_5 5^4 = 4$.

     b.   From Property 2, $\log_9 9^{-2} = -2$.

     c.   From Property 3, $6^{\log_6 5} = 5$.

     d.   From Property 3, $7^{\log_7 4} = 4$.

6. $y = \log_7 x$ means that $7^y = x$. Find some ordered pair solutions that satisfy $7^y = x$.

$x = 7^y$	y
1	0
7	1
$\frac{1}{7}$	-1
$\frac{1}{49}$	-2

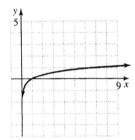

7. $y = \log_{1/4} x$ means that $\left(\dfrac{1}{4}\right)^y = x$. Find some ordered-pair solutions that satisfy $\left(\dfrac{1}{4}\right)^y = x$.

$x = \left(\frac{1}{4}\right)^y$	y
1	0
$\frac{1}{4}$	1
4	-1
16	-2

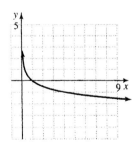

Vocabulary and Readiness Check

1. A function, such as $y = \log_2 x$ is a <u>logarithmic</u> function; **B**.

2. If $y = \log_2 x$, then $\underline{2^y = x}$; **C**.

3. Yes, the function passes both the horizontal- and vertical-line tests.

4. The function has an x-intercept of $\underline{(1, 0)}$.

5. The function has no y-intercept.

6. The domain of this function, in interval notation, is $\underline{(0, \infty)}$.

7. The range of this function, in interval notation, is $\underline{(-\infty, \infty)}$.

Exercise Set 12.4

2. $\log_2 32 = 5$
$2^5 = 32$

4. $\log_5 \dfrac{1}{25} = -2$
$5^{-2} = \dfrac{1}{25}$

6. $\log_{10} 10 = 1$
$10^1 = 10$

8. $\log_8 y = 7$
$8^7 = y$

10. $\log_e \dfrac{1}{e} = -1$
$e^{-1} = \dfrac{1}{e}$

12. $\log_{11} \sqrt[4]{11} = \dfrac{1}{4}$
$11^{1/4} = \sqrt[4]{11}$

14. $\log_{1.2} 1.44 = 2$
$1.2^2 = 1.44$

16. $\log_{1/4} 16 = -2$
$\left(\dfrac{1}{4}\right)^{-2} = 16$

18. $5^3 = 125$

$\log_5 125 = 3$

20. $10^4 = 10,000$

$\log_{10} 10,000 = 4$

22. $\pi^5 = y$

$\log_\pi y = 5$

24. $10^{-2} = \dfrac{1}{100}$

$\log_{10} \dfrac{1}{100} = -2$

26. $3^{-4} = \dfrac{1}{81}$

$\log_3 \dfrac{1}{81} = -4$

28. $4^{1/3} = \sqrt[3]{4}$

$\log_4 \sqrt[3]{4} = \dfrac{1}{3}$

30. $\log_3 9 = 2$ since $3^2 = 9$.

32. $\log_2 \dfrac{1}{32} = -5$ since $2^{-5} = \dfrac{1}{32}$.

34. $\log_8 \dfrac{1}{2} = -\dfrac{1}{3}$ since $8^{-1/3} = \dfrac{1}{2}$.

36. $\log_{2/3} \dfrac{4}{9} = 2$ since $\left(\dfrac{2}{3}\right)^2 = \dfrac{4}{9}$.

38. $\log_9 9 = 1$ since $9^1 = 9$.

40. $\log_{10} \dfrac{1}{10} = \log_{10} 10^{-1} = -1$

42. $\log_2 16 = \log_2 2^4 = 4$

44. $\log_3 \dfrac{1}{9} = \log_3 3^{-2} = -2$

46. $\log_2 8 = x$

$2^x = 8$

$2^x = 2^3$

$x = 3$

48. $\log_2 x = 3$

$2^3 = x$

$x = 8$

50. $\log_x 8 = 3$

$x^3 = 8$

$x^3 = 2^3$

$x = 2$

52. $\log_3 \dfrac{1}{81} = x$

$3^x = \dfrac{1}{81}$

$3^x = 3^{-4}$

$x = -4$

54. $\log_5 \dfrac{1}{125} = x$

$5^x = \dfrac{1}{125}$

$5^x = 5^{-3}$

$x = -3$

56. $\log_9 x = \dfrac{1}{2}$

$9^{1/2} = x$

$x = \sqrt{9}$

$x = 3$

58. $\log_2 16 = x$

$2^x = 16$

$2^x = 2^4$

$x = 4$

60. $\log_{2/3} x = 2$

$\left(\dfrac{2}{3}\right)^2 = x$

$x = \dfrac{4}{9}$

62. $\log_x 27 = 3$

$\qquad x^3 = 27$

$\qquad x^3 = 3^3$

$\qquad x = 3$

64. $\log_6 6^{-2} = x$

$\qquad 6^x = 6^{-2}$

$\qquad x = -2$

66. $5^{\log_5 7} = x$

$\qquad 7 = x$

68. $\log_x 2 = -\dfrac{1}{3}$

$\qquad x^{-1/3} = 2$

$\qquad x = 2^{-3}$

$\qquad x = \dfrac{1}{8}$

70. $\log_6 6^2 = 2$

72. $7^{\log_7 4} = 4$

74. $\log_8 (8)^{-1} = -1$

76. $y = \log_8 x$

$y = 0$: $\log_8 x = 0$

$\qquad x = 8^0 = 1$

(1, 0) is the only x-intercept.
No y-intercept exists.

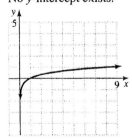

78. $f(x) = \log_{1/2} x$

$y = 0$: $\log_{1/2} x = 0$

$\qquad x = \left(\dfrac{1}{2}\right)^0 = 1$

(1, 0) is the only x-intercept.
No y-intercept exists.

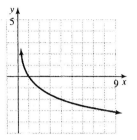

80. $f(x) = \log_6 x$

$y = 0$: $\log_6 x = 0$

$\qquad x = 6^0 = 1$

(1, 0) is the only x-intercept.
No y-intercept exists.

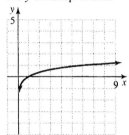

82. $f(x) = \log_{1/5} x$

$y = 0$: $\log_{1/5} x = 0$

$\qquad x = \left(\dfrac{1}{5}\right)^0 = 1$

(1, 0) is the only x-intercept.
No y-intercept exists.

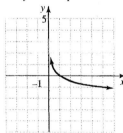

84. $\dfrac{x-5}{5-x} = \dfrac{x-5}{-1(x-5)} = -1$

86. $\dfrac{x^2 - 3x - 10}{2+x} = \dfrac{(x-5)(x+2)}{2+x} = x - 5$

88. $\dfrac{3x}{x+3} + \dfrac{9}{x+3} = \dfrac{3x+9}{x+3} = \dfrac{3(x+3)}{x+3} = 3$

90. $\dfrac{5}{y+1} - \dfrac{4}{y-1} = \dfrac{5(y-1)-4(y+1)}{(y+1)(y-1)}$

$= \dfrac{5y-5-4y-4}{(y+1)(y-1)}$

$= \dfrac{y-9}{(y+1)(y-1)}$

$= \dfrac{y-9}{y^2-1}$

92. $f(x) = \log_{0.3} x$; $g(x) = 0.3^x = f^{-1}(x)$

   a. $(3, 0.027)$ implies $g(3) = 0.027$.

   b. Since $f^{-1}(x) = g(x)$, $(0.027, 3)$ is a solution of $f(x)$.

   c. $(0.027, 3)$ implies $f(0.027) = 3$.

94. Answers may vary

96. $\log_3(2x+4) = 2$

$3^2 = 2x+4$

$9 = 2x+4$

$5 = 2x$

$x = \dfrac{5}{2}$

98. $\log_7(\log_4(\log_2 16)) = \log_7(\log_4(4))$

$= \log(1)$

$= 0$

100. $y = 3^x$; $y = \log_3 x$

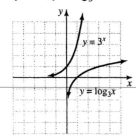

102. $y = \left(\dfrac{1}{2}\right)^x$; $y = \log_{1/2} x$

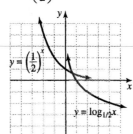

104. $\log_3 10 = x$ implies $3^x = 10$. $3^2 = 9$ and $3^3 = 27$.

Since $9 < 10 < 27$, $\log_3 10$ is between 2 and 3.

106. $\text{pH} = -\log_{10}(\text{H}^+)$; $\text{H}^+ = 0.0050$

$\text{pH} = -\log_{10} 0.0050 \approx 2.3$

The pH of lemonade is 2.3.

Section 12.5

Practice Exercises

1. a. $\log_8 5 + \log_8 3 = \log_8(5 \cdot 3) = \log_8 15$

   b. $\log_2 \dfrac{1}{3} + \log_2 18 = \log_2\left(\dfrac{1}{3} \cdot 18\right) = \log_2 6$

   c. $\log_5(x-1) + \log_5(x+1) = \log_5[(x+1)(x+1)]$
                  $= \log_5(x^2-1)$

2. a. $\log_5 18 - \log_5 6 = \log_5 \dfrac{18}{6} = \log_5 3$

   b. $\log_6 x - \log_6 3 = \log_6 \dfrac{x}{3}$

   c. $\log_4(x^2+1) - \log_4(x^2+3) = \log_4 \dfrac{x^2+1}{x^2+3}$

3. a. $\log_7 x^8 = 8\log_7 x$

   b. $\log_5 \sqrt[4]{7} = \log_5 7^{1/4} = \dfrac{1}{4}\log_5 7$

4. a. $2\log_5 4 + 5\log_5 2 = \log_5 4^2 + \log_5 2^5$
$$= \log_5 16 + \log_5 32$$
$$= \log_5 (16 \cdot 32)$$
$$= \log_5 512$$

b. $2\log_8 x - \log_8 (x+3) = \log_8 x^2 - \log_8 (x+3)$
$$= \log_8 \frac{x^2}{x+3}$$

c. $\log_7 12 + \log_7 5 - \log_7 4$
$$= \log_7 (12 \cdot 5) - \log_7 4$$
$$= \log_7 60 - \log_7 4$$
$$= \log_7 \frac{60}{4}$$
$$= \log_7 15$$

5. a. $\log_5 \frac{4 \cdot 3}{7} = \log_5 (4 \cdot 3) - \log_5 7$
$$= \log_5 4 + \log_5 3 - \log_5 7$$

b. $\log_4 \frac{a^2}{b^5} = \log_4 a^2 - \log_4 b^5$
$$= 2\log_4 a - 5\log_4 b$$

6. $\log_b 5 = 0.83$ and $\log_b 3 = 0.56$

a. $\log_b 15 = \log_b (3 \cdot 5)$
$$= \log_b 3 + \log_b 5$$
$$= 0.56 + 0.83$$
$$= 1.39$$

b. $\log_b 25 = \log_b 5^2 = 2\log_b 5 = 2(0.83) = 1.66$

c. $\log_b \sqrt{3} = \log_b 3^{1/2}$
$$= \frac{1}{2}\log_b 3$$
$$= \frac{1}{2}(0.56)$$
$$= 0.28$$

Vocabulary and Readiness Check

1. $\log_b 12 + \log_b 3 = \log_b (12 \cdot 3) = \log_b \underline{36}$; **a.**

2. $\log_b 12 - \log_b 3 = \log_b \frac{12}{3} = \log_b \underline{4}$; **c.**

3. $7\log_b 2 = \underline{\log_b 2^7}$; **b.**

4. $\log_b 1 = \underline{0}$; **c.**

5. $b^{\log_b x} = \underline{x}$; **a.**

6. $\log_5 5^2 = \underline{2}$; **b.**

Exercise Set 12.5

2. $\log_3 8 + \log_3 4 = \log_3 (8 \cdot 4) = \log_3 32$

4. $\log_2 x + \log_2 y = \log_2 (x \cdot y) = \log_2 xy$

6. $\log_5 y^3 + \log_5 (y - 7) = \log_5 [y^3 (y - 7)]$
$$= \log_5 (y^4 - 7y^3)$$

8. $\log_6 3 + \log_6 (x + 4) + \log_6 5$
$$= \log_6 [3 \cdot 5(x + 4)]$$
$$= \log_6 (15x + 60)$$

10. $\log_7 20 - \log_7 4 = \log_7 \frac{20}{4} = \log_7 5$

12. $\log_5 12 - \log_5 3 = \log_5 \frac{12}{3} = \log_5 4$

14. $\log_3 12 - \log_3 z = \log_3 \frac{12}{z}$

16. $\log_7 (x + 9) - \log_7 (x^2 + 10) = \log_7 \frac{x+9}{x^2+10}$

18. $\log_2 x^5 = 5\log_2 x$

20. $\log_6 7^{-2} = -2\log_6 7$

22. $\log_5 \sqrt[3]{x} = \log_5 x^{1/3} = \frac{1}{3}\log_5 x$

24. $\log_5 2 + \log_5 y^2 = \log_5 2y^2$

26. $2\log_3 5 + \log_3 2 = \log_3 5^2 + \log_3 2$
$$= \log_3 25 + \log_3 2$$
$$= \log_3 (25 \cdot 2)$$
$$= \log_3 50$$

28. $2\log_7 y + 6\log_7 z = \log_7 y^2 + \log_7 z^6$
$$= \log_7 y^2 z^6$$

30. $\log_6 18 + \log_6 2 - \log_6 9 = \log_6(18 \cdot 2) - \log_6 9$
$$= \log_6 \frac{36}{9}$$
$$= \log_6 4$$

32. $\log_8 5 + \log_8 15 - \log_8 20$
$$= \log_8(5 \cdot 15) - \log_8 20$$
$$= \log_8 \frac{75}{20}$$
$$= \log_8 \frac{15}{4}$$

34. $\log_9(4x) - \log_9(x-3) + \log_9(x^3+1)$
$$= \log_9 \frac{4x}{x-3} + \log_9(x^3+1)$$
$$= \log_9 \frac{4x(x^3+1)}{x-3}$$
$$= \log_9 \frac{4x^4+4x}{x-3}$$

36. $2\log_5 x + \frac{1}{3}\log_5 x - 3\log_5(x+5)$
$$= \log_5 x^2 + \log_5 x^{1/3} - \log_5(x+5)^3$$
$$= \log_5(x^2 \cdot x^{1/3}) - \log_5(x+5)^3$$
$$= \log_5 x^{7/3} - \log_5(x+5)^3$$
$$= \log_5 \frac{x^{7/3}}{(x+5)^3}$$

38. $5\log_6 x - \frac{3}{4}\log_6 x + 3\log_6 x = \left(5 - \frac{3}{4} + 3\right)\log_6 x$
$$= \frac{29}{4}\log_6 x$$
$$= \log_6 x^{29/4}$$

40. $\log_7 \frac{5x}{4} = \log_7 5x - \log_7 4$
$$= \log_7 5 + \log_7 x - \log_7 4$$

42. $\log_9 \frac{7}{8y} = \log_9 7 - \log_9 8y$
$$= \log_9 7 - (\log_9 8 + \log_9 y)$$
$$= \log_9 7 - \log_9 8 - \log_9 y$$

44. $\log_5 \frac{x}{y^4} = \log_5 x - \log_5 y^4$
$$= \log_5 x - 4\log_5 y$$

46. $\log_b \sqrt{\frac{3}{y}} = \log_b \left(\frac{3}{y}\right)^{1/2}$
$$= \log_b \frac{3^{1/2}}{y^{1/2}}$$
$$= \log_b 3^{1/2} - \log_b y^{1/2}$$
$$= \frac{1}{2}\log_b 3 - \frac{1}{2}\log_b y$$

48. $\log_2 y^3 z = \log_2 y^3 + \log_2 z$
$$= 3\log_2 y + \log_2 z$$

50. $\log_3 x^2(x-9) = \log_3 x^2 + \log_3(x-9)$
$$= 2\log_3 x + \log_3(x-9)$$

52. $\log_3 \frac{(x+5)^2}{x} = \log_3(x+5)^2 - \log_3 x$
$$= 2\log_3(x+5) - \log_3 x$$

54. $\log_b 25 = \log_b 5^2 = 2\log_b 5 = 2(0.7) = 1.4$

56. $\log_b \frac{3}{5} = \log_b 3 - \log_b 5 = 0.5 - 0.7 = -0.2$

58. $\log_b \sqrt[4]{3} = \log_b 3^{1/4} = \frac{1}{4}\log_b 3 = \frac{1}{4}(0.5) = 0.125$

60. $\log_b 81 = \log_b 3^4 = 4\log_b 3 = 4(0.68) = 2.72$

62. $\log_b \frac{4}{32} = \log_b 4 - \log_b 32$
$$= \log_b 2^2 - \log_b 2^5$$
$$= 2\log_b 2 - 5\log_b 2$$
$$= -3\log_b 2$$
$$= -3(0.43)$$
$$= -1.29$$

64. $\log_b \sqrt{\frac{3}{2}} = \log_b \frac{3^{1/2}}{2^{1/2}}$
$$= \log_b 3^{1/2} - \log_b 2^{1/2}$$
$$= \frac{1}{2}\log_b 3 - \frac{1}{2}\log_b 3$$
$$= \frac{1}{2}(0.68) - \frac{1}{2}(0.43)$$
$$= 0.34 - 0.215$$
$$= 0.125$$

66. $\log_{10} 100 = \log_{10} 10^2 = 2$

68. $\log_7 7^2 = 2$

70. $\log_3 \dfrac{14}{11} = \log_3 14 - \log_3 11; \ \mathbf{b}$

72. $\log_2 x^3 = 3\log_2 x$ is true.

74. $\dfrac{\log_7 10}{\log_7 5} = \log_7 2$ is false.

76. $\dfrac{\log_7 x}{\log_7 y} = (\log_7 x) - (\log_7 y)$ is false.

78. Yes, this is true, since $\log 1 = 0$.

Integrated Review

1. $(f+g)(x) = x - 6 + x^2 + 1 = x^2 + x - 5$

2. $(f-g)(x) = x - 6 - (x^2 + 1) = -x^2 + x - 7$

3. $(f \cdot g)(x) = (x-6)(x^2+1) = x^3 - 6x^2 + x - 6$

4. $\left(\dfrac{f}{g}\right)(x) = \dfrac{x-6}{x^2+1}$

5. $(f \circ g)(x) = f(g(x)) = f(3x-1) = \sqrt{3x-1}$

6. $(g \circ f)(x) = g(f(x)) = g\left(\sqrt{x}\right) = 3\sqrt{x} - 1$

7. one-to-one; inverse:
$$\{(6,-2),(8,4),(-6,2),(3,3)\}$$

8. not one-to-one

9. not one-to-one

10. one-to-one

11. not one-to-one

12. $\begin{aligned} f(x) &= 3x \\ y &= 3x \\ \\ x &= 3y \\ y &= \frac{x}{3} \\ f^{-1}(x) &= \frac{x}{3} \end{aligned}$

13. $\begin{aligned} f(x) &= x+4 \\ y &= x+4 \\ \\ x &= y+4 \\ y &= x-4 \\ f^{-1}(x) &= x-4 \end{aligned}$

14. $\begin{aligned} f(x) &= 5x-1 \\ y &= 5x-1 \\ \\ x &= 5y-1 \\ 5y &= x+1 \\ y &= \frac{x+1}{5} \\ f^{-1}(x) &= \frac{x+1}{5} \end{aligned}$

15. $\begin{aligned} f(x) &= 3x+2 \\ y &= 3x+2 \\ \\ x &= 3y+2 \\ 3y &= x-2 \\ y &= \frac{x-2}{3} \\ f^{-1}(x) &= \frac{x-2}{3} \end{aligned}$

16. $y = \left(\dfrac{1}{2}\right)^x$

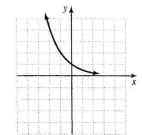

17. $y = 2^x + 1$

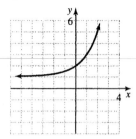

18. $y = \log_3 x$

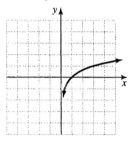

19. $y = \log_{1/3} x$

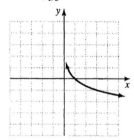

20. $2^x = 8$

$2^x = 2^3$

$x = 3$

The solution is 3.

21. $9 = 3^{x-5}$

$3^2 = 3^{x-5}$

$2 = x - 5$

$7 = x$

The solution is 7.

22. $4^{x-1} = 8^{x+2}$

$(2^2)^{x-1} = (2^3)^{x+2}$

$2^{2x-2} = 2^{3x+6}$

$2x - 2 = 3x + 6$

$-8 = x$

The solution is -8.

23. $25^x = 125^{x-1}$

$(5^2)^x = (5^3)^{x-1}$

$5^{2x} = 5^{3x-3}$

$2x = 3x - 3$

$3 = x$

The solution is 3.

24. $\log_4 16 = x$

$4^x = 16$

$4^x = 4^2$

$x = 2$

The solution is 2.

25. $\log_{49} 7 = x$

$49^x = 7$

$(7^2)^x = 7$

$7^{2x} = 7$

$2x = 1$

$x = \dfrac{1}{2}$

The solution is $\dfrac{1}{2}$.

26. $\log_2 x = 5$

$2^5 = x$

$32 = x$

The solution is 32.

27. $\log_x 64 = 3$

$x^3 = 64$

$x^3 = 4^3$

$x = 4$

The solution is 4.

28. $\log_x \dfrac{1}{125} = -3$

$x^{-3} = \dfrac{1}{125}$

$x^{-3} = 5^{-3}$

$x = 5$

The solution is 5.

29. $\log_3 x = -2$

$3^{-2} = x$

$x = \dfrac{1}{3^2} = \dfrac{1}{9}$

The solution is $\dfrac{1}{9}$

30. $5\log_2 x = \log_2 x^5$

31. $x\log_2 5 = \log_2 5^x$

32. $3\log_5 x - 5\log_5 y = \log_5 x^3 - \log_5 y^5 = \log_5 \dfrac{x^3}{y^5}$

33. $9\log_5 x + 3\log_5 y = \log_5 x^9 + \log_5 y^3$
$$= \log_5 x^9 y^3$$

34. $\log_2 x + \log_2 (x-3) - \log_2 (x^2+4)$
$$= \log_2 [x(x-3)] - \log_2 (x^2+4)$$
$$= \log_2 (x^2-3x) - \log_2 (x^2+4)$$
$$= \log_2 \dfrac{x^2-3x}{x^2+4}$$

35. $\log_3 y - \log_3 (y+2) + \log_3 (y^3+11)$
$$= \log_3 \dfrac{y}{y+2} + \log_3 (y^3+11)$$
$$= \log_3 \dfrac{y(y^3+11)}{y+2}$$
$$= \log_3 \dfrac{y^4+11y}{y+2}$$

36. $\log_7 \dfrac{9x^2}{y} = \log_7 9x^2 - \log_7 y$
$$= \log_7 9 + \log_7 x^2 - \log_7 y$$
$$= \log_7 9 + 2\log_7 x - \log_7 y$$

37. $\log_6 \dfrac{5y}{z^2} = \log_6 5y - \log_6 z^2$
$$= \log_6 5 + \log_6 y - 2\log_6 z$$

Section 12.6

Practice Exercises

1. To four decimal places, $\log 15 \approx 1.1761$.

2. a. $\log \dfrac{1}{100} = \log 10^{-2} = 2$

   b. $\log 100{,}000 = \log 10^5 = 5$

   c. $\log \sqrt[5]{10} = \log 10^{1/5} = \dfrac{1}{5}$

   d. $\log 0.001 = \log 10^{-3} = -3$

3. $\log x = 3.4$
$$x = 10^{3.4}$$
$$x \approx 2511.8864$$

4. $a = 450$ micrometers
$T = 4.2$ seconds
$B = 3.6$
$$R = \log\left(\dfrac{a}{T}\right) + B$$
$$= \log\left(\dfrac{450}{4.2}\right) + 3.6$$
$$\approx 2.0 + 3.6$$
$$= 5.6$$
The earthquake had a magnitude of 5.6 on the Richter scale.

5. To four decimal places, $\ln 13 \approx 2.5649$.

6. a. $\ln e^4 = 4$

   b. $\ln \sqrt[3]{e} = \ln e^{1/3} = \dfrac{1}{3}$

7. $\ln 5x = 8$
$$e^8 = 5x$$
$$\dfrac{e^8}{5} = x$$
$$x = \dfrac{1}{5}e^8 \approx 596.1916$$

8. $P = \$2400$
$r = 6\% = 0.06$
$t = 4$ years
$$A = Pe^{rt} = 2400e^{0.06(4)} = 2400e^{0.24} \approx 3051.00$$
The total amount of money owed is $3051.00.

9. $\log_8 5 = \dfrac{\log 5}{\log 8} \approx \dfrac{0.6989700043}{0.903089987} \approx 0.773976$

To four decimal places, $\log_8 5 \approx 0.7740$.

Vocabulary and Readiness Check

1. The base of $\log 7$ is $\underline{10}$; **c.**

2. The base of $\ln 7$ is $\underline{e}$; **a.**

3. $\log_{10} 10^7 = \underline{7}$; **b.**

4. $\log_7 1 = \underline{0}$; **d.**

5. $\log_e e^5 = \underline{5}$; **b.**

6. $\ln e^5 = \underline{5}$; **b.**

7. $\log_2 7 = \dfrac{\log 7}{\log 2} = \dfrac{\ln 7}{\ln 2}$; **a** and **b.**

Exercise Set 12.6

2. $\log 6 \approx 0.7782$

4. $\log 4.86 \approx 0.6866$

6. $\ln 3 \approx 1.0986$

8. $\ln 0.0032 \approx -5.7446$

10. $\log 25.9 \approx 1.4133$

12. $\ln 7 \approx 1.9459$

14. $\ln 41.5 \approx 3.7257$

16. Answers may vary

18. $\log 10{,}000 = \log 10^4 = 4$

20. $\log\left(\dfrac{1}{100}\right) = \log 10^{-2} = -2$

22. $\ln e^4 = 4$

24. $\ln \sqrt[5]{e} = \ln e^{1/5} = \dfrac{1}{5}$

26. $\log 10^7 = 7$

28. $\ln e^{-5} = -5$

30. $\log 0.001 = \log 10^{-3} = -3$

32. $\log \sqrt{10} = \log 10^{1/2} = \dfrac{1}{2}$

34. $\ln 5x = 9$
$$5x = e^9$$
$$x = \frac{e^9}{5} \approx 1620.6168$$

36. $\log x = 2.1$
$$x = 10^{2.1} \approx 125.8925$$

38. $\log 3x = 1.3$
$$3x = 10^{1.3}$$
$$x = \frac{10^{1.3}}{3} \approx 6.6509$$

40. $\ln x = 2.1$
$$x = e^{2.1} \approx 8.1662$$

42. $\ln(2x + 5) = 3.4$
$$2x + 5 = e^{3.4}$$
$$2x = e^{3.4} - 5$$
$$x = \frac{e^{3.4} - 5}{2} \approx 12.4821$$

44. $\log x = 3.1$
$$x = 10^{3.1} \approx 1258.9254$$

46. $\ln x = -3.7$
$$x = e^{-3.7} \approx 0.0247$$

48. $\log(3x - 2) = -0.8$
$$3x - 2 = 10^{-0.8}$$
$$3x = 2 + 10^{-0.8}$$
$$x = \frac{2 + 10^{-0.8}}{3} \approx 0.7195$$

50. $\ln 3x = 0.76$
$$3x = e^{0.76}$$
$$x = \frac{e^{0.76}}{3} \approx 0.7128$$

52. $\log_3 2 = \dfrac{\log 2}{\log 3} \approx 0.6309$

54. $\log_{1/3} 2 = \dfrac{\log 2}{\log\left(\frac{1}{3}\right)} \approx -0.6309$

56. $\log_9 4 = \dfrac{\log 4}{\log 9} \approx 0.6309$

58. $\log_6 \dfrac{2}{3} = \dfrac{\log \dfrac{2}{3}}{\log 6} \approx -0.2263$

60. $\log_6 8 = \dfrac{\log 8}{\log 6} \approx 1.1606$

62. $R = \log\left(\dfrac{a}{T}\right) + B = \log\left(\dfrac{150}{3.6}\right) + 1.9 \approx 3.5$

The earthquake measures 3.5 on the Richter scale.

64. $R = \log\left(\dfrac{a}{T}\right) + B = \log\left(\dfrac{450}{4.2}\right) + 2.7 \approx 4.7$

The earthquake measures 4.7 on the Richter scale.

66. $A = Pe^{rt} = 3500e^{0.06(1)} \approx 3716.43$
The account contains \$3716.43.

68. $A = Pe^{rt} = 2500e^{(0.10)(3)} \approx 3374.65$
The certificate of deposit is worth \$3374.65.

70. $2x + 3 = 5 - 2(3x - 1)$
$2x + 3 = 5 - 6x + 2$
$2x + 3 = 7 - 6x$
$8x = 4$
$x = \dfrac{4}{8} = \dfrac{1}{2}$

The solution is $\dfrac{1}{2}$.

72. $4x - 8y = 10x$
$-8y = 6x$
$\dfrac{-8y}{6} = x$
$-\dfrac{4y}{3} = x$

74. $x^2 + 4x = 12$
$x^2 + 4x - 12 = 0$
$(x + 6)(x - 2) = 0$
$x + 6 = 0 \quad$ or $\quad x - 2 = 0$
$x = -6 \quad$ or $\quad x = 2$
The solutions are –6 and 2.

76. $\begin{cases} 5x + y = 5 \\ -3x - 2y = -10 \end{cases}$

Multiply the first equation by 2, then add.
$10x + 2y = 10$
$\underline{-3x - 2y = -10}$
$7x = 0$
$x = 0$

Replace x with 0 in the first equation.
$5(0) + y = 5$
$y = 5$
The solution is (0, 5).

78. $\log 50^{-1}$ must be larger. Answers may vary

80. $f(x) = e^{2x}$

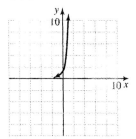

82. $f(x) = e^{-x}$

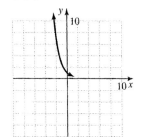

84. $f(x) = e^x - 3$

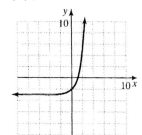

86. $f(x) = e^{x+4}$

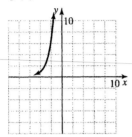

88. $f(x) = -2e^x$

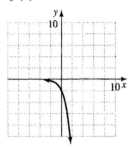

90. $f(x) = \log x$

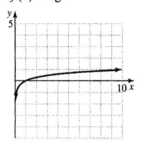

92. $f(x) = 3 \ln x$

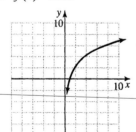

94. $f(x) = \log(x - 2)$

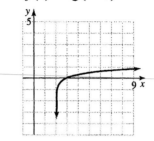

96. $f(x) = \ln x + 3$

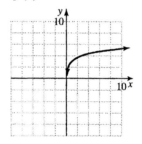

98. $f(x) = \ln x$
    $f(x) = \ln x - 3$
    $f(x) = \ln x + 3$

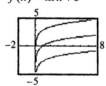

Answers may vary

Section 12.7

Practice Exercises

1. $5^x = 9$
    $\log 5^x = \log 9$
    $x \log 5 = \log 9$
    $x = \dfrac{\log 9}{\log 5} \approx 1.3652$

The solution is $\dfrac{\log 9}{\log 5}$, or approximately 1.3652.

2. $\log_2(x-1)=5$

$$2^5 = x-1$$
$$32 = x-1$$
$$33 = x$$

Check: $\log_2(x-1)=5$
$$\log_2(33-1) \overset{?}{=} 5$$
$$\log_2 32 \overset{?}{=} 5$$
$$2^5 = 32 \quad \text{True}$$

The solution is 33.

3. $\log_5 x + \log_5(x+4) = 1$

$$\log_5 x(x+4) = 1$$
$$\log_5(x^2 + 4x) = 1$$
$$5^1 = x^2 + 4x$$
$$0 = x^2 + 4x - 5$$
$$0 = (x+5)(x-1)$$
$$x+5 = 0 \quad \text{or} \quad x-1 = 0$$
$$x = -5 \qquad\qquad x = 1$$

Since $\log_5(-5)$ is undefined, -5 is rejected. The solution is 1.

4. $\log(x+3) - \log x = 1$

$$\log \frac{x+3}{x} = 1$$
$$10^1 = \frac{x+3}{x}$$
$$10x = x+3$$
$$9x = 3$$
$$x = \frac{1}{3}$$

The solution is $\frac{1}{3}$.

5. $y_0 = 60; \ t = 3$

$$y = y_0 e^{0.916t}$$
$$y = 60 e^{0.916(3)} = 60 e^{2.748} \approx 937$$

The population will be approximately 937 rabbits.

6. $P = \$3000; \ r = 7\% = 0.07; \ n = 12;$
$A = 2P = \$6000$

$$A = P\left(1 + \frac{r}{n}\right)^{nt}$$
$$6000 = 3000\left(1 + \frac{0.07}{12}\right)^{12t}$$
$$2 = \left(1 + \frac{0.07}{12}\right)^{12t}$$
$$\log 2 = \log\left(1 + \frac{0.07}{12}\right)^{12t}$$
$$\log 2 = 12t \log\left(1 + \frac{0.07}{12}\right)$$
$$\frac{\log 2}{12 \log\left(1 + \frac{0.07}{12}\right)} = t$$
$$9.9 \approx t$$

It takes nearly 10 years to double.

Graphing Calculator Explorations

1. $Y_1 = 5000\left(1 + \frac{0.05}{4}\right)^{4x}$, $Y_2 = 6000$

It takes 3.67 years, or 3 years and 8 months.

2. $Y_1 = 1000\left(1 + \frac{0.045}{365}\right)^{365x}$, $Y_2 = 2000$

It takes 15.40 years or 15 years and 5 months.

3. $Y_1 = 10,000\left(1 + \frac{0.06}{12}\right)^{12x}$, $Y_2 = 40,000$

It takes 23.16 years or 23 years and 2 months.

4. $Y_1 = 500\left(1 + \dfrac{0.04}{2}\right)^{2x}$, $Y_2 = 800$

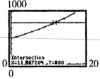

It takes 11.87 years or 11 years and 10 months.

Exercise Set 12.7

2. $4^x = 7$

$\log 4^x = \log 7$

$x \log 7 = \log 7$

$x = \dfrac{\log 7}{\log 4} \approx 1.4037$

4. $5^{3x} = 5.6$

$\log 5^{3x} = \log 5.6$

$3x \log 5 = \log 5.6$

$x = \dfrac{\log 5.6}{3 \log 5} \approx 0.3568$

6. $8^{x-2} = 12$

$\log 8^{x-2} = \log 12$

$(x-2) \log 8 = \log 12$

$x - 2 = \dfrac{\log 12}{\log 8}$

$x = 2 + \dfrac{\log 12}{\log 8} \approx 3.1950$

8. $3^x = 11$

$\log 3^x = \log 11$

$x \log 3 = \log 11$

$x = \dfrac{\log 11}{\log 3} \approx 2.1827$

10. $6^{x+3} = 2$

$\log 6^{x+3} = \log 2$

$(x+3) \log 6 = \log 2$

$x + 3 = \dfrac{\log 2}{\log 6}$

$x = -3 + \dfrac{\log 2}{\log 6} \approx -2.6131$

12. $5^{2x-6} = 12$

$\log 5^{2x-6} = \log 12$

$(2x - 6) \log 5 = \log 12$

$2x - 6 = \dfrac{\log 12}{\log 5}$

$2x = 6 + \dfrac{\log 12}{\log 5}$

$x = \dfrac{1}{2}\left(6 + \dfrac{\log 12}{\log 5}\right) \approx 3.7720$

14. $e^{2x} = 8$

$\ln e^{2x} = \ln 8$

$2x = \ln 8$

$x = \dfrac{\ln 8}{2} \approx 1.0397$

16. $\log_6 (x^2 - x) = 1$

$6^1 = x^2 - x$

$0 = x^2 - x - 6$

$0 = (x - 3)(x + 2)$

$x = 3$ or $x = -2$

18. $\log_2 x^2 = 6$

$2^6 = x^2$

$64 = x^2$

$\pm 8 = x$

20. $\log_3 5 + \log_3 x = 1$

$\log_3 5x = 1$

$3^1 = 5x$

$\dfrac{3}{5} = x$

22. $\log_4 10 - \log_4 x = 2$

$\log_4 \dfrac{10}{x} = 2$

$4^2 = \dfrac{10}{x}$

$16x = 10$

$x = \dfrac{5}{8}$

24. $\log_3 x + \log_3(x+6) = 3$

$\log_3[x(x+6)] = 3$

$3^3 = x^2 + 6x$

$0 = x^2 + 6x - 27$

$0 = (x+9)(x-3)$

$x = -9$ or $x = 3$

We discard -9 as extraneous, the solution is 3.

26. $\log_6(x+2) - \log_6 x = 2$

$\log_6 \dfrac{x+2}{x} = 2$

$6^2 = \dfrac{x+2}{x}$

$36x = x + 2$

$35x = 2$

$x = \dfrac{2}{35}$

28. $\log_2(x-5) = 3$

$2^3 = x - 5$

$8 = x - 5$

$13 = x$

30. $\log_8(x^2 - 2x) = 1$

$8^1 = x^2 - 2x$

$0 = x^2 - 2x - 8$

$0 = (x-4)(x+2)$

$x = 4$ or $x = -2$

32. $\ln 3 + \ln(x-1) = 0$

$\ln[3(x-1)] = 0$

$e^0 = 3x - 3$

$1 = 3x - 3$

$4 = 3x$

$\dfrac{4}{3} = x$

34. $2\log x - \log x = 3$

$\log x = 3$

$x = 10^3 = 1000$

36. $\log_4 x + \log_4(x+7) = 1$

$\log_4[x(x+7)] = 1$

$4^1 = x^2 + 7x$

$0 = x^2 + 7x - 4$

$x = \dfrac{-7 \pm \sqrt{7^2 - 4(1)(-4)}}{2(1)}$

$= \dfrac{-7 \pm \sqrt{65}}{2}$

Discard $\dfrac{-7 - \sqrt{65}}{2}$, the solution is

$x = \dfrac{-7 + \sqrt{65}}{2}$.

38. $\log_2 x - \log_2(3x+5) = 4$

$\log_2 \dfrac{x}{3x+5} = 4$

$2^4 = \dfrac{x}{3x+5}$

$16(3x+5) = x$

$48x + 80 = x$

$47x = -80$

$x = -\dfrac{80}{47}$ (extraneous)

No solution, or $\varnothing$

40. $\log_3 x + \log_3(x-8) = 2$

$\log_3[x(x-8)] = 2$

$3^2 = x^2 - 8x$

$0 = x^2 - 8x - 9$

$0 = (x-9)(x+1)$

$x = 9$ or $x = -1$

We discard -1 as extraneous, the solution is 9.

42.
$$y = y_0 e^{0.075t}$$
$$45,000 = 20,000 e^{0.075t}$$
$$\frac{45,000}{20,000} = e^{0.075t}$$
$$\frac{9}{4} = e^{0.075t}$$
$$\ln \frac{9}{4} = \ln e^{0.075t}$$
$$\ln \frac{9}{4} = 0.075t$$
$$t = \frac{\ln\left(\frac{9}{4}\right)}{0.075} \approx 10.81$$

45,000 people will have the flu in 10.81 weeks or $10.81 \cdot 7 \approx 76$ days.

44.
$$y = y_0 e^{0.016t}$$
$$2000 = 1730 e^{0.016t}$$
$$\frac{2000}{1730} = e^{0.016t}$$
$$\ln \frac{200}{173} = \ln e^{0.016t}$$
$$\ln \frac{200}{173} = 0.016t$$
$$t = \frac{\ln \frac{200}{173}}{0.016} \approx 9.1$$

The population will be 2 billion in 9.1 years.

46. $y = y_0 e^{0.00894t}$, $t = 2020 - 2007 = 13$,
$y_0 = 301,140,000$
$$y = 301,140,000 e^{0.00894(13)}$$
$$\approx 338,250,000$$

There will be 338,250,000 inhabitants in 2020.

48.
$$A = P\left(1 + \frac{r}{n}\right)^{nt}$$
$$1200 = 600\left(1 + \frac{0.12}{12}\right)^{12t}$$
$$2 = (1.01)^{12t}$$
$$\log 2 = \log (1.01)^{12t}$$
$$\log 2 = 12t \log 1.01$$
$$t = \frac{\log 2}{12 \log 1.01} \approx 5.8$$

It takes 5.8 years for the $600 to double.

50. $A = P\left(1 + \dfrac{r}{n}\right)^{nt}$; $P = 1500$,
$A = 1500 + 200 = 1700$, $r = 0.10$, $n = 2$
$$1700 = 1500\left(1 + \frac{0.10}{2}\right)^{2t}$$
$$\frac{17}{15} = (1.05)^{2t}$$
$$\log \frac{17}{15} = \log (1.05)^{2t}$$
$$\log \frac{17}{15} = 2t \log 1.05$$
$$t = \frac{\log\left(\frac{17}{15}\right)}{2 \log 1.05} \approx 1.3$$

It takes 1.3 years to earn $200.

52.
$$A = P\left(1 + \frac{r}{n}\right)^{nt}$$
$$2000 = 1000\left(1 + \frac{0.08}{12}\right)^{12t}$$
$$2 = \left(1 + \frac{0.08}{12}\right)^{12t}$$
$$\log 2 = \log\left(1 + \frac{0.08}{12}\right)^{12t}$$
$$\log 2 = 12t \log\left(1 + \frac{0.08}{12}\right)$$
$$t = \frac{\log 2}{12 \log\left(1 + \frac{0.08}{12}\right)}$$
$$t \approx 8.7$$

It takes 8.7 years to double.

54. $w = 0.00185 h^{2.67}$
$$w = 0.00185(43)^{2.67} \approx 42.5$$

The expected weight of a boy 43 inches tall is 42.5 pounds.

56.
$$w = 0.00185 h^{2.67}$$
$$140 = 0.00185 h^{2.67}$$
$$\frac{140}{0.00185} = h^{2.67}$$
$$\sqrt[2.67]{\frac{140}{0.00185}} = \sqrt[2.67]{h^{2.67}}$$
$$h \approx 67.2$$

The expected height of the boy is 67.2 inches.

58. $P = 14.7e^{-0.21x}$, $x = 2.7$

$P = 14.7e^{-0.21(2.7)} \approx 8.3$

The average atmospheric pressure at Pikes Peak is 8.3 pounds per square inch.

60. $P = 14.7e^{-0.21x}$

$6.5 = 14.7e^{-0.21x}$

$\dfrac{6.5}{14.7} = e^{-0.21x}$

$\ln \dfrac{6.5}{14.7} = \ln e^{-0.21x}$

$\ln \dfrac{6.5}{14.7} = -0.21x$

$x = \dfrac{\ln\left(\dfrac{6.5}{14.7}\right)}{-0.21} \approx 3.9$

The elevation is about 3.9 miles.

62. $t = \dfrac{1}{c} \ln\left(\dfrac{A}{A-N}\right)$

$t = \dfrac{1}{0.03} \ln\left(\dfrac{65}{65-30}\right) \approx 20.63$

It will take 21 weeks.

64. $t = \dfrac{1}{c} \ln\left(\dfrac{A}{A-N}\right)$

$t = \dfrac{1}{0.17} \ln\left(\dfrac{24}{24-15}\right) \approx 5.77$

It will take 6 weeks.

66. $\dfrac{x^3 - 2y + z}{2z} = \dfrac{(-2)^3 - 2(0) + 3}{2(3)} = \dfrac{-5}{6} = -\dfrac{5}{6}$

68. $\dfrac{4y - 3x + z}{2x + y} = \dfrac{4(0) - 3(-2) + 3}{2(-2) + 0} = \dfrac{9}{-4} = -\dfrac{9}{4}$

70. $f(x) = \dfrac{x-3}{4}$

$y = \dfrac{x-3}{4}$

$x = \dfrac{y-3}{4}$

$4x = y - 3$

$4x + 3 = y$

$f^{-1}(x) = 4x + 3$

72. $y = 2{,}495{,}529$, $y_0 = 2{,}018{,}456$, and $t = 6$

$y = y_0 e^{kt}$

$2{,}495{,}529 = 2{,}018{,}456 e^{k(6)}$

$\dfrac{2{,}495{,}529}{2{,}018{,}456} = e^{6k}$

$\ln \dfrac{2{,}495{,}529}{2{,}018{,}456} = \ln e^{6k}$

$\ln \dfrac{2{,}495{,}529}{2{,}018{,}456} = 6k$

$k = \dfrac{\ln \dfrac{2{,}495{,}529}{2{,}018{,}456}}{6} \approx 0.0354$

The annual rate of growth was 3.5%.

74. Answers may vary

76. $Y_1 = 10^{0.5x}$, $Y_2 = 7$

$x \approx 1.69$

78. $Y_1 = \ln(1.3x - 2.1) + 3.5x - 5$, $Y_2 = 0$

$x \approx 1.81$

80. $Y_1 = 5^{2x-6} - 12$, $Y_2 = 0$

$x \approx 3.77$

82. $Y_1 = \ln 3 + \ln(x-1)$, $Y_2 = 0$

$x \approx 1.33$

The Bigger Picture

1. $8^x = 2^{x-3}$

    $2^{3x} = 2^{x-3}$

    $3x = x - 3$

    $2x = -3$

    $x = -\dfrac{3}{2}$

2. $11^x = 5$

    $\log 11^x = \log 5$

    $x \log 11 = \log 5$

    $x = \dfrac{\log 5}{\log 11} \approx 0.6712$

3. $-7x + 3 \le -5x + 13$

    $-10 \le 2x$

    $-5 \le x$

    The solution is $[-5, \infty)$.

4. $-7 \le 3x + 6 \le 0$

    $-13 \le 3x \le -6$

    $-\dfrac{13}{3} \le x \le -2$

    The solution is $\left[-\dfrac{13}{3}, -2\right]$.

5. $|5y + 3| < 3$

    $-3 < 5y + 3 < 3$

    $-6 < 5y < 0$

    $-\dfrac{6}{5} < y < 0$

    The solution is $\left(-\dfrac{6}{5}, 0\right)$.

6. $(x - 6)(5x + 1) = 0$

    $x - 6 = 0$ or $5x + 1 = 0$

    $x = 6$ $5x = -1$

    $x = -\dfrac{1}{5}$

    The solutions are 6 and $-\dfrac{1}{5}$.

7. $\log_{13} 8 + \log_{13}(x - 1) = 1$

    $\log_{13}(8x - 8) = 1$

    $13^1 = 8x - 8$

    $21 = 8x$

    $\dfrac{21}{8} = x$

8. $\left|\dfrac{3x - 1}{4}\right| = 2$

    $\dfrac{3x - 1}{4} = 2$ or $\dfrac{3x - 1}{4} = -2$

    $3x - 1 = 8$ $3x - 1 = -8$

    $3x = 9$ $3x = -7$

    $x = 3$ $x = -\dfrac{7}{3}$

    The solutions are 3 and $-\dfrac{7}{3}$.

9. $|7x + 1| > -2$ is a true statement for all x, so the solution is $(-\infty, \infty)$.

10. $x^2 = 4$

    $x = \pm\sqrt{4} = \pm 2$

    The solutions are 2 and -2.

11. $(x + 5)^2 = 3$

    $x + 5 = \pm\sqrt{3}$

    $x = -5 \pm \sqrt{3}$

    The solutions are $-5 + \sqrt{3}$ and $-5 - \sqrt{3}$.

12. $\log_7(4x^2 - 27x) = 1$

    $7^1 = 4x^2 - 27x$

    $0 = 4x^2 - 27x - 7$

    $0 = (4x + 1)(x - 7)$

    $4x + 1 = 0$ or $x - 7 = 0$

    $4x = -1$ $x = 7$

    $x = -\dfrac{1}{4}$

    The solutions are $-\dfrac{1}{4}$ and 7.

Chapter 12 Vocabulary Check

1. For each one-to-one function, we can find its <u>inverse</u> function by switching the coordinates of the ordered pairs of the function.

2. The <u>composition</u> of functions f and g is
$(f \circ g)(x) = f(g(x))$.

3. A function of the form $f(x) = b^x$ is called an
<u>exponential</u> function if $b > 0$, b is not 1, and x is
a real number.

4. The graphs of f and f^{-1} are <u>symmetric</u> about
the line $y = x$.

5. <u>Natural</u> logarithms are logarithms to base e.

6. <u>Common</u> logarithms are logarithms to base 10.

7. To see whether a graph is the graph of a one-to-
one function, apply the <u>vertical</u> line test to see if
it is a function, and then apply the <u>horizontal</u> line
test to see if it is a one-to-one function.

8. A <u>logarithmic</u> function is a function that can be
defined by $f(x) = \log_b x$ where x is a positive
real number, b is a constant positive real number,
and b is not 1.

Chapter 12 Review

1. $(f + g)(x) = f(x) + g(x)$
$= (x - 5) + (2x + 1)$
$= x - 5 + 2x + 1$
$= 3x - 4$

2. $(f - g)(x) = f(x) - g(x)$
$= (x - 5) - (2x + 1)$
$= x - 5 - 2x - 1$
$= -x - 6$

3. $(f \cdot g)(x) = f(x) \cdot g(x)$
$= (x - 5)(2x + 1)$
$= 2x^2 + x - 10x - 5$
$= 2x^2 - 9x - 5$

4. $\left(\dfrac{g}{f}\right)(x) = \dfrac{g(x)}{f(x)} = \dfrac{2x+1}{x-5}, x \neq 5$

5. $(f \circ g)(x) = f(g(x))$
$= f(x + 1)$
$= (x + 1)^2 - 2$
$= x^2 + 2x - 1$

6. $(g \circ f)(x) = g(f(x))$
$= g(x^2 - 2)$
$= x^2 - 2 + 1$
$= x^2 - 1$

7. $(h \circ g)(2) = h(g(2)) = h(3) = 3^3 - 3^2 = 18$

8. $(f \circ f)(x) = f(f(x))$
$= f(x^2 - 2)$
$= (x^2 - 2)^2 - 2$
$= x^4 - 4x^2 + 4 - 2$
$= x^4 - 4x^2 + 2$

9. $(f \circ g)(-1) = f(g(-1)) = f(0) = 0^2 - 2 = -2$

10. $(h \circ h)(2) = h(h(2)) = h(4) = 4^3 - 4^2 = 48$

11. The function is one-to-one.
$h^{-1} = \{(14, -9), (8, 6), (12, -11), (15, 15)\}$

12. The function is not one-to-one.

13. The function is one-to-one.

Rank in Auto Thefts (Input)	2	4	1	3
U.S. Region (Output)	West	Midwest	South	Northeast

14. The function is not one-to-one.

15. $f(x) = \sqrt{x + 2}$

    a. $f(7) = \sqrt{7 + 2} = \sqrt{9} = 3$

    b. $f^{-1}(3) = 7$

16. $f(x) = \sqrt{x + 2}$

    a. $f(-1) = \sqrt{-1 + 2} = \sqrt{1} = 1$

    b. $f^{-1}(1) = -1$

17. The graph does not represent a one-to-one function.

18. The graph does not represent a one-to-one function.

19. The graph does not represent a one-to-one function.

20. The graph represents a one-to-one function.

21. $f(x) = x - 9$

$y = x - 9$

$x = y - 9$

$y = x + 9$

$f^{-1}(x) = x + 9$

22. $f(x) = x + 8$

$y = x + 8$

$x = y + 8$

$y = x - 8$

$f^{-1}(x) = x - 8$

23. $f(x) = 6x + 11$

$y = 6x + 11$

$x = 6y + 11$

$6y = x - 11$

$y = \dfrac{x - 11}{6}$

$f^{-1}(x) = \dfrac{x - 11}{6}$

24. $f(x) = 12x$

$y = 12x$

$x = 12y$

$y = \dfrac{x}{12}$

$f^{-1}(x) = \dfrac{x}{12}$

25. $f(x) = x^3 - 5$

$y = x^3 - 5$

$x = y^3 - 5$

$y^3 = x + 5$

$y = \sqrt[3]{x + 5}$

$f^{-1}(x) = \sqrt[3]{x + 5}$

26. $f(x) = \sqrt[3]{x + 2}$

$y = \sqrt[3]{x + 2}$

$x = \sqrt[3]{y + 2}$

$x^3 = y + 2$

$y = x^3 - 2$

$f^{-1}(x) = x^3 - 2$

27. $g(x) = \dfrac{12x - 7}{6}$

$y = \dfrac{12x - 7}{6}$

$x = \dfrac{12y - 7}{6}$

$6x = 12y - 7$

$12y = 6x + 7$

$y = \dfrac{6x + 7}{12}$

$g^{-1}(x) = \dfrac{6x + 7}{12}$

28. $r(x) = \dfrac{13}{2}x - 4$

$y = \dfrac{13}{2}x - 4$

$x = \dfrac{13}{2}y - 4$

$x + 4 = \dfrac{13}{2}y$

$y = \dfrac{2(x + 4)}{13}$

$r^{-1}(x) = \dfrac{2(x + 4)}{13}$

29. $y = g(x) = \sqrt{x}$

$x = \sqrt{y}$

$x^2 = y = g^{-1}(x), \ x \geq 0$

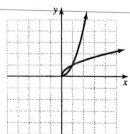

30. $h(x) = 5x - 5$
$$y = 5x - 5$$
$$x = 5y - 5$$
$$5y = x + 5$$
$$y = \frac{x+5}{5}$$
$$h^{-1}(x) = \frac{x+5}{5}$$

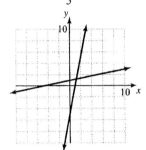

31. $f(x) = 2x - 3$
$$y = 2x - 3$$
$$x = 2y - 3$$
$$y = \frac{x+3}{2}$$
$$f^{-1}(x) = \frac{x+3}{2}$$

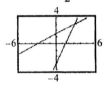

32. $4^x = 64$
$$4^x = 4^3$$
$$x = 3$$

33. $3^x = \frac{1}{9}$
$$3^x = 3^{-2}$$
$$x = -2$$

34. $2^{3x} = \frac{1}{16}$
$$2^{3x} = 2^{-4}$$
$$3x = -4$$
$$x = -\frac{4}{3}$$

35. $5^{2x} = 125$
$$5^{2x} = 5^3$$
$$2x = 3$$
$$x = \frac{3}{2}$$

36. $9^{x+1} = 243$
$$(3^2)^{x+1} = 3^5$$
$$3^{2x+2} = 3^5$$
$$2x + 2 = 5$$
$$2x = 3$$
$$x = \frac{3}{2}$$

37. $8^{3x-2} = 4$
$$(2^3)^{3x-2} = 2^2$$
$$2^{9x-6} = 2^2$$
$$9x - 6 = 2$$
$$9x = 8$$
$$x = \frac{8}{9}$$

38. $y = 3^x$

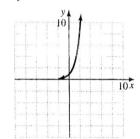

39. $y = \left(\frac{1}{3}\right)^x$

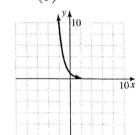

40. $y = 4 \cdot 2^x$

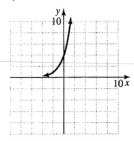

41. $y = 2^x + 4$

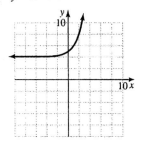

42. $A = P\left(1 + \dfrac{r}{n}\right)^{nt}$

$A = 1600\left(1 + \dfrac{0.09}{2}\right)^{(2)(7)}$

$A \approx 2963.11$

The amount accrued is $2963.11.

43. $A = P\left(1 + \dfrac{r}{n}\right)^{nt}$

$A = 800\left(1 + \dfrac{0.07}{4}\right)^{(4)(5)}$

$A \approx 1131.82$

The certificate is worth $1131.82 at the end of 5 years.

44. $y = 4 \cdot 2^x$

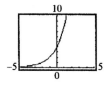

45. $49 = 7^2$

$\log_7 49 = 2$

46. $2^{-4} = \dfrac{1}{16}$

$\log_2 \dfrac{1}{16} = -4$

47. $\log_{1/2} 16 = -4$

$\left(\dfrac{1}{2}\right)^{-4} = 16$

48. $\log_{0.4} 0.064 = 3$

$0.4^3 = 0.064$

49. $\log_4 x = -3$

$x = 4^{-3} = \dfrac{1}{64}$

50. $\log_3 x = 2$

$x = 3^2 = 9$

51. $\log_3 1 = x$

$3^x = 1$

$3^x = 3^0$

$x = 0$

52. $\log_4 64 = x$

$4^x = 64$

$4^x = 4^3$

$x = 3$

53. $\log_x 64 = 2$

$x^2 = 64$

$x = \pm\sqrt{64} = \pm 8$

$x = 8$ since the base must be positive

54. $\log_x 81 = 4$

$x^4 = 81$

$x = \pm 3$

$x = 3$ since the base must be positive

55. $\log_4 4^5 = x$

$x = 5$

56. $\log_7 7^{-2} = x$

$x = -2$

57. $5^{\log_5 4} = x$

$x = 4$

58. $2^{\log_2 9} = x$

$\qquad 9 = x$

59. $\log_2(3x - 1) = 4$

$\qquad 3x - 1 = 2^4$

$\qquad 3x - 1 = 16$

$\qquad 3x = 17$

$\qquad x = \dfrac{17}{3}$

60. $\log_3(2x + 5) = 2$

$\qquad 2x + 5 = 3^2$

$\qquad 2x + 5 = 9$

$\qquad 2x = 4$

$\qquad x = 2$

61. $\log_4(x^2 - 3x) = 1$

$\qquad x^2 - 3x = 4$

$\qquad x^2 - 3x - 4 = 0$

$\qquad (x + 1)(x - 4) = 0$

$\qquad x = -1 \text{ or } x = 4$

62. $\log_8(x^2 + 7x) = 1$

$\qquad x^2 + 7x = 8$

$\qquad x^2 + 7x - 8 = 0$

$\qquad (x + 8)(x - 1) = 0$

$\qquad x = -8 \text{ or } x = 1$

63. $y = 2^x$ and $y = \log_2 x$

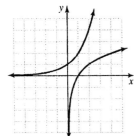

64. $y = \left(\dfrac{1}{2}\right)^x$ and $y = \log_{1/2} x$

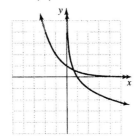

65. $\log_3 8 + \log_3 4 = \log_3(8 \cdot 4) = \log_3 32$

66. $\log_2 6 + \log_2 3 = \log_2(6 \cdot 3) = \log_2 18$

67. $\log_7 15 - \log_7 20 = \log_7 \dfrac{15}{20} = \log_7 \dfrac{3}{4}$

68. $\log 18 - \log 12 = \log \dfrac{18}{12} = \log \dfrac{3}{2}$

69. $\log_{11} 8 + \log_{11} 3 - \log_{11} 6 = \log_{11} \dfrac{(8)(3)}{6}$

$\qquad\qquad\qquad\qquad\qquad\qquad\quad = \log_{11} 4$

70. $\log_5 14 + \log_5 3 - \log_5 21$

$\quad = \log_5(14 \cdot 3) - \log_5 21$

$\quad = \log_5 \dfrac{42}{21}$

$\quad = \log_5 2$

71. $2\log_5 x - 2\log_5(x + 1) + \log_5 x$

$\quad = \log_5 x^2 - \log_5(x + 1)^2 + \log_5 x$

$\quad = \log_5 \dfrac{(x^2)(x)}{(x + 1)^2}$

$\quad = \log_5 \dfrac{x^3}{(x + 1)^2}$

72. $4\log_3 x - \log_3 x + \log_3(x + 2)$

$\quad = 3\log_3 x + \log_3(x + 2)$

$\quad = \log_3 x^3 + \log_3(x + 2)$

$\quad = \log_3\left[x^3(x + 2)\right]$

$\quad = \log_3(x^4 + 2x^3)$

73. $\log_3 \dfrac{x^3}{x + 2} = \log_3 x^3 - \log_3(x + 2)$

$\qquad\qquad\quad = 3\log_3 x - \log_3(x + 2)$

74. $\log_4 \dfrac{x+5}{x^2} = \log_4(x+5) - \log_4 x^2$
$$= \log_4(x+5) - 2\log_4 x$$

75. $\log_2 \dfrac{3x^2 y}{z} = \log_2(3x^2 y) - \log_2 z$
$$= \log_2 3 + \log_2 x^2 + \log_2 y - \log_2 z$$
$$= \log_2 3 + 2\log_2 x + \log_2 y - \log_2 z$$

76. $\log_7 \dfrac{yz^3}{x} = \log_7(yz^3) - \log_7 x$
$$= \log_7 y + \log_7 z^3 - \log_7 x$$
$$= \log_7 y + 3\log_7 z - \log_7 x$$

77. $\log_b 50 = \log_b (5)(5)(2)$
$$= \log_b(5) + \log_b(5) + \log_b(2)$$
$$= 0.83 + 0.83 + 0.36$$
$$= 2.02$$

78. $\log_b \dfrac{4}{5} = \log_b 4 - \log_b 5$
$$= \log_b 2^2 - \log_b 5$$
$$= 2\log_b 2 - \log_b 5$$
$$= 2(0.36) - 0.83$$
$$= 0.72 - 0.83$$
$$= -0.11$$

79. $\log 3.6 \approx 0.5563$

80. $\log 0.15 \approx -0.8239$

81. $\ln 1.25 \approx 0.2231$

82. $\ln 4.63 \approx 1.5326$

83. $\log 1000 = \log 10^3 = 3$

84. $\log \dfrac{1}{10} = \log 10^{-1} = -1$

85. $\ln \dfrac{1}{e} = \ln e^{-1} = -1$

86. $\ln e^4 = 4$

87. $\ln(2x) = 2$
$$2x = e^2$$
$$x = \dfrac{e^2}{2}$$

88. $\ln(3x) = 1.6$
$$3x = e^{1.6}$$
$$x = \dfrac{e^{1.6}}{3}$$

89. $\ln(2x-3) = -1$
$$2x - 3 = e^{-1}$$
$$x = \dfrac{e^{-1}+3}{2}$$

90. $\ln(3x+1) = 2$
$$3x + 1 = e^2$$
$$3x = e^2 - 1$$
$$x = \dfrac{e^2 - 1}{3}$$

91. $\ln \dfrac{I}{I_0} = -kx$
$$\ln \dfrac{0.03 I_0}{I_0} = -2.1x$$
$$\ln 0.03 = -2.1x$$
$$\dfrac{\ln 0.03}{-2.1} = x$$
$$x \approx 1.67$$
The depth is 1.67 millimeters.

92. $\ln \dfrac{I}{I_0} = -kx$
$$\ln \dfrac{0.02 I_0}{I_0} = -3.2x$$
$$\ln 0.02 = -3.2x$$
$$\dfrac{\ln 0.02}{-3.2} = x$$
$$x \approx 1.22$$
2% of the original radioactivity will penetrate at a depth of approximately 1.22 millimeters.

93. $\log_5 1.6 = \dfrac{\log 1.6}{\log 5} \approx 0.2920$

94. $\log_3 4 = \dfrac{\log 4}{\log 3} \approx 1.2619$

95. $A = Pe^{rt}$

$A = 1450e^{(0.06)(5)}$

$A \approx 1957.30$

The accrued amount is $1957.30.

96. $A = Pe^{rt}$

$A = 940e^{0.11(3)} = 940e^{0.33} \approx 1307.51$

The investment grows to $1307.51.

97. $3^{2x} = 7$

$\log 3^{2x} = \log 7$

$2x \log 3 = \log 7$

$x = \dfrac{\log 7}{2 \log 3} \approx 0.8856$

98. $6^{3x} = 5$

$\log 6^{3x} = \log 5$

$3x \log 6 = \log 5$

$x = \dfrac{\log 5}{3 \log 6} \approx 0.2994$

99. $3^{2x+1} = 6$

$\log 3^{2x+1} = \log 6$

$(2x+1) \log 3 = \log 6$

$2x = \dfrac{\log 6}{\log 3} - 1$

$x = \dfrac{1}{2}\left(\dfrac{\log 6}{\log 3} - 1\right) \approx 0.3155$

100. $4^{3x+2} = 9$

$\log 4^{3x+2} = \log 9$

$(3x+2) \log 4 = \log 9$

$3x = \dfrac{\log 9}{\log 4} - 2$

$x = \dfrac{1}{3}\left(\dfrac{\log 9}{\log 4} - 2\right) \approx -0.1383$

101. $5^{3x-5} = 4$

$\log 5^{3x-5} = \log 4$

$(3x-5) \log 5 = \log 4$

$3x = \dfrac{\log 4}{\log 5} + 5$

$x = \dfrac{1}{3}\left(\dfrac{\log 4}{\log 5} + 5\right) \approx 1.9538$

102. $8^{4x-2} = 3$

$\log 8^{4x-2} = \log 3$

$(4x-2) \log 8 = \log 3$

$4x = \dfrac{\log 3}{\log 8} + 2$

$x = \dfrac{1}{4}\left(\dfrac{\log 3}{\log 8} + 2\right) \approx 0.6321$

103. $2 \cdot 5^{x-1} = 1$

$\log(2 \cdot 5^{x-1}) = \log 1$

$\log 2 + (x-1) \log 5 = 0$

$(x-1) \log 5 = -\log 2$

$x = -\dfrac{\log 2}{\log 5} + 1 \approx 0.5693$

104. $3 \cdot 4^{x+5} = 2$

$4^{x+5} = \dfrac{2}{3}$

$\log 4^{x+5} = \log \dfrac{2}{3}$

$(x+5) \log 4 = \log \dfrac{2}{3}$

$x = \dfrac{\log\left(\frac{2}{3}\right)}{\log 4} - 5 \approx -5.2925$

105. $\log_5 2 + \log_5 x = 2$

$\log_5 2x = 2$

$2x = 5^2$

$2x = 25$

$x = \dfrac{25}{2}$

106. $\log_3 x + \log_3 10 = 2$

$\log_3(10x) = 2$

$10x = 3^2$

$10x = 9$

$x = \dfrac{9}{10}$

107. $\log(5x) - \log(x+1) = 4$

$$\log\frac{5x}{x+1} = 4$$

$$\frac{5x}{x+1} = 10^4$$

$$\frac{5x}{x+1} = 10,000$$

$$5x = 10,000x + 10,000$$

$$x = -1.0005$$

no solution, or $\varnothing$

108. $\ln(3x) - \ln(x-3) = 2$

$$\ln\left(\frac{3x}{x-3}\right) = 2$$

$$\frac{3x}{x-3} = e^2$$

$$3x = e^2x - 3e^2$$

$$3x - e^2x = -3e^2$$

$$(3 - e^2)x = -3e^2$$

$$x = \frac{3e^2}{e^2 - 3}$$

109. $\log_2 x + \log_2 2x - 3 = 1$

$$\log_2(x \cdot 2x) = 4$$

$$2x^2 = 2^4$$

$$2x^2 = 16$$

$$x^2 = 8$$

$$x = \pm 2\sqrt{2}$$

$-2\sqrt{2}$ is rejected since $\log_2\left(-2\sqrt{2}\right)$ is undefined. The solution is $2\sqrt{2}$.

110. $-\log_6(4x+7) + \log_6 x = 1$

$$\log_6\frac{x}{4x+7} = 1$$

$$\frac{x}{4x+7} = 6$$

$$x = 6(4x+7)$$

$$x = 24x + 42$$

$$x = -\frac{42}{23}$$

$-\frac{42}{23}$ is rejected since $\log_6\left(-\frac{42}{23}\right)$ is undefined.
There is no solution, or $\varnothing$.

111. $y = y_0e^{kt}$

$$y = 155,000e^{0.06(4)}$$

$$\approx 197,044$$

There will be 197,044 ducks after 4 weeks.

112. $y = y_0e^{kt}$

$$y = 2,971,650e^{-0.00129(8)}$$

$$= 2,971,650e^{-0.01032}$$

$$\approx 2,941,140$$

The population of Armenia in the year 2015 will be approximately 2,941,140.

113. $y = y_0e^{kt}$

$$1,500,000,000 = 1,321,851,888e^{0.00606t}$$

$$\frac{1,500,000,000}{1,321,851,888} = e^{0.00606t}$$

$$\ln\frac{1,500,000,000}{1,321,851,888} = \ln e^{0.00606t}$$

$$\ln\frac{1,500,000,000}{1,321,851,888} = 0.00606t$$

$$t = \frac{1}{0.00606}\ln\frac{1,500,000,000}{1,321,851,888}$$

$$t \approx 20.9$$

It will take approximately 20.9 years.

114. $y = y_0e^{kt}$

$$2(33,390,141) = 33,390,141e^{0.009t}$$

$$2 = e^{0.009t}$$

$$\ln 2 = \ln e^{0.009t}$$

$$\ln 2 = 0.009t$$

$$t = \frac{\ln 2}{0.009}$$

$$t \approx 77.0$$

It will take approximately 77.0 years.

115. $y = y_0e^{kt}$

$$2(24,821,286) = 24,821,286e^{0.018t}$$

$$2 = e^{0.018t}$$

$$\ln 2 = \ln e^{0.018t}$$

$$\ln 2 = 0.018t$$

$$t = \frac{\ln 2}{0.018}$$

$$t \approx 38.5$$

It will take approximately 38.5 years.

116.
$$A = P\left(1+\frac{r}{n}\right)^{nt}$$
$$10,000 = 5000\left(1+\frac{0.08}{4}\right)^{4t}$$
$$2 = (1.02)^{4t}$$
$$\log 2 = \log 1.02^{4t}$$
$$\log 2 = 4t \log 1.02$$
$$t = \frac{\log 2}{4\log 1.02} \approx 8.8$$

It will take 8.8 years.

117.
$$A = P\left(1+\frac{r}{n}\right)^{nt}$$
$$10,000 = 6000\left(1+\frac{0.06}{12}\right)^{12t}$$
$$\frac{5}{3} = (1.005)^{12t}$$
$$\log\frac{5}{3} = \log 1.005^{12t}$$
$$\log\frac{5}{3} = 12t \log 1.005$$
$$t = \frac{1}{12}\left(\frac{\log\left(\frac{5}{3}\right)}{\log(1.005)}\right) \approx 8.5$$

It was invested for approximately 8.5 years.

118. $Y_1 = e^x, Y_2 = 2$

$x \approx 0.69$

119. $Y_1 = 10^{0.3x}, Y_2 = 7$

$x \approx 2.82$

120. $3^x = \dfrac{1}{81}$
$$3^x = 3^{-4}$$
$$x = -4$$

121. $7^{4x} = 49$
$$7^{4x} = 7^2$$
$$4x = 2$$
$$x = \frac{1}{2}$$

122.
$$8^{3x-2} = 32$$
$$(2^3)^{(3x-2)} = 2^5$$
$$2^{9x-6} = 2^5$$
$$9x - 6 = 5$$
$$9x = 11$$
$$x = \frac{11}{9}$$

123. $\log_4 4 = x$
$$4^x = 4^1$$
$$x = 1$$

124. $\log_3 x = 4$
$$3^4 = x$$
$$81 = x$$

125. $\log_5(x^2 - 4x) = 1$
$$5^1 = x^2 - 4x$$
$$0 = x^2 - 4x - 5$$
$$0 = (x-5)(x+1)$$
$$x - 5 = 0 \quad \text{or} \quad x + 1 = 0$$
$$x = 5 \qquad\qquad x = -1$$

Both check, so the solutions are 5 and -1.

126. $\log_4(3x-1) = 2$
$$4^2 = 3x - 1$$
$$16 + 1 = 3x$$
$$\frac{17}{3} = x$$

127. $\ln x = -3.2$
$$e^{\ln x} = e^{-3.2}$$
$$x = e^{-3.2}$$

128. $\log_5 x + \log_5 10 = 2$
$$\log_5(10x) = 2$$
$$5^2 = 10x$$
$$\frac{25}{10} = x$$
$$\frac{5}{2} = x$$

129. $\ln x - \ln 2 = 1$

$$\ln \frac{x}{2} = 1$$

$$e^{\ln \frac{x}{2}} = e^1$$

$$\frac{x}{2} = e$$

$$x = 2e$$

130. $\log_6 x - \log_6 (4x + 7) = 1$

$$\log_6 \frac{x}{4x + 7} = 1$$

$$6^1 = \frac{x}{4x + 7}$$

$$24x + 42 = x$$

$$23x = -42$$

$$x = -\frac{42}{23}$$

$-\dfrac{42}{23}$ is rejected since $\log_6\left(-\dfrac{42}{23}\right)$ is undefined.

There is no solution, or $\varnothing$.

Chapter 12 Test

1. $f(x) = x$ and $g(x) = 2x - 3$

$(f \cdot g)(x) = f(x) \cdot g(x) = x(2x - 3) = 2x^2 - 3x$

2. $f(x) = x$ and $g(x) = 2x - 3$

$(f - g)(x) = f(x) - g(x)$
$= x - (2x - 3)$
$= -x + 3$
$= 3 - x$

3. $(f \circ h)(0) = f(h(0)) = f(5) = 5$

4. $(g \circ f)(x) = g(f(x)) = g(x) = x - 7$

5. $(g \circ h)(x) = g(h(x))$
$= g(x^2 - 6x + 5)$
$= x^2 - 6x + 5 - 7$
$= x^2 - 6x - 2$

6. $f(x) = 7x - 14$, $f^{-1}(x) = \dfrac{x + 14}{7}$

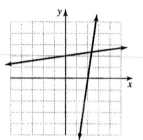

7. The graph represents a one-to-one function.

8. The graph does not represent a one-to-one function.

9. $y = 6 - 2x$ is one-to-one.
$$x = 6 - 2y$$
$$2y = -x + 6$$
$$y = \frac{-x + 6}{2}$$
$$f^{-1}(x) = \frac{-x + 6}{2}$$

10. $f = \{(0,0), (2,3), (-1,5)\}$ is one-to-one.
$$f^{-1} = \{(0,0), (3,2), (5,-1)\}$$

11. The function is not one-to-one.

12. $\log_3 6 + \log_3 4 = \log_3(6 \cdot 4) = \log_3 24$

13. $\log_5 x + 3\log_5 x - \log_5(x+1)$
$= 4\log_5 x - \log_5(x+1)$
$= \log_5 x^4 - \log_5(x+1)$
$= \log_5 \dfrac{x^4}{x+1}$

14. $\log_6 \dfrac{2x}{y^3} = \log_6 2x - \log_6 y^3$
$$= \log_6 2 + \log_6 x - 3\log_6 y$$

15. $\log_b\left(\dfrac{3}{25}\right) = \log_b 3 - \log_b 25$
$$= \log_b 3 - \log_b 5^2$$
$$= \log_b 3 - 2\log_b 5$$
$$= 0.79 - 2(1.16)$$
$$= -1.53$$

16. $\log_7 8 = \dfrac{\ln 8}{\ln 7} \approx 1.0686$

17. $8^{x-1} = \dfrac{1}{64}$
$8^{x-1} = 8^{-2}$
$x - 1 = -2$
$x = -1$

18. $3^{2x+5} = 4$
$\log 3^{2x+5} = \log 4$
$(2x+5)\log 3 = \log 4$
$2x = \dfrac{\log 4}{\log 3} - 5$
$x = \dfrac{1}{2}\left(\dfrac{\log 4}{\log 3} - 5\right)$
$x \approx -1.8691$

19. $\log_3 x = -2$
$x = 3^{-2}$
$x = \dfrac{1}{9}$

20. $\ln \sqrt{e} = x$
$\ln e^{1/2} = x$
$\dfrac{1}{2} = x$

21. $\log_8 (3x - 2) = 2$
$3x - 2 = 8^2$
$3x - 2 = 64$
$3x = 66$
$x = \dfrac{66}{3} = 22$

22. $\log_5 x + \log_5 3 = 2$
$\log_5 (3x) = 2$
$3x = 5^2$
$3x = 25$
$x = \dfrac{25}{3}$

23. $\log_4 (x+1) - \log_4 (x-2) = 3$
$\log_4 \dfrac{x+1}{x-2} = 3$
$\dfrac{x+1}{x-2} = 4^3$
$\dfrac{x+1}{x-2} = 64$
$x + 1 = 64x - 128$
$129 = 63x$
$\dfrac{129}{63} = x$
$\dfrac{43}{21} = x$

24. $\ln(3x + 7) = 1.31$
$3x + 7 = e^{1.31}$
$3x = e^{1.31} - 7$
$x = \dfrac{e^{1.31} - 7}{3} \approx -1.0979$

25. $y = \left(\dfrac{1}{2}\right)^x + 1$

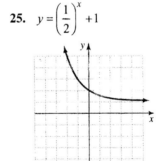

26. $y = 3^x$ and $y = \log_3 x$

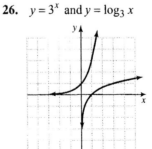

27. $A = \left(1 + \dfrac{r}{n}\right)^{nt}$, $P = 4000$, $t = 3$, $r = 0.09$,

and $n = 12$

$A = 4000\left(1 + \dfrac{0.09}{12}\right)^{12(3)}$

$\quad = 4000(1.0075)^{36}$

$\quad \approx 5234.58$

$5234.58 will be in the account.

28. $A = \left(1 + \dfrac{r}{n}\right)^{nt}$, $P = 2000$, $A = 3000$

$r = 0.07$, $n = 2$

$3000 = 2000\left(1 + \dfrac{0.07}{2}\right)^{2t}$

$1.5 = (1.035)^{2t}$

$\log 1.5 = \log 1.035^{2t}$

$\log 1.5 = 2t \log 1.035$

$t = \dfrac{\log 1.5}{2 \log 1.035} \approx 5.9$

It would take 6 years.

29. $y = y_0 e^{kt}$

$y = 57{,}000 e^{0.026(5)}$

$\quad = 57{,}000 e^{0.13}$

$\quad \approx 64{,}913$

There will be approximately 64,913 prairie dogs 5 years from now.

30.

$y = y_0 e^{kt}$

$1000 = 400 e^{0.062(t)}$

$2.5 = e^{0.062t}$

$\ln 2.5 = \ln e^{0.062t}$

$0.062t = \ln 2.5$

$t = \dfrac{\ln 2.5}{0.062} \approx 14.8$

It will take the naturalists approximately 15 years to reach their goal.

31. $\log(1 + k) = \dfrac{0.3}{D}$, $D = 56$

$\log(1 + k) = \dfrac{0.3}{56}$

$1 + k = 10^{0.3/56}$

$k = -1 + 10^{0.3/56}$

$k \approx 0.012$

The rate of population increase is approximately 1.2%.

Chapter 12 Cumulative Review

1. a. $\dfrac{4}{5} \div \dfrac{5}{16} = \dfrac{4}{5} \cdot \dfrac{16}{5} = \dfrac{4 \cdot 16}{5 \cdot 5} = \dfrac{64}{25}$

b. $\dfrac{7}{10} \div 14 = \dfrac{7}{10} \div \dfrac{14}{1} = \dfrac{7}{10} \cdot \dfrac{1}{14} = \dfrac{7 \cdot 1}{10 \cdot 2 \cdot 7} = \dfrac{1}{20}$

c. $\dfrac{3}{8} \div \dfrac{3}{10} = \dfrac{3}{8} \cdot \dfrac{10}{3} = \dfrac{3 \cdot 2 \cdot 5}{2 \cdot 4 \cdot 3} = \dfrac{5}{4}$

2. $\dfrac{1}{3}(x - 2) = \dfrac{1}{4}(x + 1)$

$4(x - 2) = 3(x + 1)$

$4x - 8 = 3x + 3$

$x = 11$

3. $f(x) = x^2$

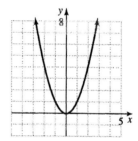

4. $y = f(x) = -3x + 4$, $m = -3$

Perpendicular line: $m = \dfrac{1}{3}$, through $(-2, 6)$

$y - y_1 = m(x - x_1)$

$y - 6 = \dfrac{1}{3}[x - (-2)]$

$y - 6 = \dfrac{1}{3}x + \dfrac{2}{3}$

$y = \dfrac{1}{3}x + \dfrac{20}{3}$

$f(x) = \dfrac{1}{3}x + \dfrac{20}{3}$

5. Equation 2 is twice the opposite of equation 1 and equation 3 is one-half of equation 1. Therefore, the system is dependent. The solution is $\{(x, y, z) | x - 5y - 2z = 6\}$.

6. The angles labeled $y°$ and $(x - 40)°$ are alternate interior angles, so $y = x - 40$. The angles labeled $x°$ and $y°$ are supplementary, so $x + y = 180$.

$\begin{cases} y = x - 40 \\ x + y = 180 \end{cases}$

Replace y with $x - 40$ in the second equation.

$$x + (x - 40) = 180$$
$$2x = 220$$
$$x = 110$$
$$y = x - 40 = 110 - 40 = 70$$

7. a. $-3 + [(-2 - 5) - 2] = -3 + [-7 - 2]$
$$= -3 + [-9]$$
$$= -12$$

b. $2^3 - |10| + [-6 - (-5)] = 2^3 - |10| + [-6 + 5]$
$$= 2^3 - |10| + (-1)$$
$$= 8 - 10 - 1$$
$$= -2 - 1$$
$$= -3$$

8. a. $(4a^3)^2 = 4^2(a^3)^2 = 16a^6$

b. $\left(-\dfrac{2}{3}\right)^3 = \dfrac{(-2)^3}{3^3} = \dfrac{-8}{27} = -\dfrac{8}{27}$

c. $\left(\dfrac{4a^5}{b^3}\right)^3 = \dfrac{4^3(a^5)^3}{(b^3)^3} = \dfrac{64a^{15}}{b^9}$

d. $\left(\dfrac{3^{-2}}{x}\right)^{-3} = \dfrac{(3^{-2})^{-3}}{x^{-3}} = \dfrac{3^6}{x^{-3}} = 729x^3$

e. $(a^{-2}b^3c^{-4})^{-2} = (a^{-2})^{-2}(b^3)^{-2}(c^{-4})^{-2}$
$$= a^4 b^{-6} c^8$$
$$= \dfrac{a^4 c^8}{b^6}$$

9. a. $C(100) = \dfrac{2.6(100) + 10,000}{100}$
$$= 102.60$$
The cost is $102.60 per disc for 100 discs.

b. $C(1000) = \dfrac{2.6(1000) + 10,000}{1000}$
$$= 12.60$$
The cost is $12.60 per disc for 1000 discs.

10. a. $(3x - 1)^2 = (3x)^2 - 2(3x)(1) + 1^2$
$$= 9x^2 - 6x + 1$$

b. $\left(\dfrac{1}{2}x + 3\right)\left(\dfrac{1}{2}x - 3\right) = \left(\dfrac{1}{2}x\right)^2 - 3^2$
$$= \dfrac{1}{4}x^2 - 9$$

c. $(2x - 5)(6x + 7) = 12x^2 + 14x - 30x - 35$
$$= 12x^2 - 16x - 35$$

11. $12a - 8a = 10 + 2a - 13 - 7$
$$4a = 2a - 10$$
$$2a = -10$$
$$a = -5$$

12. $\dfrac{5}{x - 2} + \dfrac{3}{x^2 + 4x + 4} - \dfrac{6}{x + 2}$

$$= \dfrac{5}{x - 2} + \dfrac{3}{(x + 2)^2} - \dfrac{6}{x + 2}$$

$$= \dfrac{5(x + 2)^2 + 3(x - 2) - 6(x - 2)(x + 2)}{(x - 2)(x + 2)(x + 2)}$$

$$= \dfrac{-x^2 + 23x + 38}{(x - 2)(x + 2)^2}$$

13. $\dfrac{8x^2y^2 - 16xy + 2x}{4xy} = \dfrac{8x^2y^2}{4xy} - \dfrac{16xy}{4xy} + \dfrac{2x}{4xy}$
$$= 2xy - 4 + \dfrac{1}{2y}$$

14. a. $\dfrac{\frac{a}{5}}{\frac{a-1}{10}} = \dfrac{a}{5} \cdot \dfrac{10}{a - 1} = \dfrac{2a}{a - 1}$

b. $\dfrac{\frac{3}{2+a} + \frac{6}{2-a}}{\frac{5}{a+2} - \frac{1}{a-2}} = \dfrac{\frac{3}{a+2} - \frac{6}{a-2}}{\frac{5}{a+2} - \frac{1}{a-2}}$

Multiply the numerator and the denominator by $(a + 2)(a - 2)$.

$$\dfrac{3(a - 2) - 6(a + 2)}{5(a - 2) - 1(a + 2)} = \dfrac{3a - 6 - 6a - 12}{5a - 10 - a - 2}$$
$$= \dfrac{-3a - 18}{4a - 12}$$

c. $\dfrac{x^{-1} + y^{-1}}{xy} = \dfrac{\frac{1}{x} + \frac{1}{y}}{xy} = \dfrac{\left(\frac{1}{x} + \frac{1}{y}\right)xy}{(xy)(xy)} = \dfrac{y + x}{x^2 y^2}$

15. $3m^2 - 24m - 60 = 3(m^2 - 8m - 20)$
$$= 3(m + 2)(m - 10)$$

16. $5x^2 - 85x + 350 = 5(x^2 - 17x + 70)$
$$= 5(x-10)(x-7)$$

17. $\dfrac{3x^2 + 2x}{x-1} - \dfrac{10x-5}{x-1} = \dfrac{3x^2 + 2x - (10x-5)}{x-1}$
$$= \dfrac{3x^2 + 2x - 10x + 5}{x-1}$$
$$= \dfrac{3x^2 - 8x + 5}{x-1}$$
$$= \dfrac{(3x-5)(x-1)}{x-1}$$
$$= 3x - 5$$

18. $2\,\underline{\rvert\,8 \quad -12 \quad -7}$
$$16 \quad\ \ 8$$
$$\overline{\ 8 \quad\ \ 4 \quad\ \ 1}$$

Solution: $8x + 4 + \dfrac{1}{x-2}$

19. a. $\sqrt[4]{81} = \sqrt[4]{3^4} = 3$

b. $\sqrt[5]{-243} = \sqrt[5]{(-3)^5} = -3$

c. $-\sqrt{25} = -\sqrt{5^2} = -5$

d. $\sqrt[4]{-81}$ is not a real number.

e. $\sqrt[3]{64x^3} = \sqrt[3]{4^3 x^3} = 4x$

20. $\dfrac{1}{a+5} = \dfrac{1}{3a+6} - \dfrac{a+2}{a^2+7a+10}$
$$\dfrac{1}{a+5} = \dfrac{1}{3(a+2)} - \dfrac{a+2}{(a+2)(a+5)}$$
$$3(a+2) = a+5 - 3(a+2)$$
$$3a+6 = a+5 - 3a - 6$$
$$5a = -7$$
$$a = -\dfrac{7}{5}$$

21. a. $\sqrt{x} \cdot \sqrt[4]{x} = x^{1/2} \cdot x^{1/4} = x^{3/4} = \sqrt[4]{x^3}$

b. $\dfrac{\sqrt{x}}{\sqrt[3]{x}} = \dfrac{x^{1/2}}{x^{1/3}} = x^{\frac{1}{2}-\frac{1}{3}} = x^{1/6} = \sqrt[6]{x}$

c. $\sqrt[3]{3} \cdot \sqrt{2} = 3^{1/3} \cdot 2^{1/2}$
$$= 3^{2/6} \cdot 2^{3/6}$$
$$= 9^{1/6} \cdot 8^{1/6}$$
$$= 72^{1/6}$$
$$= \sqrt[6]{72}$$

22. $y = kx$
$$\dfrac{1}{2} = 12k$$
$$k = \dfrac{1}{24}, \ y = \dfrac{1}{24}x$$

23. a. $\sqrt{3}\left(5+\sqrt{30}\right) = 5\sqrt{3} + \sqrt{90} = 5\sqrt{3} + 3\sqrt{10}$

b. $\left(\sqrt{5} - \sqrt{6}\right)\left(\sqrt{7} + 1\right) = \sqrt{35} + \sqrt{5} - \sqrt{42} - \sqrt{6}$

c. $\left(7\sqrt{x} + 5\right)\left(3\sqrt{x} - \sqrt{5}\right)$
$$= 21x - 7\sqrt{5x} + 15\sqrt{x} - 5\sqrt{5}$$

d. $\left(4\sqrt{3} - 1\right)^2$
$$= \left(4\sqrt{3}\right)^2 - 2\left(4\sqrt{3}\right)(1) + 1^2$$
$$= 16 \cdot 3 - 8\sqrt{3} + 1$$
$$= 49 - 8\sqrt{3}$$

e. $\left(\sqrt{2x} - 5\right)\left(\sqrt{2x} + 5\right) = \left(\sqrt{2x}\right)^2 - 5^2$
$$= 2x - 25$$

f. $\left(\sqrt{x-3} + 5\right)^2 = \left(\sqrt{x-3}\right)^2 + 2\sqrt{x-3}(5) + 5^2$
$$= x - 3 + 10\sqrt{x-3} + 25$$
$$= x + 22 + 10\sqrt{x-3}$$

24. a. $\sqrt[4]{81} = \sqrt[4]{3^4} = 3$

b. $\sqrt[3]{-27} = \sqrt[3]{(-3)^3} = -3$

c. $\sqrt{\dfrac{9}{64}} = \sqrt{\left(\dfrac{3}{8}\right)^2} = \dfrac{3}{8}$

d. $\sqrt[4]{x^{12}} = x^3$

e. $\sqrt[3]{-125y^6} = -5y^2$

25. $\dfrac{\sqrt[4]{x}}{\sqrt[4]{81y^5}} = \dfrac{\sqrt[4]{x}}{\sqrt[4]{81y^5}} \cdot \dfrac{\sqrt[4]{y^3}}{\sqrt[4]{y^3}} = \dfrac{\sqrt[4]{xy^3}}{3y^2}$

26. a. $a^{1/4}(a^{3/4} - a^8) = a^{4/4} - a^{33/4} = a - a^{39/4}$

    b. $(x^{1/2} - 3)(x^{1/2} + 5)$
        $= x^{2/2} + 5x^{1/2} - 3x^{1/2} - 15$
        $= x + 2x^{1/2} - 15$

27. $\sqrt{4 - x} = x - 2$
    $\left(\sqrt{4 - x}\right)^2 = (x - 2)^2$
        $4 - x = x^2 - 4x + 4$
          $0 = x^2 - 3x$
          $0 = x(x - 3)$
  $x = 0$ or $x - 3 = 0$
                 $x = 3$
$x = 0$ does not check, so the only solution is $x = 3$.

28. a. $\dfrac{\sqrt{54}}{\sqrt{6}} = \sqrt{\dfrac{54}{6}} = \sqrt{9} = 3$

    b. $\dfrac{\sqrt{108a^2}}{3\sqrt{3}} = \dfrac{1}{3}\sqrt{\dfrac{108a^2}{3}}$
               $= \dfrac{1}{3}\sqrt{36a^2}$
               $= \dfrac{1}{3}(6a)$
               $= 2a$

    c. $\dfrac{3\sqrt[3]{81a^5b^{10}}}{\sqrt[3]{3b^4}} = 3\sqrt[3]{\dfrac{81a^5b^{10}}{3b^4}}$
                    $= 3\sqrt[3]{27a^5b^6}$
                    $= 9ab^2\sqrt[3]{a^2}$

29. $3x^2 - 9x + 8 = 0$
        $x^2 - 3x + \dfrac{8}{3} = 0$
          $x^2 - 3x = -\dfrac{8}{3}$
  $x^2 - 3x + \left(\dfrac{-3}{2}\right)^2 = -\dfrac{8}{3} + \left(\dfrac{-3}{2}\right)^2$
      $x^2 - 3x + \dfrac{9}{4} = -\dfrac{8}{3} + \dfrac{9}{4}$
        $\left(x - \dfrac{3}{2}\right)^2 = -\dfrac{5}{12}$
          $x - \dfrac{3}{2} = \pm\sqrt{-\dfrac{5}{12}}$
          $x - \dfrac{3}{2} = \pm\dfrac{i\sqrt{5}}{2\sqrt{3}}$
          $x - \dfrac{3}{2} = \pm\dfrac{i\sqrt{15}}{6}$
               $x = \dfrac{3}{2} \pm \dfrac{i\sqrt{15}}{6}$
                $= \dfrac{9}{6} \pm \dfrac{i\sqrt{15}}{6}$
                $= \dfrac{9 \pm i\sqrt{15}}{6}$

The solutions are $\dfrac{9 + i\sqrt{15}}{6}$ and $\dfrac{9 - i\sqrt{15}}{6}$.

30. a. $\dfrac{\sqrt{20}}{3} + \dfrac{\sqrt{5}}{4} = \dfrac{2\sqrt{5}}{3} + \dfrac{\sqrt{5}}{4}$
                   $= \dfrac{8\sqrt{5} + 3\sqrt{5}}{12}$
                   $= \dfrac{11\sqrt{5}}{12}$

    b. $\sqrt[3]{\dfrac{24x}{27}} - \dfrac{\sqrt[3]{3x}}{2} = \dfrac{2\sqrt[3]{3x}}{3} - \dfrac{\sqrt[3]{3x}}{2}$
                     $= \dfrac{4\sqrt[3]{3x} - 3\sqrt[3]{3x}}{6}$
                     $= \dfrac{\sqrt[3]{3x}}{6}$

31.
$$\frac{3x}{x-2} - \frac{x+1}{x} = \frac{6}{x(x-2)}$$
$$3x(x) - (x+1)(x-2) = 6$$
$$3x^2 - x^2 + x + 2 = 6$$
$$2x^2 + x - 4 = 0$$
$$a = 2, b = 1, c = -4$$
$$x = \frac{-1 \pm \sqrt{1^2 - 4(2)(-4)}}{2(2)} = \frac{-1 \pm \sqrt{33}}{4}$$

32.
$$\sqrt[3]{\frac{27}{m^4 n^8}} = \frac{\sqrt[3]{27}}{\sqrt[3]{m^4 n^8}}$$
$$= \frac{3}{mn^2 \sqrt[3]{mn^2}}$$
$$= \frac{3 \cdot \sqrt[3]{m^2 n}}{mn^2 \sqrt[3]{mn^2} \cdot \sqrt[3]{m^2 n}}$$
$$= \frac{3\sqrt[3]{m^2 n}}{m^2 n^3}$$

33. $x^2 - 4x \le 0$
$$x(x-4) = 0$$
$$x = 0, x = 4$$

Region	Test Point	$x(x-4) \le 0$	Result
$x < 0$	$x = -1$	$(-1)(-5) \le 0$	False
$0 < x < 4$	$x = 2$	$2(-2) \le 0$	True
$x > 4$	$x = 5$	$5(1) \le 0$	False

Solution: $[0, 4]$

34.
$$c^2 = a^2 + b^2$$
$$8^2 = 4^2 + b^2$$
$$64 = 16 + b^2$$
$$48 = b^2$$
$$\pm 4\sqrt{3} = b$$
$b > 0$ so the length is $4\sqrt{3}$ inches.

35. $F(x) = (x-3)^2 + 1$

36. a. $i^8 = (i^2)^4 = (-1)^4 = 1$

b. $i^{21} = i(i^{20}) = i$

c. $i^{42} = i^2(i^{40}) = i^2 = -1$

d. $i^{-13} = \frac{1}{i^{13}} = \frac{1}{i(i^{12})} = \frac{1}{i} = \frac{i}{i^2} = -i$

37.
$$\frac{45}{x} = \frac{5}{7}$$
$$45 \cdot 7 = 5x$$
$$315 = 5x$$
$$63 = x$$

38.
$$4x^2 + 8x - 1 = 0$$
$$x^2 + 2x - \frac{1}{4} = 0$$
$$x^2 + 2x = \frac{1}{4}$$
$$x^2 + 2x + \left(\frac{2}{2}\right)^2 = \frac{1}{4} + \left(\frac{2}{2}\right)^2$$
$$x^2 + 2x + 1 = \frac{1}{4} + 1$$
$$(x+1)^2 = \frac{5}{4}$$
$$x + 1 = \pm\sqrt{\frac{5}{4}}$$
$$x + 1 = \pm\frac{\sqrt{5}}{2}$$
$$x = -1 \pm \frac{\sqrt{5}}{2}$$
$$= \frac{-2 \pm \sqrt{5}}{2}$$

The solutions are $\dfrac{-2 + \sqrt{5}}{2}$ and $\dfrac{-2 - \sqrt{5}}{2}$.

39. $f(x) = x + 3$
$y = x + 3$
$x = y + 3$
$y = x - 3$
$f^{-1}(x) = x - 3$

40. $\left(x - \dfrac{1}{2}\right)^2 = \dfrac{x}{2}$

$x^2 - x + \dfrac{1}{4} = \dfrac{1}{2}x$

$x^2 - \dfrac{3}{2}x + \dfrac{1}{4} = 0$

$4x^2 - 6x + 1 = 0$

$a = 4, b = -6, c = 1$

$x = \dfrac{-(-6) \pm \sqrt{(-6)^2 - 4(4)(1)}}{2(4)}$

$= \dfrac{6 \pm \sqrt{20}}{8}$

$= \dfrac{6 \pm 2\sqrt{5}}{8}$

$= \dfrac{3 \pm \sqrt{5}}{4}$

The solutions are $\dfrac{3 + \sqrt{5}}{4}$ and $\dfrac{3 - \sqrt{5}}{4}$.

41. a. $\log_4 16 = \log_4 4^2 = 2$

   b. $\log_{10} \dfrac{1}{10} = \log_{10} 10^{-1} = -1$

   c. $\log_9 3 = \log_9 9^{1/2} = \dfrac{1}{2}$

42. $f(x) = -(x + 1)^2 + 1$
Vertex: $(-1, 1)$
Axis of symmetry: $x = -1$

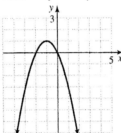

Chapter 13

1. $x = \dfrac{1}{2}y^2;\ a = \dfrac{1}{2},\ h = 0, k = 0;$ vertex: (0, 0)

x	y
2	−2
$\dfrac{1}{2}$	−1
0	0
$\dfrac{1}{2}$	1
2	2

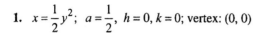

2. $x = -2(y+4)^2 - 1;\ a = -2, h = -1, k = -4;$
   vertex: (−1, −4)

x	y
−9	−6
3	−5
−1	−4
−3	−3
−9	−2

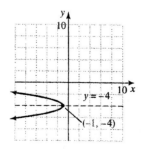

3. $$y = -x^2 + 4x + 6$$
$$y - 6 = -x^2 + 4x$$
$$y - 6 = -(x^2 - 4x)$$
$$y - 6 - (+4) = -(x^2 - 4x + 4)$$
$$y - 10 = -(x - 2)^2$$
$$y = -(x - 2)^2 + 10$$

$a = -1, h = 2, k = 10$
vertex: (2, 10)

x	y
−1	1
0	6
1	9
2	10
3	9
4	6
5	1

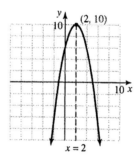

4. $x = 3y^2 + 6y + 4$
Find the vertex.
$$y = \frac{-b}{2a} = \frac{-6}{2(3)} = -1$$

$$x = 3(-1)^2 + 6(-1) + 4 = 3 - 6 + 4 = 1$$

vertex: (1, −1)
The axis of symmetry is the line $y = -1$.
Since $a > 0$, the parabola opens to the right.

$$x = 3(0)^2 + 6(0) + 4 = 4$$

The x-intercept is (4, 0).

614

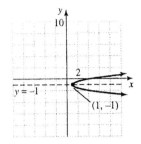

$y = -1$

$(1, -1)$

5.
$$x^2 + y^2 = 25$$
$$(x-0)^2 + (y-0)^2 = 5^2$$
center: (0, 0); radius = 5

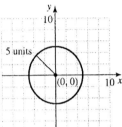

5 units

(0, 0)

6. $(x-3)^2 + (y+2)^2 = 4$

$h = 3, k = -2, r = \sqrt{4} = 2$

center: (3, −2)

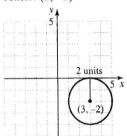

2 units

(3, −2)

7. Center: (−2, −5); radius = 9

$$(x-h)^2 + (y-k)^2 = r^2$$

$h = -2, k = -5,$ and $r = 9.$

The equation is $(x+2)^2 + (y+5)^2 = 81.$

8.
$$x^2 + y^2 + 6x - 2y = 6$$
$$(x^2 + 6x) + (y^2 - 2y) = 6$$
$$(x^2 + 6x + 9) + (y^2 - 2y + 1) = 6 + 9 + 1$$
$$(x+3)^2 + (y-1)^2 = 16$$

Center: (−3, 1); radius = $\sqrt{16}$ = 4

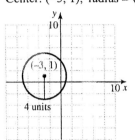

(−3, 1)

4 units

Graphing Calculator Explorations

1. $x^2 + y^2 = 55$
$$y^2 = 55 - x^2$$
$$y = \pm\sqrt{55 - x^2}$$

2. $x^2 + y^2 = 20$
$$y^2 = 20 - x^2$$
$$y = \pm\sqrt{20 - x^2}$$

3. $5x^2 + 5y^2 = 50$
$$5y^2 = 50 - 5x^2$$
$$y^2 = 10 - x^2$$
$$y = \pm\sqrt{10 - x^2}$$

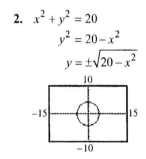

4. $6x^2 + 6y^2 = 105$

$\qquad 6y^2 = 105 - 6x^2$

$\qquad y^2 = 17.5 - x^2$

$\qquad y = \pm\sqrt{17.5 - x^2}$

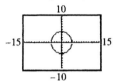

5. $2x^2 + 2y^2 - 34 = 0$

$\qquad 2y^2 = 34 - 2x^2$

$\qquad y^2 = 17 - x^2$

$\qquad y = \pm\sqrt{17 - x^2}$

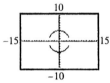

6. $4x^2 + 4y^2 - 48 = 0$

$\qquad 4y^2 = 48 - 4x^2$

$\qquad y^2 = 12 - x^2$

$\qquad y = \pm\sqrt{12 - x^2}$

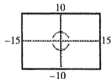

7. $7x^2 + 7y^2 - 89 = 0$

$\qquad 7y^2 = 89 - 7x^2$

$\qquad y^2 = \dfrac{89 - 7x^2}{7}$

$\qquad y = \pm\sqrt{\dfrac{89 - 7x^2}{7}}$

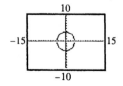

8. $3x^2 + 3y^2 - 35 = 0$

$\qquad 3y^2 = 35 - 3x^2$

$\qquad y^2 = \dfrac{35 - 3x^2}{3}$

$\qquad y = \pm\sqrt{\dfrac{35 - 3x^2}{3}}$

Vocabulary and Readiness Check

1. The circle, parabola, ellipse, and hyperbola are called the conic sections.

2. For a parabola that opens upward the lowest point is the vertex.

3. A circle is the set of all points in a plane that are the same distance from a fixed point. The fixed point is called the center.

4. The midpoint of a diameter of a circle is the center.

5. The distance from the center of a circle to any point of the circle is called the radius.

6. Twice a circle's radius is its diameter.

7. $y = x^2 - 7x + 5;\ a = 1$, upward

8. $y = -x^2 + 16;\ a = -1$, downward

9. $x = -y^2 - y + 2;\ a = -1$, to the left

10. $x = 3y^2 + 2y - 5;\ a = 3$, to the right

11. $y = -x^2 + 2x + 1;\ a = -1$, downward

12. $x = -y^2 + 2y - 6;\ a = -1$, to the left

Exercise Set 13.1

2. $x = -2y^2$

$x = -2(y - 0)^2 + 0$

Vertex: (0, 0)

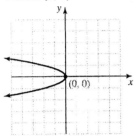

4. $x = (y - 4)^2 - 1$

Vertex: (−1, 4)

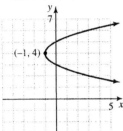

6. $x = -4(y - 2)^2 + 2$

Vertex: (2; 2)

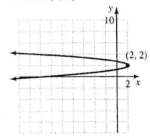

8. $x = y^2 - 6y + 6$

$x - 6 = y^2 - 6y$

$x - 6 + 9 = y^2 - 6y + 9$

$x + 3 = (y - 3)^2$

$x = (y - 3)^2 - 3$

Vertex: (−3, 3)

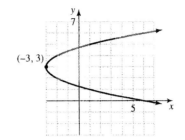

10. $y = x^2 + 4x - 5$

$y + 5 = x^2 + 4x$

$y + 5 + 4 = x^2 + 4x + 4$

$y + 9 = (x + 2)^2$

$y = (x + 2)^2 - 9$

Vertex: (−2, −9)

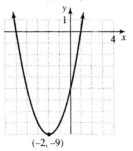

12. $x = 3y^2 + 6y + 7$

$x - 7 = 3(y^2 + 2y)$

$x - 7 + 3(1) = 3(y^2 + 2y + 1)$

$x - 4 = 3(y + 1)^2$

$x = 3(y + 1)^2 + 4$

Vertex: (4, −1)

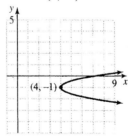

14. $x^2 + y^2 = 100$

$(x-0)^2 + (y-0)^2 = 10^2$

Center: (0, 0), radius $r = 10$.

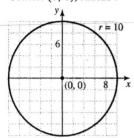

16. $(x-3)^2 + y^2 = 9$

$(x-3)^2 + (y-0)^2 = 3^2$

Center: (3, 0), radius $r = 3$.

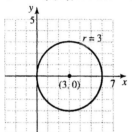

18. $(x+3)^2 + (y+3)^2 = 4$

$(x+3)^2 + (y+3)^2 = 2^2$

Center: (−3, −3), radius $r = 2$.

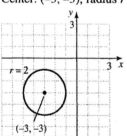

20. $\qquad x^2 + 10x + y^2 = 0$

$(x^2 + 10x) + y^2 = 0$

$(x^2 + 10x + 25) + y^2 = 25$

$(x+5)^2 + (y-0)^2 = 5^2$

Center: (−5, 0), radius $r = 5$

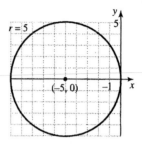

22. $\qquad x^2 + 6x - 4y + y^2 = 3$

$(x^2 + 6x) + (y^2 - 4y) = 3$

$(x^2 + 6x + 9) + (y^2 - 4y + 4) = 3 + 9 + 4$

$(x+3)^2 + (y-2)^2 = 16$

Center: (−3, 2), radius $r = \sqrt{16} = 4$.

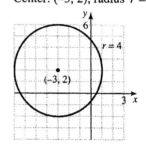

24. $\qquad x^2 + y^2 - 2x - 6y - 5 = 0$

$(x^2 - 2x) + (y^2 - 6y) = 5$

$(x^2 - 2x + 1) + (y^2 - 6y + 9) = 5 + 1 + 9$

$(x-1)^2 + (y-3)^2 = 15$

Center: (1, 3), radius $r = \sqrt{15}$.

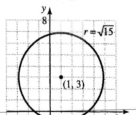

26. Center $(h, k) = (-7, 6)$, radius $r = 2$.

$[x - (-7)]^2 + (y - 6)^2 = 2^2$

$(x+7)^2 + (y-6)^2 = 4$

28. Center $(h, k) = (0, -6)$, radius $r = \sqrt{2}$.

$(x-0)^2 + [y - (-6)]^2 = \left(\sqrt{2}\right)^2$

$x^2 + (y+6)^2 = 2$

30. Center $(h, k) = (0, 0)$, radius $r = 4\sqrt{7}$.

$$(x-0)^2 + (y-0)^2 = \left(4\sqrt{7}\right)^2$$
$$x^2 + y^2 = 112$$

32. $x = y^2 + 2$

$x = (y-0)^2 + 2$

Vertex: $(2, 0)$

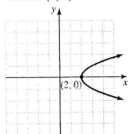

34. $y = (x+3)^2 + 3$

Vertex: $(-3, 3)$

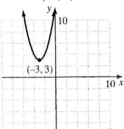

36. $x^2 + y^2 = 49$

Center: $(0, 0)$, radius $r = \sqrt{49} = 7$

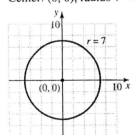

38. $x = (y-1)^2 + 4$

Vertex: $(4, 1)$

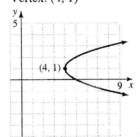

40. $(x+3)^2 + (y-1)^2 = 9$

Center: $(-3, 1)$, radius $r = \sqrt{9} = 3$

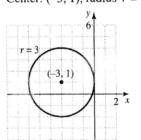

42. $x = -2(y+5)^2$

Vertex: $(0, -5)$

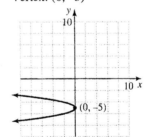

44. $x^2 + (y+5)^2 = 5$

Center: $(0, -5)$, radius $r = \sqrt{5}$

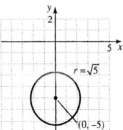

46. $y = 3(x-4)^2 + 2$

Vertex: (4, 2)

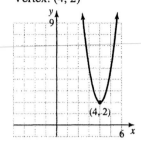

48. $2x^2 + 2y^2 = \dfrac{1}{2}$

$x^2 + y^2 = \dfrac{1}{4}$

Center: (0, 0), radius $r = \sqrt{\dfrac{1}{4}} = \dfrac{1}{2}$

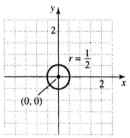

50. $y = x^2 - 2x - 15$

$y + 15 + 1 = x^2 - 2x + 1$

$y + 16 = (x-1)^2$

$y = (x-1)^2 - 16$

Vertex: (1, –16)

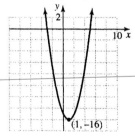

52. $x^2 + y^2 + 6x + 10y - 2 = 0$

$(x^2 + 6x) + (y^2 + 10y) = 2$

$(x^2 + 6x + 9) + (y^2 + 10y + 25) = 2 + 9 + 25$

$(x+3)^2 + (y+5)^2 = 36$

Center: (–3, –5), radius $r = \sqrt{36} = 6$

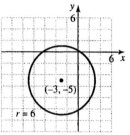

54. $x = y^2 + 6y + 2$

$x - 2 + 9 = y^2 + 6y + 9$

$x + 7 = (y+3)^2$

$x = (y+3)^2 - 7$

Vertex: (–7, –3)

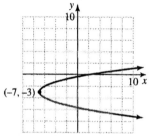

56. $x^2 + y^2 - 8y + 5 = 0$

$x^2 + (y^2 - 8y) = -5$

$x^2 + (y^2 - 8y + 16) = -5 + 16$

$x^2 + (y-4)^2 = 11$

Center: (0, 4), radius $r = \sqrt{11}$

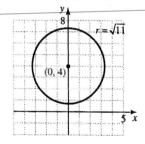

58.
$$x = -2y^2 - 4y$$
$$x + [-2(1)] = -2(y^2 + 2y + 1)$$
$$x - 2 = -2(y + 1)^2$$
$$x = -2(y + 1)^2 + 2$$

Vertex: $(2, -1)$

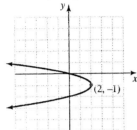

60. $\dfrac{x^2}{3} + \dfrac{y^2}{3} = 2$
$$x^2 + y^2 = 6$$

Center: $(0, 0)$, radius $r = \sqrt{6}$

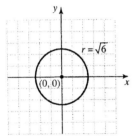

62.
$$y = 4x^2 - 40x + 105$$
$$y - 105 + 4(25) = 4(x^2 - 10x + 25)$$
$$y - 5 = 4(x - 5)^2$$
$$y = 4(x - 5)^2 + 5$$

Vertex: $(5, 5)$

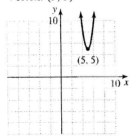

64. $y = 2x + 5$

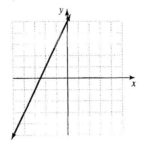

66. $y = 3$

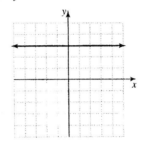

68. $\dfrac{1}{\sqrt{3}} = \dfrac{1 \cdot \sqrt{3}}{\sqrt{3} \cdot \sqrt{3}} = \dfrac{\sqrt{3}}{3}$

70. $\dfrac{4\sqrt{7}}{\sqrt{6}} = \dfrac{4\sqrt{7} \cdot \sqrt{6}}{\sqrt{6} \cdot \sqrt{6}} = \dfrac{4\sqrt{42}}{6} = \dfrac{2\sqrt{42}}{3}$

72. a. $\text{radius} = \dfrac{1}{2}(\text{diameter})$
$$= \dfrac{1}{2}(33 \text{ meters})$$
$$= 16.5 \text{ meters}$$

   b. $\text{circumference} = \pi(\text{diameter})$
$$= \pi(33 \text{ meters})$$
$$\approx 103.67 \text{ meters}$$

   c. $\dfrac{103.67}{30} \approx 3.5$ meters apart

   d. center: $(0, 16.5)$

   e. $(x - 0)^2 + (y - 16.5)^2 = 16.5^2$
$$x^2 + (y - 16.5)^2 = 16.5^2$$

74. a. $\text{radius} = \dfrac{1}{2}(\text{diameter})$
$$= \dfrac{1}{2}(250 \text{ feet})$$
$$= 125 \text{ feet}$$

b. Height $-$ diameter $= 264$ feet $- 250$ feet
$$= 14 \text{ feet}$$

c. radius $+$ distance above ground
$$= 125 \text{ feet} + 14 \text{ feet}$$
$$= 139 \text{ feet}$$

d. center: $(0, 139)$

e. $(x - 0)^2 + (y - 139)^2 = 125^2$
$$x^2 + (y - 139)^2 = 125^2$$

76. Answers may vary

78. $y = a(x - h)^2 + k$

The parabola opens downward, so $a < 0$. The vertex is at $(0, 40)$, so $h = 0$ and $k = 40$. Thus, we have $y = ax^2 + 40$. To find a, let $(x, y) = (50, 0)$.
$$0 = a(50)^2 + 40$$
$$-40 = 2500a$$
$$-\frac{2}{125} = a$$

The equation is $y = -\frac{2}{125}x^2 + 40$.

80. $\dfrac{x^2}{3} + \dfrac{y^2}{3} = 2$
$$x^2 + y^2 = 6$$
$$y^2 = 6 - x^2$$
$$y = \pm\sqrt{6 - x^2}$$

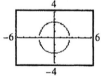

82. $y = 4x^2 - 40x + 105$

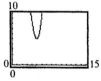

Section 13.2

Practice Exercises

1. $\dfrac{x^2}{25} + \dfrac{y^2}{4} = 1$

The equation is an ellipse with $a = 5$ and $b = 2$. The center is $(0, 0)$. The x-intercepts are $(5, 0)$ and $(-5, 0)$. The y-intercepts are $(2, 0)$ and $(-2, 0)$.

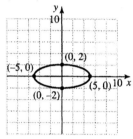

2. $9x^2 + 4y^2 = 36$
$$\frac{9x^2}{36} + \frac{4y^2}{36} = \frac{36}{36}$$
$$\frac{x^2}{4} + \frac{y^2}{9} = 1$$

This is an equation of an ellipse with $a = 2$ and $b = 3$. The ellipse has center $(0, 0)$, x-intercepts $(2, 0)$ and $(-2, 0)$, and y-intercepts $(3, 0)$ and $(-3, 0)$.

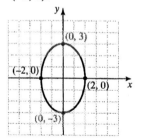

3. $\dfrac{(x - 4)^2}{49} + \dfrac{(y + 1)^2}{81} = 1$

This ellipse has center $(4, -1)$.
$a = 7$ and $b = 9$.
Find four points on the ellipse.
$(4 + 7, -1) = (11, -1)$
$(4 - 7, -1) = (-3, -1)$
$(4, -1 + 9) = (4, 8)$
$(4, -1 - 9) = (4, -10)$

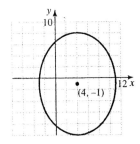

4. $\dfrac{x^2}{9} - \dfrac{y^2}{16} = 1$

This is a hyperbola with $a = 3$ and $b = 4$. It has center $(0, 0)$ and x-intercepts $(3, 0)$ and $(-3, 0)$. The asymptotes pass through $(3, 4)$, $(3, -4)$, $(-3, 4)$, and $(-3, -4)$.

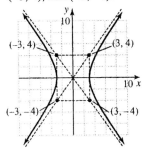

5. $9y^2 - 25x^2 = 225$

$$\frac{9y^2}{225} - \frac{25x^2}{225} = \frac{225}{225}$$

$$\frac{y^2}{25} - \frac{x^2}{9} = 1$$

This is a hyperbola with $a = 3$ and $b = 5$. The center is at $(0, 0)$ with y-intercepts $(0, 5)$ and $(0, -5)$. The asymptotes pass through $(3, 5)$, $(3, -5)$, $(-3, 5)$, and $(-3, -5)$.

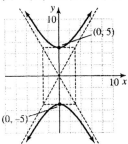

Graphing Calculator Explorations

1. $10x^2 + y^2 = 32$

$$y^2 = 32 - 10x^2$$

$$y = \pm\sqrt{32 - 10x^2}$$

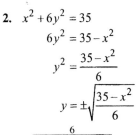

2. $x^2 + 6y^2 = 35$

$$6y^2 = 35 - x^2$$

$$y^2 = \frac{35 - x^2}{6}$$

$$y = \pm\sqrt{\frac{35 - x^2}{6}}$$

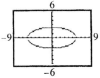

3. $20x^2 + 5y^2 = 100$

$$5y^2 = 100 - 20x^2$$

$$y^2 = 20 - 4x^2$$

$$y = \pm\sqrt{20 - 4x^2}$$

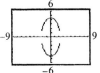

4. $4y^2 + 12x^2 = 48$

$$4y^2 = 48 - 12x^2$$

$$y^2 = 12 - 3x^2$$

$$y = \pm\sqrt{12 - 3x^2}$$

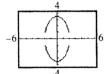

5. $7.3x^2 + 15.5y^2 = 95.2$

$$15.5y^2 = 95.2 - 7.3x^2$$

$$y^2 = \frac{95.2 - 7.3x^2}{15.5}$$

$$y = \pm\sqrt{\frac{95.2 - 7.3x^2}{15.5}}$$

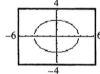

6. $18.8x^2 + 36.1y^2 = 205.8$

$$36.1y^2 = 205.8 - 18.8x^2$$

$$y^2 = \frac{205.8 - 18.8x^2}{36.1}$$

$$y = \pm\sqrt{\frac{205.8 - 18.8x^2}{36.1}}$$

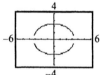

Vocabulary and Readiness Check

1. A <u>hyperbola</u> is the set of points in a plane such that the absolute value of the differences of their distances from two fixed points is constant.

2. An <u>ellipse</u> is the set of points in a plane such that the sum of their distances from two fixed points is constant.

3. The two fixed points are each called a <u>focus</u>.

4. The point midway between the foci is called the <u>center</u>.

5. The graph of $\dfrac{x^2}{a^2} - \dfrac{y^2}{b^2} = 1$ is a <u>hyperbola</u> with center <u>(0, 0)</u> and <u>x</u>-intercepts of <u>(a, 0) and (−a, 0)</u>.

6. The graph of $\dfrac{x^2}{b^2} + \dfrac{y^2}{a^2} = 1$ is an <u>ellipse</u> with center <u>(0, 0)</u> and *x*-intercepts of <u>(b, 0) and (−b, 0)</u>.

7. $\dfrac{x^2}{16} + \dfrac{y^2}{4} = 1$ is an ellipse.

8. $\dfrac{x^2}{16} - \dfrac{y^2}{4} = 1$ is a hyperbola.

9. $x^2 - 5y^2 = 3$ is a hyperbola.

10. $-x^2 + 5y^2 = 3$ or
$5y^2 - x^2 = 3$ is a hyperbola.

11. $-\dfrac{y^2}{25} + \dfrac{x^2}{36} = 1$ or
$\dfrac{x^2}{36} - \dfrac{y^2}{25} = 1$ is a hyperbola.

12. $\dfrac{y^2}{25} + \dfrac{x^2}{36} = 1$ is an ellipse.

Exercise Set 13.2

2. $\dfrac{x^2}{16} + \dfrac{y^2}{9} = 1$

$$\dfrac{x^2}{4^2} + \dfrac{y^2}{3^2} = 1$$

Center: (0, 0)
x-intercepts: (−4, 0), (4, 0)
y-intercepts: (0, −3), (0, 3)

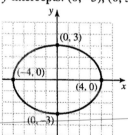

4. $x^2 + \dfrac{y^2}{4} = 1$

$$\dfrac{x^2}{1^2} + \dfrac{y^2}{2^2} = 1$$

Center: (0, 0)
x-intercepts: (−1, 0), (1, 0)
y-intercepts: (0, −2), (0, 2)

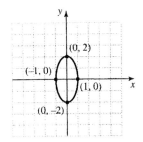

6. $x^2 + 4y^2 = 16$

$$\frac{x^2}{16} + \frac{y^2}{4} = 1$$

$$\frac{x^2}{4^2} + \frac{y^2}{2^2} = 1$$

Center: $(0, 0)$
x-intercepts: $(-4, 0), (4, 0)$
y-intercepts: $(0, -2), (0, 2)$

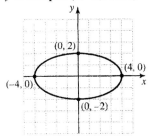

8. $36x^2 + y^2 = 36$

$$x^2 + \frac{y^2}{36} = 1$$

$$\frac{x^2}{1^2} + \frac{y^2}{6^2} = 1$$

Center: $(0, 0)$
x-intercepts: $(-1, 0), (1, 0)$
y-intercepts: $(0, -6), (0, 6)$

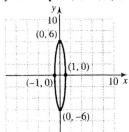

10. $\dfrac{(x-3)^2}{9} + \dfrac{(y+3)^2}{16} = 1$

$$\frac{(x-3)^2}{3^2} + \frac{(y+3)^2}{4^2} = 1$$

Center: $(3, -3)$

Other points:
$(3-3, -3) = (0, -3)$
$(3+3, -3) = (6, -3)$
$(3, -3-4) = (3, -7)$
$(3, -3+4) = (3, 1)$

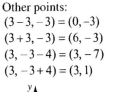

12. $\dfrac{(x+3)^2}{16} + \dfrac{(y+2)^2}{4} = 1$

$$\frac{(x+3)^2}{4^2} + \frac{(y+2)^2}{2^2} = 1$$

Center: $(-3, -2)$
Other points:
$(-3-4, -2) = (-7, -2)$
$(-3+4, -2) = (1, -2)$
$(-3, -2-2) = (-3, -4)$
$(-3, -2+2) = (-3, 0)$

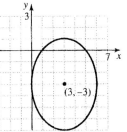

14. $\dfrac{x^2}{36} - \dfrac{y^2}{36} = 1$

$$\frac{x^2}{6^2} - \frac{y^2}{6^2} = 1$$

$a = 6, b = 6$

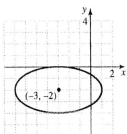

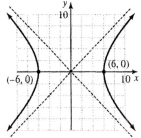

16. $\dfrac{y^2}{25} - \dfrac{x^2}{49} = 1$

$\dfrac{y^2}{5^2} - \dfrac{x^2}{7^2} = 1$

$a = 7,\ b = 5$

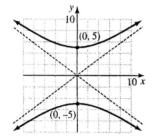

18. $4x^2 - y^2 = 36$

$\dfrac{x^2}{9} - \dfrac{y^2}{36} = 1$

$\dfrac{x^2}{3^2} - \dfrac{y^2}{6^2} = 1$

$a = 3,\ b = 6$

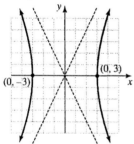

20. $4y^2 - 25x^2 = 100$

$\dfrac{y^2}{25} - \dfrac{x^2}{4} = 1$

$\dfrac{y^2}{5^2} - \dfrac{x^2}{2^2} = 1$

$a = 2,\ b = 5$

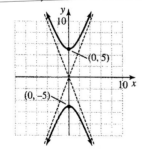

22. $(x - 7)^2 + (y - 2)^2 = 4$

Circle; center (7, 2), radius $r = \sqrt{4} = 2$

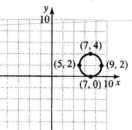

24. $y = x^2 + 12x + 36$

Parabola; $x = \dfrac{-b}{2a} = \dfrac{-12}{2(1)} = -6$

$y = (-6)^2 + 12(-6) + 36 = 0$

Vertex: (–6, 0), opens upward

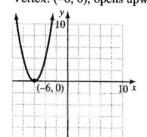

26. $\dfrac{y^2}{9} - \dfrac{x^2}{9} = 1$

$\dfrac{y^2}{3^2} - \dfrac{x^2}{3^2} = 1$

Hyperbola; center: (0, 0)

$a = 3,\ b = 3$

y-intercepts (0, –3), (0, 3)

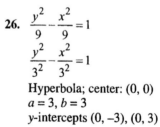

28. $\dfrac{x^2}{16} + \dfrac{y^2}{4} = 1$

$\dfrac{x^2}{4^2} + \dfrac{y^2}{2^2} = 1$

Ellipse; center: (0, 0), $a = 4,\ b = 2$

x-intercepts (–4, 0), (4, 0)

y-intercepts $(0, -2)$, $(0, 2)$

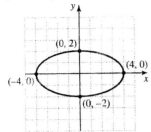

30. $x = y^2 + 4y - 1$

Parabola: $y = \dfrac{-b}{2a} = \dfrac{-4}{2(1)} = -2$

$x = (-2)^2 + 4(-2) - 1 = -5$

Vertex: $(-5, -2)$, opens to the right.

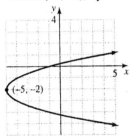

32. $9x^2 - 4y^2 = 36$

$\dfrac{x^2}{4} - \dfrac{y^2}{9} = 1$

$\dfrac{x^2}{2^2} - \dfrac{y^2}{3^2} = 1$

Hyperbola: center $= (0, 0)$

$a = 2, b = 3$

x-intercepts: $(2, 0)$, $(-2, 0)$

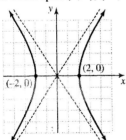

34. $\dfrac{(x-1)^2}{49} + \dfrac{(y+2)^2}{25} = 1$

$\dfrac{(x-1)^2}{7^2} + \dfrac{(y+2)^2}{5^2} = 1$

Ellipse; center: $(1, -2)$

$a = 7, b = 5$

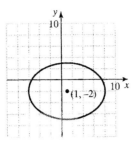

36. $\left(x + \dfrac{1}{2}\right)^2 + \left(y - \dfrac{1}{2}\right)^2 = 1$

Circle; center: $\left(-\dfrac{1}{2}, \dfrac{1}{2}\right)$, radius $r = 1$

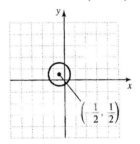

38. $x < 5$ and $x < 1$

$x < 1$

$(-\infty, 1)$

40. $2x - 1 \geq 7$ or $-3x \leq -6$

$\quad 2x \geq 8$ or $\quad x \geq 2$

$\quad\quad x \geq 4$

$x \geq 2$

$[2, \infty)$

42. $(2x^3)(-4x^2) = -8x^5$

44. $-5x^2 + x^2 = -4x^2$

46. $\dfrac{x^2}{16} + \dfrac{y^2}{25} = 1$

$\sqrt{16} = 4$, so the distance between the x-intercepts is $4 + 4 = 8$ units.

$\sqrt{25} = 5$, so the distance between the y-intercepts is $5 + 5 = 10$ units.

The distance between the y-intercepts is longer by $10 - 8 = 2$ units.

627

48. $4x^2 + y^2 = 16$

$$\frac{x^2}{4} + \frac{y^2}{16} = 1$$

$\sqrt{4} = 2$, so the distance between the *x*-intercepts
is $2 + 2 = 4$ units.
$\sqrt{16} = 4$, so the distance between the
y-intercepts is $4 + 4 = 8$ units.
The distance between the *y*-intercepts is longer
by $8 - 4 = 4$ units.

50. $x^2 + y^2 = 25$

$$\frac{x^2}{25} + \frac{y^2}{25} = 1$$

This resembles the equation of an ellipse. An
ellipse is a circle when $a = b$.

52. A: $a^2 = 36$, $b^2 = 13$

B: $a^2 = 4$, $b^2 = 4$

C: $a^2 = 25$, $b^2 = 16$

D: $a^2 = 39$, $b^2 = 25$

E: $a^2 = 17$, $b^2 = 81$

F: $a^2 = 36$, $b^2 = 36$

G: $a^2 = 16$, $b^2 = 65$

H: $a^2 = 144$, $b^2 = 140$

54. A: $d = 6$
B: $d = 2$
C: $d = 5$
D: $d = 5$
E: $d = 9$
F: $d = 6$
G: $d = 4$
H: $d = 12$

56. They are greater than 0 and less than 1.

58. They are greater than 1.

60. Answers may vary

62. Center $= (1,782,000,000,\ 356,400,000)$

64. $x^2 + 4y^2 = 16$

$$4y^2 = 16 - x^2$$

$$y^2 = 4 - \frac{x^2}{4}; \quad y = \pm\sqrt{4 - 0.25x^2}$$

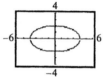

The answers are the same.

66. $\dfrac{(x+2)^2}{9} - \dfrac{(y-1)^2}{4} = 1$

Center: $(-2, 1)$
$a = 3$, $b = 2$

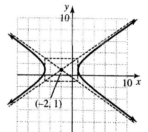

68. $\dfrac{(y+4)^2}{4} - \dfrac{x^2}{25} = 1$

Center: $(0, -4)$
$a = 5$, $b = 2$

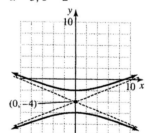

70. $\dfrac{(x-3)^2}{9} - \dfrac{(y-2)^2}{4} = 1$

Center: $(3, 2)$
$a = 3$, $b = 2$

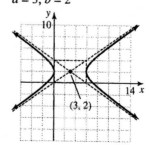

Integrated Review

1. $(x-7)^2 + (y-2)^2 = 4$

Circle; center: $(7, 2)$,

radius: $r = \sqrt{4} = 2$

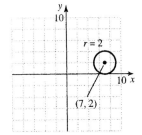

2. $y = x^2 + 4$

Parabola; vertex: $(0, 4)$

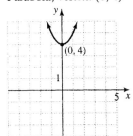

3. $y = x^2 + 12x + 36$

Parabola; $x = \dfrac{-b}{2a} = \dfrac{-12}{2(1)} = -6$

$y = (-6)^2 + 12(-6) + 36 = 0$

Vertex: $(-6, 0)$

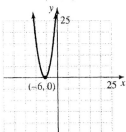

4. $\dfrac{x^2}{4} + \dfrac{y^2}{9} = 1$

Ellipse; center: $(0, 0)$

$a = 2, b = 3$

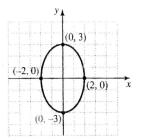

5. $\dfrac{y^2}{9} - \dfrac{x^2}{9} = 1$

Hyperbola; center: $(0, 0)$

$a = 3, b = 3$

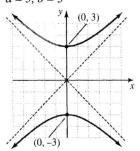

6. $\dfrac{x^2}{16} - \dfrac{y^2}{4} = 1$

Hyperbola; center: $(0, 0)$

$a = 4, b = 2$

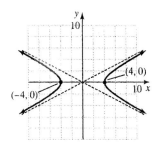

7. $\dfrac{x^2}{16} + \dfrac{y^2}{4} = 1$

Ellipse; center: $(0, 0)$

$a = 4, b = 2$

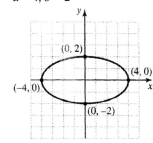

8. $x^2 + y^2 = 16$

Circle; center: $(0, 0)$

radius: $r = \sqrt{16} = 4$

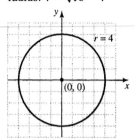

9. $x = y^2 + 4y - 1$

Parabola; $y = \dfrac{-b}{2a} = \dfrac{-4}{2(1)} = -2$

$x = (-2)^2 + 4(-2) - 1 = -5$

Vertex: $(-5, -2)$

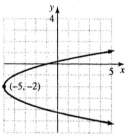

10. $x = -y^2 + 6y$

Parabola; $y = \dfrac{-b}{2a} = \dfrac{-6}{2(-1)} = 3$

$x = -(3)^2 + 6(3) = 9$

Vertex: $(9, 3)$

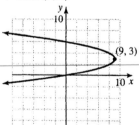

11. $9x^2 - 4y^2 = 36$

$\dfrac{x^2}{4} - \dfrac{y^2}{9} = 1$

Hyperbola; center: $(0, 0)$

$a = 2, b = 3$

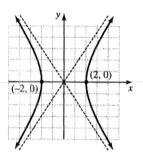

12. $9x^2 + 4y^2 = 36$

$\dfrac{x^2}{4} + \dfrac{y^2}{9} = 1$

Ellipse; center: $(0, 0)$

$a = 2, b = 3$

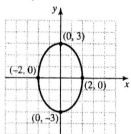

13. $\dfrac{(x-1)^2}{49} + \dfrac{(y+2)^2}{25} = 1$

Ellipse; center: $(1, -2)$,

$a = 7, b = 5$

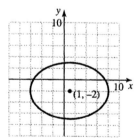

14. $\quad y^2 = x^2 + 16$

$y^2 - x^2 = 16$

$\dfrac{y^2}{16} - \dfrac{x^2}{16} = 1$

Hyperbola; center: $(0, 0)$

$a = 4, b = 4$

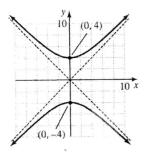

15. $\left(x+\dfrac{1}{2}\right)^2 + \left(y-\dfrac{1}{2}\right)^2 = 1$

Circle; center: $\left(-\dfrac{1}{2}, \dfrac{1}{2}\right)$, radius: $r = \sqrt{1} = 1$

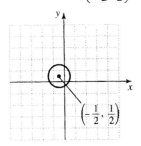

Section 13.3

Practice Exercises

1. $\begin{cases} x^2 - 4y = 4 \\ x + y = -1 \end{cases}$

Solve $x + y = -1$ for y.
$y = -x - 1$
Replace y with $-x - 1$ in the first equation and solve for x.
$$x^2 - 4(-x - 1) = 4$$
$$x^2 + 4x + 4 = 4$$
$$x^2 + 4x = 0$$
$$x(x + 4) = 0$$
$x = 0$ or $x = -4$
Let $x = 0$,   Let $x = -4$,
$y = -0 - 1 = -1$ $y = -(-4) - 1 = 3$
The solutions are $(0, -1)$ and $(-4, 3)$.

2. $\begin{cases} y = -\sqrt{x} \\ x^2 + y^2 = 20 \end{cases}$

Substitute $-\sqrt{x}$ for y in the second equation.
$$x^2 + \left(-\sqrt{x}\right)^2 = 20$$
$$x^2 + x = 20$$
$$x^2 + x - 20 = 0$$
$$(x + 5)(x - 4) = 0$$
$x = -5$ or $x = 4$
Let $x = -5$.
$y = -\sqrt{-5}$ Not a real number
Let $x = 4$.
$y = -\sqrt{4} = -2$
The solution is $(4, -2)$.

3. $\begin{cases} x^2 + y^2 = 9 \\ x - y = 5 \end{cases}$

Solve the second equation for x.
$x = y + 5$
Let $x = y + 5$ in the first equation.
$$(y + 5)^2 + y^2 = 9$$
$$y^2 + 10y + 25 + y^2 = 9$$
$$2y^2 + 10y + 16 = 0$$
$$y^2 + 5y + 8 = 0$$
By the quadratic formula,
$$y = \frac{-5 \pm \sqrt{5^2 - 4(1)(8)}}{2(1)} = \frac{-5 \pm \sqrt{-7}}{2}$$

$\sqrt{-7}$ is not a real number. There is no real solution, or $\varnothing$.

4. $\begin{cases} x^2 + 4y^2 = 16 \\ x^2 - y^2 = 1 \end{cases}$

Add the opposite of the second equation to the first.
$$\begin{array}{r} x^2 + 4y^2 = 16 \\ \underline{-x^2\ \ + y^2 = -1} \\ 0\ + 5y^2 = 15 \\ y^2 = 3 \\ y = \pm\sqrt{3} \end{array}$$

Let $y = \sqrt{3}$.

$x^2 - \left(\sqrt{3}\right)^2 = 1$

$x^2 - 3 = 1$

$x^2 = 4$

$x = \pm 2$

Let $y = -\sqrt{3}$.

$x^2 - \left(-\sqrt{3}\right)^2 = 1$

$x^2 - 3 = 1$

$x^2 = 4$

$x = \pm 2$

The solutions are $\left(2, \sqrt{3}\right)$, $\left(2, -\sqrt{3}\right)$, $\left(-2, \sqrt{3}\right)$, and $\left(-2, -\sqrt{3}\right)$.

Exercise Set 13.3

2. $\begin{cases} x^2 + y^2 = 25 & (1) \\ 3x + 4y = 0 & (2) \end{cases}$

Solve E2 for y: $y = -\dfrac{3x}{4}$.

Substitute into E1.

$x^2 + \left(-\dfrac{3x}{4}\right)^2 = 25$

$x^2 + \dfrac{9x^2}{16} = 25$

$16x^2 + 9x^2 = 400$

$25x^2 = 400$

$x^2 = 16$

$x = \pm 4$

$x = 4 : y = -\dfrac{3(4)}{4} = -3$

$x = -4 : y = -\dfrac{3(-4)}{4} = 3$

The solutions are $(4, -3)$ and $(-4, 3)$.

4. $\begin{cases} 4x^2 + y^2 = 10 & (1) \\ y = x & (2) \end{cases}$

Substitute x for y in E1.

$4x^2 + x^2 = 10$

$5x^2 = 10$

$x^2 = 2$

$x = \pm\sqrt{2}$

Substitute these values into E2.

$x = \sqrt{2} : y = x = \sqrt{2}$

$x = -\sqrt{2} : y = x = -\sqrt{2}$

The solutions are $\left(\sqrt{2}, \sqrt{2}\right)$ and $\left(-\sqrt{2}, -\sqrt{2}\right)$.

6. $\begin{cases} x^2 + y^2 = 4 & (1) \\ x + y = -2 & (2) \end{cases}$

Solve E2 for y: $y = -x - 2$

Substitute into E1.

$x^2 + (-x - 2)^2 = 4$

$x^2 + x^2 + 4x + 4 = 4$

$2x^2 + 4x = 0$

$2x(x + 2) = 0$

$x = 0$ or $x = -2$

Substitute these values into the equation $y = -x - 2$.

$x = 0 : y = -0 - 2 = -2$

$x = -2 : y = -(-2) - 2 = 0$

The solutions are $(0, -2)$ and $(-2, 0)$.

8. $\begin{cases} 4x^2 + 3y^2 = 35 & (1) \\ 5x^2 + 2y^2 = 42 & (2) \end{cases}$

Multiply E1 by 2 and E2 by -3 and add.

$8x^2 + 6y^2 = 70$

$\underline{-15x^2 - 6y^2 = -126}$

$-7x^2 = -56$

$x^2 = 8$

$x = \pm 2\sqrt{2}$

Substitute 8 for x^2 into E1.

$4(8) + 3y^2 = 35$

$3y^2 = 3$

$y^2 = 1$

$y = \pm 1$

The solutions are $\left(-2\sqrt{2}, -1\right)$, $\left(-2\sqrt{2}, 1\right)$, $\left(2\sqrt{2}, -1\right)$, and $\left(2\sqrt{2}, 1\right)$.

10. $\begin{cases} x^2 + 2y^2 = 2 & (1) \\ x^2 - 2y^2 = 6 & (2) \end{cases}$

Add E1 and E2.

$2x^2 = 8$

$x^2 = 4$

$x = \pm 2$

Substitute 4 for x^2 in E1.

$4 + 2y^2 = 2$

$2y^2 = -2$

$y^2 = -1$

There are no real solutions. The solution is $\varnothing$.

12. $\begin{cases} y = x+1 & (1) \\ x^2 - y^2 = 1 & (2) \end{cases}$

Substitute $x+1$ for y in E2.

$x^2 - (x+1)^2 = 1$

$x^2 - (x^2 + 2x + 1) = 1$

$-2x - 1 = 1$

$-2x = 2$

$x = -1$

Substitute this value into E1.

$y = -1 + 1 = 0$

The solution is $(-1, 0)$.

14. $\begin{cases} 6x - y = 5 & (1) \\ xy = 1 & (2) \end{cases}$

Solve E1 for y: $y = 6x - 5$.

Substitute into E2.

$x(6x - 5) = 1$

$6x^2 - 5x - 1 = 0$

$(6x + 1)(x - 1) = 0$

$x = -\dfrac{1}{6}$ or $x = 1$

Substitute these values into the equation $y = 6x - 5$.

$x = -\dfrac{1}{6}: y = 6\left(-\dfrac{1}{6}\right) - 5 = -6$

$x = 1: y = 6(1) - 5 = 1$

The solutions are $\left(-\dfrac{1}{6}, -6\right)$ and $(1, 1)$.

16. $\begin{cases} x^2 + y^2 = 9 & (1) \\ x + y = 5 & (2) \end{cases}$

Solve E2 for y: $y = 5 - x$.

Substitute into E1.

$x^2 + (5-x)^2 = 9$

$x^2 + (25 - 10x + x^2) = 9$

$2x^2 - 10x + 16 = 0$

$x^2 - 5x + 8 = 0$

$x = \dfrac{5 \pm \sqrt{(-5)^2 - 4(1)(8)}}{2(1)} = \dfrac{5 \pm \sqrt{-7}}{2}$

There are no real solutions. The solution is $\varnothing$.

18. $\begin{cases} x = y^2 - 3 & (1) \\ x = y^2 - 3y & (2) \end{cases}$

Substitute $y^2 - 3y$ for x in E1.

$y^2 - 3y = y^2 - 3$

$-3y = -3$

$y = 1$

Substitute this value into E2.

$x = (1)^2 - 3(1) = -2$

The solution is $(-2, 1)$.

20. $\begin{cases} 4x^2 - 2y^2 = 2 & (1) \\ -x^2 + y^2 = 2 & (2) \end{cases}$

Multiply E2 by 2 and add to E1.

$\begin{aligned} 4x^2 - 2y^2 &= 2 \\ -2x^2 + 2y^2 &= 4 \\ \hline 2x^2 &= 6 \end{aligned}$

$x^2 = 3$

$x = \pm\sqrt{3}$

Substitute 3 for x^2 into E2.

$-3 + y^2 = 2$

$y^2 = 5$

$y = \pm\sqrt{5}$

The solutions are $\left(-\sqrt{3}, -\sqrt{5}\right)$, $\left(-\sqrt{3}, \sqrt{5}\right)$, $\left(\sqrt{3}, -\sqrt{5}\right)$, and $\left(\sqrt{3}, \sqrt{5}\right)$.

22. $\begin{cases} x^2 + 2y^2 = 4 & (1) \\ x^2 - y^2 = 4 & (2) \end{cases}$

Multiply E2 by 2 and add to E1.

$\begin{aligned} x^2 + 2y^2 &= 4 \\ 2x^2 - 2y^2 &= 8 \\ \hline 3x^2 &= 12 \end{aligned}$

$x^2 = 4$

$x = \pm 2$

Replace x^2 with 4 in E1.

$4 + 2y^2 = 4$

$2y^2 = 0$

$y^2 = 0$

$y = 0$

The solutions are $(-2, 0)$ and $(2, 0)$.

24. $\begin{cases} x = -y^2 - 3 & (1) \\ x = y^2 - 5 & (2) \end{cases}$

Add E1 and E2.

$x = -y^2 - 3$
$x = y^2 - 5$
$2x = -8$
$x = -4$

Substitute this value into E1.

$-4 = -y^2 - 3$
$y^2 = 1$
$y = \pm 1$

The solutions are $(-4, -1)$ and $(-4, 1)$.

26. $\begin{cases} x^2 + y^2 = 25 & (1) \\ x = y^2 - 5 & (2) \end{cases}$

Solve E2 for y^2: $y^2 = x + 5$.

Substitute into E1.

$x^2 + (x + 5) = 25$
$x^2 + x - 20 = 0$
$(x + 5)(x - 4) = 0$
$x = -5 \text{ or } x = 4$

Substitute these values into the equation $y^2 = x + 5$.

$x = -5:\ y^2 = -5 + 5 = 0 \text{ so } y = 0$
$x = 4:\ y^2 = 4 + 5 = 9$
$\qquad\qquad y = \pm 3$

The solutions are $(-5, 0)$, $(4, -3)$, and $(4, 3)$.

28. $\begin{cases} x^2 + y^2 = 1 & (1) \\ y = x^2 - 9 & (2) \end{cases}$

Solve E2 for x^2: $x^2 = y + 9$.

Substitute into E1.

$(y + 9) + y^2 = 1$
$y^2 + y + 8 = 0$
$y = \dfrac{-1 \pm \sqrt{(1)^2 - 4(1)(8)}}{2(1)} = \dfrac{-1 \pm \sqrt{-31}}{2}$

There are no real solutions. The solution is $\varnothing$.

30. $\begin{cases} x^2 + y^2 = 16 & (1) \\ y = -\dfrac{1}{4}x^2 + 4 & (2) \end{cases}$

Solve E1 for x^2: $x^2 = 16 - y^2$.

Substitute into E2.

$y = -\dfrac{1}{4}(16 - y^2) + 4$
$y = -4 + \dfrac{1}{4}y^2 + 4$
$4y = y^2$
$0 = y^2 - 4y$
$0 = y(y - 4)$
$y = 0 \text{ or } y = 4$

Substitute these values into the equation $x^2 = 16 - y^2$.

$y = 0: x^2 = 16 - (0)^2$
$\qquad\quad x^2 = 16$
$\qquad\quad x = \pm 4$
$y = 4: x^2 = 16 - (4)^2$
$\qquad\quad x^2 = 0$
$\qquad\quad x = 0$

The solutions are $(-4, 0)$, $(4, 0)$ and $(0, 4)$.

32. $y \le 1$

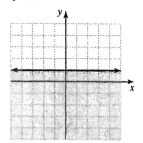

34. $3x - y \le 4$

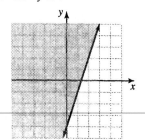

36. $P = 4(3x + 2) = (12x + 8)$ centimeters

38. $P = (4x) + (2x^2) + (3x^2 + 1) + (3x^2 + 7)$
$\quad = (8x^2 + 4x + 8)$ feet

40. Answers may vary

42. There are 0, 1, or 2 possible real solutions. Answers may vary

44. Let x and y represent the numbers.
$$\begin{cases} x^2 + y^2 = 20 \\ xy = 8 \end{cases}$$

Solve the second equation for y: $y = \dfrac{8}{x}$.

Substitute into the first equation.
$$x^2 + \left(\frac{8}{x}\right)^2 = 20$$
$$x^2 + \frac{64}{x^2} = 20$$
$$x^4 - 20x^2 + 64 = 0$$
$$(x^2 - 16)(x^2 - 4) = 0$$
$$(x+4)(x-4)(x+2)(x-2) = 0$$
$$x = \pm 4 \ \text{ or } \ x = \pm 2$$

Substitute these values into the second equation.
$$x = \pm 4: \ \pm 4y = 8$$
$$y = \pm 2$$
$$x = \pm 2: \ \pm 2y = 8$$
$$y = \pm 4$$

The numbers are –2 and –4, and 2 and 4.

46. Let x and y be the length and width.
$$\begin{cases} xy = 525 \\ 2x + 2y = 92 \end{cases}$$

Solve the first equation for y: $y = \dfrac{525}{x}$.

Substitute into the second equation.
$$2x + 2\left(\frac{525}{x}\right) = 92$$
$$x + \frac{525}{x} = 46$$
$$x^2 - 46x + 525 = 0$$
$$(x - 25)(x - 21) = 0$$
$$x = 25 \ \text{ or } \ x = 21$$

Using $x = 25$, $y = \dfrac{525}{x} = \dfrac{525}{25} = 21$.

Using $x = 21$, $y = \dfrac{525}{x} = \dfrac{525}{21} = 25$.

The dimensions are 25 feet by 21 feet.

48. $\begin{cases} p = -2x^2 + 90 \\ p = 9x + 34 \end{cases}$

Substitute.
$$9x + 34 = -2x^2 + 90$$
$$2x^2 + 9x - 56 = 0$$
$$(2x - 7)(x + 8) = 0$$

$$x = \frac{7}{2} = 3.5 \ \text{ or } \ x = -8$$

Disregard the negative.
$$p = 9x + 34 = 9(3.5) + 34 = 65.5$$

The equilibrium quantity is 3.5 thousand (3500) frames, and the corresponding price is $65.50.

50. $\begin{cases} 4x^2 + y^2 = 10 \\ y = x \end{cases}$

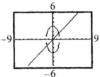

52. $\begin{cases} x = -y^2 - 3 \\ x = y^2 - 5 \end{cases}$

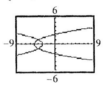

Section 13.4

Practice Exercises

1. $\dfrac{x^2}{36} + \dfrac{y^2}{16} \geq 1$

First graph the ellipse $\dfrac{x^2}{36} + \dfrac{y^2}{16} = 1$ as a solid curve. Choose $(0, 0)$ as a test point.
$$\frac{x^2}{36} + \frac{y^2}{16} \geq 1$$
$$\frac{0^2}{36} + \frac{0^2}{16} \geq 1$$
$$0 \geq 1 \quad \text{False}$$

The solution set is the region that does not contain $(0, 0)$.

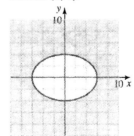

2. $16y^2 > 9x^2 + 144$

The related equation is $16y^2 = 9x^2 + 144$.

$16y^2 - 9x^2 = 144$

$\dfrac{y^2}{9} - \dfrac{x^2}{16} = 1$

Graph the hyperbola as a dashed curve.

Choose (0, 0), (0, 4), and (0, –4) as test points.

(0, 0): $16(0)^2 > 9(0)^2 + 144$
$\qquad\qquad 0 > 144$ False

(0, 4): $16(4)^2 > 9(0)^2 + 144$
$\qquad\qquad 256 > 144$ True

(0, –4): $16(-4)^2 > 9(0)^2 + 144$
$\qquad\qquad 256 > 144$ True

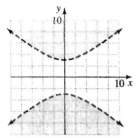

3. $\begin{cases} y \ge x^2 \\ y \le -3x + 2 \end{cases}$

Solve the related system $\begin{cases} y = x^2 \\ y = -3x + 2 \end{cases}$.

Substitute $-3x + 2$ for y in the first equation.

$x^2 = -3x + 2$

$x^2 + 3x - 2 = 0$

$x = \dfrac{-3 \pm \sqrt{3^2 - 4(1)(-2)}}{2(1)}$

$\quad = \dfrac{-3 \pm \sqrt{17}}{2}$

$\quad \approx 0.56$ or -3.56

$y = -3x + 2 \approx -3(0.56) + 2 = 0.32$

$y \approx -3(-3.56) + 2 = 12.68$

The points of intersection are approximately (0.56, 0.32) and (–3.56, 12.68).

Graph $y = x^2$ and $y = -3x + 2$ as solid curves.

The region of the solution set is above the parabola but below the line.

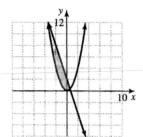

4. $\begin{cases} x^2 + y^2 < 16 \\ \dfrac{x^2}{4} - \dfrac{y^2}{9} < 1 \\ y < x + 3 \end{cases}$

Graph $x^2 + y^2 = 16$, $\dfrac{x^2}{4} - \dfrac{y^2}{9} = 1$, and $y = x + 3$.

The test point (0, 0) gives true statements for all three inequalities; thus, the innermost region is the solution set.

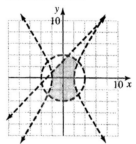

Exercise Set 13.4

2. $y < -x^2$

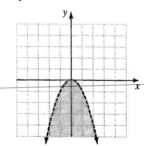

4. $x^2 + y^2 < 36$

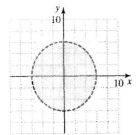

6. $x^2 - \dfrac{y^2}{9} \geq 1$

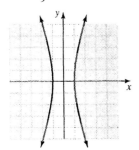

8. $y > (x+3)^2 + 2$

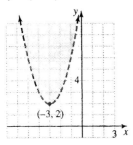

10. $x^2 + y^2 > 4$

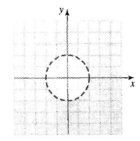

12. $y < -x^2 + 5$

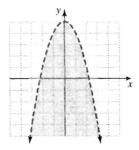

14. $\dfrac{x^2}{25} + \dfrac{y^2}{4} \geq 1$

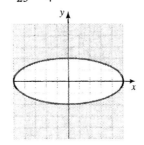

16. $\dfrac{y^2}{16} - \dfrac{x^2}{9} > 1$

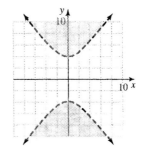

18. $y > (x-2)^2 + 1$

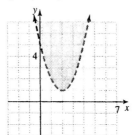

20. $y > x^2 + x - 2$

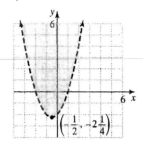

22. $\begin{cases} 3x - 4y \le 12 \\ x^2 + y^2 < 16 \end{cases}$

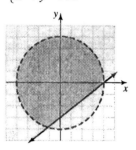

24. $\begin{cases} x^2 + y^2 \ge 9 \\ x^2 + y^2 \ge 16 \end{cases}$

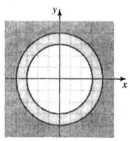

26. $\begin{cases} y \le -x^2 + 3 \\ y \le 2x - 1 \end{cases}$

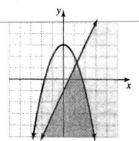

28. $\begin{cases} x^2 + y^2 \le 9 \\ y < x^2 \end{cases}$

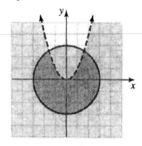

30. $\begin{cases} x^2 + (y - 2)^2 \ge 9 \\ \dfrac{x^2}{4} + \dfrac{y^2}{25} < 1 \end{cases}$

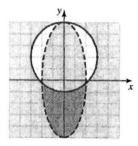

32. $\begin{cases} x^2 - y^2 \ge 1 \\ x \ge 0 \end{cases}$

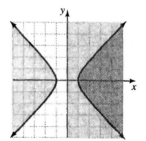

34. $\begin{cases} x - y < -1 \\ 4x - 3y > 0 \\ y > 0 \end{cases}$

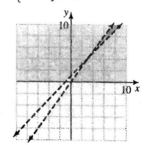

36. $\begin{cases} x^2 - y^2 \geq 1 \\ \dfrac{x^2}{16} + \dfrac{y^2}{4} \leq 1 \\ y \geq 1 \end{cases}$

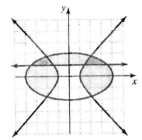

38. This is a function because a vertical line can cross the graph in no more than one place.

40. This is not a function because a vertical line can cross the graph in more than one place.

42. $f(x) = 3x^2 - 2$
$f(-3) = 3(-3)^2 - 2 = 3(9) - 2 = 25$

44. $f(x) = 3x^2 - 2$
$f(b) = 3(b)^2 - 2 = 3b^2 - 2$

46. Answers may vary

Chapter 13 Vocabulary Check

1. A <u>circle</u> is the set of all points in a plane that are the same distance from a fixed point, called the <u>center</u>.

2. A <u>nonlinear system of equations</u> is a system of equations at least one of which is not linear.

3. An <u>ellipse</u> is the set of points on a plane such that the sum of the distances of those points from two fixed points is a constant.

4. In a circle, the distance from the center to a point of the circle is called its <u>radius</u>.

5. A <u>hyperbola</u> is the set of points in a plane such that the absolute value of the difference of the distance from two fixed points is constant.

Chapter 13 Review

1. center (–4, 4), radius 3
$[x - (-4)]^2 + (y - 4)^2 = 3^2$
$(x + 4)^2 + (y - 4)^2 = 9$

2. center (5, 0), radius 5
$(x - 5)^2 + (y - 0)^2 = 5^2$
$(x - 5)^2 + y^2 = 25$

3. center (–7, –9), radius $\sqrt{11}$
$[x - (-7)]^2 + [y - (-9)]^2 = \left(\sqrt{11}\right)^2$
$(x + 7)^2 + (y + 9)^2 = 11$

4. center (0, 0), radius $\dfrac{7}{2}$
$(x - 0)^2 + (y - 0)^2 = \left(\dfrac{7}{2}\right)^2$
$x^2 + y^2 = \dfrac{49}{4}$

5. $x^2 + y^2 = 7$
Circle; center (0, 0), radius $r = \sqrt{7}$

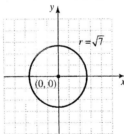

6. $x = 2(y - 5)^2 + 4$
Parabola; vertex: (4, 5)

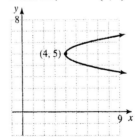

7. $x = -(y+2)^2 + 3$

Parabola; vertex: (3, –2)

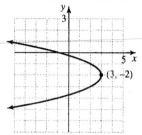

8. $(x-1)^2 + (y-2)^2 = 4$

Circle; center (1, 2), radius $r = \sqrt{4} = 2$

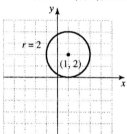

9. $y = -x^2 + 4x + 10$

Parabola; $x = \dfrac{-b}{2a} = \dfrac{-4}{2(-1)} = 2$

$y = -(2)^2 + 4(2) + 10 = 14$

Vertex: (2, 14)

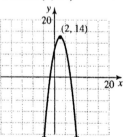

10. $x = -y^2 - 4y + 6$

Parabola; $y = \dfrac{-b}{2a} = \dfrac{-(-4)}{2(-1)} = -2$

$x = -(-2)^2 - 4(-2) + 6 = 10$

Vertex: (10, –2)

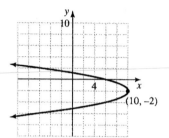

11. $x = \dfrac{1}{2}y^2 + 2y + 1$

Parabola; $y = \dfrac{-b}{2a} = \dfrac{-2}{2\left(\frac{1}{2}\right)} = -2$

$x = \dfrac{1}{2}(-2)^2 + 2(-2) + 1 = -1$

Vertex: (–1, –2)

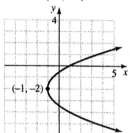

12. $y = -3x^2 + \dfrac{1}{2}x + 4$

Parabola; $x = \dfrac{-b}{2a} = \dfrac{-\frac{1}{2}}{2(-3)} = \dfrac{1}{12}$

$y = -3\left(\dfrac{1}{12}\right)^2 + \dfrac{1}{2}\left(\dfrac{1}{12}\right) + 4 = \dfrac{193}{48}$

Vertex: $\left(\dfrac{1}{12}, \dfrac{193}{48}\right)$

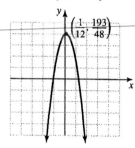

13.
$$x^2 + y^2 + 2x + y = \frac{3}{4}$$
$$(x^2 + 2x) + (y^2 + y) = \frac{3}{4}$$
$$(x^2 + 2x + 1) + \left(y^2 + y + \frac{1}{4}\right) = \frac{3}{4} + 1 + \frac{1}{4}$$
$$(x+1)^2 + \left(y + \frac{1}{2}\right)^2 = 2$$

Circle; center $\left(-1, -\frac{1}{2}\right)$, radius $r = \sqrt{2}$

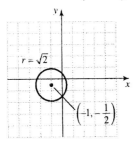

14.
$$x^2 + y^2 - 3y = \frac{7}{4}$$
$$x^2 + \left(y^2 - 3y + \frac{9}{4}\right) = \frac{7}{4} + \frac{9}{4}$$
$$x^2 + \left(y - \frac{3}{2}\right)^2 = 4$$

Circle; center $\left(0, \frac{3}{2}\right)$, radius $r = \sqrt{4} = 2$

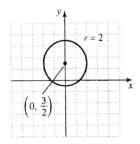

15.
$$4x^2 + 4y^2 + 16x + 8y = 1$$
$$(x^2 + 4x) + (y^2 + 2y) = \frac{1}{4}$$
$$(x^2 + 4x + 4) + (y^2 + 2y + 1) = \frac{1}{4} + 4 + 1$$
$$(x+2)^2 + (y+1)^2 = \frac{21}{4}$$

Circle; center $(-2, -1)$, radius $r = \sqrt{\frac{21}{4}} = \frac{\sqrt{21}}{2}$

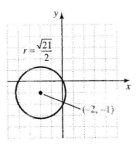

16. $x^2 + \dfrac{y^2}{4} = 1$

Center: $(0, 0)$; $a = 1$, $b = 2$

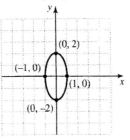

17. $x^2 - \dfrac{y^2}{4} = 1$

Center: $(0, 0)$; $a = 1$, $b = 2$

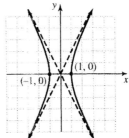

18. $\dfrac{x^2}{5} + \dfrac{y^2}{5} = 1$
$$x^2 + y^2 = 5$$

Center: $(0, 0)$; radius $r = \sqrt{5}$

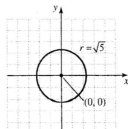

19. $\dfrac{x^2}{5} - \dfrac{y^2}{5} = 1$

Center: $(0, 0)$; $a = \sqrt{5}$, $b = \sqrt{5}$

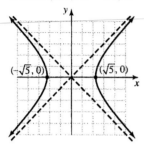

20. $-5x^2 + 25y^2 = 125$

$\dfrac{y^2}{5} - \dfrac{x^2}{25} = 1$

Center: $(0, 0)$; $a = 5$, $b = \sqrt{5}$

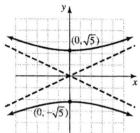

21. $4y^2 + 9x^2 = 36$

$\dfrac{y^2}{9} + \dfrac{x^2}{4} = 1$

Center: $(0, 0)$; $a = 2$, $b = 3$

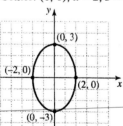

22. $x^2 - y^2 = 1$

Center: $(0, 0)$; $a = 1$, $b = 1$

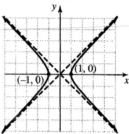

23. $\dfrac{(x+3)^2}{9} + \dfrac{(y-4)^2}{25} = 1$

Center: $(-3, 4)$; $a = 3$, $b = 5$

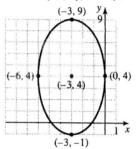

24. $\qquad y^2 = x^2 + 9$

$\qquad y^2 - x^2 = 9$

$\qquad \dfrac{y^2}{9} - \dfrac{x^2}{9} = 1$

Center: $(0, 0)$; $a = 3$, $b = 3$

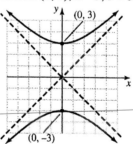

25. $x^2 = 4y^2 - 16$

$16 = 4y^2 - x^2$

$1 = \dfrac{y^2}{4} - \dfrac{x^2}{16}$

Center: $(0, 0)$; $a = 4$, $b = 2$

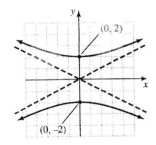

26. $100 - 25x^2 = 4y^2$

$$100 = 25x^2 + 4y^2$$

$$1 = \frac{x^2}{4} + \frac{y^2}{25}$$

Center: $(0, 0)$; $a = 2$, $b = 5$

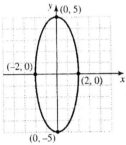

27. $\begin{cases} y = 2x - 4 & (1) \\ y^2 = 4x & (2) \end{cases}$

Substitute $2x - 4$ for y in E2.

$$(2x - 4)^2 = 4x$$

$$4x^2 - 16x + 16 = 4x$$

$$4x^2 - 20x + 16 = 0$$

$$x^2 - 5x + 4 = 0$$

$$(x - 4)(x - 1) = 0$$

$x = 4$ or $x = 1$

Use these values in E1.

$x = 4: y = 2(4) - 4 = 4$

$x = 1: y = 2(1) - 4 = -2$

The solutions are $(4, 4)$ and $(1, -2)$.

28. $\begin{cases} x^2 + y^2 = 4 & (1) \\ x - y = 4 & (2) \end{cases}$

Solve E2 for x: $x = y + 4$.

Substitute into E1.

$$(y + 4)^2 + y^2 = 4$$

$$(y^2 + 8y + 16) + y^2 = 4$$

$$2y^2 + 8y + 12 = 0$$

$$y^2 + 4y + 6 = 0$$

$$y = \frac{-4 \pm \sqrt{(4)^2 - 4(1)(6)}}{2(1)} = \frac{-4 \pm \sqrt{-8}}{2}$$

There are no real solutions. The solution is $\varnothing$.

29. $\begin{cases} y = x + 2 & (1) \\ y = x^2 & (2) \end{cases}$

Substitute $x + 2$ for y in E2.

$$x + 2 = x^2$$

$$0 = x^2 - x - 2$$

$$0 = (x - 2)(x + 1)$$

$x = 2$ or $x = -1$

Use these values in E1.

$x = 2: y = 2 + 2 = 4$

$x = -1: y = -1 + 2 = 1$

The solutions are $(2, 4)$ and $(-1, 1)$.

30. $\begin{cases} x^2 + 4y^2 = 16 & (1) \\ x^2 + y^2 = 4 & (2) \end{cases}$

Multiply E2 by -1 and add to E1.

$$\begin{aligned} x^2 + 4y^2 &= 16 \\ \underline{-x^2 - y^2} &= \underline{-4} \\ 3y^2 &= 12 \\ y^2 &= 4 \\ y &= \pm 2 \end{aligned}$$

Replace y^2 with 4 in E2.

$$x^2 + 4 = 4$$

$$x^2 = 0$$

$$x = 0$$

The solutions are $(0, 2)$ and $(0, -2)$.

31. $\begin{cases} 4x - y^2 = 0 & (1) \\ 2x^2 + y^2 = 16 & (2) \end{cases}$

Solve E1 for y^2: $y^2 = 4x$.

Substitute into E2.

$$2x^2 + 4x = 16$$

$$2x^2 + 4x - 16 = 0$$

$$x^2 + 2x - 8 = 0$$

$$(x + 4)(x - 2) = 0$$

$x = -4$ or $x = 2$

Use these values in the equation $y^2 = 4x$.

$x = -4: y^2 = 4(-4)$

$\qquad y^2 = -16$ (no real solutions)

$x = 2 : y^2 = 4(2)$

$\qquad y^2 = 8$

$\qquad y = \pm\sqrt{8} = \pm 2\sqrt{2}$

The solutions are $\left(2, -2\sqrt{2}\right)$ and $\left(2, 2\sqrt{2}\right)$.

32. $\begin{cases} x^2 + 2y = 9 & (1) \\ 5x - 2y = 5 & (2) \end{cases}$

Add E1 and E2.

$\qquad x^2 + 2y = 9$

$\qquad \underline{5x - 2y = 5}$

$\qquad x^2 + 5x = 14$

$x^2 + 5x - 14 = 0$

$(x + 7)(x - 2) = 0$

$x = -7$ or $x = 2$

Use these values in E1.

$x = -7 : (-7)^2 + 2y = 9$

$\qquad\qquad 49 + 2y = 9$

$\qquad\qquad\quad 2y = -40$

$\qquad\qquad\quad\; y = -20$

$x = 2 : (2)^2 + 2y = 9$

$\qquad\qquad 4 + 2y = 9$

$\qquad\qquad\; 2y = 5$

$\qquad\qquad\;\; y = \dfrac{5}{2}$

The solutions are $(-7, -20)$ and $\left(2, \dfrac{5}{2}\right)$.

33. $\begin{cases} y = 3x^2 + 5x - 4 & (1) \\ y = 3x^2 - x + 2 & (2) \end{cases}$

Substitute.

$3x^2 + 5x - 4 = 3x^2 - x + 2$

$\qquad\qquad 6x = 6$

$\qquad\qquad\; x = 1$

Use this value in E1.

$y = 3(1)^2 + 5(1) - 4 = 4$

The solution is $(1, 4)$.

34. $\begin{cases} x^2 - 3y^2 = 1 & (1) \\ 4x^2 + 5y^2 = 21 & (2) \end{cases}$

Multiply E1 by –4 and add to E2.

$\quad -4x^2 + 12y^2 = -4$

$\quad \underline{\; 4x^2 + \;\; 5y^2 = 21}$

$\qquad\qquad\;\; 17y^2 = 17$

$\qquad\qquad\quad\; y^2 = 1$

$\qquad\qquad\quad\;\; y = \pm 1$

Replace y^2 with 1 in E1.

$x^2 - 3(1) = 1$

$\qquad x^2 = 4$

$\qquad\; x = \pm 2$

The solutions are $(-2, -1)$, $(-2, 1)$, $(2, -1)$ and $(2, 1)$.

35. Let x and y be the length and width.

$\begin{cases} xy = 150 \\ 2x + 2y = 50 \end{cases}$

Solve the first equation for y: $y = \dfrac{150}{x}$.

Substitute into E2.

$2x + 2\left(\dfrac{150}{x}\right) = 50$

$\qquad x + \dfrac{150}{x} = 25$

$\qquad x^2 + 150 = 25x$

$x^2 - 25x + 150 = 0$

$(x - 15)(x - 10) = 0$

$x = 15$ or $x = 10$

Substitute these values into E1.

$15y = 150 \qquad\qquad 10y = 150$

$\;\; y = 10 \qquad\qquad\quad\;\; y = 15$

The room is 15 feet by 10 feet.

36. Four real solutions are possible.

37. $y \le -x^2 + 3$

Graph $y = -x^2 + 3$ as a solid curve.

Test Point	$y \le -x^2 + 3$; Result
$(0, 0)$	$0 \le -(0)^2 + 3$; True

Shade the region containing (0, 0).

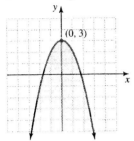

38. $x^2 + y^2 < 9$

First graph the circle as a dashed curve.

Test Point	$x^2 + y^2 < 9$; Result
(0, 0)	$0^2 + 0^2 < 9$; True

Shade the region containing (0, 0).

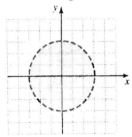

39. $\begin{cases} 2x \le 4 \\ x + y \ge 1 \end{cases}$

First graph $2x = 4$, or $x = 2$, as a solid line, and shade to the left of the line. Next, graph $x + y = 1$ as a solid line.

Test Point	$x + y \ge 1$; Result
(0, 0)	$0 + 0 \ge 1$; False

Shade the region which does not contain (0, 0). The solution to the system is the intersection.

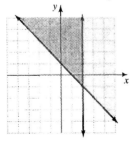

40. $\dfrac{x^2}{4} + \dfrac{y^2}{9} \ge 1$

First graph the ellipse as a solid curve.

Test Point	$\dfrac{x^2}{4} + \dfrac{y^2}{9} \ge 1$; Result
(0, 0)	$\dfrac{(0)^2}{4} + \dfrac{(0)^2}{9} \ge 1$; False

Shade the region that does not contain (0, 0).

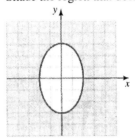

41. $\begin{cases} x^2 + y^2 < 4 \\ x^2 - y^2 \le 1 \end{cases}$

First graph the first circle as a dashed curve.

Test Point	$x^2 + y^2 < 4$; Result
(0, 0)	$0^2 + 0^2 < 4$; True

Shade the region containing (0, 0). Next, graph the hyperbola as a solid curve.

Test Point	$x^2 - y^2 \le 1$; Result
(−2, 0)	$(-2)^2 - 0^2 \le 1$; False
(0, 0)	$0^2 - 0^2 \le 1$; True
(2, 0)	$2^2 - 0^2 \le 1$; False

Shade the region containing (0, 0). The solution to the system is the intersection.

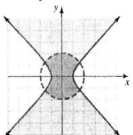

42. $\begin{cases} x^2 + y^2 \le 16 \\ x^2 + y^2 \ge 4 \end{cases}$

First graph the first circle as a solid curve.

Test Point	$x^2 + y^2 \le 16$; Result
(0, 0)	$0^2 + 0^2 \le 16$; True

Shade the region containing (0, 0). Next, graph the second circle as a solid curve.

Test Point	$x^2 + y^2 \ge 4$; Result
(0, 0)	$0^2 + 0^2 \ge 4$; False

Shade the region which does not contain (0, 0). The solution to the system is the intersection.

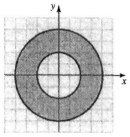

43. center: $(-7, 8)$; radius = 5
$(x - h)^2 + (y - k)^2 = r^2$
$(x + 7)^2 + (y - 8)^2 = 25$

44. $3x^2 + 6x + 3y^2 = 9$
$x^2 + 2x + y^2 = 3$
$x^2 + 2x + 1 + y^2 = 3 + 1$
$(x + 1)^2 + y^2 = 4$

This is a circle with center $(-1, 0)$ and radius 2.

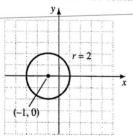

45. $y = x^2 + 6x + 9$
$y = (x + 3)^2$

This is a parabola that opens upward with vertex $(-3, 0)$.

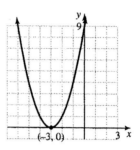

46. $x = y^2 + 6y + 9$
$x = (y + 3)^2$

This is a parabola that opens to the right with vertex $(0, -3)$.

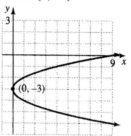

47. $\dfrac{y^2}{4} - \dfrac{x^2}{16} = 1$

This is a hyperbola with center $(0, 0)$, $a = 4$ and $b = 2$.

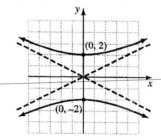

48. $\dfrac{y^2}{4} + \dfrac{x^2}{16} = 1$

This is an ellipse with center $(0, 0)$, $a = 4$ and $b = 2$. The intercepts are $(4, 0)$, $(-4, 0)$, $(0, 2)$, and $(0, -2)$.

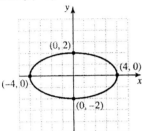

49. $\dfrac{(x-2)^2}{4} + (y-1)^2 = 1$

This is an ellipse with center $(2, 1)$, $a = 2$ and $b = 1$.

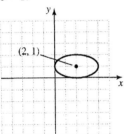

50. $\quad y^2 = x^2 + 6$

$\qquad y^2 - x^2 = 6$

$\qquad \dfrac{y^2}{6} - \dfrac{x^2}{6} = 1$

This is a hyperbola with center $(0, 0)$, $a = \sqrt{6}$ and $b = \sqrt{6}$.

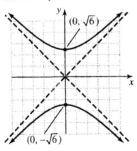

51. $\qquad\qquad y^2 + x^2 = 4x + 6$

$\qquad\qquad y^2 + (x^2 - 4x) = 6$

$\qquad\; y^2 + (x^2 - 4x + 4) = 6 + 4$

$\qquad\qquad\; y^2 + (x-2)^2 = 10$

This is a circle with center $(2, 0)$ and radius $\sqrt{10}$.

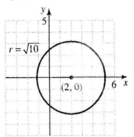

52. $\qquad\quad x^2 + y^2 - 8y = 0$

$\qquad x^2 + y^2 - 8y + 16 = 16$

$\qquad\qquad x^2 + (y-4)^2 = 16$

This is a circle with center $(0, 4)$ and radius $\sqrt{16} = 4$.

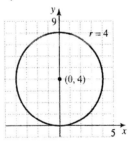

53. $6(x-2)^2 + 9(y+5)^2 = 36$

$\qquad \dfrac{(x-2)^2}{6} + \dfrac{(y+5)^2}{4} = 1$

This is an ellipse with center $(2, -5)$, $a = \sqrt{6}$, and $b = 2$.

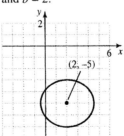

54. $\dfrac{x^2}{16} - \dfrac{y^2}{25} = 1$

This is a hyperbola with center $(0, 0)$, $a = 4$, $b = 5$, and x-intercepts $(4, 0)$ and $(-4, 0)$.

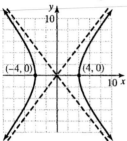

55. $\begin{cases} y = x^2 - 5x + 1 & (1) \\ y = -x + 6 & (2) \end{cases}$

Substitute $-x + 6$ for y in E2.

$-x + 6 = x^2 - 5x + 1$

$0 = x^2 - 4x - 5$

$0 = (x - 5)(x + 1)$

$x = 5$ or $x = -1$

Use these values in E2.

$x = 5: y = -(5) + 6 = 1$

$x = -1: y = -(-1) + 6 = 7$

The solutions are $(5, 1)$ and $(-1, 7)$.

56. $\begin{cases} x^2 + y^2 = 10 & (1) \\ 9x^2 + y^2 = 18 & (2) \end{cases}$

Multiply E1 by -1 and add to E2.

$\begin{array}{r} -x^2 - y^2 = -10 \\ 9x^2 + y^2 = 18 \\ \hline 8x^2 \quad\quad = 8 \\ x^2 = 1 \\ x = \pm 1 \end{array}$

Replace x^2 with 1 in E1.

$1 + y^2 = 10$

$y^2 = 9$

$y = \pm 3$

The solutions are $(-1, -3)$, $(-1, 3)$, $(1, -3)$ and $(1, 3)$.

57. $x^2 - y^2 < 1$

First graph the hyperbola as dashed curves.

Test Point	$x^2 - y^2 < 1$; Result
$(-2, 0)$	$(-2)^2 - 0^2 < 1$; False
$(0, 0)$	$0^2 - 0^2 < 1$; True
$(2, 0)$	$2^2 - 0^2 < 1$; False

Shade the region containing $(0, 0)$.

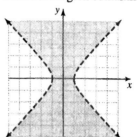

58. $\begin{cases} y > x^2 \\ x + y \geq 3 \end{cases}$

First graph the parabola as a dashed curve.

Test Point	$y > x^2$; Result
$(0, 1)$	$1 > 0^2$; True

Shade the region containing $(0, 1)$. Next, graph $x + y = 3$ as a solid line.

Test Point	$x + y \geq 3$; Result
$(0, 0)$	$0 + 0 \geq 3$; False

Shade the region which does not contain $(0, 0)$. The solution to the system is the overlapping region.

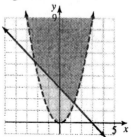

Chapter 13 Test

1. $x^2 + y^2 = 36$

   Circle; center: $(0, 0)$, radius $r = \sqrt{36} = 6$

   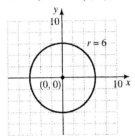

2. $x^2 - y^2 = 36$

   $\dfrac{x^2}{36} - \dfrac{y^2}{36} = 1$

   Hyperbola; center: $(0, 0)$, $a = 6$, $b = 6$

   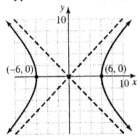

3. $16x^2 + 9y^2 = 144$

   $\dfrac{x^2}{9} + \dfrac{y^2}{16} = 1$

   Ellipse; center: $(0, 0)$, $a = 3$, $b = 4$

   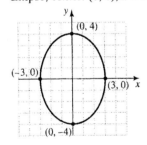

4. $y = x^2 - 8x + 16$

   $y = (x - 4)^2$

   Parabola; vertex: $(4, 0)$

   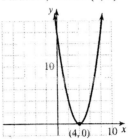

5. $x^2 + y^2 + 6x = 16$

   $(x^2 + 6x) + y^2 = 16$

   $(x^2 + 6x + 9) + y^2 = 16 + 9$

   $(x + 3)^2 + y^2 = 25$

   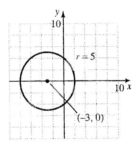

6. $x = y^2 + 8y - 3$

   $x + 16 = (y^2 + 8y + 16) - 3$

   $x = (y + 4)^2 - 19$

   Parabola; vertex: $(-4, -19)$

   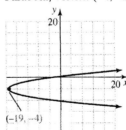

7. $\dfrac{(x-4)^2}{16} + \dfrac{(y-3)^2}{9} = 1$

Ellipse: center: $(4, 3)$, $a = 4$, $b = 3$

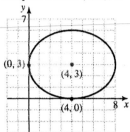

8. $y^2 - x^2 = 1$

Hyperbola: center: $(0, 0)$, $a = 1$, $b = 1$

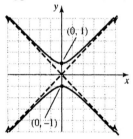

9. $\begin{cases} x^2 + y^2 = 26 & \text{(1)} \\ x^2 - 2y^2 = 23 & \text{(2)} \end{cases}$

Solve E1 for x^2: $x^2 = 26 - y^2$.

Substitute into E2.

$(26 - y^2) - 2y^2 = 23$

$-3y^2 = -3$

$y^2 = 1$

$y = \pm 1$

Replace y^2 with 1 in E1.

$x^2 + 1 = 26$

$x^2 = 25$

$x = \pm 5$

The solutions are $(-5, -1)$, $(-5, 1)$, $(5, -1)$, and $(5, 1)$.

10. $\begin{cases} y = x^2 - 5x + 6 & \text{(1)} \\ y = 2x & \text{(2)} \end{cases}$

Substitute $2x$ for y in E1.

$2x = x^2 - 5x + 6$

$0 = x^2 - 7x + 6$

$0 = (x - 6)(x - 1)$

$x = 6$ or $x = 1$

Use these values in E2.

$x = 6: y = 2(6) = 12$

$x = 1: y = 2(1) = 2$

The solutions are $(1, 2)$ and $(6, 12)$.

11. $\begin{cases} 2x + 5y \geq 10 \\ y \geq x^2 + 1 \end{cases}$

First graph $2x + 5y = 10$ as a solid line.

Test Point	$2x + 5y \geq 10$; Result
$(0, 0)$	$2(0) + 5(0) \geq 10$; False

Shade the region which does not contain $(0, 0)$.

Next, graph $y = x^2 + 1$ as a solid curve.

Test Point	$y \geq x^2 + 1$; Result
$(0, 0)$	$0 \geq 0^2 + 1$; False

Shade the region which does not contain $(0, 0)$. The solution to the system is the intersection.

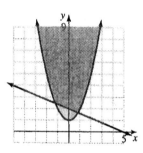

12. $\begin{cases} \dfrac{x^2}{4} + y^2 \leq 1 \\ x + y > 1 \end{cases}$

First graph the ellipse as a solid curve.

Test Point	$\dfrac{x^2}{4} + y^2 \leq 1$; Result
$(0, 0)$	$\dfrac{0^2}{4} + 0^2 \leq 1$; True

Shade the region containing $(0, 0)$. Next, graph $x + y = 1$ as a dashed line.

Test Point	$x + y > 1$; Result
$(0, 0)$	$0 + 0 > 1$; False

Shade the region which does not contain $(0, 0)$.

The solution to the system is the intersection.

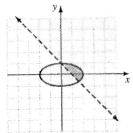

13. $\begin{cases} x^2 + y^2 \geq 4 \\ x^2 + y^2 < 16 \\ y \geq 0 \end{cases}$

First graph the circle $x^2 + y^2 = 4$ as a solid curve.

Test Point	$x^2 + y^2 \geq 4$; Result
$(0, 0)$	$0^2 + 0^2 \geq 4$; False

Shade the region which does not contain $(0, 0)$. Next graph the circle $x^2 + y^2 = 16$ as a dashed curve.

Test Point	$x^2 + y^2 < 16$; Result
$(0, 0)$	$0^2 + 0^2 < 16$; True

Shade the region containing $(0, 0)$. Now graph the inequality $y \geq 0$ by shading the region above the x-axis. The solution to the system is the intersection.

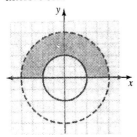

14. $100x^2 + 225y^2 = 22,500$

$\dfrac{x^2}{225} + \dfrac{y^2}{100} = 1$

$a = \sqrt{225} = 15$

$b = \sqrt{100} = 10$

Width $= 15 + 15 = 30$ feet
Height $= 10$ feet

Chapter 13 Cumulative Review

1. $2x \geq 0$ and $4x - 1 \leq -9$
   $x \geq 0$ and $4x \leq -8$
   $x \geq 0$ and $x \leq -2$
   There is no solution, or $\varnothing$.

2. $3x + 4 > 1$ and $2x - 5 \leq 9$
   $3x > -3$ and $2x \leq 14$
   $x > -1$ and $x \leq 7$
   $-1 < x \leq 7$
   $(-1, 7]$

3. $5x - 3 \leq 10$ or $x + 1 \geq 5$
   $5x \leq 13$ or $x \geq 4$
   $x \leq \dfrac{13}{5}$ or $x \geq 4$
   The solution set is $\left(-\infty, \dfrac{13}{5}\right] \cup [4, \infty)$.

4. $(3, 2), (1, -4)$
   $m = \dfrac{-4 - 2}{1 - 3} = \dfrac{-6}{-2} = 3$

5. $|5w + 3| = 7$
   $5w + 3 = 7$ or $5w + 3 = -7$
   $5w = 4$ or $5w = -10$
   $w = \dfrac{4}{5}$ or $w = -2$
   The solutions are -2 and $\dfrac{4}{5}$.

6. Let $x =$ speed of one plane. Then
   $x + 25 =$ speed of the other plane.
   $d_{\text{plane 1}} + d_{\text{plane 2}} = 650$ miles
   $2x + 2(x + 25) = 650$
   $2x + 2x + 50 = 650$
   $4x = 600$
   $x = 150$
   $x + 25 = 150 + 25 = 175$
   The planes are traveling at 150 mph and 175 mph.

7. $\left|\dfrac{x}{2}-1\right|=11$

$\dfrac{x}{2}-1=11$ or $\dfrac{x}{2}-1=-11$

$\dfrac{x}{2}=12$ or $\dfrac{x}{2}=-10$

$x=24$ or $x=-20$

The solutions are -20 and 24.

8. a. $\dfrac{4^8}{4^3}=4^{8-3}=4^5$

b. $\dfrac{y^{11}}{y^5}=y^{11-5}=y^6$

c. $\dfrac{32x^7}{4x^6}=\dfrac{32}{4}x^{7-6}=8x$

d. $\dfrac{18a^{12}b^6}{12a^8b^6}=\dfrac{18}{12}a^{12-8}b^{6-6}=\dfrac{3}{2}a^4b^0=\dfrac{3a^4}{2}$

9. $|3x+2|=|5x-8|$

$3x+2=5x-8$ or $3x+2=-(5x-8)$

$2=2x-8$ or $3x+2=-5x+8$

$10=2x$ or $8x+2=8$

$5=x$ or $8x=6$

$x=\dfrac{3}{4}$

The solutions are $\dfrac{3}{4}$ and 5.

10. a. $3y^2+14y+15=(3y+5)(y+3)$

b. $20a^5+54a^4+10a^3$

$=2a^3(10a^2+27a+5)$

$=2a^3(2a+5)(5a+1)$

c. $(y-3)^2-2(y-3)-8$

Let $u=y-3$. Then $u^2=(y-3)^2$ and

$u^2-2u-8=(u-4)(u+2)$

$=[(y-3)-4][(y-3)+2]$

$=(y-7)(y-1)$

11. $|m-6|<2$

$-2<m-6<2$

$4<m<8$

The solution set is $(4,8)$.

12. $\dfrac{2}{3a-15}-\dfrac{a}{25-a^2}$

$=\dfrac{2}{3(a-5)}+\dfrac{a}{a^2-25}$

$=\dfrac{2}{3(a-5)}+\dfrac{a}{(a+5)(a-5)}$

$=\dfrac{2(a+5)+3a}{3(a+5)(a-5)}$

$=\dfrac{2a+10+3a}{3(a+5)(a-5)}$

$=\dfrac{5a+10}{3(a+5)(a-5)}$

13. $\dfrac{x^{-1}+2xy^{-1}}{x^{-2}-x^{-2}y^{-1}}=\dfrac{\dfrac{1}{x}+\dfrac{2x}{y}}{\dfrac{1}{x^2}-\dfrac{1}{x^2y}}$

$=\dfrac{x^2y\left(\dfrac{1}{x}+\dfrac{2x}{y}\right)}{x^2y\left(\dfrac{1}{x^2}-\dfrac{1}{x^2y}\right)}$

$=\dfrac{xy+2x^3}{y-1}$

14. a. $(a^{-1}-b^{-1})^{-1}=\left(\dfrac{1}{a}-\dfrac{1}{b}\right)^{-1}$

$=\left(\dfrac{b-a}{ab}\right)^{-1}$

$=\dfrac{ab}{b-a}$

b. $\dfrac{2-\dfrac{1}{x}}{4x-\dfrac{1}{x}}=\dfrac{\left(2-\dfrac{1}{x}\right)x}{\left(4x-\dfrac{1}{x}\right)x}$

$=\dfrac{2x-1}{4x^2-1}$

$=\dfrac{2x-1}{(2x+1)(2x-1)}$

$=\dfrac{1}{2x+1}$

15. $|2x+9|+5>3$

$\quad$ $|2x+9|>-2$

The absolute value is never negative, so all real numbers are solutions. The solution set is $(-\infty, \infty)$.

16. $\quad \dfrac{2}{x+3}=\dfrac{1}{x^2-9}-\dfrac{1}{x-3}$

$\quad \dfrac{2}{x+3}=\dfrac{1}{(x+3)(x-3)}-\dfrac{1}{x-3}$

$\quad 2(x-3)=1-1(x+3)$

$\quad 2x-6=1-x-3$

$\quad 2x-6=-x-2$

$\quad 3x=4$

$\quad x=\dfrac{4}{3}$

17. $\underline{4|}\ 4\quad -25\quad 35\quad\ 0\quad\ 17\quad\ 0\quad\ 0$

$\qquad\quad\ \ 16\quad -36\quad -4\quad -16\quad\ 4\quad 16$

$\quad\overline{\ 4\quad\ -9\quad\ -1\quad -4\quad\ 1\quad\ 4\quad 16}$

Thus, $P(4)=16$.

18. $\quad y=\dfrac{k}{x}$

$\quad 3=\dfrac{k}{\dfrac{2}{3}}$

$\quad k=3\left(\dfrac{2}{3}\right)=2$

Thus, the equation is $y=\dfrac{2}{x}$.

19. a. $\sqrt[3]{1}=1$

b. $\sqrt[3]{-64}=-4$

c. $\sqrt[3]{\dfrac{8}{125}}=\dfrac{\sqrt[3]{8}}{\sqrt[3]{125}}=\dfrac{2}{5}$

d. $\sqrt[3]{x^6}=x^2$

e. $\sqrt[3]{-27x^9}=-3x^3$

20. a. $\sqrt{5}\left(2+\sqrt{15}\right)=2\sqrt{5}+\sqrt{5}\cdot\sqrt{15}$

$\qquad\qquad\qquad\quad =2\sqrt{5}+\sqrt{75}$

$\qquad\qquad\qquad\quad =2\sqrt{5}+5\sqrt{3}$

b. $\left(\sqrt{3}-\sqrt{5}\right)\left(\sqrt{7}-1\right)$

$\quad =\sqrt{3}\cdot\sqrt{7}-\sqrt{3}\cdot 1-\sqrt{5}\cdot\sqrt{7}+\sqrt{5}\cdot 1$

$\quad =\sqrt{21}-\sqrt{3}-\sqrt{35}+\sqrt{5}$

c. $\left(2\sqrt{5}-1\right)^2=\left(2\sqrt{5}\right)^2-2\cdot 2\sqrt{5}\cdot 1+1^2$

$\qquad\qquad\qquad =4(5)-4\sqrt{5}+1$

$\qquad\qquad\qquad =21-4\sqrt{5}$

d. $\left(3\sqrt{2}+5\right)\left(3\sqrt{2}-5\right)=\left(3\sqrt{2}\right)^2-5^2$

$\qquad\qquad\qquad\qquad\qquad =9(2)-25$

$\qquad\qquad\qquad\qquad\qquad =18-25$

$\qquad\qquad\qquad\qquad\qquad =-7$

21. a. $z^{2/3}(z^{1/3}-z^5)=z^{2/3+1/3}-z^{2/3+5}$

$\qquad\qquad\qquad\qquad =z^{3/3}-z^{2/3+15/3}$

$\qquad\qquad\qquad\qquad =z-z^{17/3}$

b. $(x^{1/3}-5)(x^{1/3}+2)$

$\quad =x^{1/3}\cdot x^{1/3}+2x^{1/3}-5x^{1/3}-5(2)$

$\quad =x^{2/3}-3x^{1/3}-10$

22. $\dfrac{-2}{\sqrt{3}+3}=\dfrac{-2\left(\sqrt{3}-3\right)}{\left(\sqrt{3}+3\right)\left(\sqrt{3}-3\right)}$

$\qquad\quad =\dfrac{-2\left(\sqrt{3}-3\right)}{\left(\sqrt{3}\right)^2-3^2}$

$\qquad\quad =\dfrac{-2\left(\sqrt{3}-3\right)}{3-9}$

$\qquad\quad =\dfrac{-2\left(\sqrt{3}-3\right)}{-6}$

$\qquad\quad =\dfrac{\sqrt{3}-3}{3}$

23. a. $\dfrac{\sqrt{20}}{\sqrt{5}}=\sqrt{\dfrac{20}{5}}=\sqrt{4}=2$

b. $\dfrac{\sqrt{50x}}{2\sqrt{2}}=\dfrac{1}{2}\sqrt{\dfrac{50x}{2}}=\dfrac{1}{2}\sqrt{25x}=\dfrac{5\sqrt{x}}{2}$

c. $\dfrac{7\sqrt[3]{48x^4y^8}}{\sqrt[3]{6y^2}} = 7\sqrt[3]{\dfrac{48x^4y^8}{6y^2}}$

$= 7\sqrt[3]{8x^4y^6}$

$= 7\sqrt[3]{8x^3y^6 \cdot x}$

$= 7 \cdot 2xy^2 \sqrt[3]{x}$

$= 14xy^2 \sqrt[3]{x}$

d. $\dfrac{2\sqrt[4]{32a^8b^6}}{\sqrt[4]{a^{-1}b^2}} = 2\sqrt[4]{\dfrac{32a^8b^6}{a^{-1}b^2}}$

$= 2\sqrt[4]{32a^9b^4}$

$= 2\sqrt[4]{16a^8b^4 \cdot 2a}$

$= 2 \cdot 2a^2b\sqrt[4]{2a}$

$= 4a^2b\sqrt[4]{2a}$

24. $\sqrt{2x-3} = x-3$

$\left(\sqrt{2x-3}\right)^2 = (x-3)^2$

$2x-3 = x^2 - 6x + 9$

$0 = x^2 - 8x + 12$

$0 = (x-6)(x-2)$

$x - 6 = 0$ or $x - 2 = 0$

$x = 6$ or $\quad x = 2$

Discard 2 as an extraneous solution. The solution is 6.

25. a. $\dfrac{\sqrt{45}}{4} - \dfrac{\sqrt{5}}{3} = \dfrac{3\sqrt{5}}{4} - \dfrac{\sqrt{5}}{3}$

$= \dfrac{9\sqrt{5} - 4\sqrt{5}}{12}$

$= \dfrac{5\sqrt{5}}{12}$

b. $\sqrt[3]{\dfrac{7x}{8}} + 2\sqrt[3]{7x} = \dfrac{\sqrt[3]{7x}}{2} + 2\sqrt[3]{7x}$

$= \dfrac{\sqrt[3]{7x}}{2} + \dfrac{4\sqrt[3]{7x}}{2}$

$= \dfrac{5\sqrt[3]{7x}}{2}$

26. $\quad 9x^2 - 6x = -4$

$9x^2 - 6x + 4 = 0$

$a = 9, b = -6, c = 4$

$b^2 - 4ac = (-6)^2 - 4(9)(4)$

$= 36 - 144$

$= -108$

Two complex but not real solutions

27. $\sqrt{\dfrac{7x}{3y}} = \dfrac{\sqrt{7x}}{\sqrt{3y}} = \dfrac{\sqrt{7x} \cdot \sqrt{3y}}{\sqrt{3y} \cdot \sqrt{3y}} = \dfrac{\sqrt{21xy}}{3y}$

28. $\dfrac{4}{x-2} - \dfrac{x}{x+2} = \dfrac{16}{x^2-4}$

$\dfrac{4}{x-2} - \dfrac{x}{x+2} = \dfrac{16}{(x+2)(x-2)}$

$4(x+2) - x(x-2) = 16$

$4x + 8 - x^2 + 2x = 16$

$0 = x^2 - 6x + 8$

$0 = (x-4)(x-2)$

$x - 4 = 0$ or $x - 2 = 0$

$x = 4$ or $\quad x = 2$

Discard the solution 2 as extraneous. The solution is 4.

29. $\quad \sqrt{2x-3} = 9$

$\left(\sqrt{2x-3}\right)^2 = 9^2$

$2x - 3 = 81$

$2x = 84$

$x = 42$

The solution is 42.

30. $\quad x^3 + 2x^2 - 4x \geq 8$

$x^3 + 2x^2 - 4x - 8 \geq 0$

$x^2(x+2) - 4(x+2) \geq 0$

$(x+2)(x^2-4) \geq 0$

$(x+2)(x+2)(x-2) \geq 0$

$(x+2)^2(x-2) \geq 0$

$(x+2)^2 = 0$ or $x - 2 = 0$

$x + 2 = 0$ or $\quad x = 2$

$x = -2$

Region	Test Point	$(x+2)^2(x-2) \geq 0$ Result
A: $(-\infty, -2)$	-3	$(-1)^2(-5) \geq 0$ False
B: $(-2, 2)$	0	$(2)^2(-2) \geq 0$ False
C: $(2, \infty)$	3	$(5)^2(1) \geq 0$ True

Solution: $[2, \infty)$

31. a. $i^7 = i^4 \cdot i^3 = 1 \cdot (-i) = -i$

b. $i^{20} = (i^4)^5 = 1^5 = 1$

c. $i^{46} = i^{44} \cdot i^2 = (i^4)^{11} \cdot (-1) = 1^{11}(-1) = -1$

d. $i^{-12} = \dfrac{1}{i^{12}} = \dfrac{1}{(i^4)^3} = \dfrac{1}{1^3} = 1$

32. $f(x) = (x+2)^2 - 1$

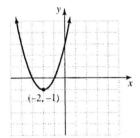

$(-2, -1)$

33.
$$p^2 + 2p = 4$$
$$p^2 + 2p + \left(\frac{2}{2}\right)^2 = 4 + 1$$
$$p^2 + 2p + 1 = 5$$
$$(p+1)^2 = 5$$
$$p + 1 = \pm\sqrt{5}$$
$$p = -1 \pm \sqrt{5}$$

The solutions are $-1 + \sqrt{5}$ and $-1 - \sqrt{5}$.

34. $f(x) = -x^2 - 6x + 4$

The maximum will occur at the vertex.
$$x = \frac{-b}{2a} = \frac{-(-6)}{2(-1)} = -3$$
$$f(-3) = -(-3)^2 - 6(-3) + 4 = 13$$
The maximum value is 13.

35.
$$\frac{1}{4}m^2 - m + \frac{1}{2} = 0$$
$$4\left(\frac{1}{4}m^2 - m + \frac{1}{2}\right) = 4(0)$$
$$m^2 - 4m + 2 = 0$$
$$a = 1, b = -4, c = 2$$
$$m = \frac{-(-4) \pm \sqrt{(-4)^2 - 4(1)(2)}}{2(1)}$$
$$= \frac{4 \pm \sqrt{16 - 8}}{2}$$
$$= \frac{4 \pm \sqrt{8}}{2}$$
$$= \frac{4 \pm 2\sqrt{2}}{2}$$
$$= 2 \pm \sqrt{2}$$

The solutions are $2 + \sqrt{2}$ and $2 - \sqrt{2}$.

36.
$$f(x) = \frac{x+1}{2}$$
$$y = \frac{x+1}{2}$$
$$x = \frac{y+1}{2}$$
$$2x = y + 1$$
$$2x - 1 = y$$
$$f^{-1}(x) = 2x - 1$$

37.
$$p^4 - 3p^2 - 4 = 0$$
$$(p^2 - 4)(p^2 + 1) = 0$$
$$(p+2)(p-2)(p^2 + 1) = 0$$
$$p + 2 = 0 \quad \text{or} \quad p - 2 = 0 \quad \text{or} \quad p^2 + 1 = 0$$
$$p = -2 \quad \text{or} \quad p = 2 \quad \text{or} \quad p^2 = -1$$
$$p = \pm i$$

The solutions are $-2, 2, -i,$ and i.

38. a. $\dfrac{\sqrt{32}}{\sqrt{4}} = \sqrt{\dfrac{32}{4}} = \sqrt{8} = \sqrt{4 \cdot 2} = 2\sqrt{2}$

b. $\dfrac{\sqrt[3]{240y^2}}{5\sqrt[3]{3y^{-4}}} = \dfrac{1}{5}\sqrt[3]{\dfrac{240y^2}{3y^{-4}}}$

$= \dfrac{1}{5}\sqrt[3]{80y^6}$

$= \dfrac{1}{5}\sqrt[3]{8y^6 \cdot 10}$

$= \dfrac{2y^3\sqrt[3]{10}}{5}$

c. $\dfrac{\sqrt[5]{64x^9y^2}}{\sqrt[5]{2x^2y^{-8}}} = \sqrt[5]{\dfrac{64x^9y^2}{2x^2y^{-8}}}$

$= \sqrt[5]{32x^7y^{10}}$

$= \sqrt[5]{32x^5y^{10} \cdot x^2}$

$= 2xy^2\sqrt[5]{x^2}$

39. $\dfrac{x+2}{x-3} \le 0$

$x+2 = 0 \quad \text{or} \quad x-3 = 0$

$\quad x = -2 \quad \text{or} \quad \quad x = 3$

Region	Test Point	$\dfrac{x+2}{x-3} \le 0$ Result
A: $(-\infty, -2)$	-3	$\dfrac{-1}{-6} \le 0$; False
B: $(-2, 3)$	0	$\dfrac{2}{-3} \le 0$; True
C: $(3, \infty)$	4	$\dfrac{6}{1} \le 0$; False

Solution: $[-2, 3)$

40. $4x^2 + 9y^2 = 36$

$\dfrac{x^2}{9} + \dfrac{y^2}{4} = 1$

Ellipse: center $(0, 0)$, $a = 3$, $b = 2$

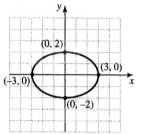

41. $g(x) = \dfrac{1}{2}(x+2)^2 + 5$

Vertex: $(-2, 5)$, axis: $x = -2$

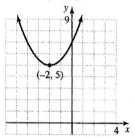

42. a. $64^x = 4$

$(4^2)^x = 4$

$4^{2x} = 4$

$2x = 1$

$x = \dfrac{1}{2}$

b. $125^{x-3} = 25$

$(5^3)^{x-3} = 5^2$

$5^{3x-9} = 5^2$

$3x - 9 = 2$

$3x = 11$

$x = \dfrac{11}{3}$

c. $\dfrac{1}{81} = 3^{2x}$

$3^{-4} = 3^{2x}$

$-4 = 2x$

$-\dfrac{4}{2} = x$

$-2 = x$

43. $f(x) = x^2 - 4x - 12$

$x = \dfrac{-b}{2a} = \dfrac{-(-4)}{2(1)} = 2$

$f(2) = (2)^2 - 4(2) - 12 = -16$

Vertex: $(2, -16)$

44. $\begin{cases} x + 2y < 8 \\ \quad y \ge x^2 \end{cases}$

First, graph $x + 2y = 8$ as a dashed line.

Test Point	$x + 2y < 8$; Result
$(0, 0)$	$0 + 2(0) < 8$; True

Shade the region containing $(0, 0)$. Next, graph the parabola $y = x^2$ as a solid curve.

Test Point	$y \ge x^2$; Result
$(0, 1)$	$1 \ge 0^2$; True

Shade the region containing $(0, 1)$. The solution to the system is the intersection.

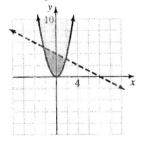

45. $(2, -5), (1, -4)$

$\begin{aligned} d &= \sqrt{[-4 - (-5)]^2 + (1 - 2)^2} \\ &= \sqrt{1^2 + (-1)^2} \\ &= \sqrt{2} \approx 1.414 \end{aligned}$

46. $\begin{cases} x^2 + y^2 = 36 & (1) \\ \quad\quad y = x + 6 & (2) \end{cases}$

Substitute $x + 6$ for y in E1.

$x^2 + (x + 6)^2 = 36$

$x^2 + (x^2 + 12x + 36) = 36$

$2x^2 + 12x = 0$

$2x(x + 6) = 0$

$2x = 0$ or $x + 6 = 0$

$x = 0$ or $\quad\quad x = -6$

Use these values in E2 to find y.

$x = 0: y = 0 + 6 = 6$

$x = -6: y = -6 + 6 = 0$

The solutions are $(0, 6)$ and $(-6, 0)$.

Chapter 14

Practice Exercises

1. $a_n = 5 + n^2$

$a_1 = 5 + 1^2 = 5 + 1 = 6$

$a_2 = 5 + 2^2 = 5 + 4 = 9$

$a_3 = 5 + 3^2 = 5 + 9 = 14$

$a_4 = 5 + 4^2 = 5 + 16 = 21$

$a_5 = 5 + 5^2 = 5 + 25 = 30$

Thus, the first five terms of the sequence are 6, 9, 14, 21, and 30.

2. $a_n = \dfrac{(-1)^n}{5n}$

a. $a_1 = \dfrac{(-1)^1}{5(1)} = -\dfrac{1}{5}$

b. $a_4 = \dfrac{(-1)^4}{5(4)} = \dfrac{1}{20}$

c. $a_{30} = \dfrac{(-1)^{30}}{5(30)} = \dfrac{1}{150}$

d. $a_{19} = \dfrac{(-1)^{19}}{5(19)} = -\dfrac{1}{95}$

3. a. 1, 3, 5, 7, ...

These numbers are the first four odd natural numbers, so a general term might be $a_n = (2n - 1)$.

b. 3, 9, 27, 81, ...

These numbers are all powers of 3 ($3 = 3^1$, $9 = 3^2$, $27 = 3^3$, and $81 = 3^4$), so a general term might be $a_n = 3^n$.

c. $\dfrac{1}{2}, \dfrac{2}{3}, \dfrac{3}{4}, \dfrac{4}{5}, \dots$

The numerators are the first four natural numbers and each denominator is one greater than the numerator, so a general term might be $a_n = \dfrac{n}{n+1}$.

d. $-\dfrac{1}{2}, -\dfrac{1}{3}, -\dfrac{1}{4}, -\dfrac{1}{5}, \dots$

The denominators are consecutive natural numbers beginning with 2 and each term is negative, so a general term might be $a_n = -\dfrac{1}{n+1}$.

4. $v_n = 3950(0.8)^n$

$v_3 = 3950(0.8)^3$

$ = 3950(0.512)$

$ = 2022.4$

The value of the copier after three years is $2022.40.

Vocabulary and Readiness Check

1. The nth term of the sequence a_n is called the <u>general</u> term.

2. A <u>finite</u> sequence is a function whose domain is $\{1, 2, 3, 4, \dots, n\}$ where n is some natural number.

3. An <u>infinite</u> sequence is a function whose domain is $\{1, 2, 3, 4, \dots\}$.

4. $a_n = 7^n$

$a_1 = 7^1 = 7$

5. $a_n = \dfrac{(-1)^n}{n}$

$a_1 = \dfrac{(-1)^1}{1} = -1$

6. $a_n = (-1)^n \cdot n^4$

$a_1 = (-1)^1 \cdot 1^4 = -1$

Exercise Set 14.1

2. $a_n = 5 - n$

$a_1 = 5 - 1 = 4$

$a_2 = 5 - 2 = 3$

$a_3 = 5 - 3 = 2$

$a_4 = 5 - 4 = 1$

$a_5 = 5 - 5 = 0$

Thus, the first five terms of the sequence are 4, 3, 2, 1, 0.

4. $a_n = (-2)^n$

$a_1 = (-2)^1 = -2$

$a_2 = (-2)^2 = 4$

$a_3 = (-2)^3 = -8$

$a_4 = (-2)^4 = 16$

$a_5 = (-2)^5 = -32$

Thus, the first five terms of the sequence are
$-2, 4, -8, 16, -32$.

6. $a_n = \dfrac{1}{7-n}$

$a_1 = \dfrac{1}{7-1} = \dfrac{1}{6}$

$a_2 = \dfrac{1}{7-2} = \dfrac{1}{5}$

$a_3 = \dfrac{1}{7-3} = \dfrac{1}{4}$

$a_4 = \dfrac{1}{7-4} = \dfrac{1}{3}$

$a_5 = \dfrac{1}{7-5} = \dfrac{1}{2}$

Thus, the first five terms of the sequence are
$\dfrac{1}{6}, \dfrac{1}{5}, \dfrac{1}{4}, \dfrac{1}{3}, \dfrac{1}{2}$.

8. $a_n = -6n$

$a_1 = -6(1) = -6$

$a_2 = -6(2) = -12$

$a_3 = -6(3) = -18$

$a_4 = -6(4) = -24$

$a_5 = -6(5) = -30$

Thus, the first five terms of the sequence are
$-6, -12, -18, -24, -30$.

10. $a_n = n^2 + 2$

$a_1 = 1^2 + 2 = 3$

$a_2 = 2^2 + 2 = 6$

$a_3 = 3^2 + 2 = 11$

$a_4 = 4^2 + 2 = 18$

$a_5 = 5^2 + 2 = 27$

Thus, the first five terms of the sequence are 3, 6,
11, 18, 27.

12. $a_n = 3^{n-2}$

$a_1 = 3^{1-2} = 3^{-1} = \dfrac{1}{3}$

$a_2 = 3^{2-2} = 3^0 = 1$

$a_3 = 3^{3-2} = 3^1 = 3$

$a_4 = 3^{4-2} = 3^2 = 9$

$a_5 = 3^{5-2} = 3^3 = 27$

Thus, the first five terms of the sequence are
$\dfrac{1}{3}, 1, 3, 9, 27$.

14. $a_n = 1 - 3n$

$a_1 = 1 - 3(1) = -2$

$a_2 = 1 - 3(2) = -5$

$a_3 = 1 - 3(3) = -8$

$a_4 = 1 - 3(4) = -11$

$a_5 = 1 - 3(5) = -14$

Thus, the first five terms of the sequence are
$-2, -5, -8, -11, -14$.

16. $a_n = (-1)^{n+1}(n-1)$

$a_1 = (-1)^{1+1}(1-1) = 1(0) = 0$

$a_2 = (-1)^{2+1}(2-1) = -1(1) = -1$

$a_3 = (-1)^{3+1}(3-1) = 1(2) = 2$

$a_4 = (-1)^{4+1}(4-1) = -1(3) = -3$

$a_5 = (-1)^{5+1}(5-1) = 1(4) = 4$

Thus, the first five terms of the sequence are 0, -1,
2, -3, 4.

18. $a_n = -n^2$

$a_{15} = -(15)^2 = -225$

20. $a_n = 100 - 7n$

$a_{50} = 100 - 7(50) = -250$

22. $a_n = \dfrac{n}{n+4}$

$a_{24} = \dfrac{24}{24+4} = \dfrac{24}{28} = \dfrac{6}{7}$

24. $a_n = 5^{n+1}$

$a_3 = 5^{3+1} = 5^4 = 625$

26. $a_n = \dfrac{n+3}{n+4}$

$a_8 = \dfrac{8+3}{8+4} = \dfrac{11}{12}$

28. $a_n = \dfrac{(-1)^n}{2n}$

$a_{100} = \dfrac{(-1)^{100}}{2(100)} = \dfrac{1}{200}$

30. $a_n = 8 - n^2$

$a_{20} = 8 - (20)^2 = 8 - 400 = -392$

32. $a_n = \dfrac{n-4}{(-2)^n}$

$a_6 = \dfrac{6-4}{(-2)^6} = \dfrac{2}{64} = \dfrac{1}{32}$

34. $a_n = 2 + 5(n-1)$ or $a_n = 5n - 3$

36. $a_n = -4(-4)^{n-1}$ or $a_n = (-4)^n$

38. $a_n = \dfrac{2}{5}\left(\dfrac{1}{5}\right)^{n-1}$ or $a_n = \dfrac{2}{5^n}$

40. $a_4 = 50(3)^{4-1} = 50(27) = 1350$ bacteria

$a_1 = 50(3)^{1-1} = 50(1) = 50$ bacteria

42. $a_n = 12 + 3(n-1)$

$a_8 = 12 + 3(8-1) = 12 + 21 = 33$ seats

44. $a_n = 2700 + 150(n-1)$

In 2000, $n = 1$ and

$a_1 = 2700 + 150(1-1) = 2700$ students

In 2001, $n = 2$ and

$a_2 = 2700 + 150(2-1) = 2850$ students

In 2002, $n = 3$ and

$a_3 = 2700 + 150(3-1) = 3000$ students

In 2003, $n = 4$ and

$a_4 = 2700 + 150(4-1) = 3150$ students

In 2004, $n = 5$ and

$a_5 = 2700 + 150(5-1) = 3300$ students

46. Answers may vary

48. $f(x) = (x-2)^2 + 1$

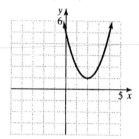

50. $f(x) = 3(x-3)^2 + 4$

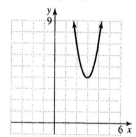

52. $(-2, -1)$ and $(-1, 5)$

$d = \sqrt{[5-(-1)]^2 + [-1-(-2)]^2}$

$\quad = \sqrt{36+1}$

$\quad = \sqrt{37}$ units

54. $(10, -14)$ and $(5, -11)$

$d = \sqrt{(5-10)^2 + [-11-(-14)]^2}$

$\quad = \sqrt{25+9}$

$\quad = \sqrt{34}$ units

56. $a_n = \dfrac{\sqrt{n}}{\sqrt{n}+1}$

$a_1 = \dfrac{\sqrt{1}}{\sqrt{1}+1} = \dfrac{1}{2} = 0.5$

$a_2 = \dfrac{\sqrt{2}}{\sqrt{2}+1} \approx 0.5858$

$a_3 = \dfrac{\sqrt{3}}{\sqrt{3}+1} \approx 0.6340$

$a_4 = \dfrac{\sqrt{4}}{\sqrt{4}+1} \approx 0.6667$

$a_5 = \dfrac{\sqrt{5}}{\sqrt{5}+1} \approx 0.6910$

58. $a_n = \left(1 + \dfrac{0.05}{n}\right)^n$

$a_1 = \left(1 + \dfrac{0.05}{1}\right)^1 = 1.05$

$a_2 = \left(1 + \dfrac{0.05}{2}\right)^2 \approx 1.0506$

$a_3 = \left(1 + \dfrac{0.05}{3}\right)^3 \approx 1.0508$

$a_4 = \left(1 + \dfrac{0.05}{4}\right)^4 \approx 1.0509$

$a_5 = \left(1 + \dfrac{0.05}{5}\right)^5 \approx 1.0510$

Section 14.2

Practice Exercises

1. $a_1 = 4$

$a_2 = 4 + 5 = 9$
$a_3 = 9 + 5 = 14$
$a_4 = 14 + 5 = 19$
$a_5 = 19 + 5 = 24$
The first five terms are 4, 9, 14, 19, 24.

2. a. $a_n = a_1 + (n-1)d$
Here, $a_1 = 2$ and $d = -3$.
$a_n = 2 + (n-1)(-3) = 2 - 3n + 3 = 5 - 3n$

b. $a_n = 5 - 3n$
$a_{12} = 5 - 3 \cdot 12 = 5 - 36 = -31$

3. Since the sequence is arithmetic, the ninth term is
$a_9 = a_1 + (9-1)d = a_1 + 8d$.
a_1 is the first term of the sequence, so $a_1 = 3$. d is the constant difference, so $d = a_2 - a_1 = 9 - 3 = 6$.
Thus,
$a_9 = a_1 + 8d = 3 + 8 \cdot 6 = 51$.

4. We need to find a_1 and d. The given facts, $a_3 = 23$ and $a_8 = 63$, lead to a system of linear equations.
$\begin{cases} a_3 = a_1 + (3-1)d \\ a_8 = a_1 + (8-1)d \end{cases}$ or $\begin{cases} 23 = a_1 + 2d \\ 63 = a_1 + 7d \end{cases}$
We solve the system by elimination. Multiply both sides of the second equation by -1.

$\begin{cases} 23 = a_1 + 2d \\ -1(63) = -1(a_1 + 7d) \end{cases}$ or $\begin{cases} 23 = a_1 + 2d \\ -63 = -a_1 - 7d \end{cases}$

$\qquad\qquad\qquad\qquad \dfrac{}{\begin{aligned} -40 &= \quad -5d \\ 8 &= d \end{aligned}}$

To find a_1, let $d = 8$ in $23 = a_1 + 2d$.
$23 = a_1 + 2(8)$
$23 = a_1 + 16$
$7 = a_1$
Thus, $a_1 = 7$ and $d = 8$, so
$a_n = 7 + (n-1)(8) = 7 + 8n - 8 = -1 + 8n$ and
$a_6 = -1 + 8 \cdot 6 = 47$.

5. The first term, a_1, is 57,000, and d is 2200.
$a_n = 57,000 + (n-1)(2200)$
$\quad\ = 54,800 + 2200n$
$a_3 = 54,800 + 2200 \cdot 3 = 61,400$
The salary for the third year is $61,400.

6. $a_1 = 8$
$a_2 = 8(-3) = -24$
$a_3 = -24(-3) = 72$
$a_4 = 72(-3) = -216$
The first four terms are 8, -24, 72, and -216.

7. $a_n = a_1 r^{n-1}$
Here, $a_1 = 64$ and $r = \dfrac{1}{4}$.
Evaluate a_n for $n = 7$.
$a_7 = 64\left(\dfrac{1}{4}\right)^{7-1}$
$\quad = 64\left(\dfrac{1}{4}\right)^6$
$\quad = 64\left(\dfrac{1}{4096}\right)$
$\quad = \dfrac{1}{64}$

8. Since the sequence is geometric and $a_1 = -3$, the seventh term must be $a_1 r^{7-1}$, or $-3r^6$. r is the common ratio of terms, so r must be $\dfrac{6}{-3}$, or -2.
$a_7 = -3r^6$
$a_7 = -3(-2)^6 = -192$

9. Notice that $\dfrac{27}{4} \div \dfrac{9}{2} = \dfrac{3}{2}$, so $r = \dfrac{3}{2}$.

$$a_2 = a_1 \left(\dfrac{3}{2}\right)^{2-1}$$

$$\dfrac{9}{2} = a_1 \left(\dfrac{3}{2}\right)^{1}, \quad \text{or} \quad a_1 = 3$$

The first term is 3, and the common ration is $\dfrac{3}{2}$.

10. Since the culture is reduced by one-half each day, the population sizes are modeled by a geometric sequence. Here, $a_1 = 4800$ and $r = \dfrac{1}{2}$.

$$a_n = a_1 r^{n-1} = 4800 \left(\dfrac{1}{2}\right)^{n-1}$$

$$a_7 = 4800 \left(\dfrac{1}{2}\right)^{7-1} = 75$$

The bacterial culture should measure 75 units at the beginning of day 7.

Vocabulary and Readiness Check

1. A geometric sequence is one in which each term (after the first) is obtained by multiplying the preceding term by a constant r. The constant r is called the common ratio.

2. An arithmetic sequence is one in which each term (after the first) differs from the preceding term by a constant amount d. The constant d is called the common difference.

3. The general term of an arithmetic sequence is $a_n = a_1 + (n-1)d$ where a_1 is the first term and d is the common difference.

4. The general term of a geometric sequence is $a_n = a_1 r^{n-1}$ where a_1 is the first term and r is the common ratio.

Exercise Set 14.2

2. $a_n = a_1 + (n-1)d$

$a_1 = 3; \ d = 10$
$a_1 = 3$
$a_2 = 3 + (2-1)10 = 13$
$a_3 = 3 + (3-1)10 = 23$
$a_4 = 3 + (4-1)10 = 33$
$a_5 = 3 + (5-1)10 = 43$

4. $a_n = a_1 + (n-1)d$

$a_1 = -20, \ d = 3$
$a_1 = -20$
$a_2 = -20 + (2-1)3 = -17$
$a_3 = -20 + (3-1)3 = -14$
$a_4 = -20 + (4-1)3 = -11$
$a_5 = -20 + (5-1)3 = -8$

6. $a_n = a_1 r^{n-1}$

$a_1 = -2, \ r = 2$
$a_1 = -2(2)^{1-1} = -2$
$a_2 = -2(2)^{2-1} = -4$
$a_3 = -2(2)^{3-1} = -8$
$a_4 = -2(2)^{4-1} = -16$
$a_5 = -2(2)^{5-1} = -32$

8. $a_n = a_1 r^{n-1}$

$a_1 = 1, \ r = \dfrac{1}{3}$

$a_1 = 1 \left(\dfrac{1}{3}\right)^{1-1} = 1$

$a_2 = 1 \left(\dfrac{1}{3}\right)^{2-1} = \dfrac{1}{3}$

$a_3 = 1 \left(\dfrac{1}{3}\right)^{3-1} = \dfrac{1}{9}$

$a_4 = 1 \left(\dfrac{1}{3}\right)^{4-1} = \dfrac{1}{27}$

$a_5 = 1 \left(\dfrac{1}{3}\right)^{5-1} = \dfrac{1}{81}$

10. $a_n = a_1 + (n-1)d$

$a_1 = 32, \ d = -4$
$a_{12} = 32 + (12-1)(-4) = -12$

12. $a_n = a_1 r^{n-1}$

$a_1 = 3, \ r = 3$
$a_5 = 3(3)^{5-1} = 3(3)^4 = 243$

14. $a_n = a_1 r^{n-1}$

$a_1 = 5, \ r = -4$
$a_6 = 5(-4)^{6-1} = 5(-4)^5 = -5120$

16. $a_n = a_1 + (n-1)d$

$a_1 = -3$ and $d = 0 - (-3) = 3$
$a_{13} = -3 + (13-1)3 = 33$

18. $a_n = a_1 r^{n-1}$

$a_1 = 5$ and $r = \dfrac{10}{5} = 2$

$a_9 = 5(2)^{9-1} = 5(2)^8 = 1280$

20. $a_n = a_1 r^{n-1}$

$a_1 = \dfrac{1}{2}$ and $r = \dfrac{3/2}{1/2} = 3$

$a_6 = \dfrac{1}{2}(3)^{6-1} = \dfrac{1}{2}(3)^5 = \dfrac{243}{2}$

22. $\begin{cases} a_2 = a_1 + (2-1)d \\ a_{10} = a_1 + (10-1)d \end{cases}$

$\begin{cases} 6 = a_1 + d \\ 30 = a_1 + 9d \end{cases}$

$\begin{cases} -6 = -a_1 - d \\ 30 = a_1 + 9d \end{cases}$

Adding yields $24 = 8d$ or $d = 3$.

Then $a_1 = 6 - 3 = 3$

$a_{25} = 3 + (25-1)3 = 3 + 72 = 75$

24. $a_2 = 15,\ a_3 = 3$

$r = \dfrac{3}{15} = \dfrac{1}{5}$

$a_2 = a_1 r^{2-1}$

$15 = a_1\left(\dfrac{1}{5}\right)$

$75 = a_1$

26. $a_3 = 4,\ a_4 = -12$

$r = \dfrac{-12}{4} = -3$

$a_3 = a_1 r^{3-1}$

$4 = a_1(-3)^2$

$\dfrac{4}{9} = a_1$

28. Answers may vary

30. Arithmetic; $a_1 = 8,\ d = 8$

32. Geometric; $a_1 = 2,\ r = 3$

34. Arithmetic; $a_1 = \dfrac{2}{3},\ d = \dfrac{2}{3}$

36. Geometric; $a_1 = y,\ r = -3$

38. Arithmetic; $a_1 = t,\ d = -1$

40. $a_1 = 8,\ r = -3$

$a_5 = 8(-3)^{5-1} = 8(-3)^4 = 648$

42. $a_1 = 9,\ d = 5$

$a_4 = 9 + (4-1)5 = 9 + 15 = 24$

44. $a_1 = 2,\ d = \dfrac{4}{3} - \dfrac{5}{3} = -\dfrac{1}{3}$

$a_{11} = 2 + (11-1)\left(-\dfrac{1}{3}\right) = 2 - \dfrac{10}{3} = -\dfrac{4}{3}$

46. $a_1 = 5,\ d = 2 - 5 = -3$

$a_{18} = 5 + (18-1)(-3) = 5 - 51 = -46$

48. $a_3 = -28,\ a_4 = -56$

$r = \dfrac{-56}{-28} = 2$

$a_3 = a_1 r^{3-1}$

$-28 = a_1(2)^2$

$-7 = a_1$

50. $a_1 = 20,\ d = 17 - 20 = -3$

$a_n = 20 + (n-1)(-3)$ or $a_n = 23 - 3n$

$a_5 = 23 - 3(5) = 8$

There are 8 cans in the fifth row. Solving $a_n \geq 0$

yields $n \leq 7\dfrac{2}{3}$ so $n = 7$ and thus there are 7 rows.

$a_7 = 23 - 3(7) = 2$

There are two cans in the top row.

52. $a_n = a_1 r^{n-1}$

$a_1 = 500,000(1.15)^0 = 500,000$

$a_2 = 500,000(1.15)^1 = 575,000$

$a_3 = 500,000(1.15)^2 = 661,250$

$a_4 = 500,000(1.15)^3 = 760,437.50$

The predicted value at the end of the third year is $760,437.60.

54. Geometric

$a_n = a_1 r^{n-1},\ a_1 = 50,\ r = 0.80$

$a_4 = 50(0.80)^3 = 25.6$

The length of the fourth swing is 25.6 inches.

56. $a_n = 15 + (n-1)5$ or $a_n = 10 + 5n$
$a_7 = 10 + 5(7) = 45$
$60 = 10 + 5n$
$50 = 5n$
$n = 10$

After 7 weeks, her riding time is 45 minutes. It takes her 10 weeks to reach 1 hour of riding time.

58. $5(1) + 5(2) + 5(3) + 5(4) = 5 + 10 + 15 + 20$
$\qquad = 50$

60. $2(2-4) + 3(3-4) + 4(4-4)$
$= 2(-2) + 3(-1) + 4(0)$
$= -4 - 3 + 0$
$= -7$

62. $\dfrac{1}{4(1)} + \dfrac{1}{4(2)} + \dfrac{1}{4(3)} = \dfrac{1}{4} + \dfrac{1}{8} + \dfrac{1}{12}$
$\qquad = \dfrac{6}{24} + \dfrac{3}{24} + \dfrac{2}{24}$
$\qquad = \dfrac{11}{24}$

64. $a_1 = \$3720,\ d = -\$268.50$
$a_1 = \$3720$
$a_2 = 3720 + (2-1)(-268.50) = \$3451.50$
$a_3 = 3720 + (3-1)(-268.50) = \$3183$
$a_4 = 3720 + (4-1)(-268.50) = \$2914.50$

66. $a_1 = 26.8,\ r = 2.5$
$a_n = a_1 r^{n-1}$
$a_1 = 26.8$
$a_2 = 26.8(2.5)^1 = 67$
$a_3 = 26.8(2.5)^2 = 167.5$
$a_4 = 26.8(2.5)^3 = 418.75$

68. Answers may vary

Section 14.3

Practice Exercises

1. a. $\displaystyle\sum_{i=0}^{4} \dfrac{i-3}{4} = \dfrac{0-3}{4} + \dfrac{1-3}{4} + \dfrac{2-3}{4} + \dfrac{3-3}{4} + \dfrac{4-3}{4}$
$= \left(-\dfrac{3}{4}\right) + \left(-\dfrac{2}{4}\right) + \left(-\dfrac{1}{4}\right) + 0 + \dfrac{1}{4}$
$= -\dfrac{5}{4},\ \text{or } -1\dfrac{1}{4}$

b. $\displaystyle\sum_{i=2}^{5} 3^i = 3^2 + 3^3 + 3^4 + 3^5$
$= 9 + 27 + 81 + 243$
$= 360$

2. a. Since the difference of each term and the preceding term is 5, the terms correspond to the first six terms of the arithmetic sequence $a_n = 5 + (n-1)5 = 5n$. Thus, in summation notation,

$$5 + 10 + 15 + 20 + 25 + 30 = \sum_{i=1}^{6} 5i.$$

b. Since each term is the product of the preceding term and $\dfrac{1}{5}$, these terms correspond to the first four terms of the geometric sequence $a_n = \dfrac{1}{5}\left(\dfrac{1}{5}\right)^{n-1} = \left(\dfrac{1}{5}\right)^n$. In summation notation,

$$\frac{1}{5} + \frac{1}{25} + \frac{1}{125} + \frac{1}{625} = \sum_{i=1}^{4}\left(\frac{1}{5}\right)^i.$$

3. $S_4 = \displaystyle\sum_{i=1}^{4} \dfrac{2+3i}{i^2}$
$= \dfrac{2+3\cdot1}{1^2} + \dfrac{2+3\cdot2}{2^2} + \dfrac{2+3\cdot3}{3^2} + \dfrac{2+3\cdot4}{4^2}$
$= \dfrac{5}{1} + \dfrac{8}{4} + \dfrac{11}{9} + \dfrac{14}{16}$
$= 5 + 2 + \dfrac{11}{9} + \dfrac{7}{8}$
$= \dfrac{655}{72},\ \text{or } 9\dfrac{7}{72}$

4. $S_5 = \displaystyle\sum_{i=1}^{5} i(2i-1)$
$= 1(2\cdot1-1) + 2(2\cdot2-1) + 3(2\cdot3-1)$
$\qquad + 4(2\cdot4-1) + 5(2\cdot5-1)$
$= 1 + 6 + 15 + 28 + 45$
$= 95$
There are 95 plants after 5 years.

Vocabulary and Readiness Check

1. A series is an <u>infinite</u> series if it is the sum of all the terms of the sequence.

2. A series is a <u>finite</u> series if it is the sum of a finite number of terms.

3. A shorthand notation for denoting a series when the general term of the sequence is known is called <u>summation</u> notation.

4. In the notation $\sum_{i=1}^{7}(5i-2)$, the Σ is the Greek uppercase letter <u>sigma</u> and the i is called the <u>index of summation</u>.

5. The sum of the first n terms of a sequence is a finite series known as a <u>partial sum</u>.

6. For the notation in Exercise 4 above, the beginning value of i is $\underline{1}$ and the ending value of i is $\underline{7}$.

Exercise Set 14.3

2. $\displaystyle\sum_{i=1}^{5}(i+6)=7+8+9+10+11=45$

4. $\displaystyle\sum_{i=2}^{3}(5i-1)=(5(2)-1)+(5(3)-1)$
$$=9+14$$
$$=23$$

6. $\displaystyle\sum_{i=3}^{5}i^3=3^3+4^3+5^3=27+64+125=216$

8. $\displaystyle\sum_{i=2}^{4}\left(\frac{2}{i+3}\right)=\frac{2}{2+3}+\frac{2}{3+3}+\frac{2}{4+3}$
$$=\frac{2}{5}+\frac{2}{6}+\frac{2}{7}$$
$$=\frac{107}{105}$$

10. $\displaystyle\sum_{i=1}^{3}\frac{1}{3i}=\frac{1}{3(1)}+\frac{1}{3(2)}+\frac{1}{3(3)}$
$$=\frac{1}{3}+\frac{1}{6}+\frac{1}{9}$$
$$=\frac{11}{18}$$

12. $\displaystyle\sum_{i=3}^{6}-4i=-4(3)-4(4)-4(5)-4(6)$
$$=-12-16-20-24$$
$$=-72$$

14. $\displaystyle\sum_{i=2}^{4}i(i-3)=2(2-3)+3(3-3)+4(4-3)$
$$=2(-1)+3(0)+4(1)$$
$$=2$$

16. $\displaystyle\sum_{i=1}^{4}3^{i-1}=3^0+3^1+3^2+3^3$
$$=1+3+9+27$$
$$=40$$

18. $\displaystyle\sum_{i=2}^{5}\frac{6-i}{6+i}=\frac{6-2}{6+2}+\frac{6-3}{6+3}+\frac{6-4}{6+4}+\frac{6-5}{6+5}$
$$=\frac{4}{8}+\frac{3}{9}+\frac{2}{10}+\frac{1}{11}$$
$$=\frac{371}{330}$$

20. $a_1=4, d=3$
$a_n=4+(n-1)3=3n+1$
$$\sum_{i=1}^{4}(3i+1)$$

22. $a_1=5, r=2$
$a_n=5(2)^{n-1}$
$$\sum_{i=1}^{6}5(2)^{i-1}$$

24. $a_1=5, d=-4$
$a_n=5+(n-1)(-4)=-4n+9$
$$\sum_{i=1}^{4}(-4i+9)$$

26. $a_1=80, r=\dfrac{1}{4}$
$a_n=80\left(\dfrac{1}{4}\right)^{n-1}=\dfrac{80}{4^{n-1}}=\dfrac{4^2\cdot 5}{4^{n-1}}=\dfrac{5}{4^{n-3}}$
$$\sum_{i=1}^{5}\frac{5}{4^{i-3}}$$

28. $1+(-4)+9+(-16)=\displaystyle\sum_{i=1}^{4}(-1)^{i-1}i^2$

30. $S_2 = \sum_{i=1}^{2} i(i-6)$

$= 1(1-6) + 2(2-6)$

$= -5 - 8$

$= -13$

32. $S_7 = \sum_{i=1}^{7} (-1)^{i-1} = 1 - 1 + 1 - 1 + 1 - 1 + 1 = 1$

34. $S_5 = \sum_{i=1}^{5} \frac{(-1)^i}{2i} = -\frac{1}{2} + \frac{1}{4} - \frac{1}{6} + \frac{1}{8} - \frac{1}{10} = -\frac{47}{120}$

36. $S_5 = \sum_{i=1}^{5} (i-1)^2 = 0^2 + 1^2 + 2^2 + 3^2 + 4^2 = 30$

38. $S_3 = \sum_{i=1}^{3} (i+4)^2 = 5^2 + 6^2 + 7^2 = 110$

40. 2, 3, 4, 5, 6, 7

$a_n = 1 + n$

$S_6 = \sum_{i=1}^{6} (1+i) = 2 + 3 + 4 + 5 + 6 + 7 = 27$

The total number of surfers is 27.

42. $a_n = 100(2)^n$, where n represents the number of 6-hour periods.

$a_4 = 100(2)^4 = 100(16) = 1600$ bacteria

The number of bacteria present after 24 hours is 1600.

44. $a_3 = (3-1)(3+3) = 2(6) = 12$

There were 12 otters born in the third year.

$S_3 = \sum_{i=1}^{3} [(i-1)(i+3)] = 0(4) + 1(5) + 2(6) = 17$

There were 17 otters born in the first three years.

46. $a_n = 200 - 6n$

2007: $a_1 = 200 - 6(1) = 194$

2008: $a_2 = 200 - 6(2) = 188$

2009: $a_3 = 200 - 6(3) = 182$

2010: $a_4 = 200 - 6(4) = 176$

The decrease in 2010 is 176 pairs.
The total decrease for the four-year period is
$194 + 188 + 182 + 176 = 740$ pairs of birds.

48. Job A: $S_5 = \sum_{i=1}^{5} (20,000 + (i-1)1200) = 112,000$

Job B: $S_5 = \sum_{i=1}^{5} (18,000 + (i-1)2500) = 115,000$

Job B pays $3000 more over the next five years.

50. Answers may vary

52. $\frac{-3}{1 - \frac{1}{7}} = \frac{-3 \cdot 7}{\left(1 - \frac{1}{7}\right) \cdot 7} = \frac{-21}{7-1} = \frac{-21}{6} = -\frac{7}{2}$

54. $\frac{\frac{6}{11}}{1 - \frac{1}{10}} = \frac{\left(\frac{6}{11}\right) \cdot 110}{\left(1 - \frac{1}{10}\right) \cdot 110} = \frac{60}{110 - 11} = \frac{60}{99} = \frac{20}{33}$

56. $\frac{2(1 - 5^3)}{1 - 5} = \frac{2(-124)}{-4} = 62$

58. $\frac{12}{2}(2 + 19) = 6(21) = 126$

60. a. $\sum_{i=1}^{6} 5i^3 = 5(1)^3 + 5(2)^3 + 5(3)^3 + 5(4)^3$

$+ 5(5)^3 + 5(6)^3$

$= 5 + 40 + 135 + 320 + 625 + 1080$

b. $5 \cdot \sum_{i=1}^{6} i^3 = 5(1^3 + 2^3 + 3^3 + 4^3 + 5^3 + 6^3)$

$= 5(1 + 8 + 27 + 64 + 125 + 216)$

c. Answers may vary

d. True; answers may vary

Integrated Review

1. $a_n = n - 3$

$a_1 = 1 - 3 = -2$

$a_2 = 2 - 3 = -1$

$a_3 = 3 - 3 = 0$

$a_4 = 4 - 3 = 1$

$a_5 = 5 - 3 = 2$

Therefore, the first five terms are $-2, -1, 0, 1, 2$.

2. $a_n = \dfrac{7}{1+n}$

$a_1 = \dfrac{7}{1+1} = \dfrac{7}{2}$

$a_2 = \dfrac{7}{1+2} = \dfrac{7}{3}$

$a_3 = \dfrac{7}{1+3} = \dfrac{7}{4}$

$a_4 = \dfrac{7}{1+4} = \dfrac{7}{5}$

$a_5 = \dfrac{7}{1+5} = \dfrac{7}{6}$

The first five terms are $\dfrac{7}{2}, \dfrac{7}{3}, \dfrac{7}{4}, \dfrac{7}{5}$, and $\dfrac{7}{6}$.

3. $a_n = 3^{n-1}$

$a_1 = 3^{1-1} = 3^0 = 1$

$a_2 = 3^{2-1} = 3^1 = 3$

$a_3 = 3^{3-1} = 3^2 = 9$

$a_4 = 3^{4-1} = 3^3 = 27$

$a_5 = 3^{5-1} = 3^4 = 81$

The first five terms are 1, 3, 9, 27, and 81.

4. $a_n = n^2 - 5$

$a_1 = 1^2 - 5 = 1 - 5 = -4$

$a_2 = 2^2 - 5 = 4 - 5 = -1$

$a_3 = 3^2 - 5 = 9 - 5 = 4$

$a_4 = 4^2 - 5 = 16 - 5 = 11$

$a_5 = 5^2 - 5 = 25 - 5 = 20$

The first five terms are −4, −1, 4, 11, and 20.

5. $(-2)^n$; a_6

$a_6 = (-2)^6 = 64$

6. $-n^2 + 2$; a_4

$a_4 = -(4)^2 + 2 = -16 + 2 = -14$

7. $\dfrac{(-1)^n}{n}$; a_{40}

$a_{40} = \dfrac{(-1)^{40}}{40} = \dfrac{1}{40}$

8. $\dfrac{(-1)^n}{2n}$; a_{41}

$a_{41} = \dfrac{(-1)^{41}}{2(41)} = \dfrac{-1}{82} = -\dfrac{1}{82}$

9. $a_1 = 7$; $d = -3$

$a_1 = 7$

$a_2 = 7 - 3 = 4$

$a_3 = 4 - 3 = 1$

$a_4 = 1 - 3 = -2$

$a_5 = -2 - 3 = -5$

The first five terms are 7, 4, 1, −2, −5.

10. $a_1 = -3$; $r = 5$

$a_1 = -3$

$a_2 = -3(5) = -15$

$a_3 = -15(5) = -75$

$a_4 = -75(5) = -375$

$a_5 = -375(5) = -1875$

The first five terms are −3, −15, −75, −375, −1875.

11. $a_1 = 45$; $r = \dfrac{1}{3}$

$a_1 = 45$

$a_2 = 45\left(\dfrac{1}{3}\right) = 15$

$a_3 = 15\left(\dfrac{1}{3}\right) = 5$

$a_4 = 5\left(\dfrac{1}{3}\right) = \dfrac{5}{3}$

$a_5 = \dfrac{5}{3}\left(\dfrac{1}{3}\right) = \dfrac{5}{9}$

The first five terms are 45, 15, 5, $\dfrac{5}{3}, \dfrac{5}{9}$.

12. $a_1 = -12$; $d = 10$

$a_1 = -12$

$a_2 = -12 + 10 = -2$

$a_3 = -2 + 10 = 8$

$a_4 = 8 + 10 = 18$

$a_5 = 18 + 10 = 28$

The first five terms are −12, −2, 8, 18, 28.

13. $a_1 = 20$; $d = 9$
$$a_n = a_1 + (n-1)d$$
$$a_{10} = 20 + (10-1)9$$
$$= 20 + 81$$
$$= 101$$

14. $a_1 = 64$; $r = \dfrac{3}{4}$
$$a_n = a_1 r^{n-1}$$
$$a_6 = 64\left(\dfrac{3}{4}\right)^{6-1}$$
$$= 64\left(\dfrac{3}{4}\right)^5$$
$$= 64\left(\dfrac{243}{1024}\right)$$
$$= \dfrac{243}{16}$$

15. $a_1 = 6$; $r = \dfrac{-12}{6} = -2$
$$a_n = a_1 r^{n-1}$$
$$a_7 = 6(-2)^{7-1} = 6(-2)^6 = 6(64) = 384$$

16. $a_1 = -100$; $d = -85 - (-100) = 15$
$$a_n = a_1 + (n-1)d$$
$$a_{20} = -100 + (20-1)(15)$$
$$= -100 + (19)(15)$$
$$= -100 + 285$$
$$= 185$$

17. $a_4 = -5$, $a_{10} = -35$
$$a_n = a_1 + (n-1)d$$
$$\begin{cases} a_4 = a_1 + (4-1)d \\ a_{10} = a_1 + (10-1)d \end{cases}$$
$$\begin{cases} -5 = a_1 + 3d \\ -35 = a_1 + 9d \end{cases}$$
Multiply eq. 2 by -1, then add the equations.
$$\begin{cases} -5 = a_1 + 3d \\ (-1)(-35) = -1(a_1 + 9d) \end{cases}$$
$$\begin{cases} -5 = a_1 + 3d \\ 35 = -a_1 - 9d \end{cases}$$
$$30 = -6d$$
$$-5 = d$$
To find a_1, let $d = -5$ in

$$-5 = a_1 + 3d$$
$$-5 = a_1 + 3(-5)$$
$$10 = a_1$$
Thus, $a_1 = 10$ and $d = -5$, so
$$a_n = 10 + (n-1)(-5) = -5n + 15$$
$$a_5 = -5(5) + 15 = -10$$

18. $a_4 = 1$; $a_7 = \dfrac{1}{125}$
$$a_n = a_1 r^{n-1}$$
$$a_4 = a_1 r^{4-1} \text{ so } 1 = a_1 r^3$$
$$a_7 = a_1 r^{71} \text{ so } \dfrac{1}{125} = a_1 r^6$$
Since $a_1 r^6 = (a_1 r^3)r^3$, $\dfrac{1}{125} = 1 \cdot r^3$ and $r = \dfrac{1}{5}$.
$$a_5 = a_4 \cdot r \text{ so } a_5 = 1 \cdot \dfrac{1}{5} = \dfrac{1}{5}$$

19. $\displaystyle\sum_{i=1}^{4} 5i = 5(1) + 5(2) + 5(3) + 5(4)$
$$= 5 + 10 + 15 + 20$$
$$= 50$$

20. $\displaystyle\sum_{i=1}^{7} (3i+2)$
$$= (3(1)+2) + (3(2)+2) + (3(3)+2)$$
$$\quad + (3(4)+2) + (3(5)+2) + (3(6)+2)$$
$$\quad + (3(7)+2)$$
$$= 5 + 8 + 11 + 14 + 17 + 20 + 23$$
$$= 98$$

21. $\displaystyle\sum_{i=3}^{7} 2^{i-4}$
$$= 2^{3-4} + 2^{4-4} + 2^{5-4} + 2^{6-4} + 2^{7-4}$$
$$= 2^{-1} + 2^0 + 2^1 + 2^2 + 2^3$$
$$= \dfrac{1}{2} + 1 + 2 + 4 + 8$$
$$= 15\dfrac{1}{2}$$
$$= \dfrac{31}{2}$$

22. $\sum\limits_{i=2}^{5} \dfrac{i}{i+1} = \dfrac{2}{2+1} + \dfrac{3}{3+1} + \dfrac{4}{4+1} + \dfrac{5}{5+1}$

$= \dfrac{2}{3} + \dfrac{3}{4} + \dfrac{4}{5} + \dfrac{5}{6}$

$= \dfrac{61}{20}$

23. $S_3 = \sum\limits_{i=1}^{3} i(i-4)$

$= 1(1-4) + 2(2-4) + 3(3-4)$

$= -3 - 4 - 3$

$= -10$

24. $S_{10} = \sum\limits_{i=1}^{10} (-1)^i (i+1)$

$= (-1)^1 (1+1) + (-1)^2 (2+1)$

$\quad + (-1)^3 (3+1) + (-1)^4 (4+1)$

$\quad + (-1)^5 (5+1) + (-1)^6 (6+1)$

$\quad + (-1)^7 (7+1) + (-1)^8 (8+1)$

$\quad + (-1)^9 (9+1) + (-1)^{10} (10+1)$

$= -2 + 3 - 4 + 5 - 6 + 7 - 8 + 9 - 10 + 11$

$= 5$

Section 14.4

Practice Exercises

1. 2, 9, 16, 23, 30

Use the formula for S_n of an arithmetic sequence, replacing n with 5, a_1 with 2, and a_n with 30.

$S_n = \dfrac{n}{2}(a_1 + a_n)$

$S_5 = \dfrac{5}{2}(2+30) = \dfrac{5}{2}(32) = 80$

2. Because 1, 2, 3, ..., 50 is an arithmetic sequence, use the formula for S_n with $n = 50$, $a_1 = 1$, and $a_n = 50$.

$S_n = \dfrac{n}{2}(a_1 + a_n)$

$S_5 = \dfrac{50}{2}(1+50) = 25(51) = 1275$

3. The list 6, 7, ..., 15 is the first 10 terms of an arithmetic sequence. Use the formula for S_n with $n = 10$, $a_1 = 6$, and $a_n = 15$.

$S_{10} = \dfrac{10}{2}(6+15) = 5(21) = 105$

There are a total of 105 blocks of ice.

4. 32, 8, 2, $\dfrac{1}{2}$, $\dfrac{1}{8}$

Use the formula for the partial sum S_n of the terms of a geometric sequence. Here, $n = 5$, the first term $a_1 = 32$, and the common ratio $r = \dfrac{1}{4}$.

$S_n = \dfrac{a_1(1-r^n)}{1-r}$

$S_5 = \dfrac{32\left[1-\left(\frac{1}{4}\right)^5\right]}{1-\frac{1}{4}}$

$= \dfrac{32\left(1-\frac{1}{1024}\right)}{\frac{3}{4}}$

$= \dfrac{32 - \frac{1}{32}}{\frac{3}{4}}$

$= \dfrac{\frac{1023}{32}}{\frac{3}{4}}$

$= \dfrac{1023}{32} \cdot \dfrac{4}{3}$

$= \dfrac{341}{8}$

$= 42\dfrac{5}{8}$

5. The donations are modeled by the first seven terms of a geometric sequence. Evaluate S_n when $n = 7$, $a_1 = 250,000$, and $r = 0.8$.

$S_7 = \dfrac{250,000[1-(0.8)^7]}{1-0.8} = 987,856$

The total amount donated during the seven years is $987,856.

6. 7, $\dfrac{7}{4}$, $\dfrac{7}{16}$, $\dfrac{7}{64}$, ...

For this geometric sequence $r = \dfrac{1}{4}$. Since $|r| < 1$, use the formula for S_∞ of a geometric sequence with $a_1 = 7$ and $r = \dfrac{1}{4}$.

$S_\infty = \dfrac{a_1}{1-r} = \dfrac{7}{1-\frac{1}{4}} = \dfrac{7}{\frac{3}{4}} = \dfrac{28}{3} = 9\dfrac{1}{3}$

7. We must find the sum of the terms of an infinite geometric sequence whose first term, a_1, is 36 and whose common ratio, r, is 0.96. Since $|r| < 1$, we may use the formula for S_∞.

$$S_\infty = \frac{a_1}{1-r} = \frac{36}{1-0.96} = \frac{36}{0.04} = 900$$

The ball travels a total distance of 900 inches before it comes to a rest.

Vocabulary and Readiness Check

1. Each term after the first is 5 more than the preceding term; the sequence is <u>arithmetic</u>.

2. Each term after the first is 2 times the preceding term; the sequence is <u>geometric</u>.

3. Each term after the first is -3 times the preceding term; the sequence is <u>geometric</u>.

4. Each term after the first is 2 more than the preceding term; the sequence is <u>arithmetic</u>.

5. Each term after the first is 7 more than the preceding term; the sequence is <u>arithmetic</u>.

6. Each term after the first is -1 times the preceding term; the sequence is <u>geometric</u>.

Exercise Set 14.4

2. $d = -4$ and $a_7 = -7 + (7-1)(-4) = -31$
$$S_7 = \frac{7}{2}[-7 + (-31)] = \frac{7}{2}(-38) = -133$$

4. $n = 8, a_1 = -1, r = -2$
$$S_8 = \frac{-1\left[1-(-2)^8\right]}{1-(-2)} = \frac{-1(-255)}{3} = 85$$

6. $n = 4, a_1 = -4, a_4 = -16$
$$S_4 = \frac{4}{2}[-4 + (-16)] = 2(-20) = -40$$

8. $n = 5, a_1 = \frac{1}{3}, r = -2$
$$S_5 = \frac{\frac{1}{3}[1-(-2)^5]}{1-(-2)} = \frac{\frac{1}{3}(33)}{3} = \frac{11}{3}$$

10. $n = 8, a_1 = -1, a_8 = -8$
$$S_8 = \frac{8}{2}[-1 + (-8)] = 4(-9) = -36$$

12. $n = 5, a_1 = -1, a_5 = -9$
$$S_5 = \frac{5}{2}[-1 + (-9)] = \frac{5}{2}(-10) = -25$$

14. $a_1 = 45, r = \frac{1}{3}$
$$S_\infty = \frac{45}{1-\frac{1}{3}} = \frac{45}{\frac{2}{3}} = 45 \cdot \frac{3}{2} = 67.5$$

16. $a_1 = \frac{3}{5}, r = \frac{1}{4}$
$$S_\infty = \frac{\frac{3}{5}}{1-\frac{1}{4}} = \frac{\frac{3}{5}}{\frac{3}{4}} = \frac{3}{5} \cdot \frac{4}{3} = \frac{4}{5}$$

18. $a_1 = -16, r = \frac{1}{4}$
$$S_\infty = \frac{-16}{1-\frac{1}{4}} = \frac{-16}{\frac{3}{4}} = -16 \cdot \frac{4}{3} = -\frac{64}{3}$$

20. $a_1 = -3, r = -\frac{1}{5}$
$$S_\infty = \frac{-3}{1-\left(-\frac{1}{5}\right)} = \frac{-3}{\frac{6}{5}} = -3 \cdot \frac{5}{6} = -\frac{5}{2}$$

22. $a_1 = 6, r = -\frac{2}{3}$
$$S_\infty = \frac{6}{1-\left(-\frac{2}{3}\right)} = \frac{6}{\frac{5}{3}} = 6 \cdot \frac{3}{5} = \frac{18}{5}$$

24. $S_{12} = \frac{12}{2}(a_1 + a_{12})$
$= 6[-3 + (-113)]$
$= 6(-116)$
$= -696$

26. $a_1 = -2, r = 3$
$$S_5 = \frac{a_1(1-r^5)}{1-r}$$
$$= \frac{-2(1-3^5)}{1-3}$$
$$= \frac{-2(-242)}{-2}$$
$$= -242$$

28. $a_1 = -\dfrac{1}{4}, r = 3$

$$S_4 = \frac{a_1(1-r^4)}{1-r}$$
$$= \frac{-\frac{1}{4}(1-3^4)}{1-3}$$
$$= \frac{-\frac{1}{4}(-80)}{-2}$$
$$= \frac{20}{-2}$$
$$= -10$$

30. $S_{15} = \dfrac{15}{2}(a_1 + a_{15})$

$$= \frac{15}{2}[-5+(-61)]$$
$$= \frac{15}{2}(-66)$$
$$= -495$$

32. $S_{18} = \dfrac{18}{2}(a_1 + a_{18})$

$$= \frac{18}{2}\left(10 + \frac{3}{2}\right)$$
$$= 9\left(\frac{23}{2}\right)$$
$$= \frac{207}{2}$$

34. $3, \$2.90, \$2.80, \$2.70, \$2.60$

$d = -0.10$ and $a_9 = 3 + 8(-0.10) = 2.20$

$$S_9 = \frac{9}{2}(3+2.20) = 4.5(5.20) = 23.40$$

The total cost of sending a nine-page document is $23.40.

36. $a_1 = 1, a_{15} = 15$

$$S_{15} = \frac{15}{2}(1+15) = \frac{15}{2}(16) = 120 \text{ points}$$

38. $a_1 = 16, d = 32$

$a_8 = 16 + (8-1)(32) = 240$

$$S_8 = \frac{8}{2}(16+240) = 4(256) = 1024$$

The parachutist drops 240 feet during the eighth second, and a total of 1024 feet during the first 8 seconds.

40. $a_1 = 5, r = 2$

$a_6 = 5(2)^{6-1} = 5(2)^5 = 160$

$$S_6 = \frac{5(1-2^6)}{1-2} = \frac{5(-63)}{-1} = 315$$

She lost $160 on the sixth bet and a total of $315 on these six bets.

42. $a_1 = 300, r = \dfrac{2}{5}$

$$S_\infty = \frac{a_1}{1-r} = \frac{300}{1-\frac{2}{5}} = \frac{300}{\frac{3}{5}} = 500$$

It makes 500 revolutions before coming to rest.

44. $a_1 = 250, d = 50$

$a_{22} = 250 + 21(50) = 1300$

$$S_{22} = \frac{22}{2}(250+1300)$$
$$= 11(1550)$$
$$= 17,050$$

He deposited $1300 on the twenty-first birthday. The total deposited over the 21 years was $17,050.

46. $a_1 = 6400, r = \dfrac{1}{4}$

$$S_5 = \frac{a_1(1-r^5)}{1-r}$$
$$= \frac{6400\left(1-\left(\frac{1}{4}\right)^5\right)}{1-\frac{1}{4}}$$
$$= \frac{6400\left(1-\frac{1}{1024}\right)}{\frac{3}{4}}$$
$$= 8525$$

8525 weevils were killed over the five days.

48. $a_1 = 80, d = 40; \ a_5 = 80 + 4(40) = 240$

$$S_5 = \frac{5}{2}(80+240) = \frac{5}{2}(320) = 800$$

They attracted 800 new customers during the first five days.

50. $8 \cdot 7 \cdot 6 \cdot 5 \cdot 4 \cdot 3 \cdot 2 \cdot 1 = 40,320$

52. $\dfrac{5 \cdot 4 \cdot 3 \cdot 2 \cdot 1}{3 \cdot 2 \cdot 1} = 5 \cdot 4 = 20$

54. $(x-2)^2 = x^2 - 2 \cdot x \cdot 2 + 2^2$
$$= x^2 - 4x + 4$$

56. $(3x+2)^3 = (3x+2)(3x+2)^2$

$= (3x+2)(9x^2+12x+4)$

$= 27x^3 + 36x^2 + 12x + 18x^2 + 24x + 8$

$= 27x^3 + 54x^2 + 36x + 8$

58. $0.5\overline{454} = \dfrac{54}{100} + \dfrac{54}{10,000} + \dfrac{54}{1,000,000} + \cdots$

$a_1 = \dfrac{54}{100}, r = \dfrac{1}{100}$

$S_\infty = \dfrac{\frac{54}{100}}{1 - \frac{1}{100}} = \dfrac{\frac{54}{100}}{\frac{99}{100}} = \dfrac{54}{99} = \dfrac{6}{11}$

60. Answers may vary

Section 14.5

Practice Exercises

1. $(p+r)^7$

The $n=7$ row of Pascal's triangle is

1   7   21   35   35   21   7   1

Using the $n=7$ row of Pascal's triangle as the coefficients, $(p+r)^7$ can be expanded as

$p^7 + 7p^6 r + 21p^5 r^2 + 35p^4 r^3 + 35p^3 r^4 + 21p^2 r^5 + 7pr^6 + r^7$

2. a. $\dfrac{6!}{7!} = \dfrac{6\cdot5\cdot4\cdot3\cdot2\cdot1}{7\cdot6\cdot5\cdot4\cdot3\cdot2\cdot1} = \dfrac{1}{7}$

b. $\dfrac{8!}{4!2!} = \dfrac{8\cdot7\cdot6\cdot5\cdot4!}{4!\cdot2\cdot1}$

$= \dfrac{8\cdot7\cdot6\cdot5}{2\cdot1}$

$= 4\cdot7\cdot6\cdot5$

$= 840$

c. $\dfrac{5!}{4!1!} = \dfrac{5\cdot4\cdot3\cdot2\cdot1}{4\cdot3\cdot2\cdot1\cdot1} = 5$

d. $\dfrac{9!}{9!0!} = \dfrac{9!}{9!\cdot1} = 1$

3. $(a+b)^9$

Let $n=9$ in the binomial formula.

$(a+b)^9 = a^9 + \dfrac{9}{1!}a^8 b + \dfrac{9\cdot8}{2!}a^7 b^2 + \dfrac{9\cdot8\cdot7}{3!}a^6 b^3 + \dfrac{9\cdot8\cdot7\cdot6}{4!}a^5 b^4 + \dfrac{9\cdot8\cdot7\cdot6\cdot5}{5!}a^4 b^5 + \dfrac{9\cdot8\cdot7\cdot6\cdot5\cdot4}{6!}a^3 b^6$

$+ \dfrac{9\cdot8\cdot7\cdot6\cdot5\cdot4\cdot3}{7!}a^2 b^7 + \dfrac{9\cdot8\cdot7\cdot6\cdot5\cdot4\cdot3\cdot2}{8!}ab^8 + b^9$

$= a^9 + 9a^8 b + 36a^7 b^2 + 84a^6 b^3 + 126a^5 b^4 + 126a^4 b^5 + 84a^3 b^6 + 36a^2 b^7 + 9ab^8 + b^9$

4. $(a+5b)^3$

   Replace b with $5b$ in the binomial formula.

   $$\begin{aligned}(a+5b)^3 &= a^3 + \frac{3}{1!}a^2(5b) + \frac{3\cdot2}{2!}a(5b)^2 + (5b)^3\\ &= a^3 + 3a^2(5b) + 3a(25b^2) + 125b^3\\ &= a^3 + 15a^2b + 75ab^2 + 125b^3\end{aligned}$$

5. $(3x-2y)^3$

   Let $a = 3x$ and $b = -2y$ in the binomial formula.

   $$\begin{aligned}(3x-2y)^3 &= (3x)^3 + \frac{3}{1!}(3x)^2(-2y) + \frac{3\cdot2}{2!}(3x)(-2y)^2 + (-2y)^3\\ &= 27x^3 + 3(9x^2)(-2y) + 3(3x)(4y^2) - 8y^3\\ &= 27x^3 - 54x^2y + 36xy^2 - 8y^3\end{aligned}$$

6. $(x-4y)^{11}$

   Use the formula with $n = 11$, $a = x$, $b = -4y$, and $r + 1 = 7$. Notice that, since $r + 1 = 7$, $r = 6$.

   $$\frac{n!}{r!(n-r)!}a^{n-r}b^r = \frac{11!}{6!5!}x^5(-4y)^6 = 462x^5(4096y^6) = 1{,}892{,}352x^5y^6$$

Vocabulary and Readiness Check

1. $0! = \underline{1}$

2. $1! = \underline{1}$

3. $4! = 4 \cdot 3 \cdot 2 \cdot 1 = \underline{24}$

4. $2! = 2 \cdot 1 = \underline{2}$

5. $3!0! = 3 \cdot 2 \cdot 1 \cdot 1 = \underline{6}$

6. $0!2! = 1 \cdot 2 \cdot 1 = \underline{2}$

Exercise Set 14.5

2. $(x+y)^4 = x^4 + 4x^3y + 6x^2y^2 + 4xy^3 + y^4$

4. $(a+b)^6 = a^6 + 6a^5b + 15a^4b^2 + 20a^3b^3 + 15a^2b^4 + 6ab^5 + b^6$

6. $(q-r)^7 = q^7 - 7q^6r + 21q^5r^2 - 35q^4r^3 + 35q^3r^4 - 21q^2r^5 + 7qr^6 - r^7$

8. 1 8 28 56 70 56 28 8 1

10. $\dfrac{6!}{0!} = \dfrac{6\cdot5\cdot4\cdot3\cdot2\cdot1}{1} = 720$

12. $\dfrac{8!}{5!} = \dfrac{8\cdot7\cdot6\cdot5!}{5!} = 8\cdot7\cdot6 = 336$

14. $\dfrac{9!}{5!3!} = \dfrac{9 \cdot 8 \cdot 7 \cdot 6 \cdot 5!}{5!3!} = \dfrac{9 \cdot 8 \cdot 7 \cdot 6}{3 \cdot 2 \cdot 1} = 9 \cdot 8 \cdot 7 = 504$

16. $\dfrac{10!}{4!6!} = \dfrac{10 \cdot 9 \cdot 8 \cdot 7 \cdot 6!}{4!6!} = \dfrac{10 \cdot 9 \cdot 8 \cdot 7}{4 \cdot 3 \cdot 2 \cdot 1} = 10 \cdot 3 \cdot 7 = 210$

18. Let $a = x, b = y,$ and $n = 8$ in the binomial theorem.

$$(x+y)^8 = x^8 + \frac{8}{1!}x^7y + \frac{8 \cdot 7}{2!}x^6y^2 + \frac{8 \cdot 7 \cdot 6}{3!}x^5y^3 + \frac{8 \cdot 7 \cdot 6 \cdot 5}{4!}x^4y^4 + \frac{8 \cdot 7 \cdot 6 \cdot 5 \cdot 4}{5!}x^3y^5 + \frac{8 \cdot 7 \cdot 6 \cdot 5 \cdot 4 \cdot 3}{6!}x^2y^6$$
$$+ \frac{8 \cdot 7 \cdot 6 \cdot 5 \cdot 4 \cdot 3 \cdot 2}{7!}xy^7 + y^8$$
$$= x^8 + 8x^7y + 28x^6y^2 + 56x^5y^3 + 70x^4y^4 + 56x^3y^5 + 28x^2y^6 + 8xy^7 + y^8$$

20. Let $a = x, b = 3y,$ and $n = 6$ in the binomial theorem.

$$(x+3y)^6 = x^6 + \frac{6}{1!}x^5(3y) + \frac{6 \cdot 5}{2!}x^4(3y)^2 + \frac{6 \cdot 5 \cdot 4}{3!}x^3(3y)^3 + \frac{6 \cdot 5 \cdot 4 \cdot 3}{4!}x^2(3y)^4 + \frac{6 \cdot 5 \cdot 4 \cdot 3 \cdot 2}{5!}x(3y)^5 + (3y)^6$$
$$= x^6 + 18x^5y + 135x^4y^2 + 540x^3y^3 + 1215x^2y^4 + 1458xy^5 + 729y^6$$

22. Let $a = b, b = c,$ and $n = 6$ in the binomial theorem.

$$(b+c)^6 = b^6 + \frac{6}{1!}b^5c + \frac{6 \cdot 5}{2!}b^4c^2 + \frac{6 \cdot 5 \cdot 4}{3!}b^3c^3 + \frac{6 \cdot 5 \cdot 4 \cdot 3}{4!}b^2c^4 + \frac{6 \cdot 5 \cdot 4 \cdot 3 \cdot 2}{5!}bc^5 + c^6$$
$$= b^6 + 6b^5c + 15b^4c^2 + 20b^3c^3 + 15b^2c^4 + 6bc^5 + c^6$$

24. Let $a = 3m, b = n,$ and $n = 4$ in the binomial theorem.

$$(3m+n)^4 = (3m)^4 + \frac{4}{1!}(3m)^3n + \frac{4 \cdot 3}{2!}(3m)^2n^2 + \frac{4 \cdot 3 \cdot 2}{3!}(3m)n^3 + n^4$$
$$= 81m^4 + 108m^3n + 54m^2n^2 + 12mn^3 + n^4$$

26. Let $a = m, b = -4,$ and $n = 6$ in the binomial theorem.

$$(m-4)^6 = m^6 + \frac{6}{1!}m^5(-4) + \frac{6 \cdot 5}{2!}m^4(-4)^2 + \frac{6 \cdot 5 \cdot 4}{3!}m^3(-4)^3 + \frac{6 \cdot 5 \cdot 4 \cdot 3}{4!}m^2(-4)^4$$
$$+ \frac{6 \cdot 5 \cdot 4 \cdot 3 \cdot 2}{5!}m(-4)^5 + (-4)^6$$
$$= m^6 - 24m^5 + 240m^4 - 1280m^3 + 3840m^2 - 6144m + 4096$$

28. Let $a = 4, b = -3x,$ and $n = 5$ in the binomial theorem.

$$(4-3x)^5 = 4^5 + \frac{5}{1!}(4)^4(-3x) + \frac{5 \cdot 4}{2!}(4)^3(-3x)^2 + \frac{5 \cdot 4 \cdot 3}{3!}(4)^2(-3x)^3 + \frac{5 \cdot 4 \cdot 3 \cdot 2}{4!}(4)(-3x)^4 + (-3x)^5$$
$$= 1024 - 3840x + 5760x^2 - 4320x^3 + 1620x^4 - 243x^5$$

30. Let $a = 3, b = 2a,$ and $n = 4$ in the binomial theorem.

$$(3+2a)^4 = 3^4 + \frac{4}{1!}(3)^3(2a) + \frac{4 \cdot 3}{2!}(3)^2(2a)^2 + \frac{4 \cdot 3 \cdot 2}{3!}(3)(2a)^3 + (2a)^4$$
$$= 81 + 216a + 216a^2 + 96a^3 + 16a^4$$

32. Let $a = x, b = -y, r = 3,$ and $n = 6$ in the formula given.

$$\frac{6!}{3!3!}x^{6-3}(-y)^3 = -20x^3y^3$$

34. Let $a = 5x, b = -y, r = 9,$ and $n = 9$ in the formula given.

$$\frac{9!}{9!0!}x^{9-9}(-y)^9 = -y^9$$

36. Let $a = 3q, b = -7r, r = 0,$ and $n = 6$ in the formula given.

$$\frac{6!}{0!6!}(3q)^{6-0}(-7r)^0 = 729q^6$$

38. Let $a = a, b = b, r = 3,$ and $n = 8$ in the formula given.

$$\frac{8!}{3!5!}a^{8-3}b^3 = 56a^5b^3$$

40. Let $a = m, b = 5n, r = 2,$ and $n = 7$ in the formula given.

$$\frac{7!}{2!5!}m^{7-2}(5n)^2 = 525m^5n^2$$

42. $g(x) = 3(x-1)^2$

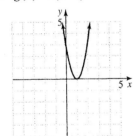

Not one-to-one

44. $F(x) = -2$

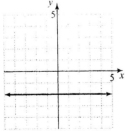

Not one-to-one

46. $h(x) = -(x+1)^2 - 4$

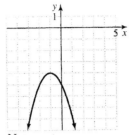

Not one-to-one

48. Let $a = \sqrt{x}, b = -\sqrt{5}, r = 2, n = 6.$

$$\frac{6!}{2!4!}\left(\sqrt{x}\right)^4\left(-\sqrt{5}\right)^2 = 75x^2$$

50. $\dbinom{4}{3} = \dfrac{4!}{3!1!} = \dfrac{4 \cdot 3 \cdot 2 \cdot 1}{(3 \cdot 2 \cdot 1) \cdot 1} = \dfrac{4}{1} = 4$

52. $\dbinom{12}{11} = \dfrac{12!}{11!1!} = \dfrac{12 \cdot 11!}{11! \cdot 1} = \dfrac{12}{1} = 12$

Chapter 14 Vocabulary Check

1. A <u>finite sequence</u> is a function whose domain is the set of natural numbers $\{1, 2, 3, ..., n\}$, where n is some natural number.

2. The <u>factorial of n</u>, written $n!$, is the product of the first n consecutive natural numbers.

3. An <u>infinite sequence</u> is a function whose domain is the set of natural numbers.

4. A <u>geometric sequence</u> is a sequence in which each term (after the first) is obtained by multiplying the preceding term by a constant amount r. The constant r is called the <u>common ratio</u> of the sequence.

5. A sum of the terms of a sequence is called a <u>series</u>.

6. The nth term of the sequence a_n is called the <u>general term</u>.

7. An <u>arithmetic sequence</u> is a sequence in which each term (after the first) differs from the preceding term by a constant amount d. The constant d is called the <u>common difference</u> of the sequence.

8. A triangle array of the coefficients of the terms of the expansions of $(a+b)^n$ is called <u>Pascal's triangle</u>.

Chapter 14 Review

1. $a_n = -3n^2$

   $a_1 = -3(1)^2 = -3$
   $a_2 = -3(2)^2 = -12$
   $a_3 = -3(3)^2 = -27$
   $a_4 = -3(4)^2 = -48$
   $a_5 = -3(5)^2 = -75$

2. $a_n = n^2 + 2n$

   $a_1 = 1^2 + 2(1) = 3$
   $a_2 = 2^2 + 2(2) = 8$
   $a_3 = 3^2 + 2(3) = 15$
   $a_4 = 4^2 + 2(4) = 24$
   $a_5 = 5^2 + 2(5) = 35$

3. $a_n = \dfrac{(-1)^n}{100}$

   $a_{100} = \dfrac{(-1)^{100}}{100} = \dfrac{1}{100}$

4. $a_n = \dfrac{2n}{(-1)^2}$

   $a_{50} = \dfrac{2(50)}{(-1)^2} = 100$

5. $\dfrac{1}{6 \cdot 1}, \dfrac{1}{6 \cdot 2}, \dfrac{1}{6 \cdot 3}, \cdots$

   In general, $a_n = \dfrac{1}{6n}$.

6. $-1, 4, -9, 16, \ldots$

   $a_n = (-1)^n n^2$

7. $a_n = 32n - 16$

   $a_5 = 32(5) - 16 = 144$ feet
   $a_6 = 32(6) - 16 = 176$ feet
   $a_7 = 32(7) - 16 = 208$ feet

8. $a_n = 100(2)^{n-1}$

   $10,000 = 100(2)^{n-1}$
   $100 = 2^{n-1}$
   $\log 100 = (n-1)\log 2$
   $n = \dfrac{\log 100}{\log 2} + 1 \approx 7.6$

   Eighth day culture will be at least 10,000. Since $n = 1$ corresponds to the end of the first day, the original amount corresponds to $n = 0$.

   $a_0 = 100(2)^{-1} = 100\left(\dfrac{1}{2}\right) = 50$

   The original measure of the culture was 50.

9. 2006: $a_1 = 660,000$
   2007: $a_2 = 660,000(2) = 1,320,000$
   2008: $a_3 = 1,320,000(2) = 2,640,000$
   2009: $a_4 = 2,640,000(2) = 5,280,000$
   2010: $a_5 = 5,280,000(2) = 10,560,000$

   There will be 10,560,000 acres of infested trees in 2010.

10. $a_n = 50 + (n-1)8$

    $a_1 = 50$
    $a_2 = 50 + 8 = 58$
    $a_3 = 50 + 2(8) = 66$
    $a_4 = 50 + 3(8) = 74$
    $a_5 = 50 + 4(8) = 82$
    $a_6 = 50 + 5(8) = 90$
    $a_7 = 50 + 6(8) = 98$
    $a_8 = 50 + 7(8) = 106$
    $a_9 = 50 + 8(8) = 114$
    $a_{10} = 50 + 9(8) = 122$

    There are 122 seats in the tenth row.

11. $a_1 = -2, r = \dfrac{2}{3}$

    $a_1 = -2$

    $a_2 = -2\left(\dfrac{2}{3}\right) = -\dfrac{4}{3}$

    $a_3 = \left(-\dfrac{4}{3}\right)\left(\dfrac{2}{3}\right) = -\dfrac{8}{9}$

    $a_4 = \left(-\dfrac{8}{9}\right)\left(\dfrac{2}{3}\right) = -\dfrac{16}{27}$

    $a_5 = \left(-\dfrac{16}{27}\right)\left(\dfrac{2}{3}\right) = -\dfrac{32}{81}$

12. $a_n = 12 + (n-1)(-1.5)$
$a_1 = 12$
$a_2 = 12 + (1)(-1.5) = 10.5$
$a_3 = 12 + 2(-1.5) = 9$
$a_4 = 12 + 3(-1.5) = 7.5$
$a_5 = 12 + 4(-1.5) = 6$

13. $a_n = -5 + (n-1)^4$
$a_{30} = 5 + (30-1)4 = 111$

14. $a_n = 2 + (n-1)\dfrac{3}{4}$
$a_{11} = 2 + 10\left(\dfrac{3}{4}\right) = \dfrac{19}{2}$

15. 12, 7, 2,...
$a_1 = 12,\ d = -5,\ n = 20$
$a_{20} = 12 + (20-1)(-5) = -83$

16. $a_n = a_1 r^{n-1},\ a_1 = 4,\ r = \dfrac{3}{2}$
$a_6 = 4\left(\dfrac{3}{2}\right)^{6-1} = \dfrac{243}{8}$

17. $a_4 = 18,\ a_{20} = 98$
$\begin{cases} a_4 = a_1 + (4-1)d \\ a_{20} = a_1 + (20-1)d \end{cases}$
$\begin{cases} 18 = a_1 + 3d \\ 98 = a_1 + 19d \end{cases}$
$\begin{cases} -18 = -a_1 - 3d \\ 98 = a_1 + 19d \end{cases}$
Adding yields $80 = 16d$ or $d = 5$.
Then $a_1 = 18 - 3(5) = 3$.

18. $a_3 = -48,\ a_4 = 192$
$r = \dfrac{a_4}{a_3} = \dfrac{192}{-48} = -4$
$a_3 = a_1 r^{3-1}$
$-48 = a_1(-4)^2$
$-48 = 16a_1$
$-3 = a_1$
$r = -4,\ a_1 = -3$

19. $\dfrac{3}{10}, \dfrac{3}{10^2}, \dfrac{3}{10^3}, \ldots$
In general, $a_n = \dfrac{3}{10^n}$

20. 50, 58, 66, ...
$a_n = 50 + (n-1)8$ or $a_n = 42 + 8n$

21. $\dfrac{8}{3}$, 4, 6, ...
Geometric; $a_1 = \dfrac{8}{3}$,
$r = \dfrac{4}{\frac{8}{3}} = 4 \cdot \dfrac{3}{8} = \dfrac{12}{8} = \dfrac{3}{2}$

22. $-10.5, -6.1, -1.7$
Arithmetic; $a_1 = -10.5$,
$d = -6.1 - (-10.5) = 4.4$

23. $7x, -14x, 28x$
Geometric; $a_1 = 7x,\ r = -2$

24. neither

25. $a_1 = 8,\ r = 0.75$
$a_1 = 8$
$a_2 = 8(0.75) = 6$
$a_3 = 8(0.75)^2 = 4.5$
$a_4 = 8(0.75)^3 \approx 3.4$
$a_5 = 8(0.75)^4 \approx 2.5$
$a_6 = 8(0.75)^5 \approx 1.9$
Yes, a ball that rebounds to a height of 2.5 feet after the fifth bounce is good, since $2.5 \geq 1.9$.

26. $a_1 = 25,\ d = -4$
$a_n = a_1 + (n-1)d$
$a_n = 25 + (n-1)(-4) = 29 - 4n$
$a_7 = 25 + 6(-4) = 1$
Continuing the progression as far as possible leaves 1 can in the top row.

27. $a_1 = 1,\ r = 2$
$a_n = 2^{n-1}$
$a_{10} = 2^9 = 512$
$a_{30} = 2^{29} = 536,870,912$
You save \$512 on the tenth day and \$536,870,912 on the thirtieth day.

28. $a_n = a_1 r^{n-1}$, $a_1 = 30$, $r = 0.7$

$a_5 = 30(0.7)^4 = 7.203$

The length is 7.203 inches on the fifth swing.

29. $a_1 = 900$, $d = 150$

$a_n = 900 + (n-1)150 = 150_n + 750$

$a_6 = 900 + (6-1)150 = 1650$

Her salary is $1650 per month at the end of training.

30. $\dfrac{1}{512}, \dfrac{1}{256}, \dfrac{1}{128}, \cdots$

first fold: $a_1 = \dfrac{1}{256}$, $r = 2$

$a_{15} = \dfrac{1}{256}(2)^{15-1} = 64$

After 15 folds, the thickness is 64 inches.

31. $\displaystyle\sum_{i=1}^{5}(2i-1) = [2(1)-1]+[2(2)-1]+[2(3)-1]$

$\qquad\qquad\qquad +[2(4)-1]+[2(5)-1]$

$\qquad = 1+3+5+7+9$

$\qquad = 25$

32. $\displaystyle\sum_{i=1}^{5} i(i+2) = 1(1+2)+2(2+2)+3(3+2)$

$\qquad\qquad\qquad +4(4+2)+5(5+2)$

$\qquad = 3+8+15+24+35$

$\qquad = 85$

33. $\displaystyle\sum_{i=2}^{4}\dfrac{(-1)^i}{2i} = \dfrac{(-1)^2}{2(2)}+\dfrac{(-1)^3}{2(3)}+\dfrac{(-1)^4}{2(4)}$

$\qquad = \dfrac{1}{4}-\dfrac{1}{6}+\dfrac{1}{8}$

$\qquad = \dfrac{5}{24}$

34. $\displaystyle\sum_{i=3}^{5} 5(-1)^{i-1} = 5(-1)^{3-1}+5(-1)^{4-1}+5(-1)^{5-1}$

$\qquad = 5(1)+5(-1)+5(1)$

$\qquad = 5-5+5$

$\qquad = 5$

35. $a_n = (n-3)(n+2)$

$S_4 = \displaystyle\sum_{i=1}^{4}(i-3)(i+2)$

$\qquad = (1-3)(1+2)+(2-3)(2+2)$

$\qquad\qquad +(3-3)(3+2)+(4-3)(4+2)$

$\qquad = -6-4+0+6$

$\qquad = -4$

36. $a_n = n^2$

$S_6 = \displaystyle\sum_{i=1}^{6} i^2$

$\qquad = (1)^2+(2)^2+(3)^2+(4)^2+(5)^2+(6)^2$

$\qquad = 91$

37. $a_n = -8+(n-1)3 = 3n-11$

$S_5 = \displaystyle\sum_{i=1}^{5}(3i-11)$

$\qquad = [3(1)-11]+[3(2)-11]+[3(3)-11]$

$\qquad\qquad +[3(4)-11]+[3(5)-11]$

$\qquad = -8-5-2+1+4$

$\qquad = -10$

38. $a_n = 5(4)^{n-1}$

$S_3 = \displaystyle\sum_{i=1}^{3} 5(4)^{i-1} = 5(4)^0+5(4)^1+5(4)^2 = 105$

39. $1+3+9+27+81+243$

$\qquad = 3^0+3^1+3^2+3^3+3^4+3^5$

$\qquad = \displaystyle\sum_{i=1}^{6} 3^{i-1}$

40. $6+2+(-2)+(-6)+(-10)+(-14)+(-18)$

$a_1 = 6$, $d = -4$

$a_n = 6+(n-1)(-4)$

$\displaystyle\sum_{i=1}^{7}[6+(i-1)(-4)]$

41. $\dfrac{1}{4}+\dfrac{1}{16}+\dfrac{1}{64}+\dfrac{1}{256} = \dfrac{1}{4^1}+\dfrac{1}{4^2}+\dfrac{1}{4^3}+\dfrac{1}{4^4}$

$\qquad\qquad = \displaystyle\sum_{i=1}^{4}\dfrac{1}{4^i}$

42. $1 + \left(-\dfrac{3}{2}\right) + \dfrac{9}{4} = \left(-\dfrac{3}{2}\right)^0 + \left(-\dfrac{3}{2}\right)^1 + \left(-\dfrac{3}{2}\right)^2$

$= \displaystyle\sum_{i=1}^{3} \left(-\dfrac{3}{2}\right)^{i-1}$

43. $a_1 = 20,\ r = 2$

$a_n = 20(2)^n$ represents the number of yeast, where n represents the number of 8-hour periods. Since $48 = 6(8)$ here, $n = 6$.

$a_6 = 20(2)^6 = 1280$

There are 1280 yeast after 48 hours.

44. $a_n = n^2 + 2n - 1$

$a_4 = (4)^2 + 2(4) - 1 = 23$

$S_4 = \displaystyle\sum_{i=1}^{4} (i^2 + 2i - 1)$

$= (1 + 2 - 1) + (4 + 4 - 1) + (9 + 6 - 1)$
$\quad + (16 + 8 - 1)$

$= 46$

23 cranes are born in the fourth year and 46 cranes are born in the first four years.

45. For Job *A*: $a_1 = 39{,}500,\ d = 2200$;

$a_5 = 39{,}500 + (5 - 1)2200 = \$48{,}330$

For Job *B*: $a_1 = 41{,}000,\ d = 1400$

$a_5 = 41{,}000 + (5 - 1)1400 = \$46{,}600$

For the fifth year, Job *A* has a higher salary.

46. $a_n = 200(0.5)^n$

$a_3 = 200(0.5)^3 = 25$

$S_3 = \displaystyle\sum_{i=1}^{3} 200(0.5)^i$

$= 200(0.5) + 200(0.5)^2 + 200(0.5)^3$

$= 175$

25 kilograms decay in the third year and 175 kilograms decay in the first three years.

47. $15, 19, 23, \ldots$

$a_1 = 15,\ d = 4,\ a_6 = 15 + (6 - 1)4 = 35$

$S_6 = \dfrac{6}{2}[15 + 35] = 150$

48. $5, -10, 20, \ldots$

$a_1 = 5,\ r = -2$

$S_n = \dfrac{a_1(1 - r^n)}{1 - r}$

$S_9 = \dfrac{5(1 - (-2)^9)}{1 - (-2)} = 855$

49. $a_1 = 1,\ d = 2,\ n = 30,\ a_{30} = 1 + (30 - 1)2 = 59$

$S_{30} = \dfrac{30}{2}[1 + 59] = 900$

50. $7, 14, 21, 28, \ldots$

$a_n = 7 + (n - 1)7$

$a_{20} = 7 + (20 - 1)7 = 140$

$S_{20} = \dfrac{20}{2}(7 + 140) = 1470$

51. $8, 5, 2, \ldots$

$a_1 = 8,\ d = -3,\ n = 20$

$a_{20} = 8 + (20 - 1)(-3) = -49$

$S_{20} = \dfrac{20}{2}[8 + (-49)]$

$= -410$

52. $\dfrac{3}{4}, \dfrac{9}{4}, \dfrac{27}{4}, \ldots$

$a_1 = \dfrac{3}{4},\ r = 3$

$S_8 = \dfrac{\dfrac{3}{4}(1 - 3^8)}{1 - 3} = 2460$

53. $a_1 = 6,\ r = 5$

$S_4 = \dfrac{6(1 - 5^4)}{1 - 5} = 936$

54. $a_1 = -3,\ d = -6$

$a_n = -3 + (n - 1)(-6)$

$a_{100} = -3 + (100 - 1)(-6) = -597$

$S_{100} = \dfrac{100}{2}(-3 + (-597)) = -30{,}000$

55. $5, \dfrac{5}{2}, \dfrac{5}{4}, \ldots$

$a_1 = 5, \ r = \dfrac{1}{2}$

$S_\infty = \dfrac{5}{1 - \frac{1}{2}} = 10$

56. $18, -2, \dfrac{2}{9}, \ldots$

$a_1 = 18, \ r = -\dfrac{1}{9}$

$S_\infty = \dfrac{18}{1 + \frac{1}{9}} = \dfrac{81}{5}$

57. $-20, -4, -\dfrac{4}{5}, \ldots$

$a_1 = -20, \ r = \dfrac{1}{5}$

$S_\infty = \dfrac{-20}{1 - \frac{1}{5}} = -25$

58. $0.2, 0.02, 0.002, \ldots$

$a_1 = 0.2 = \dfrac{1}{5}, \ r = \dfrac{1}{10}$

$S_\infty = \dfrac{\frac{1}{5}}{1 - \frac{1}{10}} = \dfrac{2}{9}$

59. $a_1 = 20{,}000, \ r = 1.15, \ n = 4$

$a_4 = 20{,}000(1.15)^{4-1} = 30{,}418$

$S_4 = \dfrac{20{,}000(1 - 1.15^4)}{1 - 1.15} = 99{,}868$

He earned \$30,418 during the fourth year and \$99,868 over the four years.

60. $a_n = 40(0.8)^{n-1}$

$a_4 = 40(0.8)^{4-1} = 20.48$

$S_4 = \dfrac{40(1 - 0.8^4)}{1 - 0.8} = 118.08$

He takes 20 minutes to assemble the fourth television and 118 minutes to assemble the first four televisions.

61. $a_1 = 100, d = -7, n = 7$

$a_7 = 100 + (7 - 1)(-7) = 58$

$S_7 = \dfrac{7}{2}(100 + 58) = 553$

The rent for the seventh day is \$58 and the rent for 7 days is \$553.

62. $a_1 = 15, \ r = 0.8$

$S_\infty = \dfrac{15}{1 - 0.8} = 75 \text{ feet downward}$

$a_1 = 15(0.8) = 12, \ r = 0.8$

$S_\infty = \dfrac{12}{1 - 0.8} = 60 \text{ feet upward}$

The total distance is 135 feet.

63. $1800, 600, 200, \ldots$

$a_1 = 1800, \ r = \dfrac{1}{3}, \ n = 6$

$S_6 = 1800 \dfrac{\left(1 - \left(\frac{1}{3}\right)^6\right)}{1 - \frac{1}{3}} \approx 2696$

Approximately 2696 mosquitoes were killed during the first six days after the spraying.

64. $1800, 600, 200, \ldots$

For which n is $a_n < 1$?

$a_n = 1800\left(\dfrac{1}{3}\right)^{n-1} < 1$

$\left(\dfrac{1}{3}\right)^{n-1} < \dfrac{1}{1800}$

$(n - 1)\log\dfrac{1}{3} < \log\dfrac{1}{1800}$

$(n - 1)\log 3^{-1} < \log 1800^{-1}$

$(n - 1)(-\log 3) < -\log 1800$

$n - 1 > \dfrac{-\log 1800}{-\log 3}$

$n > 1 + \dfrac{\log 1800}{\log 3}$

$n > 7.8$

No longer effective on the 8th day

$S_8 = \dfrac{1800\left(1 - \left(\frac{1}{3}\right)^8\right)}{1 - \frac{1}{3}} \approx 2700$

About 2700 mosquitoes were killed.

65. $0.5\overline{5} = 0.5 + 0.05 + 0.005 + \cdots$

$a_1 = 0.5, \ r = 0.1$

$S_\infty = \dfrac{0.5}{1 - 0.1} = \dfrac{0.5}{0.9} = \dfrac{5}{9}$

66. $27, 30, 33, \ldots$

$a_n = 27 + (n-1)(3)$

$a_{20} = 27 + (20-1)(3) = 84$

$S_{20} = \dfrac{20}{2}(27 + 84) = 1110$

There are 1110 seats in the theater.

67. $(x+z)^5 = x^5 + 5x^4 z + 10x^3 z^2 + 10x^2 z^3 + 5xz^4 + z^5$

68. $(y-r)^6 = y^6 + 6y^5(-r) + 15y^4(-r)^2 + 20y^3(-r)^3 + 15y^2(-r)^4 + 6y(-r)^5 + (-r)^6$
$= y^6 - 6y^5 r + 15y^4 r^2 - 20y^3 r^3 + 15y^2 r^4 - 6yr^5 + r^6$

69. $(2x+y)^4 = (2x)^4 + 4(2x)^3 y + 6(2x)^2 y^2 + 4(2x)y^3 + y^4$
$= 16x^4 + 32x^3 y + 24x^2 y^2 + 8xy^3 + y^4$

70. $(3y-z)^4 = (3y)^4 + 4(3y)^3(-z) + 6(3y)^2(-z)^2 + 4(3y)(-z)^3 + (-z)^4$
$= 81y^4 - 108y^3 z + 54y^2 z^2 - 12yz^3 + z^4$

71. $(b+c)^8 = b^8 + \dfrac{8}{1!}b^7 c + \dfrac{8 \cdot 7}{2!}b^6 c^2 + \dfrac{8 \cdot 7 \cdot 6}{3!}b^5 c^3 + \dfrac{8 \cdot 7 \cdot 6 \cdot 5}{4!}b^4 c^4 + \dfrac{8 \cdot 7 \cdot 6 \cdot 5 \cdot 4}{5!}b^3 c^5$
$\qquad\qquad + \dfrac{8 \cdot 7 \cdot 6 \cdot 5 \cdot 4 \cdot 3}{6!}b^2 c^6 + \dfrac{8 \cdot 7 \cdot 6 \cdot 5 \cdot 4 \cdot 3 \cdot 2}{7!}bc^7 + c^8$
$= b^8 + 8b^7 c + 28b^6 c^2 + 56b^5 c^3 + 70b^4 c^4 + 56b^3 c^5 + 28b^2 c^6 + 8bc^7 + c^8$

72. $(x-w)^7 = x^7 + \dfrac{7}{1!}x^6(-w) + \dfrac{7 \cdot 6}{2!}x^5(-w)^2 + \dfrac{7 \cdot 6 \cdot 5}{3!}x^4(-w)^3 + \dfrac{7 \cdot 6 \cdot 5 \cdot 4}{4!}x^3(-w)^4 + \dfrac{7 \cdot 6 \cdot 5 \cdot 4 \cdot 3}{5!}x^2(-w)^5$
$\qquad\qquad + \dfrac{7 \cdot 6 \cdot 5 \cdot 4 \cdot 3 \cdot 2}{6!}x(-w)^6 + (-w)^7$
$= x^7 - 7x^6 w + 21x^5 w^2 - 35x^4 w^3 + 35x^3 w^4 - 21x^2 w^5 + 7xw^6 - w^7$

73. $(4m-n)^4 = (4m)^4 + \dfrac{4}{1!}(4m)^3(-n) + \dfrac{4 \cdot 3}{2!}(4m)^2(-n)^2 + \dfrac{4 \cdot 3 \cdot 2}{3!}(4m)(-n)^3 + (-n)^4$
$= 256m^4 - 256m^3 n + 96m^2 n^2 - 16mn^3 + n^4$

74. $(p-2r)^5 = p^5 + \dfrac{5}{1!}p^4(-2r) + \dfrac{5 \cdot 4}{2!}p^3(-2r)^2 + \dfrac{5 \cdot 4 \cdot 3}{3!}p^2(-2r)^3 + \dfrac{5 \cdot 4 \cdot 3 \cdot 2}{4!}p(-2r)^4 + (-2r)^5$
$= p^5 - 10p^4 r + 40p^3 r^2 - 80p^2 r^3 + 80pr^4 - 32r^5$

75. The 4th term corresponds to $r = 3$.

$\dfrac{7!}{3!(7-3)!}a^{7-3}b^3 = 35a^4 b^3$

76. The 11th term corresponds to $r = 10$.

$\dfrac{10!}{10!0!}y^{10-10}(2z)^{10} = 1024z^{10}$

77. $\displaystyle\sum_{i=1}^{4} i^2(i+1) = 1^2(1+1) + 2^2(2+1) + 3^2(3+1) + 4^2(4+1)$

$$= 1\cdot 2 + 4\cdot 3 + 9\cdot 4 + 16\cdot 5$$
$$= 2 + 12 + 36 + 80$$
$$= 130$$

78. $a_1 = 14$

$d = 8 - 14 = -6$

$a_n = a_1 + (n-1)d$

$a_{15} = 14 + (15-1)(-6) = 14 + 14(-6) = 14 + (-84) = -70$

79. $a_1 = 27$

$r = \dfrac{9}{27} = \dfrac{1}{3}$

$S_\infty = \dfrac{27}{1-\frac{1}{3}} = \dfrac{27}{\frac{2}{3}} = 27\cdot\dfrac{3}{2} = \dfrac{81}{2} = 40.5$

80. $(2x-3)^4 = (2x)^4 + \dfrac{4}{1!}(2x)^3(-3) + \dfrac{4\cdot 3}{2!}(2x)^2(-3)^2 + \dfrac{4\cdot 3\cdot 2}{3!}(2x)(-3)^3 + (-3)^4$

$$= 16x^4 - 96x^3 + 216x^2 - 216x + 81$$

Chapter 14 Test

1. $a_n = \dfrac{(-1)^n}{n+4}$

$a_1 = \dfrac{(-1)^1}{1+4} = -\dfrac{1}{5}$

$a_2 = \dfrac{(-1)^2}{2+4} = \dfrac{1}{6}$

$a_3 = \dfrac{(-1)^3}{3+4} = -\dfrac{1}{7}$

$a_4 = \dfrac{(-1)^4}{4+4} = \dfrac{1}{8}$

$a_5 = \dfrac{(-1)^5}{5+4} = -\dfrac{1}{9}$

2. $a_n = 10 + 3(n-1)$

$a_{80} = 10 + 3(80-1) = 247$

3. $\dfrac{2}{5}, \dfrac{2}{25}, \dfrac{2}{125}, \ldots$

In general, $a_n = \dfrac{2}{5}\left(\dfrac{1}{5}\right)^{n-1}$ or $a_n = \dfrac{2}{5^n}$.

4. $(-1)^1 9\cdot 1, (-1)^2 9\cdot 2, \ldots, a_n = (-1)^n 9n$

5. $a_n = 5(2)^{n-1}, S_5 = \dfrac{5(1-2^5)}{1-2} = 155$

6. $a_n = 18 + (n-1)(-2)$

     $a_1 = 18, \ a_{30} = 18 + (30-1)(-2) = -40$

     $S_{30} = \dfrac{30}{2}[18 - 40] = -330$

7. $a_1 = 24, \ r = \dfrac{1}{6}$

     $S_\infty = \dfrac{24}{1 - \frac{1}{6}} = \dfrac{144}{5}$

8. $\dfrac{3}{2}, \ -\dfrac{3}{4}, \ \dfrac{3}{8}, \ldots$

     $a_1 = \dfrac{3}{2}, \ r = -\dfrac{1}{2}$

     $S_\infty = \dfrac{\frac{3}{2}}{1 - \left(-\frac{1}{2}\right)} = 1$

9. $\displaystyle\sum_{i=1}^{4} i(i-2) = 1(1-2) + 2(2-2) + 3(3-2) + 4(4-2)$

                     $= -1 + 0 + 3 + 8 - 20 + 40 - 80$

                      $= 10$

10. $\displaystyle\sum_{i=2}^{4} 5(2)^i (-1)^{i-1} = 5(2)^2(-1)^{2-1} + 5(2)^3(-1)^{3-1} + 5(2)^4(-1)^{4-1} = -20 + 40 - 80 = -60$

11. $(a-b)^6 = a^6 - 6a^5 b + 15a^4 b^2 - 20a^3 b^3 + 15a^2 b^4 - 6ab^5 + b^6$

12. $(2x+y)^5 = (2x)^5 + \dfrac{5}{1!}(2x)^4 y + \dfrac{5 \cdot 4}{2!}(2x)^3 y^2 + \dfrac{5 \cdot 4 \cdot 3}{3!}(2x)^2 y^3 + \dfrac{5 \cdot 4 \cdot 3 \cdot 2}{4!}(2x)y^4 + y^5$

            $= 32x^5 + 80x^4 y + 80x^3 y^2 + 40x^2 y^3 + 10xy^4 + y^5$

13. $a_n = 250 + 75(n-1)$

     $a_{10} = 250 + 75(10-1) = 925$

     There were 925 people in the town at the beginning of the tenth year.

     $a_1 = 250 + 75(1-1) = 250$

     There were 250 people in the town at the beginning of the first year.

14. $1, 3, 5, \ldots$

     $a_1 = 1, \ d = 2, \ n = 8$

     $a_8 = 1 + (8-1)2 = 15$

     $1 + 3 + 5 + 7 + 9 + 11 + 13 + 15$

     $S_8 = \dfrac{8}{2}[1 + 15] = 64$

     There were 64 shrubs planted in the 8 rows.

15. $a_1 = 80$, $r = \dfrac{3}{4}$, $n = 4$

$$a_4 = 80\left(\dfrac{3}{4}\right)^{4-1} = 33.75$$

The arc length is 33.75 cm on the 4th swing.

$$S_4 = \dfrac{80\left(1-\left(\frac{3}{4}\right)^4\right)}{1-\frac{3}{4}} = 218.75$$

The total of the arc lengths is 218.75 cm for the first 4 swings.

16. $a_1 = 80$, $r = \dfrac{3}{4}$

$$S_\infty = \dfrac{80}{1-\frac{3}{4}} = 320$$

The total of the arc lengths is 320 cm before the pendulum comes to rest.

17. 16, 48, 80,...

$a_{10} = 16 + (10-1)32 = 304$

He falls 304 feet during the 10th second.

$$S_{10} = \dfrac{10}{2}[16+304] = 1600$$

He falls 1600 feet during the first 10 seconds.

18. $0.4\overline{2}42 = 0.42 + 0.0042 + 0.000042$

$$a_1 = 0.42 = \dfrac{42}{100},\ r = 0.01 = \dfrac{1}{100}$$

$$S_\infty = \dfrac{\frac{42}{100}}{1-\frac{1}{100}} = \dfrac{42}{100}\cdot\dfrac{100}{99} = \dfrac{14}{33}$$

Thus, $0.4\overline{2}42 = \dfrac{14}{33}$.

Chapter 14 Cumulative Review

1. a. $(-2)^3 = (-2)(-2)(-2) = -8$

b. $-2^3 = -(2)(2)(2) = -8$

c. $(-3)^2 = (-3)(-3) = 9$

d. $-3^2 = -(3)(3) = -9$

2. a. $3a - (4a+3) = 3a - 4a - 3 = -a - 3$

b. $(5x-3) + (2x+6) = 7x + 3$

c. $4(2x-5) - 3(5x+1) = 8x - 20 - 15x - 3$
$$= -7x - 23$$

3. $(2x-3) - (4x-2) = 2x - 3 - 4x + 2 = -2x - 1$

4. Let $x =$ the price before taxes, then
$$x + 0.06x = 344.50$$
$$1.06x = 344.50$$
$$x = 325$$
The price before taxes was \$325.

5. $y = mx + b$; $m = \dfrac{1}{4}$, $b = -3$

$$y = \dfrac{1}{4}x - 3$$

6. If the line is to be parallel, then the slope has to be the same as the slope of the given line.

Therefore, $m = \dfrac{3}{2}$.

$$(y-(-2)) = \dfrac{3}{2}(x-3)$$
$$y + 2 = \dfrac{3}{2}(x-3)$$
$$y = \dfrac{3}{2}x - \dfrac{13}{2}$$
$$f(x) = \dfrac{3}{2}x - \dfrac{13}{2}$$

7. $(2, 5), (-3, 4)$
$$m = \dfrac{y_2 - y_1}{x_2 - x_1} = \dfrac{4-5}{-3-2} = \dfrac{-1}{-5} = \dfrac{1}{5}$$
$$y - y_1 = m(x - x_1)$$
$$y - 5 = \dfrac{1}{5}(x-2)$$
$$5y - 25 = x - 2$$
$$-23 = x - 5y \text{ or } x - 5y = -23$$

8.
$$y^3 + 5y^2 - y = 5$$
$$y^3 + 5y^2 - y - 5 = 0$$
$$(y^3 + 5y^2) + (-y-5) = 0$$
$$y^2(y+5) - 1(y+5) = 0$$
$$(y^2 - 1)(y+5) = 0$$
$$(y+1)(y-1)(y+5) = 0$$
$$y = -5, -1, 1$$

9. $\quad -2\,\underline{|1 \quad -2 \quad -11 \quad 5 \quad 34}$
$$\quad\quad\quad -2 \quad 8 \quad 6 \quad -22$$
$$\quad\overline{1 \quad -4 \quad -3 \quad 11 \quad 12}$$

Answer: $x^3 - 4x^2 - 3x + 11 + \dfrac{12}{x+2}$

10. $\quad \dfrac{5}{3a-6} - \dfrac{a}{a-2} + \dfrac{3+2a}{5a-10}$

$$= \dfrac{5}{3(a-2)} - \dfrac{a}{a-2} + \dfrac{3+2a}{5(a-2)}$$

$$= \dfrac{5 \cdot 5 - 3 \cdot 5a + 3(3+2a)}{3 \cdot 5(a-2)}$$

$$= \dfrac{25 - 15a + 9 + 6a}{15(a-2)}$$

$$= \dfrac{34 - 9a}{15(a-2)}$$

11. a. $\quad \sqrt{50} = \sqrt{2}\sqrt{25} = 5\sqrt{2}$

    b. $\quad \sqrt[3]{24} = \sqrt[3]{8}\sqrt[3]{3} = 2\sqrt[3]{3}$

    c. $\quad \sqrt{26} = \sqrt{26}$

    d. $\quad \sqrt[4]{32} = \sqrt[4]{16}\sqrt[4]{2} = 2\sqrt[4]{2}$

12. $\quad \sqrt{3x+6} - \sqrt{7x-6} = 0$

$$\sqrt{3x+6} = \sqrt{7x-6}$$

$$\left(\sqrt{3x+6}\right)^2 = \left(\sqrt{7x-6}\right)^2$$

$$3x+6 = 7x-6$$

$$-4x = -12$$

$$x = 3$$

13. $\quad 2420 = 2000(1+r)^2$

$$\dfrac{2420}{2000} = (1+r)^2$$

$$\dfrac{121}{100} = (1+r)^2$$

$$\pm\sqrt{\dfrac{121}{100}} = 1+r$$

$$\pm\dfrac{11}{10} = 1+r$$

$$-1 \pm \dfrac{11}{10} = r$$

Discard the negative value.

$$r = -1 + \dfrac{11}{10} = \dfrac{1}{10} = 0.10$$

The interest rate is 10%.

14. a. $\quad \sqrt[3]{\dfrac{4}{3x}} = \dfrac{\sqrt[3]{4}}{\sqrt[3]{3x}} = \left(\dfrac{\sqrt[3]{9x^2}}{\sqrt[3]{9x^2}}\right) = \dfrac{\sqrt[3]{36x^2}}{3x}$

    b. $\quad \dfrac{\sqrt{2}+1}{\sqrt{2}-1} = \dfrac{\sqrt{2}+1}{\sqrt{2}-1} \cdot \left(\dfrac{\sqrt{2}+1}{\sqrt{2}+1}\right)$

$$= \dfrac{2 + 2\sqrt{2} + 1}{2-1}$$

$$= 3 + 2\sqrt{2}$$

15. $\quad (x-3)^2 - 3(x-3) - 4 = 0$

$$x^2 - 6x + 9 - 3x + 9 - 4 = 0$$

$$x^2 - 9x + 14 = 0$$

$$(x-2)(x-7) = 0$$

$$x = 2, 7$$

16. $\quad \dfrac{10}{(2x+4)^2} - \dfrac{1}{2x+4} = 3$

$$10 - (2x+4) = 3(2x+4)^2$$

$$10 - 2x - 4 = 3(4x^2 + 16x + 16)$$

$$-2x + 6 = 12x^2 + 48x + 48$$

$$12x^2 + 50x + 42 = 0$$

$$6x^2 + 25x + 21 = 0$$

$$(6x+7)(x+3) = 0$$

$$x = -\dfrac{7}{6}, -3$$

17. $\quad \dfrac{5}{x+1} < -2$

$$x + 1 = 0$$

$$x = -1$$

Solve $\dfrac{5}{x+1} = -2$.

$$(x+1)\dfrac{5}{x+1} = (x+1)(-2)$$

$$5 = -2x - 2$$

$$7 = -2x$$

$$-\dfrac{7}{2} = x$$

Region	Test Point	$\dfrac{5}{x+1} < -2$; Result
$\left(-\infty, -\dfrac{7}{2}\right)$	$x = -6$	$\dfrac{5}{-5} < -2$; False
$\left(-\dfrac{7}{2}, -1\right)$	$x = -2$	$\dfrac{5}{-1} < -2$; True
$(-1, \infty)$	$x = 4$	$\dfrac{5}{5} < -2$; False

The solution set is $\left(-\dfrac{7}{2}, -1\right)$.

18. $f(x) = (x+2)^2 - 6$

Axis of symmetry: $x = -2$

vertex: $(-2, -6)$

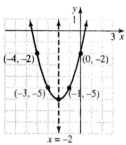

19. $f(t) = -16t^2 + 20t$

The maximum height occurs at the vertex.

$t = \dfrac{-20}{2(-16)} = \dfrac{5}{8}$

$f\left(\dfrac{5}{8}\right) = -16\left(\dfrac{5}{8}\right)^2 + 20\left(\dfrac{5}{8}\right) = \dfrac{25}{4}$

The maximum height of $\dfrac{25}{4}$ feet occurs at

$\dfrac{5}{8}$ second.

20. $f(x) = x^2 + 3x - 18$

$a = 1, b = 3, c = -18$

$x = \dfrac{-3}{2(1)} = -\dfrac{3}{2}$

$f\left(-\dfrac{3}{2}\right) = \left(-\dfrac{3}{2}\right)^2 + 3\left(\dfrac{3}{2}\right) - 18 = -\dfrac{81}{4}$

The vertex is $\left(-\dfrac{3}{2}, -\dfrac{81}{4}\right)$.

21. a. $(f \circ g)(2) = f(g(2)) = f(5) = 5^2 = 25$
$(g \circ f)(2) = g(f(2)) = g(4) = 4 + 3 = 7$

b. $(f \circ g)(x) = f(x+3)$
$= (x+3)^2$
$= x^2 + 6x + 9$
$(g \circ f)(x) = g(x^2) = x^2 + 3$

22. $f(x) = -2x + 3$
$y = -2x + 3$
$x = -2y + 3$
$x - 3 = -2y$
$\dfrac{x-3}{-2} = y$

$f^{-1}(x) = -\dfrac{x-3}{2}$ or $f^{-1}(x) = \dfrac{3-x}{2}$

23. $f^{-1} = \{(1,0), (7,-2), (-6,3), (4,4)\}$

24. a. $(f \circ g)(2) = f(g(2)) = f(3) = 3^2 - 2 = 7$
$(g \circ f)(2) = g(f(2)) = g(2) = 2 + 1 = 3$

b. $(f \circ g)(x) = f(x+1)$
$= (x+1)^2 - 2$
$= x^2 + 2x - 1$
$(g \circ f)(x) = g(x^2 - 2) = x^2 - 2 + 1 = x^2 - 1$

25. a. $2^x = 16$
$2^x = 2^4$
$x = 4$

b. $9^x = 27$
$(3^2)^x = 3^3$
$2x = 3$
$x = \dfrac{3}{2}$

c. $4^{x+3} = 8^x$
$(2^2)^{x+3} = (2^3)^x$
$2^{2x+6} = 2^{3x}$
$2x + 6 = 3x$
$x = 6$

26. a. $\log_2 32 = x$
$2^x = 32$
$2^x = 2^5$
$x = 5$

b. $\log_4 \dfrac{1}{64} = x$
$4^x = \dfrac{1}{64}$
$4^x = 4^{-3}$
$x = -3$

c. $\log_{\frac{1}{2}} x = 5$
$\left(\dfrac{1}{2}\right)^5 = x$
$x = \dfrac{1}{32}$

27. a. $\log_3 3^2 = 2$

b. $\log_7 7^{-1} = -1$

c. $5^{\log_5 3} = 3$

d. $2^{\log_2 6} = 6$

28. a. $4^x = 64$
$\left(2^2\right)^x = 2^6$
$2x = 6$
$x = 3$

b. $8^x = 32$
$\left(2^3\right)^x = 2^5$
$3x = 5$
$x = \dfrac{5}{3}$

c. $9^{x+4} = 243^x$
$(3^2)^{x+4} = (3^5)^x$
$3^{2x+8} = 3^{5x}$
$2x + 8 = 5x$
$8 = 3x$
$x = \dfrac{8}{3}$

29. a. $\log_{11} 10 + \log_{11} 3 = \log_{11}(10 \cdot 3) = \log_{11} 30$

b. $\log_3 \dfrac{1}{2} + \log_3 12 = \log_3\left(\dfrac{1}{2} \cdot 12\right) = \log_3 6$

c. $\log_2(x+2) + \log_2 x = \log_2[(x+2)x]$
$= \log_2(x^2 + 2x)$

30. a. $\log 100,000 = \log_{10} 10^5 = 5$

b. $\log 10^{-3} = \log_{10} 10^{-3} = -3$

c. $\ln \sqrt[5]{e} = \ln e^{1/5} = \dfrac{1}{5}$

d. $\ln e^4 = 4$

31. $A = Pe^{rt}$
$A = 1600e^{0.09(5)} \approx 2509.30$
$2509.30 is owed after 5 years.

32. a. $\log_6 5 + \log_6 4 = \log_6(5 \cdot 4) = \log_6 20$

b. $\log_8 12 - \log_8 4 = \log_8 \dfrac{12}{4} = \log_8 3$

c. $2\log_2 x + 3\log_2 x - 2\log_2(x-1)$
$= 5\log_2 x - \log_2(x-1)^2$
$= \log_2 x^5 - \log_2(x-1)^2$
$= \log_2 \dfrac{x^5}{(x-1)^2}$

33. $3^x = 7$
$\log 3^x = \log 7$
$x \log 3 = \log 7$
$x = \dfrac{\log 7}{\log 3} \approx 1.7712$

34. $10,000 = 5000\left(1 + \dfrac{0.02}{4}\right)^{4t}$
$2 = (1.005)^{4t}$
$\ln 2 = \ln 1.005^{4t}$
$\ln 2 = 4t \ln(1.005)$
$t = \dfrac{\ln 2}{4\ln 1.005} \approx 34.7$
It takes 34.7 years.

35. $\log_4(x-2) = 2$
$$4^2 = x - 2$$
$$x - 2 = 16$$
$$x = 18$$

36. $\log_4 10 - \log_4 x = 2$
$$\log_4 \frac{10}{x} = 2$$
$$4^2 = \frac{10}{x}$$
$$16 = \frac{10}{x}$$
$$16x = 10$$
$$x = \frac{5}{8}$$

37. $\dfrac{x^2}{16} - \dfrac{y^2}{25} = 1$

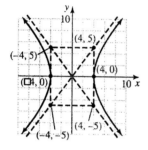

38. $(8, 5), (-2, 4)$
$$d = \sqrt{(-2-8)^2 + (4-5)^2} = \sqrt{101} \text{ units}$$

39. $\begin{cases} y = \sqrt{x} \\ x^2 + y^2 = 6 \end{cases}$

Replace y with $\sqrt{x}$ in the first equation.
$$(x)^2 + (\sqrt{x})^2 = 6$$
$$x^2 + x - 6 = 0$$
$$(x+3)(x-2) = 0$$
$$x = -3 (\text{discard}) \text{ or } x = 2$$
$$x = 2: \; y = \sqrt{x} = \sqrt{2}$$
$$(2, \sqrt{2})$$

40. $\begin{cases} x^2 + y^2 = 36 \\ x - y = 6 \Rightarrow x = y + 6 \end{cases}$

Replace x with $y + 6$ in the first equation.

$$(y+6)^2 + y^2 = 36$$
$$2y^2 + 12y = 0$$
$$2y(y+6) = 0$$

$y = 0$ or $y = -6$
$x = 0 + 6 = 6$ $x = -6 + 6 = 0$
$(0, -6); (6, 0)$

41. $\dfrac{x^2}{9} + \dfrac{y^2}{16} \le 1$

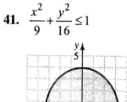

$$\frac{x^2}{9} + \frac{y^2}{16} = 1$$

42.

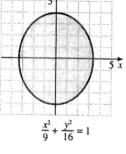

43. $a_n = n^2 - 1$
$$a_1 = 1^2 - 1 = 0$$
$$a_2 = 2^2 - 1 = 3$$
$$a_3 = 3^2 - 1 = 8$$
$$a_4 = 4^2 - 1 = 15$$
$$a_5 = 5^2 - 1 = 24$$

44. $a_n = \dfrac{n}{n+4}$
$$a_8 = \frac{8}{8+4} = \frac{8}{12} = \frac{2}{3}$$

45. $a_1 = 2, \; d = 9 - 2 = 7$
$$a_{11} = 2 + (11-1)(7) = 72$$

46. $a_1 = 2, \; r = \dfrac{10}{2} = 5$
$$a_6 = 2(5)^{6-1} = 2(5)^5 = 6250$$

47. a. $\displaystyle\sum_{i=0}^{6}\frac{i-2}{2}=\frac{0-2}{2}+\frac{1-2}{2}+\frac{2-2}{2}+\frac{3-2}{2}+\frac{4-2}{2}+\frac{5-2}{2}+\frac{6-2}{2}$

$$=-1-\frac{1}{2}+0+\frac{1}{2}+1+\frac{3}{2}+2$$

$$=\frac{7}{2}$$

b. $\displaystyle\sum_{i=3}^{5}2^{i}=2^{3}+2^{4}+2^{5}=8+16+32=56$

48. a. $\displaystyle\sum_{i=0}^{4}i(i+1)=0(0+1)+1(1+1)+2(2+1)+3(3+1)+4(4+1)$

$$=0+2+6+12+20$$

$$=40$$

b. $\displaystyle\sum_{i=0}^{3}2^{i}=2^{0}+2^{1}+2^{2}+2^{3}=1+2+4+8=15$

49. $a_{1}=1,\ a_{30}=30$

$$S_{n}=\frac{n}{2}(a_{1}+a_{n})=\frac{30}{2}(1+30)=465$$

50. $(x-y)^{6}$ where $a=x,\ b=-y,\ n=6,$ and $r=2.$

$$\frac{6!}{2!(6-2)!}x^{6-2}y^{2}=15x^{4}y^{2}$$

The third term in the expansion of $(x-y)^{6}$ is $15x^{4}y^{2}.$

Appendix A

A.2 Practice Final Exam

1. $6[5+2(3-8)-3] = 6[5+2(-5)-3]$
$$= 6[5+(-10)-3]$$
$$= 6[-5-3]$$
$$= 6[-8]$$
$$= -48$$

2. $-3^4 = -(3^4) = -81$

3. $4^{-3} = \dfrac{1}{4^3} = \dfrac{1}{64}$

4. $\dfrac{1}{2} - \dfrac{5}{6} = \dfrac{1}{2} \cdot \dfrac{3}{3} - \dfrac{5}{6} = \dfrac{3}{6} - \dfrac{5}{6} = \dfrac{-2}{6} = -\dfrac{1}{3}$

5. $(5x^3 + x^2 + 5x - 2) - (8x^3 - 4x^2 + x - 7)$
$$= 5x^3 + x^2 + 5x - 2 - 8x^3 + 4x^2 - x + 7$$
$$= 5x^3 - 8x^3 + x^2 + 4x^2 + 5x - x - 2 + 7$$
$$= -3x^3 + 5x^2 + 4x + 5$$

6. $(4x-2)^2 = (4x)^2 - 2(4x)(2) + 2^2$
$$= 16x^2 - 16x + 4$$

7. $(3x+7)(x^2+5x+2)$
$$= 3x(x^2+5x+2) + 7(x^2+5x+2)$$
$$= 3x^3 + 15x^2 + 6x + 7x^2 + 35x + 14$$
$$= 3x^3 + 22x^2 + 41x + 14$$

8. $y^2 - 8y - 48 = (y-12)(y+4)$

9. $9x^3 + 39x^2 + 12x = 3x(3x^2 + 13x + 4)$
$$= 3x(3x+1)(x+4)$$

10. $180 - 5x^2 = 5(36 - x^2)$
$$= 5(6^2 - x^2)$$
$$= 5(6+x)(6-x)$$

11. $3a^2 + 3ab - 7a - 7b = 3a(a+b) - 7(a+b)$
$$= (a+b)(3a-7)$$

12. $8y^3 - 64 = 8(y^3 - 8)$
$$= 8(y^3 - 2^3)$$
$$= 8(y-2)(y^2 + y \cdot 2 + 2^2)$$
$$= 8(y-2)(y^2 + 2y + 4)$$

13. $\left(\dfrac{x^2 y^3}{x^3 y^{-4}}\right)^2 = \left(\dfrac{y^{3-(-4)}}{x^{3-2}}\right)^2 = \left(\dfrac{y^7}{x^1}\right)^2 = \dfrac{y^{7\cdot2}}{x^{1\cdot2}} = \dfrac{y^{14}}{x^2}$

14. $-4(a+1) - 3a = -7(2a-3)$
$$-4a - 4 - 3a = -14a + 21$$
$$-7a - 4 = -14a + 21$$
$$7a - 4 = 21$$
$$7a = 25$$
$$a = \dfrac{25}{7}$$

15. $3x - 5 \geq 7x + 3$
$$-5 \geq 4x + 3$$
$$-8 \geq 4x$$
$$-2 \geq x$$
$$x \leq -2$$
$$(-\infty, -2]$$

16. $x(x+6) = 7$
$$x^2 + 6x = 7$$
$$x^2 + 6x - 7 = 0$$
$$(x+7)(x-1) = 0$$
$$x + 7 = 0 \quad \text{or} \quad x - 1 = 0$$
$$x = -7 \qquad\qquad x = 1$$

17. $5x - 7y = 10$

x	y
2	0
0	$-\dfrac{10}{7}$

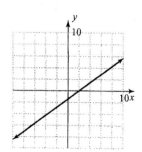

690

18. $x - 3 = 0$

$\qquad x = 3$

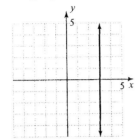

19. $m = \dfrac{y_2 - y_1}{x_2 - x_1}$

$m = \dfrac{2 - (-5)}{-1 - 6} = \dfrac{2 + 5}{-7} = \dfrac{7}{-7} = -1$

20. $-3x + y = 5$

$\qquad y = 3x + 5$

$m = 3$

21. $(x_1, y_1) = (2, -5), (x_2, y_2) = (1, 3)$

$m = \dfrac{y_2 - y_1}{x_2 - x_1} = \dfrac{3 - (-5)}{1 - 2} = \dfrac{3 + 5}{-1} = \dfrac{8}{-1} = -8$

$y - y_1 = m(x - x_1)$

$y - (-5) = -8(x - 2)$

$y + 5 = -8x + 16$

$8x + y = 11$

22. A line parallel to $x = 7$ is a vertical line. The vertical line through $(-5, -1)$ has equation $x = -5$.

23. $\begin{cases} \dfrac{1}{2}x + 2y = -\dfrac{15}{4} \\ 4x = -y \end{cases}$

Solve the second equation for y.

$y = -4x$

Substitute $-4x$ for y in the first equation.

$\dfrac{1}{2}x + 2(-4x) = -\dfrac{15}{4}$

$\dfrac{1}{2}x - 8x = -\dfrac{15}{4}$

$\dfrac{1}{2}x - \dfrac{16x}{2} = -\dfrac{15}{4}$

$-\dfrac{15}{2}x = -\dfrac{15}{4}$

$-\dfrac{2}{15}\left(-\dfrac{15}{2}x\right) = -\dfrac{2}{15}\left(-\dfrac{15}{4}\right)$

$x = \dfrac{1}{2}$

Let $x = \dfrac{1}{2}$ in $y = -4x$.

$y = -4x = -4\left(\dfrac{1}{2}\right) = -2$

The solution is $\left(\dfrac{1}{2}, -2\right)$.

24. $\begin{cases} 4x - 6y = 7 \\ -2x + 3y = 0 \end{cases}$

Multiply the second equation by 2 and add the result to the first equation.

$\begin{array}{r} 4x - 6y = 7 \\ -4x + 6y = 0 \\ \hline 0 = 7 \end{array}$

The statement $0 = 7$ is false, so the system has no solution.

25. $3x + 2 \overline{\smash{\big)}\, 27x^3 + 0x^2 + 0x - 8}$ gives quotient $9x^2 - 6x + 4$

$\begin{array}{r} 9x^2 - 6x + 4 \\ 3x + 2 \overline{\smash{\big)}\, 27x^3 + 0x^2 + 0x - 8} \\ \underline{27x^3 + 18x^2} \\ -18x^2 + 0x \\ \underline{-18x^2 - 12x} \\ 12x - 8 \\ \underline{12x + 8} \\ -16 \end{array}$

$\dfrac{27x^3 - 8}{3x + 2} = 9x^2 - 6x + 4 - \dfrac{16}{3x + 2}$

26. $h(x) = x^3 - x$

a. $h(-1) = (-1)^3 - (-1) = -1 + 1 = 0$

b. $h(0) = 0^3 - 0 = 0 - 0 = 0$

c. $h(4) = 4^3 - 4 = 64 - 4 = 60$

27. Domain: $(-\infty, \infty)$
Range: $(-\infty, 4]$

28. Let x be the smaller area code. Then the other area code is $2x$.
$x + 2x = 1203$
$3x = 1203$
$x = 401$
$2x = 2(401) = 802$
The area codes are 401 (Rhode Island) and 802 (Vermont).

29. Let x be the number of hours since the trains left. One train will have traveled $50x$ miles and the other will have traveled $64x$ miles.
$50x + 64x = 285$
$114x = 285$
$x = \dfrac{285}{114} = \dfrac{5}{2}$ or $2\dfrac{1}{2}$

The trains are 285 miles apart after $2\dfrac{1}{2}$ hours.

30. Let x be the amount of 12% solution.

Amount	Percent	Total Saline
x	$12\% = 0.12$	$0.12x$
80	$22\% = 0.22$	$0.22 \cdot 80 = 17.6$
$80 + x$	$16\% = 0.16$	$0.16(80 + x)$ $= 12.8 + 0.16x$

$0.12x + 17.6 = 12.8 + 0.16x$
$4.8 = 0.04x$
$120 = x$
120 cc of 12% saline solution should be added.

31. $x^2 + 4x + 3 = 0$
$(x + 1)(x + 3) = 0$
$x + 1 = 0$ or $x + 3 = 0$
$x = -1$ $x = -3$
The domain of $g(x)$ is
$\{x | x$ is a real number, $x \neq -1, x \neq -3\}$.

32. $\dfrac{15x}{2x+5} - \dfrac{6-4x}{2x+5} = \dfrac{15x-(6-4x)}{2x+5}$
$= \dfrac{15x-6+4x}{2x+5}$
$= \dfrac{19x-6}{2x+5}$

33. $\dfrac{x^2-9}{x^2-3x} \div \dfrac{xy+5x+3y+15}{2x+10}$
$= \dfrac{x^2-9}{x^2-3x} \cdot \dfrac{2x+10}{xy+5x+3y+15}$
$= \dfrac{(x+3)(x-3) \cdot 2(x+5)}{x(x-3) \cdot (y+5)(x+3)}$
$= \dfrac{2(x+5)}{x(y+5)}$

34. $a^2 - a - 6 = (a-3)(a+2)$
LCD $= (a-3)(a+2)$
$\dfrac{5a}{a^2-a-6} - \dfrac{2}{a-3}$
$= \dfrac{5a}{(a-3)(a+2)} - \dfrac{2 \cdot (a+2)}{(a-3) \cdot (a+2)}$
$= \dfrac{5a - 2(a+2)}{(a-3)(a+2)}$
$= \dfrac{5a - 2a - 4}{(a-3)(a+2)}$
$= \dfrac{3a - 4}{(a-3)(a+2)}$

35. $\dfrac{5 - \frac{1}{y^2}}{\frac{1}{y} + \frac{2}{y^2}} = \dfrac{y^2\left(5 - \frac{1}{y^2}\right)}{y^2\left(\frac{1}{y} + \frac{2}{y^2}\right)} = \dfrac{5y^2 - 1}{y + 2}$

36. $\dfrac{4}{y} - \dfrac{5}{3} = -\dfrac{1}{5}$
$15y\left(\dfrac{4}{y}\right) - 15y\left(\dfrac{5}{3}\right) = 15y\left(-\dfrac{1}{5}\right)$
$60 - 25y = -3y$
$60 = 22y$
$\dfrac{60}{22} = y$
$\dfrac{30}{11} = y$

37. $\dfrac{5}{y+1} = \dfrac{4}{y+2}$
$5(y+2) = 4(y+1)$
$5y + 10 = 4y + 4$
$y + 10 = 4$
$y = -6$

38.
$$\frac{a}{a-3} = \frac{3}{a-3} - \frac{3}{2}$$
$$2(a-3)\left(\frac{a}{a-3}\right) = 2(a-3)\left(\frac{3}{a-3}\right) - 2(a-3)\left(\frac{3}{2}\right)$$
$$2a = 6 - 3(a-3)$$
$$2a = 6 - 3a + 9$$
$$2a = 15 - 3a$$
$$5a = 15$$
$$a = 3$$

In the original equation, $a = 3$ makes a denominator 0, so it is extraneous. The equation has no solution.

39. Let x be the number.
$$x + 5 \cdot \frac{1}{x} = 6$$
$$x\left(x + \frac{5}{x}\right) = x \cdot 6$$
$$x^2 + 5 = 6x$$
$$x^2 - 6x + 5 = 0$$
$$(x-1)(x-5) = 0$$
$$x - 1 = 0 \quad \text{or} \quad x - 5 = 0$$
$$x = 1 \qquad\qquad x = 5$$
The number is 1 or 5.

40. $\sqrt{216} = \sqrt{36 \cdot 6} = \sqrt{36} \cdot \sqrt{6} = 6\sqrt{6}$

41. $\left(\frac{1}{125}\right)^{-1/3} = 125^{1/3} = \sqrt[3]{125} = \sqrt[3]{5^3} = 5$

42. $\left(\frac{64c^{4/3}}{a^{-2/3}b^{5/6}}\right)^{1/2} = \frac{64^{1/2}c^{\frac{4}{3} \cdot \frac{1}{2}}}{a^{-\frac{2}{3} \cdot \frac{1}{2}}b^{\frac{5}{6} \cdot \frac{1}{2}}}$

$$= \frac{8c^{2/3}}{a^{-1/3}b^{5/12}}$$

$$= \frac{8a^{1/3}c^{2/3}}{b^{5/12}}$$

43. $\sqrt{125x^3} - 3\sqrt{20x^3} = \sqrt{25x^2 \cdot 5x} - 3\sqrt{4x^2 \cdot 5x}$

$$= 5x\sqrt{5x} - 3 \cdot 2x\sqrt{5x}$$
$$= 5x\sqrt{5x} - 6x\sqrt{5x}$$
$$= (5x - 6x)\sqrt{5x}$$
$$= -x\sqrt{5x}$$

44. $\left(\sqrt{5}+5\right)\left(\sqrt{5}-5\right) = \left(\sqrt{5}\right)^2 - 5^2 = 5 - 25 = -20$

45.
$$|6x - 5| - 3 = -2$$
$$|6x - 5| = 1$$
$$6x - 5 = -1 \quad \text{or} \quad 6x - 5 = 1$$
$$6x = 4 \quad \text{or} \qquad 6x = 6$$
$$x = \frac{4}{6} \quad \text{or} \qquad x = 1$$
$$x = \frac{2}{3}$$
Both solutions check.

46.
$$-3 < 2(x - 3) \le 4$$
$$-3 < 2x - 6 \le 4$$
$$-3 + 6 < 2x - 6 + 6 \le 4 + 6$$
$$3 < 2x \le 10$$
$$\frac{3}{2} < \frac{2x}{2} \le \frac{10}{2}$$
$$\frac{3}{2} < x \le 5$$
$$\left(\frac{3}{2}, 5\right]$$

47.
$$|3x + 1| > 5$$
$$3x + 1 < -5 \quad \text{or} \quad 3x + 1 > 5$$
$$3x < -6 \qquad\qquad 3x > 4$$
$$x < -2 \qquad\qquad x > \frac{4}{3}$$
$$(-\infty, -2) \cup \left(\frac{4}{3}, \infty\right)$$

48.
$$y^2 - 3y = 5$$
$$y^2 - 3y - 5 = 0$$
$$y = \frac{-(-3) \pm \sqrt{(-3)^2 - 4(1)(-5)}}{2(1)}$$
$$y = \frac{3 \pm \sqrt{9 + 20}}{2}$$
$$y = \frac{3 \pm \sqrt{29}}{2}$$

49.
$$x = \sqrt{x - 2} + 2$$
$$x - 2 = \sqrt{x - 2}$$
$$(x - 2)^2 = \left(\sqrt{x - 2}\right)^2$$
$$x^2 - 4x + 4 = x - 2$$
$$x^2 - 5x + 6 = 0$$
$$(x - 2)(x - 3) = 0$$
$$x - 2 = 0 \quad \text{or} \quad x - 3 = 0$$
$$x = 2 \quad \text{or} \qquad x = 3$$

50.
$$2x^2 - 7x > 15$$
$$2x^2 - 7x - 15 > 0$$
$$(2x+3)(x-5) > 0$$
$$2x+3 = 0 \quad \text{or} \quad x-5 = 0$$
$$x = -\frac{3}{2} \quad \text{or} \quad x = 5$$

51. $y > -4x$

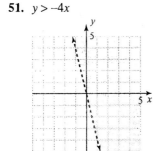

52. $g(x) = -|x+2| - 1$

x	$g(x) = -|x+2| - 1$	$g(x)$
-5	$-|-5+2| - 1 = -4$	-4
-4	$-|-4+2| - 1 = -3$	-3
-3	$-|-3+2| - 1 = -2$	-2
-2	$-|-2+2| - 1 = -1$	-1
-1	$-|-1+2| - 1 = -2$	-2
0	$-|0+2| - 1 = -3$	-3
1	$-|1+2| - 1 = -4$	-4

Domain: All real numbers, $(-\infty, \infty)$
Range: $(-\infty, -1]$

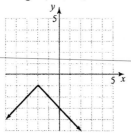

53. $h(x) = x^2 - 4x + 4$

x-intercept: Let $h(x) = 0$ and solve for x.
$$0 = x^2 - 4x + 4$$
$$0 = (x-2)^2$$
$$x - 2 = 0$$
$$x = 2$$

x-intercept: $(2, 0)$
y-intercept: Let $x = 0$.
$$h(0) = 0^2 - 4(0) + 4 = 4$$
y-intercept: $(0, 4)$
x-coordinate of vertex:
$$-\frac{b}{2a} = -\frac{-4}{2(1)} = 2$$
vertex: $(2, 0)$

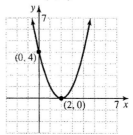

54. $f(x) = \begin{cases} -\dfrac{1}{2}x & \text{if} \quad x \le 0 \\ 2x - 3 & \text{if} \quad x > 0 \end{cases}$

If $x \le 0$

x	$-\frac{1}{2}x$	$f(x)$
0	$-\frac{1}{2}(0)$	0
-2	$-\frac{1}{2}(-2)$	1
-4	$-\frac{1}{2}(-4)$	2

If $x > 0$

x	$2x - 3$	$f(x)$
1	$2(1) - 3$	-1
2	$2(2) - 3$	1
3	$2(3) - 3$	3

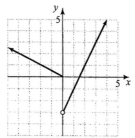

Domain: $(-\infty, \infty)$
Range: $(-3, \infty)$

55. through $(4, -2)$ and $(6, -3)$

$$\text{slope} = m = \frac{y_2 - y_1}{x_2 - x_1} = \frac{-3 - (-2)}{6 - 4} = \frac{-1}{2}$$

$$y - y_1 = m(x - x_1)$$

$$y - (-2) = -\frac{1}{2}(x - 4)$$

$$y + 2 = -\frac{1}{2}x + 2$$

$$y = -\frac{1}{2}x$$

$$f(x) = -\frac{1}{2}x$$

56. through $(-1, 2)$ and perpendicular to $3x - y = 4$

Find the slope of $3x - y = 4$ by writing the equation in slope-intercept form.

$$3x - y = 4$$

$$-y = -3x + 4$$

$$y = 3x - 4$$

The slope is 3. The slope of a line perpendicular to this line is $-\frac{1}{3}$.

Substitute $m = -\frac{1}{3}$ and $(x_1, y_1) = (-1, 2)$ in the equation:

$$y - y_1 = m(x - x_1)$$

$$y - 2 = -\frac{1}{3}[x - (-1)]$$

$$y - 2 = -\frac{1}{3}(x + 1)$$

$$y - 2 = -\frac{1}{3}x - \frac{1}{3}$$

$$y = -\frac{1}{3}x + \frac{5}{3}$$

$$f(x) = -\frac{1}{3}x + \frac{5}{3}$$

57. $(x_1, y_1) = (-6, 3);\ (x_2, y_2) = (-8, -7)$

$$d = \sqrt{(x_2 - x_1)^2 + (y_2 - y_1)^2}$$

$$= \sqrt{[-8 - (-6)]^2 + (-7 - 3)^2}$$

$$= \sqrt{(-2)^2 + (-10)^2}$$

$$= \sqrt{4 + 100}$$

$$= \sqrt{104}$$

$$= 2\sqrt{26}\ \text{units}$$

58. $(x_1, y_1) = (-2, -5);\ (x_2, y_2) = (-6, 12)$

$$\text{midpoint} = \left(\frac{x_1 + x_2}{2}, \frac{y_1 + y_2}{2}\right)$$

$$= \left(\frac{-2 + (-6)}{2}, \frac{-5 + 12}{2}\right)$$

$$= \left(\frac{-8}{2}, \frac{7}{2}\right)$$

$$= \left(-4, \frac{7}{2}\right)$$

59. $$\sqrt{\frac{9}{y}} = \frac{\sqrt{9}}{\sqrt{y}} = \frac{\sqrt{9}}{\sqrt{y}} \cdot \frac{\sqrt{y}}{\sqrt{y}} = \frac{\sqrt{9} \cdot \sqrt{y}}{\sqrt{y} \cdot \sqrt{y}} = \frac{3\sqrt{y}}{y}$$

60. $$\frac{4 - \sqrt{x}}{4 + 2\sqrt{x}} = \frac{4 - \sqrt{x}}{4 + 2\sqrt{x}} \cdot \frac{4 - 2\sqrt{x}}{4 - 2\sqrt{x}}$$

$$= \frac{\left(4 - \sqrt{x}\right)\left(4 - 2\sqrt{x}\right)}{\left(4 + 2\sqrt{x}\right)\left(4 - 2\sqrt{x}\right)}$$

$$= \frac{16 - 12\sqrt{x} + 2x}{16 - 4x}$$

$$= \frac{2\left(8 - 6\sqrt{x} + x\right)}{2(8 - 2x)}$$

$$= \frac{8 - 6\sqrt{x} + x}{8 - 2x}$$

61. $W = \dfrac{k}{V}$

Find k by substituting $W = 20$ and $V = 12$.

$$20 = \frac{k}{12}$$

$$240 = k$$

Write the inverse relation equation.

$$W = \frac{240}{V}$$

Let $V = 15$ and find W.

$$W = \frac{240}{15}$$

$$W = 16$$

62. Use the Pythagorean Theorem.

$$c^2 = a^2 + b^2$$

$$20^2 = x^2 + (x + 8)^2$$

$$400 = x^2 + x^2 + 16x + 64$$

$$0 = 2x^2 + 16x - 336$$

$$0 = 2(x^2 + 8x - 168)$$

$$x = \frac{-8 \pm \sqrt{8^2 - 4(1)(-168)}}{2(1)}$$

$$x = \frac{-8 \pm \sqrt{736}}{2}$$

$x \approx -17.6$ or $x \approx 9.6$
Discard a negative distance.
$x + 8 + x = 9.6 + 8 + 9.6 = 27.2$
$27.2 - 20 = 7.2$ or about 7
A person saves about 7 feet.

63. a. Find the vertex.

$$s(t) = -16t^2 + 32t + 256$$

t-value: $\dfrac{-b}{2a} = \dfrac{-32}{2(-16)} = 1$

$s(t)$-value:

$s(1) = -16(1)^2 + 32(1) + 256 = 272$

The maximum height is 272 feet.

b. Let $s(t) = 0$ and solve for t.

$0 = -16t^2 + 32t + 256$

$0 = -16(t^2 - 2t - 16)$

$$t = \frac{-(-2) \pm \sqrt{(-2)^2 - 4(1)(-16)}}{2(1)}$$

$$t = \frac{2 \pm \sqrt{68}}{2}$$

$$t = \frac{2 \pm 2\sqrt{17}}{2}$$

$t = 1 \pm \sqrt{17}$

$t \approx -3.12$ or $t \approx 5.12$
Discard a negative time.
The stone will hit the water in
approximately 5.12 seconds.

64. $-\sqrt{-8} = -\sqrt{4 \cdot (-1) \cdot 2} = -\sqrt{4} \cdot \sqrt{-1} \cdot \sqrt{2} = -2i\sqrt{2}$

65. $(12 - 6i) - (12 - 3i) = 12 - 6i - 12 + 3i$
$\qquad\qquad\qquad\qquad = 12 - 12 - 6i + 3i$
$\qquad\qquad\qquad\qquad = 0 - 3i$
$\qquad\qquad\qquad\qquad = -3i$

66. $(4 + 3i)^2 = (4 + 3i)(4 + 3i)$
$\qquad\qquad\quad = 16 + 12i + 12i + 9i^2$
$\qquad\qquad\quad = 16 + 24i - 9$
$\qquad\qquad\quad = 7 + 24i$

67. $\dfrac{1 + 4i}{1 - i} = \dfrac{1 + 4i}{1 - i} \cdot \dfrac{1 + i}{1 + i}$

$\qquad\quad = \dfrac{(1 + 4i)(1 + i)}{(1 - i)(1 + i)}$

$\qquad\quad = \dfrac{1 + 5i + 4i^2}{1 - i^2}$

$\qquad\quad = \dfrac{1 + 5i - 4}{1 - (-1)}$

$\qquad\quad = \dfrac{-3 + 5i}{2}$

$\qquad\quad = -\dfrac{3}{2} + \dfrac{5}{2}i$

68. $g(x) = x - 7$ and $h(x) = x^2 - 6x + 5$

$(g \circ h)(x) = (x^2 - 6x + 5) - 7 = x^2 - 6x - 2$

69. $f(x) = 6 - 2x$ is a one-to-one function since there
is only one $f(x)$ value for each x-value.
$\qquad\qquad\qquad\qquad\qquad\qquad$ Inverse:

$y = 6 - 2x \qquad\qquad \Rightarrow \qquad\qquad x = 6 - 2y$

$\qquad\qquad\qquad\qquad\qquad\qquad\qquad x + 2y = 6$

$\qquad\qquad\qquad\qquad\qquad\qquad\qquad 2y = -x + 6$

$\qquad\qquad\qquad\qquad\qquad\qquad\qquad y = \dfrac{-x + 6}{2}$

$\qquad\qquad\qquad\qquad\qquad\qquad\qquad f^{-1}(x) = \dfrac{-x + 6}{2}$

70. $\log_5 x + 3\log_5 x - \log_5(x + 1)$

$\quad = \log_5 x + \log_5 x^3 - \log_5(x + 1)$

$\quad = \log_5 x \cdot x^3 - \log_5(x + 1)$

$\quad = \log_5 x^4 - \log_5(x + 1)$

$\quad = \log_5 \dfrac{x^4}{x + 1}$

71. $8^{x-1} = \dfrac{1}{64}$

$\quad (2^3)^{x-1} = \dfrac{1}{2^6}$

$\quad 2^{3(x-1)} = 2^{-6}$

$\quad 3(x - 1) = -6$

$\quad 3x - 3 = -6$

$\quad 3x = -3$

$\quad x = -1$

72.
$$3^{2x+5} = 4$$
$$\log 3^{2x+5} = \log 4$$
$$(2x+5)\log 3 = \log 4$$
$$2x+5 = \frac{\log 4}{\log 3}$$
$$2x = \frac{\log 4}{\log 3} - 5$$
$$x = \frac{1}{2}\left(\frac{\log 4}{\log 3} - 5\right)$$
$$x \approx -1.8691$$

73. $\log_8(3x-2) = 2$
$$8^2 = 3x - 2$$
$$64 = 3x - 2$$
$$66 = 3x$$
$$22 = x$$

74. $\log_4(x+1) - \log_4(x-2) = 3$
$$\log_4 \frac{x+1}{x-2} = 3$$
$$4^3 = \frac{x+1}{x-2}$$
$$64 = \frac{x+1}{x-2}$$
$$64(x-2) = x+1$$
$$64x - 128 = x + 1$$
$$63x = 129$$
$$x = \frac{129}{63} = \frac{43}{21}$$

75.
$$\ln\sqrt{e} = x$$
$$\ln e^{1/2} = x$$
$$\frac{1}{2}\ln e = x$$
$$\frac{1}{2} = x$$

76. $y = \left(\frac{1}{2}\right)^x + 1$

x	$\left(\frac{1}{2}\right)^x + 1$	y
-3	$\left(\frac{1}{2}\right)^{-3} + 1 = 9$	9
-2	$\left(\frac{1}{2}\right)^{-2} + 1 = 5$	5
-1	$\left(\frac{1}{2}\right)^{-1} + 1 = 3$	3
0	$\left(\frac{1}{2}\right)^{0} + 1 = 2$	2
1	$\left(\frac{1}{2}\right)^{1} + 1 = 1\frac{1}{2}$	$1\frac{1}{2}$
2	$\left(\frac{1}{2}\right)^{2} + 1 = 1\frac{1}{4}$	$1\frac{1}{4}$
3	$\left(\frac{1}{2}\right)^{3} + 1 = 1\frac{1}{8}$	$1\frac{1}{8}$

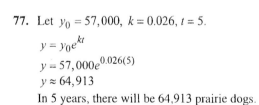

77. Let $y_0 = 57,000$, $k = 0.026$, $t = 5$.
$$y = y_0 e^{kt}$$
$$y = 57,000 e^{0.026(5)}$$
$$y \approx 64,913$$
In 5 years, there will be 64,913 prairie dogs.

78. $x^2 - y^2 = 36$
$$x^2 - y^2 = 6^2$$

hyperbola, with x-intercepts $(-6, 0)$, $(6, 0)$

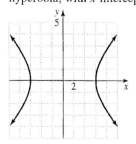

79. $16x^2 + 9y^2 = 144$

$$\frac{16x^2}{144} + \frac{9y^2}{144} = \frac{144}{144}$$

$$\frac{x^2}{9} + \frac{y^2}{16} = 1$$

Ellipse, x-intercepts $(-3, 0)$, $(3, 0)$
y-intercepts $(0, -4)$, $(0, 4)$

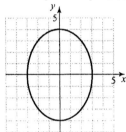

80. $x^2 + y^2 + 6x = 16$

$$(x^2 + 6x + 9) + y^2 = 16 + 9$$

$$(x + 3)^2 + y^2 = 25$$

$$[x - (-3)]^2 + (y - 0)^2 = 5^2$$

circle with center $(-3, 0)$ and radius 5

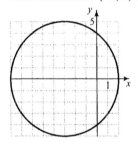

81. $\begin{cases} x^2 + y^2 = 26 \\ x^2 - 2y^2 = 23 \end{cases}$

Multiply equation (2) by -1 and add the equations.

$$\begin{array}{r} x^2 + y^2 = 26 \\ -x^2 + 2y^2 = -23 \\ \hline 3y^2 = 3 \\ y^2 = 1 \\ y = \pm 1 \end{array}$$

Substitute $y = -1$ and $y = 1$ into equation (1).

$$x^2 + (-1)^2 = 26$$

$$x^2 = 25$$

$$x = \pm 5$$

$$x^2 + 1^2 = 26$$

$$x^2 = 25$$

$$x = \pm 5$$

The solutions are $(-5, -1)$, $(-5, 1)$, $(5, -1)$, $(5, 1)$.

82. $a_n = \frac{(-1)^n}{n + 4}$

$$a_1 = \frac{(-1)^1}{1 + 4} = -\frac{1}{5}$$

$$a_2 = \frac{(-1)^2}{2 + 4} = \frac{1}{6}$$

$$a_3 = \frac{(-1)^3}{3 + 4} = -\frac{1}{7}$$

$$a_4 = \frac{(-1)^4}{4 + 4} = \frac{1}{8}$$

$$a_5 = \frac{(-1)^5}{5 + 4} = -\frac{1}{9}$$

The first five terms are $-\frac{1}{5}, \frac{1}{6}, -\frac{1}{7}, \frac{1}{8}, -\frac{1}{9}$.

83. $a_n = 5(2)^{n-1}$

$$a_1 = 5(2)^{1-1} = 5(2)^0 = 5$$

$$r = 2$$

$$n = 5$$

$$S_n = \frac{a_1(1 - r^n)}{1 - r}$$

$$S_5 = \frac{5(1 - 2^5)}{1 - 2} = \frac{5(1 - 32)}{-1} = 155$$

84. Sequence $\frac{3}{2}, -\frac{3}{4}, \frac{3}{8}, \ldots$

$$a_1 = \frac{3}{2}, \ r = -\frac{1}{2}$$

$$S_\infty = \frac{a_1}{1 - r} = \frac{\frac{3}{2}}{1 - \left(-\frac{1}{2}\right)} = \frac{\frac{3}{2}}{\frac{3}{2}} = 1$$

85. $\sum_{i=1}^{4} i(i - 2) = 1(1 - 2) + 2(2 - 2) + 3(3 - 2) + 4(4 - 2)$

$$= 1(-1) + 2(0) + 3(1) + 4(2)$$

$$= -1 + 0 + 3 + 8$$

$$= 10$$

86. $(2x+y)^5 = \binom{5}{0}(2x)^5 + \binom{5}{1}(2x)^4(y) + \binom{5}{2}(2x)^3(y)^2 + \binom{5}{3}(2x)^2(y)^3 + \binom{5}{4}(2x)^1(y)^4 + \binom{5}{5}y^5$

$\quad\quad\quad = 2^5 x^5 + 5 \cdot 2^4 x^4 y + 10 \cdot 2^3 x^3 y^2 + 10 \cdot 2^2 x^2 y^3 + 5 \cdot 2xy^4 + y^5$

$\quad\quad\quad = 32x^5 + 80x^4 y + 80x^3 y^2 + 40x^2 y^3 + 10xy^4 + y^5$

Appendix B

2.
```
    6.3
  × 0.05
  ───────
  0.315
```

4.
```
    0.0036
    7.1200
   32.5020
  + 0.0500
  ─────────
   39.6756
```

6.
```
      1.8
   4)7.2
      4
     ───
     3 2
     3 2
     ───
       0
```

8.
```
                        160
  0.25)40  becomes  25)4000
                       25
                      ────
                       150
                       150
                      ────
                         0
```

10.
```
     3.62
     7.11
    12.36
     4.15
  +  2.29
  ────────
    29.53
```

12.
```
    26.014
  −  7.800
  ─────────
    18.214
```

14.
```
     1.2366
     0.0050
    15.1700
  +  0.9700
  ──────────
    17.3816
```

16.
```
    8.09
  + 0.22
  ──────
    8.31
```

18.
```
    20.00
  − 12.29
  ───────
    7.71
```

20.
```
     8.72
     1.12
    14.86
     3.98
  +  1.99
  ────────
    30.67
```

22. $0.443 \div 100 = 0.00443$

24.
```
    3.706
  − 2.910
  ───────
    0.796
```

26.
```
                        225
  0.28)63  becomes  28)6300
                       56
                      ────
                       70
                       56
                      ────
                       140
                       140
                      ────
                         0
```

28.
```
     0.42
  + 18.00
  ───────
   18.42
```

30.
```
                          2.36
  0.47)1.1092  becomes  47)110.92
                           94
                          ────
                          169
                          141
                          ────
                          282
                          282
                          ────
                            0
```

32.
```
    7.6100
  + 0.0004
  ─────────
    7.6104
```

700

34. $0.6\overline{)444}$ becomes

$$
\begin{array}{r}
740 \\
6\overline{)4440} \\
\underline{42} \\
24 \\
\underline{24} \\
\hline
00
\end{array}
$$

36.
$$
\begin{array}{r}
3.7 \\
+\ 5.6 \\
\hline
9.3
\end{array}
$$

38. $0.54\overline{)19.872}$ becomes

$$
\begin{array}{r}
36.8 \\
54\overline{)1987.2} \\
\underline{162} \\
367 \\
\underline{324} \\
43\ 2 \\
\underline{43\ 2} \\
\hline
0
\end{array}
$$

40.
$$
\begin{array}{r}
51.77 \\
+\ \ 3.60 \\
\hline
55.37
\end{array}
$$

Appendix C

Practice Exercises

1.
$$3(x-5) = 6x - 3$$
$$3x - 15 = 6x - 3$$
$$3x - 15 - 6x = 6x - 3 - 6x$$
$$-3x - 15 = -3$$
$$-3x - 15 + 15 = -3 + 15$$
$$-3x = 12$$
$$\frac{-3x}{-3} = \frac{12}{-3}$$
$$x = -4$$

2.
$$\frac{y}{2} - \frac{y}{5} = \frac{1}{4}$$
$$20\left(\frac{y}{2} - \frac{y}{5}\right) = 20\left(\frac{1}{4}\right)$$
$$20\left(\frac{y}{2}\right) - 20\left(\frac{y}{5}\right) = 5$$
$$10y - 4y = 5$$
$$6y = 5$$
$$\frac{6y}{6} = \frac{5}{6}$$
$$y = \frac{5}{6}$$

3.
$$8(x^2 + 3) + 4 = -8x(x + 3) + 19$$
$$8x^2 + 24 + 4 = -8x^2 - 24x + 19$$
$$16x^2 + 24x + 9 = 0$$
$$(4x + 3)(4x + 3) = 0$$
$$4x + 3 = 0 \quad \text{or} \quad 4x + 3 = 0$$
$$4x = -3 \quad \text{or} \quad 4x = -3$$
$$x = -\frac{3}{4} \quad \text{or} \quad x = -\frac{3}{4}$$

The solution is $-\frac{3}{4}$.

4.
$$x - \frac{x-2}{12} = \frac{x+3}{4} + \frac{1}{4}$$
$$12\left(x - \frac{x-2}{12}\right) = 12\left(\frac{x+3}{4} + \frac{1}{4}\right)$$
$$12 \cdot x - 12\left(\frac{x-2}{12}\right) = 12\left(\frac{x+3}{4}\right) + 12 \cdot \frac{1}{4}$$
$$12x - (x - 2) = 3(x + 3) + 3$$
$$12x - x + 2 = 3x + 9 + 3$$
$$11x + 2 = 3x + 12$$
$$11x + 2 - 3x = 3x + 12 - 3x$$
$$8x + 2 = 12$$
$$8x + 2 - 2 = 12 - 2$$
$$8x = 10$$
$$\frac{8x}{8} = \frac{10}{8}$$
$$x = \frac{5}{4}$$

5.
$$4x^2 = \frac{15}{2}x + 1$$
$$2(4x^2) = 2\left(\frac{15}{2}x + 1\right)$$
$$8x^2 = 15x + 2$$
$$8x^2 - 15x - 2 = 0$$
$$(8x + 1)(x - 2) = 0$$
$$8x + 1 = 0 \quad \text{or} \quad x - 2 = 0$$
$$8x = -1$$
$$x = -\frac{1}{8} \quad \text{or} \quad x = 2$$

The solutions are $-\frac{1}{8}$ and 2.

Appendix C.1 Exercise Set

2. $y^2 - 10y + 24 = 0$
$$(y - 4)(y - 6) = 0$$
$$y - 4 = 0 \quad \text{or} \quad y - 6 = 0$$
$$y = 4 \qquad\qquad y = 6$$
The solutions are 4 and 6.

4. $13x - 15x + 8 = 4x + 2 - 24$
$$-2x + 8 = 4x - 22$$
$$8 = 6x - 22$$
$$30 = 6x$$
$$5 = x$$
The solution is 5.

6. $3y^2 - y - 14 = 0$
$(y+2)(3y-7) = 0$
$y+2 = 0 \quad \text{or} \quad 3y-7 = 0$
$\quad y = -2 \qquad\qquad 3y = 7$
$\qquad\qquad\qquad\qquad y = \dfrac{7}{3}$

The solutions are -2 and $\dfrac{7}{3}$.

8. $n^2 + n = 72$
$n^2 + n - 72 = 0$
$(n+9)(n-8) = 0$
$n+9 = 0 \quad \text{or} \quad n-8 = 0$
$\quad n = -9 \qquad\qquad n = 8$
The solutions are -9 and 8.

10. $6(y-4) = 3(y-8)$
$6y - 24 = 3y - 24$
$3y - 24 = -24$
$\quad 3y = 0$
$\quad y = 0$
The solution is 0.

12. $0.3x + 2.4 = 0.1x + 4$
$0.2x + 2.4 = 4$
$\quad 0.2x = 1.6$
$\quad 2x = 16$
$\quad x = 8$
The solution is 8.

14. $n(2n-3) = 2$
$2n^2 - 3n = 2$
$2n^2 - 3n - 2 = 0$
$(2n+1)(n-2) = 0$
$2n+1 = 0 \quad \text{or} \quad n-2 = 0$
$\quad 2n = -1 \qquad\qquad n = 2$
$\quad n = -\dfrac{1}{2}$

The solutions are $-\dfrac{1}{2}$ and 2.

16. $10x - 2(x+4) = 8(x-2) + 6$
$10x - 2x - 8 = 8x - 16 + 6$
$8x - 8 = 8x - 10$
$-8 = -10$
This is a false statement, so the equation has no solution.

18. $\dfrac{a}{2} + \dfrac{7}{4} = 5$
$2a + 7 = 20$
$\quad 2a = 13$
$\quad a = \dfrac{13}{2}$
The solution is $\dfrac{13}{2}$.

20. $n(3+n) = n^2 + 4n$
$3n + n^2 = n^2 + 4n$
$\quad 3n = 4n$
$\quad 0 = n$
The solution is 0.

22. $\dfrac{c^2}{20} - \dfrac{c}{4} + \dfrac{1}{5} = 0$
$c^2 - 5c + 4 = 0$
$(c-1)(c-4) = 0$
$c-1 = 0 \quad \text{or} \quad c-4 = 0$
$\quad c = 1 \qquad\qquad c = 4$
The solutions are 1 and 4.

24. $4(m-6) - m = 8(m-3) - 5m$
$4m - 24 - m = 8m - 24 - 5m$
$3m - 24 = 3m - 24$
$-24 = -24$
This is a true statement, so all real numbers are solutions.

26. $\dfrac{y^2}{30} = \dfrac{y}{15} + \dfrac{1}{2}$
$y^2 = 2y + 15$
$y^2 - 2y - 15 = 0$
$(y+3)(y-5) = 0$
$y+3 = 0 \quad \text{or} \quad y-5 = 0$
$\quad y = -3 \qquad\qquad y = 5$
The solutions are -3 and 5.

28. $\dfrac{5x^2}{6} - \dfrac{7x}{2} + \dfrac{2}{3} = 0$

$5x^2 - 21x + 4 = 0$

$(5x - 1)(x - 4) = 0$

$5x - 1 = 0 \quad \text{or} \quad x - 4 = 0$

$5x = 1 \qquad\qquad x = 4$

$x = \dfrac{1}{5}$

The solutions are $\dfrac{1}{5}$ and 4.

30. $4 - \dfrac{2z + 7}{9} = \dfrac{7 - z}{12}$

$36\left(4 - \dfrac{2z + 7}{9}\right) = 36\left(\dfrac{7 - z}{12}\right)$

$144 - 4(2z + 7) = 3(7 - z)$

$144 - 8z - 28 = 21 - 3z$

$116 - 8z = 21 - 3z$

$116 = 21 + 5z$

$95 = 5z$

$19 = z$

The solution is 19.

32. $\dfrac{n + 1}{8} - \dfrac{2 - n}{3} = \dfrac{5}{6}$

$24\left(\dfrac{n + 1}{8} - \dfrac{2 - n}{3}\right) = 24\left(\dfrac{5}{6}\right)$

$3(n + 1) - 8(2 - n) = 4 \cdot 5$

$3n + 3 - 16 + 8n = 20$

$11n - 13 = 20$

$11n = 33$

$n = 3$

The solution is 3.

34. $y^2 = -5y$

$y^2 + 5y = 0$

$y(y + 5) = 0$

$y = 0 \quad \text{or} \quad y + 5 = 0$

$y = -5$

The solutions are -5 and 0.

36. $z^2 - 4z + 10 = z(z - 5)$

$z^2 - 4z + 10 = z^2 - 5z$

$-4z + 10 = -5z$

$10 = -z$

$-10 = z$

The solution is -10.

38. $7c - 2(3c + 1) = 5(4 - 2c)$

$7c - 6c - 2 = 20 - 10c$

$c - 2 = 20 - 10c$

$11c - 2 = 20$

$11c = 22$

$c = 2$

The solution is 2.

40. $-4(a + 1) - 3a = -7(2a - 3)$

$-4a - 4 - 3a = -14a + 21$

$-7a - 4 = -14a + 21$

$7a - 4 = 21$

$7a = 25$

$a = \dfrac{25}{7}$

The solution is $\dfrac{25}{7}$.

42. $(2x - 1)(x + 2) = -3$

$2x^2 + 3x - 2 = -3$

$2x^2 + 3x + 1 = 0$

$(2x + 1)(x + 1) = 0$

$2x + 1 = 0 \quad \text{or} \quad x + 1 = 0$

$2x = -1 \qquad\qquad x = -1$

$x = -\dfrac{1}{2}$

The solutions are -1 and $-\dfrac{1}{2}$.

44. $\dfrac{x^2}{18} + \dfrac{x}{2} + 1 = 0$

$x^2 + 9x + 18 = 0$

$(x + 6)(x + 3) = 0$

$x + 6 = 0 \quad \text{or} \quad x + 3 = 0$

$x = -6 \qquad\qquad x = -3$

The solutions are -6 and -3.

46. $\dfrac{x^2}{10} + \dfrac{5}{2} = x$

$x^2 + 25 = 10x$

$x^2 - 10x + 25 = 0$

$(x - 5)^2 = 0$

$x - 5 = 0$

$x = 5$

The solution is 5.

48. Answers may vary

50.
$$-7.6y - 10 = -1.1y + 12$$
$$-7.6y - 10 + 10 = -1.1y + 12 + 10$$
$$-7.6y = -1.1y + 22$$

$K = 22$

52.
$$\frac{5x}{4} + \frac{1}{2} = \frac{x}{2}$$
$$4\left(\frac{5x}{4} + \frac{1}{2}\right) = 4\left(\frac{x}{2}\right)$$
$$5x + 2 = 2x$$

$K = 2$

54.
$$-9.112y = -47.537304$$
$$\frac{-9.112y}{-9.112} = \frac{-47.537304}{-9.112}$$
$$y = 5.217$$

Check:
$$-9.112y = -47.537304$$
$$-9.112 \cdot 5.217 \stackrel{?}{=} -47.537304$$
$$-47.537304 = -47.537304$$

The solution is 5.217.

56.
$$1.25x - 20.175 = -8.15$$
$$1.25x - 20.175 + 20.175 = -8.15 + 20.175$$
$$1.25x = 12.025$$
$$\frac{1.25x}{1.25} = \frac{12.025}{1.25}$$
$$x = 9.62$$

Check:
$$1.25x - 20.175 = -8.15$$
$$1.25 \cdot 9.62 - 20.175 \stackrel{?}{=} -8.15$$
$$12.025 - 20.175 \stackrel{?}{=} -8.15$$
$$-8.15 = -8.15$$

The solution is 9.62.

58. The sum of 8 and a number is $8 + x$.

60. The difference of 8 and a number is $8 - x$.

62. 5 subtracted from twice a number is $2x - 5$.

Appendix C.2

Practice Exercises

1. a.

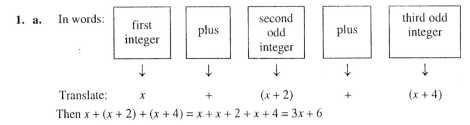

In words:

first integer	plus	second odd integer	plus	third odd integer
↓	↓	↓	↓	↓

Translate: x $+$ $(x + 2)$ $+$ $(x + 4)$

Then $x + (x + 2) + (x + 4) = x + x + 2 + x + 4 = 3x + 6$

b. In words:

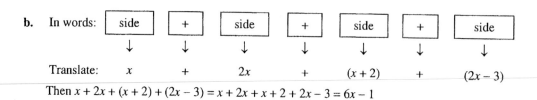

Translate: x + $2x$ + $(x + 2)$ + $(2x - 3)$

Then $x + 2x + (x + 2) + (2x - 3) = x + 2x + x + 2 + 2x - 3 = 6x - 1$

2. If x = number of arrivals and departures at Frankfurt airport, then $x + 15.7$ = number at London, and $x + 1.6$ = number at Paris.

In words:

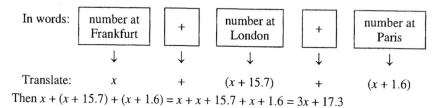

Translate: x + $(x + 15.7)$ + $(x + 1.6)$

Then $x + (x + 15.7) + (x + 1.6) = x + x + 15.7 + x + 1.6 = 3x + 17.3$

3. Let x = the first number, then $3x - 8$ = the second number, and $5x$ = the third number. The sum of the three numbers is 118.

$$x + (3x - 8) + 5x = 118$$
$$x + 3x + 5x - 8 = 118$$
$$9x - 8 = 118$$
$$9x = 126$$
$$x = 14$$

The numbers are 14, $3x - 8 = 3(14) - 8 = 34$, and $5x = 5(14) = 70$.

4. Let x = the original price. Then $0.4x$ = the discount. The original price, minus the discount, is equal to $270.

$$x - 0.4x = 270$$
$$0.6x = 270$$
$$x = \frac{270}{0.6} = 450$$

The original price was $450.

Vocabulary and Readiness Check

1. 130% of a number $\underline{>}$ the number.

2. 70% of a number $\underline{<}$ the number.

3. 100% of a number $\underline{=}$ the number.

4. 200% of a number $\underline{>}$ the number.

	First Integer	All Described Integers
5. Four consecutive integers	31	31, 32, 33, 34
6. Three consecutive odd integers	31	31, 33, 35
7. Three consecutive even integers	18	18, 20, 22
8. Four consecutive even integers	92	92, 94, 96, 98
9. Three consecutive integers	y	$y, y+1, y+2$
10. Three consecutive even integers	$z(z$ is even$)$	$z, z+2, z+4$
11. Four consecutive integers	p	$p, p+1, p+2, p+3$
12. Three consecutive odd integers	s (s is odd)	$s, s+2, s+4$

Appendix C.2 Exercise Set

2. The perimeter is the sum of the lengths of the four sides.
$$x + (x-5) + x + (x-5) = x + x + x + x - 5 - 5$$
$$= 4x - 10$$

4. Let x = first odd integer, then
$x + 2$ = second odd integer, and
$x + 4$ = third odd integer.
$$x + (x+2) + (x+4) = x + x + x + 2 + 4 = 3x + 6$$

6. Find the sum of y quarters worth 25¢ each,
$7y$ dimes worth 10¢ each, and $(2y - 1)$ nickels worth 5¢ each.
$$25y + 10(7y) + 5(2y-1) = 25y + 70y + 10y - 5$$
$$= 105y - 5$$
The total amount is $(105y - 5)$ cents.

8. $4x + 5(3x - 15) = 4x + 15x - 75 = 19x - 75$

10. The length of the side denoted by ? is
$18 - 10 = 8$. Similarly, the length of the unmarked side is
$(x + 14) - (x + 8) = x + 14 - x - 8 = 6$.
The perimeter of the floor plan is
$18 + (x + 8) + 10 + 6 + 8 + (x + 14) = 2x + 64$

12. Let x = the number.
$$2(x+3) = 5x - 1 - 4x$$
$$2x + 6 = x - 1$$
$$x = -7$$
The number is -7.

14. Let x = the first number, then
$x - 6$ = the second number, and
$2x$ = the third number.
$$x + (x - 6) + 2x = 306$$
$$4x - 6 = 306$$
$$4x = 312$$
$$x = 78$$
$x - 6 = 72$
$2x = 156$
The numbers are 78, 72, and 156.

16. $90\% \cdot 70 = 0.90 \cdot 70 = 63$
$70 - 63 = 7$
7 million acres are not federally owned.

18. 25.5% of $958 = 0.255 \cdot 958 \approx 244$
Approximately 244 tornadoes occurred during
April 2006.

20. 9.1% of $17,029,300 = 0.091 \cdot 17,029,300$
$$\approx 1,549,666$$
Approximately 1,549,666 worked in the
restaurant and food service industry in
California.

22. Look for the largest sector, which is 55%.
15–60 minutes is the most common time spent
on e-mail per day.

24. 9% of $278 = 0.09 \cdot 278 = 25.02$
About 25 employees spend between 2 and
3 hours per day using e-mail.

26. Let x = average cost in 2005.
$$x + 0.068x = 96.73$$
$$1.068x = 96.73$$
$$x \approx 90.57$$
The average hotel room cost in 2005 was
$90.57.

28. $3x + x + (x + 10) = 180$
$$5x + 10 = 180$$
$$5x = 170$$
$$x = 34$$
$3x = 3(34) = 102$
$x + 10 = 34 + 10 = 44$
The angles measure $34°$, $44°$, and $102°$.

30. $(2x) + (3.5x) + (3x + 7) = 75$
$$8.5x + 7 = 75$$
$$8.5x = 68$$
$$x = 8$$
$2x = 2(8) = 16$
$3.5x = 3.5(8) = 28$
$3x + 7 = 3(8) + 7 = 31$
The sides measure 16 centimeters,
28 centimeters, and 31 centimeters.

32. $7.3x + (9.2x - 3) + 7.3x + (9.2x - 3) = 324$
$$33x - 6 = 324$$
$$33x = 330$$
$$x = 10$$
$7.3x = 7.3(10) = 73$
$9.2x - 3 = 9.2(10) - 3 = 89$
The sides measure 73 feet, 73 feet, 89 feet, and
89 feet.

34. Let x = the first odd integer, then
$x + 2$ = the second odd integer and
$x + 4$ = the third odd integer.
$$x + x + 2 + x + 4 = 327$$
$$3x + 6 = 327$$
$$3x = 321$$
$$x = 107$$
The numbers are 107, 109, 111.

36. Let x = first integer, then
$x + 1$ = second integer, and
$x + 2$ = third integer.
$$x + (x + 1) + 3(x + 2) = 2637$$
$$x + x + 1 + 3x + 6 = 2637$$
$$5x + 7 = 2637$$
$$5x = 2630$$
$$x = 526$$
$x + 1 = 527$
$x + 2 = 528$
The score for Alabama was 526, for Louisiana
was 527, and for Michigan was 528.

38. $\left(\dfrac{3}{2}x + 1\right) + x + (x - 1) = 105$
$$\dfrac{7}{2}x = 105$$
$$x = 105 \cdot \dfrac{2}{7}$$
$$x = 30$$
$\dfrac{3}{2}x + 1 = \dfrac{3}{2}(30) + 1 = 46$
$x - 1 = 30 - 1 = 29$

Occupation	Percent Increase in Number of Jobs from 2000 to 2012
Computer software engineers	46%
Management analysts	30%
Receptionist and information clerks	29%
Total	105%

40. Let x = thousands of fishers, then
$2x + 8$ = thousands of telephone operators, and
$10x - 1$ = thousands of sewing machine operators
$$x + (2x + 8) + (10x - 1) = 137$$
$$13x + 7 = 137$$
$$13x = 130$$
$$x = 10$$
$2x + 8 = 2(10) + 8 = 28$
$10x - 1 = 10(10) - 1 = 99$
The declines are as follows: telephone operators: 28 thousand;
sewing machine operators: 99 thousand; fishers: 10 thousand.

42. Let x = NY governor's salary, then
$x + 27,500$ = CA governor's salary, and
$x + 27,500 - 120,724$ = AK governor's salary.
$$x + (x + 27,500) + (x + 27,500 - 120,724) = 471,276$$
$$3x - 65,724 = 471,276$$
$$3x = 537,000$$
$$x = 179,000$$
$x + 27,500 = 206,500$
$x + 27,500 - 120,724 = 85,776$
The governor salaries are as follows: CA: \$206,500; NY: \$179,000; AK: \$85,776

44. Let x = price before taxes.
$$x + 0.09x = 158.60$$
$$1.09x = 158.60$$
$$x = 145.50$$
The price of the book was \$145.50.

46. Let x = population in 2005.
$$33.2 = x + 0.015x$$
$$33.2 = 1.015x$$
$$32.7 = x$$
The population in 2005 was 32.7 million.

48. Let x = measure of complement; then $2x + 30$ = measure of angle.
$$x + 2x + 30 = 90$$
$$3x = 60$$
$$x = 20$$
$2x + 30 = 2(20) + 30 = 70$
The angles measure $20°$ and $70°$.

50. Let x = base angle; then $3x - 10$ = third angle.
$$2x + 3x - 10 = 180$$
$$5x - 10 = 180$$
$$5x = 190$$
$$x = 38$$
$3x - 10 = 3 \cdot 38 - 10 = 104$
The angles measure 38°, 38°, and 104°.

52. Let x = length of side of pentagon, then
$x + 7$ = length of side of square.
$$5x = 4(x + 7)$$
$$5x = 4x + 28$$
$$x = 28$$
$x + 7 = 28 + 7 = 35$
The pentagon has a side length of 28 inches and the square has a side length of 35 inches.

54. Let x = first integer, then
$x + 1$ = second integer, and
$x + 2$ = third integer, and
$x + 3$ = fourth integer.
$$(x + 1) + (x + 3) = 110$$
$$2x + 4 = 110$$
$$2x = 106$$
$$x = 53$$
$x + 1 = 54$
$x + 2 = 55$
$x + 3 = 56$
The integers are 53, 54, 55, and 56.

56.
$$(x + 2) + 2x + x + (2x - 3) = 110$$
$$6x - 1 = 110$$
$$6x = 111$$
$$x = 18.5$$
$x + 2 = 18.5 + 2 = 20.5$
$2x = 2(18.5) = 37$
$2x - 3 = 2(18.5) - 3 = 34$
The bases measure 18.5 meters and 37 meters, and the sides measure 20.5 meters and 34 meters.

58.
$$x + (x + 15.7) + (x + 1.6) = 173.9$$
$$3x + 17.3 = 173.9$$
$$3x = 156.6$$
$$x = 52.2$$
$x + 15.7 = 52.2 + 15.7 = 67.9$
$x + 1.6 = 52.2 + 1.6 = 53.8$
The arrivals and departures are as follows:
London: 67.9 million, Paris: 53.8 million, Frankfurt: 52.2 million

60. Let x = height of Galter Pavilion; then
$x + 67$ = height of Guy's Tower and
$x + 47$ = height of Queen Mary
$$x + (x + 67) + (x + 47) = 1320$$
$$3x + 114 = 1320$$
$$3x = 1206$$
$$x = 402$$
$x + 67 = 402 + 67 = 469$
$x + 47 = 402 + 47 = 449$
Galter Pavilion: 402 ft
Guy's Tower: 469 ft
Queen Mary: 449 ft

62. Let x = number of seats in Heinz Field; then
$x + 11,675$ = number of seats in Mile High.
$$x + (x + 11,675) = 140,575$$
$$2x + 11,675 = 140,575$$
$$2x = 128,900$$
$$x = 64,450$$
$x + 11,675 = 64,450 + 11,675 = 76,125$
Mile High stadium has 76,125 seats and Heinz Field has 64,450 seats.

Appendix C.3

Practice Exercises

1. The six points are graphed as shown.

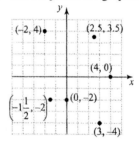

a. $(3, -4)$ lies in quadrant IV.

b. $(0, -2)$ is on the y-axis.

c. $(-2, 4)$ lies in quadrant II.

d. $(4, 0)$ is on the x-axis.

e. $\left(-1\frac{1}{2}, -2\right)$ is in quadrant III.

f. $(2.5, 3.5)$ is in quadrant I.

2. $y = -3x - 2$
This is a linear equation. (In standard form, it is $3x + y = -2$.) Since the equation is solved for y,

we choose three x-values.

Let $x = 0$.

$y = -3x - 2$

$y = -3 \cdot 0 - 2$

$y = -2$

Let $x = -1$.

$y = -3x - 2$

$y = -3(-1) - 2$

$y = 1$

Let $x = -2$.

$y = -3x - 2$

$y = -3(-2) - 2$

$y = 4$

The three ordered pairs $(0, -2)$, $(-1, 1)$, and $(-2, 4)$ are listed in the table.

x	y
0	-2
-1	1
-2	4

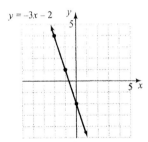

$y = -3x - 2$

3. $y = -\dfrac{1}{2}x$

To avoid fractions, we choose x-values that are multiples of 2. To find the y-intercept, we let $x = 0$.

If $x = 0$, then $y = -\dfrac{1}{2}(0)$, or 0.

If $x = 2$, then $y = -\dfrac{1}{2}(2)$, or -1.

If $x = -2$, then $y = -\dfrac{1}{2}(-2)$, or 1.

x	y
0	0
2	-1
-2	1

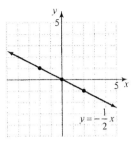

$y = -\dfrac{1}{2}x$

Appendix C.3 Exercise Set

2. Point B is $(2, 5)$.

4. Point D is $(-1, 3)$.

6. Point F is $(-3, 5)$.

8. Point H is $(0, -3)$.

10. $(0, 5)$; y-axis

12. $(-3, 0)$; x-axis

14. $(4, -2)$; QIV

16. $(10, 30)$; QI

18. $(0, 0)$; x- and y-axis

20. $(-42, 17)$; QII

22. $(-x, y)$ lies in quadrant II.

24. $(0, -y)$ lies on the y-axis.

26. $(0, 0)$ is the origin.

28. $y = 2x + 1$

Let $x = 0$.

$y = 2(0) + 1 = 1$

Let $x = -1$.

$y = 2(-1) + 1 = -2 + 1 = -1$

Let $x = 1$.

$y = 2(1) + 1 = 2 + 1 = 3$

x	y
0	1
-1	-1
1	3

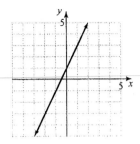

30. $x - 9y = 3$
Let $x = 0$.
$0 - 9y = 3$
$-9y = 3$
$y = -\dfrac{1}{3}$
Let $y = 0$.
$x - 9(0) = 3$
$x = 3$
Let $y = -1$.
$x - 9(-1) = 3$
$x + 9 = 3$
$x = -6$

x	y
0	$-\dfrac{1}{3}$
3	0
-6	-1

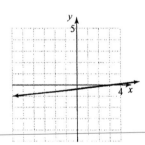

32. $y = \dfrac{3}{2}x$
Let $x = 0$.
$y = \dfrac{3}{2}(0) = 0$
Let $x = 2$.
$y = \dfrac{3}{2}(2) = 3$
Let $x = -2$.
$y = \dfrac{3}{2}(-2) = -3$

x	y
0	0
2	3
-2	-3

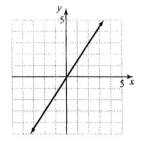

34. $x = -1.5$
This is a vertical line.

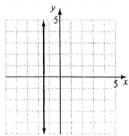

36. The point $(0, 1)$ is on the graph of f.
Thus, $f(0) = 1$.

38. The point $(-1, -2)$ is on the graph of g.
Thus, $g(-1) = -2$.

40. The point on the graph of g with y-value of 0 is $(-2, 0)$. Thus, $g(x) = 0$ when $x = -2$.

42. $f(-1) = 2$

Appendix C.4

Practice Exercises

1. a. $12x^2y - 3xy = 3xy(4x) + 3xy(-1)$
$= 3xy(4x - 1)$

b. $49x^2 - 4 = (7x)^2 - 2^2 = (7x + 2)(7x - 2)$

c. $5x^2 + 2x - 3 = (5x - 3)(x + 1)$

d. $3x^2 + 6 + x^3 + 2x = 3(x^2 + 2) + x(x^2 + 2)$
$= (x^2 + 2)(3 + x)$

e. $4x^2 + 20x + 25 = (2x)^2 + 2 \cdot 2x \cdot 5 + 5^2$
$$= (2x+5)^2$$

f. $b^2 + 100$ cannot be factored.

2. a. $64x^3 + y^3 = (4x)^3 + y^3$
$$= (4x+y)[(4x)^2 - 4x \cdot y + y^2]$$
$$= (4x+y)(16x^2 - 4xy + y^2)$$

b. $7x^2y^2 - 63y^4 = 7y^2(x^2 - 9y^2)$
$$= 7y^2[x^2 - (3y)^2]$$
$$= 7y^2(x-3y)(x+3y)$$

c. $3x^2 + 12x + 12 - 3b^2$
$$= 3(x^2 + 4x + 4 - b^2)$$
$$= 3[(x+2)^2 - b^2]$$
$$= 3(x+2+b)(x+2-b)$$

d. $x^5y^4 + 27x^2y$
$$= x^2y(x^3y^3 + 27)$$
$$= x^2y[(xy)^3 + 3^3]$$
$$= x^2y(xy+3)(x^2y^2 - 3xy + 9)$$

e. $(x+7)^2 - 81y^2 = (x+7)^2 - (9y)^2$
$$= (x+7+9y)(x+7-9y)$$

Appendix C.4 Exercise Set

2. $(5z^4 - 6z^2 + z + 1) - (7z^4 - 2z + 1)$
$$= 5z^4 - 6z^2 + z + 1 - 7z^4 + 2z - 1$$
$$= -2z^4 - 6z^2 + 3z$$

4. $(2x^2 + 6x - 5) + (5x^2 - 10x) = 7x^2 - 4x - 5$

6. $\dfrac{5x^2 - 14x - 3}{5x+1} = \dfrac{(x-3)(5x+1)}{5x+1} = x - 3$

8.
$$\begin{array}{r} x^2 - 3x - 2 \\ \times \qquad 4x - 1 \\ \hline -x^2 + 3x + 2 \\ 4x^3 - 12x^2 - 8x \quad\;\; \\ \hline 4x^3 - 13x^2 - 5x + 2 \end{array}$$

10. $12x^2 - 22x - 20 = 2(6x^2 - 11x - 10)$
$$= 2(3x+2)(2x-5)$$

12. Let $y = 2x + 1$. Then
$$(2x+1)^2 - 3(2x+1) + 2$$
$$= y^2 - 3y + 2$$
$$= (y-2)(y-1)$$
$$= [(2x+1)-2][(2x+1)-1]$$
$$= (2x-1)(2x)$$
$$= 2x(2x-1)$$

14. $24ab^2 - 6ab = 6ab(4b-1)$

16. $9x^2 - 81 = 9(x^2 - 9) = 9(x+3)(x-3)$

18. $5x^2 - 2x - 3 = (5x+3)(x-1)$

20. $6x^2 - 6x - 12 = 6(x^2 - x - 2)$
$$= 6(x-2)(x+1)$$

22. $25x^2 + 40x + 16 = (5x)^2 + 2 \cdot 5x \cdot 4 + 4^2$
$$= (5x+4)^2$$

24. $27x^3 - 64y^3 = (3x)^3 - (4y)^3$
$$= (3x-4y)(9x^2 + 12xy + 16y^2)$$

26. $27x^5y^4 - 216x^2y$
$$= 27x^2y(x^3y^3 - 8)$$
$$= 27x^2y[(xy)^3 - 2^3]$$
$$= 27x^2y(xy-2)(x^2y^2 + 2xy + 4)$$

28. $(y-1)^3 + 27x^3$
$$= (y-1)^3 + (3x)^3$$
$$= [(y-1)+3x][(y-1)^2 - (y-1)(3x) + (3x)^2]$$
$$= (y-1+3x)(y^2 - 2y + 1 - 3xy + 3x + 9x^2)$$

30. Let $y = 4r + 1$. Then
$$(4r+1)^2 + 8(4r+1) + 16 = y^2 + 8y + 16$$
$$= (y+4)(y+4)$$
$$= (y+4)^2$$
$$= [(4r+1)+4]^2$$
$$= (4r+5)^2$$

32. $20x^2 + 23x + 6 = (4x+3)(5x+2)$

34. $20x^2 - 220x + 600 = 20(x^2 - 11x + 30)$
$$= 20(x-6)(x-5)$$

36. $15x^2 - 20x = 5x(3x - 4)$

38. $45m^3n^3 - 27m^2n^2 = 9m^2n^2(5mn - 3)$

40. $x^4 + x = x(x^3 + 1)$
$$= x(x^3 + 1^3)$$
$$= x(x+1)(x^2 - x + 1)$$

42. $20x^3 + 20y^3 = 20(x^3 + y^3)$
$$= 20(x+y)(x^2 - xy + y^2)$$

44. $9y^2 - 42y + 49 = (3y)^2 - 2 \cdot 3y \cdot 7 + 7^2$
$$= (3y - 7)^2$$

46. $y^4 - 16 = (y^2)^2 - 4^2$
$$= (y^2 + 4)(y^2 - 4)$$
$$= (y^2 + 4)(y + 2)(y - 2)$$

48. $2sr + 10s - r - 5 = 2s(r + 5) - 1(r + 5)$
$$= (2s - 1)(r + 5)$$

50. $64a^2 + b^2$ is a prime polynomial.

52. $250x^4 - 16x = 2x(125x^3 - 8)$
$$= 2x[(5x)^3 - 2^3]$$
$$= 2x(5x - 2)(25x^2 + 10x + 4)$$

54. $2a^5 - a^4 + 6a - 3 = a^4(2a - 1) + 3(2a - 1)$
$$= (a^4 + 3)(2a - 1)$$

56. Let $x = c + 2$. Then
$(c+2)^2 - 6(c+2) + 5 = x^2 - 6x + 5$
$$= (x - 5)(x - 1)$$
$$= [(c+2) - 5][(c+2) - 1]$$
$$= (c - 3)(c + 1)$$

Appendix C.5

Practice Exercises

1. a. $\dfrac{\dfrac{2+5n}{3n}}{\dfrac{6n+3}{5n^2 - 3n - 2}}$

$$= \dfrac{2 + 5n}{3n} \cdot \dfrac{3(2n+1)}{(5n+2)(n-1)}$$

$$= \dfrac{2n+1}{n(n-1)}$$

b. $\dfrac{x^3 - 8}{-6x + 12} \cdot \dfrac{6x^2}{x^2 + 2x + 4}$

$$= \dfrac{(x-2)(x^2 + 2x + 4)}{-6(x-2)} \cdot \dfrac{6x^2}{x^2 + 2x + 4}$$

$$= \dfrac{(x-2)(x^2 + 2x + 4) \cdot 6 \cdot x^2}{-1 \cdot 6(x-2)(x^2 + 2x + 4)}$$

$$= \dfrac{x^2}{-1}$$

$$= -x^2$$

2. a. $\dfrac{6y^3}{3y^2 - 27} \div \dfrac{42}{3-y} = \dfrac{6y^3}{3y^2 - 27} \cdot \dfrac{3-y}{42}$

$$= \dfrac{6y^3(3-y)}{3(y+3)(y-3) \cdot 42}$$

$$= \dfrac{6y^3 \cdot (-1)(y-3)}{3(y+3)(y-3) \cdot 6 \cdot 7}$$

$$= -\dfrac{y^3}{21(y+3)}$$

b. $\dfrac{10x^2 + 23x - 5}{5x^2 - 51x + 10} \div \dfrac{2x^2 + 9x + 10}{7x^2 - 68x - 20}$

$$= \dfrac{10x^2 + 23x - 5}{5x^2 - 51x + 10} \cdot \dfrac{7x^2 - 68x - 20}{2x^2 + 9x + 10}$$

$$= \dfrac{(5x-1)(2x+5)}{(5x-1)(x-10)} \cdot \dfrac{(7x+2)(x-10)}{(2x+5)(x+2)}$$

$$= \dfrac{7x+2}{x+2}$$

3. a. The LCD is $5p^4q$.

$$\frac{4}{p^3q}+\frac{3}{5p^4q}=\frac{4\cdot 5p}{p^3q\cdot 5p}+\frac{3}{5p^4q}$$

$$=\frac{20p}{5p^4q}+\frac{3}{5p^4q}$$

$$=\frac{20p+3}{5p^4q}$$

b. The LCD is the product of the two denominators: $(y+3)(y-3)$.

$$\frac{4}{y+3}+\frac{5y}{y-3}$$

$$=\frac{4\cdot(y-3)}{(y+3)\cdot(y-3)}+\frac{5y\cdot(y+3)}{(y-3)\cdot(y+3)}$$

$$=\frac{4y-12}{(y+3)(y-3)}+\frac{5y^2+15y}{(y+3)(y-3)}$$

$$=\frac{4y-12+5y^2+15y}{(y+3)(y-3)}$$

$$=\frac{5y^2+19y-12}{(y+3)(y-3)}$$

c. The LCD is either $z-5$ or $5-z$.

$$\frac{3z-18}{z-5}-\frac{3}{5-z}=\frac{3z-18}{z-5}-\frac{3}{-1(z-5)}$$

$$=\frac{3z-18}{z-5}-\frac{-1\cdot 3}{z-5}$$

$$=\frac{3z-18-(-3)}{z-5}$$

$$=\frac{3z-18+3}{z-5}$$

$$=\frac{3z-15}{z-5}$$

$$=\frac{3(z-5)}{z-5}$$

$$=3$$

4. $x^2-4=(x+2)(x-2)$

The LCD is $(x+2)(x-2)$.

$$\frac{2}{x-2}-\frac{5+2x}{x^2-4}=\frac{x}{x+2}$$

$$(x+2)(x-2)\cdot\frac{2}{x-2}-(x+2)(x-2)\cdot\frac{5+2x}{(x+2)(x-2)}$$

$$=(x+2)(x-2)\cdot\frac{x}{x+2}$$

$$2(x+2)-(5+2x)=x(x-2)$$

$$2x+4-5-2x=x^2-2x$$

$$x^2-2x+1=0$$

$$(x-1)(x-1)=0$$

$$x-1=0$$

$$x=1$$

Since 1 does not make any denominator 0, the solution is 1.

Appendix C.5 Exercise Set

2. $\dfrac{x}{4}=\dfrac{3}{2}+\dfrac{x}{10}$

The LCD is 20.

$$20\cdot\frac{x}{4}=20\cdot\frac{3}{2}+20\cdot\frac{x}{10}$$

$$5x=30+2x$$

$$3x=30$$

$$x=10$$

The solution is 10.

4. $\dfrac{3}{2}+\dfrac{x}{10}=\dfrac{5}{5}\cdot\dfrac{3}{2}+\dfrac{x}{10}=\dfrac{15}{10}+\dfrac{x}{10}=\dfrac{15+x}{10}$

6. $\dfrac{5}{x-2}-\dfrac{10}{x+4}=\dfrac{5}{x-2}\cdot\dfrac{x+4}{x+4}-\dfrac{10}{x+4}\cdot\dfrac{x-2}{x-2}$

$$=\frac{5(x+4)}{(x-2)(x+4)}-\frac{10(x-2)}{(x-2)(x+4)}$$

$$=\frac{5x+20-10x+20}{(x-2)(x+4)}$$

$$=\frac{-5x+40}{(x-2)(x+4)}$$

$$=\frac{-5(x-8)}{(x-2)(x+4)}\text{ or }-\frac{5(x-8)}{(x-2)(x+4)}$$

8. $\dfrac{5}{x-2} = \dfrac{10}{x+4}$

The LCD is $(x-2)(x+4)$.

$$(x-2)(x+4)\cdot\dfrac{5}{x-2} = (x-2)(x+4)\cdot\dfrac{10}{x+4}$$
$$5(x+4) = 10(x-2)$$
$$5x + 20 = 10x - 20$$
$$5x = 10x - 40$$
$$-5x = -40$$
$$x = 8$$

The solution is 8.

10. $x^2 - 25 = (x+5)(x-5)$

The LCD is $(x+5)(x-5)$.

$$\dfrac{3}{x^2-25} = \dfrac{1}{x+5} + \dfrac{2}{x-5}$$
$$(x+5)(x-5)\cdot\dfrac{3}{(x+5)(x-5)} = (x+5)(x-5)\cdot\dfrac{1}{x+5} + (x+5)(x-5)\cdot\dfrac{2}{x-5}$$
$$3 = (x-5) + 2(x+5)$$
$$3 = x - 5 + 2x + 10$$
$$3 = 3x + 5$$
$$-2 = 3x$$
$$-\dfrac{2}{3} = x$$

The solution is $-\dfrac{2}{3}$.

12. $\dfrac{5}{x^2-3x} \div \dfrac{4}{2x-6} = \dfrac{5}{x^2-3x}\cdot\dfrac{2x-6}{4}$

$$= \dfrac{5}{x(x-3)}\cdot\dfrac{2(x-3)}{4}$$
$$= \dfrac{5}{2x}$$

14. $\left(1-\dfrac{y}{x}\right) \div \left(1-\dfrac{x}{y}\right) = \left(\dfrac{x}{x}-\dfrac{y}{x}\right) \div \left(\dfrac{y}{y}-\dfrac{x}{y}\right)$

$$= \left(\dfrac{x-y}{x}\right) \div \left(\dfrac{y-x}{y}\right)$$
$$= \dfrac{x-y}{x}\cdot\dfrac{y}{y-x}$$
$$= \dfrac{x-y}{x}\cdot\dfrac{y}{-(x-y)}$$
$$= -\dfrac{y}{x}$$

16. $\dfrac{2}{a-6} + \dfrac{3a}{a^2-5a-6} - \dfrac{a}{5a+5} = \dfrac{2}{a-6} + \dfrac{3a}{(a-6)(a+1)} - \dfrac{a}{5(a+1)}$

$$= \frac{2}{a-6} \cdot \frac{5(a+1)}{5(a+1)} + \frac{3a}{(a-6)(a+1)} \cdot \frac{5}{5} - \frac{a}{5(a+1)} \cdot \frac{a-6}{a-6}$$

$$= \frac{10a+10}{5(a+1)(a-6)} + \frac{15a}{5(a+1)(a-6)} - \frac{a^2-6a}{5(a+1)(a-6)}$$

$$= \frac{10a+10+15a-a^2+6a}{5(a+1)(a-6)}$$

$$= \frac{-a^2+31a+10}{5(a+1)(a-6)}$$

18. The LCD is $2x(4x+1)$.

$$\frac{5x-3}{2x} = \frac{10x+3}{4x+1}$$

$$2x(4x+1) \cdot \frac{5x-3}{2x} = 2x(4x+1) \cdot \frac{10x+3}{4x+1}$$

$$(4x+1)(5x-3) = 2x(10x+3)$$

$$20x^2-12x+5x-3 = 20x^2+6x$$

$$20x^2-7x-3 = 20x^2+6x$$

$$-7x-3 = 6x$$

$$-3 = 13x$$

$$-\frac{3}{13} = x$$

The solution is $-\dfrac{3}{13}$.

20. $\dfrac{3}{4a-8} - \dfrac{a+2}{a^2-2a} = \dfrac{3}{4(a-2)} - \dfrac{a+2}{a(a-2)}$

$$= \frac{3}{4(a-2)} \cdot \frac{a}{a} - \frac{a+2}{a(a-2)} \cdot \frac{4}{4}$$

$$= \frac{3a}{4a(a-2)} - \frac{4(a+2)}{4a(a-2)}$$

$$= \frac{3a}{4a(a-2)} - \frac{4a+8}{4a(a-2)}$$

$$= \frac{3a-4a-8}{4a(a-2)}$$

$$= \frac{-a-8}{4a(a-2)}$$

$$= -\frac{a+8}{4a(a-2)}$$

22. $\dfrac{x}{2x+6} + \dfrac{5}{x^2-9}$

$= \dfrac{x}{2(x+3)} + \dfrac{5}{(x-3)(x+3)}$

$= \dfrac{x}{2(x+3)} \cdot \dfrac{x-3}{x-3} + \dfrac{5}{(x-3)(x+3)} \cdot \dfrac{2}{2}$

$= \dfrac{x(x-3)}{2(x+3)(x-3)} + \dfrac{10}{2(x+3)(x-3)}$

$= \dfrac{x^2-3x}{2(x+3)(x-3)} + \dfrac{10}{2(x+3)(x-3)}$

$= \dfrac{x^2-3x+10}{2(x+3)(x-3)}$

24. $x^2 - x - 2 = (x-2)(x+1)$

The LCD is $(x-2)(x+1)$.

$$\dfrac{x-8}{x^2-x-2} + \dfrac{2}{x-2} = \dfrac{3}{x+1}$$

$$(x-2)(x+1) \cdot \dfrac{x-8}{(x-2)(x+1)} + (x-2)(x+1) \cdot \dfrac{2}{x-2} = (x-2)(x+1) \cdot \dfrac{3}{x+1}$$

$$(x-8) + 2(x+1) = 3(x-2)$$

$$x - 8 + 2x + 2 = 3x - 6$$

$$3x - 6 = 3x - 6$$

$$-6 = -6 \quad \text{True}$$

The solution set is
$\{x \mid x \text{ is a real number and } x \neq 2,\ x \neq -1\}$.

26. $\dfrac{7}{3z-9} + \dfrac{5}{z} = \dfrac{7}{3(z-3)} + \dfrac{5}{z}$

$= \dfrac{7}{3(z-3)} \cdot \dfrac{z}{z} + \dfrac{5}{z} \cdot \dfrac{3(z-3)}{3(z-3)}$

$= \dfrac{7z}{3z(z-3)} + \dfrac{15(z-3)}{3z(z-3)}$

$= \dfrac{7z + 15z - 45}{3z(z-3)}$

$= \dfrac{22z - 45}{3z(z-3)}$

28. a. $\dfrac{x}{5} - \dfrac{x}{4} = \dfrac{1}{10}$ is an equation.

b. The first step to solve this equation is to clear the equation of fractions by multiplying each term by the LCD, 20.

c.

$$\frac{x}{5} - \frac{x}{4} = \frac{1}{10}$$

$$20 \cdot \frac{x}{5} - 20 \cdot \frac{x}{4} = 20 \cdot \frac{1}{10}$$

$$4x - 5x = 2$$

$$-x = 2$$

$$x = -2$$

The solution is -2.

30.

$$\frac{\triangle}{\square} + \frac{\square}{\triangle} = \frac{\triangle}{\square} \cdot \frac{\triangle}{\triangle} + \frac{\square}{\triangle} \cdot \frac{\square}{\square}$$

$$= \frac{\triangle\triangle}{\square\triangle} + \frac{\square\square}{\square\triangle}$$

$$= \frac{\triangle\triangle + \square\square}{\square\triangle}$$

d is the correct answer.

32.

$$\frac{\triangle}{\square} \div \frac{\bigcirc}{\triangle} = \frac{\triangle}{\square} \cdot \frac{\triangle}{\bigcirc} = \frac{\triangle\triangle}{\square\bigcirc}$$

a is the correct answer.

Appendix D

2. Yes, since every coordinate is between -10 and 10.

4. No, since 15 is greater than 10.

6. Answers may vary; any values such that $Xmin < -18$, $Ymin < 20$, $Xmax > 20$, and $Ymax > 90$.

8. Answers may vary; any values such that $Xmin < -3$, $Ymin < -5$, $Xmax > 15$, and $Ymax > 5$.

10. Answers may vary; any values such that $Xmin < -30$, $Ymin < 0$, $Xmax > 40$, and $Ymax > 800$.

12. $Xmin = -20$ $Ymin = -20$
$Xmax = 20$ $Ymax = 20$
$Xscl = 5$ $Yscl = 5$

14. $Xmin = -27$ $Ymin = -6$
$Xmax = 27$ $Ymax = 6$
$Xscl = 3$ $Yscl = 1$

16. $Xmin = -50$ $Ymin = -20$
$Xmax = 50$ $Ymax = 20$
$Xscl = 10$ $Yscl = 4$

18. $Xmin = -100$ $Ymin = -20$
$Xmax = 100$ $Ymax = 20$
$Xscl = 10$ $Yscl = 2$

20. $Xmin = -500$ $Ymin = -800$
$Xmax = 700$ $Ymax = 400$
$Xscl = 100$ $Yscl = 200$

Graphing Equations and Square Viewing Window Exercise Set

2. Setting A:

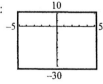

Setting B:

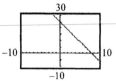

Setting B shows all intercepts.

4. Setting A:

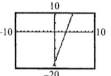

Setting B:

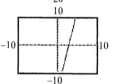

Setting A shows all intercepts.

6. Setting A:

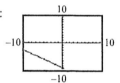

Setting B:

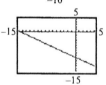

Setting B shows all intercepts.

8. $7y = -3x$, or $y = -\dfrac{3}{7}x$

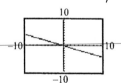

10. $4x + 6y = 20$, or $y = -\dfrac{2}{3}x + \dfrac{10}{3}$

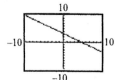

12. $y = 2$

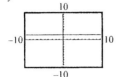

14. $x - 5y = 9$, or $y = \dfrac{1}{5}x - \dfrac{9}{5}$

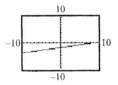

16. $y = \sqrt{2x}$

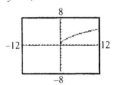

18. $y = x^2 - 5$

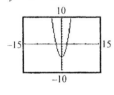

20. $y = |x - 2|$

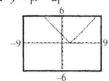

22. $1.5x - 3.7y = 40.3$

$\qquad -3.7y = -1.5x + 40.3$

$\qquad\quad y = \dfrac{1.5x - 40.3}{3.7}$

Standard window:

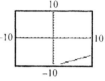

Adjusted window:

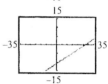

Appendix E

Practice Exercises

1. $\begin{cases} x+4y=-2 \\ 3x-y=7 \end{cases}$

The corresponding matrix is $\begin{bmatrix} 1 & 4 & | & -2 \\ 3 & -1 & | & 7 \end{bmatrix}$. The element in the first row, first column is already 1. Multiply row 1 by -3 and add to row 2 to get a 0 below the 1.

$\begin{bmatrix} 1 & 4 & | & -2 \\ -3(1)+3 & -3(4)+(-1) & | & -3(-2)+7 \end{bmatrix}$

$\begin{bmatrix} 1 & 4 & | & -2 \\ 0 & -13 & | & 13 \end{bmatrix}$

We change -13 to a 1 by dividing row 2 by -13.

$\begin{bmatrix} 1 & 4 & | & -2 \\ 0 & \frac{-13}{-13} & | & \frac{13}{-13} \end{bmatrix}$

$\begin{bmatrix} 1 & 4 & | & -2 \\ 0 & 1 & | & -1 \end{bmatrix}$

The last matrix corresponds to $\begin{cases} x+4y=-2 \\ y=-1 \end{cases}$

To find x, we let $y=-1$ in the first equation.

$x+4y=-2$
$x+4(-1)=-2$
$x-4=-2$
$x=2$

The solution is $(2,-1)$.

2. $\begin{cases} x-3y=3 \\ -2x+6y=4 \end{cases}$

The corresponding matrix is $\begin{bmatrix} 1 & -3 & | & 3 \\ -2 & 6 & | & 4 \end{bmatrix}$. The element in the first row, first column is already 1. Multiply row 1 by 2 and add to row 2 to get a 0 below the 1.

$\begin{bmatrix} 1 & -3 & | & 3 \\ 2(1)+(-2) & 2(-3)+6 & | & 2(3)+4 \end{bmatrix}$

$\begin{bmatrix} 1 & -3 & | & 3 \\ 0 & 0 & | & 10 \end{bmatrix}$

The corresponding system is $\begin{cases} x-3y=3 \\ 0=10 \end{cases}$

The equation $0=10$ is false. Hence, the system is inconsistent and has no solution. The solution set is $\varnothing$.

3. $\begin{cases} x+3y-z=0 \\ 2x+y+3z=5 \\ -x-2y+4z=7 \end{cases}$

The corresponding matrix is $\begin{bmatrix} 1 & 3 & -1 & | & 0 \\ 2 & 1 & 3 & | & 5 \\ -1 & -2 & 4 & | & 7 \end{bmatrix}$.

The element in the first row, first column is already 1. Multiply row 1 by -2 and add to row 2 to get a 0 below the 1 in row 2. Add row 1 to row 3 to get a 0 below the 1 in row 3.

$\begin{bmatrix} 1 & 3 & -1 & | & 0 \\ -2(1)+2 & -2(3)+1 & -2(-1)+3 & | & -2(0)+5 \\ 1+(-1) & 3+(-2) & -1+4 & | & 0+7 \end{bmatrix}$

$\begin{bmatrix} 1 & 3 & -1 & | & 0 \\ 0 & -5 & 5 & | & 5 \\ 0 & 1 & 3 & | & 7 \end{bmatrix}$

Now we want a 1 where the -5 is now. Interchange rows 2 and 3.

$\begin{bmatrix} 1 & 3 & -1 & | & 0 \\ 0 & 1 & 3 & | & 7 \\ 0 & -5 & 5 & | & 5 \end{bmatrix}$

Now we want a 0 below the 1. Multiply row 2 by 5 and add to row 3.

$\begin{bmatrix} 1 & 3 & -1 & | & 0 \\ 0 & 1 & 3 & | & 7 \\ 5(0)+0 & 5(1)+(-5) & 5(3)+5 & | & 5(7)+5 \end{bmatrix}$

$\begin{bmatrix} 1 & 3 & -1 & | & 0 \\ 0 & 1 & 3 & | & 7 \\ 0 & 0 & 20 & | & 40 \end{bmatrix}$

Finally, divide row 3 by 20.

$\begin{bmatrix} 1 & 3 & -1 & | & 0 \\ 0 & 1 & 3 & | & 7 \\ 0 & 0 & \frac{20}{20} & | & \frac{40}{20} \end{bmatrix}$

$\begin{bmatrix} 1 & 3 & -1 & | & 0 \\ 0 & 1 & 3 & | & 7 \\ 0 & 0 & 1 & | & 2 \end{bmatrix}$

This matrix corresponds to the system

$\begin{cases} x+3y-z=0 \\ y+3z=7 \\ z=2 \end{cases}$

The z-coordinate is 2. Replace z with 2 in the second equation and solve for y.

$$y + 3z = 7$$
$$y + 3(2) = 7$$
$$y + 6 = 7$$
$$y = 1$$

To find x, we let $z = 2$ and $y = 1$ in the first equation.
$$x + 3y - z = 0$$
$$x + 3(1) - 2 = 0$$
$$x + 1 = 0$$
$$x = -1$$

The solution is $(-1, 1, 2)$.

Appendix E Exercise Set

2. $\begin{cases} 2x - y = 8 \\ x + 3y = 11 \end{cases}$

$\begin{bmatrix} 2 & -1 & | & 8 \\ 1 & 3 & | & 11 \end{bmatrix}$

Interchange R1 and R2.

$\begin{bmatrix} 1 & 3 & | & 11 \\ 2 & -1 & | & 8 \end{bmatrix}$

Multiply R1 by –2 and add to R2.

$\begin{bmatrix} 1 & 3 & | & 11 \\ 0 & -7 & | & -14 \end{bmatrix}$

Divide R2 by –7.

$\begin{bmatrix} 1 & 3 & | & 11 \\ 0 & 1 & | & 2 \end{bmatrix}$

This corresponds to $\begin{cases} x + 3y = 11 \\ y = 2 \end{cases}$.

$$x + 3(2) = 11$$
$$x = 5$$

The solution is $(5, 2)$.

4. $\begin{cases} 4x - y = 5 \\ 3x + 3y = 0 \end{cases}$

$\begin{bmatrix} 4 & -1 & | & 5 \\ 3 & 3 & | & 0 \end{bmatrix}$

Interchange R1 and R2.

$\begin{bmatrix} 3 & 3 & | & 0 \\ 4 & -1 & | & 5 \end{bmatrix}$

Divide R1 by 3.

$\begin{bmatrix} 1 & 1 & | & 0 \\ 4 & -1 & | & 5 \end{bmatrix}$

Multiply R1 by –4 and add to R2.

$\begin{bmatrix} 1 & 1 & | & 0 \\ 0 & -5 & | & 5 \end{bmatrix}$

Divide R2 by –5.

$\begin{bmatrix} 1 & 1 & | & 0 \\ 0 & 1 & | & -1 \end{bmatrix}$

This corresponds to $\begin{cases} x + y = 0 \\ y = -1 \end{cases}$.

$$x + (-1) = 0$$
$$x = 1$$

The solution is $(1, -1)$.

6. $\begin{cases} -x + 3y = 6 \\ 3x - 9y = 9 \end{cases}$

$\begin{bmatrix} -1 & 3 & | & 6 \\ 3 & -9 & | & 9 \end{bmatrix}$

Multiply R1 by 3 and add to R2.

$\begin{bmatrix} -1 & 3 & | & 6 \\ 0 & 0 & | & 27 \end{bmatrix}$

This corresponds to $\begin{cases} -x + 3y = 6 \\ 0 = 27 \end{cases}$.

This is an inconsistent system. The solution set is $\varnothing$.

8. $\begin{cases} 9x - 3y = 6 \\ -18x + 6y = -12 \end{cases}$

$\begin{bmatrix} 9 & -3 & | & 6 \\ -18 & 6 & | & -12 \end{bmatrix}$

Multiply R1 by 2 and add to R2.

$\begin{bmatrix} 9 & -3 & | & 6 \\ 0 & 0 & | & 0 \end{bmatrix}$

This corresponds to $\begin{cases} 9x - 3y = 6 \\ 0 = 0 \end{cases}$.

This is a dependent system. The solution set is $\{(x, y) | 9x - 3y = 6\}$.

10. $\begin{cases} 5x = 5 \\ 2x + y = 4 \\ 3x + y - 5z = -15 \end{cases}$

$\begin{bmatrix} 5 & 0 & 0 & | & 5 \\ 2 & 1 & 0 & | & 4 \\ 3 & 1 & -5 & | & -15 \end{bmatrix}$

Divide R1 by 5.

$\begin{bmatrix} 1 & 0 & 0 & | & 1 \\ 2 & 1 & 0 & | & 4 \\ 3 & 1 & -5 & | & -15 \end{bmatrix}$

Multiply R1 by –2 and add to R2.
Multiply R1 by –3 and add to R3.

$$\begin{bmatrix} 1 & 0 & 0 & | & 1 \\ 0 & 1 & 0 & | & 2 \\ 0 & 1 & -5 & | & -18 \end{bmatrix}$$

Multiply R2 by –1 and add to R3.

$$\begin{bmatrix} 1 & 0 & 0 & | & 1 \\ 0 & 1 & 0 & | & 2 \\ 0 & 0 & -5 & | & -20 \end{bmatrix}$$

Divide R3 by –5.

$$\begin{bmatrix} 1 & 0 & 0 & | & 1 \\ 0 & 1 & 0 & | & 2 \\ 0 & 0 & 1 & | & 4 \end{bmatrix}$$

This corresponds to $\begin{cases} x = 1 \\ y = 2 \\ z = 4 \end{cases}$.

The solution is (1, 2, 4).

12. $\begin{cases} 4y + 3z = -2 \\ 5x - 4y = 1 \\ -5x + 4y + z = -3 \end{cases}$

$$\begin{bmatrix} 0 & 4 & 3 & | & -2 \\ 5 & -4 & 0 & | & 1 \\ -5 & 4 & 1 & | & -3 \end{bmatrix}$$

Interchange R1 and R2.

$$\begin{bmatrix} 5 & -4 & 0 & | & 1 \\ 0 & 4 & 3 & | & -2 \\ -5 & 4 & 1 & | & -3 \end{bmatrix}$$

Add R1 and R3.

$$\begin{bmatrix} 5 & -4 & 0 & | & 1 \\ 0 & 4 & 3 & | & -2 \\ 0 & 0 & 1 & | & -2 \end{bmatrix}$$

Divide R2 by 4.

$$\begin{bmatrix} 5 & -4 & 0 & | & 1 \\ 0 & 1 & \frac{3}{4} & | & -\frac{1}{2} \\ 0 & 0 & 1 & | & -2 \end{bmatrix}$$

This corresponds to $\begin{cases} 5x - 4y = 1 \\ y + \frac{3}{4}z = -\frac{1}{2} \\ z = -2 \end{cases}$.

$y + \frac{3}{4}(-2) = -\frac{1}{2}$

$y - \frac{3}{2} = -\frac{1}{2}$

$y = 1$

$5x - 4(1) = 1$

$5x = 5$

$x = 1$

The solution is (1, 1, –2).

14. $\begin{cases} 3y = 6 \\ x + y = 7 \end{cases}$

$$\begin{bmatrix} 0 & 3 & | & 6 \\ 1 & 1 & | & 7 \end{bmatrix}$$

Interchange R1 and R2.

$$\begin{bmatrix} 1 & 1 & | & 7 \\ 0 & 3 & | & 6 \end{bmatrix}$$

Divide R2 by 3.

$$\begin{bmatrix} 1 & 1 & | & 7 \\ 0 & 1 & | & 2 \end{bmatrix}$$

This corresponds to $\begin{cases} x + y = 7 \\ y = 2 \end{cases}$.

$x + 2 = 7$

$x = 5$

The solution is (5, 2).

16. $\begin{cases} x + 2y + z = 5 \\ x - y - z = 3 \\ y + z = 2 \end{cases}$

$$\begin{bmatrix} 1 & 2 & 1 & | & 5 \\ 1 & -1 & -1 & | & 3 \\ 0 & 1 & 1 & | & 2 \end{bmatrix}$$

Multiply R1 by –1 and add to R2.

$$\begin{bmatrix} 1 & 2 & 1 & | & 5 \\ 0 & -3 & -2 & | & -2 \\ 0 & 1 & 1 & | & 2 \end{bmatrix}$$

Interchange R2 and R3.

$$\begin{bmatrix} 1 & 2 & 1 & | & 5 \\ 0 & 1 & 1 & | & 2 \\ 0 & -3 & -2 & | & -2 \end{bmatrix}$$

Multiply R2 by 3 and add to R3.

$$\begin{bmatrix} 1 & 2 & 1 & | & 5 \\ 0 & 1 & 1 & | & 2 \\ 0 & 0 & 1 & | & 4 \end{bmatrix}$$

This corresponds to $\begin{cases} x + 2y + z = 5 \\ y + z = 2 \\ z = 4 \end{cases}$.

$y + 4 = 2$

$y = -2$

$$x + 2(-2) + 4 = 5$$
$$x = 5$$

The solution is (5, –2, 4).

18. $\begin{cases} 4x - y = 9 \\ 2x + 3y = -27 \end{cases}$

$$\begin{bmatrix} 4 & -1 & | & 9 \\ 2 & 3 & | & -27 \end{bmatrix}$$

Divide R1 by 4.

$$\begin{bmatrix} 1 & -\frac{1}{4} & | & \frac{9}{4} \\ 2 & 3 & | & -27 \end{bmatrix}$$

Multiply R1 by –2 and add to R2.

$$\begin{bmatrix} 1 & -\frac{1}{4} & | & \frac{9}{4} \\ 0 & \frac{7}{2} & | & -\frac{63}{2} \end{bmatrix}$$

Multiply R2 by $\frac{2}{7}$.

$$\begin{bmatrix} 1 & -\frac{1}{4} & | & \frac{9}{4} \\ 0 & 1 & | & -9 \end{bmatrix}$$

This corresponds to $\begin{cases} x - \dfrac{1}{4}y = \dfrac{9}{4} \\ \quad\quad y = -9 \end{cases}$.

$$x - \frac{1}{4}(-9) = \frac{9}{4}$$
$$x + \frac{9}{4} = \frac{9}{4}$$
$$x = 0$$

The solution is (0, –9).

20. $\begin{cases} 2x - 5y = 12 \\ -4x + 10y = 20 \end{cases}$

$$\begin{bmatrix} 2 & -5 & | & 12 \\ -4 & 10 & | & 20 \end{bmatrix}$$

Multiply R1 by 2 and add to R2.

$$\begin{bmatrix} 2 & -5 & | & 12 \\ 0 & 0 & | & 44 \end{bmatrix}$$

This corresponds to $\begin{cases} 2x - 5y = 12 \\ \quad\quad 0 = 44 \end{cases}$.

This is an inconsistent system. The solution set is $\varnothing$.

22. $\begin{cases} 5y - 7z = 14 \\ 2x + y + 4z = 10 \\ 2x + 6y - 3z = 30 \end{cases}$

$$\begin{bmatrix} 0 & 5 & -7 & | & 14 \\ 2 & 1 & 4 & | & 10 \\ 2 & 6 & -3 & | & 30 \end{bmatrix}$$

Interchange R1 and R2.

$$\begin{bmatrix} 2 & 1 & 4 & | & 10 \\ 0 & 5 & -7 & | & 14 \\ 2 & 6 & -3 & | & 30 \end{bmatrix}$$

Divide R1 by 2.

$$\begin{bmatrix} 1 & \frac{1}{2} & 2 & | & 5 \\ 0 & 5 & -7 & | & 14 \\ 2 & 6 & -3 & | & 30 \end{bmatrix}$$

Multiply R1 by –2 and add to R3.

$$\begin{bmatrix} 1 & \frac{1}{2} & 2 & | & 5 \\ 0 & 5 & -7 & | & 14 \\ 0 & 5 & -7 & | & 20 \end{bmatrix}$$

Multiply R2 by –1 and add to R3.

$$\begin{bmatrix} 1 & \frac{1}{2} & 2 & | & 5 \\ 0 & 5 & -7 & | & 14 \\ 0 & 0 & 0 & | & 6 \end{bmatrix}$$

This corresponds to $\begin{cases} x + \dfrac{1}{2}y + 2z = 5 \\ \quad\quad 5y - 7z = 14 \\ \quad\quad\quad\quad 0 = 6 \end{cases}$.

This is an inconsistent system. The solution set is $\varnothing$.

24. $\begin{cases} x + y + z = 9 \\ 3x - y + z = -1 \\ -2x + 2y - 3z = -2 \end{cases}$

$$\begin{bmatrix} 1 & 1 & 1 & | & 9 \\ 3 & -1 & 1 & | & -1 \\ -2 & 2 & -3 & | & -2 \end{bmatrix}$$

Multiply R1 by –3 and add to R2.
Multiply R1 by 2 and add to R3.

$$\begin{bmatrix} 1 & 1 & 1 & | & 9 \\ 0 & -4 & -2 & | & -28 \\ 0 & 4 & -1 & | & 16 \end{bmatrix}$$

Add R2 to R3.

$$\begin{bmatrix} 1 & 1 & 1 & | & 9 \\ 0 & -4 & -2 & | & -28 \\ 0 & 0 & -3 & | & -12 \end{bmatrix}$$

Divide R2 by –3.

$$\begin{bmatrix} 1 & 1 & 1 & | & 9 \\ 0 & -4 & -2 & | & -28 \\ 0 & 0 & 1 & | & 4 \end{bmatrix}$$

This corresponds to $\begin{cases} x+y+z=9 \\ -4y-2z=-28. \\ \qquad z=4 \end{cases}$

$$-4y-2(4)=-28$$
$$\qquad -4y=-20$$
$$\qquad\quad y=5$$
$$x+5+4=9$$
$$\quad x+9=9$$
$$\qquad x=0$$

The solution is (0, 5, 4).

Appendix F

2. $\begin{vmatrix} -5 & 1 \\ 1 & -4 \end{vmatrix} = ad - bc = -5(-4) - 1(1) = 20 - 1 = 19$

4. $\begin{vmatrix} 4 & 0 \\ 9 & 8 \end{vmatrix} = ad - bc = 4(8) - (0)(9) = 32 + 0 = 32$

6. $\begin{vmatrix} -40 & 8 \\ 70 & -14 \end{vmatrix} = -40(-14) - 8(70) = 560 - 560 = 0$

8. $\begin{cases} 4x - y = 5 \\ 3x - 3 = 0 \end{cases}$ or $\begin{cases} 4x - 1y = 5 \\ 3x + 0y = 3 \end{cases}$

$D = \begin{vmatrix} 4 & -1 \\ 3 & 0 \end{vmatrix} = 0 - (-3) = 3$

$D_x = \begin{vmatrix} 5 & -1 \\ 3 & 0 \end{vmatrix} = 0 - (-3) = 3$

$D_y = \begin{vmatrix} 4 & 5 \\ 3 & 3 \end{vmatrix} = 12 - 15 = -3$

$x = \dfrac{D_x}{D} = \dfrac{3}{3} = 1$

$y = \dfrac{D_y}{D} = \dfrac{-3}{3} = -1$

The solution is $(1, -1)$.

10. $\begin{cases} y = 2x - 5 \\ 8x - 4y = 20 \end{cases}$ or $\begin{cases} -2x + y = -5 \\ 8x - 4y = 20 \end{cases}$

$D = \begin{vmatrix} -2 & 1 \\ 8 & -4 \end{vmatrix} = 8 - 8 = 0$

Since $D = 0$, Cramer's Rule cannot be used. Notice equation (2) is equation (1) multiplied by -4. The solution is $\{(x, y) | y = 2x - 5\}$.

12. $\begin{cases} 4x - y = 9 \\ 2x + 3y = -27 \end{cases}$

$D = \begin{vmatrix} 4 & -1 \\ 2 & 3 \end{vmatrix} = 12 + 2 = 14$

$D_x = \begin{vmatrix} 9 & -1 \\ -27 & 3 \end{vmatrix} = 27 - 27 = 0$

$D_y = \begin{vmatrix} 4 & 9 \\ 2 & -27 \end{vmatrix} = -108 - 18 = -126$

$x = \dfrac{D_x}{D} = \dfrac{0}{14} = 0$ and $y = \dfrac{D_y}{D} = \dfrac{-126}{14} = -9$

The solution is $(0, -9)$.

14. Expand by column 1.

$\begin{vmatrix} -6 & 4 & 2 \\ 1 & 0 & 5 \\ 0 & 3 & 1 \end{vmatrix} = -6\begin{vmatrix} 0 & 5 \\ 3 & 1 \end{vmatrix} - 1\begin{vmatrix} 4 & 2 \\ 3 & 1 \end{vmatrix} + 0\begin{vmatrix} 4 & 2 \\ 0 & 5 \end{vmatrix}$

$\quad = -6(0 - 15) - 1(4 - 6) + 0$

$\quad = 90 + 2$

$\quad = 92$

16. Expand by column 3.

$\begin{vmatrix} 5 & 2 & 1 \\ 3 & -6 & 0 \\ -2 & 8 & 0 \end{vmatrix} = 1\begin{vmatrix} 3 & -6 \\ -2 & 8 \end{vmatrix} - 0\begin{vmatrix} 5 & 2 \\ -2 & 8 \end{vmatrix} + 0\begin{vmatrix} 5 & 2 \\ 3 & -6 \end{vmatrix}$

$\quad = 1(24 - 12) - 0 + 0$

$\quad = 12$

18. Expand by row 1.

$\begin{vmatrix} 2 & -2 & 1 \\ 4 & 1 & 3 \\ 3 & 1 & 2 \end{vmatrix} = 2\begin{vmatrix} 1 & 3 \\ 1 & 2 \end{vmatrix} + 2\begin{vmatrix} 4 & 3 \\ 3 & 2 \end{vmatrix} + 1\begin{vmatrix} 4 & 1 \\ 3 & 1 \end{vmatrix}$

$\quad = 2(2 - 3) + 2(8 - 9) + 1(4 - 3)$

$\quad = -2 - 2 + 1$

$\quad = -3$

20. $\begin{cases} 4y - 3z = -2 \\ 8x - 4y = 4 \\ -8x + 4y + z = -2 \end{cases}$

$D = \begin{vmatrix} 0 & 4 & -3 \\ 8 & -4 & 0 \\ -8 & 4 & 1 \end{vmatrix} = 0 - 4\begin{vmatrix} 8 & 0 \\ -8 & 1 \end{vmatrix} - 3\begin{vmatrix} 8 & -4 \\ -8 & 4 \end{vmatrix}$

$\quad = 0 - 4(8 - 0) - 3(32 - 32)$

$\quad = -32$

$D_x = \begin{vmatrix} -2 & 4 & -3 \\ 4 & -4 & 0 \\ -2 & 4 & 1 \end{vmatrix} = -3\begin{vmatrix} 4 & -4 \\ -2 & 4 \end{vmatrix} - 0 + 1\begin{vmatrix} -2 & 4 \\ 4 & -4 \end{vmatrix}$

$\quad = -3(16 - 8) + 1(8 - 16)$

$\quad = -32$

$D_y = \begin{vmatrix} 0 & -2 & -3 \\ 8 & 4 & 0 \\ -8 & -2 & 1 \end{vmatrix} = 0 + 2\begin{vmatrix} 8 & 0 \\ -8 & 1 \end{vmatrix} - 3\begin{vmatrix} 8 & 4 \\ -8 & -2 \end{vmatrix}$

$\quad = 2(8 - 0) - 3(-16 + 32)$

$\quad = -32$

$D_z = \begin{vmatrix} 0 & 4 & -2 \\ 8 & -4 & 4 \\ -8 & 4 & -2 \end{vmatrix} = 0 - 4\begin{vmatrix} 8 & 4 \\ -8 & -2 \end{vmatrix} - 2\begin{vmatrix} 8 & -4 \\ -8 & 4 \end{vmatrix}$

$\quad = -4(-16 + 32) - 2(32 - 32)$

$\quad = -64$

$x = \dfrac{D_x}{D} = \dfrac{-32}{-32} = 1, \quad y = \dfrac{D_y}{D} = \dfrac{-32}{-32} = 1,$

$z = \dfrac{D_z}{D} = \dfrac{-64}{-32} = 2$

The solution is $(1, 1, 2)$.

22. $\begin{cases} 5x + y + 3z = 1 \\ x - y - 3z = -7 \\ -x + y = 1 \end{cases}$

$D = \begin{vmatrix} 5 & 1 & 3 \\ 1 & -1 & -3 \\ -1 & 1 & 0 \end{vmatrix}$

$= 5\begin{vmatrix} -1 & -3 \\ 1 & 0 \end{vmatrix} - 1\begin{vmatrix} 1 & -3 \\ -1 & 0 \end{vmatrix} + 3\begin{vmatrix} 1 & -1 \\ -1 & 1 \end{vmatrix}$

$= 5(0+3) - 1(0-3) + 3(1-1)$

$= 15 + 3 + 0$

$= 18$

$D_x = \begin{vmatrix} 1 & 1 & 3 \\ -7 & -1 & -3 \\ 1 & 1 & 0 \end{vmatrix}$

$= 1\begin{vmatrix} -1 & -3 \\ 1 & 0 \end{vmatrix} - 1\begin{vmatrix} -7 & -3 \\ 1 & 0 \end{vmatrix} + 3\begin{vmatrix} -7 & -1 \\ 1 & 1 \end{vmatrix}$

$= 1(0+3) - 1(0+3) + 3(-7+1)$

$= 3 - 3 + (-18)$

$= -18$

$D_y = \begin{vmatrix} 5 & 1 & 3 \\ 1 & -7 & -3 \\ -1 & 1 & 0 \end{vmatrix}$

$= 5\begin{vmatrix} -7 & -3 \\ 1 & 0 \end{vmatrix} - 1\begin{vmatrix} 1 & -3 \\ -1 & 0 \end{vmatrix} + 3\begin{vmatrix} 1 & -7 \\ -1 & 1 \end{vmatrix}$

$= 5(0+3) - 1(0-3) + 3(1-7)$

$= 15 + 3 - 18$

$= 0$

$D_z = \begin{vmatrix} 5 & 1 & 1 \\ 1 & -1 & -7 \\ -1 & 1 & 1 \end{vmatrix}$

$= 5\begin{vmatrix} -1 & -7 \\ 1 & 1 \end{vmatrix} - 1\begin{vmatrix} 1 & -7 \\ -1 & 1 \end{vmatrix} + 1\begin{vmatrix} 1 & -1 \\ -1 & 1 \end{vmatrix}$

$= 5(-1+7) - 1(1-7) + 1(1-1)$

$= 30 + 6 + 0$

$= 36$

$x = \dfrac{D_x}{D} = \dfrac{-18}{18} = -1, \quad y = \dfrac{D_y}{D} = \dfrac{0}{18} = 0,$

$z = \dfrac{D_z}{D} = \dfrac{36}{18} = 2$

The solution is $(-1, 0, 2)$.

24. $\begin{vmatrix} -6 & 2 \\ 5 & -1 \end{vmatrix} = -6(-1) - 2(5) = 6 - 10 = -4$

26. Expand by row 1.

$\begin{vmatrix} 0 & 1 & 2 \\ 3 & -1 & 2 \\ 3 & 2 & -2 \end{vmatrix} = 0\begin{vmatrix} -1 & 2 \\ 2 & -2 \end{vmatrix} - 1\begin{vmatrix} 3 & 2 \\ 3 & -2 \end{vmatrix} + 2\begin{vmatrix} 3 & -1 \\ 3 & 2 \end{vmatrix}$

$= 0 - 1(-6 - 6) + 2(6 + 3)$

$= 12 + 18$

$= 30$

28. $\begin{vmatrix} \frac{5}{7} & \frac{1}{3} \\ \frac{6}{7} & \frac{2}{3} \end{vmatrix} = \dfrac{5}{7}\left(\dfrac{2}{3}\right) - \left(\dfrac{1}{3}\right)\left(\dfrac{6}{7}\right) = \dfrac{10}{21} - \dfrac{6}{21} = \dfrac{4}{21}$

30. Expand by row 1.

$\begin{vmatrix} 1 & 5 & 0 \\ 7 & 9 & -4 \\ 3 & 2 & -2 \end{vmatrix} = 1\begin{vmatrix} 9 & -4 \\ 2 & -2 \end{vmatrix} - 5\begin{vmatrix} 7 & -4 \\ 3 & -2 \end{vmatrix} + 0\begin{vmatrix} 7 & 9 \\ 3 & 2 \end{vmatrix}$

$= 1(-18 + 8) - 5(-14 + 12) + 0$

$= -10 + 10$

$= 0$

32. Expand by row 1.

$\begin{vmatrix} 5 & -2 & 4 \\ -1 & 5 & 3 \\ 1 & 4 & 2 \end{vmatrix} = 5\begin{vmatrix} 5 & 3 \\ 4 & 2 \end{vmatrix} - (-2)\begin{vmatrix} -1 & 3 \\ 1 & 2 \end{vmatrix} + 4\begin{vmatrix} -1 & 5 \\ 1 & 4 \end{vmatrix}$

$= 5(10 - 12) + 2(-2 - 3) + 4(-4 - 5)$

$= -10 - 10 - 36$

$= -56$

34. $\begin{cases} 3x - y = 2 \\ -5x + 2y = 0 \end{cases}$

$D = \begin{vmatrix} 3 & -1 \\ -5 & 2 \end{vmatrix} = 6 - 5 = 1$

$D_x = \begin{vmatrix} 2 & -1 \\ 0 & 2 \end{vmatrix} = 4 - 0 = 4$

$D_y = \begin{vmatrix} 3 & 2 \\ -5 & 0 \end{vmatrix} = 0 + 10 = 10$

$x = \dfrac{D_x}{D} = \dfrac{4}{1} = 4 \text{ and } y = \dfrac{D_y}{D} = \dfrac{10}{1} = 10$

The solution is $(4, 10)$.

36. $\begin{cases} 3x + 6y = 15 \\ 2x + 4y = 3 \end{cases}$

$D = \begin{vmatrix} 3 & 6 \\ 2 & 4 \end{vmatrix} = 12 - 12 = 0$

Since $D = 0$, Cramer's rule cannot be used. Multiply the first equation by 2 and the second equation by -3, then add.

$\begin{array}{r} 6x + 12y = 30 \\ -6x - 12y = -9 \\ \hline 0 = 21 \end{array}$

This is a false statement, so the system has no solution, or $\varnothing$.

38. $\begin{cases} 2x - 3y + z = 5 \\ x + y + z = 0 \\ 4x + 2y + 4z = 4 \end{cases}$

$D = \begin{vmatrix} 2 & -3 & 1 \\ 1 & 1 & 1 \\ 4 & 2 & 4 \end{vmatrix} = 2\begin{vmatrix} 1 & 1 \\ 2 & 4 \end{vmatrix} + 3\begin{vmatrix} 1 & 1 \\ 4 & 4 \end{vmatrix} + 1\begin{vmatrix} 1 & 1 \\ 4 & 2 \end{vmatrix}$

$\qquad = 2(4-2) + 3(4-4) + 1(2-4)$
$\qquad = 4 + 0 + (-2)$
$\qquad = 2$

$D_x = \begin{vmatrix} 5 & -3 & 1 \\ 0 & 1 & 1 \\ 4 & 2 & 4 \end{vmatrix} = 5\begin{vmatrix} 1 & 1 \\ 2 & 4 \end{vmatrix} + 3\begin{vmatrix} 0 & 1 \\ 4 & 4 \end{vmatrix} + 1\begin{vmatrix} 0 & 1 \\ 4 & 2 \end{vmatrix}$

$\qquad = 5(4-2) + 3(0-4) + 1(0-4)$
$\qquad = 10 - 12 - 4$
$\qquad = -6$

$D_y = \begin{vmatrix} 2 & 5 & 1 \\ 1 & 0 & 1 \\ 4 & 4 & 4 \end{vmatrix} = 2\begin{vmatrix} 0 & 1 \\ 4 & 4 \end{vmatrix} + 5\begin{vmatrix} 1 & 1 \\ 4 & 4 \end{vmatrix} + 1\begin{vmatrix} 1 & 0 \\ 4 & 4 \end{vmatrix}$

$\qquad = 2(0-4) + 5(4-4) + 1(4-0)$
$\qquad = -8 + 0 + 4$
$\qquad = -4$

$D_z = \begin{vmatrix} 2 & -3 & 5 \\ 1 & 1 & 0 \\ 4 & 2 & 4 \end{vmatrix} = 2\begin{vmatrix} 1 & 0 \\ 2 & 4 \end{vmatrix} + 3\begin{vmatrix} 1 & 0 \\ 4 & 4 \end{vmatrix} + 5\begin{vmatrix} 1 & 1 \\ 4 & 2 \end{vmatrix}$

$\qquad = 2(4-0) + 3(4-0) + 5(2-4)$
$\qquad = 8 + 12 + (-10)$
$\qquad = 10$

$x = \dfrac{D_x}{D} = \dfrac{-6}{2} = -3, \quad y = \dfrac{D_y}{D} = \dfrac{-4}{2} = -2,$

$z = \dfrac{D_z}{D} = \dfrac{10}{2} = 5$

The solution is $(-3, -2, 5)$.

40. $\begin{cases} \dfrac{1}{2}x - \dfrac{1}{3}y = -3 \\ \dfrac{1}{8}x + \dfrac{1}{6}y = 0 \end{cases}$

$D = \begin{vmatrix} \frac{1}{2} & -\frac{1}{3} \\ \frac{1}{8} & \frac{1}{6} \end{vmatrix} = \dfrac{1}{12} + \dfrac{1}{24} = \dfrac{1}{8}$

$D_x = \begin{vmatrix} -3 & -\frac{1}{3} \\ 0 & \frac{1}{6} \end{vmatrix} = -\dfrac{1}{2} - 0 = -\dfrac{1}{2}$

$D_y = \begin{vmatrix} \frac{1}{2} & -3 \\ \frac{1}{8} & 0 \end{vmatrix} = 0 + \dfrac{3}{8} = \dfrac{3}{8}$

$x = \dfrac{D_x}{D} = \dfrac{-\frac{1}{2}}{\frac{1}{8}} = -4 \ \text{ and } \ y = \dfrac{D_y}{D} = \dfrac{\frac{3}{8}}{\frac{1}{8}} = 3$

The solution is $(-4, 3)$.

42. $\begin{cases} -0.7x + 0.6y = 1.3 \\ 0.5x - 0.3y = -0.8 \end{cases}$

$D = \begin{vmatrix} -0.7 & 0.6 \\ 0.5 & -0.3 \end{vmatrix} = 0.21 - 0.30 = -0.09$

$D_x = \begin{vmatrix} 1.3 & 0.6 \\ -0.8 & -0.3 \end{vmatrix} = -0.39 + 0.48 = 0.09$

$D_y = \begin{vmatrix} -0.7 & 1.3 \\ 0.5 & -0.8 \end{vmatrix} = 0.56 - 0.65 = -0.09$

$x = \dfrac{D_x}{D} = \dfrac{0.09}{-0.09} = -1$

$y = \dfrac{D_y}{D} = \dfrac{-0.09}{-0.09} = 1$

The solution is $(-1, 1)$.

44. $\begin{cases} -x - y + 3z = 2 \\ 4x + 4y - 12z = -8 \\ -3x - 3y + 9z = 6 \end{cases}$

$$D = \begin{vmatrix} -1 & -1 & 3 \\ 4 & 4 & -12 \\ -3 & -3 & 9 \end{vmatrix} = (-1)\begin{vmatrix} 4 & -12 \\ -3 & 9 \end{vmatrix} - (-1)\begin{vmatrix} 4 & -12 \\ -3 & 9 \end{vmatrix} + 3\begin{vmatrix} 4 & 4 \\ -3 & -3 \end{vmatrix}$$

$$= -1(36 - 36) + 1(36 - 36) + 3(-12 + 12)$$

$$= 0$$

Since $D = 0$, Cramer's rule cannot be used. Note that the second equation is -4 times the first, and the third equation is 3 times the first. Thus, the system is dependent and the solution set is $\{(x, y, z) | -x - y + 3z = 2\}$.

46. $\begin{cases} 4x + 5y \quad\ = 10 \\ \quad\ 3y + 2z = -6 \\ x + y + z = 3 \end{cases}$

$$D = \begin{vmatrix} 4 & 5 & 0 \\ 0 & 3 & 2 \\ 1 & 1 & 1 \end{vmatrix} = 4\begin{vmatrix} 3 & 2 \\ 1 & 1 \end{vmatrix} - 5\begin{vmatrix} 0 & 2 \\ 1 & 1 \end{vmatrix} + 0$$

$$= 4(3 - 2) - 5(0 - 2)$$

$$= 4 + 10$$

$$= 14$$

$$D_x = \begin{vmatrix} 10 & 5 & 0 \\ -6 & 3 & 2 \\ 3 & 1 & 1 \end{vmatrix} = 10\begin{vmatrix} 3 & 2 \\ 1 & 1 \end{vmatrix} - 5\begin{vmatrix} -6 & 2 \\ 3 & 1 \end{vmatrix} + 0$$

$$= 10(3 - 2) - 5(-6 - 6)$$

$$= 10 + 60$$

$$= 70$$

$$D_y = \begin{vmatrix} 4 & 10 & 0 \\ 0 & -6 & 2 \\ 1 & 3 & 1 \end{vmatrix} = 4\begin{vmatrix} -6 & 2 \\ 3 & 1 \end{vmatrix} - 10\begin{vmatrix} 0 & 2 \\ 1 & 1 \end{vmatrix} + 0$$

$$= 4(-6 - 6) - 10(0 - 2)$$

$$= -48 + 20$$

$$= -28$$

$$D_z = \begin{vmatrix} 4 & 5 & 10 \\ 0 & 3 & -6 \\ 1 & 1 & 3 \end{vmatrix} = 4\begin{vmatrix} 3 & -6 \\ 1 & 3 \end{vmatrix} - 5\begin{vmatrix} 0 & -6 \\ 1 & 3 \end{vmatrix} + 10\begin{vmatrix} 0 & 3 \\ 1 & 1 \end{vmatrix}$$

$$= 4(9 + 6) - 5(0 + 6) + 10(0 - 3)$$

$$= 60 - 30 + (-30)$$

$$= 0$$

$$x = \frac{D_x}{D} = \frac{70}{14} = 5, \quad y = \frac{D_y}{D} = \frac{-28}{14} = -2, \quad z = \frac{D_z}{D} = \frac{0}{14} = 0$$

The solution is $(5, -2, 0)$.

48. $\begin{vmatrix} 6 & 1 \\ -2 & x \end{vmatrix} = 26$

$$6 \cdot x - 1 \cdot (-2) = 26$$

$$6x + 2 = 26$$

$$6x = 24$$

$$x = 4$$

50. 0; answers may vary

52. Answers may vary

54. Expand by row 1.

$$\begin{vmatrix} 1 & 7 & 0 & -1 \\ 1 & 3 & -2 & 0 \\ 1 & 0 & -1 & 2 \\ 0 & -6 & 2 & 4 \end{vmatrix} = 1\begin{vmatrix} 3 & -2 & 0 \\ 0 & -1 & 2 \\ -6 & 2 & 4 \end{vmatrix} - 7\begin{vmatrix} 1 & -2 & 0 \\ 1 & -1 & 2 \\ 0 & 2 & 4 \end{vmatrix} + 0\begin{vmatrix} 1 & 3 & 0 \\ 1 & 0 & 2 \\ 0 & -6 & 4 \end{vmatrix} - (-1)\begin{vmatrix} 1 & 3 & -2 \\ 1 & 0 & -1 \\ 0 & -6 & 2 \end{vmatrix}$$

$$= 1\left[3\begin{vmatrix} -1 & 2 \\ 2 & 4 \end{vmatrix} - (-2)\begin{vmatrix} 0 & 2 \\ -6 & 4 \end{vmatrix} + 0\begin{vmatrix} 0 & -1 \\ -6 & 2 \end{vmatrix}\right] - 7\left[1\begin{vmatrix} -1 & 2 \\ 2 & 4 \end{vmatrix} - (-2)\begin{vmatrix} 1 & 2 \\ 0 & 4 \end{vmatrix} + 0\begin{vmatrix} 1 & -1 \\ 0 & 2 \end{vmatrix}\right]$$

$$+ 0 + 1\left[\begin{vmatrix} 0 & -1 \\ -6 & 2 \end{vmatrix} - 3\begin{vmatrix} 1 & -1 \\ 0 & 2 \end{vmatrix} + (-2)\begin{vmatrix} 1 & 0 \\ 0 & -6 \end{vmatrix}\right]$$

$$= 1[3(-4-4) + 2(0+12) + 0] - 7[1(-4-4) + 2(4-0) + 0] + 1[1(0-6) - 3(2-0) - 2(-6-0)]$$

$$= 1(-24+24) - 7(-8+8) + 1(-6-6+12)$$

$$= 1(0) - 7(0) + 1(0)$$

$$= 0$$

56. Expand by column 2.

$$\begin{vmatrix} 2 & 0 & -1 & 4 \\ 6 & 0 & 4 & 1 \\ 2 & 4 & 3 & -1 \\ 4 & 0 & 5 & -4 \end{vmatrix} = -0\begin{vmatrix} 6 & 4 & 1 \\ 2 & 3 & -1 \\ 4 & 5 & -4 \end{vmatrix} + 0\begin{vmatrix} 2 & -1 & 4 \\ 2 & 3 & -1 \\ 4 & 5 & -4 \end{vmatrix} - 4\begin{vmatrix} 2 & -1 & 4 \\ 6 & 4 & 1 \\ 4 & 5 & -4 \end{vmatrix} + 0\begin{vmatrix} 2 & -1 & 4 \\ 6 & 4 & 1 \\ 2 & 3 & -1 \end{vmatrix}$$

$$= 0 + 0 - 4\left[2\begin{vmatrix} 4 & 1 \\ 5 & -4 \end{vmatrix} - (-1)\begin{vmatrix} 6 & 1 \\ 4 & -4 \end{vmatrix} + 4\begin{vmatrix} 6 & 4 \\ 4 & 5 \end{vmatrix}\right] + 0$$

$$= -4[2(-16-5) + 1(-24-4) + 4(30-16)]$$

$$= -4(-42-28+56)$$

$$= -4(-14)$$

$$= 56$$

Appendix G

2. 42, 35, 36, 40, 50

$$\bar{x} = \frac{42+35+36+40+50}{5} = \frac{203}{5} = 40.6$$

35, 36, 40, 42, 50
median = 40
no mode

4. 4.9, 7.1, 6.8, 6.8, 5.3, 4.9

$$\bar{x} = \frac{4.9+7.1+6.8+6.8+5.3+4.9}{6} = \frac{35.8}{6} = 6.0$$

4.9, 4.9, 5.3, 6.8, 6.8, 7.1

$$\text{median} = \frac{5.3+6.8}{2} = 6.05$$

mode = 4.9 and 6.8

6. 0.6, 0.6, 0.8, 0.4, 0.5, 0.3, 0.7, 0.8, 0.1

$$\bar{x} = \frac{0.6+0.6+0.8+0.4+0.5+0.3+0.7+0.8+0.1}{9}$$

$$= \frac{4.8}{9}$$

$$= 0.5$$

0.1, 0.3, 0.4, 0.5, 0.6, 0.6, 0.7, 0.8, 0.8
median = 0.6
mode = 0.6 and 0.8

8. 451, 356, 478, 776, 892, 500, 467, 780

$$\bar{x} = \frac{451+356+478+776+892+500+467+780}{8}$$

$$= \frac{4700}{8}$$

$$= 587.5$$

356, 451, 467, 478, 500, 776, 780, 892

$$\text{median} = \frac{478+500}{2} = 489$$

no mode

10. 1454, 1250, 1136, 1127, 1107
median = 1136 feet

12. Sum = 1454 + 1250 + 1136 + 1127 + 1107
$$\qquad + 1046 + 1023 + 1002$$

$$= 9145$$

$$\bar{x} = \frac{9145}{8} = 1143.1 \text{ feet}$$

14. 4.7, 6.9, 6.9, 7.0, 7.5, 7.8

$$\text{median} = \frac{6.9+7.0}{2} = 6.95 \text{ seconds}$$

16. $$\bar{x} = \frac{86+95+91+74+77+85}{6} = \frac{508}{6} = 84.67$$

18. 74, 77, 85, 86, 91, 95
no mode

20. 64, 65, 66, 68, 70, 70, 71, 71, 72, 75, 77, 78, 80, 82, 86
median = 71

22. 64, 65, 66, 68, 70, 70, 71, 71, 72, 75, 77, 78, 80, 82, 86
$$\qquad\qquad\qquad\qquad\qquad\qquad \uparrow$$
$$\qquad\qquad\qquad\qquad\qquad \text{mean} = 73$$
6 rates were higher than the mean.

24. Answers may vary

26. __, __, __, __, 40;

Since the mode is 35, at least two of the missing numbers must be 35. The median will be the middle value, so one number must be 37, the median. The mean is 38. Let the one unknown number be x.

$$\bar{x} = \frac{35+35+37+40+x}{5} = 38$$

$$\frac{147+x}{5} = 38$$

$$147+x = 190$$

$$x = 43$$

The missing numbers are 35, 35, 37, 43.

Appendix H

2. $90° - 65° = 25°$

4. $90° - 45\frac{2}{3}° = 44\frac{1}{3}°$

6. $90° - 19.6° = 70.4°$

8. $180° - 90° = 90°$

10. $180° - 81.9° = 98.1°$

12. $180° - 165\frac{8}{9}° = 14\frac{1}{9}°$

14. $m\angle 1 = 60°$
$m\angle 2 = 180° - 70° - 60° = 50°$
$m\angle 3 = 70°$
$m\angle 4 = 180° - 70° = 110°$
$m\angle 5 = 180° - 60° = 120°$

16. $180° - 8° - 102° = 70°$

18. $180° - 44° - 19° = 117°$

20. $180° - 67° - 23° = 90°$

22. $90° - 60° = 30°$
$30°, 90°$

24. $90° - 30° = 60°$
$60°, 90°$

26. $90° - 72.6° = 17.4°$
$17.4°, 90°$

28. $\dfrac{7}{14} = \dfrac{4}{x}$
$14x\left(\dfrac{7}{14}\right) = 14x\left(\dfrac{4}{x}\right)$
$7x = 56$
$x = 8$

30. $\dfrac{5}{60} = \dfrac{4}{x}$
$60x\left(\dfrac{5}{60}\right) = 60x\left(\dfrac{4}{x}\right)$
$5x = 240$
$x = 48$

32. $a^2 + b^2 = c^2$
$5^2 + 12^2 = c^2$
$25 + 144 = c^2$
$169 = c^2$
$13 = c$

34. $a^2 + b^2 = c^2$
$12^2 + b^2 = 20^2$
$144 + b^2 = 400$
$b^2 = 256$
$b = 16$